Unless Recalled Earlier

DATE DUE

DEMCO, INC. 38-2931

THE TORRE-BUENO
GLOSSARY OF ENTOMOLOGY

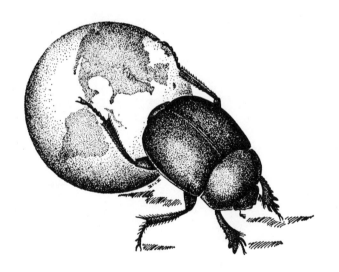

THE TORRE-BUENO
GLOSSARY OF ENTOMOLOGY

Revised Edition of
A GLOSSARY OF ENTOMOLOGY
by J. R. de la Torre-Bueno
including
SUPPLEMENT A
by George S. Tulloch

Compiled by
Stephen W. Nichols
Department of Entomology,
Cornell University, Ithaca, New York

Managing Editor
Randall T. Schuh
Department of Entomology,
American Museum of Natural History,
New York, New York

Published by
The New York Entomological Society
Incorporating the Brooklyn Entomological Society
in cooperation with the
American Museum of Natural History

Printed in the United States of America

Library of Congress Cataloging-in-Publication Data

Torre-Bueno, J. R. de la (José Rollin), 1871–1948
  The Torre-Bueno glossary of entomology / compiled by Stephen W. Nichols; including Supplement A by George S. Tulloch.——Rev. ed.
  p. cm.
  Rev. ed. of: A glossary of entomology. 1937.
  Bibliography: p.
  1. Entomology—Dictionaries.   I. Nichols, Stephen W., 1956–   .
II. Tulloch. George S.   III. Torre-Bueno, J. R. de la (José Rollin), 1871–1948. Glossary of Entomology.   IV. American Museum of Natural History.   V. Title.
QL462.3.T67   1989
595.7′003——dc20
ISBN 0-913424-13-7

Limited portions were reprinted from the following works with permission of the publishers: Taxonomist's Glossary of Genitalia in Insects, 2nd rev. and enl. ed., by S. L. Tuxen, copyright © 1970 by Munksgaard; International Code of Zoological Nomenclature. Third Edition, copyright © 1985 by International Trust for Zoological Nomenclature in association with British Museum (Natural History) and University of California Press; The Insect Societies by E. O. Wilson, copyright © 1971 by The Belknap Press of Harvard University Press; Taxonomist's Glossary of Mosquito Anatomy by R. E. Harbach and K. L. Knight, copyright © 1980 by Plexus Publishing, Inc.; Principles of Systematic Zoology by E. Mayr, copyright © 1969 by McGraw-Hill Book Company, Inc.; Fundamentals of Applied Entomology, Third Edition, R. E. Pfadt (ed.), copyright © 1978 by MacMillan Publishing Company, Inc.; and An Introduction to the Study of Insects, Fifth Edition, by D. J. Borror, D. M. DeLong, and C. A. Triplehorn, copyright © 1981 by Saunders College Publishing, a division of Holt, Rinehart and Winston, Inc.

Order from:
New York Entomological Society
c/o Department of Entomology
American Museum of Natural History
Central Park West at 79th Street
New York, New York 10024

EDITORIAL CONTRIBUTORS

C. VAN ACHTERBERG, Rijksmuseum van Natuurlijke Historie, Leiden, The Netherlands

T. R. ADKINS, JR., Clemson University, Clemson, South Carolina, USA

PETER H. ADLER, Clemson University, Clemson, South Carolina, USA

DAVID ALSOP, Queens College, City University of New York, Queens, New York, USA

PETER F. BELLINGER, California State University, Northridge, California, USA

ART BORKENT, Agriculture Canada, Salmon Arm, British Columbia, Canada

WILLIAM L. BROWN, JR., Cornell University, Ithaca, New York, USA

GEORGE W. BYERS, University of Kansas, Lawrence, Kansas, USA

ULF CARLBERG, Nacka, Sweden

JAE C. CHOE, Museum of Comparative Zoology, Harvard University, Cambridge, Massachusetts, USA

JAMES M. CARPENTER, Museum of Comparative Zoology, Harvard University, Cambridge, Massachusetts, USA

IAN F. B. COMMON, CSIRO, Canberra, A. C. T., Australia

DONALD R. DAVIS, Smithsonian Institution, Washington, D. C., USA

WILLIAM R. DOLLING, British Museum (Natural History), London, England, UK

GEORGE C. EICKWORT, Cornell University, Ithaca, New York, USA

OLIVER S. FLINT, JR., Smithsonian Institution, Washington, D. C., USA

GORDON GORDH, University of California, Riverside, California, USA

DAVID A. GRIMALDI, American Museum of Natural History, New York, New York, USA

BRUCE HEMING, University of Alberta, Edmonton, Alberta, Canada

LEE HERMAN, American Museum of Natural History, New York, New York, USA

K. H. L. KEY, CSIRO, Canberra, A. C. T., Australia

R. KINZELBACH, Technische Hochschule, Darmstadt, Federal Republic of Germany

MICHAEL KOSZTARAB, Virginia Polytechnic Institute and State University, Blacksburg, Virginia, USA

KUMAR KRISHNA, City College, City University of New York, New York, New York, USA

ROBERT E. LEWIS, Iowa State University, Ames, Iowa, USA

JAMES K. LIEBHERR, Cornell University, Ithaca, New York, USA

CHRISTOPHER H. C. LYAL, British Museum (Natural History), London, England, UK

WOLFRAM MEY, Museum für Naturkunde der Humbold-Universität, Berlin, German Democratic Republic

JAMES S. MILLER, American Museum of Natural History, New York, New York, USA

EDWARD L. MOCKFORD, Illinois State University, Normal, Illinois, USA

JOHN C. MORSE, Clemson University, Clemson, South Carolina, USA

Lois O'Brien, Florida Agricultural and Mechanical University, Talahassee, Florida, USA

John D. Oswald, Cornell University, Ithaca, New York, USA

Daniel Otte, Academy of Natural Sciences, Philadelphia, Pennsylvania, USA

Norman D. Penny, California Academy of Sciences, San Francisco, California, USA

William L. Peters, Florida Agricultural and Mechanical University, Talahassee, Florida, USA

Edward J. Popham, Mellor Brook, Blackburn, England, UK

Edward S. Ross, California Academy of Sciences, San Francisco, California, USA

Louis Roth, Sherborn, Massachusetts, USA

Seiroku Sakai, Daito Bunka University, Tokyo, Japan

Michael E. Schauff, USDA Systematic Entomology Laboratory, Washington, D. C., USA

Malcolm J. Scoble, British Musem (Natural History), London, England, UK

Richard J. Snider, Michigan State University, East Lansing, Michigan, USA

Manya B. Stoetzel, USDA Systematic Entomology Laboratory, Beltsville, Maryland, USA

Helmut Sturm, Hochschule Hildesheim, Hildesheim, Federal Republic of Germany

Pavel Štys, Charles University, Prague, Czechoslovakia

Barbara Thorne, Museum of Comparative Zoology, Harvard University, Cambridge, Massachusetts, USA

I. W. B. Thornton, La Trobe University, Bundoora, Victoria, Australia

Norman E. Woodley, USDA Systematic Entomology Laboratory, Washington, D. C., USA

Peter Zwick, Max-Planck-Instituts für Limnologie, Schlitz, Federal Rupublic of Germany

TABLE OF CONTENTS

PREFACE

A revision of José Rollin de la Torre-Bueno's *A Glossary of Entomology*, published in 1937, was long overdue. For over half a century the *Glossary*, itself an expanded and modified version of John B. Smith's *An Explanation of Terms Used in Entomology*, published in 1906, has served as the most important reference for entomological terms in the English language. *Supplement A* by George S. Tulloch, published in 1962, enhanced the value of the *Glossary*, but even it is long out of date.

Because of the diversity of insects, a comprehensive glossary would consist of many volumes and cost a king's ransom to produce. Such an encyclopedic work would also be out of date almost as soon as it was published. This more modest, affordable revision nonetheless includes twice the number of terms found in the previous edition. Furthermore, all terms are now stored in a computerized listing which will facilitate more frequent updates.

The original version of the *Glossary* was intended as a general reference in entomology. This objective is maintained here with the addition of many new entries in such diverse subdisciplines as morphology, ethology, taxonomy, physiology, pathology, medical entomology, and applied entomology.

The preparation of the current *Glossary* was made possible by bequests to the New York Entomological Society from the late Patricia Vaurie and Charles P. Alexander. Suggestions for improvement should be sent to the Society, c/o the American Museum of Natural History, New York.

ACKNOWLEDGMENTS

The preparation of this volume required the cooperation of a large number of individuals.

We particularly thank Peter Adler, Ian Common, Michael Kosztarab, John Morse, Lois O'Brien, John Oswald, Pavel Štys, Norman Woodley, and other editorial contributors for providing numerous new entries as well as suggestions on how the original manuscript might be improved.

For assistance with production we thank Thomas Kelly, Lee Ewing, Mark Abraham, and Garrett Yankou of the American Museum of Natural History. Brenda Massie entered a large portion of the original *Glossary* into the computer file and made most of the modifications derived from review comments. Allma Edwards typed part of the manuscript and prepared the correspondence during the review process. Charles Myers and Richard Zweifel of the American Museum assisted in the conversion of word processing files.

We thank those publishers who gave permission to use material from glossaries in copyrighted sources. We have given an appropriate bibliographic citation and indicate the source of the entry in the body of the *Glossary*.

Finally, we thank Dennis Joslyn (President), Durland Fish (Vice President), and Louis Sorkin (Treasurer) of the New York Entomological Society for their enthusiasm for this project and their continued support from its inception to conclusion.

INTRODUCTION TO THE REVISED GLOSSARY

The primary sources for this revision are general text books and glossaries, which are widely used in the entomological community, and from which terms and definitions could be easily extracted. In this regard, it should be remembered, that the *Glossary* does not attempt to establish who first used a term, but only to indicate the various meanings attached to terms in the literature. While compiling terms and definitions we discovered that the world of terminology is a battle ground, made even more unseemly because there are no established rules of conduct comparable to the *International Code of Zoological Nomenclature* for taxonomic names, leaving disputes to be settled by he who barks the loudest or who has the most clout. Because the *Glossary* is not fully comprehensive, a considerable amount of effort was spent adding and rechecking terms of broadest application, e.g., "thorax" and "protocerebrum." This choice will leave some specialists dissatisfied, especially when terms they themselves coined are ommited—or even worse, synonymized!

As in the work of Torre-Bueno, we have attempted to include definitions for terms that will reflect usage, more than personal preference. The extensive commentary provided by editorial contributors made it clear that no two specialists view terminology in exactly the same way. Rather than eliminate terms just to simplify the presentation, we have included definitions ranging from the archaic to the current, in the hope that the *Glossary* will be useful in interpreting older literature as well as understanding current terminology. As did Torre-Bueno, we warn the reader that the terminology of a certain author, or from a certain time, may fall into disuse. A prime example may be the work of A. D. MacGillivray. We have not included terms coined by MacGillivray if they could not be associated with better known synonyms or had not been seen in the literature subsequent to their original introduction. We have also eliminated terms from the work of Torre-Bueno where they appeared to represent misspellings or simple errors.

The many synonymous terms found in the literature made it impossible to define each term separately. It was often necessary to determine with which term a definition should be associated. Thus, the reader may find a preferred term treated as a synonym of some other. We have used the Latin "q.v." (*quod vide*, which see) to indicate that one term has been used in the same sense as another.

We have also incorporated extensive cross referencing. Terms with a related but different meaning, as well as those pertaining to the same or a related subject, are cross referenced with "see."

The reader will find substantial numbers of terms taken from the primary literature. These derive in large part from submitting the original manuscript to the scrutiny of a dedicated and capable group of Editorial Contributors. This process was achieved by sorting the *Glossary* into subsets on the basis of the the occurrence of ordinal names in the entries, an extremely variable aspect of the 1937 version, but one which was made much more uniform during the course of revision. Nonetheless, certain subdisciplines of entomology could not be easily recognized through computer sorting, and therefore entries pertaining to them rely on the thoroughness of our search of the secondary literature, the integrity of the sources used, and the care with which the entire *Glossary* manuscript was edited.

The sorting mentioned above required a consistent ordinal nomenclature. The current conception of the orders of insects differs somewhat from that used at the time Torre-Bueno prepared his *Glossary*. The ordinal classification presented below is intended to assist *Glossary* users in interpreting unambiguously the meanings of ordinal level categories and definitions associated with them.

In addition to implementing a consistent ordinal-level nomenclature, we have added to the *Glossary* entries for higher category names at the level of superfamily and above, for all hexapod orders as well as many other groups of arthropods. We have indicated the rank and composition of all groups, and have included characters useful in recognizing those groups where such was feasible.

Even though many terms included in the *Glossary* are taken directly from the primary literature, we have followed the method of citation found in the Torre-Bueno edition, and not included dates. Thus, the reader wishing to track down a source may have to search through more than one reference by a given author, in order to find exactly where and how the term was used. Reference to the original Torre-Bueno Glossary is indicated by "T-B," to Supplement A by "Tulloch." In some cases we were not able to easily associate the use of a term with a published source, and have used the attribution "pers. comm.," in every instance referring to one of the editorial contributors. Because of the large numbers of terms and sources, there are bound to be cases where terms are attributed to authors for whom no reference exists. Some such examples exist in the compilations of both Torre-Bueno and Tulloch. We have tried to keep such occurrences to a minimum.

In addition to listing those sources from which terms have been drawn, we also include three lists of references which we believe serve to supplement this *Glossary*: Non-English Language Glossaries and Sources, Sources to English Common Names of Insects, and Other Useful References, the last including primarily dictionaries, glossaries, lexicons, and bibliographic sources.

Stephen W. Nichols
Randall T. Schuh

New York, New York
March 1, 1989

INTRODUCTION TO THE ORIGINAL EDITION

The broad general purpose of a vocabulary or dictionary of technical terms is solely to reflect usage. Its basic principle is to furnish information to those seeking to know a terminology. It is not for the lexicographer to read meanings into terms nor to redefine them according to preconceived ideas that may have found lodgement in his mind. He, indeed, must take the language or the terminology as he finds it; and must refer back to the originator of the term or to the consensus of usage for meanings. Nor is it the function of a word book to set standards; these must be the fruit of cooperative and self-denying effort on the part of many specialists in the science of entomology. All terms, so far as practicable or known, must be included, and defined as used by those experts in the matter or who specialize in any given branch. Hence, it is necessary to include also the special terms and technicisms applicable to restricted groups, not alone the more general terms which may almost be deemed to be elementary and known to all. In the modern extensions of entomology, which touch so many branches of science, almost any student is likely to meet with special terms outside of his own particular field. Thus, Snodgrass originates or redefines many terms; we must interpret these according to his intent.

The entomologist of the early days was the closet naturalist *par excellence*. He was a distiguisher and namer of things not heretofore discriminated. In consequence, an undue value was set on the bare description of species and the higher categories. The natural result flowed from this: a new technical vocabulary came into being; and since so much of the work done was independent and so much on very limited groups, practically each investigator invented new terms for his group, or improved on those of his predecessors, or by misinterpretation misnamed structures already recognized and named. But this condition naturally made any explanation of terms refer practically to nothing other than those structures employed in entomography or descriptive entomology.

The fundamental definitions of early terminology are to be found in Kirby and Spence. These terms are given herein as defined by them. Many are now obsolete; but many others have become crystallized into definite and fixed meanings and are still in current usage. Moreover, such fundamental definitions are the key to the sense of their predecessors—a key needed by all who attempt definitive work based on the earlier post-Linnaean authors—perhaps even to the last quarter of the XIXth century. Again, workers in the several Orders at times have given definite and distinct meanings to established terms to meet an exacting requirement of taxonomy in a given Order; such meanings, with the Order in which they apply, are set forth and defined accordingly.

Time moves inexorably. Entomology is now definitely past the descriptive stage pure and simple. Today, no entomological vocabulary can dissociate itself from the many aspects of biology in general, which derive from insects; even the physical sciences are embraced in this purview. Accordingly, terms are included in this revision covering not only entomology single and alone, but likewise the sciences into which it enters—embryology, cytology, physiology, morphology, development, genetics, ecology; and also certain terms in chemistry, physics, botany, medicine, etc., to be met in modern general and special treatises on insects—all to be defined in those fields and senses in which they apply to insects as such and as parts of the bios.

The rise of medical entomology has brought in its train a twilight zone of terminology impinging on both medicine and entomology. Acquaintance with certain of these terms is necessary to make easy the understanding of the terse references in texts on insects, as well as the more technical papers, by physicians and other non-entomologists, on the biology of certain insects as carriers of disease. A selection of such is given and the terms defined.

Some—but very few—mathematical terms are also included, for the reason that a certain stream of biological thought (which includes entomology) is endeavoring to express life mathematically; and also, that in certain insect descriptions, particular characters are expressed numerically, mostly ratios.

In general, terms are in the singular, sometimes in the plural, when the latter is the general usage, but both singular and plural are indicated, especially when there is any question as to the correct form of either. Plurals are given for the root-word, at least. In most of the older terms, which are anglicizings of Latin, the Latin form is also indicated. There are naturally included many straight Latin terms found in such general works as Imms, Snodgrass, Tillyard, etc. No words in other languages are included, with the few rare exceptions which seem to have crept into standard English usage in the general works.

Many highly specialized usages are doubtless omitted. So many authors prone to improvise terms for structures or functions in limited groups, that short of a complete revision of *all* the literature for each and every group, it becomes unavoidable to omit them. Many of these improvised terms have died with the author; others have gone out of use because they were new, and perhaps less felicitous, expressions to take the place of terms crystallized by long usage and thoroughly understood by all workers.

As a rule, the terms defined are referable back for usage to the general works mentioned in the Bibliography. The authority for the terms as defined is added in parentheses at the end of the definition, as (Snodgrass). In the case of this author, the terms are taken verbatim or with slight changes from his Insect Morphology, by kind permission of the publishers, the McGraw-Hill Book Co., of New York.

The terms as used or invented by MacGillivray in his External Insect Anatomy are included. They are general, separately lined from other like terms. They are also defined *in his own terminology*, which may be ascertained by consulting any of the words in its proper alphabetical place in this Glossary. In many cases his terms are straight substitutions for others already in general accepted usage, hence redundant. The same holds true for the MacGillivray terms in Coccids, certain of which, however, appear to be coming into usage. All these terms bear the indication (MacGillivray).

The purpose in the definitions as given is to fix a strict meaning of a term or word. The general definition is given as well as the several special usages in various groups, and the applications of specific authors. It has been the endeavor to make the definitions as clear as possible, and in consequence, the plates are only to clarify any obscurity. Colors are defined as nearly as may be in words. They are not referred to any standard color-keys or charts, for the reason that few descriptive entomologists are likely to have any of these at their elbows.

The MS and the proofs have had over twenty-five readings: any errors or misprints are the consequence of the imperfect human element.

Appreciation is due to Dr. G. C. Crampton, who kindly furnished a list of terms in morphology, here accredited to him; to Dr. A. B. Klots, who kindly has furnished definitions of some hundred or more elusive terms, and who with Dr. A. G. Richards, Jr., has made the drawings for genitalia and wing-venation in Lepidoptera; to Mrs. Lenore Reese Sias, who has defined many of the chemical terms; and to her and to my dear wife, Mrs. Lillian R. de la Torre-Bueno, for carrying the burden of collating and correcting proof with me; both have helped greatly in the clarification of many obscurities in expression or definition. And finally, my gratitude is without stint to my friend Mr. George P. Englehardt for his encouragement and understanding in the accomplishment of this work; and the to the Brooklyn Entomological Society for their unwavering support in the preparation and publication of this Glossary.

J. R. de la Torre-Bueno

Tucson, Arizona
September 1, 1937.

INTRODUCTION TO SUPPLEMENT A

In the twenty-three years since the Torre-Bueno Glossary was issued, entomology has grown rapidly both in its substance and its vocabulary. The purpose of Supplement A is to provide students with additional terms as well as to furnish modifications and modernizations of some of the definitions in the Glossary to reflect present understanding. Insofar as practicable, the format of this Supplement follows that of the parent work and provision is made for cross-referencing the two as occasion demands.

Supplement A has been compiled from text and journal sources, and also from information solicited from specialists in various fields. The Society is indebted to Professor Jack C. Jones of the University of Maryland, Dr. C. B. Philip of the Rocky Mountain Laboratory, Professor A. G. Richards of the University of Minnesota, Professor Morris Rockstein of New York University, Mr. George C. Steyskal of Grosse Ile, Michigan, Dr. Alan Stone of the U.S. National Museum, and Professor and Mrs. G. C. Wheeler of the University of North Dakota for their aid.

The first entomological vocabulary published in America appeared in 1883 as part of volume 6 of the Bulletin of the Brooklyn Entomological Society. It included about 800 terms and definitions. Twenty-three years later (1906) the Society sponsored the publication of Dr. John B. Smith's "An Explanation of Terms Used in Entomology" which contained about 4,000 entries. The Glossary of Entomology by J. R. de la Torre-Bueno (1937) containing 10,000 terms and 12,000 definitions was the third dictionary published by the Society. Like the two earlier ones, this last was designed to provide workers, from the beginner to the advanced student, with a ready reference to the many terms used in the various phases of insect study. In their respective times, all three of these works gained wide acceptance, both here and abroad, and the Torre-Bueno Glossary, translated in Chinese, was incorporated into "A Dictionary of Entomological Terms" by SoSome Jame (1956) of the Taiwan Provincial College of Agriculture.

[George S. Tulloch]

[July, 1960]

ORDINAL NAMES USED IN THE GLOSSARY

Collembola
Protura
Diplura
Archaeognatha
Zygentoma
Ephemeroptera
Odonata
Plecoptera
Dermaptera
Grylloblattodea
Blattaria

Isoptera
Mantodea
Orthoptera
Phasmida
Zoraptera
Embiidina
Psocoptera
Phthiraptera
Thysanoptera
Hemiptera
Megaloptera

Raphidioptera
Planipennia
Coleoptera
Strepsiptera
Mecoptera
Trichoptera
Lepidoptera
Diptera
Siphonaptera
Hymenoptera

a-, prefix: wanting or without (T-B; Harris).

a posteriori weighting, the weighting of taxonomic characters on the basis of their proved contribution to the establishment of natural classification, i.e., monophyletic taxa (Mayr); see a priori weighting.

a priori, applied to a form of reasoning that deduces consequences from assumed principles; without a determining examination (T-B).

a priori weighting, the weighting of taxonomic characters on the basis of preconceived criteria, e.g., their physiological importance (Mayr); see a posteriori weighting.

ab-, prefix: off; away from (T-B; Harris).

Abate (trade name), temephos, q.v. (Pfadt).

abbreviate, abbreviatus (Latin), disproportionate shortness in a part; cut short; not of usual length (T-B).

abbreviate fascia, a fascia traversing less than half of a wing (T-B).

abdomen, the third or posterior, major division of the insect body, consisting primitively of eleven segments, but normally with 9 or ten apparent segments and bearing no functional legs in the adult stage (T-B; Chapman); see metasoma.

abdomere, abdominal segment, q.v. (Tulloch).

abdominal, belonging or pertaining to the abdomen (T-B).

abdominal appendages, in an embryo, pleuropodia, q.v. (Chapman); cerci, q.v., and external genitalia, q.v. (Chapman); in Collembola, ventral tube, retinaculum, and furcula, q.v. (Chapman); in Protura, paired appendages on each of the first 3 abdominal segments (Chapman); in Archaeognatha, Zygentoma, and Diplura, styli, eversible vesicles and cerci, q.v. (Chapman; von Kéler); in aquatic insects, abdominal gills, q.v. (Chapman); in larval Lepidoptera, Mecoptera, some Diptera, and sawflies (Hymenoptera: Symphyta), prolegs, q.v. (Chapman); in larval Lepidoptera and Trichoptera, anal prolegs, q.v. (Chapman); in Zygentoma and Ephemeroptera, filum terminale, q.v. (Chapman; von Kéler); in larval Sphingidae, the terminal spine arising from the dorsum of abdominal segment X (Chapman); in nymphs of Zygoptera, caudal gills, q.v. (Chapman); in larval Coleoptera, urogomphi, q.v. (Chapman); in Aphididae (Hemiptera: Sternorrhyncha), cornicles, q.v. (Chapman).

abdominal feet, prolegs, q.v. (T-B).

abdominal filaments, in Ephemeroptera, cerci, q.v. (Tulloch; Tuxen, after Stephens).

abdominal forceps, in ♂ Mecoptera, stylus, q.v. (Tuxen, after Hobby and Killington).

abdominal ganglia, ganglia of the ventral nerve cord which innervate the abdomen, variable in number, each giving off a pair of principal nerves to the muscles of the segment (T-B, after Imms), generally one to a segment, lying between the alimentary canal and the large ventral muscles (T-B).

abdominal gills, in nymphs of Ephemeroptera, 4 to 8 pairs of platelike or filamentous gills arising from the pleural region of the abdomen

(Chapman); in nymphs of Plecoptera, gill tufts or filaments on abdominal segments I to VI or on the anal region, including cerci and terminal filament (Chapman: Zwick, pers. comm.); in larval *Sialis* (Megaloptera: Sialidae), 7 pairs of five-segmented gills, each arising from a basal sclerite on the side of the abdomen (Chapman); in other larval Megaloptera and some larval Coleoptera, unsegmented gills, on the side of the abdomen (Chapman); in larval Trichoptera, filamentous gills, in tufts, on a common stalk, or as single filaments, in dorsal, lateral, and ventral series on the abdomen (Chapman; Morse, pers. comm.).

abdominal groove, in some butterflies (Lepidoptera), the concave lobe of the inner margin of the hind wings enveloping the abdomen beneath (T-B).

abdominal plate, in ♂ Lepidoptera, mappa, q.v. (Tuxen, after Buchanan White).

abdominal pouch, in adult Lepidoptera, sphragis, q.v. (T-B; Tulloch; Tuxen, after Elwes).

abdominal puncture, in larval and pupal Culicidae (Diptera), puncture occurring medially on the dorsolateral area of abdominal segments III–V (Harbach and Knight).

abdominal region, the third of 3 regions into which the embryonic trunk segments become segregated, the appendages of which are obliterated or reduced (T-B, after Snodgrass); see abdomen.

abdominal segment, one of the annular subdivisions of the insect abdomen (Harbach and Knight, after Theobald).

abdominal spiracle, one of a pair of spiracles of an abdominal segment (Harbach and Knight, after Christophers).

abdominal sucker, in larval Blepharoceridae (Diptera), adhesive organ on abdominal segments II–VII (Chapman, after Hinton).

abduction, drawing back; retraction (T-B); movement of the coxa away from the body (Chapman, after Hughes).

abductor, abductor muscle, q.v. (T-B).

abductor muscle, any muscle that opens out or extends an appendage or draws it away from the body (T-B); see adductor muscle.

abductor coxae, the muscle of the coxa, which directs it outward (T-B); see adductor coxae.

abductor mandibulae, the muscle that opens the mandibles (T-B).

aberrant, departing from the regular or normal type (T-B).

aberration, a form that departs in some striking way from the normal type, occurring either singly, or rarely, at regular intervals (T-B); a number of individuals within a species, unequivocally signifying infrasubspecific rank (ICZN).

abiogenesis, spontaneous generation (T-B).

abnormal, outside of the usual range or course; not normal (T-B).

abnormality, the quality or state of being abnormal; a deviation from the normal; a structure, function, or condition different from the usual; a malformation or teratology; a state of disease (Steinhaus and Martignoni).

aboral, in a direction away from the mouth (T-B).

aboriginal, first; original; native (T-B).

aborted, developed so as to be unfit for normal function; obsolete or atrophied (T-B).

abortion, imperfect or nondevelopment of any normally present part or organ (T-B).

abraded, scraped or rubbed (T-B).

abrupt, sudden or without gradation (T-B).

abscised, abscissus (Latin), cut off squarely, with a straight margin (T-B).

abscissa, in the wing, a more or less segregated or distinct segment or section of a vein; e.g., abscissa of radius (T-B).

absconding, departure of a whole colony of highly eusocial bees for a new nest site (Michener).

absconditus (Latin), hidden; concealed (T-B).

absolute, that to which all else is relative, existing in and of itself, independently and actually; a philosophical something not existing in nature (T-B).

absolute hemocyte count, the number of hemocytes within the insect, including both sessile and circulating forms (Tulloch, after Jones).

absolute refractory period, in the presence of an action potential, the period during which no further stimulation can initiate another impulse, nor can an impulse from elsewhere pass through the area (Chapman).

absolute tautonymy, the identical spelling of a generic or subgeneric name and the specific or subspecific name of one of its originally included nominal species or subspecies (Tulloch; ICZN).

absorption, passive or active process in which products of digestion are taken up by cells of the midgut and hind gut (Chapman).

Acalypterae, Acalyptratae, q.v. (T-B, after Imms).

Acalypteratae, Acalyptratae, q.v. (T-B, after Curran).

Acalyptrata, Acalyptratae, q.v. (T-B).

Acalyptratae, section within the division Schizophora (Diptera: Brachycera), including the superfamilies Conopoidea, Nerioidea, Diopsoidea, Tephritoidea, Opomyzoidea, Sciomyzoidea, Lauxanioidea, Sphaeroceroidea, and Ephydroidea, characterized by adults with antennal pedicel with dorsal seam usually absent or incomplete except in Drosophiloidea and greater ampula usually absent (Borror et al; McAlpine).

acalyptrate Diptera, Diptera with lower calypter absent or vestigial (Colless and McAlpine, in CSIRO).

acanthae, very fine cuticular bristles, occurring in the proventriculus (Boudreaux), and elsewhere.

acanthoparia (pl., **acanthopariae**), in larval Scarabaeoidea (Coleoptera), spiny marginal parts of the paria, the lateral paired regions of the epipharynx (T-B, after Böving).

acanthophorites, in ♀ Asiloidea (Diptera), lamelliform dorsal appendages at base of proctiger (Tuxen, after Hardy); in many ♀ Orthorrhapha (Diptera), pair of hemitergites representing divided tergum IX, bearing strong spines (Colless and McAlpine, in CSIRO).

acanthus, a spine, spur or prickle (T-B).

Acaraben (trade name), chlorobenzilate, q.v. (Pfadt).

Acaralate (trade name), chloropropylate, q.v. (Pfadt).

acariform, shaped like a mite (Acari) (Peterson).

Acari, order within the class Arachnida, including mites and ticks, characterized by an unsegmented opisthosoma which is broadly joined to the prosoma (Borror et al.).

acaricide, a chemical employed to kill and control mites and ticks (Acari) (Pfadt).

Acarida, Acari, q.v. (Borror et al.).

Acarina, Acari, q.v. (T-B; Tulloch).

acarine disease, a disease of adult bees (Hymenoptera: Apoidea) caused by the parasitic mite *Acarapsis woodi* (Acari), which infests the tracheae leading from the first pair of thoracic spiracles, causing the bees to lose their ability to fly and shortening the life of overwintering bees (Steinhaus and Martignoni).

Acarol (trade name), bromopropylate, q.v. (Pfadt).

acaudal, acaudate, without a tail (T-B).

accessory, secondary; adjoined to any primary structure (T-B).

accessory appendages, in ♂ Odonata, accessory genitalia, q.v. (T-B, after Garman; Tuxen).

accessory blade, in larval Chironomidae (Diptera), a thin, flat appendage of blade, q.v., on basal antennal segment, joined with blade at base (Saether) or on mandible, seta subdentalis, q.v (Saether).

accessory boss, in Hypogastruridae (Collembola), a condition where the posterior arms of the postantennal organ encircle a knob or prominence (Christiansen and Bellinger).

accessory burrows, in ground-nesting species, blind-end false tunnels close beside the true nest burrow, e.g., in some Sphecidae (Hymenoptera) (Matthews and Matthews).

accessory canal of spermatheca, diverticulum ductus, q.v. (Tuxen, after Scudder).

accessory carinae, in Orthoptera, lateral facial carinae, q.v. (T-B).

accessory cell, a wing cell not commonly present (T-B); in adult Lepidoptera, a closed cell in the front wing formed from the fusion of 2 branches of the radius (T-B, after Comstock, Klots; Borror et al.).

accessory cilia, in Thysanoptera, long, usually straight hairs borne at tip of wing in addition to the fringe in many Tubulifera (Mound et al).

accessory circulatory organ, pulsatile organ, q.v. (T-B).

accessory clasper, in ♂ Micropterigidae (Lepidoptera), a protrusion, bearing heavy setae, near base of uncus (Tuxen, after Heath).

accessory copulatory processes, accessory copulatory sclerites, q.v. (Tuxen, after Walker).

accessory copulatory sclerites, in ♂ Grylloblattodea, 2 small sclerites carried by the right phallomere (Tuxen, after Scudder).

accessory diverticulum, in ♀ Siphonaptera, duplicatura vaginalis, q.v. (Lewis, pers. comm.).

accessory fecundation canal, in ♀ Heteroptera (Hemiptera), diverticulum ductus, q.v. (Tuxen, after Scudder).

accessory genital glands, glands opening in ♀ primarily on venter of abdominal segment IX, secreting an adhesive substance or material forming a covering or case (ootheca) for eggs; in ♂, opening into ejaculatory duct (Tuxen); see colleterial glands, ectadenia, glandulae accessoriae, glandulae sebaceae, and sebific glands.

accessory genitalia, in ♂ Odonata, the genitalia of abdominal segment II (T-B, after Garman; Tuxen).

accessory gland, in general, any secondary gland of a glandular system (T-B); in ♀ Ensifera (Orthoptera), a gland opening into the genital chamber (Tuxen); in ♀ Heteroptera (Hemiptera), vermiform gland, q.v. (Tuxen, after Scudder); in, e.g. *Oncopeltus* (Hemiptera: Heteroptera: Lygaeidae), a long tubular portion of the salivary gland that produces some of the mucoids of the more fluid saliva (Chapman, after Miles); in ♀ *Dysdercus* (Hemiptera: Heteroptera: Pyrrhocoridae), diverticulum ductus, q.v. (Tuxen, after Freeman); in ♀ Osmylidae (Planipennia), spermatheca, q.v.(Tuxen, after Kimmins); in ♀ Diptera, accessory genital gland, q.v. (McAlpine).

acessory gland duct, a duct of an accessory gland in the insect reproductive system (Harbach and Knight, after Jones and Wheeler).

accessory gland duct base, in ♀ Culicidae (Diptera), the usually pigmented part of the accessory gland duct near its opening into the vagina (Harbach and Knight).

accessory gonopore, in adult insects, external opening of accessory genital or colleterial glands, primitively through paired papillae (labia, phalli) on abdominal segment IX, but united with gonadal gonopore in Hymenoptera and most other orders (Tuxen, after E. L. Smith); see collatoria.

accessory heart, pulsatile organ, q.v. (Leftwich).

accessory lobes, corpora ventralia, q.v. (T-B; Chapman).

accessory male genitalia, in some Schizopteridae (Heteroptera), complex dorsoabdominal pregenital structures assumed to perform the actual insemination after receiving sperm from the primary genitalia (Štys).

accessory mandibular sclerite, in larval Tabanoidea (Diptera), barlike sclerite of head capsule bearing mandibular brush (Teskey, in McAlpine).

accessory oral sclerites, in some larval Calliphoridae and Muscidae (Diptera), sclerites closely associated with and located below or between the mandibles (Teskey, in McAlpine).

accessory organ, in ♀ Lepidoptera, appendix bursae, q.v. (Tuxen, after Brown).

accessory papilla, in Collembola, an integumental papilla of antennal apex, lateral and additional to the normal apical retractile papilla (Christiansen and Bellinger).

accessory parempodia, in Heteroptera (Hemiptera), small, secondary parempodia, q.v. (Cobben).

accessory process of antenna, in larval Coleoptera, a short or long secondary process arising from the distal portion of the second, occasionally the first, segment of the antenna; supplemental process, q.v.; tactile papilla, q.v.; sensory appendix, q.v. (Peterson).

accessory pulsatory organ, pulsatile organ, q.v. (T-B).

accessory sac, in ♀ insects, accessory genital glands, q.v. (T-B; Tulloch).

accessory salivary gland, in Heteroptera (Hemiptera), tubular (Enicocephalidae, Pentatomomorpha) or vesicular gland associated by a duct with the principal salivary gland (Cobben; Miyamoto).

accessory scent glands, in Heteroptera (Hemiptera), small scent glands associated with the scent reservoir of the metathoracic scent gland (Štys, pers. comm.).

accessory seta, in Entomobryidae (Collembola), one of a group of microsetae associated with the base of the bothriotrix or macrochaeta (Christiansen and Bellinger); in ♂ *Anopheles* (Diptera: Culicidae), one of usually a pair of prominent setae located near the mesal margin of the dorsal (prerotation sense) surface of the gonocoxite, being dorsal to the internal seta and distal to the parabasal setae (Harbach and Knight, after Gater).

accessory sexual characters, structures and organs (except the gonads) of which the genital tract is composed, including accessory glands and external genitalia (Mayr); see secondary sexual characters.

accessory subcostal vein, in adult Plecoptera, the vein given off from the subcosta and branching toward the apex of the wing (T-B).

accessory teeth, in anopheline larvae (Diptera: Culicidae), a group of peglike teeth borne on the mesodorsal margin of the mandible, located immediately posterior to and closely associated with the base of the posterior dorsal tooth (Harbach and Knight, after Foote); in some culicine larvae (Diptera: Culicidae), a smaller group of similar structures closely associated with the posterior dorsal tooth (Harbach and Knight).

accessory tergal plate, in some anopheline larvae (Diptera: Culicidae), one of the small median or submedian dorsal sclerites located posterior to the tergal plates of abdominal segments I–VII (Harbach and Knight, after Belkin).

accessory testis, in many ♂ Coleoptera, tightly coiled middle section of the vas deferens, being a reservoir for the sperm (Tulloch).

accessory tympanal membrane, in adult Lepidoptera, a secondary membrane of the tympanum; morphologically a membranized part of the postnotum (T-B, after Richards).

accessory vein, secondarily developed vein in the wings of insects (T-B, after Comstock and Kellogg); an extra branch of a longitudinal vein (Borror et al); in adult Symphyta (Hymenoptera), the most posterior vein in the anal area of the forewing, i.e., the third anal vein (A_3) (Borror et al.; Riek, in CSIRO); see intercalary vein.

accessory ventral condyle, an additional condyle or articulating process on the ventral side of the mandible and located mesad of the regular ventral condyle (Peterson).

accidental host, in invertebrate pathology, a host in which the pathogenic microorganism (or parasite) is not commonly found; nevertheless one suitable for the pathogen's development (Steinhaus and Martignoni, after Hopps and Price).

acclimation, response to temperature varying according to previous experience of the insect (Chapman).

acclimatization, acclimation, q.v. (Chapman).

acclivous, rising gently (T-B).

accommodation, in vision, the ability to change the focus of the eye (T-B).

accrescent, accrescente, increasing gradually in thickness toward the apex (T-B).

accretion, in Lepidoptera, sphragis, q.v. (Tulloch).

aceous, aceus, suffix; similar to, or of the nature of (T-B).

acephalic head capsule, in larval Muscomorpha (Diptera: Brachycera), reduced head capsule retracted into the thorax (Teskey, in McAlpine).

acephalous, without a head (T-B); without a distinct head (Peterson).

acephalous larva, in Muscomorpha (Diptera), larva without a distinct head capsule (Chapman); see acephalic head capsule.

acephate, a synthetic insecticide, plant systemic; an organophosphate, *O, S*-dimethyl acetylphosphoramidothioate; slightly toxic to mammals, acute oral LD_{50} for rats 866 to 945 mg/kg (Pfadt).

acerata, arthropods without true antennae, e.g., Arachnida and *Xyphosura* (T-B).

Acercaria, a group of hemimetabolous insects, including the extant orders Psocoptera, Phthiraptera, Thysanoptera, and Hemiptera, characterized by the lack of abdominal cerci, reduced abdominal sternum I, and lacinia of the maxilla developed into a stylet drawn deep into the head capsule (Hennig); see Psocodea and Condylognatha.

Acercarida, Acercaria, q.v. (Boudreaux).

Acerentomoidea, a suborder of Protura containing the families Protentomidae and Acerentomidae, lacking spiracles, and abdomen with pectinated structure (Nosek).

acerous, without antennae, e.g., the Protura (T-B; (Leftwich).

acetabular angle, in adult Siphonaptera, the angle formed by the 2 margins of the acetabular projection (Hopkins and Rothschild).

acetabular bristle(s), in adult Siphonaptera, acetabular setae, q.v. (Lewis, pers. comm.).

acetabular caps, in Hemiptera, coxal cavity, q.v. (T-B).

acetabular projection, in ♂ Siphonaptera, processus acetabuli, q.v. (Tuxen, after Hopkins and Rothschild); in ♂ Siphonaptera, a projection of the fixed process of the clasper bearing the acetabular seta(e) (Lewis, pers. comm.).

acetabular setae, in ♂ Siphonaptera, one or 2 long setae arising on the posterior margin of the fixed process of the clasper, frequently from a caudal projection of the latter (Lewis, pers. comm.).

acetabuliform, like a shallow saucer with more or less incurved sides; of the shape of an acetabulum or coxal cavity (T-B).

acetabulum (pl., **acetabula**), the cavity into which an appendage is articulated, e.g., coxal cavity (T-B); in larval Diptera, a cuplike cavity in the mouth (T-B); in ♂ Siphonaptera, the point of articulation of the movable process with the body (fixed process) of the clasper (Hopkins and Rothschild).

acetic acid, glacial, a clear, colorless liquid, with a pungent characteristic odor resembling vinegar and with an acid taste when well diluted with water; miscible with water, alcohol and glycerine; used in hardening tissues and for other histological purposes (T-B).

acetylcholine, chemical transmitter at excitatory synapses within the central nervous system, produced in the presynaptic fiber (Chapman).

acetylcholine esterase, enzyme that destroys acetylcholine postsynaptically (Chapman).

acetyl coenzyme A, enzyme involved in acetylcholine synthesis, energy metabolism, and intermediate metabolism (Chapman).

acetyl dopamine quinone, aromatic ring linking proteins in a sclerotization process known as quinone tanning (Chapman).

acetyl glucosomine, major subunit of the polysaccharide chitin, a constituent of insect cuticle (Chapman).

achatine, achatinus (Latin), resembling the lines of a agate in more or less concentric circles (T-B).

Achreioptera, an ordinal term proposed for the Platypsyllidae (Coleoptera) (T-B).

achrestogonomes, in a few species of Isoptera, alates which remain in the nest after swarming, loosing their wings, their gonads becoming atrophied, and playing no role in the maintenance of the colony (Grassé).

achromatic, free from color (T-B).

achromatin, that part of the cell nucleus which does not stain with chromatin (T-B).

acia, a thin cuticular plate of the mandible (T-B, after MacGillivray).

acicula (pl., **aciculae**), needle or spine (T-B); a small, slender, rigid, needle- or thornlike spicule (Harbach and Knight); in ♀ Tubulifera (Thysanoptera), paired, sclerotized thickenings in the marginal cuticle of the common oviduct appearing in macerated whole mounts as curved needles in abdominal segments VIII and IX (Heming).

acicular, needle-shaped; with a long slender point (T-B).

aciculate, aciculatus (Latin), appearing as if superficially scratched with a needle (T-B; Harris); furnished with aciculae (Harbach and Knight); see rastrate and scarified.

aciculate seta, a seta funished with slender needlelike processes along the stem (Harbach and Knight).

acid, a chemical compound having a sour taste and turning blue litmus red when in solution, that is, containing the H$^+$ radical; a salt of hydrogen (T-B).

acid alcohol, 70% alcohol to which is added 0.1% to 1% hydrochloric acid; used for destaining (T-B).

acid glands, poison glands, q.v. (T-B, after Imms; Leftwich).

acid scent, a pungent, sour smell (T-B).

acidopore, in adult Formicinae (Hymenoptera: Formicidae), pore of the modified hypopygium through which venomous secretions are squirted (Gauld and Bolton); see nozzle.

acidotheca, the pupal sheath of the ovipositor (T-B).

acies, the extreme termination of a margin (T-B).

acinacicate, acinaciform, falchion-shaped; curved and growing wider toward the bend, with a truncate apex (T-B).

acinose, acinous, continuously set with granulations like those on a blackberry (T-B; Harris); see colliculate, granulate, and papillate.

acinus (pl., **acini**), granulations, like those on a blackberry; the terminal secreting tubes of glands (T-B).

acone eye, a type of insect eye in which the ommatidium has neither a crystalline nor a liquid cone, in place of which there is a group of elongate transparent cells (T-B, after Imms); see acone ommatidia.

acone ommatidia, ommatidia in which the Semper cells do not produce a separate lens, but have a clear cytoplasm and occupy the region normally filled by the cone, e.g., some Coleoptera (Coccinellidae, Staphylinidae, and Tenebrionidae), some Diptera, and Heteroptera (Chapman).

acoustic communication, in Cicadellidae and Fulgoroidea (Hemiptera: Auchenorrhyncha), sound transmission through the plant substrate (O'Brien, pers. comm.); see calling song.

acoustic nerve, auditory nerve, q.v. (T-B).

acraein, a protective or distasteful secretion of certain butterflies (Lepidoptera) (Leftwich).

Acridoidea, superfamily belonging to the Caelifera (Orthoptera), including the short-horned grasshoppers and locusts, characterized by having all the tarsi with 3 tarsomeres (Key, in CSIRO).

acridophagus, feeding on grasshoppers (Orthoptera) (T-B); feeding on substances which (to man) have a sharp, biting taste (Tulloch).

acroblast, in the development of an acrosome, a cup that embraces the proacrosomal granule (Chapman, after Kaye).

acrocercus (pl., **acrocerci**), cercus, q.v. (Tulloch); in ♂ Lepidoptera, structure on inner face of valva (Tuxen, after Berlese).

acrodendrophily, the tendency of certain sylvan insects to inhabit the tree-tops (Tulloch).

acrogynium (pl., **acrogynia**), in ♀ Protura, supposed distal part of squama genitalis, retractable into perigynium and consisting of stipes and paired styli; however, only the nonretractible styli exist (Tuxen, after Berlese).

acron, the prostomium, q.v. (T-B); in the arthropod embryo, the head region anterior to the tritocerebral somite (T-B, after Snodgrass); the first preoral segment of the head (McAlpine).

acroparia (pl., **acropariae**), in larval Scarabaeidae (Coleoptera), anterior part of paria bearing bristles that are usually long (T-B, after Böving).

acroperiphallus (pl., **acroperiphalli**), in ♂ Protura, distal part of periphallus that may be retractable into basiperiphallus (Tuxen).

acrophallus, in ♂ Diptera, part of distiphallus bearing the gonopore (McAlpine).

acropod, pretarsus, q.v. (McAlpine).

acrosome, anterior end of the head of a mature sperm, in front of the nucleus, probably concerned with attachment of the sperm to the egg and possibly also with lysis of the egg membrane, thus permitting sperm entry (Chapman).

acrosternite, narrow marginal flange of abdominal sternum anterior to the antecosta of a definite sternal plate that includes the preceding primary intersegmental sclerotization (T-B, after Snodgrass); in ♂ Lycaenidae (Lepidoptera), sclerite of intersegmental membrane between sterna VIII and IX, more or less fused with cephalic margin of vinculum, sometimes bearing specialized hair-plumes (Tuxen, after Shirozu and Yamamoto).

acrostichal(s), in adult Diptera, acrostichal setae, q.v. (T-B, after Curran; Saether).

acrostichal area, in adult Diptera, the median longitudinal area of the scutum bearing the acrostichal setae (Harbach and Knight, after Belkin).

acrostichal bristles, in adult Diptera, acrostichal setae, q.v. (T-B; Borror et al.).

acrostichal hairs, in adult Diptera, hairs lying between the dorsocentral bristles (T-B, after Curran); see acrostichal setae.

acrostichal setulae, in adult Diptera, very short hairs between the dorsocentral bristles (T-B, after Curran); see acrostichal setae.

acrostichal scale, in adult Culicidae (Diptera), one of the scales usually occurring in one or 2 lines on the acrostichal area of the scutum, being borne on either side of the acrostichal setae when 2 rows are present (Harbach and Knight).

acrostichal setae, in adult Diptera, 2 longitudinal rows of setae along midline of scutum (McAlpine); see presutural acrostichal setae and postsutural acrostichal setae.

acrostichal suture, in adult Nematocera (Diptera), median scutal suture, q.v. (McAlpine).

acrostylus (pl., **acrostyli**), in Protura, distal part of stylus (Tuxen); in ♂ Lepidoptera, structure on inner face of valva (Tuxen, after Berlese).

acrotergal, of or pertaining to an acrotergite (T-B).

acrotergite, the anterior, precostal part of the tergal plate of a secondary segment, usually in the form of a narrow flange, sometimes greatly enlarged but frequently reduced or obliterated (T-B, after Snodgrass).

acrotrophic, in the ovary, having the trophic cells remain in the apical chamber (T-B).

acrotrophic egg tube, telotrophic ovariole, q.v. (T-B, after Snodgrass).

acrotrophic ovariole, telotrophic ovariole, q.v. (T-B, after Snodgrass; Leftwich).

acrydian, a grasshopper; grasshopperlike (T-B).

actin, protein filament, being a major component of muscle fibrils (Chapman).

actinomycete symbiont, in *Rhodnius* (Heteroptera: Reduviidae), fungal symbiont (*Actinomyces*), living in crypts between the cells of the anterior midgut, providing precursors of B vitamins to the insect (Chapman).

action potential, self-generating standard signal that travels through nerve cells (Matthews and Matthews), arising from a depolarization of the axon membrane associated with a change in permeability (Chapman).

activation center, region near the posterior pole of the egg involved in production of the germ band and its subsequent development (Chapman); see differentiation centre.

active ingredient, the toxic part of a pesticide formulation (Pfadt).

active space, the space within which the concentration of a pheromone (or any other behaviorally active substance) is at or above threshold concentration (Wilson).

actual penis, in ♂ Heteroptera (Hemiptera), endosoma, q.v., (Tuxen, after Ekblom).

acuductate, acuducted, acuductus (Latin), aciculate, q.v. (T-B; Harris).

aculea (pl., **aculeae**), microtrichium, q.v. (T-B, after Comstock, Tillyard; Mackerras, in CSIRO); spinelike seta (Boudreaux); in adult Diptera, one of the microtrichiumlike spicules comprising the tomentum (Harbach and Knight); aculeus, q.v. (Leftwich).

Aculeata, group of Hymenoptera, including the superfamilies Chrysidoidea, Tiphioidea, Formicoidea, Scolioidea, Vespoidea, Sphecoidea, and Apoidea, in which the ovipositor is modified into a sting (T-B; Wilson; Brown, in Parker); see Apocrita.

aculeate, pointed (T-B); armed with short sharp points (T-B); furnished with prickles (T-B); with aculeae (Borrow et al.); armed with a sharp sting, as in the Hymenoptera (T-B); pertaining to the Aculeata (Wilson).

aculeate-serrate, armed with numerous short points inclined toward one end, like the teeth of a saw (T-B).

aculeate Hymenoptera, members of the Aculeata, q.v. (Riek, in CSIRO).

aculeatus (Latin), aculeate, q.v. (T-B).

aculeus (pl., **aculei**), a prickle; a small sharp point (T-B); in ♀ Odonata, applied to combined anterior and median gonapophyses (Tuxen, after Tillyard); in adult Lepidoptera, microtrichium, q.v. (T-B); in ♂ Tipulidae (Diptera), a sharp spine jutting from beneath the margin of the eighth sternite (T-B; Tulloch); in ♀ Hymenoptera, stinglike ovipositor (Tuxen).

acumen (pl., **acumina**), in ♂ some Chrysopidae (Planipennia), central tooth of tignum (Tuxen, after Tjeder).

acuminate, acuminated, acuminatus (Latin), tapering to a long point (T-B).

acupunctate, acupunctatus (Latin), punctate, q.v. (T-B; Harris).

acus, in aculeate Hymenoptera, second gonapophyses, q.v. (Tuxen, after Eaton).

acutangulate, forming, or meeting in an acute angle (T-B).

acute, pointed (T-B); terminating in or forming less than a right angle (T-B); in invertebrate pathology, of short duration (Steinhaus and Martignoni) or characterized by sharpness or severity, e.g., an acute disease (Steinhaus and Martignoni).

acute paralysis, a fatal disease of adult honey bees and of certain bumble bees (Hymenoptera: Apidae), caused by a virus, with infected bees not feeding and unable to fly, and walking around with trembling legs and wings (Steinhaus and Martignoni).

acutilingual, with a sharp pointed tongue or mouth structure, as in some bees (Hymenoptera: Apoidea) (T-B).

acutilingues, bees (Hymenoptera: Apoidea), with a short pointed tongue (T-B); see obtusilingues.

acutolobus (pl., **acutolobi**), in ♂ Blattopteroidea, dorsoexternal process of left epiphallus (Tuxen, after Crampton).

acyl-coenzyme A, intermediate metabolite in the production of triglyceride in cell of the fat body (Gilmour, in CSIRO).

adanal lobes, in larval Scatopsidae (Diptera), a pair of sclerotized lobes above and behind the anus (Teskey, in McAlpine).

adanale, the fourth axillary sclerite of the wing (T-B, after Crampton).

adaptation, the condition of showing fitness for a particular environment, as applied to characteristics of a structure, function, or entire organism; or process by which such fitness is acquired (Mayr); the capacity of a living system to adjust to changing environmental conditions (Tulloch); the capacity of the eye to adjust to varying light intensities, which is controlled in part by pigment migration in the retinal cells (Tulloch).

adaptive ocelli, stemmata, q.v. (T-B, after Comstock).

adaptive radiation, evolutionary divergence of members of a single phyletic line into a series of rather diverse niches or adaptive zones (Mayr).

additional lateral plates, in ♀ Mecoptera, laterotergites, q.v. (Tuxen, after Tjeder).

addled, term used by apiculturalists to describe eggs that fail to hatch, larvae that fail to pupate, and pupae and adult honey bees (Hymenoptera: Apidae), that die without infection but rather the result of genetic anomalies (Steinhaus and Martignoni).

addorsal, close to but not quite on the middle of the dorsum (T-B).

addorsal line, in larval Lepidoptera, a longitudinal line, a little to one side of the dorsal line and between it and the subdorsal line (T-B).

adduction, the movement of the coxa towards the body (Chapman, after Hughes).

adductor, adductor muscle, any muscle that draws an appendage to the body or brings parts into apposition (T-B); see abductor.

adductor coxae, the muscle of the coxa which directs it inward (T-B); see abductor coxae.

adductor mandibulae, the muscle that draws in or closes the mandible (T-B).

adecticous pupa, pupa with immobile mandibles, e.g., Diptera, Coleoptera, Siphonaptera, most most Lepidoptera and Hymenoptera (Chapman, after Hinton).

Adelgoidea, superfamily proposed for the families Adelgidae and Phylloxeridae (Hemiptera: Sternorrhyncha), generally included within the Aphidoidea (Ilharco and Van Harten, after Shaposhnikov).

adeloceratous, with concealed antennae (T-B).

Adelomorpha, Incurvarioidea, q.v. (Munroe, in Parker).

adelphoparasite, heteronomous hyperparasitoid, q.v. (Gauld and Bolton).

adenopodites, cerci arising from abdominal segment XI of Symphyla, provided with spinning glands (Hennig).

adenosine diphosphate (ADP), high-energy phosphoric ester, or nucleotide, of the nucleoside adenosine (Allaby); see adenosine triphosphate.

adenosine triphosphate (ATP), high-energy phosphoric ester, or nucleotide, of the nucleoside adenosine, which functions as the principal energy-carrying compound in the cells of all living organisms, being hydrolyzed to ADP and inorganic phosphate and releasing energy (Allaby); see adenosine triphosphate.

adenosma, in larval Lepidoptera, cervical gland, q.v.

adenotrophic viviparity, viviparity in which fully developed eggs with chorion are produced and passed to the uterus; embryonic development follows as in ovoviparity, but when the larva hatches it remains in the uterus and is nourished by special maternal glands; parturition occurs when the larva is fully developed and pupation follows within a short time, there being no free-living feeding phase; e.g., *Glossina* (Glossinidae) and Pupipara (Diptera) (Chapman).

adenylluciferin, in light production, activated form of luciferin and precursor of adenyloxyluciferin (Chapman).

adenyloxyluciferin, oxydized form of adenylluciferin that produces light through spontaneous decay to low energy adenyloxyluciferin (Chapman).

Adephaga, one of the 4 suborders of Coleoptera, including predominantly predaceous and terrestrial or aquatic beetles; the adults having notopleural sutures and the basal abdominal sternite divided into 2 lateral pieces by the hind coxae; the larva lacking a mola on the mandible, a lacinia on the maxilla, and a labrum (Britton, in CSIRO); see Polyphaga, Archostemata, and Myxophaga.

adephagan, of or pertaining to the Adephaga; a member of the Adephaga.

adephagid, adephagan, q.v. (T-B).

adephagous, adephagan, q.v. (T-B).

adermata, pupae in which the wings and other parts of the forming imago show through the pupal skin (T-B).

adfrontal areas, in larval Lepidoptera, the areas between the ecdysial lines and the adfrontal sutures (T-B, after Imms; Common, in CSIRO).

adfrontal pieces, adfrontal areas, q.v. (Peterson).

adfrontal sclerites, in larval Lepidoptera, adfrontal areas, q.v. (T-B; Peterson).

adfrontal setae, in larval Lepidoptera, a pair of setae, AF1 and AF2, on the adfrontal areas of head capsule (Stehr).

adfrontal sutures, in larval Lepidoptera, sutures separating adfrontal areas from frontoclypeus (Hinton; Common, in CSIRO; Stehr).

adfrontals, in larval Lepidoptera, adfrontal areas, q.v. (T-B).

adhesive anal macrosetae, in some pupal Pentaneurini (Diptera: Chironomidae), filamentous anal macrosetae surrounded by sticky, jellylike substance on apical two-thirds (Saether).

adhesive discs, in some ♂ Siphonaptera, an array of mushroom-shaped projections on the inner surface of the antennae that are applied to sternum II of the ♀ during copulation (Rothschild and Traub).

adhesive hair, tenent hair, q.v. (Tulloch).

adhesive sacs, in Aleyrodidae (Hemiptera: Sternorrhyncha), a pair of saclike extentions of the body wall mesad of the midlegs (Russell).

adiaphanous, adiaphanus, having only a surface transparency; opaque, not transmitting light at all (T-B, after Kirby and Spence).

adipohemocyte, in Lepidoptera, Diptera, and representatives of other orders, hemocyte characterized by refringent fat droplets and other inclusions (Chapman, after Rizki).

adipokinetic hormone, hormone from the glandular lobes of the corpora cardiaca that initiates metabolism of fats, usually triglycerides, stored in the fat body (Chapman, after Jutsum and Goldsworthy).

adipoleucocyte, adipohemocyte, q.v. (T-B; Tulloch).

adipose tissue, fat body, q.v. (T-B).

Adiscota, old term for insects which develop into adults without forming imaginal discs (T-B); see Discota.

admedian sclerites, in ♀ Cimicidae (Heteroptera), gonocoxites of abdominal segment VIII (Tuxen, after Rothschild).

adminiculum (pl., **adminicula**), support or prop (T-B); one of the minute teeth on the dorsal abdominal surface in subterranean pupae (T-B); the elevated or indented lines found in certain pupae (T-B); in ♂ Diptera, gonostern, q.v. (Tuxen, after Rubzov), or aedeagal guide, q.v. (McAlpine); in ♂ Tipulidae (Diptera), aedeagal guide, q.v. (van Emden and Hennig, in Tuxen).

adnate, adjoining; adhering or growing together; closely connected (T-B).

adoption substance, a secretion presented by a social parasite that induces the host insects to accept it as a member of their colony (Wilson).

adoral, to, toward, or in the direction of the mouth (T-B).

ADP, adenosine diphosphate, q.v. (Allaby).

adpressed, laid or pressed to; contiguous (T-B).

adscensio (pl., **adscenciones**), in some ♂ Neuropteroidea, dorsally directed process of parameres (Tuxen, after Tjeder).

adsperse, adspersus (Latin), marked with closely crowded, small spots (T-B; Harris); see atomarius, irrorate, and maculate.

adult, the fully-grown, sexually mature insect (T-B); the final stage in the arthropod life cycle (Harbach and Knight).

adult transport, the carrying or dragging of one adult social insect by a nestmate, usually during colony emigrations, being a very frequent and stereotyped form of behavior in ants (Hymenoptera: Formicidae) (Wilson).

adultoid reproductive, in the higher termites (Isoptera), a replacement reproductive that becomes a fully developed imago which does not disperse and instead becomes a functional reproductive (morphologically indistinguishable from the founding king or queen) within the natal nest, but rarely developing in colonies with a vigorous primary reproductive of the same sex (Noirot); see supplementary reproductive.

aduncate, aduncatus, aduncus, gradually bent through its whole extent; employed in regard to parts (T-B).

adventitia, the outer layer of elastic connective tissue of the insect heart (T-B, after Folsom and Wardle).

adventitious, occurring accidentally; out of the ordinary course; without apparent reason (T-B).

adventitious suture, in adult Diptera, lateral transverse suture of syntergite (McAlpine).

adventitious veins, secondary wing veins which are neither accessory veins nor intercalary veins, usually the result of crossveins lined up to form a continuous line (T-B, after Comstock; Borror et al.).

adventral line, in larval Lepidoptera, a line which extends the length of the body along the venter between the midline and the leg bases (T-B).

adventral tubercle, in larval Lepidoptera, the most ventral tubercle on abdominal segments I–IX, bearing primary seta V1 (Stehr) or sigma (Fracker) (T-B, after Dyar; Peterson, after Fracker); see ventral group.

aedaeagus, aedoeagus, q.v. (Tuxen).

aedagus, aedeagus, q.v. (Tuxen).

aedalati, in ♂ Auchenorrhyncha (Hemiptera), paired lateral sheathlike portions of aedeagus (Tuxen, after Delong and Freitag).

aedeagal apodemal rod, in ♂ Siphonaptera, apophysis, q.v. (Tuxen, after Traub).

aedeagal apodeme, an apodeme of aedeagus (T-B); in ♂ Siphonaptera, plate arising from base of aedeagus and extending foward above endophallus, consisting of lamina media and laminae laterales (Tuxen, after Snodgrass); in most ♂ Diptera, phallapodeme, q.v. (McAlpine); in ♂ Hymenoptera, apodeme of penis valve, q.v. (Tuxen, after Snodgrass).

aedeagal appendages, in ♂ Achilidae (Hemiptera: Auchenorrhyncha: Fulgoroidea), long sclerotized moveable rods attached to the transverse strut (O'Brien, pers. comm.).

aedeagal blade, in ♂ Chironomidae (Diptera), blade, q.v. (Saether).

aedeagal brace, in ♂ Auchenorrhyncha (Hemiptera), genital phragm, q.v. (Tuxen).

aedeagal crypt, in ♂ Trichoptera, phallocrypt, q.v. (Tuxen, after Snodgrass).

aedeagal foramen, in ♂ Heteroptera (Hemiptera), basal foramen, q.v., (Tuxen, after Michener); in ♂ Hymenoptera, basal opening into lumen of aedeagus when penis valves are fused or approximate dorsally and ventrally (Tuxen, after Michener).

aedeagal fulcrum, in ♂ Lepidoptera, juxta, q.v. (Tuxen, after Snodgrass).

aedeagal furrow, in ♂ Gelastocoridae (Heteroptera), groove in the right paramere (Nieser).

aedeagal guide, in many ♂ Diptera, partially fused lobes occurring medially at the posterior margin of the hypandrium, between the inner ventral bases of the gonocoxites and the anteroventral base of the aedeagus (McAlpine).

aedeagal lamellae, in ♂ Siphonaptera, ventrolateral lobes of palliolum (Tuxen).

aedeagal lobe, in ♂ some Chironomidae (Diptera), weak, membranous lobe of intromittent organ attached to phallapodeme (Saether); see also aedeagus lobes.

aedeagal paraphysis, in ♂ Auchenorrhyncha (Hemiptera), paired or unpaired process belonging to phallobase, as a rule attached to connective, sometimes also to shaft of aedeagus (Tuxen, after Oman, Beirne).

aedeagal pouch, in ♂ Culicidae (Diptera), the membranous depression or pocket into which the aedeagus is retracted at rest (Harbach and Knight, after Spielman); in ♂ Siphonaptera, a sheathlike pouch from which the aedeagus arises (Lewis, pers. comm., after Snodgrass).

aedeagal rods, in ♂ Hymenoptera, parameres, q.v. (Tuxen, after Snodgrass).

aedeagal sclerite, in ♂ Dixidae and certain Culicidae (Diptera), e.g., *Aedes* subgenus *Verrallina*, a supporting sclerite on either side of the phallus, being in most ♂ mosquitoes one of a pair of lateral sclerotizations of the aedeagus (Harbach and Knight, after Belkin).

aedeagal shaft, in Fulgoroidea (Hemiptera: Auchenorrhyncha), proximal part of aedeagus before distal flagellum (O'Brien, pers. comm.); in Delphacidae (Fulgoroidea), aedeagus, q.v. (Kramer).

aedeagal sheath, in ♂ Tabanoidea (Diptera), cone-shaped sheath of aedeagus formed from lateral fusion of aedeagal guide with the fused parameres (McAlpine).

aedeagal spicule, in some ♂ Culicidae (Diptera), one of the usually flattened spicules borne at the apex of the aedeagus (Harbach and Knight).

aedeagal strut, in ♂ Heteroptera (Hemiptera), inferior process, q.v. (Tuxen, after Leston).

aedeagal support, in ♂ Heteroptera (Hemiptera), inferior process, q.v. (Tuxen, after Leston).

aedeagal tines, in ♂ Tabanoidea (Diptera), lateral branches of three-branched aedeagus (McAlpine).

aedeagal valves, in ♂ Caelifera (Orthoptera), a dorsal and ventral pair of sclerotizations in endophallic membrane limiting phallotreme duct; see also dorsal and ventral aedeagal valve (Tuxen).

aedeagus, in ♂ insects, the terminal part of phallus as distinct from phallobase or just the united mesomeres (Tuxen, after Snodgrass); intromittent organ resulting from combination of gonapophyses of abdominal segment IX (Tuxen, after E. L. Smith); in ♂ Archaeognatha and Zygenotoma, penis, q.v. (Tuxen, after Denis); in ♂ Ephemeroptera, penis, q.v. (Tuxen, after Imms); in ♂ Plecoptera, penis, q.v. (Tuxen, after Helson); in ♂ Psocoptera, internal parameres, q.v. (Tuxen, after Badonnel); in ♂ Phthiraptera, complete genital apparatus (Tuxen, after authors); in ♂ Anoplura (Phthiraptera), genital sac together with the various sclerotizations of its walls (Tuxen, after Ferris); in ♂ some Phthiraptera, part of phallus bearing gonopore (Tuxen, after Schmutz); in ♂ Auchenorrhyncha (Hemiptera), tubular sclerotized copulatory organ continuating ductus ejaculatorius, constituting together with phallobase the true penis or phallus (Tuxen); in ♂ Heteroptera (Hemiptera), distal segment of phallus (endosoma) + distal part (basiconjunctiva) of its proximal segment (phallosoma) (Tuxen, after Bonhag and Wick); in ♂ Coleoptera, penis, q.v. (Tuxen, after Snodgrass) or penis + tegmen (Tuxen); in ♂ Strepsiptera, upwards curved sclerotized, acute appendage of abdominal sternum IX, sometimes ending in a hook (Tuxen); in ♂ Neuroptera, penis and accessory structures (parameres, hypomeres) (Tuxen, after authors); in ♂ Raphidiidae (Raphidioptera), hypovalva, q.v. (Tuxen, after Carpenter); in ♂ *Chrysopa* (Planipennia: Chrysopidae), pseudopenis, q.v. (Tuxen, after Killington); in ♂ *Wesmaelius* (Planipennia: Hemerobiidae), mediuncus, q.v. (Tuxen, after Killington); in some ♂ Hemerobiidae (Planipennia), arcessus, q.v. (Tuxen, after Killington); in ♂ *Neochauliodes* (Megaloptera: Corydalidae), parameres, q.v. (Tuxen, after Tjeder); in ♂ Mecoptera, penis and accessory structures (Tuxen, after authors) or penis (Tuxen, after Michener); in ♂ Trichoptera, distal part of phallus, if divided (Tuxen) or whole copulatory organ (Tuxen, after Snodgrass); in ♂ Lepidoptera, aedoeagus, q.v. (Tuxen); in ♂ Diptera, intromittent organ as a whole (Tuxen, after authors), intromittent organ as far as fused with penis valves (Tuxen, after Abul Nasr), or distiphallus, q.v. (Tuxen, after authors, Snodgrass); in ♂ Chironomidae (Diptera), intromittent organ resulting from combination of gonapophyses IX and surrounding phalli (Saether); in ♂ Culicidae (Diptera), central body of phallosome or distal part of phallus (Harbach and Knight); in ♂ Siphonaptera, the external part of the phallosome including the end chamber that bears a large basal

apodeme (Rothschild and Traub); in ♂ Hymenoptera, bilobate intromittent organ (Gauld and Bolton), penis and penis valves (Tuxen,
after Beck), or entire genitalia (Tuxen, after Timberlake).

aedeagus lobes, in ♂ Bittacidae (Mecoptera), penunci, q.v. (Cheng).

aedeagus s. ampl., in ♂ Heteroptera (Hemiptera), phallus as a whole
(Tuxen, after Singh-Prithi).

aedeagus s. pr., in ♂ Heteroptera (Hemiptera), endosoma, q.v.
(Tuxen, after Snodgrass).

aedeagus s. str., in ♂ Heteroptera (Hemiptera), vesica *sensu* Singh-
Pruthi, q.v. (Tuxen, after Snodgrass).

aedoeagus, in ♂ Lepidoptera, the tubular, sclerotized, distal or subdis-
tal, and more or less extrusible part of penis, enclosing the eversible
vesica and enclosed by manica (Tuxen, after Pierce); in ♂ Coleoptera, aedeagus, q.v. (Tuxen); in ♂ Culicidae (Diptera), mesosome, parameres and basal plates (Tuxen, after Marshall); in ♂
Thysanoptera, the fusion product of the mesomeres consisting of
phallotheca, endotheca and pseudovirga (Heming) or endophallus
(Lyal).

aedoeotype, aedoeotypus, q.v. (Tulloch).

aedoeotypus (pl., **aedoeotypi**), in adult Lepidoptera, the first specimen
of a species of which the genitalia are studied and described or fig-
ured (Tuxen, after Toxopeus).

Aegerioidea, Sesioidea, q.v. (Borror et al.).

aeneous, aeneus (Latin), bright brassy or golden green color (T-B).

aenescent, becoming or appearing brassy (T-B).

aequale, aequata, equal (T-B).

aequilate, aequilatus (Latin), of equal breadth throughout (T-B).

Aequipalpia, former suborder of Trichoptera, including species with
adults with isopalpi (Riek, in CSIRO; Mey, pers. comm., after Kolenati), see Inaequipalpia.

aerial, by extension, flying forms of insects, especially of those which
also have nonwinged or otherwise flightless forms (T-B).

aerial plankton, small insects dispersed by air currents (Mackerras, in
CSIRO).

aeriduct, aeriductus, spiracle, q.v. (T-B); tracheal gill, q.v. (T-B); the
taillike extensions of rat-tailed maggots (Diptera: Syrphidae); in
some aquatic Heteroptera, respiratory siphon, q.v. (T-B).

aerobic, growing or thriving only in the presence of atmospheric air
(T-B).

aerobiosis, the respiratory state in which oxygen is available to meet
the oxidative needs of the organism; applied to carbohydrate metabolism, specifically, in which complete breakdown of sugar is accomplished in the presence of oxygen (Tulloch, after Rockstein).

aerodynamics, performance in flight (Chapman).

aeropyles, in the insect egg, fine pores connected to air spaces in the
outer and inner meshworks of the chorion (Chapman); in a spiracular gill, fine pores connecting plastron with spiracle (Chapman); in
pupal Chironomidae (Diptera), opening from respiratory atrium to
plastron (Saether).

aeroscepsin, a hypothetical sense supposed to be lodged in the insect antennae (T-B).

aeroscepsy, perception of sound or odor through the medium of the air, through the antennae (T-B).

aerosol, finely dispersed particles in air (Pfadt).

aerostatic, in insects, able to maintain balance in the air (T-B).

aerostats, in adult Diptera, a pair of large air sacs at the base of the abdomen (T-B).

aeruginose, aeruginous, aeruginus (Latin), the color of verdigris; i.e., blueish-green (T-B).

Aeshnidea, Aeshnoidea, q.v. (Hennig, after Rodendorf).

Aeshnoidea, superfamily of Anisoptera (Odonata), including Petaluridae, Gomphidae, Aeshnidae, and Cordulegastridae, characterized by adults with triangles in front and hind wings similar in shape and about equidistant from arculus; most of costal and subcostal crossveins not in a line; and usually a brace vein behind proximal end of pterostigma (O'Farrell, in CSIRO; Borror et al.); a paraphyletic group within the Anisoptera (Odonata), basal to the Libelluloidea (Hennig, after Fraser, Watson).

aestival, occurring in summer (T-B).

aestivation, quiescence resulting from continued high temperature or xeric conditions (T-B, after Folsom and Wardle); see diapause and hibernation.

aetiology, etiology, q.v. (T-B).

afferent, carrying inwardly, or toward the center, as a nerve (T-B).

afferent canal, in ♀ Lepidoptera, the more membranous of 2 closely intertwined ducts that together comprise the ductus spermathecae; the afferent, external, or transport canal serves to transport sperm from the ductus seminalis to the utriculus (Mitter); see efferent canal.

afferent nerve, axon, q.v. (T-B, after Snodgrass).

afferent neuron, sensory nerve cell, q.v. (T-B, after Snodgrass).

affinis (Latin), related to; similar in structure or development (T-B).

African sleeping sickness, disease of man and other animals in Equatorial Africa caused by the flagellate protozoan *Trypanosoma gambiense rhodesiense* (Trypanosomatidae) transmitted by tsetse flies, *Glossina* spp. (Diptera: Glossinidae) (Borror et al.).

African tick fever, disease of man in South Africa, Australia, and the western United States caused by *Rickettsia* spp. (Rickettsiaceae) transmitted by various ticks (Acari: Ixodidae) (Borror et al.).

afterbody, in Coleoptera, all the body behind the pronotum (T-B, after Tillyard).

afternose, a triangular piece below the antennae and above the clypeus (T-B); see postclypeus.

AGA, killing solution, especially used for Thysanoptera, containing 8 parts of 95% ethyl alcohol, 5 parts of distilled water, 1 part of glycerine, and 1 part of glacial acetic acid (Borror et al.).

agamic, agamous, parthenogenetic, q.v. (T-B; Mayr).

agamospecies, a species without sexual reproduction, i.e., an asexual species (Mayr).

agamogenesis, parthenogenesis, q.v. (T-B).

Agathiphagoidea, only superfamily of suborder Aglossata (Lepidoptera), containing the single family Agathiphagidae, the adults being small Trichoptera-like moths lacking a proboscis and ocelli, with mandibles, homoneurous wing venation, media 3- or 4-branched, wings with primitive, solid scales; ♀ with apophyses on both sternum and tergum of abdominal segment VIII; larvae apodous, with enormous, asymmetrical mandibles (Kristensen; Common).

age polyethism, the regular changing of labor roles by colony members as they age (Wilson).

agglomerate, heaped or massed together (T-B).

agglomerate pores, in Aleyrodidae (Hemiptera: Sternorrhyncha), compound wax pores, q.v. (Gill).

agglutinate, stuck or glued together; welded into one mass (T-B).

aggregate, a group of species, other than a subgenus, within a genus; a group of species within a subgenus; or a group of subspecies within a species, being denoted by a species group name interpolated in parentheses (ICZN).

aggregated, crowded together (T-B).

aggregation, a group of individuals, comprised of more than just a mated pair or a family, that have gathered together in the same place but do not construct nests or rear offspring in a cooperative manner (Wilson); see colony.

aggressive display, ritualized display in territorial animals which usually concludes with the departure of one of the combatants before actual physical contact (Matthews and Matthews).

aggressive mimicry, mimicry in which a predator resembles a potential food source or potential mate of prey (Matthews and Matthews).

Aglossata, a suborder of Lepidoptera containing a single superfamily, Agathiphagoidea, q.v. (Kristensen).

Agnatha, Ephemeroptera, q.v. (Martynov).

agnathous, without jaws; specifically those neuropteroids in which the mouth structures are obsolescent (T-B).

Agrioidea, Zygoptera, q.v. (Hennig, after Tillyard and Fraser).

Agrionidea, extinct group of Odonata, including the families Amphipterygidae and Epallagidae, possibly belonging to the Lestinoidea (Hennig, after Rodendorf).

Agrionoidea, Lestinoidea, q.v. (Hennig).

agroecosystem, the relatively artificial ecosystem in an agricultural environment (Pfadt).

aheneus, aeneous, q.v. (T-B).

AI, active ingredient, q.v. (Pfadt).

aileron, tegula, q.v. (T-B); in adult Diptera, inner squama, outer squama, or alula, q.v. (T-B).

air sacs, expanded, thin-walled areas in the tracheae, in which taenidia are absent or poorly developed and often irregularly arranged, playing an important part in ventilation of the tracheal system as well as having other functions (Chapman).

air speed, movement of a flying insect relative to the air (Chapman); see ground-speed.

air stores, plastron, q.v., or physical gill, q.v. (Tulloch).

air straps, in Belostomatidae (Heteroptera), a pair of straplike appendages derived from abdominal segment VIII used like the respiratory siphon in the Nepidae to obtain atmospheric air (Menke, in Menke).

air tube, in larval Culicidae (Diptera), siphon, q.v. (T-B; Harbach and Knight, after Dyar).

air vesicles, air sacs, q.v. (T-B).

akinesis, a motionless state resembling sleep, particularly after loss of, or damage to, sensory organs such as antennae (Tulloch; Leftwich).

ala (pl., **alae**), the distal expanse of the wings containing veins; a wing or any winglike structure (T-B); see blade.

alae cordis, winglike bands of fibrous tissue suspending the heart from the pericardium in insects and other arthropods (Leftwich).

alacardo, disticardo, q.v. (T-B, after MacGillivray).

alacercus, filum terminale, q.v. (T-B, after MacGillivray).

alae, in ♂ Siphonaptera, dorsolateral flanges of palliolum (Tuxen, after Günther); see ala.

alae valvae, in ♂ Lithosiinae (Lepidoptera: Arctiidae), distal part of valva (Tuxen, after Birket-Smith).

alaforamen, the opening in the foramen through which passes the alimentary canal (T-B, after MacGillivray); see occipital foramen.

alaglossa, the glossae of the labium when fused into a single plate (Tulluch, after MacGillivray); see ligula.

alar, alary, relating to the wings (T-B); winglike (Leftwich).

alar appendage, alulet, q.v. (T-B).

alar area, in larval Coleoptera, the tergal area immediately above the epipleural area, on the abdominal segments usually carrying the spiracles (Peterson, after Böving and Craighead).

alar brush, in adult Chironomidae (Diptera), scopula alaris, q.v. (Saether).

alar frenum, in adult Diptera, a small ligament dividing the supraalar cavity into an anterior and a posterior part (T-B, after Comstock); in adult Hymenoptera, a small ligament crossing the supraalar groove toward the base of the wing (T-B, after J. B. Smith).

alar pocket, in ♂ Danaidae (Lepidoptera), glandular area on the surface of the hind wing, producing a pheromone (Chapman, after Boppré).

alar squama, in some Diptera, outer squama, q.v. (Chapman).

alariae, notal wing processes, q.v. (T-B, after MacGillivray).

alaraliae (pl., **alaraliaes**), the prealaraliae and postalaraliae collectively (T-B, after MacGillivray).

alarima, the fissure between the 2 paraglossae (T-B, after MacGillivray).

alarm-defense system, defensive behavior which also functions as an alarm signaling device within the colony, including the use by certain ant species (Hymenoptera: Formicidae), of chemical defensive secretions that double as alarm pheromones (Wilson).

alarm pheromone, a chemical substance exchanged among the members of the same species that induces a state of alertness or alarm in the face of a common threat (Wilson).

alarm-recruitment system, a communication system that rallies nestmates to some particular place to aid in the defense of the colony, e.g., the odor trail system of lower termites (Isoptera), which is used to recruit colony members to the vicinity of intruders and breaches in the nest wall (Wilson).

alarm signals, intraspecific signals of alarm characteristic of social insects (Matthews and Matthews).

alarm substance, in Formicidae, Vespidae, and Apoidea (Hymenoptera) and Isoptera, alarm pheromone, q.v. (CSIRO; Carpenter, pers. comm., after Jeanne).

alary muscles, the paired, transverse muscles attached to and supporting the heart, usually arranged in fan-shaped groups of fibers (T-B, after Snodgrass, Imms)

alary polymorphism, 2 or more forms of wings in the same species, correlated with sex or not (T-B).

alatae, the winged forms of the Aphididae (Hemiptera: Sternorrhyncha) (T-B).

alatate, having lateral winglike expansions, as in the tibiae or eggs of certain insects (T-B).

alate, alatus (Latin), winged form; possessing wings (T-B; Leftwich); see apterous.

alate lobes of aedeagal apodeme, in some adult Siphonaptera, flaplike circular or elliptical extensions of the aedeagal apodeme that flank part of the middle lamina (Rothschild and Traub).

alavertex, the part of the vertex on its ventral aspect (T-B); occiput, q.v. (T-B, after MacGillivray).

albi, combining form for albus, q.v.

albicans, formed or made of white (T-B).

albidus, white with a dusky tinge (T-B).

albinism, absense of pigmentation, particularly melanins, in individuals of a species that is usually colored (T-B; Mayr).

albinistic, tending to whiteness or fading to white in normally dark forms (T-B).

albino, a depigmented individual in a species that is normally pigmented (T-B).

albumen, the white of an egg (T-B); see albumin.

albumin, the protein substance forming the white of egg (T-B); see albumen.

albuminoid, like or of the character of albumin (T-B).

albuminoid spheres, eosinophilic bodies formed by extruded chromatin granules of fat cells which are liberated into blood during moulting and metamorphosis (Chapman).

albus (Latin), pure white; the color of chalk (T-B, after Kirby and Spence).

alcohol, simple organic molecule containing a hydroxyl group (OH⁻); see ethyl alcohol and methyl alcohol.

aldicarb, $C_7H_{14}N_2O_2S$, a systemic insecticide, acaricide, and nematicide; a carbamate, 2-methyl-2-(methylthio)propionaldehyde-(O-methylcarbamoyl) oxime; highly toxic to mammals, acute oral LD_{50} for rats 1 mg/kg (Pfadt).

aldrin, $C_{12}H_8Cl_6$, a synthetic insecticide; a chlorinated hydrocarbon of not less than 95 percent 1,2,3,4,10,10-hexachloro-1,4,4a,5,8,8a-hexahydro-1,4-$endo$-exo-5,8-dimethanonaphthalene; highly toxic to mammals, acute oral LD_{50} for rats 44 mg/kg (Pfadt).

alecithal egg, small eggs provided with very little nutritive substance (Gauld and Bolton); see lecithal egg.

aleuritic acid, one of the organic acids contained in lac (T-B).

Aleurodidea, name used for fossil Aleyrodoidea (Hennig, after Bekker-Migdisova).

aleyrodiform, resembling *Aleyrodes* (Hemiptera: Sternorrhyncha: Aleyrodidae) in form and shape (T-B).

Aleyrodina, Aleyrodoidea, q.v. (Hennig, after Börner).

Aleyrodoidea, superfamily belonging to the Sternorrhyncha (Hemiptera), including the single family Aleyrodidae (whiteflies), with adults possessing tarsi with 2 tarsomeres, membranous forewings, and antennae normally with 7 articles (Woodward et al., in CSIRO).

aleutaceous, aleutaceus (Latin), rather pale leather-brown; covered with minute cracks like the human skin and leathery in texture (T-B; Harris); see coriaceous and coriarious.

alfalfa mosaic, disease of alfalfa, beans, and tobacco caused by rhabdovirus with nonpersistent transmission by many species of aphids (Hemiptera: Sternorrhyncha: Aphididae) (Borror et al.).

alfalfa witches'-broom, disease of alfalfa caused by mycoplasm with propagative transmission by leafhopper *Scaphytopius acutus cirrus* (Hemiptera: Auchenorrhyncha: Cicadellidae) (Borror et al.).

algophagous, algae-eating (T-B).

alienicola (pl., **alienicolae**), in Aphididae (Hemiptera: Sternorrhyncha), parthenogenetic viviparous females developing for the most part on the secondary host, often differing markedly from the fundatrices and migrantes (T-B, after Imms).

alifer, pleural wing process, q.v. (T-B, after Crampton).

alifera (pl., **aliferae**), pleural wing process, q.v. (T-B, after MacGillivray).

aliform, winglike (Leftwich).

aliform muscles, alary muscles, q.v. (Chapman).

alimentary canal, the food tube traversing the body from the mouth to the anus, consisting of an endodermal mesenteron and an ectodermal stomodaeum and proctodaeum (T-B).

alimentary castration, sterility of worker and soldier castes of some social insects, brought about by a deficiency in their diet (Leftwich).

alimentary water, water taken in with food, or as food (T-B).

alimentation, feeding or taking in nourishment (T-B).

alinotum, the wing-bearing plate of the dorsum of the meso- or met-athorax (T-B); see eunotum.

aliphatic, a term applied to the open chain or fatty series of hydrocarbons (Pfadt).

alitrunk, in adult Apocrita (Hymenoptera), mesosoma, q.v., including the true thorax and (fused anteriorly to the thorax) the first abdominal segment (propodeum) (T-B; Wilson); see pterothorax.

alizarine, a transparent orange red (T-B).

alkaline, having the reaction of an alkali resulting from an excess of hydroxyl ions (OH⁻) over hydrogen ions (H⁺) in solution; pH greater than 7.0 (T-B; Pfadt).

alkaline alcohol, 70% alcohol to which a few drops of 0.1% solution of bicarbonate of soda ($NaHCO_3$) are added (T-B).

alkaline gland, Dufour's gland, q.v. (T-B, after Imms).

alkaloid, substance found in plants, many having powerful pharmacological action, and characterized by content of nitrogen and the property of combining with acids to form salts (Pfadt).

allantoic acid, waste product of nitrogen metabolism occurring in the excreta of larval and adult Lepidoptera and larval Hymenoptera, being a product of allantoin acted upon by allantoinase.

allantoicase, enzyme converting allantoic acid into urea and glycolic acid (Chapman).

allantoin, oxidized form of uric acid excreted by aquatic insects (Chapman).

allantoinase, enzyme converting allantoin into allantoic acid (Chapman).

Alleghanian faunal area, the part of North America comprising the greater part of New England, southeastern Ontario, New York, Pennsylvania, Michigan, Wisconsin, Minnesota, eastern N. Dakota, northeastern S. Dakota, and the Alleghanies from Pennsylvania to Georgia (T-B).

allele, any of the alternative expressions (states) of a gene (locus) (Tulloch; Mayr).

allelochemic, a substance that affects individuals or populations of a species different from the source (Matthews and Matthews, after Whittaker and Feeny).

allelomorph, allele, q.v. (T-B; Tulloch).

allethrin, $C_{19}H_{26}O_3$, a synthetic insecticide related to the plant derived pyrethrins; slightly toxic to warmblooded animals, acute oral LD_{50} for rats 920 mg/kg (Pfadt).

alliaceous, smelling like garlic (T-B).

alligate, alligatus, fastened or suspended by a thread, like the chrysalis of *Papilio* (Lepidoptera: Papilionidae) (T-B).

alliogenesis, a form of development which includes an alternation of generations (q.v.) as in Cynipidae (Hymenoptera) (T-B).

allochronic species, in paleontology, species which do not occur at the same time level (Mayr); see synchronic species.

allochthonous, a type of input into aquatic ecosystems that consists of external sources of mineral nutrients and organic matter and that contributes to the productivity of the system (Ricklefs); see autochthonous.

allometric growth, development from which the parts of the body grow at rates peculiar to themselves (Tulloch); growth in which the growth rate on one part of an organism is different from that of another part or of the body as a whole (Mayr); growth exhibiting allometry (Wilson).

allometrosis, the presence of different species of social insects, or of different races of gynes in one colony at one time (Forel).

allometry, any size relation between 2 body parts that can be expressed by $y = bx^a$, where a and b are fitted constants (Wilson); see allometric growth.

allomone, allelochemic of adaptive advantage to the organism sending it (Matthews and Matthews).

alloparalectotype, a specimen from the original material, of another sex than the holotype, and designated later than the original publication of the species (Tulloch, after Frizzell).

alloparasitoid, heteronomous parasitoid, q.v. (Gauld and Bolton).

allopatric, of populations or species, occupying mutually exclusive geographical areas (Mayr).

allopatric hybridization, hybridization between 2 allopatric populations (species or subspecies) along a well-defined contact zone (Mayr); see sympatric hybridization.

allopatric speciation, speciation dependent on geographic barriers to maintain reproductive isolation (Tulloch); species formation during geographical isolation (Mayr); see sympatric speciation.

allosematic resemblance, in Batesian mimicry, the resemblance of a harmless animal to a poisonous or distasteful one, giving protection to the former, since predators will tend to avoid both (Leftwich); see aposematic.

allotectomy, total excision of the corpora allata (Tulloch).

allotype, a paratype of opposite sex to the holotype (T-B, after Banks and Caudell); not regulated by the International Code of Zoological Nomenclature, a designated specimen of opposite sex to the holotype (T-B; ICZN).

alluring coloration, in predators, those patterns or colors which attract other species of insects; a form of aggressive mimicry (T-B).

alluring scent glands, glandular structures diffusing an odor supposed to be attractive to the opposite sex (T-B); see scent glands.

allux, in adult Curculionoidea (Coleoptera), the next to the last joint of the tarsus (T-B).

alpha-chlorophyll, a form of chlorophyll which produces colors in insects (T-B, after Wardle); see beta-chlorophyll.

alpha female, α-female, in ants (Hymenoptera: Formicidae), the normal ♀ when it coexists with the aberrant β-female (T-B, after Imms); or an intermediate in structure between the teratogyne, q.v., and normal ♀ (Tulloch, after Wheeler).

alpha portion, in adult Siphonaptera, the anterior or dorsal portion of Ford's sclerite, usually heavily sclerotized (Rothschild and Traub).

alpha taxonomy, the level of taxonomy concerned with the characterization and naming of species (Mayr); see beta taxonomy and gamma taxonomy.

Alpine Zone, Arctic Zone, q.v.

altaceratubae, in certain Coccoidea (Hemiptera: Sternorrhyncha), the ceratubae in the form of large broad cylinders, with usually oblique mouths, located at or near the margin of the pygidium (T-B, after MacGillivray).

alternation of generations, cyclical alternation between parthenogenetic and bisexual generations, e.g., Cynipidae (Hymenoptera) and Aphididae (Hemiptera: Sternorrhyncha) (T-B; Mayr; Chapman); see heterogeny.

Altosid, (trade name), methoprene, q.v.(Pfadt).

altruism, self-destructive behavior performed for the benefit of others (Wilson).

altus, high; raised above the usual level (T-B).

Alucitoidea, superfamily of infraorder Ditrysia (Lepidoptera) containing the Tineodidae and Alucitidae; adults are small moths with naked proboscis, wings entire or deeply cleft into up to 7 segments, tympanal organs absent, abdominal terga III to VI with anterior band of spines; larvae with 2 prespiracular (L) setae on prothorax, crochets uniordinal; pupae without dorsal spines, not protruded from cocoon at ecdysis (Common).

alula (pl., **alulae**), in adult Diptera, restricted membranous basal portion of posterior wing margin, distal to upper calypter and basal to anal lobe (T-B, after Comstock, J. B. Smith; Chapman, after Oldroyd; Saether; Harbach and Knight; McAlpine) or calypter, q.v. (Saether); in ♂ Lepidoptera, paired flaps of manica, laterad of its attachment to aedoeagus (Tuxen, after Nabokov); in adult Coleoptera, the expanded axillary membrane of the wing (T-B).

alular incision, marginal indentation separating alula from the rest of the wing distally (McAlpine).

alular lobe, alula, q.v. (McAlpine).

alulet, in adult Diptera, the lobe at the basal posterior part of the wing (T-B); see alula and anal lobe.

alutaceous, alutaceus (Latin), rather pale leather-brown; covered with minute cracks like the human skin and leathery in texture (T-B; Harris); see coriaceous and coriarious.

alveolate, alveolatus (Latin), honeycombed; with regular, deep, angular cavities (alveoli) separated by thin partitions (Harris, after Jaegar); furnished with cells or alveoli (T-B; Harris); see areolate, goffered, and reticulate.

alveolation, formation of cells or alveoli; or condition of having cells or alveoli (T-B).

alveole, alveolus, q.v. (T-B); a cell, like that of a honeycomb (T-B).

alveolus (pl., **alveoli**), membranous ring or socket surrounding base of seta or scale (T-B; Harbach and Knight; McAlpine); see tormogen cell.

am-, amb-, Latin prefix; round about (T-B).

amazons, obligatory slave-making ants of the genus *Polyergus* (Hymenoptera: Formicidae) (T-B; Borror et al.).

amber, the fossilized resin of coniferous trees, being a transparent, clear, pale yellowish-brown color (T-B).

ambient vein, a vein partially encircling the wing close to the margin (T-B, after Tillyard); the veinlike structure stiffening the margin of the wing (T-B, after Comstock).

ambipharynx, the membrane along the mesal margin of the proximal end of each mandible, forming the lateral aspect of the prepharynx (T-B, after MacGillivray).

Amblycera, suborder within the Phthiraptera, including the Abrocomophagidae, Boopiidae, Gyropidae, Laemobothriidae, Menoponidae, Ricinidae, and Trimenoponidae, possessing antennae concealed in grooves, horizontal mandibles, pedunculate first flagellomere, maxillary palpi 2–4 segmented, and meso- and metathorax usually separated (Calaby, in CSIRO; Lyal, pers. comm.; Emerson, in Parker); see Anoplura, Ischnocera, and Rhyncophthirina.

Amblypygi, order within the class Arachnida, including the tailless whipscorpions and whipspiders of tropical regions, characterized by distinctly segmented opisthosoma, being constricted at base and without a taillike prolongation; raptorial pedipalps; first pair of legs very long, with long tarsi; and prosoma wider than long (Borror et al).

Amblypigida, Amblypygi, q.v. (Borror et al.).

ambrosia, the fungus cultivated by wood-boring Scolytidae (Coleoptera), or, more specifically, the part of the fungus that grows out into the burrows and is eaten by the beetles (Wilson); in Apidae (Hymenoptera), bee bread, q.v. (T-B).

ambrosia beetle, a wood-boring beetle, e.g., *Xyleborus* spp. (Coleoptera: Scolytidae), that cultivates fungus ("ambrosia") as larval food (Wilson; Leftwich).

ambulacra, the walking legs of insects (T-B).

ambulate, to move backward and forward; to walk, in general (T-B).

ambulatoria, among the orthopteroid orders, those members in which the legs are fitted for walking only, e.g., Phasmida (T-B).

ambulatorial, fitted for walking or making progress on the surface (T-B).

ambulatorial setae, specialized hairs or bristles, situated on the ventral segments of the abdomen of some Coleoptera (T-B).

ambulatorial warts, in larval insects, ampullae used as organs of locomotion, usually confined to the abdominal segments, ventral or dorsal, rarely lateral, in position (Peterson); see callus.

ambulatory, ambulatorial, q.v. (T-B).

ambulatory combs, in larval Dixidae (Diptera), transverse rows of backward directed setae on the venter of abdominal segments V–VII (Teskey, in McAlpine).

ambulatory ridges, in larval Diptera, creeping welts, q.v. (Teskey, in McAlpine).

ambulatory rosette, a cluster of soft pads found on the tips of the last abdominal segment of some snakefly larvae (Raphidioptera) which functions as a holdfast (Tulloch).

amebocyte, plasmatocyte, q.v. (Tulloch).

ameiotic parthenogenesis, apomictic parthogenesis, q.v. (Chapman).

amensalism, a type of symbiotic relationship in which one of the partners is inhibited and the other is not affected (Steinhaus and Martignoni).

American foulbrood, a disease of larval honey bees (Hymenoptera: Apidae) caused by *Bacillus larvae* White, with the infection occurring in the youngest larvae and with death occurring most frequently in the prepupal or pupal stage after the cells have been capped (Steinhaus and Martignoni).

Ametabola, old term for primitively wingless hexapods with ametabolous development, including Protura, Collembola, Diplura, Archaeognatha, and Zygentoma (T-B; Leftwich; von Kéler).

ametabolic, ametabolous, q.v. (T-B).

ametabolion, an ametabolous insect (T-B).

ametabolous, having no metamorphosis, i.e., primitively wingless, emerging from the egg in a form essentially resembling the adult apart from the small size and lack of developed of genitalia, e.g., Collembola, Diplura, Protura, Archaeognatha, and Zygentoma (T-B; Chapman); see heterometabolous and holometabolous.

ametaboly, the condition of being ametabolous (T-B).

ametamorphic, ametabolous, q.v. (Leftwich).

amethystine, amethystinus, bright blue with a reddish admixture; clear like an amethyst (T-B).

amide, a compound derived from carboxylic acids by replacing the hydroxyl of the -COOH by the amino group, $-NH_2$ (Pfadt).

amine, an organic compound containing nitrogen, derived from ammonia, NH_3, by replacing one or more hydrogen atoms by as many hydrocarbon radicals (Pfadt).

amino acid, any of the thirty or more organic compounds containing amino (NH2-) and carboxyl (-COOH) groups, being the basic building blocks of proteins (T-B; Tulloch); essential elements in the diet of insects, including arginine, glycine, histidine, isoleucine, leucine, lysine, methionine, phenylalanine, threonine, tryptophan, and valine (Gilmour, in CSIRO).

amitosis, cell division by cleavage without change in the structure of the nucleus; cell division without formation of chromosomes or spindle fibers (T-B).

amitotic, not mitotic or without mitosis (T-B).

ammochaeta, (pl., **ammochaetae**), a stiff type of long, curved, bristle occurring in bunches on the underside of the head in adult ants (Hymenoptera: Formicidae), used for cleaning the legs, etc. (T-B, after W. M. Wheeler; Brown, pers. comm.); in adult Masarinae (Hymenoptera: Vespidae), elongate bristles on head, used to carry soil (Carpenter, pers. comm., after Snelling); see psammophore.

ammonia, a gaseous compound of nitrogen and hydrogen (NH^{3}, being a toxic nitrogenous waste product of protein catabolism and excreted by some aquatic insects as NH_4^+ (T-B; Gilmour, in CSIRO; Chapman); see uric acid.

ammonium carbonate, an unstable salt of ammonia and carbon (NH_4CO_3) which decomposes readily, liberating ammonia (T-B).

ammophilous, psammophilous, q.v. (T-B).

amnion, the inner envelope covering the germ band and ultimately the entire embryo in the development of the ovum (T-B).

amnion cavity, amniotic cavity, q.v. (T-B).

amnion folds, amniotic folds, q.v. (T-B, after J. B. Smith).

amnios, the first cast skin of the larva when a moult occurs almost immediately after emergence from the egg (T-B).

amniotic, of or pertaining to the amnion (T-B).

amniotic cavity, in the developing egg, a space or cavity formed by the amniotic folds, which contains the germ band (T-B, after Imms).

amniotic folds, folds arising from the edge of the germ band in the ovum, which meet closing the mouth of the amnion cavity in the embryo (T-B, after Imms, J. B. Smith).

amniotic fluid, the liquid surrounding the embryo within the egg which is swallowed by the insect prior to hatching.

amniotic pore, a permanent opening in the amniotic cavity in the development of certain insects (T-B).

amoeba, any eukaryotic single-celled organism that is naked and that changes shape due to the irregular extension and retraction of pseudopodia (Allaby).

amoeba disease, a disease of adult honey bees (Hymenoptera: Apidae) caused by *Malpighamoeba mellificae,* an amoeba that develops and ultimately encysts in the lumen of the Malpighian tubules (Steinhaus and Martignoni); a disease of grasshoppers in which an amoeba, *Malemba locustae,* infects primarily the Malpighian tubules (Steinhaus and Martignoni).

amoebiasis, any disease in which the causal agent is an amoeba (Allaby); see amoeba disease and amoebic dysentery.

amoebic disease, amoeba disease, q.v. (Steinhaus and Martignoni).

amoebic dysentery, disease of man and livestock caused by *Entamoeba histolytica* and spread by the house fly, *Musca domestica* (Muscidae), various blow flies (Calliphoridae), and various flesh flies (Sarcophagidae) (Diptera) (Borror et al.).

amoebiform, having the appearance or properties of an amoeba (T-B); see amoeboid.

amoebocyte, plasmatocyte, q.v. (T-B; Tulloch).

amoeboid, amoebalike in form or movements (T-B); see amoebiform.

amorpha, those insects in which the pupa bears no resemblance to the imago (T-B).

ampherotoky, amphitoky, q.v. (Tulloch).

Amphibicorisae, Amphibiocorisae, division of the Heteroptera, including semiaquatic bugs, in earlier works often including Gerromorpha and Leptopodomorpha, more recently usually only the Gerromorpha.

amphibiotica, pseudoneuropterous insects with aquatic larvae and aerial imagos, including Plecoptera, Ephemeroptera, and Odonata (T-B).

Amphientometae, group within the suborder Troctomorpha (Psocoptera), including Amphientomidae, Musapsocidae, Troctopsocidae, Manicapsocidae, and Compsocidae in which there is more than one anal vein (Pearman; Badonnel).

Amphiesmenoptera, group within the Holometabola, including the Trichoptera and Lepidoptera (Hennig).

amphigony, sexual reproduction (Tulloch).

amphimixis, the mingling of the germ plasm of 2 individuals (T-B); reproduction involving fusion of haploid nuclei, i.e., gamete nuclei (Tulloch).

amphiodont, mesodont, q.v. (T-B).

amphiploid, a polyploid produced by the chromosome doubling of a species hybrid, i.e., an individual with 2 rather different chromosome sets (Mayr).

amphipneustic respiration, amphipneustic respiratory system, q.v. (T-B).

amphipneustic respiratory system, larval respiratory system in which only the first (thoracic) and the last or last 2 (abdominal) pairs of spiracles are open (Peterson); respiratory system with mesothoracic and one pair of posterior abdominal spiracles functional, e.g., larval Psychodidae (Chapman, after Keilin); in larval Tanyderidae, Axymyiidae, most Psychodidae, Trichoceridae, Anisopodidae, Thaumaleidae, and most Brachycera (Diptera), respiratory system with only the anterior spiracles and posterior spiracles functional (Teskey, in McAlpine).

Amphipoda, order of Crustacea, including marine and freshwater amphipods (Borror et al.).

amphitoky, parthenogenesis in which individuals of either sex may be produced (Chapman); see arrhenotoky and telytoky.

ample, broad; large; sufficient in size (T-B).

amplected, having the head set into a concavity of the prothorax; e.g., *Hister* (Coleoptera: Histeridae) (T-B).

amplexiform coupling, a type of wing-coupling mechanism in Lepidoptera in which there is no frenulum and the large humeral lobe of the hind wing projects under the forewing (T-B, after Wardle); in Papilionoidea and some Bombycoidea (Lepidoptera), wing coupling by virtue of an extensive area of overlap between the forewing and hind wing (Chapman).

ampliate, ampliatus, moderately dilated (T-B).

amplificate, amplificatus, dilated; enlarged (T-B).

amplixicate, amplixicatus, dilatate, q.v. (T-B).

ampulla (pl., **ampullae**), a blister or blisterlike structure (T-B); in ♂ insects, distal part of embryonic gonoducts (Tuxen, after Heymons); in nymphal Orthoptera, an extensile sac between the head and prothorax used by the young in escaping from the ootheca, and later, in moulting (T-B); in orthopteroid orders, dilation of the heart where the ostia pierce the wall (Chapman); in Heteroptera (Hemiptera), a blisterlike enlargement at the middle of the anterior margin of the prothorax (T-B); in ♂ Noctuidae (Lepidoptera), digitoid or rounded process of inner surface of central area of valva (Tuxen, after Pierce); in ♂ Geometridae and Noctuidae (Lepidoptera), a major division of valva occupying the central inner surface (Tuxen); in ♂ Rhopalocera (Lepidoptera), a major terminal part of valva (T-B, after Klots; Tuxen, after Sibatani et al.); in adult Diptera, greater or lesser ampulla, q.v.

ampulla mold, in ♂ Orthoptera, ventral phallic lobes, q.v. (Tuxen, after Alexander and Otte).

ampullaceous, ampullalike, flask-shaped (T-B).

ampullaceous sensillum, sensillum ampullaceum, q.v. (T-B).

ampulliform, resembling an ampulla (T-B).

amygdaliform, almond-shaped (T-B).

amylase, digestive enzyme, commonly contained in the saliva produced by the labial glands, catalyzing the hydrolysis of 1:4-alpha-glucosidic linkages in polysaccharides, thus converting starches to maltose into dissaccharide and glycogen to glucose (T-B; Chapman).

amyloidosis, a pathologic condition in mated queen honey bees (Hymenoptera: Apidae), causing premature drone production, associated with the deposition of amyloid in the cytoplasm of the spermathecal epithelium of the affected queens (Steinhaus and Martignoni).

amylolitic, of or pertaining to the enzyme amylase (T-B); having the action or effect of amylase (T-B).

an-, ana-, Greek prefix; up, all through; back; again (T-B).

anabolic, relating to the constructive change from food material to animal tissue (T-B); see katabolic.

anabolism, the building up metabolic processes; those reactions of the animal body which produce proteins, fats and carbohydrates from food materials (T-B); constructive metabolism, in which simple compounds are converted into more complex ones in an energy-requiring reaction (Tulloch).

anacerores, in Coccoidea (Hemiptera: Sternorrhyncha), rectal wax pores, q.v. (T-B, after MacGillivray).

anaerobic, able to live without oxygen (T-B); see aerobic.

anaerobiosis, the respiratory state under oxygen-free or oxygen-deficient conditons (applied to carbohydrate metabolism, specifically, in which sugar breakdown proceeds without the intervention of oxygen) (Rockstein).

anagenesis, evolution of a lineage, as opposed to speciation; see cladogenesis.

anagram, a name formed by the rearrangement of letters of a word or phrase (ICZN).

anal, in the direction of, pertaining or attached to the anus or to the last segment of the abdomen (T-B).

anal angle, on the hind wing, the angle nearest the end of the abdomen when the wings are expanded; the angle between the inner and outer margins of any wing; hind angle of forewings (T-B); in ♂ Noctuidae (Lepidoptera), an angle of cucullus, forming the ventro-caudal angle of valva (Tuxen, after Pierce).

anal apparatus, in Heteroptera (Hemiptera), abdominal segments X and XI (transl. "Analapparat" Larsén, after Tuxen).

anal appendages, the external genital parts (T-B, after Smith); in Odonata, movable appendages at the end of the abdomen (T-B, after Garman); in ♂ Embiidina, cerci, q.v. (Tuxen, after Melander); in adult Planipennia, ectoproct, q.v. (Tuxen, after McLachlan); in ♂ Bittacidae (Mecoptera), branches of epiandrium, q.v. (Byers, pers. comm., after Esben-Petersen); in ♂ Lepidoptera, short, lateral processes of tegumen (transl. "anale Anhänge" Zander, after Tuxen).

anal area, the posterior part of the wing supported by the anal veins (T-B; Borror et al.); see vannus.

anal block, in ♂ Auchenorrhyncha (Hemiptera), anal tube + anal style (transl. "bloc anal" Ribaut, after Tuxen).

anal blood sinus, in wings of ♂ Embiidina, a tapered sinus in position of anal vein that becomes turgid with blood pressure during flight (Ross).

anal bristle, in pupal Chironomidae (Diptera), anal macroseta, q.v. (Saether).

anal cell, cell posterior to an anal vein (T-B, after Comstock); in Diptera, anal cell, exclusive of alula (McAlpine); in Diptera, posterior cubital cell, q.v. (T-B, after Williston).

anal cerari, in Pseudococcidae (Hemiptera: Sternorrhyncha: Coc-coidea), the eighteenth (or last) pair of pores on the anal lobes (T-B, after MacGillivray).

anal claspers, in larval Amphiesmenoptera, anal prolegs, q.v.

anal claw, in larval Trichoptera, a sclerotized hook at the end of an anal proleg, sometimes with one or more accessory hooks, q.v. (Wiggins).

anal cleft, in nymphs and ♀ Coccoidea, e.g., Coccidae (Hemiptera: Sternorrhyncha), a space or crack leading from the anal opercula to the posterior body margin (T-B; Miller, in Stehr).

anal collar, in ♂ Auchenorrhyncha (Hemiptera), a transverse or annuliform intersegmental sclerite between pygofer and anal tube (Tuxen); in ♂ Psyllidae (Hemiptera: Sternorrhyncha), a sclerite basally of proctiger (Tuxen).

anal comb, in larval Lepidoptera, the sclerotized prong, fork, or comb ventrad of the anal plate, located on the meson and adjacent to the anal opening, and used to eject feces; in larval Coleoptera, urogomphi, q.v. (Peterson); in adult Chironomidae (Diptera), comb of anal point (transl. "Analkamm", Saether).

anal cone, in ♂ Cryptostemmatidae (Heteroptera), anal tube, q.v. (Tuxen, after Wygodzinsky); in ♀ Lepidoptera, a sclerite below the ovipositor (transl. "Analconus" Hering, after Tuxen).

anal crossing, in adult Odonata, where anal vein branches posteriorly from CuP + A (Borror et al.; O'Farrell, in CSIRO).

anal crossvein, in adult Diptera, second branch of cubitus anterior

(CuA$_2$), extending posterior to meet first anal vein (1A), thus closing the posterior cubital cell (T-B, after Curran; McAlpine); not a true crossvein.

anal disc, in larva of Simuliidae (Diptera), the suckerlike point of attachment at the end of the abdomen (T-B).

anal fan, vannus, q.v. (T-B, after Tillyard).

anal field, in Mastotermitidae (Isoptera), the numerous branched veins in the anal lobe of the hind wing (Emerson); in Orthoptera, the area on the tegmina corresponding to the anal area of the hind wings (T-B).

anal filaments, in Ephemeroptera, cerci, q.v. (T-B; Tulloch).

anal fimbria, in Hymenoptera, fringes about the anus (T-B).

anal fin, in pupal Chironomidae (Diptera), anal lobe, q.v. (Saether).

anal flap, in ♂ Auchenorrhyncha (Hemiptera), the posterior lobe of anal tube, being the complete abdominal segment X (Tuxen; L. O'Brien, pers. comm.); in ♂ Embiidina, epiproct, q.v. (Ross, in Tuxen).

anal fold, claval furrow, q.v. (T-B, after Snodgrass); in the Mastotermitidae (Isoptera) and cockroaches (Blattaria), a distinctive fold in the hind wing, situated between the first anal vein and the anal field, reduced or absent in other termite families, which lack the anal lobe (Emerson).

anal foot, in larval Chironomidae (Diptera), the tip of the body which is modified to serve as a hold-fast (T-B).

anal forceps, in some ♂ Coleoptera, a strongly chitinized structure of the genitalia which projects from the abdomen (T-B, after Tillyard); in ♂ Aleyrodidae (Hemiptera: Sternorrhyncha), claspers, q.v. (Tuxen).

anal fork, in larval Coleoptera, urogomphi, q.v. (T-B).

anal fringe, irregular posterior body margin made up of supraanal plates and anal ring setae, e.g., in Tachardiidae (Hemiptera: Sternorrhyncha: Coccoidea) (Miller, in Stehr); see fringe.

anal furrow, claval furrow, q.v., of wing (T-B, after Comstock).

anal gills, in larval Culicidae (Diptera), anal papillae, q.v. (Tulloch; Harbach and Knight, after J. B. Smith); in larval Chironomidae (Diptera), anal tubules, q.v. (Saether); in some larval aquatic Syrphidae (Diptera: Muscomorpha), fingerlike processes of the wall of the rectum, extrusible into the larval medium, thought to have respiratory or osmoregulatory function (Ferrar).

anal glands, ectodermal glands of the alimentary canal, opening into it near the posterior extremity of the anus, secreting either a lubricant, a silk-gum, or some other specialized material (T-B); in adult Coleoptera, pygidial glands, q.v. (Britton, in CSIRO).

anal hooks, in ♂ Auchenorrhyncha (Hemiptera), sclerotized paired processes of anal tube or anal collar (Tuxen); in pupal Lycaenidae (Lepidoptera), an area of many tiny hooks which attaches the posterior end to a pad of silk (Common and Waterhouse).

anal horn, in Collembola, anal spine, q.v. (T-B); in most larval Sphingidae (Lepidoptera), a spinelike horn located dorsally on the meson of abdominal segment VIII (Peterson).

anal legs, anal prolegs, q.v. (T-B).

anal lid, in Heteroptera (Hemiptera), anal tube, q.v. (Tuxen, after Ekblom).

anal lobe(s), a lobe at the posterior part of the wing (Borror et al.); a distinctive, fanlike portion of the hind wing of Mastotermitidae (Isoptera) and cockroaches (Blattaria), containing the veins of the anal field, folded at rest beneath the anterior part of the wing, along the anal fold, being greatly reduced in the forewing of Mastotermitidae and the hind wing of all other families of Isoptera (Emerson); in Eriococcidae, Cerococcidae, and Lecanodiaspididae (Hemiptera: Sternorrhyncha: Coccoidea), posterior protrusion of derm at posterior apex of body, one on each side of body (T-B; Miller, in Stehr); in adult Hymenoptera, jugal lobe, q.v. (Gauld and Bolton); in adult Diptera, basal part of wing behind and below anal vein and distal to alula (T-B, after Curran; Saether); in adult Diptera, flexible, more or less triangular area, containing at most 2 branches of the anal vein (McAlpine); in pupal Chironomidae (Diptera), lateral paratergites of anal segment (a complex of segments IX, X, and XI), occasionally absent in some Orthocladinae (Saether) (see paddle).

anal loop, in adult Anisoptera (Odonata), an area of hind wing including a group of cells between posterior cubitus (CuP) and anal veins (1A and 2A), which may be rounded, elongate, or foot-shaped (T-B, after Garman; O'Farrell, in CSIRO; Borror et al.).

anal macroseta, in pupal Chironomidae (Diptera), usually strong, mostly apical, lateral, often hook-shaped seta (usually 3) on each lobe (Saether).

anal margin, the line extending along the lower or interior edge of the wing from the base to the anal angle (T-B; Chapman).

anal membrane, in adult Odonata, membranule, q.v. (T-B, after Garman).

anal opening, anus, q.v. (Tuxen) (term attributed to Tillyard by T-B).

anal operculum, the dorsal arch of abdominal segment X (T-B); in Coccoidea (Hemiptera: Sternorrhyncha), operculum, q.v. (Miller, in Stehr); in larval Lepidoptera, anal plate, q.v. (T-B).

anal organ(s), in Collembola, the 2 modified hairs arising from a tubercle ventrocephalad of anus and usually curving caudodorsad (T-B); in larval Muscomorpha (Diptera), large cells inside the anal plate, generally thought to have an osmoregulatory function (Ferrar).

anal orifice, anus, q.v. (Tuxen).

anal pads, paired padlike structures lying on either side of the anus (Peterson).

anal papilla(e), in Collembola, tubercle bearing the anus, q.v. (T-B; Wallace and Mackerras, in CSIRO); in larval Chironomidae (Diptera), procercus, q.v. (Saether); see anal papillae; in many aquatic and semiaquatic larvae of Nematocera (Diptera), delicate, thin outgrowths arising from the perianal pad (Teskey, in McAlpine); in larval Culicidae (Diptera), 4 soft white protuberances on the ninth abdominal segment involved in the uptake of ions (T-B; Harbach and Knight, after Meinert; Chapman); in larval Chironomidae (Diptera), anal tubules, q.v. (Chapman; Saether); in larval Trichoptera, elongate lobes arising from within the anal opening (Wiggins).

anal plate(s), in embryonic larvae, the eleventh tergite (T-B); in Orthoptera, epiproct + paraprocts (transl. "Analplatten" Brunner v. Wattenwyl, after Tuxen); in Coccoidea (Hemiptera: Sternorrhyncha), sclerotized structure associated with anal apparatus that does not contain pores and is not in the form of a ring (T-B, after Comstock; Miller, in Stehr); in Aphididae (Hemiptera: Sternorrhyncha), sternum X (Tuxen); in Neuropteroidea, ectoproct, q.v. (Tuxen, after Killington); in ♀ Coleoptera, remaining sclerite of tergum X (transl. "Analplatte" Tuxen); in larval Muscomorpha (Diptera), a more or less distinct plate surrounding the anus ventrally on the last abdominal segment, with thinner cuticle than on the rest of the larval body (Ferrar); in larval Lepidoptera, the shieldlike covering of the dorsum of the last segment (T-B), anal shield, q.v.

anal pore field, in Psylloidea (Hemiptera: Sternorrhyncha), an area formed by a concentric pair of pore rings (inner and outer circumanal rings) around the anus (White and Hodkinson).

anal processes, in many pupal Trichoptera, sclerotized projections (other than those containing developing genitalia) of various shapes at the apex of the abdomen (Ross).

anal prolegs, in larval Amphiesmenoptera, paired prolegs of the last abdominal segment (Peterson; Chapman).

anal pyramid, in nymphal Anisoptera (Odonata), group of posterior appendages forming spiny armature around anus, including epiproct, cerci, and paraprocts (O'Farrell, in CSIRO).

anal ring, in nymphs and ♀ Coccoidea (Hemiptera: Sternorrhyncha), an elevated ringlike structure surrounding anus, normally with pores and setae (T-B, after MacGillivray; Kosztarab and Kozár) (see anal plate); in Auchenorrhyncha (Hemiptera), anal tube, q.v. (Tuxen); in ♀ Plecoptera, abdominal segment X (transl. "Analring" Klapálek, after Tuxen).

anal ring hairs, anal ring setae, q.v. (T-B).

anal ring setae, in ♀ Coccoidea (Hemiptera: Sternorrhyncha), stout setae of anal ring, of varying numbers (T-B, after Comstock; Woodward et al., in CSIRO; Kosztarab and Kozár).

anal ring spines, in Coccoidea (Hemiptera: Sternorrhyncha), anal ring setae, q.v. (T-B, after Comstock).

anal scale, one of the lateral processes of the ovipositor in Cynipidae (Hymenoptera), lying outside and below the lateral scale (T-B, after J. B. Smith).

anal sclerite, in ♂ Rhyacophilidae (Trichoptera), heavy sclerotized, paired or unpaired process below apex of tergite X (Ross).

anal segment, the most caudal segment of the abdomen (Peterson); in Auchenorrhyncha (Hemiptera), anal tube, q.v. (Tuxen); in Heteroptera (Hemiptera), abdominal segment XI invaginated into abdominal segment X (Tuxen, after Dupuis and Carvalho); in adult Diptera, proctiger, q.v. (Tuxen, after Crampton); in adult Siphonaptera, the anal lobes, one dorsal, one ventral to the anus (Rothschild and Traub).

anal setae, in Coccoidea (Hemiptera: Sternorrhyncha), one or more prominent setae of the anal lobes (T-B, after Comstock); in larval Chironomidae (Diptera), apical setae of procercus, or, when procercus lacking, setae inserted at caudomesal angle of preanal segment (Saether).

anal shield, anal plate, q.v.

anal siphon, in larval Culicidae (Diptera), respiratory siphon, q.v. (T-B).

anal slit, slitlike anal opening, being either transverse or parallel with meson (Peterson).

anal spine(s), in Poduromorpha and Isotomidae (Collembola), an enlarged seta, usually blunt and conical and commonly set on a raised papilla, on or near the posterior margin of the eighth abdominal segment (Christiansen and Bellinger); in ♂ Noctuidae (Lepidoptera), long bristle or spine of cucullus or valvula, at or near anal angle (Tuxen, after Pierce); in ♂ Auchenorrhyncha (Hemiptera), anal style, q.v. (Tuxen) or anal hooks, q.v. (Tuxen, after Muir).

anal strut, in larval Siphonaptera, the paired terminal abdominal appendages (Lewis, pers. comm.).

anal style, in Auchenorrhyncha (Hemiptera), abdominal segment XI (T-B; Tulloch; Tuxen); cerci, q.v. (Tulloch).

anal stylet(s), cercus, q.v. (Tulloch); in most ♀ Siphonaptera, an elongate projection, bearing one long apical seta and one or a few small preapical setae, on each side of the anal tergum, behind the sensilium (Smit).

anal tergal bands, in adult Chironomidae (Diptera), basal and sublateral to median darkened bands or apodemes of tergite IX (Saether).

anal tergal setae, in adult Chironomidae (Diptera), setae of tergite IX (transl. "Analtergitborsten," Saether).

anal triangle, in the wings of some Anisoptera (Odonata), a well-marked triangular area bounded in front by vein A' and distally by vein A_3 (T-B, after Comstock).

anal tube, in ♂ Zoraptera, uncus, q.v. (Tuxen, after Snodgrass); in Auchenorrhyncha (Hemiptera), abdominal segment X as a tubular dorsal projection behind pygofer (Tuxen); in Psyllidae (Hemiptera: Sternorrhyncha), proctiger, q.v. (Tuxen); in Heteroptera (Hemiptera), abdominal segment X surrounding the invaginated abdominal segment XI (Tuxen, after Myers and China); in Lepidoptera, tuba analis, q.v. (Tuxen).

anal tube collar, in ♂ Psyllidae (Hemiptera: Sternorrhyncha), anal collar, q.v., (Tuxen).

anal tubercle, in Collembola, anal papilla, q.v. (T-B).

anal tubercles, in certain Coccoidea (Hemiptera: Sternorrhyncha), a pair of prominent, rounded or conical processes, one on each side of anus (T-B).

anal tubules, in larval Chironomidae (Diptera), 1–3 (usually 2) pairs of mostly oblong (but also ovoid, tapering, etc.) appendages of the anal segment above and between posterior parapods (Saether); see anal papillae.

anal valve(s), in Collembola, one of the 3 lobes (1 dorsal, 2 ventrolateral) of abdominal segment VI, surrounding the anal opening (Christiansen and Bellinger); in nymphs of Anisoptera (Odonata), musculated valves located behind the branchial chamber, controlling the size of the anal aperture (Chapman); in Isoptera, paraprocts, q.v. (Tuxen); in Phasmida, epiproct + paraprocts (transl. "Analklappen" Tuxen); in ♂ Psyllidae (Hemiptera: Sternorrhyncha), proctiger, q.v. (Tuxen, after Crawford); in ♀ Psyllidae (Hemiptera: Sternorrhyncha), dorsal plate, q.v. (Tuxen); in ♂ Auchenorrhyncha (Hemiptera), sclerites of anal style (Tuxen); in ♂ Lepidoptera, valvae, q.v. (Tuxen, after Wallace); in ♀ Lepidoptera, papillae anales, q.v. (Tuxen, after Jackson).

anal veins, in pterygote insects, longitudinal unbranched veins posterior to the cubitus posterior (CuP), articulating at the wing base with the third axillary sclerite and occupying the clavus of the wing (T-B, after J. B. Smith; Chapman; Common, pers. comm.); all the undivided longitudinal veins (1A, 2A, etc.) with generally neutral fluting arising from a common sclerite ("anal brace") behind the empusal vein and, in Neoptera, between the claval furrow and the jugal fold, q.v. (Ross et al, after Hamilton); in adult Odonata, the sixth to the ninth longitudinal veins, being commonly short or abbreviated (T-B, after Garman).

analis, a projection formed by the anal and cubital veins (T-B, after MacGillivray).

analogous, similar in function, but differing in origin and structure, e.g., wings of birds and insects (T-B); similar, but cannot be traced back to the same feature in the common ancestor of the 2 taxa being compared (Mayr); see homologous.

Anamorpha, subclass of Chilopoda, including the orders Scutigeromorpha and Lithobiomorpha, being characterized by adults with 15 pairs of legs and newly hatched young with 7 pairs (Borror et al.).

anamorphic development, anamorphosis, q.v. (Chapman).

anamorphosis, type of metamorphosis in which the juvenile stages present fewer abdominal segments than the adults; in Protura, the addition of 3 abdominal segments after hatching of the first instar from the egg (T-B; Chapman; Janetschek); see epimorphosis.

Anaplasmataceae, family of bacteria in which the cells are very small and obligately parasitic in the blood of vertebrates, being transmitted from one host to another by arthorpod vectors, e.g., ticks (Acari: Ixodida) (Allaby).

anaplasmosis, infection with bacteria of the family Anaplasmataceae (Pfadt).

anapleural, of or pertaining to the anapleurite (T-B).

anapleural suture, in adult Diptera, suture separating anepisternum from katepisternum (McAlpine).

anapleurite, the dorsal supracoxal sclerotization of a generalized thoracic pleuron (T-B, after Snodgrass).

anapophysis, in ♀ Lepidoptera, apophyses anteriores, q.v. (Tuxen, after Diakonoff).

anapterygota, apterous insects which have degenerated from winged ancestors (T-B).

Anareolatae, Phasmatidea, q.v. (Kevan).

anasa, a wilt disease of cucurbits caused by the feeding of squash bugs, *Anasa* spp. (Hemiptera: Heteroptera: Coreidae), no parasitic microorganism being involved (Pfadt).

anastomosing, running together, like lines or the veins of an insect's wing (T-B).

anastomosis, the running together or intimate connection of any 2 lines, such as wing veins, blood vessels or nerves; usually applied to wing veins, often to markings (T-B); stigma, q.v. (T-B); a connecting series of veinlets (T-B); in Plecoptera, transverse cord, q.v. (T-B, after Comstock).

anatergite, in some adult Diptera, dorsal division of laterotergite of postnotum (Colless and McAlpine, in CSIRO).

anatomical planes, imaginary planes of the insect body (Mackerras, in CSIRO; McAlpine); see horizontal plane, sagittal plane, and transverse plane.

anatomy, science of internal morphology, as revealed by dissection (Mayr); see morphology.

anatrepsis, in blastokinesis, the passage of the embryo from the ventral to the dorsal aspect of the ovum (T-B, after W. M. Wheeler).

Anatriata, Lonchopteroidea (Diptera), q.v. (Colless and McAlpine, in CSIRO).

anautogenous, in some ♀ mosquitoes (Culicidae), black flies (Simuliidae), and other blood-feeding Diptera, and some Hymenoptera parasitoids, laying no eggs until after a meal (Chapman; Gauld and Bolton); see autogenous.

anautogeny, the inability of ♀ insects to develop eggs without a prior meal of proteinaceous food, e.g., blood in the case of ♀ Culicidae (Diptera) (Tulloch; Adkins, pers. comm.); see autogeny.

anceps, ensiform, q.v. (T-B, after Say).

ancestor, an early form or type from which a later organism is developed; see stem group and stem species.

ancestral, primitive; inherited from an earlier form or ancestor (T-B).

anchor process, in some larval Diptera (e.g. Cecidomyiidae), breastbone, q.v. (T-B); see sternal spatula.

ancipital, with 2 opposite edges or angles (T-B).

ancora (pl., **ancorae**), in ♂ Caelifera (Orthoptera), a pair of anterior hornlike processes of epiphallus (Tuxen).

andrium, in ♂ muscoid Diptera, the posterior portion of the postabdomen, comprising abdominal segments IX and X and including the copulatory apparatus (Tulloch, after Steyskal); in ♂ Muscomorpha (Diptera), modified segment IX of abdomen (Colless and McAlpine, in CSIRO); in ♂ Diptera, genital segment, q.v. (McAlpine); see hypopygium.

androconia, in ♂ Lepidoptera and Trichoptera, elongate scent scales, often occurring on the wings, emitting aphrodisiac pheromones (T-B; Chapman; Morse, pers. comm.); in Scutelleridae and some other Pentatomomorpha (Heteroptera), unicellular glands grouped in patches on the abdominal venter, with the hollow bristlelike androconium set into an alveolus (Carayon).

androecium, hypopygium, q.v. (Crampton.

androgynous, uniting the characters of both sexes (T-B).

andromorph, in adult Odonata, especially Coenagrionidae, a ♀ brightly colored like the ♂ (O'Farrell, in CSIRO); see heteromorph.

androparae, in Aphidoidea (Hemiptera: Sternorrhyncha), viviparous females that produce males exclusively (Miyazaki).

androphore, in Cynipidae (Hymenoptera), a parthenogenetic ♀ that lays only ♂ eggs (Gauld and Bolton); see gynophore.

andropodites, in ♂ Diptera, parameres, q.v. (Tuxen, after Christophers).

androtraumatic insemination, in ♂ *Phallopirates* (Heteroptera: Enicocephalidae), presumed mode of insemination when the ♂ can pass the sperm to the ♀ only after breaking off the tip of his own copulatory organ (Štys).

androtype, a designated ♂ type specimen (T-B, after Banks and Caudell; Tulloch); see type.

anecdysis, a long passive period between 2 moults of an insect or other arthropod during which there appears to be no preparation for the next moult (Leftwich).

Anectropoda, Orthandria, q.v. (Hennig, afte Börner).

anellifer (pl., **anelliferi**), in ♂ Lepidoptera, the caudolateral part of the anellus, in contact with, and more or less joined to, the inner surface of proximal region of valva, sometimes appearing as a distinct structure (Tuxen, after Sabatini et al.).

anellus (pl., **anelli**), in ♂ insects, a sclerotization of the inner wall of the phallocrypt or phallotheca, often forming a ring or tube about base of the aedeagus (T-B, after Snodgrass); in ♂ Lepidoptera, a sclerotized structure supporting and often surrounding the terminal part of the aedoeagus, often articulating with the bases of the harpes, its ventral part forming a median plate below the aedoeagus, called the juxta (T-B, after Klots); in some adult Hymenoptera, one or more very short ringlike segments at base of antennal flagellum, immediately distal to pedical (Gauld and Bolton).

anellus lobes, in ♂ Geometridae (Lepidoptera), paired lateral processes of anellus (Tuxen, after Pierce).

anemic, deficient in blood quantity or quality (Pfadt).

anemophilous, applied to plants adapted for wind pollination (see entomophilous) (Matthews and Matthews).

anemotaxis, orientation or reaction to air currents (T-B); a tendency of some insects to fly into a current of air (Leftwich).

anemotropism, reaction to currents of air or wind movement (T-B).

anepimeral suture, in adult Diptera, transepimeral suture, q.v. (McAlpine).

anepimeron, the division of the epimeron into 2 parts by a suture (T-B, after Comstock); in adult Diptera, upper portion of mesepimeron, separated from katepimeron by transepimeral suture (McAlpine).

anepisternal cleft, in many adult Diptera, vertical cleft dividing anepisternum (Harbach and Knight, after Crampton; McAlpine).

anepisternal membrane, in adult Simuliidae (Diptera), unusually large anepisternal cleft (McAlpine).

anepisternal seta, in adult Diptera, seta borne on anepisternum (McAlpine).

anepisternal suture, in adult Diptera, anapleural suture, q.v. (Saether).

anepisternite, anepisternum, q.v. (T-B, after Curran).

anepisternum, the division of the episternum into 2 parts by a suture (T-B); in adult Diptera, the upper division of the mesepisternum, separated from the katepisternum by the anapleural suture (McAlpine).

anepisternum II, in adult Chironomidae (Diptera), dorsal portion of episternal part of anapleuron separated from central portion or preepisternum by anapleural suture, being divided into 3 parts: anterior, median, and posterior anepisternum II (Saether).

aner, a ♂ insect, applied especially to ants (Hymenoptera: Formicidae) (T-B, after W. M. Wheeler; Leftwich).

aneurose, of a wing, without veins except near the costa (T-B).

angle, of tegmina, longitudinal ridge formed along the internomedian by the sudden flexure from the horizontal to the vertical portion when closed (T-B, after J. B. Smith).

ångstrom (Å), one hundred millionth of a centimeter, unit used in measuring the length of light waves (Pfadt).

angular area, in Hymenoptera, the posterior of the 3 areas on the metanotum between the lateral and pleural carinae; third pleural area (T-B).

angular pupa, pupa angularis, q.v. (T-B).

angulate, angulatus (Latin), forming an angle; when 2 margins meet in an angle (T-B).

angulate setae, in adult Chironomidae (Diptera), golf-club like lamellate setae of median volsella with slender stem and broader angled apex (Saether).

angulation, in ♂ Lepidoptera, Bayard's point, q.v. (Tuxen).

anguli frontales, in larval Coleoptera, anterior projections from the frons located laterad of the nasale (Peterson).

angulose, angled; having angles (T-B).

anguloso-undulate, going more or less in zig-zags or having alternating acute sinuses (T-B).

angulus, an angle; forming an angle; angulate (T-B); in ♂ Lepidoptera, angulus valvae, q.v. (Tuxen, after Dampf).

angulus valvae, in ♂ Lepidoptera, dorsocephalic angle of valva (Tuxen, after Petersen).

angustate, angustatus (Latin), disproportionately narrow (T-B).

angustate antenna, one in which the intermediate and terminal articles are thinner than the others (T-B).

anholocyclic species, in Aphididae (Hemiptera: Sternorrhyncha), those species in which the host plants are entirely of the summer herbaceous type and in which no winged sexual forms are ever produced, reproduction being always by parthenogenesis (T-B, after Wardle).

anhydrobiose, anhydrobiosis, dormancy in insects induced by low humidity or by desiccation (T-B); see aestivation.

anhydropic egg, lecithal egg, q.v. (Gauld and Bolton).

aniso-, prefix; unequal (T-B).

anisomorpha, groups in which the metamorphosis is of a varying character (T-B).

Anisopodoidea, superfamily within the suborder Nematocera (Diptera), including the family Anisopodidae, belonging to the Bibionomorpha (Colless and McAlpine, in CSIRO; Borror et al.) or Psychodomorpha (McAlpine).

Anisoptera, suborder of Odonata, including the dragonflies belonging to superfamilies Aeshnoidea and Libelluloidea, in which the forewings and hind wings of the adult are dissimilar in venation and usually in shape and in which the nymphs are rather stout and lack caudal gills (T-B; O'Farrell, in CSIRO); see Anisozygoptera and Zygoptera.

anisopterous, of or pertaining to the Anisoptera (Odonata) (T-B).

anisopterous penis, in ♂ Anisoptera (Odonata), organ for transfer of spermatophore, orginating from abdominal segment III (Tuxen).

anisotropic, the dark part of the sarcostyle (T-B).

Anisozygoptera, suborder of Odonata, including the single family Epiophlebiidae of Japan and the Himalayas, generally resembling Anisoptera, but adult having zygopteron-like wings and nymphs having 5 antennal articles (O'Farrell, in CSIRO); see Anisoptera and Zygoptera.

ankylosed, grown together at a joint (T-B).

ankylosis, the union or welding together of hard parts to form one structure (T-B); stiffening or growing together of a joint (T-B).

annectant, connecting or intermediate (T-B).

annelet, in adult Hymenoptera, anellus, q.v., of antenna (T-B).

annelid, any one of the segmented worms (Annelida) (T-B).

Annelida, phylum containing the segmented worms, e.g., the earthworm (T-B; Tulloch).

annellus, in adult Hymenoptera, anellus, q.v., of antenna (T-B).

annual colony, in social Hymenoptera, a colony that lasts only one season and dies out at its end (T-B).

annular, ring-shaped or ringlike (T-B).

annular-biforous spiracle, a spiracle with the principal opening usually round, but having 2 small or large accessory or secondary chambers (air tubes) usually adjacent to the margin (Peterson).

annular lamina, in ♂ Formicidae (Hymenoptera), sternum IX (Tuxen).

annular organ, campaniform sensillum, q.v. (Saether).

annular spiracle, a simple, ringlike spiracle, having a single opening with no accessory chambers (Peterson).

annular zone, peripheral pad, q.v.(T-B, after Künckel).

Annulata, the segmented animals, including Annelida, Arthropoda, and Onychophora (T-B, after Say).

annulate, annulatus (Latin), ringed (T-B); surrounded by a ring of a different color (T-B); formed in ringlike segments (T-B); ringlike (T-B).

annulate aedeagus, in ♂ Phytophaga and some other forms (Coleoptera), aedeagus in which basal piece forms a complete ring around the penis with which it is loosely connected, allowing extensive movements of the latter, and parameres usually reduced, sometimes to a pair of processes firmly fixed to the basal piece (Tuxen).

annulet(s), a narrow circle or ring of a different color (T-B); a ring-shaped spot (T-B, after Kirby and Spence); in insect larvae, one of the small rings into which a segment is divided by complete transverse constrictions, crenulations, or plicae (Peterson).

annuliform, in the form of rings or ringlike segments (T-B).

Annulipalpia, suborder of Trichoptera, including the infraorders Spicipalpia and Curvipalpia, including species with campodeiform, rheophillic larvae with elongated anal prolegs possessing lateral sclerites and elongate apical claws, dilation of midtibia and tarsus, and and adults with reduced dorsal tentorial arms (Hennig, after Martynov; Weaver); see Integripalpia.

Annulosa, Annulata, q.v. (T-B).

annulus (pl., **annuli**), a ring encircling an article, segment, spot or mark (T-B); annulet, q.v. (T-B); ringlike subdivision of the antennal flagellum (Chapman); in ♂ Tubulifera (Thysanoptera), incorrectly applied to periandrium or phallobase, q.v. (Tuxen, after Priesner; Heming); in Heteroptera (Hemiptera), anal tube, q.v. (Tuxen, after Verhoeff); in ♂ Lycaenidae (Lepidoptera), vinculum, q.v. (Tuxen, after van Eecke); in Hymenoptera, reinforcing struts at one or both ends of a segment of a gonapophysis (Tuxen, after Smith); in ♀ Hymenoptera, basal ring, q.v. (Tuxen, after Beck).

annulus antennalis, the ring sclerite of the head into which the basal segment of the antenna is inserted (T-B).

annulus receptaculi, in ♀ Carabidae (Coleoptera), sclerotized ring in wall of spermatheca (Tuxen, after Holdhaus).

annulus sterni IX, in ♂ Geometridae (Lepidoptera), part of vinculum, q.v. (Tuxen, after Schroeder).

annulus tergi IX, in ♂ *Eupithecia* (Lepidoptera: Geometridae), tegumen, q.v. (Tuxen, after Schroeder).

anogenital segments, in Sminthuridae (Collembola), the fifth and sixth abdominal segments (Christiansen and Bellinger).

anogenital tagma, terminalia, q.v. (Mackerras, in CSIRO).

anomaladensa, in certain Coccoidea (Hemiptera: Sternorrhyncha), ventral thickening, q.v. (T-B, after MacGillivray).

anomalous, unusual; departing widely from the usual type (T-B).

anophore, in ♂ Dipsocoromorpha (Heteroptera), anal tube, q.v. (Tuxen, after Wygodzinsky).

anopleure, epimeron, q.v. (T-B, after MacGillivray).

Anoplura, suborder of Phthiraptera, including sucking lice parasitic on mammals, in which the head is relatively small and the mouthparts are developed into an unjointed, more or less pointed beak (T-B; Calaby, in CSIRO); see Amblycera, Ischnocera, and Rhyncophthirina.

anoprocessus, in adult Neuroptera, uppermost process of each half of anal segment (Tuxen, after Tjeder).

Anostraca, order of Branchiopoda (Crustacea), including fairy shrimp (Borror et al).

ansa, in Geometridae (Lepidoptera) a sclerotized arm on the inner side of each tympanic membrane (Minet).

ant(s), member of the superfamily Formicoidea (Hymenoptera) (Hennig).

ant hill, hill, q.v., of ants.

ant mimicry, resemblance to ants (Hymenoptera: Formicidae), occurring in many orders of insects, as e.g., first instar nymphs of the Australian *Extatosoma tiaratum* (Phasmida: Phasmatidae) (Key, in CSIRO); see myrmecomorphy.

antacava, torulus, q.v. (T-B, after MacGillivray).

antacoila, antennifer, q.v. (T-B, after MacGillivray).

antacoria, the coria or segmental membrane of each antennomere (T-B); the narrow ring of membrane connecting an antenna with the head (T-B, after MacGillivray); see annulus.

antafossa, antennal groove, q.v. (T-B, after MacGillivray).

antapophysis, in ♀ Lepidoptera, apophyses anteriores, q.v. (Tuxen).

Antarctoperlaria, suborder of the Plecoptera, including the superfamilies Eusthenioidea and Gripterygoidea of the southern hemisphere (Zwick, in Hennig); see Arctoperlaria.

antarolium, the large pulvillus (T-B, after MacGillivray).

antartis, scape, q.v., of antenna (T-B, after MacGillivray).

antaxial setae, in larval Chironomidae (Diptera), long setae on ventral side of galea of maxilla at about the level of middle dorsal chaetae on lacinia, occasionally situated on a high slender tubercle; interpreted as a pectinate sensillum chaeticum by Sublette (Saether).

ante-, Latin prefix; before (T-B); see anti-.

antealar, situated anterior to the front wing (T-B, after Tillyard).

antealar area, in adult Culicidae (Diptera), the lateral area of the scutum at the level of the paratergite, bearing the antealar scales and setae (Harbach and Knight, after Belkin).

antealar scale, in adult Culicidae (Diptera), one of the scales occurring on the antealar area of the scutum (Harbach and Knight).

antealar seta, in adult Culicidae (Diptera), one of the setae occurring in a longitudinal row on the antealar area of the scutum immediately above the paratergite, being sometimes more or less continuous with the supraalar setae posteriorly (Harbach and Knight).

antealar sinus, in adult Odonata, a grooved area extending transversely immediately in front of the base of each front wing (T-B).

anteapical, just proximad of the apex (T-B; Borror et al.).

anteapical cell, in adult Cicadellidae (Hemiptera: Auchenorrhyncha), a cell in the distal part of the wing, being the first cell posterior to R_{4+5} (Borror et al.).

anteclypeus, the inferior half of the clypeus whenever there is an apparent line of demarcation between it and the labrum (T-B); in Odonata, the lower of the 2 divisions of the clypeus (T-B); see postclypeus.

antecosta, the anterior submarginal ridge on the inner surface of a tergal or sternal plate corresponding to the primary intersegmental fold, on which typically the longitudinal muscles are attached (T-B, after Snodgrass); in Trichoptera, suture on tergites and sternites close to the anterior margin (Nielsen).

antecostal ridge, antecosta, q.v. (Chapman).

antecostal sulcus, antecoxal suture, q.v. (Chapman).

antecostal suture, the groove through the base of a phragma which marks the base of the antecosta, i.e., the external groove of the antecosta (T-B, after Snodgrass).

antecoxal piece, an inner sclerite between the single or divided trochantin and the episternum, or between the trochantin and the precoxal bridge (T-B); clypealia, q.v. (T-B, after J. B. Smith); in some adult Coleoptera, a plate in front of the hind coxa, being the posterior portion of the metasternum.

antecoxal sclerite, a sclerite of the metasternum, just anterior to the hind coxae (Borror et al.).

antecubital, in adult Odonata, antenodal crossveins, q.v., or antenodal costal spaces, q.v. (T-B).

antecubital crossveins, in adult Odonata, antenodal crossveins, q.v. (T-B, after Comstock).

antefurca, an internal forked process from the prosternum, to which muscles are attached (T-B); see furca.

antehumeral, relating to the space just before the origin of the wings (T-B).

antehumeral stripe, in adult Odonata, a discolored stripe, approximately parallel to, but to the inner side of the humeral suture (T-B).

antemedial line, in adult Lepidoptera, transverse anterior line, q.v. (T-B).

antemedian, leg-bristles situated before the middle (T-B).

antenna (pl., **antennae**), in larval and adult insects, paired segmental appendages, borne one on each side of head (T-B, Peterson), functioning as sense organs and bearing a large number of sensilla (Chapman).

antenna cleaner, in adult Hymenoptera, an excavation on the interior base of the first tarsomere of the anterior tarsus fringed with a row of bristles (antenna comb), covered by a movable process from the end of the tibia (strigilis), forming an opening through which the antenna may be drawn (T-B); any structure on the anterior tibia resembling or functioning similarly to the antenna cleaner of adult Hymenoptera (T-B); in adult Lepidoptera, epiphysis, q.v. (Common, pers. comm.).

antenna comb, in adult Hymenoptera, row of bristles lining a groove at the proximal end of the anterior tarsus, forming comblike structure of the antenna cleaner, q.v. (Leftwich); see strigil.

antennal appendage, in ♂ Phthiraptera (Amblycera and Ischnocera), a projecting process of the first or third segment (T-B, after J. B. Smith).

antennal base, in Collembola (esp. Onychiuridae), a differentiated area of cuticle around the point of origin of the antenna (Christiansen and Bellinger).

antennal blade, in larval Chironomidae (Diptera), blade usually at apex of basal antennal segment, having a common base with accessory blade (Saether).

antennal clava, in adult Siphonaptera, the terminal apical segment of the antenna usually subdivided into 9 flagellomeres (Smit).

antennal club, the more or less enlarged distal articles of a clubbed antenna (T-B; Borror et al.).

antennal comb, in adult Hymenoptera, strigil, q.v. (T-B).

antennal file, in Hypogastruridae (Collembola), a field of small, short, sometimes hooked, ventral setae found on the fourth antennal segment (Christiansen and Bellinger).

antennal formula, in Coccoidea (Hemiptera: Sternorrhyncha), enumeration of the antennal segments in the order of their length, beginning with the longest and bracketing together those of the same length; in other insects, the arrangement of the antennal joints in point of length, or in a proportion in serial order, beginning with the first (T-B).

antennal fossa, a groove or cavity in which antenna is located or concealed (T-B); in adult Diptera, antennal groove, q.v. (T-B, after Comstock); in adult Siphonaptera, the deep grooves on the sides of the head in which the antennae rest (Smit); see scrobe and torulus.

antennal fovea, in some Derbidae (Hemiptera: Auchenorrhyncha: Fulgoroidea), U-shaped area formed by the foliaceous extension of the ventrolateral carinae of the pronotum which appears to surround the antenna (Fennah); in adult Diptera, antennal groove, q.v. (T-B); in some adult Hymenoptera, the depressed area surrounding torulus, frequently connected with the antennal furrows and the lateral foveae (T-B).

antennal foveolae, in Orthoptera, the pits between the frontal costa and the lateral carinae, in which the antennae are inserted (T-B).

antennal furrows, in some adult Hymenoptera, furrows or grooves extending from the anterior tentorial pits along the lateral margin of the toruli across the frons to near the lateral ocelli, thence across the vertex to the occipital ridge; most frequently complete, but at times with certain sections obsolete (T-B); see antennal scrobe, antennal fovea, vertical furrows, lateral foveae, ocellar furrows, and interocellar furrows.

antennal groove, in adult Diptera, one of a pair of grooves on the facial plate which receive the antennae (T-B, McAlpine); in adult Curculionoidea (Coleoptera), scrobe, q.v. (Borror et al); in Hymenoptera, the curved portion of the antennal furrow extending on each side of the head between the anterior tentorial pits and the frontal crest around the lateral margin of the toruli (T-B); in fleas (Siphonaptera) a sulcus just behind the eye which divides the head into 2 regions (T-B); see antennal fossa and antennal fovea.

antennal lobes, paired lobes of the deutocerebrum (T-B).

antennal organ(s), in Collembola, sensory structures on the distal segment of the antenna (T-B); in Eumastacidae (Orthoptera), a small organ situated at the ventrodistal angle of one of the distal articles (Key, in CSIRO).

antennal nerve, nerve extending from deutocerebrum, that innervates the antenna (Chapman).

antennal papillae, in Collembola, papillae found subapically and laterodorsally on antennal segment III; blunt, thin walled, free or set in individual depressions or common groove, sometimes concealed in separate pockets (Richards).

antennal process, in adult Diptera, the frontal protuberance upon which the antennae are inserted (T-B).

antennal prominence, in larval Culicidae (Diptera), the anterolateral antenna-bearing lobe of the cranium (Harbach and Knight, after Christophers).

antennal puncture, in larval Culicidae (Diptera), a small puncture located dorsally near the base of the antenna (Harbach and Knight, after Laffoon and Knight).

antennal ratio (AR), in larval Chironomidae (Diptera), ratio of length of the basal segment to the combined length of the remaining segments (Saether); in adult Chironomidae (Diptera), ratio of apical flagellomere plus any flagellomeres distal to it divided by the combined length of the more basal flagellomeres (Saether).

antennal sclerite, annulus antennalis, q.v. (T-B).

antennal scrobe, in some adult Hymenoptera, one of a pair of excavations on frons, receiving the basal part of the antenna (Gauld and Bolton); see antennal groove and antennal fovea.

antennal seam, in adult Calyptratae and some other Muscomorpha (Diptera), a dorsalateral longitudinal groove on antennal pedicel (McAlpine).

antennal segment, antennomere, q.v. (Boudreaux); the second preoral segment of the head, bearing the antennae, between the acron and the intercalary segment (T-B; McAlpine).

antennal socket, torulus, q.v.(T-B, after Snodgrass).

antennal spine, in larval Chironomidae (Diptera), antennal blade, q.v. (Saether).

antennal suture, an external inflection forming an internal ridge to strengthen the rim of the antennal socket (T-B, after Snodgrass); in adult *Culiseta annulata* (Schrank), margin of scape adjacent to antennal socket (Harbach and Knight, after Schiemenz).

antennale, antennaria, q.v. (T-B, after MacGillivray).

antennaria, the annular sclerite forming the periphery of each anta-coria (T-B).

antennary fossa, antennal fossa, q.v. (T-B).

antennary furrow, in Amblycera (Phthiraptera), a groove on the under side of the head in which each antenna lies (T-B; Lyal, pers. comm.).

antennary nerve, antennal nerve, q.v. (T-B).

Antennata, Mandibulata, q.v. (Hennig).

antennate, antennatus (Latin), having antennae (T-B).

antennation, touching with antennae, serving as a sensory probe or as a tactile signal to another insect (Wilson).

antennifer, a pivotlike process at the rim of the antennal socket form-ing a special support and articular point for the base of the scape, to allow the antenna free movement in all directions (T-B, after Snod-grass); in adult Culicidae (Diptera), a process of the scape which articulates with the pedicel (Harbach and Knight, after Patton and Evans); see torulus.

antenniferous, bearing antennae (T-B).

antenniform, made up like, or having the appearance of, antennae.

antenno-ocular pouches, in larval Muscidae (Diptera), a pair of lateral pouches which contain the histoblastic rudiments of the antennae and comound eyes, which are formed by the invagination of the areas of the dorsal wall of the head on which the antennae and eyes are to be formed (T-B, after Snodgrass).

antennomaxillary lobes, in larval Muscomorpha (Diptera), lobe of cephalic segment bearing an antennal and a maxillary sensory pa-pilla (Teskey, in McAlpine).

antennomere, a subunit of the antenna, including scape, pedicel, and flagellomeres.

antennular region, deutocerebrum, q.v. (T-B).

antennule, a small antenna (T-B); the first antennae of Crustacea (T-B; Borror et al.).

antenodal, before or preceding a node, specifically, the node in the dragonfly (Odonata) wing (T-B); in adult Odonata, anternodal crossvein, q.v. (T-B, after Tillyard).

antenodal cells, in adult Agrionidae (Odonata), the cells included be-tween the short sector (M_4) and the upper sector of the triangle (Cu_1), and between the quadrilateral (or quadrangle) and the vein descending from the nodus (T-B).

antenodal costal spaces, in Odonata, the cells between the costa and subcosta, from the base to the nodus (T-B).

antenodal crossveins, in adult Odonata, crossveins extending between the costa and the subcosta proximad to nodus (T-B; Borror et al).

anteocular, before the eye (T-B); in Collembola, a peculiar structure of undefined function in front of the eyes (T-B).

anteoculus, in Heteroptera (Hemiptera), the part of head capsule ex-tending in front of eyes in dorsal view (Nieser).

antepectus, the under side of the prothorax (T-B).

antepenultimate, the second before the last (T-B).

antepleuron, episternum, q.v. (T-B, after MacGillivray).

anteprocoxal membrane, in adult Culicidae (Diptera), the membrane anterior to the forecoxa, between it and the proepisternum, sometimes with anteprocoxal scales (Harbach and Knight, after Knight and Laffoon).

anteprocoxal scale, in adult Culicidae (Diptera), one of the scales occurring in a small group on the anteprocoxal membrane (Harbach and Knight).

antepronotal lobes, in adult Nematocera (Diptera), enlarged lateral portions of antepronotum (McAlpine).

antepronotal scale, in adult Culicidae (Diptera), one of the scales occurring in a group on the antepronotum, sometimes forming a tuft (Harbach and Knight).

antepronotal seta, in adult Culicidae (Diptera), any seta occurring on the antepronotum (Harbach and Knight, after Knight and Laffoon).

antepronotals, in adult and pupal Chironomidae (Diptera), setae of antepronotum, divided into median and lateral antepronotals (Saether).

antepronotum, in adult Diptera, especially Nematocera, the anterior division of the pronotum, visible as a setose lobe just above the proepisternum (T-B, after Crampton; Harbach and Knight; McAlpine).

antepygidial bristles, antepygidial setae, q.v. (Dunnet, in CSIRO; Borror et al.).

antepygidial setae, in adult Siphonaptera, one or more large setae on the apical margin of tergum VII, rarely absent (Lewis, pers. comm.).

anterior, in front; before (T-B); see cephalad.

anterior acrostichals, in adult Diptera, preacrostichals, q.v. (T-B).

anterior angle, the angle of the thorax near the head (T-B).

anterior apodeme of endophallic plate, in ♂ Orthoptera, endophallic apodeme, q.v. (Tuxen, after Snodgrass).

anterior apophyses, in ♀ Lepidoptera, apophyses anteriores, q.v. (T-B, after Klots; Tuxen).

anterior arculus, in wing veins, that part of the arculus which is a section of the media (T-B, after Comstock).

anterior arms of tentorium, anterior tentorial arms, q.v. (T-B, after Imms).

anterior basalare, in adult Diptera, anterior part of divided basalare (McAlpine); see posterior basalare.

anterior branch, convex anterior branch of primary longitudinal vein of wing (McAlpine, after Kukulova-Peck).

anterior branch of third vein, in Diptera, fourth radial vein (R_4) of Comstock (T-B, after Williston).

anterior clypeus, anteclypeus, q.v. (T-B).

anterior connecting leaf of gonapophysis VIII (connective VIII A), in ♀ Heteroptera (Hemiptera), generally membranous connective between gonapophysis VIII and gonocoxite VIII (transl. "feullet connectif antérior de la gonapophyse VIII" Dupuis, after Tuxen).

anterior connecting leaf of gonapophysis IX (connective IX A), in ♀

Heteroptera (Hemiptera), connective between gonapophysis IX and gonocoxite IX (transl. "feullet connectif antérieur de la gonapophyse IX" Dupuis, after Tuxen).

anterior cornu, precornua, q.v. (T-B, after MacGillivray).

anterior crop, in many Auchenorrhyncha and Sternorrhyncha (Hemiptera), the anterior part of the filter chamber (T-B, after Hickernell).

anterior crossvein, in adult Diptera, radial-medial crossvein, q.v. (T-B, after Curran; Borror et al.).

anterior cubitus, cubitus anterior, q.v.

anterior dorsal tooth, in larval Culicidae (Diptera), the more anterior of the 2 dorsal teeth of the mandible, usually bearing one or 2 cusps (Harbach and Knight, after Pao and Knight).

anterior dorsocentral area, in adult Culicidae (Diptera), the part of the dorsocentral area cephalad of about the level of the antealar area, bearing setae and scales (Harbach and Knight, after Belkin).

anterior dorsocentral bristles, in adult Diptera, a row of bristles on each side before the scutal transverse suture (T-B, after Comstock); see dorsocentral setae.

anterior dorsocentral scale, in adult Culicidae (Diptera), one of the scales occurring in a more or less distinct line located cephalad of the posterior scutal fossal scales on the anterior dorsocentral area of the scutum (Harbach and Knight).

anterior dorsocentral seta, in adult Culicidae (Diptera), a dorsosentral seta occurring on the anterior dorsocentral area, occurring in one or more rows (Harbach and Knight); see anterior dorsocentral bristles.

anterior fibula(e), in ♀ Heteroptera (Hemiptera), fibulae anteriores, q.v. (Tuxen) or posterior connecting leaf of gonapophysis VIII, q.v. (Tuxen, after Štys).

anterior field, in the tegmina of Orthoptera, costal field, q.v. (T-B).

anterior gonapophyses, in ♂ Muscomorpha (Diptera), pregonites, q.v. (Tuxen); in adult ♂ Diptera, gonopods, q.v. (McAlpine); in ♀ Odonata, Orthoptera, Psocoptera, and Heteroptera, first gonapophyses, q.v. (Tuxen; Broadhead).

anterior gonopods, in ♀ Psocoptera, first valvulae, q.v. (Tuxen, after Pearman).

anterior hard plate, in adult Culicidae (Diptera), the irregular platelike anterior area of the clypeopalatum, bearing one or more palatal setae (Harbach and Knight, after Thompson).

anterior hooklike processes, in ♂ Orthoptera, ancora, q.v., of epiphallus (Tuxen, after Snodgrass).

anterior intercalary vein, in adult Diptera, a branch of media posterior (M_2) (T-B).

anterior intervalvula, in ♀ Orthoptera, inferior intervalvula, q.v. (Tuxen, after Snodgrass).

anterior intestine, the part of the hind gut between the midgut and the rectum (T-B, after Snodgrass; Gilmour, in CSIRO); see colon and ileum.

anterior labral muscles, one of the 2 pairs of long muscles which move the labrum, inserted on the anterior margin of the labral base (T-B, Snodgrass).

anterior lacinial chaeta, in larval Chironomidae (Diptera), most anterior chaeta of lacinia placed above galear sensillum basiconicum and posterior to paraxial seta (Saether).

anterior lamina, in ♂ Odonata, lamina anterior, q.v. (Tuxen).

anterior lateral sclerites, in ♂ Dermaptera, anterior side wall of basal region of penis (Tuxen).

anterior mandibular articulation, in larval Diptera, dorsal point of articulation of mandible with head capsule (Teskey, in McAlpine); junction line along which the preartis and precoila come into contact during mandibular movements (Harbach and Knight).

anterior media, media anterior, q.v.

anterior median process, in anopheline larvae (Diptera: Culicidae), an elevated dome- or knoblike membranous area situated posteriorly on the midline of the anterior spiracular lobe of the spiracular apparatus (Harbach and Knight).

anterior mesanepisternum, in some adult Diptera, the somewhat triangular anterior part of the mesanepisternum bearing the mesothoracic spiracle, separated from the posterior mesanepisternum and meskatepisternum by the anepisternal cleft (Harbach and Knight).

anterior mesenteron rudiment, in the insect embryo, the anterior group of cells of the ventral endoderm remnant that regenerates the mesenteron (T-B, after Snodgrass).

anterior mesepimeral scale, in adult Culicidae (Diptera), one of the mesepimeral scales occurring in a group on the cephalodorsal quarter of the mesanepimeron (Harbach and Knight).

anterior nodule of median flap, in some ♂ *Dihybocercus* (Embiidina: Embiidae), an anterior nodule, usually microspiculate, on the median flap of tergum X (Ross, in Tuxen).

anterior notal process, anterior notal wing process, q.v. (Chapman).

anterior notal wing process, the anterior lobe of the lateral margin of the alinotum supporting the neck of the first axillary sclerite (T-B, after Snodgrass).

anterior oblique suture, in many adult Aculeata (Hymenoptera), a groove extending from subalar pit to the epicnemal carina (Gauld and Bolton).

anterior orbit, facial orbit, q.v. (T-B, after MacGillivray).

anterior palatal bar, in larval Culicidae (Diptera), a transverse labropalatal structure formed by a pair of well-sclerotized lateral parts articulating on the mesal tormal processes and a short, flexible, interposed mesal unit (Harbach and Knight, after Cook).

anterior palpi, labial palpi, q.v. (T-B).

anterior parameres, in ♂ (Muscomorpha) Diptera, pregonites, q.v. (Tuxen; Griffiths, after Black); in some ♂ Machilidae (Archaeognatha), gonapophyses of abdominal segment VIII (transl. "paramères antérieurs" Denis, after Tuxen).

anterior parapods, in some larval Chironomidae (Diptera), parapods on prothorax, which are occasionally fused (Saether); prolegs, q.v. (Teskey, in McAlpine).

anterior pharynx, the precerebral part of the pharynx, in those insects in which there is a differentiated posterior pharynx behind the brain (T-B, after Snodgrass).

anterior phragma, one of a pair of internal lobes borne by the antecosta, which project into the cavity of the mesothorax and serve for the attachment of a muscle (T-B, after Needham).

anterior plate, in ♀ Lepidoptera, lamella antevaginalis, q.v. (Tuxen, after Alman).

anterior point, in ♂ Auchenorrhyncha (Hemiptera), anterolateral angle of foot of style (Tuxen, after Young).

anterior process, in ♂ Siphonaptera, telomeres dorsalis, q.v. (Tuxen, after Hubbard).

anterior process of terebra, in ♀ Odonata, anterior gonapophyses, q.v. (Tuxen, after Tillyard).

anterior promontory, in adult Culicidae (Diptera), the broad median area of the mesonotum at the anterior end of the acrostichal area which more or less projects cephalad over the cervix (Harbach and Knight, after Cristophers).

anterior pronotal setae, in pupal Chironomidae (Diptera), median antepronotals, q.v. (Saether).

anterior pronotum, in adult Nematocera (Diptera), antepronotum, q.v. (McAlpine).

anterior ramus, in ♀ Heteroptera (Hemiptera), posterior connecting leaf of gonapophysis VIII, q.v. (Tuxen, after Slater).

anterior sclerite of second coxopodite, in ♀ insects, gonangulum, q.v. (Tuxen, after Snodgrass).

anterior scutal fossal seta, in adult Culicidae (Diptera), one of the setae occurring in a group on the anterolateral margin of the scutal fossa above the posterior margin of the antepronotum (Harbach and Knight).

anterior scutellar ridge, in adult Culicidae (Diptera), the external ridge extending from the anterolateral angle of the scutellum to the base of the posterior notal wing process (Harbach and Knight, after Owen).

anterior spiracles, in adult and larval Diptera, paired mesothoracic spiracles that have migrated forward, being situated on the anterodorsal angle of the anepisternum near the junction of the pronotum and mesonotum (Teskey, in McAlpine).

anterior spiracular lobe, in larval Culicidae and Dixidae (Diptera), anterior, unpaired flaplike projection of the spiracular apparatus (Harbach and Knight).

anterior spiracular lobe plate I, in larval Culicidae (Diptera), the inner sclerite (that nearest the spiracular openings) of the anterior spiracular lobe of the spiracular apparatus (Harbach and Knight).

anterior spiracular lobe plate II, in larval Culicidae (Diptera), the somewhat weakly developed outer sclerite (that nearest abdominal segment VIII or the distal margin of the siphon) of the anterior spiracular lobe of the spiracular apparatus (Harbach and Knight).

anterior squama, in adult Diptera, outer squama, q.v. (T-B).

anterior stigmatal tubercle, in larval Lepidoptera, a prominence on the thoracic and abdominal segments (T-B).

anterior surstylar lobe, in adult Muscomorpha (Diptera), secondary lobe of epandrium (McAlpine).

anterior tentorial arms, the cuticular invaginations arising from the anterior tentorial pits in the subgenal sutures or in the epistomal suture, which form part of the tentorium (T-B, after Snodgrass); see posterior tentorial arms.

anterior tentoral pits, the external depressions in the subgenal or epistomal ridges, sometimes elongate (T-B, after Snodgrass); see anterior tentorial arms.

anterior tentorium, in adult Diptera, anterior tentorial arms, q.v. (Harbach and Knight, after Robinson; McAlpine).

anterior trapezoidal tubercle, in larval Lepidoptera, protuberance on the thoracic and abdominal segments (T-B).

anterior tuberosity, in most insects, the anterior of 2 prominent, elevated, shoulderlike areas at the base of the wing (T-B, after Comstock).

anterior valves, in ♀ insects, first gonapophyses, q.v. (Tuxen); in ♀ Plecoptera, ventrovalvulae, q.v. (Tuxen, after Crampton) or ventral valves of ovipositor, q.v. (Tuxen, after Walker).

anterior valvulae, in ♀ insects, first gonapophyses, q.v. (Tuxen); in Phasmida, inferior valvulae, q.v. (Tuxen); in ♀ Orthoptera, first gonapophyses, q.v. (Tuxen); in ♀ Heteroptera (Hemiptera), first gonapophyses, q.v. (Tuxen, after Rawat).

anterior ventral cervical sclerite, in Dermaptera, front ventral neck sclerite (Popham).

anterior vertical ridge, in adult Siphonaptera, a ridge lying close to, and parallel with, the anterior margin of the metepisternum (Hopkins and Rothschild).

anterior wall, in ♀ Miridae (Hemiptera: Heteroptera), the part of the bursa copulatrix lying between the anterior fibulae and below the roof (transl. "vordere Wand" Kullenberg, after Tuxen).

anterior wing-root, in adult Culicidae (Diptera), the proximal area of the wing including the basal parts of the costa, radius and remigium (Harbach and Knight, after Prashad).

anterior wings, forewings, q.v. (T-B).

antero-, Latin prefix; before; to the front of (T-B).

anteroadmedian lines, in adult Hymenoptera, anterior paramedial lines of the mesoscutum (Gibson).

anterodorsal, toward the front and dorsum (T-B); in adult Diptera, leg bristles at the meeting of the anterior and the dorsal faces (T-B).

anterodorsal endomere, in ♂ Anoplura (Phthiraptera), dorsal sclerotization near base of genital sac (Tuxen, after Ewing).

anterolateral, located anteriorly and to the side.

anterolateral spiracular lobe, in larval mosquitoes (Diptera: Culicidae and Dixidae), one of the anterior of the 2 bilateral pairs of flaplike projections of the spiracular apparatus, being weakly developed (indistinct) in the tribe Mansoniini (Harbach and Knight).

anterolateral spiracular lobe plate I, in larval Culicidae and Dixidae (Diptera), the inner sclerite (that nearest the spiracular openings) of one of the anterolateral spiracular lobes of the spiracular apparatus (Harbach and Knight).

anterolateral spiracular lobe plate II, in larval Culicidae and Dixidae (Diptera), the often poorly delimited outer sclerite (that nearest abdominal segment VIII or the distal margin of the siphon) of one of the anterolateral spiracular lobes of the spiracular apparatus (Harbach and Knight).

anteromedian bare space, in adult Culicidae (Diptera), the area between the acrostichal and dorsocentral setae on roughly the anterior half of the scutum (Harbach and Knight, after Christophers).

anteromedian palatal brush, in most larval Culicidae (Diptera), the distal, unpaired palatal brush formed by some of the long filaments attached to the anteromedian palatal lobe (Harbach and Knight, after Laffoon and Knight).

anteromedian palatal filament, in larval Culicidae (Diptera), any labropalatal filament between the inner edges of the lateral palatal penicular areas (Harbach and Knight).

anteromedian palatal lobe, in larval Culicidae (Diptera), the distal, unpaired labropalatal lobe, usually bearing a brush of filaments (Harbach and Knight, after Laffoon and Knight).

anteromedian palatal penicular area, in many larval Culicidae (Diptera), the specialized cuticular area bearing a brush on the anterolateral palatal lobe (Harbach and Knight, after Laffoon and Knight).

anteromesal, in the front and along the midline (Borror et al.).

anteroventral, in the front and underneath or on the lower side (T-B; Borror et al); in adult Diptera, leg bristles at the meeting of the anterior and the ventral faces (T-B).

anteroventral endomere, in ♂ Anoplura (Phthiraptera), ventral sclerotization near base of genital sac (Tuxen, after Ewing).

antescutal depression, in adult Zelinae (Hymenoptera: Braconidae), a transverse depression between the dorsoanterior part of the pronotum and the middle lobe of the mesoscutum (van Achterberg).

antevaginal plate, lamella antevaginalis, q.v. (Tuxen, after Rothschild and Jordan).

anthobian, feeding on flowers, being applied to certain lamellicorn Coleoptera in which the labium extends beyond the mentum (T-B).

anthocyanins, plant pigments which may be incorporated in the tissues and contribute to the blue or red coloration of some insects (Tulloch).

anthogenesis, the production of males and females parthenogenetically, as in certain aphids (Hemiptera: Sternorrhyncha: Aphididae).

anthonome, a larval mine occurring in a flower (Hering).

anthophila, in Hymenoptera, species in which the basal joint of the hind tarsus is dilated and pubescent, i.e., bees (Apoidea) (T-B).

anthophilous, flower-frequenting or flower-loving (T-B); feeding on flowers (Leftwich); describing insects that serve as pollen vectors (Matthews and Matthews); describing mouthparts modified for flower feeding (Gauld and Bolton).

anthracine, anthracinus (Latin), coal black; a deep shiny black with a bluish tinge (T-B).

anthraquinone, in Coccoidea (Hemiptera: Sternorrhyncha), quinone pigment formed from the condensation of 3 benzene rings, e.g., carminic acid, q.v. (Chapman); see aphin.

anthrax, bacterial disease of man and other animals caused by *Bacillus anthracis* Cohn and transmitted by horse flies, *Tabanus* spp. (Diptera: Tabanidae) (Borror et al).

anthropomorphism, attributing human characteristics to other species of animals (Matthews and Matthews).

anthropophilous, man-loving, applied to insects which show a preference for human blood.

anti-, Latin prefix; against; opposite; contrary (T-B); see ante-.

antibiosis, an association between 2 or more organisms that is detrimental to one or more or them (Pfadt).

antibody, in vertebrates, a serum globin which is produced in the blood of an immunized animal in response to the introduction of a foreign antigen (Mayr; Steinhaus and Martignoni); see antigen, antiserum, and serology.

anticlyepus, anteclypeus, q.v. (T-B, after Sharp).

anticoagulant, any substance which prevents the clotting or coagulation of blood, e.g., in saliva of blood-sucking insects (T-B; Gilmour, in CSIRO).

anticoagulatory, acting to prevent coagulation (T-B).

anticoagulin, an animal secretion which acts to prevent the coagulation of the blood (T-B); a substance secreted by certain sucking arthopods which prevents the blood of their prey from coagulating or inhibits the action of coagulin (T-B).

anticrypsis, concealing coloration and behavior (crypsis) enabling a predator to apprach its prey unobserved, or, more usually, allowing the prey to approach the predator without seeing it (Norris, in CSIRO).

anticryptic colors, colors which are used for concealment in order to facilitate attack on prey (T-B).

anticus, frontal; belonging to or directed toward the front (T-B).

antidiuretic hormone, a hormone that increases resorbtion of water by the rectum as well as decreasing the rate of water secretion by the Malpighian tubules, resulting in reduced water excretion (Chapman).

antigen, a substance, especially a protein, capable of inducing the formation of antibodies when introduced into the bloodstream of vertebrates or, in insects, other protective, lytic, or cidal substance (Mayr; Steinhaus and Martignoni); see immunogen.

antigenic, with the properties of an antigen (Mayr).

antigeny, opposition or antagonism of the sexes, embracing all forms of sexual diversity (T-B).

antigonadotrophin, hormone that blocks vitellogenesis in younger oocytes (Chapman, after Pratt and Davey).

antiperistalsis, the reversed muscular contractions, or peristalsis, of the gut (T-B).

antipygidial bristles, in adult Siphonaptera, antepygidial bristles, q.v. (T-B, after Comstock).

antiserum, blood serum containing specific antibodies (Mayr); see antibody and precipitin reaction.

antisquama, in adult Diptera, upper calypter, q.v. (T-B).

antistyle, in ♂ Hesperiidae (Lepidoptera), a process of stylifer of valva (Tuxen, after Chapman).

antitegula, in adult Diptera, antisquama, q.v. (T-B).

antlered larvae, in certain Notodontidae (Lepidoptera), freshly-hatched larvae which have a pair of large antlerlike horns dorsally on the first thoracic segment and other horns on the abdominal segments (T-B, after Comstock).

antlia, in adult Lepidoptera, proboscis, q.v. (T-B; Leftwich); in adult Diptera, pharyngeal pump, q.v. (T-B, after MacGillivray).

Antliata, an old name for sucking insects, especially Lepidoptera and Diptera (T-B; Leftwich).

Antliophora, hypothesized monophyletic within the Holometabola, including the Mecoptera and Diptera (Hennig).

antovipositor, in ♀ Telmatogetoninae (Diptera: Chironomidae), egg-laying device consisting of elements other than gonapophyses VIII and IX and gonostyli VIII and IX only, but including cerci and tergite IX (Saether).

antrorse, antrorsum (Latin), directed toward the front (T-B).

antrum (pl., **antra**), in ♀ Lepidoptera (Lepidoptera: Nymphalidae), caudal-most part of ductus bursae when more heavily sclerotized and differentiated from remainder of ductus (Tuxen, after Higgins; Davis, pers. comm).

ants' eggs, pupae of ants (Hymenoptera: Formicidae), commonly and erroneously called eggs when they are used for feeding fish, etc. (Leftwich).

anullus, in ♂ Sphingidae (Lepidoptera), region of aedoeagus, sometimes especially sclerotized, perhaps produced, immediately caudad of zone (Tuxen, after Oiticica).

anus (pl., **ani**), the opening at the posterior end of the digestive tract, through which food remnants are passed (T-B); in armored scales (Hemiptera: Sternorrhyncha: Coccoidea), a more or less circular opening on the dorsal surface of the pygidium, varying in location as regards the circumgenital pore orifices (T-B; Kosztarab, pers. comm.).

aorta, the anterior, nonchambered, narrow part of the dorsal vessel, opening into the head and lacking ostia (T-B; Chapman); see heart.

aortal chamber, a thoracic enlargement of the aorta (T-B, after Packard).

aortic valve, the closing mechanism of the insect dorsal vessel at the junction of the aorta and the heart proper (T-B).

apatetic colors, in insects, colors resembling some part of the environment or the appearance of another species (T-B, after Folsom and Wardle).

apertum, in adult Coleoptera, a special cell opening basally in the hind wing (T-B, after Tillyard).

aperture opening, in ♀ Heteroptera (Hemiptera), orificium receptaculi, q.v. (Tuxen, after Pendergrast).

apex (pl., **apices**), end of any structure distad to the base (T-B); apical angle, q.v., of wing (T-B, after Comstock); in ♂ Orthoptera, ventral aedeagal valve, q.v. (Tuxen, after Walker); in ♂ Coleoptera, distal part of penis, distad of ostium (Tuxen); in ♂ Siphonaptera, distal arm, q.v. (Tuxen); in ♂ Lepidoptera, apical angle q.v. (Tuxen, after John).

apex abdominis, the end of the abdomen (T-B); cremaster, q.v. (T-B).

aphagia, in invertebrate pathology, the inability to ingest (Steinhaus and Martignoni).

Aphaniptera, Siphonaptera, q.v. (T-B, after Kirby and Spence).

Aphelocheiroidea, superfamily with infraorder Nepomorpha (Hemiptera: Heteroptera), including only Aphelocheiridae; generally included in the Naucoroidea.

aphid, a member of the superfamily Aphidoidea (Hemiptera: Sternorrhyncha) (Kosztarab, in Parker); see plant-louse.

aphideine, aphidilutein, q.v. (T-B).

aphidicolous, frequenting aphid (Hemiptera: Sternorrhyncha: Aphididae) colonies, being applied to ants (Hymenoptera: Formicidae) (T-B).

Aphidina, Aphidoidea, q.v. (Hennig).

Aphidiformes, Aphidimorpha, q.v. (Hennig, after Schlee).

aphidilutein, a yellowish fluid found in aphids (Hemiptera: Sternorrhyncha: Aphididae) (T-B).

aphidivorous, aphidophagous, q.v. (T-B).

Aphidoidea, superfamily within the Sternorrhyncha (Hemiptera), including the families Aphididae, Adelgidae, and Phylloxeridae (Woodward et al., in CSIRO).

Aphidomorpha, group within the Sternorrhyncha (Hemiptera), including the superfamilies Aphidoidea and Coccoidea (Hennig).

aphidophagous, feeding or praying upon aphids (Hemiptera: Auchenorrhyncha: Aphidoidea) (Gauld and Bolton).

aphin, quinone pigment with a nucleus of 7 condensed benzene rings, found in the hemolymph of aphids (Hemiptera: Sternorrhyncha: Aphididae) and imparting a purple or black color to the whole insect (Chapman); see anthraquinone.

aphrodisiac, a substance produced by either sex that facilitates courtship or prepares the opposite sex for copulation after the pair has been brought together (Matthews and Matthews).

aphrodisiac pheromone, aphrodisiac, q.v. (Chapman).

apiary, a place where honeybees are kept or more specifically a group of hives (Wilson).

apicad, toward the apex (T-B).

apical, at, near or pertaining to the apex of any structure (T-B).

apical angle, the angle of the wing at its apex (T-B, after Wardle); in ♂ Lepidoptera, dorsocaudal angle of valva (Tuxen).

apical appendage, in ♂ Diptera, dististylus, q.v. (Tuxen, after Snodgrass); gonostylus, q.v. (McAlpine); in ♂ Siphonaptera, the tendril-like extension of the proximal end of the median lamina (Rothschild and Traub).

apical area, apical cell, q.v., of wing (T-B); in ♂ Ensifera (Orthoptera), distal end of the dorsal field of the forewing, posterior to the mirror (Otte, pers. comm.); in adult Aprocrita (Hymenoptera), petiolar area, q.v., of propodeum (T-B).

apical arm, in ♂ Siphonaptera, distal arm, q.v. (Tuxen).

apical bulb, in Collembola, a papilla at or near the tip of antennal segment 4, usually set in a deep socket, sometimes retracted, and therefore visible only by transparency (Christiansen and Bellinger); in ♀ Heteroptera (Hemiptera), capsula seminalis, q.v. (Tuxen, after Scudder).

apical cell, a specialized, usually large, trophic cell of the upper end of the testicular tube in some insects (T-B, after Snodgrass); a cell near the wing tip (T-B; Borror et al.); in adult Trichoptera, the principal cells along the wing apex, from anterior to posterior: S_1, S_3, M_1, M_3, and Cu_1 (according to Ross et al.), numbered 1 through 5, respectively, variously present or absent (McLachlan).

apical chamber, a germarium in a telotrophic ovariole (T-B, after Snodgrass).

apical comb, in ♂ Psocoptera, comb on tergum IX (transl. "peigne apical" after Tuxen).

apical complex, in ♂ Heteroptera and Diptera, syncytium with many nuclei in germarium of testis follicle, providing nutriment to the spermatogonia (Chapman).

apical crossvein, in wing of some adult Syrphidae and many Calyptratae (Diptera), relatively sharply bent portion of M_{1+2} (McAlpine).

apical filament, in Collembola, terminal projection of one of the unguicular lamellae, extending beyond the rest of the organ (Christiansen and Bellinger).

apical intersegmental fold, in ♀ Culicidae (Diptera), the usually cephalad-directed fold of the intersegmental membrane between the posterior margin of sternum VIII and the lower vaginal lip, carrying the insula on its posterior median area (Harbach and Knight, after Reinert).

apical lateral spines, in ♂ Auchenorrhyncha (Hemiptera), anal hooks, q.v. (L. O'Brien, pers. comm.).

apical lobe, in ♂ Culicidae (Diptera), subapical lobe, q.v. (Tuxen; Harbach and Knight, after Dyar).

apical margin, the outer margin of the insect wing (T-B, after Wardle; Chapman).

apical membrane, in ♂ Siphonaptera, vexillum, q.v. (Tuxen).

apical opening, in ♂ Coleoptera, ostium, q.v., of penis (Tuxen).

apical orifice, in ♂ Coleoptera, ostium, q.v., of penis (Tuxen).

apical plate, an external sensory structure of the primitive annelid-arthropod nervous system or group of nerve cells at the anterior pole of the body (T-B, after Snodgrass); in many Heteroptera (Hemiptera), a median ventral structure on the labial apex (Cobben).

apical portion of upper organ, in ♂ Hesperiidae (Lepidoptera), uncus, q.v. (Tuxen, after Scudder and Burgess).

apical process, in ♂ Lygaeidae (Hemiptera: Heteroptera), processus gonopori, q.v. (Tuxen, after Kumar); in some ♀ Helotrephidae (Hemiptera: Heteroptera), distal part of transformed ovipositor pertaining to abdominal segment IX (Papáček, Tonner, and Štys).

apical processes, processus terminales, q.v. (Tuxen, after Tjeder).

apical processes of aedeagus, in ♂ Orthoptera, the free parts of the aedeagal valves (Tuxen, after Snodgrass); in ♂ Mecoptera, doral valves, q.v. (Tuxen, after Cheng).

apical sector, in adult Planipennia, one of the longitudinal veins in the apical part of the wing (T-B).

apical sclerite, in ♂ Siphonaptera, Ford's sclerites, q.v. (Tuxen, after Wagner).

apical sclerite of phallosome, in ♂ Siphonaptera, hamuli, q.v. (Tuxen, after Jordan).

apical scutellars, in adult Diptera, apical scutellar setae, q.v. (T-B, after Curran).

apical scutellar setae, in adult Diptera, apical pair of marginal setae on the scutellum of mesonotum (McAlpine); see subapical and basal scutellar setae.

apical setae, on antenna of adult Chironomidae (Diptera), straight, stiff, dark setae at or near apex (Saether).

apical spurs, in adult Diptera, tibial spurs, q.v. (T-B, after Curran; McAlpine).

apical sternite, in ♀ Cicadoidea (Hemiptera: Auchenorrhyncha), "last" abdominal sternum, q.v. (Tuxen).

apical style, some ♀ Helotrephidae (Heteroptera), apical process, q.v. (Esaki and Miyamoto from Papáček, Tonner, and Štys).

apical transverse carina, in adult Hymenoptera, the carina which crosses the metanotum behind the middle and separates the median area from the petiolar area (T-B); see area.

apical tube, in ♀ Gerromorpha (Hemiptera: Heteroptera), spermathecal tube, q.v. (Štys).

apical tuft, in adult Lepidoptera, prominent masses of hairs or scales on posterior abdominal segments, presumably for display, scent dispersal, or covering the eggs (Tuxen); see corethrogyne.

apical valves, in ♂ Caelifera (Orthoptera), distal valves of penis if divided, or distal half of undivided penis (Tuxen, after Dirsh).

apically, toward, or directed toward, the apex (T-B).

apicodorsal lobe, in ♂ Culicidae (Diptera), subapical lobe, q.v. (Harbach and Knight).

apicodorsals, in ♂ Tanypodinae (Diptera: Chironomidae), stronger apicodorsal seta of gonocoxite (Saether).

apicolateral, located apically and to the side.

apicomedian sclerite, in ♂ Siphonaptera, Ford's sclerites, q.v. (Tuxen).

apicoventral lobe, in ♂ Culicidae (Diptera), the most distal area of the ventral (prerotation sense) surface of the gonocoxite, being an apical ventromesal lobe (Harbach and Knight, after Christophers and Barraud).

apiculate, apiculatus (Latin), covered with erect fleshy short points (T-B).

apiculis, an erect, fleshy, short point (T-B).

apiculus, in Hesperiidae (Lepidoptera), tapering apical portion of the antennal club (Common and Waterhouse).

apimyiasis, myiasis of the adult honey bee (Hymenoptera: Apidae) caused by larvae of *Senotainia tricuspis* Meigen (Diptera: Sarcophagidae), *Rondanioestrus apivorus* de Villers (Oestridae), and certain other fly species (Steinhaus and Martignoni).

apisthognathous, opisthognathous, q.v. (Peterson).

apitoxin, the poison of bees' stings (Hymenoptera: Apoidea) consisting chiefly of histamine-producing enzymes and proteins of low molecular weight (Leftwich).

apivorous, bee-eating (T-B).

aplasia, the failure of organs or tissues to develop; the congenital absense of an organ or tissue (Steinhaus and Martignoni).

apneustic respiration, respiration through the skin or through tracheal gills (T-B, after Smith); respiration without specific external breathing organs, either spiracles or gills, and with the tracheal system usually absent or rudimentary (T-B, after Snodgrass).

apneustic respiratory system, in aquatic larval Diptera, tracheal system without functional spiracles (Peterson; Teskey, in McAlpine).

Apocrita, suborder of Hymenoptera in which segment I of the abdomen is fused to the thorax to form the propodeum in the adult and in which the larvae are apodous (T-B; CSIRO); see Symphyta.

apodal, apodous, q.v. (T-B).

apode, an organism which has no feet (T-B).

apodema, in ♂ Coccoidea (Hemiptera: Sternorrhyncha), a conspicuous transverse band crossing the thorax in front of the scutellum (T-B) or, a thin, vertical cuticular plate extending into the body cavity from the inner surface of each episternum (sensu MacGillivray) (T-B, after MacGillivray).

apodemal, of, or pertaining to, or of the character of, an apodeme (T-B).

apodemal plate, in ♂ Dermaptera, basal attachment of genital armature (Tuxen, after Snodgrass).

apodemal rod of endophallus, in ♂ Siphonaptera, a rod closely following the curvature of the endophallus, providing a point of attachment for muscles arising dorsally on the aedeagal apodeme, from the base of the aedeagus, sternum IX or the wall of the aedeagal pouch, depending on the family (Tuxen, after Snodgrass; Lewis, pers. comm.).

apodemal strut, in ♂ Siphonaptera, an extension of the median lamina of the aedeagal apodeme caudally into the aedeagus, supporting the tubus interior (Tuxen, after Snodgrass; Rothschild and Traub).

apodeme(s), a chitinous ingrowth of the exoskeleton to which the muscles are attached, serving as tendons in insects, crustaceans, and other arthropods (T-B; Leftwich); in ♀ Trichoptera and Lepidoptera, rodlike projections issuing from the anterior margin of the sclerites on segment VIII and IX (Nielsen); see apophysis, furca, and phragma.

apodeme of aedeagus, in Auchenorrhyncha and Sternorrhyncha (Hemiptera), dorsal paired or single process at base of aedeagal shaft (Tuxen); in Cixiidae, (Hemiptera: Auchenorrhyncha: Fulgoroidea), base of aedeagus before flagellum (Mead) or, in Derbidae base of aedeagus before shaft (Flynn and Kramer).

apodeme of gonobase, in ♂ insects, projection from united Section 1 (gonobase) of gonocoxite IX on which muscles from gonocoxite IX insert, and from which many intrinsic muscles of gonocoxites and gonapophyses originate (Tuxen, after E. L. Smith).

apodeme of gonocoxite, in ♂ Culicidae (Diptera), an apodematous continuation of the proximal mesal dorsal (prerotation sense) corner of the gonocoxite, being fused or articulated with basal piece (Harbach and Knight, in Knight and Laffoon); see gonocoxal apodeme.

apodeme of hemitergite IX, in ♀ Hymenoptera, an anterior apodeme of hemitergite IX (Tuxen, after Michener).

apodeme of penis valve, in ♂ Hymenoptera, basal apodeme of penis valve usually extending into lumen of gonobase (Tuxen, after Michener).

apodeme of stylet, in ♀ Hymenoptera, apodeme at base of sting bulb (Tuxen, after Michener).

apodeme of tergum IX, in ♂ Siphonaptera, anterior apodeme of tergum IX (Tuxen, after Snodgrass).

apodeme lobe, in ♀ Chironomidae (Diptera), small lobe either with apodeme or with sclerotized base, situated between principal ventrolateral and dorsomedian lobes of gonapophysis VIII (Saether).

apodemes of cingulum, in ♂ Caelifera (Orthoptera), a pair of cephalad-directed arms from the cingulum (Tuxen).

apodemes of male hypopygium, in ♂ Chironomidae (Diptera), inner, sclerotized parts of hypopygium (Saether).

Apoditrysia, a collective name for all Ditrysia (Lepidoptera), except the tineoid superfamilies Tineoidea, Yponomeutoidea and Gelechioidea (Minet).

apodous larva, larva without thoracic legs (Peterson; Chapman); see oligopod larva and polypod larva.

apoid, resembling larvae of honey bee (Hymenoptera: Apidae) (Peterson).

Apoidea, superfamily within the Aculeata (Hymenoptera), including the bees, characterized by branched hairs on the body and the basitarsus of the hind leg much broader than following segments (Riek, in CSIRO); Apoidea + Sphecoidea (Gauld and Bolton).

apolar, without differentiated poles; without apparent radiating processes; being applied to cells (T-B).

apolysis, in moulting the separation of the old cuticle from the underlying epidermal cells (Chapman, after Jenkin and Hinton).

apomictic parthenogenesis, parthenogenesis in which no reduction division occurs in the maturation division of the oocyte so that the offspring have the same genetic constitution as the mother and all are females, commonly occurring in Blattidae (Blattaria), Aphididae (Hemiptera: Sternorrhyncha), Tenthredinidae (Hymenoptera), and Curculionidae (Coleoptera) (Chapman); see automictic parthenogenesis and thelytoky.

apomorphic, relatively derived or specialized, when comparing 2 or more homologous character states (Hennig).

apomorphy, a derived character or character state (Hennig).

apophyseal cup, in adult Culicidae (Diptera), a cuplike process borne on the free end of a sternal apophysis, receiving the attachment of certain thoracic muscles (Harbach and Knight, after Owen).

apophysis (pl., **apophyses**), an elongate projection from the exosketeton (body wall), either internally or externally (T-B, after Comstock, Folsom and Wardle; Leftwich) (see apodeme, furca, and phragma); in ♂ Blattopteroidea, dorsoproximal appendage of right epiphallus (Tuxen); in ♂ Miridae (Heteroptera), apical process of paramere (transl. "apophyse" Ribaut, after Tuxen); in ♂ Siphonaptera, apodemal rod, q.v. (Tuxen, after Dampf); in ♀ Lepidoptera, apophyses anteriores and posteriores, q.v. (Tuxen, after Lacaze-Duthiers); see apophyses.

apophysis anterior (pl., **apophyses anteriores**), in ♀ Lepidoptera, strongly sclerotized, paired apodemes of abdominal segment VIII extending cephalad, serving for muscle attachment, sometimes very long, sometimes forked (Tuxen, after Kusnezov).

apophysis interna (pl., **apophyses internae**), in ♀ Blattopteroidea, a pair of sclerites situated at base of ovipositor (Tuxen).

apophysis lateralis (pl., **apophyses laterales**), in ♂ Planipennia, lateral extensions of fused parameres (Tuxen, after Tjeder).

apophysis posterior (pl., **apophyses posteriores**), in ♀ Lepidoptera, strongly sclerotized paired apodemes of papillae anales (abdominal segment IX) extending cephalad, serving for muscle attachment, sometimes very long, sometimes forked (Tuxen, after Kusnezov).

apophysis inferior, phallapodeme, q.v. (Tuxen, after Hewitt et al.).

apophysis of tergum IX, in ♀ Orthoptera, acrotergite, q.v. (Tuxen, after Walker).

apophysis of valvifer, intervalvular apodeme, q.v. (Tuxen, after Ford).

apophysis proxima (pl., **apophyses proximae**), in ♂ Planipennia, adpressed proximal ends of fused parameres (Tuxen, after Tjeder).

apophysis superior, in ♂ Diptera, epiphallus, q.v. (Tuxen, after Hewitt et al.).

apophystegal plates, in ♀ Orthoptera, posterior valvulae, q.v. (T-B).

apopygeal appendages, in ♂ Podopinae (Hemiptera: Heteroptera: Pentatomidae), parandria, q.v. (Tuxen, after McDonald).

aposematic, having warning coloration, indicating that an animal is unpalatable (Norris, in CSIRO).

aposematic coloration, warning coloration, q.v. (Chapman).

aposematic colors, warning coloration, q.v. (T-B).

apostatic selection, a situation in which the relative rate of predation rises more rapidly than does the relative rate of encounter (Matthews and Matthews).

aposymbiotic, symbiont-free, i.e., separated from mutualistic (generally) symbionts (Steinhaus and Martignoni).

apotheca (pl., **apothecae**), in ♂ Arrhenophanidae (Lepidoptera), membranous sac, formed by invagination of diaphragma, lying in abdominal segment VIII, sometimes extending into abdominal segment VII, its opening joined to anellus and ventral wall of tuba analis and serving as container for the very long, coiled and permanently extruded vesica (Tuxen, after Bradley).

apotome, in general, part of an organ (von Kéler); in Japygidae (Diplura), a short anterior subdivision of each abdominal sternum separated by a membranous fold from the rest of the plate (T-B, after Snodgrass); in larval Diptera, frontoclypeal apotome, q.v. (Teskey, in McAlpine, after Snodgrass).

apotorma (pl., **apotormae**), in larval Scarabaeoidea (Coleoptera), the process extending forward from the torma between the pternotorma and the interior end of the torma, always located exterior to phobae (T-B, after Böving).

apotype, hypotype, q.v. (T-B).

apparatus vestibularis, in ♀ Mecoptera, medigynium, q.v. (Tuxen, after Tjeder).

appeasement, active inhibition of normal aggressive or predatory instincts (Matthews and Matthews).

appeasement substance, a secretion presented by a social parasite that reduces aggression in the host insects and aids the parasite's acceptance by the host colony (Wilson).

appendage, any part, piece, or organ attached by a joint to the body or to any other main structure (T-B).

appendage vein, in adult Diptera, a short vein at the angle of a bend (T-B, after Curran).

appendages, in adult Planipennia, ectoproct, q.v. (Tuxen, after Morton); in ♂ Mecoptera, hypovalvae, q.v. (Tuxen, after Hine).

appendices, in ♂ Ephemeroptera, genostyles, q.v. (Tuxen, after Hagen); in ♂ Caelifera (Orthoptera), lateral sclerites of epiphallus, q.v. (Key, pers. comm., after Eades and Kevan); in adult Planipennia, ectoproct, q.v. (Tuxen, after McLachlan) and in *Sisyra* (Sisyridae) entoprocessus, q.v. (Tuxen, after McLachlan); in ♂ Mecoptera, hypovalvae, q.v. (Tuxen, after McLachlan).

appendices conjunctivae, in ♂ Heteroptera (Hemiptera), processus conjunctivae, q.v. (Tuxen, after Piotrowski).

appendices copulatorii, in ♂ Lepidoptera, valvae, q.v. (Tuxen, after Cholodkowsky).

appendices genitales, in general, gonapophyses, q.v. (von Kéler); in ♂ Japygidae (Diplura), 2 fingerlike appendages on sides of papilla genitalis (Tuxen).

appendices inferiores, in ♂ Lepidoptera, valvae, q.v. (Tuxen, after McLachlan).

appendices preanales, in ♂ Trichoptera other than Limnephilidae, paired, setose, dorsolateral processes of abdominal segment X, q.v. (Schmid); see dorsal process and superior appendages.

appendices subapicales, in ♂ Planipennia, pleuritosquamae, q.v. (Tuxen, after McLachlan).

appendices superiores, in ♂ Bittacidae (Mecoptera), epiandrium, q.v. (Tuxen, after Esben-Petersen).

appendices vesicae, in ♂ Heteroptera (Hemiptera), processus vesicae, q.v. (Tuxen, after Piotrowski).

appendicial, supplementary; relating to appendices (T-B).

appendicle, appendicula, a small appendix (T-B); in some insects, a small sclerite at the tip of the labrum (T-B).

appendicular, of or pertaining to an appendage (T-B).

appendicular gland, in ♀ Diptera, accessory genital gland, q.v. (McAlpine).

appendicular ovipositor, in some ♀ insects, ovipositor formed from appendicular parts of abdominal segments VIII and IX (Tuxen); see oviscapt.

appendiculate, bearing appendages (T-B).

appendiculate marginal cell, in adult Hymenoptera, marginal cell with the vein forming the posterior margin extending a short distance beyond the apex of the cell (Borror et al.).

appendigerous, bearing appendages (T-B).

appendix (pl., **appendices**), a supplementary or additional piece or part (T-B); in adult Heteroptera, cuneus, q.v. (T-B); in adult Cicadellidae (Hemiptera: Auchenorrhyncha), distal lobe along anal margin of forewing (Borror et al); in ♀ *Leucanitis* (Lepidoptera: Noctuidae), a short tubular arm of bursa copulatrix from which ductus seminalis departs (Tuxen, after John); in ♀ Lepidoptera, appendix bursae, q.v. (Tuxen, after Wehrli).

appendix analis (pl., **appendices anales**), in ♂ Trichoptera, superior appendages, q.v. (Tuxen, after Zander).

appendix angularis (pl., **appendices angulares**), in ♂ *Argynnis* (Lepidoptera: Nymphalidae), paired, often triangular processes, presumably derivatives of tegumen or its pedunculi, usually serving to articulate tegumen and dorsocephalic angles of valvae (Tuxen, after Petersen).

appendix bursae, in ♀ Lepidoptera, an anterior, secondary evagination of corpus bursae (Tuxen, after Kusnezov).

appendix dorsalis (pl., **appendices dorsales**), in Ephemeroptera, filum terminale, q.v. (Tuxen, after Eaton); in nymphal and ♂ Anisoptera (Odonata), the inferior anal appendage lying above the anus

(Tuxen); in ♂ *Bittacus* (Mecoptera: Bittacidae), upwardly directed process from abdominal tergum XI (Tuxen).

appendix dorsalis teguminis, in ♂ Noctuidae (Lepidoptera), lobe-shaped appendix on tegumen (Tuxen, after Boursin).

appendix externa supera, in ♂ Diptera, appendix supera, q.v. (Tuxen).

appendix genitalis, in ♂ Strepsiptera, aedeagus, q.v. (Tuxen, after Silvestri).

appendix intermedia (pl., **appendices intermediae**), in ♂ Tipulidae (Diptera), rest of dististylus after separation of appendix supera (Tuxen).

appendix of spermatheca, in ♀ Siphonaptera, hilla, q.v. (Tuxen).

appendix of tail of spermatheca, in some ♀ Siphonaptera the hilla, or tail of the spermatheca, bearing a small, apical papilla (Lewis, pers. comm.).

appendix preanalis (pl., **appendices preanales**), in ♂ *Rhyacophila* (Trichoptera: Rhyacophilidae), lateral lobes, q.v. (Tuxen, after Ulmer); in other ♂ Trichoptera, superior appendages, q.v. (Tuxen, after Ulmer).

appendix seta, in larval Chironomidae (Diptera), digitiform, blade- to bristlelike or reduced appendage of labial margin (Saether).

appendix supera (pl., **appendices superae**), in ♂ Tipulidae (Diptera), separated outer part of dististylus (Tuxen).

appendotomy, loss of appendages by arthropods, including autotomy, autoplasy, and autotilly (Tulloch).

appetitive flight, flight involving local movements of varying length and orientation concerned with food and mate finding, escape from potential enemies, location of suitable oviposition sites, territorial defense, and other such activities (Matthews and Matthews).

applied entomology, economic entomology; the application of pure entomology to the control of insect pests (T-B).

apposed, having the surfaces against each other (T-B).

apposed image, apposition image, q.v. (T-B).

apposition eye, in diurnal insects, a compound eye which absorbs oblique rays of light in the pigmented walls of the ommatidium (T-B, after Snodgrass); compound eye that forms a mosaic image, i.e., an erect image composed of a large number of dots or points of light (Leftwich).

apposition image, mosaic image produced by light-adapted eyes (T-B; Gilmour, in CSIRO); see superposition image.

appress, to press against (T-B).

appressed, closely applied to (T-B).

appressed setae, extending parallel to and often in contact with the surface of the body or appendage from which the seta arises (Christiansen and Bellinger).

approximate, approximatus (Latin), near to; applied to any parts close together (T-B).

Aptera, a Linnaean name for a taxon including fleas and other wingless insects (T-B; Lewis, pers. comm.); Siphonaptera, q.v. (Lewis, pers. comm., after Leach); Zygentoma, q.v. (Boudreaux); see Apterygota.

Apterata, Zygentoma, q.v. (Boudreaux).

apterergate, in vespid wasps (Hymenoptera: Vespidae), a wingless worker in a species of normally winged workers (Tulloch, after Gaul).

apterodicera, wingless, and with 2 antennae (T-B).

apterogyne, in social insects, a wingless ♀ in a species of normally winged females (Tulloch).

apterous, apterus (Latin), without wings; wingless (T-B); see brachypterous, macropterous, and micropterous.

apterous neotenic, in termites (Isoptera), ergatoid reproductive, q.v. (Wilson).

aptery, apterous condition, i.e., winglessness (CSIRO); see brachyptery, macroptery, and microptery.

apterygogenea, those insects that are wingless in all stages and hence presumed to be descended from ancestors which never were winged (T-B); see pterygogenea.

Apterygota, old name for primitively wingless and ametabolous insects including, Protura, Collembola, Diplura, Zygentoma, and Archaeognatha (T-B, after Imms; Leftwich; Borror et al); old name for primitively wingless, ectognathous hexapods, including primitively wingless orders, including Archaeognatha, Thysanura, and the extinct order Monura (Mackerras, in CSIRO; Hennig).

aquamarine, aquamarinus (Latin), sea green; pale green with predominant blue and a little gray (T-B).

aquatic, adapted to life in water (Norris, in CSIRO); living in water (T-B; Borror et al.); see semiaquatic.

Aquatilia, old name given to aquatic forms of Nepomorpha, q.v. (T-B; Schuh, pers. comm.).

Arachnida, class of Arthropoda within the subphylum Chelicerata, including the recent orders Scorpiones, Uropygi, Schizomida, Amblypygi, Palpigradi, Araneae, Ricinulei, Pseudoscorpionida, Solpugida, Opiliones, and Acari; possessing book lungs, pedipalps, typically 4 pairs of ambulatory legs (on third through sixth metameres), and lacking compound eyes (T-B; Borror et al.; Boudreaux).

arachnoideous, arachnoideus, cobweblike; resembling cobweb (T-B).

Aradoidea, superfamily of fungus feeding Heteroptera, including the Aradidae and Termitaphididae, characterized by flattened body form, found under bark or associated with termites (Woodward et al., in CSIRO).

Araneae, order within the Arachnida, including the spiders, which possess a petiolate opisthosoma that possesses spinnerets posteriorly (Borror et al).

Araneida, Araneae, q.v. (Tulloch; Borror et al.).

araneiform, spiderlike in appearance (T-B).

arbitrary combination of letters, a scientific name that was not based by its author on an existing word of a language (ICZN).

arboreal, living in, on, or among trees (T-B).

arborescent, branching like the twigs of a tree (T-B).

arborizations, the fine, branching, terminal fibers of axons or collaterals (T-B, after Snodgrass).

arboviruses, group of viruses man and other vertebrates transmitted especially by Diptera, including those causing yellow fever, dengue fever, and various encephalitides (Colless and McAlpine, in CSIRO).

arcessus (pl., **arcessi**), in ♂ Planipennia, structure moveably attached ventrally to upper median part of gonarcus (Tuxen, after Tjeder).

arch, in ♂ Orthoptera, ponticulus, q.v. (Tuxen, after Roberts, Dirsh); in ♂ Orthoptera, zygoma, q.v. (Tuxen, after Walker); in some adult Siphonaptera, paired, sclerotized, curved bars in the genal region, forming part of the tentorium, and frequently hidden by the eye in eyed forms (Rothschild and Traub).

Archaeococcoidea, superfamily proposed for families Margarodidae, Ortheziidae, and Phenacoleachiidae, of the Coccoidea (Hemiptera: Sternorrhyncha) (Hennig, after Balachowsky; Kosztarab, in Parker).

Archaeognatha, primitively wingless order Insecta, differing from the Zygentoma by possessing monocondylar mandibles, well-developed compound eyes which meet dorsomedially; large maxillary palps with 7 segments; and an appendix dorsalis that is longer than the cerci (Mackerras, in CSIRO; Hennig); see Monura and Zygentoma.

Archaeoptera, extinct pterygote order of Insecta, based on *Eopterum devonicum* from the Devonian, too poorly known to be placed confidently in the Paleoptera or the Neoptera (Riek, in CSIRO).

archaic, ancient; generalized, q.v.; no longer dominant (T-B).

archecerebrum, archicerebrum, q.v. (Chapman).

arched nerves, 2 nerves arising from the 2 upper basal parts of the circumoesophageal connectives, connecting the central and the stomatogastric nervous systems (T-B).

arched plate, in Lecanodiaspididae (Hemiptera: Sternorrhyncha: Coccoidea), a narrow, sclerotized bar in form of half circle, surrounding anterior margin of anal apparatus, associated with anal plates (Miller, in Stehr).

archedictyon, the primitive original vein network characterizing the wings of many of the most ancient insect fossils (T-B, after Needham; Mackerras, in CSIRO); in Mastotermitidae and Hodotermitidae (Isoptera), the complex network or reticulum of irregular veinlets between the veins in the apical 3 quarters of both wings, including the anal lobe (Emerson).

archencephalon, see archicerebrum, q.v. (T-B).

archenteric, of or pertaining to the archenteron (T-B).

archenteron, primitive stomach, a simple food-pocket walled by specialized digestive cells (T-B, after Snodgrass); see gastrocoele.

Archentomata, Monura, q.v. (Boudreaux).

Archeognathata, Archaeognatha, q.v. (Boudreaux).

archetype, hypothetical type or form from which a whole group of existing forms is supposed to have sprung (T-B, after Tillyard); hypothetical ancestral type arrived at by the elimination of specialized characters (Mayr).

Archiannelida, group within the Annelida, including *Dinophilus* and *Nerilla,* in which all segmentation is primary and in which there is only one gamete-producing somite (Boudreaux).

archicephalon, the primitive annelid-arthropod head, or prostomium (T-B, after Snodgrass).

archicerebrum, the ganglionic nerve mass of the prostomium in Annelida; the primitive suprastomodaeal nerve mass of the prostomium (T-B, after Snodgrass).

Archicoleoptera, extinct order of insects, phylogenetically near the Coleoptera, including the Permophilidae, Permosynidae, Permarrhaphidae, and Sojanocoleidae (Hennig, after Jeannel).

Archidermaptera, extinct suborder of Dermaptera, based upon *Protodiplatys* from the middle Jurassic, differing from recent forms by possessing tarsi of hind leg with 5 tarsomeres and segmented cerci (Riek, in CSIRO); these features together with the fact that the tergites of the thorax and the abdomen are situated virtually immediately dorsal to the corresponding sternites renders the dermapteran affinities of this taxon doubtful (Popham, pers. comm.).

archidictyon, archedictyon, q.v. (Leftwich).

Archidiptera, extinct group of insects based upon Upper Triassic fossils, doubtfully placed within the Diptera as a suborder and doubtfully giving rise to the recent Nymphomyiidae and Deuterophlebiidae (Hennig, after Rohdendorf); see Nymphomyioidea and Deuterophlebioidea.

Archiperlaria, Eusthenioidea, q.v. (Riek, in CSIRO; Zwick, pers. comm.).

Archiptera, Pseudoneuroptera, q.v. (T-B); Ephemeroptera + Archodonata (Hennig, after Demoulin).

Archizygoptera, extinct suborder of Odonata from the Mesozoic (Riek, in CSIRO).

Archodonata, extinct order of Palaeoptera (Insecta) from the Permian of North America and Russia, possessing a greatly developed mesothorax and a pterostigma and few crossveins in the forewing (Riek, in CSIRO).

Archoptera, infraclass of the class Insecta, including extinct orders Archaeoptera and Protoptera, characterized by an oblique position of the wings at rest (Riek, after Sharov, in CSIRO); see Neoptera and Paleoptera.

Archostemata, suborder of beetles (Coleoptera) including recent families Ommatidae, Cupedidae, and Micromalthidae, and fossils back to the Mesozoic, possessing adults with filiform antennae with 11 articles, prothorax with notopleural sutures, well-developed hind wing venation, and complete basal abdominal sternite; larvae woodboring and lacking urogomphi (Britton, in CSIRO; Lawrence, in Parker).

arch-shaped chitinous framework, in ♂ Planipennia, gonarcus, q.v. (Tuxen, after Killington and Kimmins).

Arctic Realm, see Holarctic Realm, q.v. (T-B).

Arctic Zone, that part of the Boreal Region above the limits of tree growth in latitude or altitude, and having mean summer maxima not exceeding 10°C (T-B).

Arctoperlaria, suborder of Plecoptera, including the Systellognatha and Euholognatha (Zwick, in Hennig); see Antarctoperlaria.

arcuate, arcuatus (Latin), arched or bowlike (T-B).

arcuate thickening, in larval Culicidae (Diptera), a partial or complete looplike band of cuticle extending anteriorly from the dorsal part of the U-shaped rod of the mandible, representing the rim of the depression in which is borne mandibular sweeper 2 (Harbach and Knight).

arcuate vein, vena arcuata, q.v. (T-B, after Snodgrass).

arcuato-emarginate, with a bowlike or curved excision (T-B).

arculus, a crossvein apparently giving rise to the media (T-B); in adult Odonata, an arch-shaped vein connecting radius and media near the base of the wing, forming an elongate triangle between them (T-B); in adult Auchenorrhyncha, a crossveinlet nearly reaching posteroapical margin of the forewing (T-B); in wing of adult Diptera, anterior branch of media, q.v. (McAlpine); in wing of adult Chironomidae (Diptera), small, strong, L-shaped sclerite found at tip of brachiolum at level of humeral crossvein and distalmost indentation of alula (Saether); in adult Culicidae (Diptera), crossvein between the radius and cubitus near the wing base (Harbach and Knight, after Christophers and Barraud); in adult Trichoptera, small vein bulla, often hyaline, at the posterior apical margin of the forewing formed by the apical fusion of one or more of the following veins: the plical, empusal, and first and second anal veins (P + E + 1A + 2A of Ross et al = Cu_2 + 1A + 2A + 3A of Comstock) (T-B; Betten).

arcus (pl., **arcus**), a bow (T-B); part of a circle, but less than one half (T-B); in ♂ Caelifera (Orthoptera), the median part of the epiphallus, when this is medially incised (Tuxen); in ♀ Caelifera (Orthoptera), the arch formed by the anterior arms of the ventral basivalvulae in the chamber (Agarwala); in some ♀ Helotrephidae (Heteroptera), arcuately fused 2nd valvulae (Papáček, Tonner, and Štys,); in ♀ Pentatomoidea (Heteroptera), the fused gonapophyses of abdominal segment IX forming a V-shaped sclerite in the dorsal wall of the vagina between the mouth of the oviductus communis (proximally) and the orificium receptaculi (distally) (Tuxen, after Verhoeff).

area (pl., **areae**), cell, q.v., of wing (T-B); in adult Apocrita (Hymenoptera), one of more cells enclosed by keels on the propodeum (Gauld and Bolton); see areola.

area apicalis, in Phasmida, a triangular depression on the underside of the tibia of the second and third pairs of legs (Carlberg, pers. comm.).

area communis, in adult Siphonaptera, a pale circular or oval area in the head capsule formed by the fusion of the 2 sides to form a central tuber, and frequently hidden by the first antennal segment (Rothschild and Traub).

area cribiformis (pl., **areae cribiformes**), in ♀ Siphonaptera, zone of minute pores in wall of bulga surrounding orifice of ductus spermathecae (Tuxen, after Fox).

area fusoria (pl., **areae fusoriae**), in ♂ Siphonaptera, dorsal area of fusion of the 2 sides of the apodeme of tergum IX (Tuxen, after Smit).

area mediastinal, in adult Orthoptera, mediastinal area, q.v. (T-B, after J. B. Smith).

area porosa (pl., **areae porosae**), in many ♂ Thysanoptera, glandular areas on sternites (Mound et al).

area scapularis, in adult Orthoptera, radial area, q.v. (T-B, after J. B. Smith).

area spiculosa (pl., **areae spiculosae**), in ♂ Siphonaptera, area covered with spicules on inner side of dorsal part of tergum VIII (Tuxen, after Ioff).

area ulnaris, in adult Orthoptera, median area, q.v. (T-B, after J. B. Smith).

area valvularum pilosa (pl., **areae valularum pilosae**), in ♂ *Zygaena* (Lepidoptera: Zygaenidae), bushy, long-haired, preapical region of valvula (Tuxen, after Loritz).

area verticalis, in Poduromorpha (Collembola), a region on the head, between and just posterior to the eyes, usually bearing 1–2 pairs of "v" setae (Christiansen and Bellinger).

areate, furnished with open areas or with areas defined on the surface (T-B; Harris, after Munz); see areolate.

arenaceous, sandy or sandlike (T-B); see arenose.

arenicolous, frequenting or living in sandy areas (T-B); psammophilous.

arenose, superficially sandy or gritty (T-B); see arenaceous.

areocel, in adult Lepidoptera, the closed cell of the forewing formed by the fusion of the areole with the basal cell (T-B, after Tillyard).

areola (pl., **areolae**), in certain Hemiptera, a small cell on the wings (T-B); in Lepidoptera, a small space or window on the obverse surface of a scale (Downey and Allyn); in adult Apocrita (Hymenoptera), the central of 3 median areas on the propodeum (T-B); see area.

areola postica, in adult Psocoptera, open cell between the branches of the anterior cubitus (CuA) in the forewing (Smithers, in CSIRO).

areolate, furnished with areolae, like a network (T-B); divided into a number of small irregular spaces (Harris, after R. W. Brown, and Stearn); see alveolate, goffered, and reticulate.

areole, in adult Lepidoptera, accessory cell, q.v. (T-B, after Tillyard; Common, in CSIRO); see basal areole.

areolet, a small wing cell (T-B; Borror et al.); in adult Ichneumonidae (Hymenoptera), the small submarginal cell opposite the second recurrent vein (Borror et al.).

argentate, shining, silvery white (T-B); see argenteous.

argenteous, argenteus (Latin), silver color; silvery; see argentate (T-B).

argentophilic cells, cells found in the anal papillae or rectal gills of aquatic larvae specialized for ion uptake (Tulloch).

argillaceous, argillaceus (Latin), of the texture, appearance, or color of clay (T-B).

arginase, enzyme that splits urea from arginine (Gilmour, in CSIRO).

arginine, essential amino acid in the diet of insects (Gilmour, in CSIRO).

argol, impure potassium bitartrate or cream of tartar; the solid residue left in wine casks by fermentation (T-B).

arid, dry; any region in which the normal rainfall is insufficient to produce ordinary farm crops without irrigation, and in which desert conditions prevail (T-B); see humid.

arid transition area, the faunal division which comprises the western part of the Dakotas, northern Montana east of the Rockies, southern Assiniboia, small areas in southern Manitoba and Alberta, the higher parts of the Great Basin and the plateau region generally, the eastern base of the Cascade-Sierras and local areas in Oregon and California (T-B).

arista, in higher Diptera, reduced flagellomeres of antenna following the usually enlarged, first flagellomere (postpedicel) of the antenna (T-B, after Tillyard, Imms; McAlpine).

aristate, bristlelike (Borror et al.); having or bearing an arista, e.g., the antenna of higher Diptera (T-B; McAlpine).

aristiform, of the form or appearance of an arista (T-B).

aristomere, article of arista (McAlpine); see flagellomere.

aristopedia, a developmental anomaly in which the arista may mature as a leg (Tulloch).

Arixeniina, originally regarded as a separate suborder within the Dermaptera, including the family Arixeniidae being associated with bats in South East Asia (Giles, in CSIRO), but regarded by Popham as a specialized neotonous family within the Forficulina (Labioidea).

arm(s), in Hypogastruridae (Collembola), an elongate lobe of postantennal organ (Snider, pers. comm.); in Orthoptera, brachium, q.v. (Tuxen, after Snodgrass); in ♂ Heteroptera (Hemiptera), superior lateral process, q.v. (Tuxen, after McDonald); in ♂ Heteroptera (Hemiptera), suspensorial apodemes, q.v. (Tuxen, after Bonhag and Wick); in ♂ Aradidae (Heteroptera), suspensorial apodemes, q.v. (Tuxen, after Leston); in ♀ Dytiscus (Coleoptera: Dytiscidae), the halves of tergum IX (Tuxen, after Böving); in ♀ Mecoptera, lamnae, q.v. (Tuxen, after Carpenter); in adult Chironomidae (Diptera), coxosternapodeme, q.v. (Saether); genital fork, q.v. (McAlpine).

armatura genitalis (pl., **armaturae genitales**), in ♀ and ♂ adult insects, modifications of abdominal segments VII–X and their appendages for secondary reproductive functions (Tuxen).

armature, the spinous or chitinous processes on the legs, body or wings, or the corneous parts of genitalic structures (T-B); in ♂ Siphonaptera, structures of apex of tubus interior, including dorsal, lateral and ventral sclerotization or tooth (Tuxen, after Traub).

armatus (Latin), set with spines, claws, or other chitinous processes (T-B).

armillate, armillatus (Latin), with a ring or annulus of raised or different tissue (T-B).

armlike part, in ♂ Lepidoptera, caulis, q.v. (Tuxen, after Heinrich).

army ant, a member of an ant species, particulary of the subfamily Dorylinae (Hymenoptera: Formicidae), that shows both nomadic and group-predatory behavior, i.e., the nest site is changed at relatively freqent intervals, in some cases daily, and the workers forage in groups (Wilson).

Arnhart's black-egg disease, H-melanosis, q.v. (Steinhaus and Martignoni).

arolanna (pl., **arolannae**), in adult Hymenoptera, arolium, q.v. (T-B, after MacGillivray).

arolella, in Hemiptera, arolium, q.v. (T-B, after MacGillivray).

arolium (pl., **arolia**), in Orthoptera, the terminal pad between the claws of the pretarsus (T-B; Borror et al.); in Heteroptera (Hemiptera), bristle- or bladderlike, single or double (then: dorsal arolium, ventral arolium) pretarsal structure, originating dorsad of the unguitractor and between but isolated from bases of the claws (Cobben; Andersen) (sometimes incorrectly called empodium, parempodium, or rarely puvillus); in some adult Diptera, a median, more or less saclike protrusion from the end of the pretarsus (McAlpine); see empodium, euplantulae, and pulvillus.

aromatic, in chemistry, describing a compound that has a ring structure similar to that of benzene (Pfadt).

Arrhenatherum blue dwarf, disease of grasses (*Arrhenathrum*) caused by a reovirus (*Fijivirus*) transmitted propagatively by *Javesella* and *Dicranotropis* (Hemiptera: Auchenorrhyncha: Delphacidae) (Nault and Ammar).

arrhenotokous, capable of producing ♂ offspring only, as in worker bees and some sawflies (Hymenoptera) (T-B).

arrhenotoky, parthenogenetic production of males from unfertilized eggs, e.g., drone bees (Hymenoptera: Apoidea) (T-B; Wilson).

artatendon, pretarsal tendon, q.v. (T-B, after MacGillivray).

Artematopoidea, a superfamily within Elateriformia (Coleoptera) that includes Artematopidae, Callirhipidae, and Brachypsectridae (Crowson).

Artenkreis (German), superspecies, q.v. (Mayr, after Rensch).

arthrium, in adult Coleoptera, the minute, concealed taromere in pseudotetramera and trimera (T-B).

arthroderm, integument, q.v. (T-B).

arthrodial, of articulations permitting motion in any direction (T-B).

arthrodial membrane, a term used by some authors for the flexible joint and intersegmental membranes (Tulloch, after Richards).

arthromere, somite, q.v. (T-B).

Arthropleona, suborder of Collembola, including Poduridae, Hypogastruridae, Onychiuridae, Isotomidae, Oncopuridae, and Entomobryidae, the members of which possess an elongate body and most of the thoracic and abdominal segments distinctly separate (Wallace and Mackerras, after Gisin, in CSIRO; Snider, pers. comm.); see Symphypleona.

Arthropleurida, very large (up to 180 cm long), centipedelike, mandibulate arthopods living in the Carboniferous Period (Boudreaux, after Waterlot).

arthropleuron, pleuron, q.v. (T-B).

arthropod, member of the phylum Arthropoda (Gauld and Bolton).

Arthropoda, large phylum including crustaceans, chelicerates, hexapods, and myriapods, the members of which possess a segmented body, a thick exoskeleton that is moulted from time to time, a number of jointed appendages modified in various ways to form legs, jaws, antennae, cerci, etc., a nervous system consisting of a double ventral cord, 2 ganglia in each segment and a collar around the pharynx, and a brain formed by the fusion of some ganglia in the head segments (T-B; Leftwich).

arthropodins, the family of characteristic proteins that are found associated with chitin in the insect cuticle (Tulloch, after Richards).

arthropodization, the evolutionary acquisition of sclerotized, jointed appendages (Boudreaux).

arthrostyli, in ♂ Ephemeroptera, genostyles, q.v. (Tuxen, after Crampton); in larval Megalodontoidea (Hymenoptera: Symphyta), subanal appendages, q.v. (Gauld and Bolton).

article, a subdivision of any segmented or jointed part or structure (T-B).

articular area, wing base, q.v. (T-B, after Snodgrass).

articular corium, the membrane of the insect leg joint (T-B).

articular membrane, articular corium, q.v. (T-B): the ring of thin membrane uniting a seta at its base with the wall of the trichopore (T-B, after Comstock).

articular pan, the cup- or dishlike depression forming the socket into which a condyle is fitted (T-B).

articular sclerite, a sclerite occupying an intermediate position between the body and its appendage (T-B, after Comstock).

articular surface, area of basal plate articulating and pivoting on suspensorial apodemes (transl. "Gelenkfläche" Ludwig, after Tuxen).

articularis, pretarsus, q.v. (T-B, after MacGillivray).

Articulata, Annulata, q.v. (T-B).

articulate, verb; to connect by a joint; adj., jointed or segmented (T-B).

articulate aedeagus, in most ♂ Adephaga and Staphylinoidea (Coleoptera), usually asymmetrical aedeagus with basal piece often unsclerotized and seemingly absent and parameres articulating to the penis by a true condyle (Lindroth and Palmén, in Tuxen).

articulate fascia, a fascia composed of contiguous spots; fascia articulata (T-B, after Kirby and Spence).

articulated apex, in ♂ Culicidae, dististylus, q.v. (T-B).

articulating plate, in ♂ Heteroptera (Hemiptera), capitate processes, q.v. (Tuxen, after Tang).

articulation, a moveable point or place where 2 parts or segments join (T-B); see joint.

articulatory apparatus, in ♂ Heteroptera (Hemiptera), system of plates and apodemes for suspension of phallus and attachment of its motor muscles, drawn out along phallosoma into ligamentary processes, comprising 1) basal plates s. str. (major part of the apparatus) attached to suspensory apodemes and united to ponticulus transversalis and ductifer, and 2) dorsal connectives, ending in capitate processes (Tuxen, after Bonhag and Wick).

articulatory epideme, the partly chitinized membrane by which the wings are attached to the thorax (T-B).

articulatory processes, in ♂ Lepidoptera, appendices angulares, q.v., of tegumen (Tuxen, after Klots).

artificial classification, classification based on convenient and conspicuous diagnositic characters without attention to characters indicating relationship, often being a classification based upon a single arbitrarily chosen character instead of an evaluation of the totality of characters (Mayr); see natural classification.

artificial medium, a substance with an agar base incorporating various chemicals or other constituents and designed to replace normal foodstuffs for rearing insects.

artificial selection, the opposite to natural selection; selection by animal and plant breeders, e.g., the purposed selection in strains of *Drosophila* (Diptera: Drosophilidae), for genetic study (T-B); see natural selection.

artis, the point of articulation of an appendage with the body itself (T-B, after MacGillivray).

artus, a limb; a locomotor appendage (T-B).

ascending arm (of sternum IX), in ♂ Siphonaptera, proximal arm, q.v. (Tuxen).

ascending frontal bristles, in adult Diptera, the uppermost of one to 4 frontal bristles (T-B, after Comstock).

ascending intestine, in generalized Auchenorrhyncha (Hemiptera), the third part or section of the ventriculus, a long slender tube which turns foward to reenter the filter chamber (T-B, after Snodgrass).

Aschelmenthes, phylum of unsegmented worms possessing a pseudocoelom and straight intestine (Allaby); see Nematoda and Nematomorpha.

Aschiza, series of Muscomorpha (Diptera), including superfamilies Lonchopteroidea, Phoroidea, and Syrphoidea, characterized by the absence of a ptilinal fissure in the adult (Colless and McAlpine, in CSIRO); or including the superfamilies Lonchopteroidea, Platypezoidea, and Syrphoidea (McAlpine).

ascoid, a type of trichoid sensillum with 2 or more palmate branches, occurring on the antenna of certain Diptera (Psychodidae) and Lepidoptera (Micropterigidae, Opostegidae) (Feuerborn).

-ase, the termination of the technical name of enzymes, the first part of the word indicating the substance on which the enzyme acts, e.g., protease, an enzyme acting on proteins (T-B).

asexual, parthenogenetic, q.v. (T-B).

asexual reproduction, parthenogenesis, q.v. (Mayr).

Asiloidea, superfamily belonging to the Orthorrhapha (Diptera: Brachycera), including Therevidae, Scenopinidae, Asilidae, Apioceridae, Mydidae, and Bombyliidae, the empodium of the adult being bristlelike, reduced, or absent, and the posterior abdominal spiracles of the larvae placed laterally on the penultimate segment (Colless and McAlpine, in CSIRO).

Asilomorpha, infraorder within the suborder Brachycera (Diptera), including the superfamilies Asiloidea, Bombylioidea, and Empidoidea (McAlpine).

Asiopsocoidea, superfamily with group Caecilietae (Psocoptera), including Asiopsocidae, in which mandibles are relatively short and ventral abdominal vesicles are absent (Mockford and Garcia Aldrete).

aspect, the direction to which a surface faces or in which it is viewed; it may be dorsal, ventral, caudal, cephalic or lateral (T-B).

asper, asperous, q.v. (T-B; Harris).

asperate, asperatus (Latin), asperous, q.v. (T-B; Harris).

asperites, surface roughenings or dotlike elevations (T-B); small spinelike structures frequently arranged in rows or confined to specific areas (Peterson).

asperous, rough and uneven (T-B; Harris); see salebrose, scabrous, and squarrose.

aspersus, rugged, with distinct elevated dots (T-B).

asphyxiation, loss of consciousness as a result of too little oxygen and too much carbon dioxide.

aspirator, a suction device for picking up insects (Borror et al.).

assembling, gathering together of insects into an assembly (T-B; Matthews and Matthews).

assembly, situations in which members of a species congregate prior to some activity, such as feeding, mating, or hibernation, with the signals which call them unrelated in any direct manner to the subsequent activity (Matthews and Matthews).

association neurone, a nerve cell lying within the central system that intermediates between sensory and motor nerve cells, or between other association nerve cells (T-B, after Snodgrass).

associative learning, the ability to form associations between previously meaningless stimuli and reinforcements such as reward or punishment (Matthews and Matthews).

associative memory, associative learning, q.v. (T-B, after J. Loeb).

assurgent, down-curved at base, then upcurved to an erect position (T-B).

astaxanthin, xanthophyll pigment commonly found in arthropods (Tulloch, after Richards; Chapman).

Asteioidea, superfamily within the Schizophora of the Muscomorpha (Diptera: Brachycera), including the Teratomyzidae, Periscelididae, Aulacigastridae, Anthomyzidae, and Asteiidae), including small or minute flies lacking preapical tibial bristles and possessing a short postabdomen without a piercing organ in the ♀ (Colless and McAlpine, in CSIRO).

astelocyttarous nests, nests of social wasps (Hymenoptera: Vespidae), in which the comb is attached directly to a support and lacks pillars (Wilson, after Richards and Richards).

aster yellows, disease of aster, celery, squash, cucumber, wheat, and barley caused by a mycoplasma and transmitted by leafhoppers, e.g., *Macrosteles fascifrons* (Hemiptera: Auchenorrhyncha: Cicadellidae), the symptoms being stunting, sterility, and chlorosis of foliage (Borror et al; Pfadt).

asteriform, starlike; star-shaped (T-B).

asteronome, a digitate or star shaped larval mine (Hering).

asthenia, loss of strength, debility (T-B).

asthenobiose, asthenobiosis, q.v. (T-B).

asthenobiosis, arrested growth which occurs cyclically after a number of active generations, caused by an intoxication of the tissues by excretory products which may be transmitted from one generation to the next (T-B; Tulloch, after Roubaud); theoretical explanation of the phenomenon of diapause or arrested growth of an insect which supposes that an accumulation of waste products hinders normal development in much the same way it can cause muscular fatigue, followed by the gradual disappearance of waste products during the resting stage because excretion continues while normal metabolism is slowed down (Leftwich).

asymmetric, asymmetrical, q.v. (T-B).

asymmetrical, not symmetrical (T-B).

asymmetrical scale, a lamellar scale (modified seta) which is obviously unevenly developed on opposite sides of a plane which is parallel to the plane of the squame (Harbach and Knight).

asymmetry, a state of unlikeness in lateral development; absence of symmetry in form or in the development of members (T-B).

atavism, reversion to ancestral characters (T-B).

atavistic, of or pertaining to atavism; of the nature of atavism (T-B).

Atelocera, Atelocerata, q.v. (Hennig).

Atelocerata, hypothesized monophyletic lineage including the Myriapoda and Hexapoda (Mackerras, in CSIRO; Boudreaux).

Atelopoda, hypothesized monophyletic group including the Symphyla, Chilopoda, and Hexapoda, the members of which possess a head capsule consisting of 4 somites plus the acron and last 2 trunk somites lacking typical legs (Boudreaux).

ater, atrous, q.v. (T-B).

aterrimus, of the deepest black (T-B).

athericerous, aristate, q.v. (T-B).

athermobiosis, dormancy in insects induced by cold or by relatively low temperatures (T-B); the process of eliminating toxic materials from the body during a prolonged resting stage at low temperature (Tulloch, after Roubaud); see hibernation.

athrocytes, nephrocytes, q.v. (Tulloch, after DuPorte).

atlas, in taxonomy, a method of presenting taxonomic materials primarily by means of comparative illustrations rather than by comparative descriptions (Mayr); see monograph.

atmosphere, the exterior circle of an ocellate spot (T-B).

atom, atomus (Latin), a minute dot or point (T-B).

atomarius, with minute dots or points (T-B; Harris); see adsperse, irrorate, and maculate.

atomization, process of breaking a liquid into a fine spray (Pfadt).

atonia, atony, in insect pathology, flaccidity, i.e., lack of tone or tension (Steinhaus and Martignoni).

ATP, adenosine triphosphate, q.v. (Allaby).

atracheate, without tracheae (T-B).

Atrachelia, Coleoptera in which there is no visible constriction between head and prothorax, e.g., Curculionoidea and some Heteromera (T-B).

atrial orifice, the external opening of the spiracular atrium (T-B, after Snodgrass).

atrial plate, in ♀ Culicidae (Diptera), upper vaginal sclerite, q.v. (Tuxen, after Christophers; Harbach and Knight).

atrial rim, in ♀ Auchenorrhyncha (Hemiptera), border of genital atrium (Tuxen, after Young); in Coccoidea (Hemiptera: Sternorrhyncha), outer rim of spiracular atrium (Kosztarab, pers. comm.).

atrial sclerotizations, in ♂ Heteroptera (Hemiptera), superior lateral process, q.v. (Tuxen, after Leston).

atrial wall, in pupal Culicidae (Diptera), the wall of the spiracular atrium, clothed in network of specialized spicules (Harbach and Knight, after Snodgrass).

atriate, having an atrium (T-B).

atrium (pl., **atria**), any chamber at the entrance of a body opening (T-B); in larval Muscomorpha (Diptera), preoral cavity, q.v. (T-B; Teskey, in McAlpine); in ♀ Culicidae (Diptera), vagina, q.v. (Tuxen, after Christophers; Harbach and Knight); in ♀ Chironomidae, vagina, q.v. (Saether); in Siphonaptera, the tubular or bottle-shaped structure, the walls of which are strongly ringed, connecting the ostium and fossa of the spiracle with the trachea (Rothschild and Traub); see spiracular atrium.

atrium genitale, in ♂ Psocoptera, the chamber formed by the hypandrium and containing the penis (Tuxen); in ♂ Heteroptera (Hemiptera), genital chamber, q.v. (Tuxen, after Piotrowski); in ♂ Coleoptera, second connecting membrane, q.v. (Tuxen); in ♀ Scarabaeidae (Coleoptera), the vulvar part of the cloaca (as contrasted) with the anal or rectal part) (Tuxen).

atrium of spiracle, spiracular atrium, q.v. (Peterson).

atroceruleous, atroceruleus, atrocoeruleus, a deep blue-black (T-B).

Atropetae, group within the suborder Trogiomorpha (Psocoptera), including the Lepidopsocidae, Trogiidae, and Psoquillidae in which the head is short and transverse, segment 2 of the maxillary palpus possesses a sensillum on the inner side, and veins CuP and 1A reach the wing margin separately (Smithers, in CSIRO).

atrophied, reduced in size (T-B; Borror et al.); see embryonic and rudimentary.

atrophy, decrease in size of a tissue, organ, or part after full development has been obtained, due to disuse, old age, injury, or disease, in which the affected cells undergo degenerative and autolytic changes, becoming smaller and having lessened functional capacity (T-B; Steinhaus and Martignoni); quantitative atrophy, q.v. (Steinhaus and Martignoni); see hypoplasia.

atropine, $C_{17}H_{23}NO_3$, a poisonous, crystalline alkaloid used in medicine; a specific antidote for poisoning by organophosphate insecticides (Pfadt).

atropurpureus, dark purplish, nearly black (T-B).

atrous, of a pure intense black (T-B).

atrovelutinus, velvety black (T-B).

atrovirens, dark green, approaching blackish (T-B).

atrus, atrous, q.v. (T-B).

attachment fibers, dense fibers passing through pore canals between the epicuticle and hemidesmosomes where muscles attach to the cuticle (Chapman); see microtubules.

attachment plates, in ♂ *Embiophila* (Heteroptera: Plokiophilidae), capitate processes, q.v. (Tuxen, after China).

attapulgite, a magnesium silicate clay mined in Florida and Georgia and used as a dust carrier for pesticides (Pfadt).

attenuate, attenuated, attenuatus (Latin), gradually tapering apically (T-B).

attenuated infection, in invertebrate pathology, an infection which is not immediately followed by overt disease or an infection following an overt infection, including microbial persistence, latent infection, and carrier state (Steinhaus and Martignoni).

attenuation, in invertebrate pathology, the process of decreasing the virulence of a microorganism (Steinhaus and Martignoni).

attingent, touching (T-B).

attractant, substance that elicits a positive directive response; chemicals having positive attraction for animals such as insects, usually in low concentration and at considerable distances (Pfadt).

-atus, Latin suffix; denotes possession of a quality or structure (T-B).

atypic, atypical, not conforming to type; not of the usual form (T-B).

Auchenorrhyncha, suborder of the Hemiptera, including Fulgoroidea, Cicadoidea, Cercopoidea, and Cicadelloidea, in which the beak appears to issue from the inferior portion of the head and in which the tarsi possess 3 tarsomeres (T-B; Woodward et al., in CSIRO); see Coleorrhyncha, Heteroptera, and Sternorrhyncha.

auchenorrhynchus, with the beak issuing from the inferior portion of the head, as in Auchenorrhyncha (Hemiptera) (T-B).

auctorum (Latin), of authors (T-B).

auditory, relating to the sense of hearing (T-B).

auditory nerve, nerve connecting chordotonal organ with ganglion of nervous system (Tulloch; Chapman).

auditory organ, tympanal organ, q.v. (T-B).

auditory peg, scolopale, q.v. (T-B).

auditory sense, hearing, q.v. (T-B).

aulaeum, in mosquito larvae (Diptera: Culicidae), ventromentum, q.v. (Tilloch; Harbach and Knight).

aulax (pl., **aulaces**), in ♀ Hymenoptera, groove on dorsal ramus of gonapophysis VIII into which fits a tongue, rhachis, from ventral ramus of gonapophysis IX (Tuxen, after E. L. Smith).

aurantiacus, aurantius, the color of an orange (T-B).

aurate, with ears or earlike expansions (T-B); see auratus.

auratus, golden yellow (T-B); see aurate.

aurelia, chrysalis, q.v. (T-B).

aurelian, a lepidopterist (T-B).

aureolate, with a diffuse colored ring (T-B).

aureole, a ring of color which is usually diffuse outwardly (T-B).

aureous, aureus (Latin), gold colored (T-B); see auratus.

aurichalceous, aurichalceus (Latin), between gold and brass in color (T-B).

auricle(s), an appendage resembling a little ear (T-B, after J. B. Smith); a chamber of the insect heart (T-B); in some ♂ Anisoptera (Odonata), oreillets, q.v. (T-B, after Imms; O'Farrell, in CSIRO); in Heteroptera (Hemiptera), variously shaped structure on metapleuron of adult bugs assisting in spreading the products of scent glands from the ostiolar groove upon the evaporatorium of the metathoracic scent gland (Slater); in ♀ *Melitaea* (Lepidoptera: Nymphalidae), small, paired invaginations of sides of lamella postvaginalis which extend mediad and dorsad on antrum (Tuxen, after Higgins); in honey bee (Hymenoptera: Apoidea), pollen press, q.v. (T-B; Borror et al); in andrenid bees (Hymenoptera: Andrenidae), a short membranous process placed laterally on the ligula (T-B, after J. B. Smith).

auricula (pl., **auriculae**), in ♂ Caelifera (Orthoptera), outer process of lophus of epiphallus when divided (Tuxen); in ♂ Tipulidae (Diptera), apodeme of ejaculator besides ejaculator apodeme (Tuxen, after Bodenheimer); see auricle.

auricular, of or pertaining to the auricle, the space or cavity surrounding the dorsal vessel (T-B).

auricular openings, ostia, q.v., of heart (T-B).

auricular valve, a mechanism of the insect heart, at each ostium, which prevents the return flow of the blood into the dorsal sinus (T-B).

auriculate, earlike (T-B); see aurate.

auriculate antennae, those in which one of the basal joints is dilated into an earlike shield or cap partly covering the rest (T-B, after Westwood).

auriculo-ventricular, the outer valves of the heart between the auricular space and the chamber (T-B).

auritate, earlike; applied to appendages (T-B).

auritus, having 2 ears or earlike spots or appendages (T-B).

auroral spot, in *Anthocharis* (Lepidoptera: Pieridae), the bright orange-colored spot at the apical area (T-B).

auroreous, auroreus, red, like the aurora borealis (T-B).

Austral region, that faunal area which covers the whole of the United States and Mexico except the boreal mountains and tropical low-

lands; divided into Transition, Upper, Lower and Gulf Strip: see
Boreal and Tropical (T-B); faunal region including Australia, New
Zealand, the eastern Malay Islands and Polynesia (T-B); see Australian region; faunal region including Australia and Tasmania, sometimes including New Guinea and Wallacea depending upon the author, but not including New Zealand (Mackerras, in CSIRO).

Australian Region, faunal region including Australia and Tasmania,
sometimes including New Guinea and Wallacea depending on the
author, but not including New Zealand (Mackerras, in CSIRO).

Australoperloidea, Gripopterygoidea, q.v. (Hennig, after Illies).

Austroriparian Faunal Area, that part of the lower Austral Zone of
North America covering the greater part of the South Atlantic and
Gulf States (T-B).

autapomorphy, an apomorphy unique to a terminal taxon on a cladogram (Hennig).

autecology, the ecology of individual organisms and populations, including physiological ecology, behavioral ecology, and population
ecology (T-B, after Folsom and Wardle; Allaby); see synecology.

authority citation, the custom of citing the name of the author of a
scientific name or name combination, e.g., X-us Jones, X-us albus
Jones, Y-us albus (Jones) (Mayr).

autochthonous, native or aboriginal; used for those species which are
considered to have arisen as a part of the native or aboriginal fauna
or flora, as contrasted with those which are considered to have im-
migrated from outside regions (Tillyard); a type of input into aquatic
ecosystems that comes from within the system in the form of primary
production (Ricklefs); see allochthounous.

autogenous, in some ♀ mosquitoes (Culicidae), other biting Diptera,
and other insect orders, laying a first batch of eggs without prior
feeding (Chapman; Gauld and Bolton); see anautogenous.

autogeny, the laying of eggs by adults that have not injested any pro-
teinaceaus food, e.g., short-lived mayflies (Ephemeroptera) (Matthews and Matthews); the ability of ♀ mosquitoes (Culicidae) and
other biting Diptera to develop eggs without a prior blood meal
(Tulloch).

autoinfection, in invertebrate pathology, infection of a host by a microorganism or virus produced within or upon the body of the same
host individual (Steinhaus and Martignoni).

automictic parthenogenesis, parthenogenesis in which there is a normal reduction division in the maturation division of the oocyte, followed by the fusion of 2 nuclei so that the diploid number of chromosomes is restored so that only females are produced, occurring in
Phasmidae (Phasmida), Coccoidea (Hemiptera: Sternorrhyncha),
and Psychidae (Lepidoptera), (Chapman).

automimicry, Batesian mimicry in which palatable individuals mimic
unpalatable individuals of the same species, e.g., monarch butterfly
(Matthews and Matthews, after Brower).

autonomic ganglia, stomatogastric nervous system, q.v. (T-B).

autonomic nerves, nerves of the stomatogastric nervous system, q.v. (T-B).

autonomic nervous system, stomatogastric nervous system, q.v. (T-B).

autoparasitism, in ants (Hymenoptera: Formicidae), return of mated females to former colony resulting in polygyny (Gauld and Bolton).

autoparasitoid, heteronomous hyperparasitoid, q.v. (Gauld and Bolton).

autophagocytosis, the absorption of contractile muscular tissue by cells originating from the muscular fiber itself instead of by leucocytes (T-B, after Henneguy).

autopolyploid, a polyploid originating through the doubling of a diploid chromosome set (Mayr).

autosome, one of the chromosomes other than a sex chromosome (Mayr).

autospasy, loss of appendages in arthropods by an extrinsic force (Tulloch, after L. C. Woodruff).

autotilly, loss of appendages in arthropods by self amputation (Tulloch, after L. C. Woodruff).

autotomize, to perform autotomy, as in spiders (Araneae) which caste off legs (T-B).

autotomy, loss of appendages in arthropods by reflex sloughing (T-B; Tulloch, after L. C. Woodruff), in Phasmida often associated with problems during ecdysis, and in some species also used defensively (Carlberg, pers. comm.); see autospasy and autotilly.

autotype, any specimen identified by the author of the species and compared with the type or cotype (T-B, after J. B. Smith).

auxilia (pl., **auxiliae**), small plate beneath the base of a pretarsal claw, in some insects bearing a pulvillus when the latter are present (T-B, after Snodgrass; Chapman).

auxiliary, additional or supplementing (T-B); gyne (potential reproductive) which, in association with a queen, becomes a worker in a social insect colony (Michener).

auxiliary plates, auxiliae, q.v. (Tulloch).

auxiliary sclerites, in ♂ *Arixenia* (Dermaptera: Arixeniidae), sclerites on penis lobe (Tuxen, after Rehn).

auxiliary vein, in adult Diptera, subcosta, q.v. (T-B, after Williston, Meigen).

auxiliary ventral tooth, in some mosquito larvae (Diptera: Culicidae), a small tooth located posterior to and in line with the ventral teeth of the mandible, and usually bearing 2 or 3 cusps (Harbach and Knight).

auxiliary worker, in ants (Hymenoptera: Formicidae), slave of slave-making ants (T-B); see dulosis.

auxillae, auxiliae, q.v. (Tulloch).

available name, a scientific name that is not excluded under the Code and that conforms to the provisions of the Code (ICZN).

available nomenclatural act, a nomenclatural act that is published in an available work and conforms to the provisions of the Code (ICZN).

available work, a work that was published within the meaning of the Code after 1757, in which the Principle of Binominal Nomenclature is consistently applied, and has not been suppressed by the Commission for nomenclatural purposes; or is a work entered in the Official List of Works Approved as Available for Zoological Nomenclature by a decision of the Commission (ICZN).

avian, of or pertaining to birds (Aves) (T-B).

avicephaliform, in ♂ Derbidae (Hemiptera: Auchenorrhyncha: Fulgoroidea), shaped like the head of a bird, referring to lobes of the flagellum of the aedeagus (Kramer).

avidity index, in invertebrate pathology, the mean number of particles per positive phagocytic cell (Steinhaus and Martignoni); see phagocytic index.

axenic, in invertebrate pathology, free from associated organisms (Steinhaus and Martignoni).

axenic cultivation, in invertebrate pathology, the rearing of one or more individuals of a single species in or on a nonliving medium (Steinhaus and Martignoni).

axial, of or pertaining to an axis (T-B).

axial filament, filament arising behind nucleus of sperm, in most cases consisting of 2 central tubes with a ring of 9 doublets and 9 accessory tubules on the outside (Chapman).

axilla (pl., **axillae**), in some Symphyta and Chalcididae (Hymenoptera), posterior portion of mesoscutum separated off by transcutal articulation (Gauld and Bolton); in many Apocrita (Hymenoptera), one of 2 small posterolateral plates formed from the mesoscutum, separated from rest of scutum by transcutal articulation (T-B, after MacGillivray; Riek, in CSIRO; Gibson; Gauld and Bolton).

axillar carina, in adult Apocrita (Hymenoptera), carina that delineates the dorsal axillar surface from the lateral axillar surface (Gibson).

axillaries, pteralia, q.v. (T-B, after Imms).

axillaris, the second and third anal veins of Comstock (T-B, after Enderlein).

axillary, placed in the crotch or angle of origin of 2 bodies; arising from the angle of ramification (T-B).

axillary area, vannus, q.v. (T-B); in adult Diptera, axillary region, q.v. (McAlpine).

axillary cell, in adult Diptera, anal cell, q.v., of wing (T-B, after Williston, Comstock, Curran; McAlpine).

axillary cord, the produced posterior angle of the notum, which forms the posterior margin of the basal membrane of the wing (T-B, after Comstock); continuation of posterior fold of scutellum along the trailing edge of the wing (Chapman, after Snodgrass); in adult Diptera, the thickened posterior edge of the upper and lower calypteres, being continuous with the posterior scutellar ridge (Harbach and Knight, after Snodgrass).

axillary excision, in adult Diptera, axillary incision, q.v. (T-B, after Comstock).

axillary fossa, in adult Eumeninae (Hymenoptera: Vespidae), depression in axilla (Carpenter, pers. comm., after Carpenter and Cumming).

axillary furrow, jugal fold, q.v. (T-B).

axillary incision, in adult Diptera, a notch on the posterior margin of the wing between the alula and the distal part (T-B; Harbach and Knight, after Giles).

axillary membrane, the membrane of the insect wing base extending from the tegula at the base of the costal margin to the axillary cord, q.v. (Comstock).

axillary muscles, muscles arising from the pleuron of a wing-bearing segment and inserting on the first and third axillary sclerites (T-B, after Snodgrass; Borror et al.).

axillary plate, the posterior sclerite of the wing base in Odonata, supporting the subcostal, radial, medial, cubital, and vannal veins (T-B, after Snodgrass).

axillary plates, in adult Diptera, axillary sclerites, q.v. (McAlpine).

axillary region, the region of the wing base containing the axillary sclerites (T-B, after Snodgrass).

axillary sclerites, the sclerites of the axillary region in the wing-flexing insects, being partially differentiated in Ephemeroptera and represented by the axillary plate in Odonata (T-B, after Snodgrass); see first, second, third, and fourth axillary sclerites.

axillary vein, in adult Ephemeroptera and Orthoptera, intercalary vein, q.v. (T-B, after J. B. Smith); in adult Diptera, the second branch of anal vein (A_2), when present (T-B, after Curran; McAlpine); in hind wing of Symphyta (Hymenoptera), third anal vein (3A) (Borror et al.).

Axioidea, superfamily of the infraorder Ditrysia (Lepidoptera) containing one family Axiidae; adults are fairly stout, without chaetosemata, but with naked proboscis, atrophied maxillary palpi, antennae bipectinate in both sexes, wings fairly broad, paired invaginated, lateral organs on abdominal segment VII; larvae with inconspicuous setae, anal prolegs massive; pupae stout, without dorsal spines, not protruded from cocoon at ecdysis (Minet).

axis (pl., **axes**), the process at the base of an elytron on which it turns (T-B); the central line of anything, about which it is constructed or about which it turns or rotates (T-B); in ♀ Panorpidae (Mecoptera), median portion of medigynium, q.v., consisting of apodemes alongside spermathecal duct (Byers, after Carpenter).

axis-cylinder, that part of a nerve fiber made up of fibrillae, which is covered with a membrane sheath (T-B, after Folsom and Wardle).

axon, the principal process, or nerve fiber, of a nerve cell (T-B, after Snodgrass); projections of a nerve cell that conduct nerve impulses from one cell to another (Chapman).

axoneme, axial filament, q.v. (Chapman).

Axymyioidea, superfamily within the Nematocera (Diptera), including the single family Axymyiidae (McAlpine).

Axymyiomorpha, infraorder within the suborder Nematocera (Diptera), including only the superfamily Axymyioidea (McAlpine).

azinphosethyl, $C_{12}H_{16}N_3O_3PS_2$, a synthetic insecticide and acaricide; an organophosphate, O,O-diethyl S-4-oxo-1,2,3-benzotriazin-3(4H)-ylmethyl phosphorodithioate; highly toxic to mammals; acute oral LD_{50} for rats 7 to 18 mg/kg (Pfadt).

azinophosmethyl, $C_{10}H_{12}N_3O_3PS_2$, a synthetic, broad-spectrum insecticide and acaricide; an organophosphate, O,O-dimethyl S-(4-oxo-1,2,3-benzotriazin-3(4H)-ylmethyl) phosphorodithioate; extremely toxic to mammals, acute oral LD_{50} for rats 15–25 mg/kg (Pfadt).

azobenzene, $C_{12}H_{10}N_2$, a synthetic acaricide; chronic toxicity 1000 ppm in diet kills rats in a few days (Pfadt).

Azodrin (trade name), monocrotophos, q.v. (Pfadt).

azure, azureus, clear sky-blue (T-B).

azygos, in ♂ Coleoptera, unpaired portion of genitalia, i.e., genital tube beyond junction of seminal ducts (Tuxen).

azygos tube, in ♂ Lepidoptera, the embryonic tube that develops into aedoeagus (Tuxen, after Sharp).

azygotic portion, in ♂ Coleoptera, azygos, q.v. (Tuxen).

azygous, unpaired (T-B); sometimes applied to an unpaired oviduct (i.e., common oviduct) (T-B).

B

B-melanosis, melanosis caused by a bacterium, probably *Aerobacter cloacae* (Steinhaus and Martignoni).

babesioses, diseases of vertebrates caused by *Babesia* (Piroplasmea) infecting red blood cells (Adkins, pers. comm.; Allaby); see red-water fever.

baccate, baccatus, berrylike; applied to bladderlike ovaries from the surface of which the short ovarian tubes arise (T-B).

bacillary dysentery, disease of man caused by bacteria, *Bacillus* spp., and transmitted by the house fly, *Musca domestica* L. (Muscidae), various blow flies (Calliphoridae), and various flesh flies (Sarcophagidae) (Diptera) (Borror et al.).

bacillary paralysis, a disease of silkworm larvae (Lepidoptera: Bombycidae), caused by ingestion of spores and parasporal of bacteria, *Bacillus thurengensis* var. *alesti* and var. *sotto*, involving usually irreversible paralysis followed by death (Steinhaus and Martignoni).

Bacillidea, infraorder of the Phasmida, including the Bacilloidea, Phylloidea, Nescroscioidea and Phasmatoidea (Kevan).

bacilliform sclerite, in ♂ Calyptratae (Diptera), processus longus, q.v. (Tulloch, after Steyskal; Tuxen, after Crampton; McAlpine).

Bacilloidea, in Phasmida, superfamily within the infraorder Bacillidea, containing the families Bacillidae and Bacunculidae (Kevan).

bacillus (pl., **bacilli**), in ♀ *Melitaea* (Lepidoptera: Nymphalidae), sclerotized, longitudinal rods in walls of ductus bursae (Tuxen, after Higgins).

Bacillus chitinivorous, the soil bacterium which attacks and breaks up the chitinous skeleton of dead insects in the soil (T-B, after Folsom and Wardle).

back, dorsum, q.v. (T-B).

bacteremia, presence of bacteria in the hemolymph without production of harmful toxins or other deleterious effects (Steinhaus and Martignoni).

bacteria (sing., **bacterium**), group of microscopic, prokaryotic organisms (Allaby).

bacterial wilts, plant diseases in which the causative bacteria produce slime that plugs the water-conducting tissue of the invaded plant (Pfadt).

bacteriocyte, a cell containing mutualistic and commensalistic bacteria (Steinhaus and Martignoni); see mycetocyte.

bacteriosis, any morbid or diseased condition caused by bacteria (T-B).

baculi (sing., **baculus**), in ♀ Coleoptera, rodlike apophyses of tergum or sternum IX (Tuxen).

baculiform, rod- or stafflike (T-B).

baculum (pl., **bacula**), in some ♂ Osmylidae (Planipennia), a narrow strut situated on either side of gonarcus (Tuxen, after Tjeder); stiffening sclerotic rod running parallel with rami of gonopods used in oviposition (Tuxen, after E. L. Smith).

badius, bay-colored; of the color of a bay horse (T-B).

baenomere, thoracic segment, q.v. (T-B).

baenopoda, thoracic legs, q.v. (T-B).

baenosome, thorax, q.v. (T-B).

Baetiscoidea, superfamily of Ephemeroptera, including Baetiscidae and Prosopistomatidae (McCafferty and Edmunds).

Baetoidea, superfamily of Ephemeroptera, including Siphlonuridae, Baetidae, Oniscigastridae, Ameletopsidae, and Ametropodidae (sensu Landa and Sold n), and Oligoneuriidae and Heptageniidae (sensu McCafferty and Edmunds).

balance of nature, a fluctuating biotic equilibrium, in which interdependent organisms bear quantitative relations each to all the others, as modified by variable elements, such as weather, food, physiography, vegetation, etc. (T-B, after Folsom and Wardle).

balancer, in adult Diptera, halter, q.v. (T-B).

bald, investitus, q.v. (T-B).

ballooning, aerial dispersal by newly hatched spiderlings (Arachnida: Araneae) (Matthews and Matthews).

Baltic amber, Oligocene-aged amber from Europe, containing many insect inclusions (Riek, in CSIRO).

band, a transverse marking broader than a line (T-B); see stripe.

Banksian line(s), in some Myrmeleontidae (Neuroptera), a prominent longitudinal line on the wings formed by the bending and alignment of the branches of the radial sector (anterior Banksian line) or of the branches of the CuA [in the forewing] or MP2 [in the hind wing] (posterior Banksian line) (Stange, after Tillyard); also called, respectively, the linea plicata anterioris and linea plicata posterioris (Markl, after Nav s), and the radial planate and trigonal planate (Comstock).

bar, a short, straight band of equal width (T-B); in ♂ *Phoebis* (Lepidoptera: Pieridae), sclerotized strip along line of juncture of sacculus and base of harpe (Tuxen, after Klots).

barb(s), a minute, short, pointed process projecting obliquely from a surface (T-B; Harbach and Knight); in Heteroptera (Hemiptera), barblike microtrichia on apices of maxillary stylets (Cobben); in larval *Aedes communis* DeGeer (Diptera: Culicidae), one of the minute, pointed processes occurring on some of the maxillary brush filaments (Harbach and Knight); see barbed filament.

barbate, barbatus (Latin), bearded; in antennae, with tufts or fascicles of hair or short bristles on each side of each joint; on the abdomen, with flat tufts at the sides or tip (T-B).

barbed, furnished with barbs (T-B).

barbed filament, a filament with minute, short, pointed processes projecting obliquely from the surface (Harbach and Knight).

barbed seta, seta with minute, short, heavy pointed processes projecting obliquely from the surface (Harbach and Knight).

barbula (pl., **barbulae**), in larval Scarabaeidae (Coleoptera), the tuft or patch of hairs or short bristles at the sides of the abdomen near the anal region (T-B, after Böving).

barbule, a small barb, beard, or filiform appendage (T-B).

bar eye, a name given to one of the mutations of *Drosophila* (Diptera: Drosophilidae), in which the number of optical units in the compound eye is greatly reduced (Leftwich).

bare, without clothing structures of any kind (T-B); see glabrous.

bark, all the tissues outside of the cambium layer of a plant (T-B).

barley yellow dwarf, a virus disease of cereals, marked by leaves rapidly turning light green and yellow, beginning at the tips; transmitted by certain species of aphids (Hemiptera: Sternorrhyncha: Aphididae) (Pfadt).

barrette, in adult Diptera, katepimeron, q.v. (McAlpine).

Barth's Organ, in some ♂ Notodontidae (Lepidoptera), a pleated sacculus (q.v.) that can be inflated during courtship, usually folded accordionlike, enclosing a large tuft of hairlike androconia (Barth).

Bartonellaceae, family of bacteria which are parasitic in vertebrate hosts, usually within red blood cells (Allaby).

bartonelloses, diseases of vertebrates caused by bacteria of the Bartonellaceae (Adkins, pers. comm.; Allaby).

basad, in the direction of or toward the base (T-B).

basal, at or pertaining to the base or point of attachment or nearest the main body (T-B); see apical.

basal abdominal sternum, in adult Siphonaptera, sternum II, sternum I having been lost (Lewis, pers. comm.).

basal anal area, in Anisoptera (Odonata), a definitely outlined area at the base of the wing, bounded by Cu + A, the anal crossing and the secondary anal vein A′ (T-B, after Comstock).

basal anal cell, in adult Plecoptera, a wing cell near the base of wing between first (1A) and second (2A) anal veins (Borror et al.).

basal anchor, in ♂ Setipalpia (Plecoptera), a sclerotized plate between hemitergites of tergum X, connected with supraanal lobe via the basal bar (Tuxen, after Ricker).

basal apodeme(s), in Protura, apodemes from basal part of periphallus or perigynium (Tuxen); in ♂ most Teratembiidae (Embiidina), projection of basal margin (mostly the medial sclerite) of abdominal tergum X beneath abdominal tergum IX (Ross, in Tuxen); in ♂ Phthiraptera, sclerite articulating with, or fused to, parameres and mesomeres and continues with endophallus and wall of genital chamber (Lyal); in ♂ Diptera, phallapodeme, q.v. (Tuxen, after Snodgrass).

basal apparatus, in Heteroptera (Hemiptera), articulatory apparatus, q.v. (Tuxen, after Ashlock).

basal arch, in ♀ Blattaria, curved, strongly sclerotized area, cephalad of the first gonapophyses (T-B).

basal area, wing base, q.v. (T-B); in ♂ Ensifera (Orthoptera), the dorsal area of forewing between the pronotum and the stridulum (Otte, pers. comm.); in adult Apocrita (Hymenoptera), the anterior of the 3 median areas on the propodeum (T-B) (see area).

basal areole, a small cell at the base of the wing (Borror et al.); in some adult Lepidoptera, the cell at the base of the wing between the subcosta (Sc) and radius (R) (Borror et al.).

basal arm (of sternum IX), proximal arm, q.v. (Tuxen).

basal arms of sting sheath, rami of second valvulae, q.v. (Tuxen, after Michener).

basal articulating membrane, antacoria, q.v., of antenna (Peterson).

basal aula, in ♂ Leptopodomorpha (Hemiptera: Heteroptera), phallosoma, q.v. (Tuxen, after Cobben).

basal band, in many mosquito larvae (Diptera: Culicidae), a semicircular or linear band of cuticle representing the rim of the depression bearing the mandibular rake (Harbach and Knight, after Pao and Knight).

basal bar, in ♂ Isogeniinae (Plecoptera: Perlodidae), a sclerotized bladelike plate connecting the supraanal lobe with the basal anchor (Tuxen, after Walker).

basal bridge, in ♂ Hymenoptera, dorsal bridge of penis valves, q.v. (Tuxen, after Beck).

basal bulb, in ♀ Gerridae (Hemiptera: Heteroptera), basal bulb of ductus receptaculi excluding fecundation canal (before the pump) (Tuxen, after Pendergrast).

basal callus, in adult Tabanidae (Diptera), one of several calli on the frons (McAlpine).

basal cell, in Odonata, an elongate cell between radius and cubitus, just before the arculus (T-B); in adult Diptera, basal radial or basal medial cells, q.v. (T-B, after Comstock, Williston; McAlpine); in adult Trichoptera, one, 2, or 3 cells enclosed by the plical, empusal, and first and second anal veins ($P + E + 1A + 2A$ of Ross et al. = $Cu_2 + 1A + 2A + 3A$ of Comstock) (T-B; Betten).

basal costal cell (bc), in adult Diptera, cell at base of wing bounded by costa and subcosta, and apically by humeral crossvein (McAlpine).

basal dash, in adult Noctuidae (Lepidoptera), basal streak, q.v. (Tulloch).

basal dorsomesal lobe, in ♂ Culicidae (Diptera), a basal lobe on the mesal margin of the dorsal (prerotation sense) surface of the gonocoxite (Harbach and Knight).

basal fold, in the wing, a line of flexion between the base of the mediocubital field and the axillary region, forming a prominent convex fold in the flexed wing, extending between the median plates from the articulation of the radius with the second axillary sclerite to the articluation of the anal veins with the third axillary sclerite (T-B, after Snodgrass); in ♂ Caelifera (Orthoptera), an extension as a free soft fold of ectophallic membrane above the zygoma (Tuxen); in ♂ Heteroptera (Hemiptera), articulatory apparatus, q.v. (Tuxen, after Christophers and Gragg).

basal foramen, in ♂ Heteroptera (Hemiptera), entrance to phallic cavity surrounded by basal plates and ponticulus transversalis, closed or not by a septum (Tuxen, after Singh-Pruthi); in Heteroptera (Hemiptera), incorrectly applied to foramen ductus, q.v. (Tuxen, after Dupuis and Carvalho).

basal lateral arm, in ♂ *Culex* (Diptera: Culicidae), a laterally-directed basal process of the paraproct that may bend in caudal and/or ventral directions (Harbach and Knight, after Barraud).

basal line, in many Lepidoptera, a transverse line extending half way across the forewing very close to base (T-B).

basal lobe, in most ♂ Coleoptera, basal piece, q.v. (Tuxen, after Hinton); in ♂ Coccinellidae (Coleoptera), the distal unpaired part of the tegmen, sometimes surrounding the penis (Tuxen, after Wilson); in ♂ Culicidae (Diptera), a lobe near basal end of basistylus (coxite) (Tuxen); in ♂ Chironomidae (Diptera), inferior volsella, q.v. (Saether); in most ♂ Diptera, basistylus, q.v. (Tuxen).

basal lobe of tegumen, in ♂ *Catopsilia* (Lepidoptera: Pieridae), uncus anticus, q.v. (Tuxen, after Klots).

basal mandibular sclerite, in larvae of most orthorraphous Brachycera (Diptera), basal portion of divided mandible (Teskey, in McAlpine).

basal medial cell (bm), in wing of adult Diptera, cell between media and cubitus (or anterior branch of cubitus) and proximal to basal-medial or medial-cubital crossvein, located posterior to basal radial cell (McAlpine).

basal median apodeme, in ♀ Culicidae (Diptera), an apodeme arising on the midline at the base of the ventral surface of the postgenital lobe (Harbach and Knight, after Reinert).

basal median lobe, in ♂ Chironomidae (Diptera), superior volsella, q.v. (Saether).

basal mesal lobe, in ♂ Culicidae (Diptera), a small lobe or sclerite located anteromesally on the gonocoxite, usually being connected with its mate, and possibly homologous with the claspette (Harbach and Knight, after Belkin).

basal metabolism, the slow rate of metabolism of the resting animal (T-B).

basal notch, in some culicine larvae (Diptera: Culicidae), a small gap or slit between the galeastipital stem and the laciniastipes on the ventrobasal margin of the maxilla (Harbach and Knight, after Gardner et al.).

basal orifice, in ♂ Coleoptera, basal (proximal) opening of penis through which ejaculatory duct enters, often displaced to ventral side of penis (Tuxen).

basal palpal hair, in certain ♀ *Anopheles* (Diptera: Culicidae), one of several conspicuous setae arising from the basal palpomere of the maxillary palpi (Harbach and Knight, after Christophers).

basal piece, in ♂ Coleoptera, the unpaired basal (proximal) part of tegmen, usually sclerotized and may form a complete ring or tube around penis, often provided with single (manubrium) or paired processes (struts, apophyses) (Tuxen); in ♂ Culicidae (Diptera), one of the pair of supporting sclerotizations of the phallosome, lying within abdominal segment IX and often extending anteriorly into VIII, being articulated with the paramere, sometimes with the base of the proctiger, and often connected with the apodeme of the gonocoxite, probably being primitively an apodeme of the mesal margin of the gonocoxite (Harbach and Knight, after Belkin); in larval Muscomorpha (Diptera), tentoropharyngeal sclerite, q.v. (Ferrar).

basal plate(s), at base of wing, tegula, humeral plate, and median plates (McAlpine); in adult Ephemeroptera, the single basal wing sclerite from which most of the longitudinal veins originate (Ross et al., after Hamilton); in Embiidina, cercus-basipodites, q.v. (Tuxen, after Imms); in ♂ insects, sclerites of phallobase (T-B, after Snodgrass); in ♂ *Zorotypus zimmermani* Gurney (Zoraptera), unpaired sclerite articulating basally with lateral lobes (Tuxen); in ♂ Auchenorrhyncha (Hemiptera), connective, q.v. (Tuxen, after Singh-Pruthi); in ♂ Heteroptera (Hemiptera), articulatory apparatus, q.v. (Tuxen, after Singh-Pruthi); in ♂ Heteroptera (Hemiptera), the 2 major plates of the articulatory apparatus, considered separately (Tuxen, after Singh-Pruthi), sometimes incorrectly applied to entire articulatory apparatus (Tuxen); in ♂ Trichoptera, unpaired sclerite united with bases of dorsal sides of gonopods (Tuxen); in ♂ Culicidae (Diptera), basal piece, q.v. (Tuxen; Harbach and Knight, after Edwards); in ♂ Chironomidae (Diptera), superior volsella, q.v. (Saether).

basal plate apodemal rod, in ♂ Tingidae (Hemiptera: Heteroptera), dorsal connectives, q.v. (Tuxen, after Livingstone).

basal plate apodemes, in ♂ Tingidae (Hemiptera: Heteroptera), capitate processes, q.v. (Tuxen, after Livingstone).

basal plate apparatus, in ♂ Heteroptera (Hemiptera), articulatory apparatus, q.v. (Tuxen, after Schaefer).

basal plate foramen, in ♂ Tingidae (Hemiptera: Heteroptera), basal foramen, q.v. (Tuxen, after Livingstone).

basal plate (median) extension, in ♂ Reduviidae (Hemiptera: Heteroptera), basal plates' prolongation, q.v. (Tuxen, after China and Usinger).

basal plate notches, in ♂ Tingidae (Hemiptera: Heteroptera), area of basal plate articulating and pivoting on suspensorial apodemes (Tuxen, after Livingstone).

basal plate process, in ♂ Gerridae (Hemiptera: Heteroptera), ligamentary process, q.v. (Tuxen, after Brinkhurst).

basal plate struts, in ♂ Heteroptera (Hemiptera), free dorsoproximal end of each basal plate dorsal to basal plate notches (Tuxen, after Livingstone); in ♂ Reduviidae (Hemiptera: Heteroptera), struts, q.v. (Tuxen, after China and Usinger).

basal plates bridge, in ♂ Heteroptera (Hemiptera), applied both to ductifer, q.v. (Tuxen, after Singh-Pruthi) and to ponticulus transversalis, q.v. (Tuxen, after Dupuis and Carvalho).

basal plates' prolongation, in ♂ Reduviidae (Hemiptera: Heteroptera), coalescent ligamentary process ventrally to the proximal segment (true phallosoma) of phallus (Tuxen, after Singh-Pruthi).

basal postcostal vein, in adult Agrionidae (Odonata), one of the cubitoanal crossveins (T-B).

basal process, in ♂ Lepidoptera, a type of armature on inner face of valva (Tuxen, after Scudder and Burgess).

basal process of subgenital plate, in ♂ Plecoptera, vesicle, q.v. (Tuxen).

basal prong of penis, in ♂ *Anteos* (Lepidoptera: Pieridae), midventral, ventrad or ventrocaudad sclerotized process of proximal part of aedoeagus. being morphologically a hypomere (Tuxen, after Klots).

basal prong of uncus, in ♂ *Anteos* (Lepidoptera: Pieridae), uncus anticus, q.v. (Tuxen, after Klots).

basal radial cell (br), in wing of adult Diptera, cell in basal half of wing between radius and media, limited distally by radial-medial crossvein (McAlpine).

basal region, in ♂ Dermaptera, penis, q.v. (Tuxen); in ♂ Heteroptera (Hemiptera), phallosoma, q.v. (Tuxen, after Drake and Davis).

basal ring, in ♂ Protura, basiperiphallus, q.v. (Tuxen); in ♂ Diptera, e.g., Trichoceridae, ring-shaped amalgamation of tergum and sternum IX (Tuxen); in larval Culicidae (Diptera), a pedicel supporting one or more setae (Harbach and Knight, after Tanaka et al.); in ♂ Hymenoptera, sclerotized ring surrounding parameres proximally, q.v. (Tuxen, after Crampton; Gauld and Bolton).

basal sac, in ♀ Gerridae (Hemiptera: Heteroptera), basal sac of ductus receptaculi excluding fecundation canal (before the pump) (Tuxen, after Pendergrast).

basal sclerite, in ♂ Blattopteroidea, proximal plate separated from left epiphallus (transl. "Basalsklerit" Tuxen); in ♂ Heteroptera (Hemiptera), articulatory apparatus, q.v. (Tuxen, after Yang); in ♂ Noctuidae (Lepidoptera), oblique or V-shaped, sclerotized process of clasper serving for attachment of insertion of flexor muscle (Tuxen, after Forbes); in larval Chironomidae (Diptera), triangular to rectangular sclerite attached to ungula posteriorly (Saether); in larval Muscomorpha (Diptera), tentoropharyngeal sclerite, q.v. (McAlpine).

basal segment of clasp, in ♂ Culicidae (Diptera), basistylus, q.v. (T-B); gonocoxite, q.v. (McAlpine).

basal segment of gonostyli, in ♂ Mecoptera, gonocoxite, q.v. (Tuxen, after Issiki).

basal segment of penis, vesicula spermalis, q.v. (Tuxen, after Borror).

basal setae, in adult Chironomidae (Diptera), anterior transverse row of setae on tergites (Saether).

basal space, in certain Lepidoptera, that area on the forewings between the base and transverse anterior line (T-B).

basal spur, in adult Culicidae (Diptera), a longitudial proximal extension of the radial sector (R_s) or R_{4+5} when these are sharply bent in the form of a crossvein near their points of origin (Harbach and Knight, after Belkin).

basal streak, in adult Noctuidae (Lepidoptera), streak extending from the base of the wing, through the submedian interspace to the transverse anterior line (T-B).

basal supporting plate, in anopheline larvae (Diptera: Culicidae), a sclerite located anteriorly at the base of the spiracular apparatus and extending laterally to the pecten plate on each side of abdominal segment VIII (Harbach and Knight, after Imms).

basal suture, in Isoptera, a line of weakness along which the fracture and consequent shedding of the wings takes place (T-B).

basal thickening, in ♀ Heteroptera (Hemiptera), that portion of the fecundation canal lying in the ventral wall of the gynatrial sac (Andersen).

basal transverse carina, in adult Apocrita (Hymenoptera), a carina which crosses the propodeum before the middle and separates the basal area from the areola (T-B); see area.

basal valves, in ♂ Caelifera (Orthoptera), proximal valves of penis when divided, or proximal part of undivided penis (Tuxen, after Dirsh).

basal vein, in adult Chironomidae (Diptera), brachiolum, q.v. (Saether) (see stem vein); in some adult Hymenoptera, short branch of media (M) extending between M + CuA and R_s + M, located about the middle of the wing (Borror et al.; Riek, in CSIRO).

basal ventromesal lobe, in ♂ Culicidae (Diptera), a basal lobe on the mesal margin of the ventral (prerotation sense) surface of gonocoxite (Harbach and Knight).

basal vesicle, in ♂ Dermaptera, enlargement of base of virga where it joins the rest of the ejaculatory duct (Tuxen, after Burr).

basal wedge, in ♂ Chironomidae (Diptera), pars ventralis, q.v. (Saether).

basalar apodeme, in adult Culicidae (Diptera), an apodeme of the mesothorax arising from the posterior mesanepisternum slightly below the basalare (Harbach and Knight, after Owen).

basalar cleft, in adult Diptera, anepisternal cleft, q.v. (McAlpine).

basalar muscles, muscles arising from the coxa and episternum of a wing-bearing segment, inserting on the basalare (T-B, after Snodgrass; Borror et al.).

basalar plate, in Miridae (Hemiptera: Heteroptera), the plate or sclerite at the base of the front wing below the posterior edge of the pronotum and behind the upper margin of the propleuron (T-B).

basalar sclerites, small pleural sclerites located at the base of the wings (T-B, after Crampton); basalare, q.v. (Chapman); see basilare and subalare.

basalare, the episternal epipleurite (sometimes double) giving insertion to the anterior pleural muscles of the wing, often being represented by a partially detached lobe of the episternum before the pleural wing process (T-B, after Snodgrass); see anterior basalare and posterior basalare.

basale, in ♂ Coleoptera, basal piece, q.v. (Tuxen).

basalis, the principal mandibular sclerite, when sclerites are distinguishable, to which all other parts are jointed, corresponding to the stipes in the maxilla (T-B).

basanale, third axillary sclerite, q.v. (T-B, after Crampton).

basantenna, antacoria, q.v. (T-B, after MacGillivray).

basantra, in certain Tubulifera (Thysanoptera), prepectus, q.v. (Heming, pers. comm., after Bhatti).

basarcus, in ♀ Blattaria, basal arch, q.v. (T-B, after MacGillivray).

base, that part of any appendage or structure that is nearest the body; on the thorax, that part nearest the abdomen; on the abdomen that part nearest the thorax; the bottom on which anything stands (T-B); in adult Diptera, proximal portion of halter that articulates with the body (McAlpine); in ♀ Diplura, basal part of papilla genitalis carrying tubercula sensitiva and valvae (Tuxen, after Pagés); in ♂ Auchenorrhyncha (Hemiptera), posterior outline of foot of style, between heel and posterior point (Tuxen, after Young).

basement membrane, the membrane covering the inner surface of the eye in insects, continuous with that of the surrounding epidermis (T-B, after Snodgrass); the membrane underlying an epithelial layer (T-B); a membrane, underlying epidermal cells, consisting of an amorphous glandular material, probably a mucopolysaccharide, which in some species has collagen fibers imbedded in it (Tulloch, after Richards; Chapman, after Neville).

basendite, an endite of the base of an appendage (T-B).

basiala, in adult Diptera, prearcular field, q.v. (Hennig, after Rodendorf).

basiandropodite, in ♂ Diptera, basistylus, q.v. (Tuxen, after Christophers); gonocoxite, q.v. (McAlpine).

basicalypter, in adult Diptera, lower calypter, q.v. (McAlpine).

basicardo, the basal region of the cardo (T-B, after Crampton).

basicercus, in ♀ Culicidae (Diptera), first segment of cercus (Tuxen, after Gerry); in Orthoptera, cercal basipodite, q.v. (Tuxen).

basiconic peg, a thin-walled, peg-shaped sensillum with minute pores, functioning in chemoreception (Chapman).

basiconic receptor, basiconic peg, q.v. (Leftwich).

basiconic sensillum, basiconic peg, q.v. (T-B).

basiconjunctiva, in ♂ Heteroptera (Hemiptera), distal membranous part of phallosoma reaching to, but not including, ejaculatory reservoir (Tuxen, after Bonhag and Wick).

basicosta, in adult Diptera, humeral plate, q.v. (T-B, after Curran; McAlpine); the proximal submarginal ridge of the inner wall of a leg segment (T-B, after Snodgrass).

basicostal, of or pertaining to the basicosta (T-B).

basicostal sulcus, the external groove of a leg segment forming the basicosta (Chapman, after Snodgrass).

basicostal suture, basicostal sulcus, q.v. (T-B, after Snodgrass).

basicoxa, in adult Diptera, the basal portion of the divided eucoxa (McAlpine); see disticoxa.

basicoxite, the usually narrow rim of the coxa proximal to the basicoxal sulcus and its internal ridge, the basicosta (T-B, after Snodgrass; Chapman).

basidorsal lobe, in ♂ Chironomidae (Diptera), inferior volsella, q.v. (Saether).

basigalea, the basal division of the galea (T-B, after Crampton).

basilaire, the jugulum (T-B, after Straus).

basilar, of or pertaining to the base (T-B).

basilar crossvein, in adult Odonata, the vein crossing the basilar space (T-B).

basilar membrane, a thin fenestrate membrane separating the rods and cones of the insect eye from the optic tract (T-B, after Packard).

basilar space, in adult Odonata, a cell at the base of the wing bounded by radius, cubitus, arculus and the base of the wing; median space (T-B, after Garman).

basimandibula, trochantin of the mandible, q.v. (T-B, after MacGillivray).

basimere, in ♂ insects, basal segment of paramere (Tuxen); in ♂ Siphonaptera, main part of paramere (Tuxen); in ♂ Diptera, basistylus, q.v. (Tuxen, after Crampton) or gonocoxite, q.v. (Saether; McAlpine); in ♂ Trichoptera, the basal segment of a divided paramere (= inferior appendage), q.v. (T-B, after Snodgrass), coxopodite, q.v. (Nielsen).

basiparamere, in ♂ Hymenoptera, gonocoxite, q.v. (Tuxen, after Snodgrass).

basipenalis, in ♂ Blattopteroidea, hypophallus, q.v. (Tuxen, after Berlese).

basiperiphallus (pl., **basiperiphalli**), in ♂ Protura, basal ring of periphallus into which acroperiphallus may or may not retract, and carrying basal apodemes (Tuxen).

basiphallus (pl., **basiphalli**), in ♂ Diptera, basal part of intromittent organ (Tuxen; McAlpine).

basipharynx, a slender chitinized tube formed by the greatly reduced epigusta and subgusta (T-B, after MacGillivray); in adult Chironomidae (Diptera), cibarial pump, q.v. (Saether).

basipodial plate, in Orthoptera, cercal basipodite, q.v. (Tuxen).

basipodite, the segment next following the coxopodite in the insect maxilla (T-B, after Imms); in Arthropoda, the second podomere of the leg, being homologous with the trochanter of Hexapoda (T-B, after Tillyard; Boudreaux).

basiproboscis, in adult Diptera, the region proximal to the constriction of the proboscis (T-B, after MacGillivray).

basipulvillus, in Heteroptera (Hemiptera) and Diptera, auxilia, q.v. (T-B, after Holway; McAlpine; Goel and Schaefer).

basis (pl., **bases**), foundation or base, with regard to an insectan structure; the whole lower part of the theca from the mouth as far as the labella (T-B, after Jardine); in ♂ Heteroptera, articulatory apparatus, q.v. (Tuxen, after Kullenberg).

basis capituli, the basal part of the capitulum in ticks (Acari) (T-B, after Matheson).

basis parameri, in ♂ Heteroptera (Hemiptera), basal part of paramere on which insert the muscles of this appendage (Tuxen, after Dupuis).

basis valvae, in ♂ Lepidoptera, proximal part of valva (Tuxen, after Birket-Smith).

basisternal, of or pertaining to the basisternum (T-B).

basisternal carina, in acalyptrate Muscomorpha and other Diptera, a median inflection of the prothoracic basisternum, which forms an internal, keellike apodeme to which the promotor muscle of the coxa attaches (Speight).

basisternum, the principal sclerite of the eusternum anterior to the roots of the sternal apophyses or the sternocostal suture, between the presternum and the sternellum (T-B; Chapman, after Snodgrass).

basistyle, in ♂ Mecoptera and ♂ Diptera, gonocoxite, q.v. (Tuxen, after Crampton; Saether; McAlpine).

basistylar lobe, in ♂ Chironomidae (Diptera), median volsella, q.v. (Saether).

basistylus (pl., **basistyli**), in ♂ Protura, basal part of stylus (Tuxen); basistyle, q.v. (Tuxen).

basitarsal, of or pertaining to the basitarsus (T-B).

basitarsus, the proximal or basal tarsomere (T-B; Mackerras, in CSIRO).

basitibial plate, in adult Aculeata (Hymenoptera), a small plate or scalelike projection at the base of the hind tibia (Michener).

basituberculum (pl., **basitubercula**), in ♂ Mecoptera, basal tooth on inner margin of stylus (Tuxen).

basivalves, in ♀ Isoptera, basivalvulae, q.v. (Tuxen, after Browman).

basivalvula (pl., **basivalvulae**), in ♀ Grylloblattodea, sclerite at base of first valvulae (Tuxen); in ♀ Orthoptera, one (Ensifera) or more (Caelifera) sclerites at base of anterior valvulae (Tuxen); see basivalvulae.

basivalvulae, in ♀ insects, small sclerites sometimes occurring at the bases of the first valvulae, often confused with first valvifers (T-B, after Snodgrass); in ♂ Isoptera, paired sclerites in intersegmental membrane between sternum VIII and IX (Tuxen, after Geyer); in ♀ Isoptera, small paired sclerites sometimes differentiated at base of ventral valves) (Tuxen, after Crampton); in ♀ Psyllidae (Hemiptera: Sternorrhyncha), a pair of mediodorsal processes from ventral valvulae (Tuxen).

basivolsella (pl., **basivolsellae**), in ♂ Hymenoptera, the main plate of the volsella, i.e., the volsella except for chelate apex (Tuxen, after Peck).

basivolsellar apodeme, in ♂ Hymenoptera, apodeme from anterior end of volsellar strut (Tuxen, after Peck).

basking, positioning the body in such a way relative to the suns rays as to raise body temperature, especially to a level permitting flight (Chapman).

basolateral seta, in ♀ Culicidae (Diptera), a small seta which may be present on either the anterolateral corner of tergum VIII or sternum VIII, being occasionally replaced by a small bulla (Harbach and Knight, after Reinert).

Batesian mimicry, that form of mimicry described by H. W. Bates, in which an edible species (the mimic) obtains security by counterfeiting the appearance of an inedible species (the model), e.g., clearwing moth (Lepidoptera: Sesiidae) resembling a bee (Hymenoptera: Apoidea) (T-B, after Folsom and Wardle; Leftwich); see Müllerian mimicry.

Bateson's law, an observational rule relating to regenerative abnormalities of the distal portion of appendages, which holds that in the case of triplications the parts must be in one plane and that the middle branch must be the mirror image of the outer and inner branches (Tulloch).

bathmis, pterostigma, q.v. (T-B).

batumen, in stingless bees (Hymenoptera: Apidae), a protective layer of propolis or hard cerumen (sometimes vegetable matter, mud, or various mixtures) that encloses the nest cavity of a colony (Wilson).

bave, the fluid silk as it is spun by caterpillars (Lepidoptera).

Bayard's point (or angulation), in ♂ Plebeiinae (Lepidoptera: Lycaenidae), point on dorsal margin of valva where this attains its greatest breadth; apex of a more or less rounded, dorsal hump or bulge of valva (Tuxen, after Nabokov).

Baygon (trade name), propoxur, q.v. (Pfadt).

Baytex (trade name), fenthion, q.v. (Pfadt).

beak, the protruding mouthpart structures of a sucking insect (Borror et al.); proboscis, q.v. (Borror et al.); rostrum, q.v. (T-B).

bean golden yellow mosaic, disease of bean plants caused by an isometric virus and transmitted by the whitefly *Bemisia tabaci* (Gennadius) (Hemiptera: Sternorrhyncha: Aleyrodidae) (Borror et al.).

beard, in adult Diptera (e.g., Asilidae), mystax, q.v. (T-B); in larval Chironomidae (Diptera), cardinal beard, q.v., or ventromental beard, q.v. (Saether); in adult Chironomidae (Diptera), group of setae on tibia or tarsomeres that are more than 4 times as long as diameter (Saether).

bearded, fringed with hair (T-B); see barbated.

beating umbrella, an umbrella frame covered with white muslin or light canvas used to catch insects that drop from vegetation which is beaten (Borror et al.).

bedegaur, bedegaur gall, q.v. (T-B).

bedegaur gall, a red and green hairy or bristly gall occurring on wild rose bushes and produced by the cynipid gall wasp *Diplolepis rosae* (Hymenoptera: Cynipoidea) (Leftwich); see pea gall.

bee bread, in honey bees (Hymenoptera: Apidae), a mixture of honey and pollen fed to larvae of developing workers (Norris, in CSIRO).

bee milk, royal jelly, q.v. (Leftwich).

bee paralysis, a fatal disease of adult honey bees and certain bumble-bees, (Hymenoptera: Apidae) including acute paralysis and chronic paralysis (Steinhaus and Martignoni).

bees, Hymenoptera belonging to the superfamily Apoidea (Riek, in CSIRO).

beeswax, material from which honeycomb is made, consisting of a mixture of esters, fatty acids and hydrocarbons of high molecular weight, secreted by worker bees from glands under the abdomen (Leftwich; Chapman).

beet curly top, disease of beet plants caused by a geminivirus transmitted circulatively by *Circulifer* (Hemiptera: Auchenorrhyncha: Cicadellidae) (Nault and Ammar).

beet mosaic, viral disease of beet plants transmitted by *Aphis rumicus* (Hemiptera: Sternorrhyncha: Aphididae) (Borror et al.).

beetle, a member of the order Coleoptera (Britton, in CSIRO).

behavior, an organism's muscular and glandular response or responses to stimuli, especially those responses that can be observed.

bell organ, campaniform sensillum, q.v. (T-B).

bell-shaped capsule, in ♂ Lygaeidae (Hemiptera: Heteroptera), cricoid sclerite (?) (transl. "glockenförmige Kapsel" Ludwig, after Tuxen).

belly, venter, q.v., of abdomen (T-B).

belonoid, needlelike (T-B).

bend of fourth vein, in adult Schizophora (Diptera: Brachycera), the curve of the media (M) beyond the discal medial-cubital (dm-cu) crossvein (T-B, after Curran; McAlpine).

bendiocarb, a synthetic insecticide; a carbamate, 2,2-Dimethyl-1,3-benzodioxol-4-yl *N*-methylcarbamate; moderately toxic to mammals, acute oral LD_{50} for rats 179 mg/kg (Pfadt).

benign tertian malaria, widespread type of malaria caused by *Plasmodium vivax* (Borror et al.).

benthic, of or pertaining to the sea bottom; by extension, to the bottom of any permanent body of water, such as lakes or ponds; especially of organisms.

benthos, in freshwater and marine ecogystems, the collection of organisms attached to or resting on the bottom sediments (Allaby); see nekton and plankton.

bentonite, a clay composed mainly of silica and aluminum silicate; mine in Mississippi, Wyoming and elsewhere; used as dust diluent and for lining ponds to hold water (Pfadt).

benzaldehyde, aromatic aldehyde secreted as a defense chemical by some beetles (Coleoptera) (Gilmour, in CSIRO).

benzene, benzol, C_6H_6, a colorless, oily liquid produced from coal;

volatile; inflammable; miscible with alcohol; used in clearing tissues in histology (T-B).

benzene hexachloride (BHC), a synthetic insecticide, a chlorinated hydrocarbon, 1,2,3,4,5,6-hexachlorocyclohexane, with mixed insomers and a specified percentage of gamma; slightly more toxic to mammals than DDT, acute oral LD_{50} for rats about 200 mg/kg (Pfadt).

Berlese funnel, collection apparatus, consisting of a funnel containing a piece of screen or hardware cloth, with a light mounted above and a killing jar or container of alcohol below, for catching small arthropods that exit and fall from material (e.g., leaf litter or soil) that is placed on the screen (Borror et al.).

Berlese's fluid, Hoyer's mounting medium, q.v. (Borror et al.).

Berlese's organ, in some ♀ Cimicoidea (Hemiptera: Heteroptera), mesospermalege, q.v., or spermalege, q.v., as a whole (Carayon, in Usinger).

bermudagrass etched-line, disease of bermudagrass caused by marafivirus transmitted propagatively by *Aconurella* (Hemiptera: Auchenorrhyncha: Cicadellidae) (Nault and Ammar).

beset, thickly set with anything, specifically with cuticular outgrowths (T-B).

beta-chlorophyll, a form of chlorophyll which produces color in insects (T-B, after Wardle).

beta-female, teratogyne, q.v. (Tulloch).

beta group, in larval Lepidoptera, dorsal group, q.v. (Peterson, after Fracker).

beta taxonomy, natural classification, q.v. (Mayr).

Bethyloidea, Chrysidoidea, q.v. (Gauld and Bolton).

Bettlach May disease, a paralysis of adult honey bees (Hymenoptera: Apidae), reported chiefly from Switzerland, caused by poisonous substances in the pollen of *Ranunculus* species (buttercups) (Steinhaus and Martignoni).

bi-, Latin prefix; two or two-fold (T-B).

bialar, bialate, bialatus, two-winged (T-B).

biarcuate, biarcuatus, twice curved (T-B).

biareolate, biareolatus, with 2 cells or aeroles (T-B); see bilocular.

biarticulate, biarticulatus, two-jointed (T-B).

Bibioniformia, Bibionoidea, q.v. (Hennig).

Bibionoidea, superfamily within the Nematocera (Diptera), including the Bibionidae and Pachyneuridae, belonging to the infraorder Bibionomorpha (Borror et al.).

Bibionomorpha, infraorder of the suborder Nematocera (Diptera), including the the superfamilies Pachyneuroidea, Bibionoidea, and Sciaroidea, characterized by adults in which there is a more or less complete fusion of the lobes of the postphragma and in which there is an absence of chiasma formation during spermatogenesis (Colless and McAlpine, in CSIRO).

bibliographical reference, for nomenclatural purposes, the citation of the author and date of publication for a scientific name, with a full bibliographical reference also including the citation of the exact place of publication of a scientific name (i.e., title of book or journal, volume, page, etc.) (Mayr).

bicarinate, bicarinatus (Latin), with 2 carinae or keels (T-B).

bicaudate, bicaudatus, having 2 tails or anal processes.

bichloride of mercury, $HgCl_2$; a chemical compound of mercury and chlorine in the form of crystals or a white powder; highly poisonous; soluble in water, glycerine and alcohol; used as a preservative of tissues in aqueous solution (T-B).

bicolor (Latin), **bicolorate, bicoloratus** (Latin), **bicolored, bicolorous,** with 2 colors that contrast to some extent (T-B).

biconvex, double convex, i.e., lenticular or lens-shaped (T-B).

bicornua, in ♂ Plecoptera, hemitergal processes, q.v. (Tuxen, after Crampton); in ♂ *Notiothauma* (Mecoptera: Notiothaumidae), paired lateral processes of tergum VI and/or VII (Tuxen).

bicornute, bicornutus (Latin), with 2 horns or cephalic processes (T-B).

bicuspidate, bicuspidatus (Latin), two-pointed; having 2 cusps (T-B).

bidactylate, bidactylus, with 2 fingers or fingerlike processes (T-B).

bidentate, bidentatus (Latin), having 2 teeth (T-B).

bidenticulate, bidenticulatus (Latin), set with 2 small teeth (T-B).

biemarginate, biemarginatus (Latin), twice emarginate; with 2 excisions (T-B).

bifarious, bifarius (Latin), pointing in opposite direction (T-B).

bifasciate, bifasciatus (Latin), with 2 bands or fasciae (T-B).

bifid, bifidus (Latin), cleft or divided into 2 parts; forked (T-B); see bipartite.

bifid process, in ♂ *Eusthenes eurytus* (Hemiptera: Heteroptera: Tessaratomidae), flagellum, q.v. (Tuxen, after Sharp).

biflabellate, biflabellatus (Latin), twice-flabellate; applied to antennae in which both sides of the articles have fanlike or flabellate processes (T-B).

bifollicular, consisting of 2 follicles (T-B).

biforous, having 2 openings (T-B).

biforous spiracles, in larval Coleoptera, spiracles having 2 pouches of the atrium, originally thought to open separately to the exterior (T-B, after Snodgrass); spiracles having 2 entrances, provided with a pair of distinct air tubes (Peterson).

bifurcate, bifurcatus (Latin), **bifurcous,** divided partly, or forked into 2 (T-B).

bifurcation, a forking or division into 2; the point at which a forking occurs (T-B).

bigibbous, possessing paired, large, rounded, dorsal swellings (Peterson).

biguttate, biguttatus (Latin), with 2 droplike spots (T-B).

bijugum, in 2 parts (T-B).

bilabiate spiracle, an elongate or annular spiracle with a pair of projecting lips interior to the spiracular frame (peritreme); one having 2 lips at the slitlike entrance (Peterson, after Roberts).

bilamellar, bilamellate, bilamellatus (Latin), having or divided into 2 laminae or plates (T-B).

bilateral, bilateriter, with 2 equal or symmetrical sides (T-B).

bilateral symmetry, a type of symmetry in which the various parts are arranged more or less symmetrically on either side of a plane (T-B; Borror et al.).

Bidrin, dicrotophos, q.v. (Pfadt).

bile pigment, blue or green pigments in Orthoptera, larval Lepidoptera, and adult Chironomidae (Diptera) (Chapman).

biliary vessels, Malpighian tubules, q.v. (T-B).

bilin, a tetrapyrole with a linear arrangement of the pyrroles, typically imparting a blue or green color (Chapman); see bilirubin and biliverdin.

bilineate, bilineatus (Latin), marked with 2 lines (T-B).

biliverdin, in *Rhodnius* (Heteroptera: Reduviidae), a bilin that is a product of the breakdown of hemoglobin by the midgut cells and which is accumulated in the pericardial cells giving them a green color (Chapman).

bilobate, bilobatus (Latin), bilobed, q.v. (T-B).

bilobed, divided into 2 lobes (T-B; Borror et al.).

bilocular, having 2 cells or compartments (T-B); see biareolate.

bilocular pores, in Coccoidea (Hemiptera: Sternorrhyncha), small dermal pores of various types, with 2 loculi (Kosztarab and Kozár).

bimaculate, bimaculatus (Latin), with 2 spots or maculae (T-B).

binapacryl, a synthetic acaricide; a nitrophenol; derivative, 2-*sec*-butyl-4,6-dinitrophenyl 3-methyl-2-butenoate; moderate mammalian toxicity; acute oral LD_{50} for rats 136 to 225 mg/kg (Pfadt).

binary, in zoological nomenclature, binominal, q.v. (T-B).

binary name, binomen, q.v. (T-B).

binary nomenclature, binominal nomenclature, q.v. (T-B).

binate, consisting of a single pair; in pairs (T-B).

binomen (pl., **binomina**), the combination of 2 names, the first being a genus name and the second a specific name, that together constitute the scientific name of a species (ICZN).

binomial, binominal, q.v. (T-B).

binomial nomenclature, binominal nomenclature, q.v. (T-B; Mayr).

binominal, of or pertaining to 2 names; consisting of 2 names; having 2 terms, not necessarily names (T-B).

binominal name, binomen, q.v. (ICZN).

binominal nomenclature, the system of nomenclature whereby a species, but no other taxon, is denoted by a binomen (ICZN); see Principle of Binomial Nomenclature and zoological nomenclature.

binotate, binotatus (Latin), with 2 rounded spots (T-B).

binucleate eggs, eggs containing 2 nuclei which may have different gene contents and may be fertilized by 2 different spermatozoa, accounting for the existence of gynandromorphs (Leftwich).

binus, paired; doubled (T-B).

bioassay, the measurement of the potency of any stimulus, physical, chemical, biological, physiological, or psychological, by means of the response which it produces in living matter (Steinhaus and Martignoni).

biochemistry, biological chemistry; the chemistry of living organisms and of their functions, secretions, and parts; that branch of chemistry which concerns itself with the formation, constitution, and reactions of the chemical components of living organism (T-B).

biochemical lesion, in invertebrate pathology, the initial change in tissue cells which precedes any damage visible with the light microscope (Steinhaus and Martignoni).

bioclimatic law, Hopkins bioclimatic law, q.v. (T-B).

biocoenosis, a community of living beings where the sum of the species and individuals, being mutually limited and selected under the average external conditions of life, have by means of transmission, continued in possession of a certain territory (T-B, after K. Mobius).

bioecology, the sociology of organisms; the study of the living organism in relation to the totality of its environment (T-B, after Shelford).

biogenesis, the production of life from antecedent life (T-B); see abiogenesis.

biological assay, bioassay, q.v. (Steinhaus and Martignoni).

biological classification, natural classification, q.v. (Mayr).

biological control, the use, by man, of living organisms to control (usually meaning to suppress) undesirable animals and plants, e.g., control of the greenhouse whitefly *Trialeurodes* (Hemiptera: Sternorrhyncha: Aleyrodidae) by the chalcidoid wasp *Encarsia* (Hymenoptera) (T-B; Steinhaus and Martignoni; Leftwich); the action of parasites, predators, or pathogens on a host or prey population which produces a lower general equilibrium position than would prevail in the absence of these agents (Steinhaus and Martignoni); see microbial control.

biological species, a population with a common heredity (T-B, after Kinsey); see species.

biological species concept, a concept of the species category stressing reproductive isolation, and the possession of a genetic program effecting such isolation (Mayr); see species.

bioluminescence, the production of cold light by certain insects, fish, and other organisms, involving the oxidation of luciferin through the action of luciferase, e.g., *Onychiurus armatus* (Collembola), a few larval and pupal Diptera belonging to the Mycetophilidae, e.g., *Arachnocampa,* and in Lampyridae, Phengodidae, and Elateridae (*Pyrophorus*) (Matthews and Matthews; Chapman).

biomechanics, the mechanics of the structure of living organisms (T-B).

biometrician, a student of biometrics or biometry (T-B).

biometry, the application of mathematical statistical methods to biological facts or phenomena (T-B).

biomorphotica, those neuropterous insects in which the pupa is active (T-B).

bionomics, the habits, breeding and adaptations of living forms (T-B).

biophore, a supposed ultimate constituent of germ plasm or hereditary substance (T-B).

biopterin, a pterine with a blue flourescence, being a pigment found in the accessory pigment cells between ommatidia of the compound eye of *Drosophila* (Diptera: Drosophilidae) (Chapman).

biordinal crochets, in larval Lepidoptera, crochets in a uniserial circle or row but of 2 alternating lengths (T-B; Peterson); see uniordinal crochets.

biosystematics, taxonomy, q.v.

biota, the fauna and flora of a given habitat (T-B); the fauna and flora of a region (Mayr); see fauna and flora.

biotic, of or pertaining to biota (T-B).

biotic insecticide, an organism used to suppress a local insect pest population (Steinhaus and Martignoni); see microbial insecticide.

biotic potential, an estimate of the maximum rate of increase of any species of animal if left to itself and isolated from its natural enemies, disease or other inhibitory factors (Leftwich).

biotically, in a biotic manner or way (T-B).

biotin, essential water-soluble vitamin in insects (Gilmour, in CSIRO).

biotype, groups of insects primarily distinguishable on the basis of interaction with relatively genetically stable varieties or clones of host plants; a strain of an insect species (Pfadt).

bipartite, bipartitus, divided into 2 parts (T-B).

bipectinate, bipectinatus (Latin), pectinate on 2 sides (T-B).

bipectinate blade, a flattened spicule with 2 rows of acicula, or small toothlike processes (Harbach and Knight).

bipolar, with 2 poles, one at each end of an axis (T-B).

bipolar cell, bipolar nerve cell, q.v. (T-B).

bipolar nerve cell, peripheral sense cell with a short dendrite receiving stimuli and a proximal axon extending to the central ganglion (Chapman).

bipupillate, bipupillatus, having 2 pupils; as ocellate spots in insects which have 2 pupils or central spots, sometimes of different colors (T-B).

biradiate, biradiatus, consisting of, or with 2 rays or spokes (T-B).

biramose, biramosus (Latin), biramous, q.v. (T-B).

biramous, with 2 branches (Borror et al.); having two-branched or double appendages, consisting of an endopodite and exopodite, e.g., Crustacea (T-B; Borror et al.).

bisensillum of labrum (S IV), in larval Chironomidae (Diptera), 2 pairs (one in Tanytarsini) of short, thick-walled pegs or basiconic pegs to each side of and above setae posteriores and setae minuscula, occasionally on a common tubercle (Saether).

bisensillum (of maxillary palp), in larval Chironomidae (Diptera), 2 central, nearly cylindrical and roughly equal-sized sensilla of maxillary palp (Saether).

biserial crochets, in larval Lepidoptera, crochets with their proximal ends arranged in 2 rows, usually concentric (Peterson; Stehr).

biseriately, arranged in double rows or series (T-B).

biserrate, biserratus, doubly saw-toothed; with a saw tooth on each side of each antennal article (T-B).

bisetose, bisetosus, bisetous, bearing 2 setae (T-B).

bisexual, having 2 sexes, ♂ and ♀, distinct and separate within a species (T-B; Mayr) (see unisexual); hermaphrodite, q.v. (Mayr).

bisinuate, bisinuatus, with 2 sinuations or incisions (T-B).

biting lice, members of the suborders Amblycera and Ischnocera (Phthiraptera) (Calaby, in CSIRO).

biting mouthparts, chewing mouthparts, q.v. (Peterson).

bituberculate, bituberculatus (Latin), with 2 distinct tubercles (T-B).

biuncinate, biuncinatus, with 2 hooks (T-B).

bivalvate, bivalvatus (Latin), bivalved, q.v. (T-B).

bivalved, made up of 2 parts or valves united to form a tube, being applied to the proboscis (T-B); clamlike (Borror et al.).

bivittate, bivittatus, with 2 longitudinal stripes or vittae (T-B).

bivoltine, having 2 generations in a year (T-B); see multivoltine and univoltine.

bivouac, in army ants (Hymenoptera: Formicidae), the mass of workers within which the queen and brood find refuge (Wilson).

Blaberoidea, one of 2 superfamilies of Blattaria, including Polyphagidae, Blattellidae, and Blaberidae, in which the males lack or have a greatly reduced ventral phallomere, and females have genital crosspieces and an unforked spermatheca (Mackerras, after McKittrick, in CSIRO; Alsop, pers. comm.); see Blattoidea

black brood, American foulbrood, q.v. (Steinhaus and Martignoni).

black spot, a fungus disease of roses caused by *Diplocarpon rosae,*and characterized by black spots on the leaves and yellowing and premature dropping of leaves (Pfadt).

black-spot area, in larval Culicidae (Diptera), the darkly pigmented, ventromesally directed middle division of the paraclypeal lobe (Harbach and Knight, after Thompson).

blade, any thin, flat structure like a leaf or a sword or knife (T-B); an elongate, flattened, usually stiff spicule (Harbach and Knight); lacinia, q.v. (T-B); in Collembola, the principle ramus of the maxilla (Christiansen and Bellinger); in adult ♂ Diptera, main area of wing distal to stalk (McAlpine); in adult Hymenoptera, lamnium, q.v. (Tuxen).

blastem, a nucleated protoplasmic layer preceding the blastoderm (T-B).

blastocephalon, acron, q.v. (Boudreaux).

blastocoel, in the embryo, the cavity within the blastula (T-B, after Snodgrass).

blastoderm, the continuous, peripheral cell layer surrounding the yolk of the insect egg following cleavage (T-B; Borror et al.); see blastula.

blastodermic cells, blastomeres, q.v. (T-B).

blastogenesis, the origin of different caste traits from variation in the ovarian environment of the egg or the nongenetic contents of the egg (opposed to genetic control of caste and trophogenesis) (Wilson).

blastogenic, relating to or inherent in the germ or blast (T-B).

blastokinesis, the movements of the embryo by which it changes orientation in the egg (T-B).

blastomeres, the cleavage cells, or cells produced by the division of the egg or its nucleus, which form the blastoderm (T-B, after Snodgrass; Chapman).

blastopore, the mouth of the gastrulation cavity in embryonic development (T-B).

blastula, the early stage of the embryo in which the only cell layer is the blastoderm (T-B, after Snodgrass).

Blattaeformia, Blattiformida, q.v. (Boudreaux, after Handlirsch).

Blattaria, order of exopterygote Neoptera (Insecta), comprising the cockroaches, including the superfamilies Blattoidea and Blaberoidea, possessing dorsoventrally compressed bodies, cursorial legs, forewings (when present) modified into tegmina, complex, asymmetrical ♂ genitalia, concealed beneath sternum IX, females wity reduced ovipositor concealed by abdominal sternum VII, cerci with one to numerous segments, and eggs contained in an ootheca (Mackerras, in CSIRO; Alsop, pers. comm., after McKittrick; Hennig).

Blattariae, Blattaria, q.v. (Hennig).

Blattarida, Blattopteroidea, q.v. (Boudreaux).

Blattiformia, Blattaria + Mantodea (Boudreaux, after Werner).

Blattiformida, group of Polyneoptera, including the recent orders Dermaptera, Grylloblattodea, Zoraptera, Isoptera, Blattaria, and Mantodea, and the extinct orders Protelytroptera and Protoblattodea (Boudreaux).

Blattodea, Blattaria, q.v. (Mackerras, in CSIRO); Blattaria and Isoptera (Hennig); Blattaria and Mantodea (Boudreaux, after Brunner).

blattoid neck, in Forficulina (Dermaptera), with the posterior ventral cervical sclerite small, e.g. Pygidicranoidea (Steinmann).

blattoid orders, Blattopteroidea, q.v. (Mackerras, in CSIRO).

blattoid-orthopteroid orders, Polyneoptera, q.v. (Mackerras, in CSIRO).

Blattoidea, one of 2 superfamilies of Blattaria, including Blattidae and Cryptocercidae, characterized by presence of large ventral phallomere in males and a forked spermatheca and lack of genital crosspieces in females (Mackerras, after McKittrick, in CSIRO; Alsop, pers. comm.); see Blattopteroidea.

Blattoprosboloidea, extinct group from the Upper Carboniferous, sometimes considered to belong within the Hemiptera, but probably better placed among the blattoid-orthopteroid orders (Mackerras, in CSIRO).

Blattoprosbolomorpha, Blattoprosboloidea, q.v. (Hennig).

Blattopteriformia, group within the Polyneoptera, including the Blattopteroidea, Grylloblattodea, and Dermaptera (Hennig).

blattopteroid orders, orders of the Blattopteroidea, q.v. (Alsop, pers. comm., after Boudreaux).

Blattopteroidea, superorder encompasing the cockroaches (Blattaria), mantids (Mantodea), and termites (Isoptera) (Hennig).

Blephariceroidea, superfamily within the infraorder Blepharicero-

morpha, including the family Blephariceridae (Diptera: Nematocera) (McAlpine).

Blephariceromorpha, infraorder within the suborder Nematocera
(Diptera), including the superfamily Blephariceroidea (McAlpine).

blind, without eyes (T-B).

blind duct, in ♀ Siphonaptera, duct of degenerate spermatheca in
species with one rather than 2 spermathecae (Lewis, pers. comm.).

blind ocellus, an ocellate spot without any central spot (T-B).

blinding filarial disease, onchocerciasis, q.v. (Adkins, q.v.).

Blochmann's corpuscles, in the insect egg, minute greenish bodies,
which are independent organisms capable of cultivation in artificial
media (T-B, after Imms).

blood, in insects, hemolymph, q.v. (T-B; Leftwich).

blood-brain barrier, maintenance of the ionic concentration within the
central nervous system through active regulation by the glial cells
(Chapman).

blood cells, hemocytes, q.v. (T-B; Tulloch).

blood channel, in certain predaceous larval Coleoptera, a channel,
either internal in the form of a duct or tube (Gyrinidae) or external
in the form of an excavation or groove (Cantharidae) usually extending the full lenth of the inner margin of the mandible (Peterson).

blood corpuscles, hemocytes, q.v. (T-B).

blood forming organ, hemopoietic organ, q.v. (Tulloch).

blood gills, in aquatic larvae, hollow, nontracheated, usually tubular
filamentous or digitiform respiratory evaginations of the body wall
or the proctodeum within which blood circulates (T-B); in some
larval Chironomidae (Diptera), lateral tubules, q.v., or ventral tubules, q.v. (Saether).

blood plasma, plasma, q.v. (T-B).

blood sugar, sugar within the hemolymph, usually dissacharide
trehalose (Gilmour, in CSIRO).

blood tube, in larval Coleoptera, blood channel, q.v. (Peterson).

bloodworm, larva of some Chironominae (Diptera: Chironomidae)
that is bright red due to the presence of hemoglobin (Colless and
McAlpine, in CSIRO).

bloom, pruinescence, q.v. (T-B).

blotch, a large irregular spot or mark (T-B); in certain sawflies (Hymenoptera: Symphyta), a large whitish membrane between the abdomen and the thorax (T-B).

blotch mine, a discolored patch or blister on a leaf caused by a minute
insect larva "mining" or burrowing between the upper and lower
epidermis, e.g., larvae of small moths such as the Gracillariidae (Lepidoptera) and of Diptera such as the Agromyzidae; see stigmatonome.

blow-fly strike, cutaneous myiasis in sheep produced by larvae of certain species of Calliphoridae (Diptera) (Colless and McAlpine, in
CSIRO).

blue disease, a rickettsial disease of the larvae of the Japanese beetle,
Popillia japonica Newman (Coleoptera: Scarabaeidae), and of other

related larval Scarabaeidae, caused by *Rickettsiella popilliae* (Dutky and Goodin) Philip, and producing a bluish appearance in diseased grubs (Steinhaus and Martignoni).

bluetongue, serious disease of sheep and other ruminants caused by a virus transmitted by biting flies (Diptera) (Colless and McAlpine, in CSIRO; Allaby).

blunt, not sharp; obtuse at the edge or tip (T-B).

blunt seta, a differentiated seta with a rounded apex, frequently thicker than, or with a thinner cuticle than, ordinary setae; in Collembola found commonly on th fourth antennal segment and sometimes elsewhere (Christiansen and Bellinger).

boat-shaped lobe, in ♂ *Acentropus* (= *Acentria*) (Lepidoptera: Pyralidae), tegumen, q.v. (Tuxen, after McLachlan).

boat-shaped mucro, in Collembola, mucro with subequal dorsal lamellae, elevated above the median portion and meeting at the apex (Christiansen and Bellinger).

body, the trunk; the thorax alone, the abdomen alone, or sometimes the thorax and abdomen combined (T-B); corpus, q.v. (T-B); in ♂ Coleoptera, penis, q.v. (Tuxen, after Hopkins).

body angle, relative angle of body with the horizontal during flight (Chapman).

body cavity, the definitive cavity of the body and appendages, being not strictly equivalent in all animals (T-B, after Snodgrass).

body of clasper, in ♂ Siphonaptera, basimere, q.v. (Tuxen).

body of the tentorium, a median plate of the tentorium, often large (T-B).

body of penis, in ♂ Odonata, second segment of prophallus (Tuxen).

body of spermatheca, in ♀ Siphonaptera, bulga, q.v. (Tuxen).

body wall, integument, q.v. (T-B, after Snodgrass).

Böhm bristles, in Lepidoptera, small patches, or hair plates, of trichoid sensilla arising from the intersegmental membrane between head and scape and between scape and pedicel of the antenna (Schneider).

bombifrons, having a blisterlike protuberance on the front of the head (T-B).

bombous, blisterlike; spherically enlarged or dilated (T-B).

bombycic acid, the acid constituent of the fluid with which certain moths (Lepidoptera) dissolve the gum binding the silk threads of the cocoon at the emergence of the imago (T-B, after Packard).

bombycinous, bombycinus, a very pale yellow, like fresh spun silk (T-B).

Bombycoidea, superfamily within the Ditrysia (Lepidoptera), including Apatelodidae, Bombycidae, Eupterotidae, Anthelidae, Brahmaeidae, Lasiocampidae, Endromidae, Lemoniidae, Ratardidae, Carthaeidae, Oxytenidae, Cercophanidae, and Saturniidae; medium to large-sized moths lacking ocelli and chaetosemata, antenna bipectinate in males, wings broad, and tympanal organs absent; larvae with dense secondary setae (Common, in CSIRO; Munroe, in Parker).

Bombylioidea, superfamily within the infraorder Asilomorpha

(Diptera: Brachycera), including the families Acroceridae, Nemestrinidae, Bombyliidae, and Hilarimorphidae (McAlpine).

Bordeaux mixture, primarily a fungicide but also a repellent to many insects, consisting of copper sulfate, hydrated lime, and water; ingestion of large quantities sometimes causing fatal gastroenteritis in mammals (Pfadt).

Boreal, from or belonging to the north; the faunal region that extends from the polar sea southward to near the northern boundary of the United States and farther south occupies a narrow strip along the Pacific Coast and the higher parts of the Sierra-Cascade, Rocky and Alleghany Mountain ranges; divided into Arctic, Hudsonian and Canadian (T-B); see Austral and Tropical.

borer, an insect or larva that burrows or makes channels in woody or other vegetable tissue (T-B).

bordering line, in larval mosquitos (Diptera: Culicidae), a "line" believed to be an effect given by seeing the clypeal ridge through the part of the clypeus which overlaps it (Harbach and Knight, after Thompson).

boring bristle, in ♀ Hymenoptera, first gonapophyis, q.v. (Tuxen).

boss, in larval mosquitos (Diptera: Culicidae), a more or less sclerotized elevated area without a grid at the base of the ventral brush (Harbach and Knight, after Belkin).

Bostrychiformia, group within the Polyphaga (Coleoptera), including the superfamilies Dermestoidea and Bostrychoidea, having adults with 5-5-5 tarsal formula, 5 or fewer visible abdominal sternites, functional spiracles on abdominal segment VIII, and oligopod larvae (Britton, in CSIRO).

Bostrychoidea, superfamily within the Bostrychiformia (Coleoptera: Polyphaga), including the Bostrychidae, Anobiidae, Ptinidae, and Lyctidae, in which the mesepimeron does not form part of the mid-coxal cavity in the adult and the larvae are scarabaeiform and lack urogomphi (Britton, in CSIRO).

bothriotrichial pattern, in Sminthuridae (Collembola), the arrangement of the characteristic lateral trunck bothriotrichia (Christiansen and Bellinger).

bothriotrix (pl., **bothriotricha**), in Collembola, unusually thin, flexible, elongate setae, found in characteristic positions on certain Isotomidae (trunk: smooth or ciliate), Entomobryidae (trunk and sometimes head: ciliate), and Sminthuridae (trunk: smooth) (Christiansen and Bellinger); see trichobothria.

bothrium (pl., **bothrium**), in Heteroptera (Hemiptera) and other groups, a pit or tubercle from which a trichobothrium arises.

botryoidal, clustered like a bunch of grapes (T-B).

boubas, yaws, q.v. (Adkins, pers. comm.).

bouclier (French, meaning: shield), pronotum, q.v. (T-B).

Bouin's solution, preservation fluid consisting of 150 ml of 80% ethyl alcohol, 60 ml of formaldehyde, 15 ml of glacial acetic acid, and 1 gram of picric acid (Borror et al.).

bound pupa, see pupa contigua, q.v. (T-B).

bound water, in any chemical compound, such as protoplasm, water molecules so incorporated that when they are driven off by evaporation, the chemical structure of the remaining compound is changed (T-B).

bouton (French, meaning: button), in adult bees (Hymenoptera: Apoidea), flabellum, q.v. (T-B).

boutonneuse fever, disease of man caused by *Rickettsia conori* (Rickettsiaceae), transmitted by ticks (Acari) (Allaby).

bovine piroplasmosis, red-water fever, q.v. (Adkins, pers. comm.).

brace vein, a slanting crossvein (Borror et al.); in adult Odonata, a slanting crossvein just behind the proximal end of pterostigma (Borror et al.; O'Farrell, in CSIRO); in wing of adult Diptera, anterior branch of media, q.v. (McAlpine).

brachelytra, abbreviated wing covers or elytra (T-B).

brachelytrous, having short elytra (T-B).

brachia (sing., **brachium**), in ♂ Lepidoptera, paired gnathos arms not fused at their distal ends (Tuxen, after Muschamp); in ♂ *Eupithecia* (Lepidoptera: Geometridae), paired, hairy, clavate processes of transtilla, also regarded as parts of sides of fultura inferior, q.v. (Tuxen, after Schroeder).

brachial, relating to an arm; armlike (T-B).

brachial cells, in adult Hymenoptera, closed cells of the wing, near the base (T-B, after Norton).

brachial nerves, in adult Hymenoptera, brachial veins, q.v. (T-B).

brachial nervures, brachial veins, q.v. (T-B).

brachial plate, in some nymphs and ♀ Coccoidea, e.g., Tachardidae (Hemiptera: Sternorrhyncha), a pair of lobes on thoracic dorsum, laterad of spiracle (Woodward et al., after J. Chamberlin, in CSIRO; Miller, in Stehr).

brachial veins, in adult Hymenoptera, the longitudinal veins of the forewing, near the base (T-B).

brachiola (pl., **brachiolae**), in ♂ Tortricidae (Lepidoptera), weak, hairy, digitoid process of cucullus (Tuxen, after Diakonoff).

brachiolum, in wing of adult Chironomidae (Diptera), enlarged and strongly sclerotized base of radius and subcosta (Saether); see stem vein.

brachium (pl., **brachia**), arm (T-B); a raptorial foreleg (T-B); foretibia q.v. (T-B); in ♂ Caelifera (Orthoptera), an upper ventrocaudad process of laminae phalli joining the ventral aedeagal sclerite (Tuxen, after Ander); in Heteroptera (Hemiptera), cubitus anterior, q.v., of wing (T-B); see brachia.

brachones, in ♂ Auchenorrhyncha (Hemiptera), upper genital styles, q.v. (Tuxen, after Lower).

Brachycera, suborder of Diptera, including the infraorders Tabanomorpha, Asilimorpha, and Muscomorpha, possessing adults with relatively short antennae (usually with 8 or fewer flagellomeres), maxillary palps with 1 or 2 segments, and larvae with a reduced or incomplete head capsule (Colless and McAlpine, in CSIRO; McAlpine); see Nematocera.

brachycerous, with short antennae (T-B).

brachyosis, a bacterial disease of tent caterpillars, *Malacosoma* spp. (Lepidoptera: Lasiocampidae), caused by *Clostridium brevifaciens* and *C. malacosomae,* and producing a form of dysentery, sluggishness, shortening of the larval body, and death in younger larvae, while older larvae may survive (Steinhaus and Martignoni).

Brachyostomata, brachycerous Diptera with a short proboscis (T-B).

brachypterism, brachyptery, q.v. (T-B).

brachypterous, with short or abbreviated wings (T-B); see apterous, macropterous, and micropterous.

brachypterous neotenic, in termites (Isoptera), nymphoid reproductive, q.v. (Wilson).

brachyptery, the condition of being brachypterous (CSIRO); see microptery.

bracteae, in certain Coccoidea (Hemiptera: Sternorrhyncha), projections of the lateral portions of the segments of the preabdomen (T-B, after MacGillivray).

brain, the supraoesophageal ganglion of the nervous system which lies in the head above the oesophagous, being the principal association center of the body, and consisting of the protocerebrum, deutocerebrum, and tritocerebrum (T-B; Chapman).

brain appendages, in larval Muscidae (Diptera), 2 sacs, one applied to each side of the brain (T-B, after Comstock).

brain hormone, prothoracotrophic hormone, q.v. (Borror et al.).

brancheae, in spiders, book lungs, q.v. (T-B, after Imms).

branched hairs, in adult Chironomidae (Diptera), ramose setae, q.v. (Saether).

branchia (pl., **branchiae**), gill, q.v. (T-B, after J. B. Smith).

branchial, relating to branchiae or gills (T-B).

branchial basket, in Anisoptera (Odonata), branchial chamber, q.v. (T-B; O'Farrell, in CSIRO).

branchial chamber, in nymphs of Anisoptera (Odonata), anterior part of rectum containing gills, the contraction of which can force water out rapidly driving the insect foward (Chapman); see rectal gills.

branchiate, supplied with gills (T-B).

Branchiopoda, subclass within the Crustacea, including mostly freshwater orders Notostraca, Cladocera, Conchostraca, and Anostraca, possessing appendages on all body segments except for the last few of the abdomen and with flattened thoracic segments (Borror et al.).

branchiopneustic, a form of respiration in larvae in which the spiracles are functionally supplanted by gills (T-B).

branch-tipped blade, a flattened spicule with a few short branches arising apically or subapically (Harbach and Knight).

brand, in some adult Hesperiidae (Lepidoptera), a conspicuous patch crossing the disc of the forewings and appearing to the naked eye like a scorched streak, being a complicated organ of tubular scales and androconia and other scales (T-B, after Comstock); see sex-brand.

brassy, yellow with the lustre of metallic brass (T-B).

breakbone fever, dengue, q.v. (Adkins, pers. comm.).

breast, pectus, q.v. (T-B).

breastbone, in larval Cecidomyiidae (Diptera), sternal spatula, q.v. (T-B; McAlpine).

breathing, respiration, q.v. (Leftwich).

breathing pore, spiracle, q.v. (T-B).

brevaceratubae, in Coccoidea (Hemiptera: Sternorrhyncha), ceratubae which do not open at the margin of the pygidium (T-B, after MacGillivray).

breviate, shortened; a term applied to antennae that are about the length of the head (T-B).

breviorate, a term applied to antennae longer than the head but shorter than the body (T-B).

brevis, short (T-B).

brevissimate antennae, antennae shorter than the head (T-B).

Brevitentoria, infraorder within the Integripalpia (Trichoptera), including the superfamilies Sericostomatoidea and Leptoceroidea, characterized by dorsal atrofication of the adult tentorium and the loss of spicules on all abdominal segments except VIII in larvae (Weaver); see Plenitentoria.

bridge, in adult Odonata, bridge vein, q.v. (T-B, after Comstock); in ♂ Heteroptera (Hemiptera), ponticulus transversalis, q.v. (Tuxen, after Lansbury).

bridge crossveins, in adult Odonata, one or more crossveins extending between R_{2+3} and proximal portion of intercalary vein IR(3) proximal to oblique vein (T-B; O'Farrell, after Tillyard and Fraser, in CSIRO).

bridge of anterior phallotreme sclerites, in ♂ Orthoptera, a transverse archlike connecting structure between dorsal aedeagal sclerites (Tuxen, after Snodgrass, Roberts).

bridge of epiphallus, in ♂ Orthoptera, arcus, q.v. (Tuxen, after Snodgrass, Roberts).

bridge vein, basal portion of intercalary vein IR(3) proximal to oblique vein (Borror et al.; O'Farrell, after Tillyard and Fraser, in CSIRO).

brin, in silk worms (Lepidoptera: Bombycidae), the fluid silk thread from each salivary gland (T-B).

Brindley's glands, in adult Reduviidae and some other Cimicomorpha (Hemiptera: Heteroptera), paired scent glands with openings situated dorsolaterally at thoracic-abdominal junction (Štys, pers. comm.).

bristle, a stiff, usually short and blunt, seta (T-B; McAlpine); see macrotrichia.

bristle bearer, in larval Chironomidae (Diptera), procercus, q.v. (Saether).

bristle comb, in Zygentoma, rows of macrochaetae (macrosetae) (Wygodzinsky).

bristle valve, in ♀ Hymenoptera, first gonapophysis, q.v. (Tuxen).

broad-spectrum, relating to pesticides, killing a wide range of target organisms.

brochosomes, ultramicroscopic reticulated bodies produced in the Malpighian glands of leafhoppers (Hemiptera: Auchenorrhyncha: Cicadellidae), which later are found on the surfaces of the body, especially on the wings (Tulloch).

brochus (pl., **brochi**), in ♀ Hymenoptera, dorsal serrula at apices of gonapophyses IX (Tuxen, after E. L. Smith).

broken, interrupted in continuity, as a line or band (T-B).

bromatia, the swellings on the fungi cultivated by ants, which are used for food (T-B).

bromopropylate, an experimental specific miticide related to DDT; isoprpyl 4,4'-dibromobenzilate; slightly toxic to mammals, acute oral LD$_{50}$ for rats 5000 mg/kg (Pfadt).

bronchiae, tracheoles, q.v. (T-B, after Kirby and Spence).

bronze, bronzus, bronze-colored (T-B).

brood, all the individuals that hatch at about one time, from eggs laid by one series of parents and which normally mature at about the same time (T-B); in social insects, the immature members of a colony collectively, including eggs, nymphs, larvae, and pupae (Wilson).

brood canal, in ♀ Strepsiptera, passage between cuticle and last larval cuticle into which open genital canals (Tuxen).

brood cannibalism, among the social Hymenoptera, eating of immature stages by workers in the same colony (Tulloch, after Gaul; Matthews and Matthews).

brood care, feeding and protection of immatures by adults, extending past the time of oviposition or birth (Matthews and Matthews).

brood cell, a special chamber or pocket built to house immature stages (Wilson).

brood chamber, in ♀ Kermesidae (Hemiptera: Sternorrhyncha: Coccoidea), a pouch formed by the true venter (sternum) and false venter in which the eggs are laid and protected (Miller, in Stehr; Bullington and Kosztarab); in ♀ Strepsiptera, brood canal, q.v. (T-B, after Comstock; Tuxen).

brood food, in honeybees (Hymenoptera: Apidae), a secretion of the hypopharyngeal and mandibular glands of workers fed to larvae, especially to larvae destined to become queens (Chapman); see royal jelly.

brood passage, in ♀ Strepsiptera, brood canal, q.v. (Riek, in CSIRO).

brood sac, in ovoviviparous Blattaria (Blaberoidea: Blaberidae), an anterior median extension of the vestibular wall into which the ootheca is withdrawn after being rotated 90° and held until parturition (Alsop, pers. comm., after McKittrick).

Brook's Rule, Dyar's Rule, q.v. (Crosby).

brosse, a brush of hairs; in Apoidea (Hymenoptera), the scopa, q.v. (T-B).

Brunner's organ, in grasshoppers (Orthoptera), a soft tubercle or process located proximad in the ventral sulcus of the caudal femora, and against which, when in the usual inactive position, the caudal tibiae are closely pressed (Tulloch).

brunneus, a pure reddish dark brown (T-B).

brush-footed butterflies, the Nymphalidae (Lepidoptera), so-called because the foretarsi are short and clothed with long hairs, especially in males (T-B).

brush pedestal, in larval Chironomidae (Diptera), procercus, q.v. (Saether).

brush-tipped seta, a seta with numerous moderately long slender processes arising apically (Harbach and Knight).

brushes of posterior edge of sternum VIII, in adult Chironomidae (Diptera), gonapophysis VIII, q.v. (Saether).

brustia, bands or areas of spinulae or setae on the mandibles (T-B, after MacGillivray); in Acrididae (Orthoptera), 2 spiney knobs at the bases of the cerci of embryonic cuticle that hold it so that the hind legs of the first instar larva can be withdrawn (Chapman, after Bernays).

bubonic plague, bacterial disease of man and rodents caused by *Yersina pestis* transmitted by fleas (Siphonaptera), esp. *Xenopsylla cheopis*, marked by chills, fever, and inflammatory swelling of lymphatic glands (Pfadt; Borror et al.).

Bux (trade name), metalkamate, q.v. (Pfadt).

bucca (pl., **buccae**), mouth, q.v. (T-B); in adult Diptera, gena, q.v. (T-B, after Comstock; Tulloch; McAlpine).

buccal, relating to the mouth cavity; rarely to the cheeks (T-B).

buccal appendages, the mouthparts excluding the labrum (T-B).

buccal armature, in larval Muscomorpha (Diptera), cephalopharyngeal skeleton, q.v. (Ferrar).

buccal cavity, the foregut between the mouth and the pharynx (T-B; Chapman); see preoral cavity.

buccal cone, in some Neanurinae (Collembola: Hypogastruridae), elongate, pointed mouth region, formed mainly of the labium (Christiansen and Bellinger).

buccal fissure, opening on each side of the mentum (T-B).

buccal funnel, in Phthiraptera, the tubular foreintestine in the region of the head, extending into the pharynx (T-B, after Imms).

buccal teeth, in Phthiraptera, the minute denticles in the trophi (T-B).

buccate, buccatus, blown up, distended; especially the cheeks (T-B).

buccopharyngeal, of or pertaining to the mouth (bucca) and the pharnyx together (T-B).

buccopharyngeal armature, in larval Muscomorpha (Diptera), pharyngeal skeleton, q.v. (T-B); in adult Culicidae and *Phlebotomus* (Psychodidae and in many larval Nematocera) (Diptera), sclerites of buccal cavity and pharyngeal pump (Colless and McAlpine, in CSIRO; Harbach and Knight, after Sinton and Covell).

buccula (pl., **bucculae**), a little cheek or distended area (T-B); in most Heteroptera, a flange of the gena, on each side of the first segment of the resting labium (T-B; Woodward et al., in CSIRO).

bucina (pl., **bucinae**), in ♂ *Terias* (Lepidoptera: Pieridae), elongate structure in anellus region, chiefly ventrad (Tuxen, after Fruhstorfer).

bud, in agamic viviparous aphids (Hemiptera: Sternorrhyncha: Aphididae), an internal protuberance which develops into a new individual (T-B).

budding, producing buds (T-B); in social insects, colony fission, q.v. (Wilson); agamic reproduction in aphids (Hemiptera: Sternorrhyncha: Aphidoidea) (T-B); see parthenogenesis.

bug, a term often loosely used for a number of insects but which should strictly be used only for members of the suborder Heteroptera (Hemiptera) (Woodward et al., in CSIRO; Leftwich); true bug, q.v.

Bügel (German), in adult Noctuoidea (Lepidoptera), an invagination of the tympanal frame in the tympanal organs (Chapman, after Roeder and Treat).

bulb of sting, in ♀ Aculeata (Hymenoptera), enlarged basal part of fused second valvulae (Tuxen, after Snodgrass).

bulbous, bulblike; swollen to form a bulb (T-B).

bulbus (pl., **bulbi**), base of antennal scape which inosculates in the torulus, frequently subglobose and appearing like a distinct joint (T-B); in ♂ Lepidoptera, vesica, q.v. (Tuxen, after Stitz).

bulbus arteriosus, a swelling of the insect aorta at its junction with the heart (T-B, after Imms).

bulbus ejaculatorius (pl., **bulbi ejaculatorii**), in ♂ Lepidoptera, termination of ductus ejaculatorius at the base of the aedoeagus (T-B, after Imms); in ♂ Diptera, a strongly-muscled, syringelike structure of the ductus ejaculatorius (Tuxen).

bulbus epiphalli, in ♂ Caelifera (Orthoptera), a pair of backward directed processes laterad of the ancora (Tuxen).

bulga (pl., **bulgae**), in ♀ Siphonaptera, larger, basal part of spermatheca (Tuxen, after Peus).

bulla (pl., **bullae**), in wing of adult Hymenoptera, fenestra, q.v. (Gauld and Bolton).

bulla dentis, in ♂ *Zygaena* (Lepidoptera: Zygaenidae), inflated bases of spinose structures of lamina dorsalis of aedoeagus (Tuxen, after Loritz).

bulla seminalis (pl., **bullae seminales**), in ♀ ditrysian Lepidoptera, saclike evagination of ductus seminalis which presumably stores spermatozoa received via ductus seminalis from bursa copulatrix (Tuxen, after Petersen); in ♀ *Tegeticula* (Lepidoptera: Incurvariidae: Prodoxinae), vesicle in proximal portion of ductus bursae in monotrysian type of genitalia sometimes having a paired, rod-shaped sclerite (Tuxen, after Busck).

bulla spermatica, in ♀ Lepidoptera, bulla seminalis, q.v. (Tuxen).

bullate, bullatus (Latin), pustulate, q.v. (T-B; Harris).

Bulletin of Zoological Nomenclature (1943–), the official organ of the International Commission on Zoological Nomenclature (ICZN).

bullula (pl., **bullulae**), in ♂ Lycaenidae (Lepidoptera), membranous swelling between rostellum and mentum of valva (Tuxen, after Nabokov).

bullule, a small blister (T-B).

Buprestoidea, superfamily within the Elateriformia (Coleoptera: Polyphaga), including only the family Buprestidae, with adults characterized by a 5-5-5 tarsal formula, basal 2 segments of abdomen fused or immovably joined, globular forecoxae, penultimate tarsomere lobed or bilobed beneath, and larvae that are apodous with a markedly exanded and flattened prothorax (Britton, in CSIRO).

bursa (pl., **bursae**), a pouch or sac (T-B); in ♂ Trichoptera, a wing pouch in connection with a stalked hair pencil (T-B); in ♀ Diptera, a saccate, dorsal invagination of the genital chamber (McAlpine); in ♂ *Apis* (Hymenoptera: Apidae), large proximal part of endophallus (Tuxen).

bursa conceptionis, in ♀ Coleoptera, bursa copulatrix, q.v. (Tuxen).

bursa copulatrix (pl., **bursae copulatrices**), in ♀ insects, a pouch supposed to function during copulation, being either the genital chamber or part of this, or sometimes with a separate outer entrance (Tuxen); in ♀ Phasmida, pocket between first valvifers into abdominal segment VIII (Tuxen); in ♀ *Aphanus* (Hemiptera: Heteroptera: Lygaeidae), capsula seminalis, q.v. (Tuxen, after Ekblom); in ♀ Heteroptera (Hemiptera), vagina, q.v. (Tuxen, after Kullenberg); in ♀ Apelocheiridae (Hemiptera: Heteroptera), vaginal pouch, q.v. (Tuxen, after Larsén); in ♀ *Lygaeus* (Heteroptera: Lygaeidae), vagina + vestibulum (Tuxen, after Ludwig); in ♀ *Pyrrhocoris* (Heteroptera: Pyrrhocoridae), orificium receptaculi (when broadened), q.v. (Tuxen, after Mayer); in ♀ Coreoidea (Hemiptera: Heteroptera), ductus receptaculi (when broadened), q.v. (Tuxen, after Schaefer); in ♀ Coleoptera, proximal blind end of vagina, with which it is broadly or narrowly connected (Tuxen); in ♀ Neuroptera, copulatory pouch (Tuxen, after Tjeder); in ♀ Trichoptera, cul-de-sac from anterior end of genital chamber (Tuxen); in ♀ Lepidoptera, invagination of the primitive genital chamber (sinus vaginalis) forming a sac for the primary reception and storage of the spermatozoa received in copula, but usually differentiated into a proximal duct (ductus bursae) and distal sac (corpus bursae) which may become further subdivided (Tuxen, after von Siebold), corpus bursae, q.v. (Tuxen, after authors), or receptaculum seminis, q.v. (Tuxen, after Kirby and Spence); in ♀ Siphonaptera, genital duct, often dilated apically, between vagina and ductus spermathecae (Rothschild and Traub); in ♀ Diptera, bursa, q.v. (McAlpine).

bursa inseminalis, in ♀ Diptera, bursa, q.v. (McAlpine).

bursal duct, in ♀ Coleoptera, duct connecting bursa copulatrix and vagina (Tuxen).

bursal sac, in ♀ Coleoptera, bursa copulatrix, q.v. (Tuxen).

bursicon, hormone controlling hardening and darkening of the cuticle following ecdysis, produced by neurohemal organs associated with the abdominal ganglia (Chapman).

bursiform, shaped like a purse; subspherical (T-B).

bursula, in ♀ Lepidoptera, cervix bursae (Tuxen, after Nordström and Wahlgren).

butterfly, a popular term for a member of the Rhopalocera (Lepidoptera), including the superfamilies Hesperioidea, Papilionoidea, and sometimes Hedyloidea (Common, in CSIRO).

button, in ♂ Plecoptera, hammer, q.v. (Tuxen, after Wu); in larval Muscomorpha (Diptera), a scar on the posterior spiracle remaining in second and third instars after moulting, representing the spiracle of the previous instar (Ferrar).

buttress, in pupal Culicidae (Diptera), the thickened, sclerotized, basolateral part of the paddle (Harbach and Knight, after Ingran and Macfie).

byrrhoid type, in ♂ Coleoptera, trilobate type, q.v. (Tuxen, after Sharp and Muir).

Byrrhoidea, superfamily within the Polyphaga (Coleoptera), including the single family Byrrhidae, possessing adults lacking either a median ocellus on the frons or a distinct clypeus, 5 visible abdominal sternites, widely separated midcoxae, and a trilobate aedeagus in the ♂ (Britten, in CSIRO; Lawrence, in Parker).

C

caddisfly, a member of the order Trichoptera (Riek, in CSIRO).

caducous, caducus (Latin), deciduous, q.v. (T-B); easily detached or shed (T-B).

caducous muscles, larval muscles persisting for a short time in the adult (Hinton and Mackerras, in CSIRO).

caecal pouch, midgut caecum, q.v. (T-B).

caecal tube, midgut caecum, q.v. (T-B).

Caecilietae, group within the suborder Psocomorpha (Psocoptera), including the Caeciliidae, Amphipsocidae, Stenopsocidae, Polypsocidae, and Asiopsocidae, in which the pretarsal claws lack a preapical denticle and the valva externa rarely bears more than 2 setae (Mockford and Garcia Aldrete).

Caecilioidea, superfamily within group Caecilietae (Psocoptera), including the family Caeciliidae, in which mandibles are relatively long and ventral abdominal vesicles are present (Mockford and Garcia Aldrete).

caecum (pl., **caeca**), a saclike or tubelike structure, open at only one end (Borror et al.); midgut caecum, q.v. (T-B).

caelate, caelatus (Latin), with superficial plane elevations of varying form (T-B; Harris, after R. W. Brown).

Caelifera, suborder of Orthoptera, including the superfamilies Acridoidea, Tetrigoidea, and Tridactyloidea, the members of which have antennae with fewer than 30 segments (Key, in CSIRO); see Ensifera.

Caeliferoidea, group proposed for the Caelifera (Orthoptera) + Phasmida (Hennig, after Sharov).

caenogenesis, cenongenesis, q.v.

caenogenetic, cenogenetic, q.v.

Caenoidea, superfamily of Ephemeroptera, including the families Neoephemeridae, Caenidae, Baetiscidae, and Prosopistomatidae (Landa and Soldán), but excluding Baetiscidae and Prosopistomatidae (McCafferty and Edmunds).

caeruleous, caeruleus, sky-blue (T-B).

caerulescent, with a tinge of sky-blue (T-B).

caeseous, caesious, caesius, a greyish or dirty blue; a very pale blue with a little black (T-B, after Kirby and Spence).

caespiticolous, frequenting or living in grassy pastures or lawns (T-B).

caespitose, caespitosus, cespitose, cespitosus, tufted or matted together (T-B).

calathiform, shaped like a deep bowl (T-B).

calcanea (pl., **calcaneae**), unguitractor, q.v. (T-B, after MacGillivray).

calcar, a movable spur or spinelike process (T-B); spur, q.v. (T-B); in advanced Symphyta (e.g. Tenthredinidae and Cephidae), modified, curved anterior tibial spur (Riek, in CSIRO) (see strigil); in some adult Calyptratae (Diptera), a posterodorsal bristle on the hind tibia at or beyond the middle (McAlpine); in ♂ *Xanthorhoe* (Lepidoptera: Geometridae), single, median arm of ventral part of anellus, formed by union of anellus lobes (Tuxen, after Pierce).

calcarate, calcaratus, with a moveable spur or spinelike process (T-B).

calcarium (pl., **calcaria**), spur, q.v. (T-B).

calceoliform, oblong in shape with a somewhat coarctate middle (T-B).

calcipala, in some ♂ Simuliidae (Diptera), an apical process on the first tarsomere of the hind leg (Tulloch, after Stone; Peterson, in McAlpine).

calcium, Ca, a white metal not found in a free state, but important as an element in lime, bone and other common compounds (T-B).

calcium chloride, CaCl$_2$, a chemical compound of calcium and chlorine; a white salt used to absorb water in desiccation (T-B).

calcium citrate, calcium salt of citric acid, produced by the sternal gland of some ♀ Mantodea and incorporated into their egg masses (Alsop, pers. comm, after Parker and Rudell).

calcium oxalate, calcium salt of oxalic acid, produced by ♀ accessory genital glands of some ♀ Blattaria and Mantodea and incorporated into ootheca (Gilmour, in CSIRO).

calcospherites, in larvae of phytophagous Diptera, calcium deposits in the fat body (T-B, after Henneguy; Chapman).

calculi, deposits of calcium salts stored in parts of the Malpighian tubules (Gilmour, in CSIRO).

calie, an individual unit of a subterranean termite (Isoptera) nest, connected to the other units by galleries (Noirot, in Krishna and Weesner).

calipers, in Dermaptera, forceps, q.v. (T-B).

callar area, in Heteroptera (Hemiptera), the middle part of the pronotum behind the collum and containing the calli, and corresponding in size to the prothoracic body cavity (Štys).

calles, in certain Coccoidea (Hemiptera: Sternorrhyncha), a curved transverse band of thickenings in the cephalic region of the dorsal aspect of the pygidium (T-B, after MacGillivray).

Calliduloidea, superfamily within the Ditrysia (Lepidoptera), including medium-sized moths of the families Callidulidae and Pterothysanidae; the larvae and pupae are unknown (Common, in CSIRO).

calling organ, in ♂ Orthoptera, stridulating organ, q.v (T-B).

calling song, sounds made by Cicadellidae and Fulgoroidea (Hemiptera: Auchenorrhyncha), transmitted through plants, which attract the other sex of the same species, consisting of trains of damped pulses repeated at characteristic rates or indistinctive temporal patterns (Claridge, in Nault).

calliphorin, in larval *Calliphora* (Diptera: Calliphoridae), protein synthesized in the fat body and stored in the hemolymph, providing major source of amino acids during metamorphosis (Chapman).

Callipodida, order within the Helminthomorpha (Diplopoda), including the families Callipodidae, Schizopetalidae, Dolypetalidae, and Caspiopetalidae (Hoffman, in Parker).

callose, calloused, furnished with calli (T-B).

callosity, a thick swollen lump, harder than its surroundings; callus; also a rather flattened elevation not necessarily harder than the surrounding tissue (T-B).

callow, teneral, q.v. (T-B; Leftwich).

callow workers, newly eclosed workers whose exoskeleton is still relatively soft and lightly pigmented (Wilson).

callus (pl., **calli**), a hard lump or swelling of the cuticle (T-B); a rounded swelling (Borror et al.); in Heteroptera (Hemiptera), paired or fused impressions or elevations in the anterior part of the pronotum behind the collum (Štys); in ♂ Heteroptera (Hemiptera), superior lateral process, q.v. (T-B; Tuxen, after McDonald); in adult Tabanidae (Diptera), shining area on frons (McAlpine) (see median callus, basal callus, and subcallus); see calli.

callus cerci, in most adult Planipennia and Megaloptera, callus of the ectoproct bearing trichobothria (Tuxen, after Tjeder).

calobiosis, a form of symbiosis in social insects, in which one species, often only the ♀, lives in the nest of and at the expense of another either for a time (temporary calobiosis), or altogether (permanent calobiosis) (T-B, after J. B. Smith).

Caloneurodea, extinct order of pterygote insects from Carboniferous-Permian of North America and Russia, possessing long antennae, slender legs, subequal membranous wings, slender abdomen, short cerci, and a distinctive venation with a double stem to the radial sector (R_s), and lacking paranotal lobes (Riek, in CSIRO).

calotodomous, pertaining to nests, especially wasp nests (Hymenoptera), in which the combs are surrounded by an envelope (Wilson).

caltrops spines, in larval Limacodidae (Lepidoptera), the branched and otherwise specialized irritating spines (T-B).

calva, epicranium, q.v. (T-B).

calvescens, becoming bald; or growing bald; in the act of becoming bald (T-B).

calvus, bald; hairless (T-B).

calx (pl., **calces**), in ♂ Siphonaptera, foward pointing extension of ventroanterior part of palliolum, usually below fulcrum, and from which an apophysis arises (Tuxen, after Peus).

calyciform, calyx or goblet-shaped (T-B).

calyciform cell, goblet cell, q.v. (T-B, after Snodgrass).

calyculate, applied to antennae, with cup-shaped joints so arranged as to fit one into the other (T-B).

calypter (pl., **calypteres**), in wing of adult Diptera, 2 basal lobes formed from the posterobasal portion of axillary membrane, proximal to alula (T-B; Colless and McAlpine, in CSIRO; McAlpine); see lower calypter and upper calypter.

Calypterae, Calyptratae, q.v. (T-B, after Curran).

Calypteratae, Calyptratae, q.v. (T-B, after Curran).

Calypterygoidea, superfamily within the Zygoptera (Odonata), including the families Calypterigidae, Chlorocyphidae, Heliocharitidae, Polythoridae, and Epallagidae, possessing 5 or more antenodal crossveins in the wing (O'Farrell, in CSIRO).

calyptodomous, applied to wasp nests (Hymenoptera: Vespidae) which are enclosed in a layer or layers of carton (T-B, after Gaul).

calyptra, calypter, q.v. (T-B).

calyptral fold, fold between lower and upper calypteres (McAlpine).

calyptral fringe, fringe of hairs along posterior margin of calypteres (McAlpine).

Calyptrata, capyptrate Diptera, q.v. (T-B).

Calyptratae, section of the Schizophora within the infraorder Muscomorpha (Diptera: Brachycera), including the superfamilies Muscoidea, Oestroidea, and Hippoboscoidea (McAlpine).

calyptrate Diptera, Diptera with a well-developed lower calypter, e.g., Tabanidae, Acroceridae, and many Calyptratae (Colless and McAlpine, in CSIRO; McAlpine).

calyptron, calypter, q.v. (T-B).

calyx (pl., **calyses**), a cup into which certain structures are set (T-B); the cap or crown of the corpus pedunculatum of the protocerebrum (T-B); expansion of the oviduct into which the ovarioles open (T-B; Chapman); in ♀ Phthiraptera, modified area at junction of sac and tube of spermatheca (Tuxen); in ♂ Lepidoptera, funnel-shaped dilation of basal part of each vas deferens (Tuxen, after Spichardt).

calyx glomeruli, the calyx or cup of the glomerules (T-B).

cambium, in the stems and roots of vascular plants, a layer of cells lying between the xylem and phloem (Allaby).

camera, in adult Hymenoptera and other orders, auxilia, q.v., of tarsus (T-B, after MacGillivray).

camera genitalis (pl., **camerae genitales**), in ♀ Siphonaptera, cavity below proctiger enclosed laterally by flanges of tergum VIII and often ventrally by sternum VIII, its anterior wall containing the gonotreme (Tuxen, after Smit).

camera lucida, a device enabling one to make accurate drawings of objects seen through a microscope, in which the image of the drawing paper is projected into the field of the microscope (Borror et al.).

camerostome, in ticks (Acari), an emargination at the anterior end of the body in which the specialized head, false head or capitulum is set (T-B).

camouflage, coloration that blends with the background (Borror et al.).

campaniform organ, campaniform sensillum, q.v. (T-B).

campaniform receptor, campaniform sensillum, q.v. (Leftwich).

campaniform sensillum, mechanoreceptor visible externally as an area of thin cuticle, domed and usually oval in shape, with a long diameter commonly 20–30μ, commonly found in groups at the base of the wing or halter in Diptera, functioning to sense stress on the surrounding cuticle (T-B; Chapman; McAlpine).

campanulate, campanulatus, bell-shaped; more or less ventricose at the base and a little recurved at the margin (T-B).

campestral, inhabiting open fields (T-B).

campodeiform larvae, larvae which, in their early stages at least, resemble *Campodea* (Diplura: Campodeidae) (T-B); oligopod, pronathous, usually predatory larvae having well-developed sense organs and legs but no abdominal appendages other than cerci, e.g., many larval Coleoptera, Trichoptera, and Planipennia (Leftwich; von Kéler).

campus (pl., **campi**), in larval Scarabaeoidea (Coleoptera), the bare or almost bare ventral region of the tenth or fused ninth and tenth abdominal segments in front of an entire or anteriorly split teges or in front of the paired tegilla (T-B, after Böving).

Canadian Zone, that part of the Boreal Region comprising the southern part of great transcontinental coniferous forests of Canada, the northern parts of Maine, New Hampshire and Michigan, and a strip along the Pacific Coast reaching south to Cape Mendocino and the greater part of the high mountains of the United States and Mexico (T-B).

canal, a channel or groove (T-B).

canal of fecundation, in ♀ Coleoptera, seminal canal, q.v. (T-B, after Imms; Tuxen).

canaliculate, canaliculatus (Latin), channelled or grooved; longitudinally grooved; in general body form, long and concave so as to resemble a gutter or channel (T-B; Harris, after Stearn); see porcate and sulcate.

canaliculus (pl., **canaliculi**), in ♂ *Ortholitha* (Lepidoptera: Geometridae), elongate, median sclerotized structure formed by the caudad projection of dorsocaudal edge of fultura inferior, serving as a support or guide for aedoeagus (Tuxen, after Pierce); tiny (0.1μ or less) opening in inner wall of hairlike scale which communicates to the hair chamber (Downey and Allyn).

canalis (pl., **canales**), in ♀ Lepidoptera, ductus bursae, q.v. (Tuxen),

canalis receptaculi, in ♀ Lepidoptera, the proximal, not spiralled, part of ductus receptaculi (Tuxen, after Stitz).

canalis seminalis, in ♀ Lepidoptera, ductus seminalis or (in part) ductus bursae, q.v. (Tuxen, after Petersen).

canalis spiralis (pl., **canales spirales**), in ♀ Lepidoptera, the median, spiralled part of ductus receptaculi, often containing a narrow, band-shaped sclerite (Tuxen, after Petersen) or entire ductus receptaculi, q.v. (Tuxen).

canalis vestibuli, in ♀ Lepidoptera, the distal, not spiralled, part of ductus receptaculi, emptying into vestibulum (Tuxen, after Stitz).

cancellate, cancellatus (Latin), cross-barred; latticed; with longitudinal lines decussate by transverse lines (T-B); a latticework or qrid; a series of enclosed cells or chambers (Harris, after R. W. Brown, Marchant and Charles, and Funk); see clathrate and reticulate.

canella, in Coccoidea (Hemiptera: Sternorrhyncha), spiracular furrow, q.v. (T-B, after MacGillivray).

canescent, hoary, with more white than gray (T-B).

canines, in Ephemeroptera, 2 heavily chitinized spines arising from the mandibles, adapted for holding food (T-B, after Needham).

cannibalism, the act of preying on other members of the same species (Common, pers. comm.); see brood cannibalism.

cannibalistic, feeding on other individuals of the same species (Borror et al.).

cannula, a tubule or small tube (T-B).

cantharidin, in adult Meloidae (e.g, Spanish fly, *Lytta vesicatoria*) and Oedemeridae (Coleoptera), chemical found mainly in the elytra, producing blisters on human skin (T-B; Britton, in CSIRO; Leftwich).

cantharophily, insect-flower pollination syndrome involving beetles (Matthews and Matthews, after Baker and Hurd).

Cantharoidea, superfamily within the Elateriformia (Coleoptera: Polyphaga), including the Cantharidae and other families, possessing adults with antennae lacking a club, 6 or 7 visible abdominal sternites, a 5-5-5 tarsal formula, a bilobed fourth tarsomere, transverse hind coxae, and a loosely articulated body (Britton, in CSIRO).

canthus, the chitinous process more or less completely dividing the eyes of some insects into an upper and lower half (T-B).

canus, the color of grey hair (T-B).

cap cell, the distal or peripheral cell of a sense organ, or of one of the component units of the organ, probably corresponding to the tormogen, or socket-forming cell of a seta (T-B, after Snodgrass).

capacitation, maturation of sperm within the ♀ (Chapman).

capillaceous, capillaceus (Latin), hairlike (T-B).

capillaris (Latin), of hair (T-B; R. W. Brown).

capillarity, capillary action; the rising or moving of liquids in minute tubes by surface tension (T-B).

capillary, long and slender like a hair; applied to those antennae in which the articles are long, slender and loosely articulated (T-B); a very slender hairlike tube (T-B).

capillate, capillatus (Latin), clothed with long slender hair (T-B).

capillitium, in some adult Noctuidae, e.g. *Cucullia* (Lepidoptera), a hoodlike collar (T-B).

capillus (pl. **capilli**), hair, q.v. (T-B).

capitate, capitatus (Latin), with a head (T-B); with an apical knoblike enlargement, e.g., capitate antenna, q.v. (T-B; Borror et al.); see clavate.

capitate antenna, antenna in which there is an abrupt and strongly marked capitulum (T-B).

capitate hairs, hairs with knobbed apices (T-B).

capitate processes, in ♂ Heteroptera (Hemiptera), the mushroomlike ends of dorsal connectives (apodemes) of basal plates, on which are inserted the protractor muscles of the phallus (Tuxen, after Marks).

capitellum, in adult Culicidae (Diptera), knob, q.v., of halter (Harbach and Knight, after Prashad).

capitulate, having an enlarged terminal part or capitulum, typical of some setae (Peterson).

capitulum (pl., **capitula**), a small head (T-B); the enlarged tip of an antenna (T-B); in some Phasmida, a structure attached to the operculum of some species (Clark; Sellick); in adult Diptera, knob, q.v., of halter, or labella, q.v. (T-B); in ticks, the false head (T-B); in ♀ Lepidoptera, a clavate process of a signum on outer wall of corpus bursae (Tuxen, after Diakonoff).

capricorn beetle, long-horned beetle (Coleoptera: Cerambycidae) (T-B).

caprification, fertilization of ♀ fruit-producing fig, with pollen from ♂ inedible fig by species of Agaonidae, e.g., *Blastophaga psenes* (Hymenoptera: Chalcidoidea) (T-B; Riek, in CSIRO).

caprifier, a minute hymenopterous wasp, e.g., *Blastophaga psenes* (Hymenoptera: Agaonidae), which fertilizes certain figs by carrying pollen from the ♂ to ♀ plant (T-B).

caprifig, a form of ♂ pollen-producing inedible fig, the pollen of which is carried to the ♀ edible fig to fertilize and form it (T-B).

capsid, the protein coat or shell of a virus particle (Steinhaus and Martignoni) (see nucleocapsid and virion); in Heteroptera (Hemiptera), member of the family Miridae (Schuh, pers. comm.).

capsomere, one of the structural units on the surface of a nucleocapsid, in viruses possessing cubic symmetry (Steinhaus and Martignoni).

capsula (pl., **capsulae**), in ♂ Siphonaptera, cavity overarched by tectum (Tuxen, after Jordan), now applied to outer wall of this cavity, in particular to the larger sclerotized part (Tuxen).

capsula seminalis (pl., **capsulae seminales**), in ♀ Heteroptera (Hemiptera), anatomically proximal and ontogenetically distal part of receptaculum seminis (and its homologous vermiform gland), if differentiated into ductus receptaculi, pars intermedialis and capsula seminalis (Tuxen, after von Siebold); in ♀ Coleoptera, spermatheca, q.v. (Tuxen).

capsula seminis, in ♀ Heteroptera (Hemiptera), capsula seminalis, q.v. (Tuxen, after von Siebold).

capsular, in the form of a capsule or little cuplike container (T-B).

capsule, in general, any small, closed vessel or structure containing another (T-B); in invertebrate pathology, the protein material surrounding the granulosis-virus rod, i.e., the granule inclusion body produced in tissue cells with granulosis infection (Steinhaus and Martignoni); in Phasmida, corion of egg excluding operculum (Clark).

capsule rod, in larval Diptera, metacephalic rod, q.v. (McAlpine).

captan, a protective fungicide, particularly for foliage application or seed treatment; cis-*N*-(trichloromethyl)thio-4-*cyclo*hexene-1,2-dicarboximide; low acute toxicity to warmblooded animals, acute oral LD_{50} for rats 9000 mg/kg (Pfadt).

capulus, in ♂ Siphonaptera, aedeagal apodeme (in part), q.v., lamina media (in part), q.v. (Tuxen, after Oudemans).

caput, head, q.v. (T-B).

capylus, a hump on the upper side of the segments of many larvae (T-B).

carabidoid, the second stage of a meloid larva (Coleoptera: Meloidae), when it resembles that of a carabid (Coleoptera: Carabidae) (T-B).

carabiform, when an insect resembles a carabid larva (Coleoptera: Carabidae) (Peterson); see caraboid.

Carabiformia, Adephaga, q.v. (Crowson).

caraboid, *Carabus*-like (Coleoptera: Carabidae); somewhat resembling a carabid beetle (Coleoptera: Carabidae) (T-B).

Caraboidea, single superfamily within the suborder Adephaga (Coleoptera), including the Rhysodidae, Carabidae, Haliplidae, Hygrobiidae, Amphizoidae, Noteridae, Dytiscidae, and Gyrinidae, possessing the same characteristics as the Adephaga (Britton, in CSIRO).

carapace, in Crustacea, a hard dorsal covering consisting of the fused dorsal sclerites (T-B; Borror et al.); in adult *Chelonus* (Hymenoptera: Braconidae), fused abdominal tergites II–IV, covering reduced posterior segments (Gauld and Bolton).

carbaryl, $C_{12}H_{11}NO_2$, a synthetic insecticide; a carbamate, 1-naphthyl methylcarbamate; moderately toxic to mammals, acute oral LD_{50} for rats 500–700 mg/kg (Pfadt).

carbofuran, $C_{12}H_{15}NO_3$, a synthetic insecticide, plant systemic applied to soil; a carbamate, 2,3-dihydro-2,2-dimethyl-7-benzofuranyl methylcarbamate; highly toxic to mammals; acute oral LD_{50} for rats 11 mg/kg (Pfadt).

carbohydrase, a digestive enzyme which splits or breaks up carbohydrates in the food (T-B; Chapman); see amylase, chitinase, fructidase, invertase, and trehalase.

carbohydrates, class of compounds, including starches and sugars, which contain only carbon, hydrogen, and oxygen, the later 2 atoms usually being in a ratio of 2 to 1 (T-B; Tulloch).

carbol-xylene, a mixture of 3 parts xylene and 1 part melted crystal carbolic acid; used in clearing for whole mounts of insects, chitinous parts (e.g., genitalia) and other preparations (T-B).

carbol-xylol, carbol-xylene, q.v. (T-B)

carbolic acid, C_6H_6O; when pure, needle-shaped crystals which form a crystalline, colorless, white or light pink mass; extremely hygroscopic and caustic; soluble in water, alcohol, glycerin, ether, chloroform and xylene; used in dehydration in microscopy and histology (T-B).

carbon dioxide, CO_2; a colorless, odorless gas, heavier than air (of which it is a constituent), somewhat soluble in water and not a supporter of combustion, an end-product of animal respiration (T-B).

carbon dioxide sensitivity, a disease of adult fruit flies, *Drosophila* spp.

(Diptera: Drosophilidae), caused by sigma virus in the presence of carbon dioxide (Steinhaus and Marignoni).

carbon disulfide, CS_2; an insecticidal fumigant for treatment of stored grain, also a soil fumigant for Japanese and Asiatic beetles (Coleoptera: Scarabaeidae), also used to rid horses of bots (Diptera: Gasterophilidae, Oestridae) and roundworms (Nematoda); highly toxic to mammals and toxic to plants and certain seeds (Pfadt).

carbon tetrachloride, CCl_4; an aromatic colorless liquid compound of carbon and chlorine; a strong solvent of greases and oils; used to clean greasy or dirty insects; also in disinfecting collections and as an anesthetic for insects; nonflammable, unexplosive; a carcinogen (T-B).

carbonarius, coal black (T-B).

carbonate, a salt of carbonic acid (T-B).

carbonphenothion, $C_{11}H_{16}ClO_2PS_3$, a synthetic insecticide and acaricide; an organophosphate, S-(p-chlorophenylthio) methyl $0,0$-diethyl phosphorodithioate; highly toxic to mammals, acute oral LD_{50} for rats 30 mg/kg (Pfadt).

cardia, gizzard, q.v. (T-B, after Snodgrass); heart, q.v. (T-B, after Smith).

cardiac, belonging or relating to the heart (T-B).

cardiac sinus, the channel of the hemocoele in the embryo dorsal to the yolk or alimentary canal, a part of which becomes the lumen of the dorsal vessel (T-B, after Snodgrass).

cardiac sphincter, stomodaeal valve, q.v. (Tulloch).

cardiac valve, stomodaeal valve, q.v. (T-B, after Imms; Tulloch).

cardiac valvule, stomodaeal valve, q.v. (T-B).

cardinal, of or pertaining to the cardo (T-B).

cardinal beard, in larval Chironomidae (Diptera), setae on medial, membranous part of cardo in some Orthocladiinae and most Prodiamesinae often appearing as setae underneath ventromental plates (Saether).

cardinal cell, in adult Odonata, triangle, q.v. (T-B).

cardinal striae, in larval Chironominae (Diptera: Chironomidae), structures on medial, membranous part of cardo contacting striae on ventromedial plates and often appearing as part of these (Saether).

cardinales, the rods joining the labium to the head; the cardines (T-B).

cardinate coxae, in Heteroptera (Hemiptera), hinged and elongate hind coxae in pagiopodous taxa (Drake and Davis, after Schiödte).

cardinosternal, of or pertaining to the cardo and the sternum of the labial segment (T-B, after Snodgrass).

cardinostipital, of or pertaining to the cardo and stipes taken together (T-B).

cardioblasts, a string or row of cells in the embryo giving rise to the heart (T-B; Chapman).

cardiocoelomic, applied to the venous openings from the heart to the body cavity (T-B).

cardiocoelum, pericardial sinus, q.v. (T-B).

cardo (pl., **cardines**), the proximal joint of the protopodite (T-B); the basal division of the maxilla (T-B, after Tillyard; Borror et al.); in ♂ Coleoptera, basal piece, q.v. (Tuxen, after Kerschner); in Hymenoptera, basal ring, q.v. (T-B; Tuxen, after Thomson); in millipedes (Diplopoda), one of 2 small laterobasal sclerites in the gnathochilarium (Borror et al.).

cardolacinial line, in larval Culicidae (Diptera), the line formed by the bases of the spicules forming laciniasternum 2 (Harbach and Knight, after Pao and Knight).

cardostipes, in adult Chironomidae (Diptera), stipes, q.v. (Saether).

cardosubmental, of or pertaining to the cardo and the submentum together (T-B).

carina (pl., **carinae**), an elevated ridge or keel, not necessarily high or acute (T-B); in Syrphidae (Diptera), the ridge on which the posterior spiracles are sometimes elevated in the larva or a dorsal ridge of the puparium (Peterson, after Heiss); in ♂ Lycaenidae (Lepidoptera), a sharp distal part of the aedoeagus (Tuxen, after van Eecke); in ♂ Siphonaptera, keel, q.v. (Tuxen, after Peus).

carina penis, in ♂ Scythridae (Lepidoptera), dorsodistal keel of aedoeagus (Tuxen, after Petersen); in ♂ *Neptis* (Lepidoptera: Nymphalidae), a series of dentations along dorsal rim of orifice of aedoeagus (Tuxen, after Roepke).

carinal, keellike; pertaining to a carina (T-B).

carinate, carinatus (Latin), keeled; having keels or carinae; with one, or several, longitudinal narrow raised lines (T-B; Harris); see carinulate, costate, cristate, ecarinate, and porcate.

carinula (pl., **carinulae**), a little carina or keellike ridge; in Curculionoidea (Coleoptera), the longitudinal elevation on the middle of the rostrum (T-B).

carinulate, carinulatus (Latin), with several small, elevated, longitudinal ridges or carinae (T-B; Harris); see costulate and cristulate.

cariose, cariosus (Latin), **carious,** carroded; appearing worm eaten; with cavities or ulcerations (T-B; Harris, after Funk); see vermicular and vermiculate.

carminate, carminated, mixed or tinged with carmine (T-B).

carmine, a red insoluble compound formed by treating an extract of cochineal with a solution of alum; a stain used in microscopic preparations (T-B).

carminic acid, anthraquinone pigment purified from cochineal (Chapman).

carneose, carneous, carneus, fleshlike in substance; flesh colored; white tinged with red (T-B, after Kirby and Spence).

carnitine, essential chemical involved in fatty-acid oxidation (Gilmour, in CSIRO).

carnivore, a flesh-eater, i.e., an insect preying on other insects or feeding on their flesh (T-B).

carnivorous, predaceous, q.v. (T-B; Chapman).

carnose, carnosus, of a soft, fleshy substance (T-B).

Carnoy fluid, general insect fixative and collection fluid consisting of

10 parts glacial acetic acid, 60 parts 95% ethanol, and 30 parts chloroform (Borror et al.).

Carolinian Faunal Area, moist, cold-temperate, eastern North America (T-B).

carotene, a type of carotinoid pigment (Chapman); see xanthophyll.

carotin, carotinoid, q.v. (T-B, after Wardle).

carotinalbumen, a substance in the insect blood which produces the pink, purple, and green colors in certain insects (T-B).

carotinoid, plants pigments built up from isoprene residues, including carotenes and xanthophylls, found in the hemolymph and tissues of insects (T-B; Chapman).

carotinoid pigment, carotinoid, q.v. (Tulloch).

carpophagous, fruit-eating (T-B).

carpopodite, the fifth segment of a generalized appendage; tibia, q.v. (T-B, after Snodgrass).

carpus, the pterostigma of Odonata; the extremity of the radius and cubitus of the forewings; that point in the wings at which they are transversely folded (T-B).

carrier state, in invertebrate pathology, type of attenuated infection characterized by the presence of a pathogenic microorganism within or upon host tissues, in which there is no evidence of overt disease in the host but the pathogen retains its virulence towards members of the host's species (Steinhaus and Martignoni).

Carrion's disease, bartonellosis of man, caused by the bacterium *Bartonella bacilliformis* (Bartonellaceae), vectored by sand flies (Diptera: Psychodidae); see oroya fever and verruga peruana.

cartilaginous, cartilagineus, resembling cartilage in structure or appearance (T-B).

cartilago ensiformis (Latin), sternum collare, q.v. (T-B).

carton, the paper manufactured by Hymenoptera for nest construction (T-B); substance consisting largely of excreta or semidigested wood or grass and organic matter forming the walls of the innermost galleries in termitaria of Isoptera (Norris, in CSIRO).

caruncle, caruncula, a soft, naked, fleshy excrescence or protuberance (T-B).

caryolite, a group of sarcolytes accompanied by a knot of muscular origin (T-B, after Henneguy); a fragment of muscular fiber with a nucleus (T-B, after Imms.)

caryophylleous, nut or clove brown (T-B).

Carzol SP (trade name), formetanate, q.v. (Pfadt).

case fatality rate, in invertebrate pathology, the number of deaths in every 100 cases of a particular disease (Steinhaus and Martignoni); see mortality rate.

castaneous, castaneus, chestnut brown; bright red-brown (T-B).

caste(s), the various forms or kinds of matured individuls among social insects, e.g., workers, soldiers, queens, etc. (T-B); any set of individuals in a given colony that are both morphologically distinct and specialized in behavior (Wilson).

caste determination, mechanism by which castes are produced (Chapman).

caste polyethism, polyethism in which morphological castes are specialized to serve different functions (Matthews and Matthews).

Castnioidea, superfamily within the Ditrysia (Lepidoptera: Glossata), including only the family Castniidae (Common, in CSIRO).

castration, any process that interferes with or inhibits the production of mature ova or sperm in the gonads of an organism (T-B, after Imms; Steinhaus and Martignoni).

catabolism, the breaking-down metabolic processes; those reactions of the animal body which break down or destroy protein, fats, or carbohydrates (T-B); destructive metabolism, in which complex compounds are converted to simpler ones in an energy releasing-reaction (Tulloch); see anabolism.

Catadermaptera, suborder with Dermaptera, including the infraorders Protodermaptera, Mesodermaptera, and Paradermaptera (Steinmann).

catalepsy, a state of immobilization in which the insect is insensible to stimulation, the muscles are plastic and the limbs retain any unusual position in which they are placed, e.g., in walking sticks (Phasmida) (Tulloch; Key, in CSIRO).

catalog, an index to taxonomic literature arranged by taxa so as to provide ready reference to at least the most important taxonomic and nomenclatural references to the taxon involved (Mayr); see checklist.

catalyst, a substance which can alter (usually accelerate) the speed of a reaction without itself being consumed in the process (T-B; Tulloch, after Rockstein).

cataphracted, cataphractus (Latin), clad in closely set scales (T-B; Harris, after Marchant and Charles); see imbricate, scutate, and squamate.

catatrepsis, in blastokinesis of insects, when the embryo leaves the dorsal aspect to resume its primitive condition on the ventral aspect of the ovum (T-B, after W. M. Wheeler).

catch, in Collembola, tenaculum, q.v. (T-B).

category, taxonomic category, q.v. (Mayr).

catena (pl., **catenae**), in ♂ *Anophia* (Lepidoptera: Noctuidae) a series of scalelike dentations, arranged longitudinally along membranous plate, covering proximal part of aedoeagus (Tuxen, after Roepke).

catenate, catenatus (Latin), with longitudinal, connected elevations like links of a chain (T-B; Harris); see catenulate and consute.

cateniform, catenulate, q.v. (T-B; Harris).

catenulate, catenulatus (Latin), chainlike; with smaller links than catenate (T-B; Harris).

caterpillar(s), polypod or eruciform larva of butterflies and moths (Lepidoptera), i.e., a soft-bodied larva having, in addition to the 6 true legs on the thorax, a number of prolegs on the abdomen (T-B; Borror et al.; Leftwich); see eruciform larva.

cathrema, in ♂ Nepticulinae (Lepidoptera: Nepticulidae), a striated thickening at the base of the ductus ejaculatorius (Common).

catoprocessus, in adult Planipennia, lower most process of each half of the anal segment (Tuxen, after Tjeder).

cattle tick fever, a specific infectious disease of the blood of cattle caused by a protozoan, *Babesia bigemina,* which attacks the red blood cells; characterized by fever, anemia, jaundice, and red urine; transmitted by the bite of the cattle tick, *Boophilus annulatus* (Acari: Ixodidae) (Pfadt); see red-water fever and Texas cattle fever.

cauda (pl., **caudae**), the tail (T-B); any process resembling a tail (T-B); any extension of the anal segment or appendage terminating the abdomen (T-B); in Aphidoidea (Hemiptera: Sternorrhyncha), a modified structure of abdominal tergum IX, in adults varying in shape from elongate to short and fingerlike to triangular (Stoetzel, in Stehr); in Heteroptera (Hemiptera), anal tube, q.v. (Tuxen, after Sharp; Woodward et al., in CSIRO); see caudula.

caudad, toward or in the direction of the tail; posteriad (T-B).

caudal, of or pertaining to the cauda or to the anal end of the insect body (T-B).

caudal comb, in some ♂ Psocoptera, a row of toothlike projections on the posterior margin of the clunium (Pearman).

caudal fan, in mosquito larvae (Diptera: Culicidae), the feathery bristles arranged fanlike on the ninth abdominal segment (T-B).

caudal filaments, threadlike processes at the posterior end of the abdomen (Borror et al.); in Ephemeroptera, cerci, q.v., and filum terminale, q.v. (Tuxen, after Berner; Chapman); in nymphal Zygoptera (Odonata), caudal gills, q.v. (Chapman); in *Cryptochetum iceryae* (Diptera: Cryptochetidae), an endoparasite of mealy bugs of the family Margarodidae (Hemiptera: Sternorrhyncha: Coccoidea), 2 respiratory filaments at the end of the body, which in the third instar larva are 10 times as long as the body and are packed with tracheae (Woodward et al., in CSIRO; Chapman, after Thorpe).

caudal gills, in nymphal Zygoptera (Odonata), the 3 foliaceous caudal external tracheal gills (T-B).

caudal lamellae, in Zygoptera (Odonata), caudal gills, q.v. (Chapman).

caudal postanal setae, in Coccoidea (Hemiptera: Sternorrhyncha), obanal setae, q.v. (T-B, after MacGillivray).

caudal protuberances, in larval Nematinae (Hymenoptera: Tenthredinidae), a pair of conical protuberances on the posterior margin of the tergite above the suranal lobe (Gauld and Bolton).

caudal ridge of sacculus, in ♂ Coleophoridae (Lepidoptera), caudadprojecting edge of valva (Tuxen, after Toll).

caudal setae, long, threadlike processes at the end of the abdomen in many insects (T-B); in Ephemeroptera, cerci, q.v (T-B; Tulloch; Tuxen, after Eaton).

caudal style, appendix dorsalis, q.v. (CSIRO); see filum terminale.

caudal sympathetic system, stomatogastric nervous system, q.v. (Tulloch).

caudal vesicle, in larval Braconidae (Hymenoptera), eversible hind gut functioning in gas exchange (Chapman).

caudalabiae, in Coccoidea (Hemiptera: Sternorrhyncha), cicatrices, q.v., of the abdomen (T-B, after MacGillivray).

caudalaria, posterior notal wing process, q.v. (T-B, after MacGillivray).

caudate, caudatus, with taillike extensions or processes (T-B).

caudate larva, in Apocrita (Hymenoptera), rather unspecialized, distinctly segmented larva with a long fleshy caudal appendage arising from the last abdominal segment, e.g., first instar larva of *Pygostolus falcatus* (Braconidae) (Gauld and Bolton).

caudocephalic, in a line from the head to the tail (T-B).

caudula (pl., **caudulae**), a little tail (T-B); see cauda.

caul, fat body, q.v. (T-B).

cauliculus, the larger of the 2 stalks supporting the calyx of the mushroom body (T-B).

caulis (pl., **caules**), funicle, q.v., of antenna (T-B); the corneous basal part of the jaws (T-B); in ♂ Tortricidae (Lepidoptera), median rodlike structure, ventrad of aedoeagus, connecting juxta with anellus (Tuxen, after Obraztsov); in ♂ Hymenoptera, gonobase + gonocoxites + volsellae, q.v. (Tuxen, after Snodgrass).

caulis paramerus, in ♂ Heteroptera (Hemiptera), esp. Saldidae, the shaft of the paramere (Polhemus).

caulonome, a larval mine occurring on a plant stem (Hering).

cavaera, in Coccoidea (Hemiptera (Hemiptera: Sternorrhyncha), tracheal tube connecting with each spiracle, expanded into a chamber of varying size and shape (T-B, after MacGillivray).

cavate, cavatus, hollowed out; cavelike (T-B).

cavernicolous, cave-inhabiting (T-B).

cavernicula vaginae (pl., **caverniculae**), in ♀ Siphonaptera, postbursal dorsal ingrowths of vagina caudad of vestibulum vaginae (Tuxen, after Smit).

cavernous, divided into small spaces or little caverns (T-B).

cavity, a hollow space or opening (T-B).

cecidium, gall, q.v. (T-B).

cecidogenic, gall-forming; instigating physiological changes in plant tissue which result in gall formation (Gauld and Bolton).

cecidogenous larvae, in Cecidomyiidae (Diptera), larvae which cause and live in galls (T-B).

cecum of colleterial gland, in ♀ Lepidoptera, ductus sebaceus, q.v. (Tuxen, after Alman).

cecum of spermathecal gland, in ♀ Lepidoptera, ductus receptaculi, q.v. (Tuxen, after Alman).

cell, a unit mass of protoplasm, surrounded by a cell membrane and containing one or more nuclei or nuclear material (T-B; Borror et al.); see brood cell and wing cell.

cell culture, the growing of cells in vitro, including the culture of single cells (Steinhaus and Martignoni); see tissue culture and organ culture.

cell of Semper, Semper cell, q.v. (T-B, after Snodgrass).

cellobiose, dissacharide, consisting of 2 glucose molecules with a beta linkage, found primarily in plants (Chapman).

cellular, composed of cells (T-B).

cellulase, digestive enzyme capable of hydrolysing cellulose, produced by the insect itself or by symbiotic microorganisms in the gut (T-B; Chapman).

cellule, wing cell, q.v., especially a closed cell, q.v. (T-B).

cellulose, polysaccharide consisting of repeated glucose units, being a major constituent of plant cell walls (Chapman).

cement glands, in ♀ Lepidoptera, glandulae sebaceae, q.v. (Tuxen, after Janse).

cement layer, a very thin layer of the epicuticle outside most of the wax formed by the hardened secretion of the dermal glands (Tulloch, after Richards; Chapman); in *Rhodnius* (Hemiptera: Heteroptera: Reduviidae), extrachorion, q.v., of egg (Cobben); see suprachorionic layers.

cement sac, in ♀ Lepidoptera, saccus sebaceus, q.v. (Tuxen, after Janse).

cenchrus (pl., **cenchri**), in adult Symphyta (Hymenoptera), specialized lobes on the metanotum which engage with rough areas on the undersides of the forewings to hold then in place (T-B, after Comstock; Chapman).

cenogenesis, that form of development of an individual plant or animal which does not repeat the evolutionary history of its group; see palingenesis.

cenogenetic, describing insects having secondary adaptations to special ways of life in larvae (T-B, after Comstock).

cenogenous, producing young at one time oviparously, at another viviparously; as in aphids (Hemiptera: Sternorrhyncha: Aphididae) (T-B).

cenosis, coenosis, biocenosis, q.v. (T-B).

Cenozoic Era, era of the geological time scale, including the Tertiary and Quaternary Periods, extending between about 70 million years ago and the present (Riek, in CSIRO).

center of distribution, center of origin, q.v. (T-B).

center of origin, the hypothsized geographical area from which any group or particular species has spread.

Centigrade, the temperature scale which divides the interval between the melting point of ice and the boiling point of water at sea level (760 mm pressure) into 100 parts or degrees; 1° C = 1.8° Fahrenheit (T-B).

centimeter, abbrev., cm; .01 meter; .394 inch; roughly 2.5 cm = one inch (T-B).

centipede, a member of the class Chilopoda (Borror et al.).

centrad, toward the center or interior (T-B).

central area, in ♂ Geometridae (Lepidoptera), diaphragma, q.v. (Tuxen, after Pierce).

central body, a mass of neuropile in the center of the protocereburm, being proportionately larger in insects exhibiting higher levels of behavioral complexity, e.g., social insects (Chapman); in ♂ *Zorotypus zimmermani* Gurney (Zoraptera), part of the complicated genital structure (Tuxen).

central bone, in ♀ Coleophoridae (Lepidoptera), sclerotized, central ridge of ductus bursae (Tuxen, after Toll).

central foveola, in Orthoptera, median foveola, q.v. (T-B).

central girdle, in some pupal Lepidoptera, a rope of silk which gives central support, in addition to the cremaster (Common and Waterhouse).

central nervous system, the longitudinal series of connected ganglia extending the whole length of the body, including the brain and ventral nerve cord, containing the motor perikarya and the synaptic junctions between nerve cells (T-B).

central pattern generator hypothesis, hypothesis that most behavioral patterns are generated in the central nervous system (Matthews and Matthews).

central plate, in ♂ Rhyacophilidae (Trichoptera), the dorsal process of abdominal segment IX (Tuxen, after Mosely).

central region, costal region, q.v., of wing (T-B).

central sclerite, in ♂ Siphonaptera, the ventralmost of the 2 prongs of the fork of the fulcral medial lobe, sometimes fused with the main medial lobe to form the floor of the capsule, or forming additional support to the lateral wall of the capsule (Tuxen, after Jordan; Rothschild and Traub).

central symmetry system, in some Lepidoptera, the median field of the wing pattern bounded basally and distally by the light central line of the transverse anterior and transverse posterior lines respectively (T-B, after Richards).

central triangular piece, in ♀ *Apatania* (Trichoptera: Limnephilidae), either the greater part of the processus spermathecae or the internal part of gonopods VIII (Tuxen, after Morton; Nielsen).

central tuber, in adult Siphonaptera, area communis, q.v. (Rothschild and Traub).

centripital, toward the center (T-B).

centris, in aculeate Hymenoptera, sting, q.v. (T-B).

centrolecithal egg, in insects and other arthropods, an egg having the yolk concentrated in the center (T-B; Leftwich).

centrosome, a spherical body that appears outside the nucleus of a cell; a spherical region of differentiated cytoplasm of a cell which frequently contains one or 2 deeply staining bodies called centrioles (T-B).

cephalad, toward or in the direction of the head end of the insect (T-B); see cephalic.

cephalic, belonging or attached to the head (T-B); see cephalad.

cephalic apotome, in larval Nematocera and orthorrhaphous Brachycera (Diptera), frontoclypeal apotome, q.v. (Colless and McAlpine, in CSIRO; Teskey, in McAlpine).

cephalic artery, one of the divisons of the aorta entering the insect head (T-B).

cephalic bristles, in adult Diptera, specialized bristles occuring on the head (T-B).

cephalic fans, mobile, brushlike structures on the labrum of larval Culicidae, Dixidae and Simuliidae (Diptera) (Colless and McAlpine, in CSIRO); see lateral palatal brush.

cephalic foveae, in ♀ Eumeninae (Hymenoptera: Vespidae), pits posterior to ocelli on vertex (Carpenter, pers. comm., after Carpenter and Cumming).

cephalic foramen, occipital foramen, q.v. (T-B).

cephalic gland(s), in Isoptera, frontal gland, q.v. (Krishna, pers. comm.); in *Zorotypus barberi* Gurney (Zoraptera), a gland on the head (Choe); in Heteroptera (Hemiptera), maxillary glands, q.v. (Cobben).

cephalic heart, in Odonata, a peculiar pulsating organ which exerts pressure against the egg shell in hatching and forces out a caplike operculum (T-B, after Imms).

cephalic lobes, the head lobes of the embryo, comprising the region of the prostomium and usually that of the tritocerebral somite (T-B, after Snodgrass); in larval Muscomorpha (Diptera), 2 lobes of the head segment demarcated by a ventral longitudinal furrow.

cephalic neck, in Heteroptera (Hemiptera), constricted proximal part of head, for the most part inserted within the prothorax (Štys, pers. comm.).

cephalic papilla, in certain larval Culicidae (Diptera), one of one or more paired protruding vesicular expansions of cephalic articulatory membranes (Harbach and Knight, after Lewis).

cephalic pole, in the insect egg, that end of an elongated egg which points to the head of the parent while in the ovariole (Imms).

cephalic salivary glands, in the honey bee (Hymenoptera: Apidae), a pair of glands lying against the posterior wall of the head (Imms).

cephalic segment, in larval Muscomorpha (Diptera), outer membranous part of head bearing anteriorly the antennal and maxillary sensory papillae (McAlpine); see cephalopharyngeal skeleton.

cephalic setae 1--12, in larval Chironomidae (Diptera), dorsal and lateral setae of head capsule starting with setae on labral sclerite (Saether); see labral setae (S1, S2), clypeal seta (S3), frontal setae (S4, S5), suborbital seta (S6), supraorbital seta (S7), parietal seta (S8), genal setae (S9, S10), and coronal setae (S11, S12) (Saether).

cepahlic skeleton, in larval Muscomorpha (Diptera), cephalopharyngeal skeleton, q.v. (Ferrar).

cephalic stomodaeum, the part of the stomodaeum continued in the head.

cephalic tubercles, in pupal Chironomidae (Diptera), tubercles mostly on frontal apotome, usually carrying frontal setae (Saether)

cephalic vesicle, a single sac formed by the union of the larval pharynx and its diverticula (T-B, after Imms).

cephaliger, in adult Diptera, the anterior process of the cervical sclerite which articulates with the occipital condyle of the cranium (Harbach and Knight, after Crampton).

cephalization, the concentration of the sense organs in the anterior part of the body toward the head, or in the head itself (T-B).

cephalocaudal suture, in Vespidae (Hymenoptera), the median suture dividing the mesepisternum (T-B, after Viereck).

cephalomere, one of the head segments of an arthropod (T-B).

cephalon, the head (T-B); the vertical surface of the head end of the insect body (T-B, after MacGillivray); the vertical or frontal surface of the head end of the insect body, especially among hypognathous insects (Peterson).

cephalonotal sulcus, in Helotrephidae (Hemiptera: Heteroptera), partly obliterated sulcus between the fused head capsule and pronotum in adults and the ecdysial line in larvae (Papáček, Tonner, and Štys, after Esaki and China).

cephalopharyngeal skeleton, in larval Muscomorpha (Diptera), portion of head forming a heavily sclerotized, internal pharyngeal skeleton withdrawn into the thoracic segments, being an invaginated portion of the mouthparts (T-B; Colless and McAlpine, in CSIRO; Teskey, in McAlpine); buccal armature, cephalic skeleton, cephaloskeleton, head skeleton, q.v.; see cephalic segment.

cephalophragma, in some Orthoptera, a V-shaped partition which divides the head into an anterior and posterior chamber (T-B).

cephaloskeleton, in larval Muscomorpha (Diptera), cephalopharyngeal skeleton, q.v. (Farrar).

cephalosome, prosoma, q.v. (T-B).

cephalotheca, the head covering in the pupal stage (T-B).

cephalothorax, the united head and thorax in Arachnida and Crustacea (T-B); cephalotheca, q.v., of an obtect pupa (T-B); the anterior segments of larvae that have no obviously separated head (T-B), e.g., instars 6 and 7 of larval Strepsiptera (Chapman); in Coccoidea (Hemiptera: Sternorrhyncha), the fused head and thorax (T-B); in ♀ Strepsiptera, the more or less fused head, thorax, and first abdominal segment (Riek, in CSIRO); in pupal Culicidae (Diptera), the combined head and thorax (Harbach and Knight, after Mitchell).

Cephoidea, superfamily within the suborder Symphyta (Hymenoptera), including stem sawflies of the family Cephidae, in which the adults lack cenchri, the single foretibial spur developed into a calcar, and the venation approaching that in Apocrita, and in which the larvae are stem borers in Gramineae and Rosaceae (Riek, in CSIRO).

cerago, bee bread, q.v. (T-B).

cerambycoid, resembling larval Cerambycidae (Coleoptera); straight, flattened or cylindrical, naked, smooth, and distinctly segmented (Peterson).

Ceraphronoidea, superfamily within the suborder Apocrita (Hymenoptera), including the Ceraphronoidea and Megaspilidae (both formerly included in the Proctotrupoidea) (Gauld and Bolton, after Masner and Dessart).

ceraran setae, in Coccoidea (Hemiptera: Sternorrhyncha), cerarian setae, q.v. (T-B).

cerarian setae, in Coccoidea (Hemiptera: Sternorrhyncha), conical setae of the cerari (T-B, after MacGillivray).

cerari, cerarii, q.v. (T-B).

cerarii (sing., **cerarius**), in nymphs and ♀ Pseudococcidae (Hemiptera: Sternorrhyncha: Coccidoidea), clusters of trilocular pores and stout setae located dorsolaterally on body, often on a sclerotized surface (Woodward et al., in CSIRO; Kosztarab and Kozár).

ceras (pl., **cerata**), in ♂ Geometridae (Lepidoptera), paired, pointed, sclerotized processes, extending caudad from caudal part of abdominal segment VIII, lying in lateral grooves of abdomen, usually projecting beyond caudal end of body, being hairy, scobinate or bristled, and asymmetrical, the right one being usually larger (Tuxen, after Prout).

ceratheca, ceratotheca, q.v. (T-B).

Ceratophylloidea, one of 2 superfamilies of fleas (Siphonaptera), including Ceratophyllidae and many other families, characterized by adults lacking spiniform setae on inner surface of hind coxa and possessing an outer internal ridge on middle coxa, pseudosetae under collar of mesonotum, and a sensilium with 16 or more pits on each side (Dunnet, in CSIRO).

ceratotheca, the part of the pupal skin that encloses the antennae (T-B; Leftwich).

cercal appendage, in ♂ Taeniopterygidae (Plecoptera), a large process of basal lobe of cercus (Tuxen).

cercal basipodite, in Orthoptera, sclerite at base of cercus (Tuxen, after Walker).

cercal callus, in adult Neuroptera, callus cercus, q.v. (Tuxen, after Tjeder).

cercal sclerite, in ♂ Culicidae (Diptera), the more or less distinctly sclerotized area between the paraprocts on the dorsal (prerotation sense) surface of the proctiger or one of a pair of sclerites in the same area (Harbach and Knight, after Belkin).

cercal setae, in ♂ Culicidae (Diptera), setae on the proctiger (Harbach and Knight, after Belkin).

cercaria, cercal basipodite, q.v. (Tuxen, after MacGillivray).

cerci inferiores, in ♂ Panorpidae (Mecoptera), hypovalvae, q.v. (Tuxen, after Navás).

cerci superiores, in ♂ Bittacidae (Mecoptera), epiandrium, q.v (Tuxen, after Navás).

cerciform appendage, filum terminale, q.v. (Tuxen, after Walker).

cercina (pl., **cercinae**), in ♂ *Argynnis* (Lepidoptera: Nymphalidae), serrate sclerotized process on dorsal part of valva (Tuxen, after Fruhstorfer).

cercobranchiate, in nymphs of Zygoptera (Odonata), caudal gills, q.v. (T-B).

cercoid, in ♂ *Troides* (Lepidoptera: Papilionidae), ventral process of uncus (transl. "cercoïde" Roepke, after Tuxen).

cercopod (pl. **cercopoda**), in Ephemeroptera, cerci, q.v. (Tuxen, after

Packard; Leftwich); a footlike appendage on the last abdominal segment (T-B; Leftwich).

Cercopoidea, superfamily within the Auchenorrhyncha (Hemiptera), including the families Cercopidae, Aphrophoridae, Machaerotidae, and sometimes Clastopteridae, characterized by short, conical hind coxae, short approximate middle coxae, short cylindrical hind tibiae with 1 or 2 strong spines, slender forefemora, 2 or no ocelli, and lacking tegula on mesothorax (Woodward et al., in CSIRO).

cercus (pl., **cerci**), an appendage (generally paired) of abdominal segment XI, but often appearing to belong to abdominal segment X (T-B; Tuxen; Chapman); in ♂ Thysanoptera, incorrectly applied to parameres (in part), q.v. (Tuxen, after Buffa); in adult Neuroptera, ectoproct, q.v. (Tuxen, after Gerstäcker); in ♂ *Sialis* (Megaloptera: Sialidae), utriculi, q.v. (Tuxen, after Seitz); in ♂ *Coniopteryx* (Planipennia: Coniopterygidae), entoprocessus, q.v. (Tuxen, after Tjeder); in larval Coleoptera, urogomphi, q.v. (Peterson); in ♀ Annulipalpia (Trichoptera), usually unsegmented, small, slender, thin-walled processes, carrying a small number of sensilla, on the posterior end of segment X (Nielsen), in ♂ Trichoptera, appendices preanales, q.v., or superior appendages, q.v. (Mey, pers. comm., after authors) in ♀ Lepidoptera, papillae anales, q.v. (Tuxen, after Alman); in ♀ Chironomidae (Diptera), appendages of segment XI apparently originating on segment X (Saether); in ♀ Culicidae (Diptera), a pair of more or less conspicuous lobes posterior to tergum IX, being appendages of the proctiger (Harbach and Knight, after Edwards).

cercus basipodites, in ♂ Embiidina, small sclerites in the membrane at base of cerci (Ross, in Tuxen).

cereal chlorotic mottle, disease of cereal grains caused by a rhabdovirus transmitted propagatively by *Nesoclutha* and *Cicadulina* (Hemiptera: Auchenorrhyncha: Cicadellidae) (Nault and Ammar).

cereal tillering disease, disease of cereal grains caused by a reovirus (*Fijivirus*) transmitted propagatively *Laodelphax* and *Dicranotropis* (Hemiptera: Auchenorrhyncha: Delphacidae) (Nault and Ammar).

cerebellum, suboesophageal ganglion, q.v. (T-B).

cerebral ganglion, brain, q.v. (T-B).

cerebrum, brain, q.v. (T-B).

cereous, waxlike (T-B).

cernuous, cernuus (Latin), drooping; with the apex bent downward (T-B; R. W. Brown).

cerodecyte, a wax-producing oenocyte (T-B, after Snodgrass).

ceroris (pl., **cerores**), in Coccoidea (Hemiptera: Sternorrhyncha), wax pore, q.v. (T-B, after MacGillivray).

cerumen, a mixture of resin and wax, used for nest construction by stingless bees and honey bees (Hymenoptera: Apoidea: Apinae, Meloponinae) (T-B, after Rau; Wilson).

cervical, relating or belonging to the cervix or neck (T-B).

cervical ampullae, in many Orthoptera, paired lobes dorsally on the neck membrane which are inflated to break the egg shell or old cuticle during ecdysis (T-B, after Imms; Chapman).

cervical condyle, in adult Culicidae (Diptera), the posterior process of the cervical sclerite which articulates with the proepisternum (Harbach and Knight, after Owen).

cervical foramen, in larval Coleoptera, occipital foramen, q.v. (T-B).

cervical glands, in some larval Lepidoptera (especially Notodontidae, Noctuidae and Arctiidae), an eversible defensive gland on the prothorax located ventrally, immediately behind the head (Stehr); in larval Xyelidae (Hymenoptera), dorsolateral glands located between the head and thorax (Peterson).

cervical link plate, in Siphonaptera, small paired sclerites linking the caudolateral margin of the head capsule with the prothorax in the vicinity of the angle formed between the pronotum and the prosternosome (Lewis, pers. comm.).

cervical organ, in adult Diptera, a pair of hair plates arising from a sclerite located between the lateral cervical sclerites, equipped with sensilla and probably functioning as a position-indicating proprioceptive organ (Speight).

cervical organ sclerite, in Diptera, the sclerite upon which the cervical organ lies (Speight).

cervical sclerites, small chitinous plates on the membrane between head and thorax (T-B).

cervical shield, in larval Lepidoptera, prothoracic shield, q.v. (T-B).

cervical triangle, epicranial notch, q.v. (Stehr); vertical triangle, q.v.

cervicalia, cervical sclerites, q.v. (T-B, after Crampton).

cervicum, cervix, q.v. (T-B).

cervinus, reddish, deer-gray (T-B).

cervix (pl., **cervices**), the membranous region between the head and the prothorax (T-B; Borror et al.); in adult Diptera, membranous area of prothorax united with head (McAlpine); in ♀ Lepidoptera, ductus bursae (Tuxen, after Chapman); see collar.

cervix bursae, in ♀ Lepidoptera, a differentiated region between the ductus bursae and corpus bursae, often with special sclerotizations or invaginations in its wall (Tuxen, after Stitz).

cespiticolous, inhabiting grassy places (T-B).

cespitose, caespitose, q.v. (T-B).

cestiform, girdle-shaped (T-B).

Cestoda, class of endoparasitic platyheminth worms, including tapeworms, all of which lack a gut, with mature individuals living as vertebrate endoparasites (Allaby).

cestus (pl., **cesti**), in ♀ Tortricidae (Lepidoptera), one or more sclerites of the the median, and sometimes of the basal, portion of the ductus bursae, usually forming a tortuous band (Tuxen).

chaeta(e), a thin, elongate outgrowth of the cuticle, being either articulated (seta) or not (spine); in larval Chironomidae (Diptera), 2–11 (usually 6–9) pairs of nonsensitive, nonarticulated, simple or mostly mesally serrated, occasionally bilaterally serrated blades to each side of setae anteriores (Saether).

chaeta media, in some larval Chironomidae (Diptera), somewhat isolated, and differentiated chaeta on labrum (Saether).

chaetoparia (pl., **chaetopariae**), in larval Scarabaeidae (Coleoptera),
the inner part of the paria covered with bristles, strongest toward
pedium gradually decreasing in size toward gymnoparia, or toward
the acanthoparia when the gymnoparia is absent (T-B, after Böving);
see paria.

chaetophorous, bristle-bearing (T-B).

chaetosema (pl., **chaetosemata**), a cluster of sensory bristles on the
head of some adult Lepidoptera (Common, after Jordan, in CSIRO;
Leftwich).

chaetotaxal, of or pertaining to chaetotaxy (T-B).

chaetotaxy, the arrangement and nomenclature of the setae or bristles
on any part of the exoskeleton of an insect or the study of such
arrangement (T-B).

chaetulae basales, in larval Chironomidae (Diptera), mostly 2 pairs of
simple or pectinate blades or rods inserted at lower corners of the
ungula below insertion of chaetulae laterales (Saether).

chaetulae laterales, in larval Chironomidae (Diptera), mostly 6–8 pairs
of simple or pectinate blades to each side of pecten epipharyngis
(Saether).

chaetulae of palpiger, in larval Chironomidae (Diptera), chitinous processes varying from tetrahedral or apically serrate lamellae to thornlike chaetae dorsally on palpiger behind maxillary palp (Saether).

chaetulae of prementum, in larval Chironomidae (Diptera), flat, apically serrated chaetulae present caudolaterally on prementum at
least in Orthocladiinae and Chironominae (Saether).

Chagas' disease, disease of man and other mammals in South and
Central America, Mexico, and Texas, caused by the flagellate protozoan *Trypanosoma cruzi* (Trypanosomatidae) and transmitted by assassin bugs (Hemiptera: Heteroptera: Reduviidae), esp. *Triatoma* and
Rhodnius (Borror et al.).

chagrined, shagreened, q.v. (T-B; Harris).

chain, in chemistry, a series of atoms connected by bonds, forming the
skeleton of a number of compounds (Pfadt).

chain transport, the relaying of food from one worker to another in
the course of transporting it back to the nest (Wilson).

Chalastrogastra, Symphyta, q.v. (T-B; Borror et al.).

chalastrogastrous, with the abdomen broadly sessile and with no
marked constriction at its base, referring to adult Symphyta (Hymenoptera) (T-B); see clistogastrous.

chalaza (pl., **chalazae**), a pimplelike swelling of the insect body wall
bearing a seta (T-B, after MacGillivray), e.g., larval Coccinellidae
(Coleoptera) (Peterson, after Gage).

chalceous, chalceus, brassy in color or appearance (T-B).

Chalcidoidea, superfamily of Apocrita (Hymenoptera), including
Chalcididae and many other families, characterized by adults with
reduced forewing venation, a pronotum separated from the tegula
by the prepectus, no subantennal groove, and hind tibia without a

spur modified for preening, including small to minute parasitic and phytophagous species (Riek, in CSIRO).

chalk brood, a disease of larval honey bees (Hymenoptera: Apidae) caused by the fungus *Ascosphaera apis* killing larvae within the first 2 days after the cells have been sealed with the cadavers drying up to form a hard, shrunken chalklike lump (Steinhaus and Martignoni).

chalybeate, chalybeatus, chalybeous, chalybeus, metallic steel-blue in color (T-B).

chamber, a segmental dilatation of the insect heart (T-B).

champagne-cork organs, ampullaceous sensilla, from their shape (T-B, after Forel).

channeled, having deep grooves or channels (T-B; Harris); see caniculate, fluted, striate, and strigate.

channel of processus gonopori, in ♂ Heteroptera (Hemiptera), median groove, q.v. (Tuxen, after Štys).

chaperon, clypeus, q.v., or anteclypeus, q.v. (T-B).

chaplet, a little crown; a circle of hooks or other small processes terminating a member or appendage (T-B).

Chapman's process, in ♂ Lycaenidae (Lepidoptera), spinose or filamentous sclerotized process, formed by prolongation of dorsal lining of manica, running along vesica (Tuxen, after Nabokov).

character, a quality of form, color or structure (T-B); any characteristic or its attributes used for recognizing, describing, defining, or differentiating taxa (ICZN); see taxonomic character.

character gradient, cline, q.v. (Mayr).

character matrix, a tabular presentation of the observed states of various characters for a group of taxa under study.

character weighting, in taxonomy, assigning relative importance values to characters based either upon some preconceived criterion (a priori weighting) or upon character consistency (a posteriori weighting).

checklist, usually a skeleton classification of a group used for quick reference and as an aid in the arrangement of collections (Mayr); see catalog.

cheek, the lateral part of the head between the compound eye and the mouth, including the gena and the subgena (T-B; Borror et al.; McAlpine); see parafacial.

cheek groove, in adult Diptera, genal groove, q.v. (T-B, after Comstock; McAlpine).

chela, the terminal portion of a limb bearing a lateral moveable claw, like that of a crab; specifically applied to the feet in some Parasitica in which the opposable claw forms a clasping structure (T-B).

chelae, in ♂ Mecoptera, styli, q.v. (Tuxen, after Esben-Petersen).

chelate, pincerlike, i.e., having 2 opposable claws (T-B; Borrow et al.).

Cheleutoptera, Phasmida, q.v. (Kevan).

chelicera (pl., **chelicerae**), the pincerlike first pair of appendages of adult Chelicerata, homologous with the second antennae of Crustacea (T-B); also, the grasping claws of the forelegs in Phymatinae (Hemiptera: Heteroptera: Reduviidae).

Chelicerata, subphylum of Arthropoda, including the Merostomata and Arachnida, the members of which lack antennae and typically have 6 pairs of legs, the first pair being chelicerae and the rest being leglike (Borror et al.).

cheliferous, cheliferus, bearing, or terminating, in a very thick forceps or chela (T-B, after Kirby and Spence).

cheliform, shaped like a pincer or chela (T-B).

Chelonethida, Pseudoscorpiones, q.v. (Borror et al.).

cheloniform, turtle or tortoise-shaped (Peterson).

chemical communication, communication via pheromones (Borror et al.).

chemoreception, perception through chemical stimuli, i.e., taste, smell (T-B); see contact chemoreception and olfaction.

chemoreceptive, susceptible to chemical stimuli (T-B).

chemoreceptor, a sense organ having a group of cells supposedly sensitive to chemical properties of matter (T-B, after Snodgrass); see basiconic peg, coeloconic sensillum, plate organ.

chemotaxis, reaction to chemical stimuli (T-B).

chemotropism, reaction to chemical stimuli, e.g., smell and taste (T-B).

chewing lice, biting lice, q.v. (Borror et al.; Lyal, pers. comm.).

chewing mouthparts, mouthparts with mandibles fitted for chewing (Peterson).

chiasma, an X-like crossing of nerve tracts within a nerve center (T-B).

chiasmata, points of genetic crossing-over during meiosis (White, in CSIRO).

Chiastomyaria, Opisthoptera, q.v. (Hennig, after Shvanvich).

chiclero ulcer, espundia, q.v. (Adkins, pers. comm.).

chigger, the parasitic larval mite belonging to the family Trombiculidae (Pfadt).

Chilognatha, subclass of the Diplopoda, including the superorders Helminthomorpha and Pentazonia (Borror et al.).

Chilopoda, class of myriapods, including the centipedes, the members of which are elongate with 15 or more pairs of legs with a single pair per body segment, antennae consisting of 14 or more segments; genital openings located at the posterior end of the body, and the appendages of the first segment behind the head clawlike and functioning as poison jaws (T-B; Borror et al.).

chiloscleres, in larval Camponotini (Hymenoptera: Formicidae), a pair of conspicuous dark brown spots, one on either side of the labrum (Wheeler and Wheeler).

Chironomoidea, superfamily within the infraorder Culicimorpha (Diptera: Nematocera), including the families Chironomidae, Ceratopogonidae, Simuliidae, and Thaumaleidae, possessing adult flies with a radial sector with fewer than 3 branches (Hennig; McAlpine).

chironym, manuscript name, q.v. (Mayr).

chirotype, the specimen upon which a manuscript name is based (T-B).

chirping, stridulation, q.v. (Leftwich).

chisel, in Psocoptera, lacinia, q.v. (T-B).

chitin, a major polysaccharide constituent of arthropod cuticle, being composed of acetyl glucosamine and glucosamine subunits and secreted by the epidermis, being insoluble in water, alcohol, ether and other solvents and resistant to acids and alkalis (T-B; Tulloch; Leftwich; Borror et al.; Chapman).

chitinase, enzyme in moulting fluid or secreted by chitinovore that initiates the digestion of chitin (Tulloch, after Richards; Chapman).

chitine, chitin, q.v. (T-B).

chitinization, the process of depositing or filling with chitin (T-B); see sclerotization.

chitinized, filled in with or hardened by chitin (T-B); see sclerotized.

chitinized lobe on sternum VIII, in ♂ Plecoptera, median lobe of sternum VIII, q.v. (Tuxen, after Hynes).

chitinophilus, applied to microorganisms found in association with chitin and presumably deriving nourishment therefrom (Richards).

chitinous, composed of chitin or like it in structure (T-B); as a color term, amber yellow (T-B); sclerotized, q.v. (Peterson).

chitinous apodeme of epipharynx, in larval Culicidae (Diptera), torma, q.v. (Harbach and Knight, after Pucat).

chitinous bag, in ♀ Nabidae (Hemiptera: Heteroptera), (unpaired saclike) pseudospermatheca, q.v. (Tuxen, after Ekblom).

chitinous cradle, in Coccoidea (Hemiptera: Sternorrhyncha), the chitinized arms or bars forming the endoskeleton of the head (T-B, after MacGillivray).

chitinous plate, in larval Scarabaeoidea, (right) nesium, q.v. (T-B, after Hayes).

chitinous receptacle, in ♀ Pyrrhocoridae (Hemiptera: Heteroptera), (enlarged) orificium receptaculi, q.v. (Tuxen, after Stehlik)

chitinous rods, in ♂ Heteroptera (Hemiptera), struts, q.v. (Tuxen, after Singh-Pruthi).

chitinovore, a microorganism capable of digesting chitin (Tulloch, after Richards).

chitosan, a product from chitin by treating with an hydroxide at high temperature; a deacetylated derivative of chitin which gives a characteristic violet color with iodine (Tulloch, after Richards).

chitose, a decomposition product of chitin; a glucosamine salt (T-B).

chlamydate, chlamydatus (Latin), cloaked; or bearing a cloak- or mantellike structure (T-B).

chloral hydrate mounting medium, Hoyer's mounting medium, q.v. (Borror et al.).

chlordane, $C_{10}H_6Cl_8$, a synthetic insecticide; a chlorinated hydrocarbon, 1,2,4,5,6,7,8,8-octachloro-3a,4,7,7a-tetrahydro-4,7-methanoindane; moderately toxic to mammals, oral LD_{50} for rats about 250 mg/kg (Pfadt).

chlordimeform, a synthetic insecticide and acaricide; a formamidine, N'(4-chloro-o-tolyl)-N,N-dimethylformamidane; moderately toxic to mammals, acute oral LD_{50} for rats 127 to 352 mg/kg (Pfadt).

chlorfenethol, a synthetic acaricide, a chlorinated hydrocarbon and relative of DDT; chemically, 1,1-bis(p-chlorophenyl)ethanol; moderately toxic to mammals, acute oral LD_{50} for rats 500 mg/kg (Pfadt).

chloride, a salt of hydrochloric acid, e.g., table salt, NaCl (T-B).

chloride cells, in aquatic insects, specialized concentrated cells in the epithelium of abdominal gills that absorb salts as a function of osmoregulation (Komnick).

chloride epithelium, in larval Trichoptera, ovoid areas of modified cuticle each surrounded by a thin sclerotized line on the venter, dorsum, or pleural regions of certain abdominal segments, involved in ion absorption (Wiggins, after Wichard).

chlorinated, of a greenish-yellow color (T-B).

Chloris striate mosaic, disease of grass (*Choris*) caused by a geminivirus transmitted circulatively *Mesoclutha* (Hemiptera: Auchenorrhyncha: Cicadellidae) (Nault and Ammar).

chlorobenside, $C_{13}H_{10}Cl_2S$, a synthetic acaricide, a sulfide; chemically, *p*-chlorobenzyl, *p*-chlorophenyl sulfide; single dose of 3000 mg/kg administered to rats without sigs of systemic toxicity (Pfadt).

chlorobenzilate, $C_{13}H_{10}Cl_2S$, a synthetic acaricide, a chlorinated hydrocarbon and relative of DDT; chemically, ethyl 4,4'-dichlorobenzilate; slightly toxic to mammals, acute oral LD_{50} for rats 960 mg/kg (Pfadt).

chlorocresol, 4-Chloro-*m*-cresol, a crystalline chemical used to prevent mold attack on dried insect specimens (Common).

chloroform, $CHCl_3$; a clear, colorless, nonpolar liquid with a characteristic ethereal odor and a burning sweet taste; not inflammable; anesthetic (T-B).

chlorophane, an oily, greenish yellow pigment found in insects (T-B).

chlorophyll, green plant pigment (T-B; Gilmour, in CSIRO); the green, light energy-trapping pigment of plants essential for photosynthesis.

chloropicrin, CCl_3NO_2, insecticidal fumigant for treatment of stored grain and cereal products and for soil treatment to control insects, nematodes, weeds, fungi; 0.05 oz/1000 cu ft lethal in 10 minutes to mammals (Pfadt).

chloroplast, one of the chlorophyll bodies of the green plant (T-B).

Chloropoidea, superfamily proposed for the single family Chloropidae (Diptera), more generally included within the Drosophiloidea or Ephydroidea (sensu McAlpine) (Borror et al.; Colless and McAlpine, in CSIRO; McAlpine); superfamily within the Schizophora-Acalyptratae (Diptera: Brachycera), including the families Chloropidae, Milichiidae, Carnidae, Tethinidae, and Canacidae, including adult flies with weak or absent oral vibrissae, costa of wing broken near the end of the subcosta, reduced anal vein, and vestigial ♀ spermatheca (Bickel, in Parker).

chloropropylate, a synthetic acaricide related to DDT; isopropyl 4,4'-dichlorobenzilate; acute oral LD_{50} for rats 5000 mg/kg (Pfadt).

chlorosis, fading of the color of the chlorophyll of plant leaves, caused by disease (T-B).

chlorpyrifos, $C_9H_{11}Cl_3NO_3PS$, a synthetic insecticide and acaricide; an organophosphate, *O,O*-diethyl *O*-(3,5,6-trichloro-2-pyridyl) phosphororthioate; moderately toxic to mammals, acute oral LD_{50} for ♂ rats 163 mg/kg (Pfadt).

cholera, bacterial disease of man caused by *Vibrio comma* and transmitted by *Musca domestica* (Muscidae), various blow flies (Calliphoridae), and various flesh flies (Sarcophagidae) (Diptera) (Borror et al.).

choline, $C_5H_{15}O_2N$, an essential water-soluble vitamin in insects belonging to the vitamin B complex (Gilmour, in CSIRO).

cholinesterase, an enzyme (or enzymes) present in body tissues which hydrolyzes or breaks down acetylcholine (Pfadt).

chorda, in the forewing of Lepidoptera, stem of veins R_{4+5} in the discal cell (T-B, after Turner; Common, in CSIRO); basal part of R_{4+5} separating areole from the basal cell in Lepidoptera (T-B, after Tillyard).

chordal area, in ♂ Grylloidea (Orthoptera), the area bounded by the mirror, the harp, and the outer wing edge (Otte, pers. comm.).

Chordeumatida, order within the Helminthomorpha (Diplopoda), characterized by a body composed of 26 to 32 segments, each consisting of a coalesced pleurotergum with a prominent dorsal median suture (Hoffman, in Parker).

Chordeumida, Chordeumatida, q.v. (Borror et al.).

chordotonal, responsive to vibrations (T-B).

chordotonal ligament, a ligamentous structure connecting a scolopophore with the body wall (T-B, after Comstock).

chordotonal organ, a sense organ, the cellular elements forming an elongate structure attached at both ends of the body wall, not necessarily containing sense rods or scolopes (T-B, after Snodgrass; Chapman); see Johnston's organ, subgenual organ, and tympanal organ.

chordotonal nerve, auditory nerve, q.v. (T-B, after Klots).

chordotonal receptor, chordotonal organ, q.v. (Leftwich).

chords, in ♂ Grylloidea (Orthoptera), bowed veins (anal and cubital) in the chordal area of the forewing (Otte, pers. comm.).

chorion, the outer shell or covering of the insect egg (T-B), produced by the follicle cells while the egg is in the ovary (Chapman); see endochorion and exochorion.

chorionic, of or pertaining to the chorion or shell of the insect egg (T-B).

chorionin, scleroprotein forming the chief part of the chorion of an insect's egg (T-B, after Tillyard; Hinton and Mackerras, in CSIRO; Leftwich).

choriothete, in the uterus of ♀ *Glossina* (Diptera: Glossinidae), a small pad of glandular cells with a cushion of muscles beneath and other muscles running to the ventral body wall, serving to remove the chorion and cuticle of first-instar larvae (Chapman).

choroid, choroides, in the insect eye, the black basal membrane of the ommatidium (T-B, after Kirby and Spence).

chorology, biogeography, q.v. (T-B; Mayr).

chorotype, a fossil specimen collected from the same stratum as the type, but from a neighboring locality (Tulloch).

chorusing, collective and synchronous song of an entire population (Matthews and Matthews).

Chresmododea, extinct suborder of Phasmida from the Mesozoic differing from recent members of the order in having long forewings with the longitudinal veins parallel and connected by many crossveins (Riek, in CSIRO).

chromatic spheres, chromatin masses extruded by dividing cells and engulfed by phagocytes (Tulloch).

chromatin, the minute granules that make up the chromoplasm of a cell nucleus (T-B).

chromatocyte cells, chromatocytes, q.v. (Teskey, in McAlpine).

chromatocytes, in some larval Nematocera (Diptera), pigmented mesodermal cells of the fat body that can migrate forming new color patterns (Hinton and Mackerras, in CSIRO).

chromatography, an analytical method for the purification and separation of inorganic or organic compounds, in the presence of suitable solvents, through a porous medium (Tulloch, after Rockstein).

chromatolysis, a phase of histolysis in larvae in which the chromatin condenses in the nodules of histolyzing tissue into compact masses (Henneguy).

chromatophore, a pigment-bearing intracellular body (Mayr).

chromidia, protein spheres which first appear near the nucleus of a yolk cell and later migrate to the periphery and enlarge (Tulloch).

chromogen, raw material used in the synthesis of melanin (Tulloch).

chromogenic phase, in Muscomorpha (Diptera), the last pupal phase preceding emergence of the adult, in which the pigment of the body and its appendages occurs (Peterson, after Dean).

chromophile, intermediate or transitional form between prohemocytes and plasmatocytes and perhaps some other types of blood cells (T-B; Tulloch, after Jones).

chromophilic leucocyte, chromophile, q.v. (T-B).

chromophore, color-producing molecule (Chapman).

chromoprotein, chromophore conjugated with a protein molecule (Chapman).

chromoptic phase, in Muscomorpha (Diptera), the pupal phase following the teleomorphic phase in which pigmentation of the compound eyes commences; considered a subphase of the chromogenic phase (Peterson, after Dean).

chromosomal inversion, reversal of the linear order of the genes in a segment of a chromosome (Mayr).

chromosomal polymorphism, the occurrence of cytologically distinct chromosomal arrangements among individuals within the same population, arising predominantly through chromosomal inversions (White, in CSIRO).

chromosomal puffs, in polytene chromosomes of certain Diptera, swellings indicating transcriptional activity at certain loci, specific for various stages of development and in particular tissues (White, after Beermann, in CSIRO).

chromosome, a deeply staining DNA-containing body in the nucleus of the cell, best seen during cell division (T-B; Mayr).

chromosome cytology, study of the chromosome sets of animal and plant species (White, in CSIRO); see cytogenetics.

chronic, in invertebrate pathology, of long duration, e.g., chronic disease (Steinhaus and Martignoni); see acute.

chronic paralysis, a fatal disease of adult honey bees and of certain bumblebees (Hymenoptera: Apidae), caused by virus, in which the bees are able to feed but are feeble and trembly in movement (Steinhaus and Martignoni); see acute paralysis.

chrymosymphily, friendly relations between ants (Hymenoptera: Formicidae) and larval Lepidoptera, based upon the attractive scent emitted by the larvae (Tulloch, after Gaul).

chrysalis, chrysalid, (pl., **chrysalides** or **chrysalids**), obtect pupa of butterfly or moth (Lepidoptera) (T-B; Peterson; Leftwich); pupa, q.v.

chrysargyrus, silvery gilt (T-B).

Chrysidoidea, superfamily within the Apocrita (Hymenoptera), including the families Cryinidae, Embolemidae, Bethylidae, Plumariidae, Sclerogibbidae, Scolebythidae, and Chrysididae, possessing the same number of antennal segments in both sexes, ♀ second gonocoxa 9 comprising proximal and distal portions which articulate at their point of contact, and ♀ abdominal tergite VIII (seventh gastral tergite) complete, not deeply cleft medially (Gauld and Bolton).

Chrysomeloidea, superfamily within the Polyphaga (Coleoptera), including the families Chrysomelidae, Cerambycidae, and Bruchidae, adults possessing 5-5-5 pseudotetramerous tarsi (penultimate tarsomere very small and hidden in the emargination of the 3rd tarsomere), a head that is not produced into a rostrum, 2 gular sutures, metasternum with a transverse suture, antennae never elbowed, abdomen with 5 visible sternites, and hind coxae without a declivity or cavity into which the femora can retract (Britton, in CSIRO).

chrysopterin, pterine pigment producing yellow color in the brimstone butterfly, *Gonepteryx rhamni* (Lepidoptera: Pieridae) (Chapman).

chyle, the food mass after it has passed through the gizzard and is mixed with the secretions of the salivary glands and caecal structures, ready to be assimilated (T-B).

chyle stomach, midgut, q.v. (T-B, after Comstock).

chylific ventricle, midgut, q.v. (T-B).

chyme, the semidigested food in the small intestine (T-B).

CI, consistency index, q.v.

cibarial, of or pertaining to the cibarium (T-B).

cibarial apparatus, the mouth organs which operate on the food (T-B).

cibarial armature, in some ♀ Culicidae (Diptera), a series of specialized spicules, cibarial teeth, borne on a transverse ridge, cibarial crest, and a group of spiculate ridges, cibarial ridges, lying ventrally at the posterior margin of the cibarium (Harbach and Knight, after Knight and Laffoon); see buccopharyngeal armature.

cibarial bar, in larval Culicidae and some other Nematocera (Diptera), a paired cranial element of the cibarial wall just anterior to the mouth (Harbach and Knight, after Cook; Teskey, in McAlpine).

cibarial crest, in adult Culicidae (Diptera), the transverse ridge located ventrally at the posterior margin of the cibarium which supports the cibarial teeth (Harbach and Knight).

cibarial dome, in adult Culicidae (Diptera), a hemispherical, spiculate structure projecting from the clypeopalatum, at the posterior margin of the cibarium (Harbach and Knight, after Valencia).

cibarial pump, modified cibarium and associated structures, forming a sucking pump (T-B; Chapman).

cibarial ridge, in some ♀ Culicidae (Diptera), one of a series of short spiculate ridges lying just posterior to the cibarial crest and forming part of the cibarial armature (Harbach and Knight, after Knight and Laffoon).

cibarial sclerite, in Psocoptera and Amblycera (Phthiraptera), sclerite, forming part of floor of cibarium, by which moisture taken from atmosphere by the lingual sclerites is transported to the pharynx (Rudolph).

cibarial seta, in adult Culicidae (Diptera), one of the various types of setae borne within the cibarium, in groups designated by location as dorsal, palatal and ventral (Harbach and Knight).

cibarial teeth, in some ♀ Culicidae (Diptera), a series of specialized spicules borne on the cibarial crest located ventrally at the posterior margin of the cibarium, being commonly of 2 kinds called cones and rods (Harbach and Knight, after Reid).

cibarian, referring to mouthparts (T-B).

cibarious, relating to food (T-B).

cibarium, preoral cavity between base of hypopharynx and under surface of clypeus (T-B, after Snodgrass; Chapman); see cibarial pump.

cibarium-pharynx, in larval Diptera, pharynx, q.v., in Muscomorpha lying posterior to the atrium (Teskey, in McAlpine).

cibivia, food canal, q.v. (T-B, after MacGillivray).

Cicadellidea, Cicadelloidea, q.v. (Hennig, after Bekker-Migdisova).

Cicadelloidea, superfamily within the Auchenorrhyncha (Hemiptera), including the families Cicadellidae, Membracidae, Aetalionidae, Hylicidae, and Eurymelidae, possessing long hind tibiae usually with numerous spines in conspicuous rows, tranverse platelike hind coxae, slender forefemora, 2 or no ocelli, tegulae lacking, middle coxae short and approximate, and pedicel of antenna not or scarcely thicker than scape (Woodward et al., in CSIRO).

Cicadidea, Cicadoidea, q.v. (Hennig, after Bekker-Migdisova).

Cicadiformes, group within the Auchenorrhyncha (Hemiptera), including the Cicadoidea, Cicadelloidea, and Cercopoidea (Hennig).

Cicadoidea, superfamily within the Auchenorrhyncha (Hemiptera), including the families Cicadidae and Tettigarctidae, characterized by 3 ocelli on crown, thickened forefemora, no tegula, middle coxae short and approximate, and pedicel of antenna not or scarcely thicker than scape (Woodward et al., in CSIRO).

Cicadomorpha, Cicadoidea, q.v. (Hennig).

Cicadopsyllidea, group of fossil insects from the Permian, including the Cicadopsyllidae and Coleoscytidae, belonging to the Psyllomorpha together with the recent superfamilies Psylloidea and Aleyrodoidea (Hemiptera: Sternorrhyncha) (Hennig, after Bekker-Migdisova).

cicatrices, in Margarodidae (Hemiptera: Sternorrhyncha: Coccoidea), large porelike structures on venter, often surrounded by a sclerotized rim (Kosztarab and Kozár); in Pseudococcidae (Hemiptera: Sternorrhyncha: Coccoidea), ventral circuli, q.v. (T-B, after MacGillivray); see cicatrix.

cicatricose, cicatricosus, having superficial scars with elevated margins (T-B).

cicatrix (pl., **cicatrices**), a scar; an elevated, rigid spot; a scarlike structure (T-B); see cicatrices.

cicatrose, cicatrosus (Latin), having scars with elevated margins (T-B; Harris); see impressed, lacunose, and variolate.

cilia (sing., **cilium**), series of moderate or thin hairs arranged in tufts or single lines (T-B); thin scattered hairs on a surface or margin (T-B); in Lepidoptera, the fringe scales present along the wing margin (Downey and Allyn); see fimbria and fringe.

cilia of the posterior orbit, in adult Diptera, postocular setae, q.v. (T-B, after Comstock).

ciliate, ciliated, ciliatus, fringed with a row of parallel hairs or cilia (T-B, after Kirby and Spence).

ciliations, in Collembola, e.g., some Isotomidae, fine projections forming one or more transverse rows on the ventral (inner) surface of labrum (Christiansen and Bellinger).

cimicine, in Heteroptera (Hemiptera), secretions of the metathoracic scent glands, of disagreeable odor and variable composition, at least in part defensive (T-B); old term for bug, q.v. (T-B); a bed bug (Hemiptera: Heteroptera: Cimicidae).

Cimicoidea, superfamily within the infraorder Cimicomorpha of the Heteroptera, including the families Anthocoridae, Cimicidae, Plokiophilidae, and Polyctenidae; used in sense of Cimicomorpha in older literature (Schuh).

Cimicomorpha, group within the Heteroptera, including the superfamilies Cimicoidea, Reduvioidea and additional families, Miridae, Tingidae, Nabidae, Thaumastocoridae and others, whose interfamilial relationships are not well established (Woodward et al., in CSIRO, after Leston et al.).

cimier, the head crest in chrysalides of Pieridae (Lepidoptera) (T-B).

cinctus, with a colored band; cingulatus (T-B).

cinerous, cinereus, ash-colored; gray tinged with blackish (T-B).

cinerescent, ashen in color or appearance (T-B).

cingula (pl., **cingulae**), a colored band (T-B); in Lepidoptera, girdle, q.v.; in ♂ Lepidoptera, saccus + vinculum (Tuxen, after Cockayne).

cingulate, cingulatus, belted with one or more cingula or bands; see also cinctus (T-B).

cingulum (pl., **cingula**), in ♂ Caelifera (Orthoptera), a large sclerite in the ectophallic membrane (Tuxen); in ♂ Siphonaptera, membranous diaphragm encompassing aedeagus and forming base of phallocrypt (Tuxen, after Peus).

cinnabarine, vermilion red; of the color of cinnabar, or red oxide of mercury (T-B).

cinnamomeous, cinnamomeus, cinnamon brown (T-B).

Cinura, name previously used for a taxon including Diplura, Archaeognatha, and Zygentoma (T-B; Paclt, after Packard).

Ciodrin (trade name), crotoxyphos, q.v. (Pfadt).

circa (Latin), about or near to (T-B).

circadian rhythm, reiterative behavioral rhythm having a periodicity of about 24 hours (Borror et al.; Chapman).

circinal, circinate, circinatus, spirally rolled like a watch spring or a butterfly proboscis (T-B).

circiter, about, or round about (T-B).

circular overlap, phenomenon in which a chain of contiguous and intergrading populations curves back until the terminal links overlap geographically and behave like good (noninterbreeding) species (Mayr).

circular plate, in larval Syrphidae (Diptera), either a relatively weakly sclerotized, retractile area on the dorsal inner sector of the posterior spiracular plate, or in saprophytic forms, a sunken area located at or just above the posterior spiracular plate; the inner stigmatic scar of Snodgrass (Peterson, after Heiss).

circular-seamed flies, members of the Cyclorrhapha (= Muscomorpha) (Diptera) (Borror et al.).

circulation, movement of the hemolymph brought about by pulsations of the heart and accessory pulsatile organs (Borror et al.).

circulative transmission, viral transmission in which the viruses pass through the gut wall into the hemolymph of the vector, subsequently passing to the salivary glands and being discharged with the salivary secretions (Nault and Ammar); see viral transmission.

circulatory system, hemocoel and dorsal vessel though which circulates the hemolymph (Leftwich; Chapman).

circulus, in nymphal and ♀ Pseudococcidae and Putoidae (Hemiptera: Sternorrhyncha: Coccoidea), an adhesive organ, being either a ring or hourglasslike structure between the 4th and 5th or on the 4th sternite of the abdomen (T-B, after Ferris and Murdock; Kosztarab, pers. comm.; Miller, in Stehr); see cicatrices.

circum-, Latin prefix; around, about, on all sides, or in a circle (T-B).

circumanal, about or surrounding the anus (T-B).

circumanal papilla, in Collembola, anal papilla, q.v. (Snider, pers. comm.).

circumanal pore ring, in ♀ Psyllidae (Hemiptera: Sternorrhyncha), a ring of gland pores surrounding the anus (Tuxen; Kosztarab, pers. comm.).

circumanal ring, in Psyllidae (Hemiptera: Sternorrhyncha), circumanal pore ring, q.v. (Stoetzel, in Stehr).

circumanal setae, in Collembola (esp. some Sminthuridae), characterisitc setae of the anal valves (Christiansen and Bellinger).

circumantennal sulcus, antennal suture, q.v. (Chapman).

circumfili, in most Cecidomyiidae (Diptera), curious looped filaments or sometimes tortuous threads in the antennal joints arranged in whorls (Imms).

circumgenital glands, in Coccoidea (Hemiptera: Sternorrhyncha), circumgenital pores, q.v. (T-B, after MacGillivray).

circumgenital pores, in Diaspididae (Hemiptera: Sternorrhyncha: Coccoidea), small circular pores, disposed in groups about the genital orifice (T-B, after MacGillivray); in other Coccoidea, scattered pores on the ventral aspect of the abdomen, cephalad and lateral of opercula (Kosztarab and Kozár).

circumocular, roundabout or surrounding the eye (T-B).

circumocular sulcus, ocular suture, q.v. (Chapman).

circumoesophageal commissures, circumoesophageal connectives, q.v. (Leftwich).

circumoesophageal connectives, the connectives between the brain and the ventral nerve cord embracing the stomodaeum; primitively, the connectives from the archicerebrum to the first ventral ganglia; in insects the connectives between the tritocerebral ganglia and the mandibular ganglia (T-B, after Snodgrass).

circumoral, about, or surrounding, the mouth (T-B).

circumsepted, with a vein all around the wing (T-B).

circumpharyngeal commissures, circumoesophageal connectives, q.v. (Leftwich).

circumversion, a turning around (T-B); in ♂ Muscomorpha (Diptera: Brachycera), the rotation of the terminalia 360° (Tulloch, after Feuerborn; McAlpine); see inversion.

cirrate antenna, a pectinate antenna (q.v.) with very long curved lateral branches, sometimes fringed with hair; see plumose (T-B).

Cirripedia, group within the Crustacea with sessile marine adults, e.g., barnacles (Borror et al.).

cirrose, cirrous, cirrosus, furnished with a fringe of hair; fringed; having one or more cirri (T-B, after Kirby and Spence).

cirrus (pl., **cirri**), a curled lock of hair placed on a thin stalk (T-B).

cirrus acuum (pl., **cirri acuum**), in ♂ *Zygaena* (Lepidoptera: Zygaenidae), rounded sclerotized areas, often bearing dense spine-hairs, on vesica of aedoeagus (Tuxen, after Loritz).

cisanal setae, in Coccoidea (Hemiptera: Sternorrhyncha), the shorter and further 2 of the 4 setae near the caudal ring (T-B, after MacGillivray).

cisanal cista acustica, an elongated ridge or crest of scolopophores of the integumental type (T-B, after Imms).

cismontane, on this side of the mountains (T-B); see transmontane.

citric acid, organic acid that is an intermediate in glucose oxidation and commonly found in high concentrations in insect hemolymph (Gilmour, in CSIRO).

citrine, citrinus, lemon yellow (T-B).

citrus stubborn, disease of orange and other citrus and periwinkle caused by a spiroplasma transmitted propagatively by leafhoppers (Hemiptera: Auchenorrhyncha: Cicadellidae) (Borror et al.).

clade, a hypothesized monophyletic group (Hennig).

cladism, cladistics, q.v. (Mayr).

cladistic, pertaining to cladistic analysis or cladistic classification.

cladistic analysis, phylogenetic analysis in which taxa, defined by synapomorphies, are grouped on the basis of relative recency of common ancestry; see paleontological method and phenetic analysis.

cladistic classification, a form of natural classification which only recognizes hypothesized monophyletic taxa; see evolutionary classification.

cladistics, the principles of cladistic analysis and cladistic classification.

Cladocera, order of Branchiopoda, including the water fleas (Borror et al.).

cladocerous, with branched horns or antennae (T-B).

cladogenesis, diversification of a lineage by splitting, i.e., speciation; see anagenesis.

cladogram, a branching diagram based on the distribution of synapomorphies; a diagram showing only the sequence in which groups of organisms are interpreted to have originated and diverged in the course of evolution (Wilson).

clam shrimps, members of the Conchostraca (Borror et al.).

clasp, in Collembola, tenaculum, q.v. (T-B).

clasp filament, in ♂ Culicidae (Diptera), dististylus, q.v. (T-B, after J. B. Smith; Tuxen); gonostylus, q.v. (McAlpine).

clasper(s), in ♂ insects, clasping organs functioning in holding ♀ during coition (Tuxen, after Imms); in ♂ Ephemeroptera, gonostyles, q.v. (Tuxen, after Phillips); in ♂ Blattopteroidea, apophysis, q.v. (Tuxen, after Walker); in ♂ Embiidina, left cercus (Ross, in CSIRO); in ♂ Psocoptera, large hook on hypandrium or paraprocts (Tuxen); in ♀ Anoplura (Phthiraptera), paraprocts, q.v. (Calaby, in CSIRO); in ♂ Auchenorrhyncha (Hemiptera), anal hooks and styles, q.v. (Tuxen, after Brittain) or styles (Tuxen, after McAtee); in ♂ Psyllidae (Hemiptera: Sternorrhyncha), forceps, q.v. (Tuxen); in ♂ Aleyrodidae (Hemiptera: Sternorrhyncha), a forceps-shaped pair of moveable processes from abdominal segment IX (Tuxen); in ♂ Aphididae (Hemiptera: Sternorrhyncha), a pair of cone-shaped ventral processes on either side of penis (Tuxen); in ♂ Heteroptera (Hemiptera), parameres, q.v. (Tuxen, after Baker); in ♂ Mecoptera, gonocoxite, q.v. (Tuxen, after Esben-Petersen), in ♂ *Bittacus* (Mecoptera: Bittacidae), epiandrium, q.v. (Tuxen, after Wood); in ♂ Trichoptera, inferior appendages, q.v. (Tuxen), or gonopods, q.v. (Tuxen, after Nielsen); in ♂ Noctuidae (Lepidoptera), a more or less median, ental process attached to the valva, often with separate musculature perhaps derived from the stylus of the gonopod if valva is derived from the coxite (Tuxen, after Pierce); in ♂ Lepidoptera, valvae, q.v. (Tuxen, after Griffith) or clavus, q.v. (Tuxen, after Heinrich); in ♂ Diptera, gonopods, q.v.; in ♂ Diptera, basistyle, dististylus, surstyli, q.v. (Tuxen); gonostylus, q.v. (McAlpine); in ♂ Siphonaptera, parameres, q.v. (Tuxen, after Rothschild), basimere, q.v. (Tuxen); or (in *Cediopsylla,* Pulicidae), processus basimeris ventralis, q.v. (Tuxen, after Hopkins and M. Rothschild).

clasper lobe, in ♂ Siphonaptera, basimere, q.v. (Tuxen, after authors) or processus basimeris, q.v. (Tuxen, after Snodgrass).

clasperlike sclerites, in ♂ Aradidae (Hemiptera: Heteroptera), parandria, q.v. (Tuxen, after Wygodzinsky).

claspette, in some ♂ Nematocera (Diptera), appendage of basistylus (T-B; Tuxen); in ♂ Culicidae (Diptera), variably shaped lobe arising mesally at the base of the gonocoxite (T-B; Harbach and Knight, after Edwards; McAlpine); in ♂ Chironomidae (Diptera), volsella, q.v., or superior volsella, q.v. (Saether).

claspette filament, in ♂ Culicidae (Diptera), a specialized apical seta of the claspette, being usually simple or foliform (Harbach and Knight, after Carpenter and LaCasse).

claspette stem, in ♂ Culicidae (Diptera), the basal part of the claspette, bearing the claspette filament apically (Harbach and Knight, after Carpenter and LaCasse).

clasping apparatus, in ♂ Siphonaptera, parameres, q.v. (Tuxen).

clasping organ(s), in ♂ *Sminthurides* (Collembola: Sminthuridae), the modified second and third antennal segments (Christiansen and Bellinger); in ♂ Zoraptera, a pair of dorsal lobes and a pair of lateral lobes hinged to the horseshoe-shaped basal plate and protrusible (Tuxen, after Gurney); in ♂ Siphonaptera, parameres, q.v. (Tuxen).

clasps, in ♂ Lepidoptera, valvae, q.v. (Tuxen, after Scudder and Burgess).

class, a subdivision of a phylum or subphylum, containing a group of related orders, e.g., class Insecta (T-B; Borror et al.).

classification, the delimitation, ordering, and ranking of taxa (T-B; Mayr); see artificial classification, natural classification, and taxonomy.

clathrate, clathratus (Latin), latticed; with elevated ridges decussing at right angles (T-B; Harris); see cancellate and reticulate.

clathrose, clathrosus (Latin), clathrate, q.v. (T-B; Harris).

claustral colony founding, in Isoptera, the procedure during which queens (or royal pairs) seal thmeselves off in cells and rear the first generation of workers on nutrients obtained mostly or entirely from their own storage tissues, including fat body and histolysed wing muscles (Wilson).

claustrum, wing-coupling mechanism, q.v. (T-B).

clava, a club (T-B); antennal club, q.v. (T-B).

clava (penis), in ♂ Lepidoptera, vesica, q.v. (Tuxen, after Baltzer).

claval commissure, in Heteroptera (Hemiptera), the junction of the hemelytra along the clavus on the midline of the body posterior to the apex of the scutellum and anterior to the membrane (Štys, pers. comm.).

claval furrow, furrow separating clavus from remigium of wing (Chapman).

claval lobe, in adults of some Hymenoptera, posterior marginal lobe of wing between claval furrow and jugal fold (Gauld and Bolton).

claval organ, in Heteroptera (Hemiptera), microtrichia-bearing organ at the posteroventral surface of clavus of the forewing, grasping the leading edge of the hind wing during expansion and flexion of wings and during flight (Wygodzinsky and Štys).

claval suture, in adult Heteroptera, suture of the forewing separating the clavus from the corium (T-B; Borror et al.).

claval vein, in adult Hemiptera, apically fused anal veins (Borror et al.).

clavate, clavatus, clublike, i.e., thickening gradually toward the tip, e.g., clavate antenna (T-B; Borror et al.); see capitate.

clavate antenna, an antenna terminating in a gradual club (Borror et al.).

clavate hairs, in Collembola, tenent hairs (T-B).

clavate process, in some ♂ Myrmeleontidae (Planipennia), a process with a dense hair tuft at the base of the posterior margin of the hind wing (Riek, in CSIRO).

clavate setae, in Coccoidea (Hemiptera: Sternorrhyncha), certain marginal setae with enlarged or dilated ends (T-B, after MacGillivray).

Clavicornia, a subgroup of Coleoptera having the antennae more or less distinctly enlarged or clubbed at tip (T-B).

clavicula, procoxae, q.v. (T-B, after Kirby and Spence).

clavicular lobe, in Auchenorrhyncha (Hemiptera), that portion of hind wing behind the anal veins (T-B).

claviform, clublike in form (T-B); in Noctuidae (Lepidoptera), an elongate spot or mark extending from the transverse anterior line through the submedian interspace, toward and sometimes to the transverse posterior line (T-B).

clavigerate antenna, clavate antenna, q.v. (T-B).

claviola, antennal club, q.v. (T-B, after J. B. Smith); flagellum, q.v., of antenna (T-B, after Comstock).

clavopruina, in Corixidae (Hemiptera: Heteroptera), a narrow, white frosted area along the anterior lateral margin of the clavus (Lauck, in Menke).

clavulus, frenulum, q.v. (T-B).

clavus (pl., **clavi**), in the wing, the area behind the claval furrow (Chapman); antennal club, q.v. (T-B); in Heteroptera (Hemiptera), the usually parallel-sided and sharply pointed anal area of the hemelytron (T-B); in Coccoidea (Hemiptera:Sternorrhyncha), clypeus, q.v. (T-B, after MacGillivary); in ♂ Noctuidae (Lepidoptera), rounded, peaked or brushlike process of dorsal margin of sacculus (Tuxen, after Pierce); in adult Hymenoptera, area of wing between claval furrow and jugal fold (Gauld and Bolton); in adult Chalcidoidea (Hymenoptera), the knob at the end of the stigmal vein (T-B).

claw(s), a sharp, hooked, structure resembling the nail of a bird or mammal; pretarsal claw, q.v. (T-B); one (or more) corneous sharp structures on the lobes of the maxillae (T-B, after Kirby and Spence); in Collembola, unguis, q.v. (Christiansen and Bellinger); in ♂ Culicidae (Diptera), apical or subapical articulating part of dististylus (stylus) (Tuxen); in ♂ Mecoptera, styli, q.v. (Tuxen, after Hine); in ♂ Siphonaptera, lobes of aedeagus, q.v. (Tuxen).

claw hairs, in Heteroptera (Hemiptera), setiform microtrichia on outer surface of a claw (Schuh).

claw plate, in Heteroptera (Hemiptera), unguitractor (plate), q.v. (Andersen).

claws of last segment, in ♂ Mecoptera, styli, q.v. (Tuxen, after McLachlan).

cleavage, in embryological development, the division of the original single-celled egg into a number of cells called blastomeres (T-B; Tulloch; Hinton and Mackerras, in CSIRO); see holoblastic cleavage and meroblastic cleavage.

cleavage cells, blastomeres, q.v. (T-B).

cleft, split or forked (T-B; Borror et al.); in ♂ Caelifera (Orthoptera), slitlike ventral opening of phallotreme (Tuxen, after Roberts).

Cleistogastra, Clistogastra, q.v. (Leftwich).

cleptobiosis, a form of symbiosis in ants (Hymenoptera: Formicidae) in which small ants have nests near or in the nests of larger species, feeding on refuse or waylaying the workers and stealing their food (T-B).

cleptoparasitism, the parasitic relation in which a ♀ seeks out prey or stored food of another ♀, usually belonging to a different species, and appropriates it for the rearing of her own offspring (Wilson); see social parasitism.

Cleroidea, superfamily within the suborder Polyphaga (Coleoptera), including the families Cleridae, Trogossitidae, Chaetosomatidae, and Phloeophilidae, adults possessing 5-5-5 tarsal formula, transverse forecoxae with exposed trochantins, hind coxae without a steep or concave posterior face for reception of the femur, and abdomen with 5 (rarely 6) visible sternites, and larvae with a strongly sclerotized prothorax, fixed urogomphi arising from basal plate, free labrum, fused galea and lacinia, and lacking a mola on the mandible (Britton, after Crowson, in CSIRO).

click mechanism, wing movement resulting from rapid movement of cuticular hinge into down position resulting in release of tension produced from contraction of the dorsal longitudinal muscles (Gilmour, in CSIRO); in Cicadidae (Hemiptera: Auchenorrhyncha), sudden deformation of tymbal resulting from release of tension produced by contraction of tymbal muscle (Gilmour, in CSIRO); in adult Elateridae (Coleoptera), the sudden forcing of long prosternal process into cavity in the mesosternum, causing sudden movement of the prothorax relative to the hind body (Britton, in CSIRO).

climate, the sum total of weather at a particular point (T-B, after Shelford).

climax area, in ecology, the most stable and permanent type of biotic environment attainable over a major geographic area, e.g. northern coniferous forest (Klots).

climograph, a diagram of climate plotted in the form of a mean monthly wet-bulb temperature and humidity (T-B, after Shelford).

clinal, varying gradually, of characters (Mayr).

cline, a gradual or nearly continuous change of a character in a series of contiguous populations (Mayr); a character gradient in which the structure or physiology of an organism changes over its geographical range (Common and Waterhouse).

clinical pathology, study of disease by laboratory methods (Steinhaus and Martignoni).

clinopus (pl., **clinopodes**), in ♂ *Argynnis* (Lepidoptera: Nymphalidae), geniculate, serrate process of inner face of valva, arising from sacculus or harpe (Tuxen, after Fruhstorfer).

clintheriform, shaped like a plate (T-B).

clip, in ♀ Coleophoridae (Lepidoptera), tubular structures, thickly covered with short dark spines, lying lateral to central ridge of ductus bursae (Tuxen, after Toll).

Clistogastra, Apocrita, q.v. (T-B; Borror et al.).

clistogastrous, having a petiolate abdomen, referring to adult Apocrita (Hymenoptera) (T-B); see chalastrogastrous.

clithrum (pl., **clithra**), in some larval Scarabaeidae (Coleoptera), a paired short sclerome in the anterior part of the margin of the epipharynx, separating the corypha and the paria (T-B, after Böving).

clitoris, in ♀ Lepidoptera, signum, q.v. (Tuxen).

cloaca (pl., **cloacae**), a common chamber into which open the intestine (rectum) and the genital ducts, e.g., Dermaptera, Coleoptera, and ♀ monotrysian Lepidoptera (T-B; Tuxen).

cloaca valves, in ♀ Dytiscidae (Coleoptera), the halves of sternum VIII (Tuxen, after Böving).

cloacal, pertaining to cloaca or rectum (Peterson).

clone, all of the offspring of a single asexually producing individual (Mayr).

closed cell, a wing cell completely surrounded by veins (T-B, after Comtock); see open cell.

closed clavus, in Fulgoroidea (Hemiptera: Auchenorrhyncha), claval suture extending to wing margin (O'Brien and Wilson, in Nault).

closed coxal cavity, in adult Coleoptera, coxal cavity bounded posteriorly by a sclerite of the same thoracic segment (front coxal cavities) or one completely surrounded by sternal sclerites and not touched by any pleural sclerites (middle coxal cavities) (Borror et al.).

closing apparatus of spiracle, the closing and opening mechanism formed either of the lips of the atrium or by a valve at the inner end of the atrium (T-B, after Snodgrass).

closing band, the moveable valvular fold of the inner closing mechanism of a spiracle (T-B, after Snodgrass).

closing bow, the rigid but elastic lip of the inner closing mechanism of a spiracle opposite the valve (T-B, after Snodgrass).

clothing hairs, the hairs, setae, or chaetae investing or covering the surface of the insect body or its appendages, frequently more or less specialized, giving it a downy appearance (T-B).

clover phyllody, disease of clover caused by a mycoplasma transmitted propagatively by leafhoppers (Hemiptera: Auchenorrhyncha: Cicadellidae) (Borror et al.).

club, antennal club, q.v. (T-B, after Comstock).

clubbed, with the distal part (or segments) enlarged, e.g., clubbed antenna (T-B; Borror et al.); see capitate and clavate.

clunial prolongation, in ♀ Psocoptera, ventral prolongation of clunium, bearing terminally a set of paired gonapophyses (Tuxen, after Pearman).

clunicula (pl., **cluniculae**), in ♂ *Ornithoptera* (Lepidoptera: Papilionidae), spoonlike, serrate process of inner face of valva, sometimes clublike, arising from valvula or harpe (Tuxen, after Fruhstorfer).

clunium (pl., **clunia**), in ♀ Psocoptera, fused terga VIII–X (Tuxen, after Pearman); in ♂ Psocoptera, fused terga IX–X (Mockford, pers. comm.).

cluster, a group set close together (T-B).

cluster pore plate, in Cryptococcidae (Hemiptera: Sternorrhyncha: Coccoidea), structure on venter, just posterior to hind spiracles, apparently resulting from the reduction of the hind legs (Kosztarab and Kozár).

clustering, the habit of gathering in groups prior to mating or prior to hibernation, or due to low temperature, e.g, among *Polistes* wasps (Hymenoptera: Vespidae) (Tulloch, after Fernald, Rau, Gaul).

clustering methods, methods for grouping related or similar species into species groups or higher taxa (Mayr).

clypanguli, the parts of the clypeus bearing the precoila (T-B, after MacGillivray).

clypealia (pl., **clypealiae**), the small subtriangular or quadrangular area at each lateral end of the postclypeus; antecoxal piece of the mandible; paraclypeus, lateroclypeus (T-B, after MacGillivray).

clypeal phragma, in adult Culicidae (Diptera), a flat, sheetlike apodeme extending from the exposed part of the clypeus to the lateral margin of the cibarium (Harbach and Knight, after Knight and Laffoon); see clypeal phragmata.

clypeal phragmata, in larval Muscomorpha (Diptera), dorsal cornua, q.v. (Teskey, after Roberts, in McAlpine).

clypeal setae, in larval Chironomidae (Diptera), labral setae (S1,S2) + clypeal seta (S3) (Saether); in larval Lepidoptera, 2 pairs of setae (C1 and C2) on the clypeus (Stehr).

clypeal suture, epistomal suture, q.v. (T-B); transverse suture dividing the clypeus into an anteclypeus and a postclyepus (T-B, after MacGillivray; Harbach and Knight).

clypealia (pl., **clypealiae**), the small subtriangular or quadrangular area at each lateral end of postclypeus (T-B); antecoxal piece of the mandible, e.g., larval *Corydalus* (Megaloptera: Corydalidae) (Peterson); in larval Chironomidae (Diptera), triangular sclerite, q.v. (Saether).

clypeate, clypeatus, shieldlike in form (T-B).

clypeate constriction, a constriction formed when a surface is drawn in from the sides so as to produce a shield or saddlelike form (T-B).

clypeate head, caput clypeatum; a flattish head, with broad flat margins in the clypeus and frons (T-B).

clypeiform, shield-shaped; clypeus-shaped (T-B).

clypeocephalic prolongment, in Ephemeroptera, a small rounded projection arising from the anterior border of the head between the antennae (T-B, after Needham).

clypeofrontal, of or pertaining to the clypeus and the front (T-B).

clypeofrontal phragmata, in larval Muscomorpha (Diptera), dorsal cornua, q.v. (Teskey, after Hartley, in McAlpine).

clypeofrontal suture, frontoclypeal suture, q.v. (T-B).

clypeolabral, of or pertaining to the clypeus and the labrum together (T-B).

clypeolabral membrane, membrane between clypeus and labrum (McAlpine).

clypeolabral ridge, the internal ridge associated with the clypeolabral suture when this suture is not entirely membranous (Harbach and Knight).

clypeolabral shield, in ♀ Coccoidea (Hemiptera: Sternorrhyncha), the usually subrectangular or pentagonal shield located anterior to the labium, enclosing the clypeus, labrum, and the bases of the mandibles and maxillae (Kosztarab and Kozár).

clypeolabral strap, in larval Culicidae (Diptera), a paired straplike cranial process comprising of the end of the clypeolabral ridge and the adjacent lateral corners of the paraclypeal lobe and median labral plate, articulating distally with the base of the torma (Harbach and Knight, after Laffoon and Knight).

clypeolabral suture, the flexible junction or suture between the clypeus and the labrum (T-B); in larval Chironomidae (Diptera), interantennal suture, q.v. (Saether).

clypeolabrum, in larval Chironomidae (Diptera), sclerite or delineated area carrying clypeal seta (S3) and at least one of the labral setae (S1,S2) (Saether) or area in front of frontal apotome whether or not this is differentiated into a clypeus and labral sclerites (Saether).

clypeolus, anteclypeus, q.v. (T-B).

clypeopalatum, in adult Culicidae (Diptera), the part of the palatum formed by the under surface of the clypeus, the roof of the cibarium (Harbach and Knight).

clypeus, that part of the insect head below the frons, to which the labrum is attached anteriorly (T-B); area of head separated from frons by epistomal suture (Chapman); in Coccoidea (Hemiptera: Sternorrhyncha), the broad band bounding the ventral aspect of the head (T-B, after Green); in some larval Chironomidae (Diptera), plate carrying clypeal seta (S3) and separated from frontal apotome and labral sclerites by sutures (Saether) (see frontoclypeal apotome).

clypeus anterior, anteclypeus, q.v. (T-B).

clypeus posterior, postclypeus, q.v. (T-B).

clypofrons, the transverse line forming the caudal limit of the clypeus on the external surface of the head, and its invaginated part (T-B, after MacGillivray).

co-, Latin prefix; together (T-B); see con-.

CO₂ carbon dioxide, q.v. (T-B).

Co-Ral (trade name), coumaphos, q.v. (Pfadt).

coactus, condensed; of a short stout form (T-B).

coadaptation, coevolution, q.v. (Matthews and Matthews).

coadapted, formed so as to work together to one end (T-B).

coadunate, joined together at base; 2 or more joined together; said of elytra when permanently united at the suture (T-B).

coagulate, to congeal; to change from a fluid to a jelly; to form a clot (T-B).

coagulation, clot formation or jell formation involving cystocytes (Gilmour, in CSIRO; Chapman)

coagulin, a constituent of blood which aids in blood-clotting (T-B).

coagulocyte, cystocyte, q.v. (Tulloch; Chapman).

coagulum, a clotted mass, as of blood (T-B).

coalescent, united or grown together (T-B).

coalite, coalitus, fused; of any 2 parts usually separated and distinct (T-B, after Kirby and Spence).

coalite stilt prolegs, stilt prolegs united for a part of their length into one organ, which has a bifid apex (T-B).

coarctate, coarctatus (Latin), contracted or compacted (T-B); beginning with a narrow base, then dilated and thickened (T-B).

coarctate larva, larva somewhat similar to dipterous puparium, in which the skin of the preceding instar is not completely shed but remains attached to the caudal end of the body (Borror et al.); in larval Meloidae (Coleoptera), sixth instar with fifth instar exuvium present (Borror et al.).

coarctate pupa, pupa in which all the members of the future adult are concealed by a thickened, usually cylindrical case or covering, which is often the hardened skin of the larva (T-B); in many Diptera, pupa which remains enclosed in the old larval skin (puparium) (T-B, after Wardle; Leftwich).

coarsely granular hemocyte, spherule cell, q.v. (Tulloch, after Bogojavlensky).

cocardes, retractile vesicular bodies on each side of the thorax in certain Malachiidae (Coleoptera) (T-B).

coccidicolous, having the habit of feeding on honey-dew secreted by Coccoidea (Hemiptera: Sternorrhyncha) (Gaul).

coccidivorous, feeding or preying on scale insects, mealy bugs, etc (Hemiptera: Sternorrhyncha: Coccoidea) (Gauld and Bolton).

Coccidomorpha, Coccoidea, q.v. (Hennig, after Bekker-Migdisova).

coccids, scale insects, q.v.; members of the family Coccidae, the soft scale (Hemiptera: Sternorrhyncha) (Kosztarab and Kozár).

Coccina, Coccoidea, q.v. (Hennig).

Coccinea, suborder within the Hemiptera, proposed for the superfamily Coccoidea (Kosztarab and Kozár).

coccineous, coccineus, cochineal red; scarlet (T-B).

coccoid, a member of the superfamily Coccoidea (Hemiptera: Sternorrhyncha).

Coccoidea, superfamily within the Sternorrhyncha (Hemiptera), including scale insects and mealy bugs, characterized by tarsi with 2 or fewer tarsomeres, neoteinic, apterous females, and flightless or dipterous males with wings without or with few closed cells (Woodward et al., in CSIRO); Neococcoidea, q.v. (Kosztarab and Kozár).

cocephalic, having a prognathous head in which only the foramen exists (T-B, after MacGillivray).

cochineal, red dye made from the dried bodies of scale insects, *Dactylopius cacti* or *Dactylopius coccus* (Hemiptera: Sternorrhyncha: Eriococcidae), (T-B; Leftwich; Chapman); see carminic acid.

cochineal insect, *Dactylopius coccus*, a coccoid (Hemiptera: Sternorrhyncha: Dactylopiidae) of Mexican *Opuntia* (prickly pear cacti), from which a red dye is obtained; a word derived from the Spanish "cochinillo," a little pig, given because of the gregarious habit of this form (T-B); see cochineal.

cochleariform setae, in *Micropsectra* (Diptera: Chironomidae), spoonshaped, apical, lamellate setae of median volsella (Saether).

cochleate, cochleatus, cochleiform, twisted spirally, like a snail shell (T-B).

cochlearium, in ♂ Hymenoptera, gonostylus, q.v. (Tuxen, after Hartig).

cockroach, a member of the order Blattaria (Mackerras, in CSIRO).

cockscomb gall, leaf gall on elm caused by *Colopha ulmicola* (Fitch) (Hemiptera: Sternorrhyncha: Aphididae) (Borror et al.).

cocoon, a covering of the pupa, composed partly or wholly of silk, spun or constructed by many larvae (T-B), e.g., in Lepidoptera (Bombycoidea), Siphonaptera, Trichoptera, and many Hymenoptera (Chapman); in *Hydrophilus* (Coleoptera: Hydrophilidae), a silken sac produced by the ♀ accessory glands into which eggs are laid, equipped with a silken mast which serves a respiratory function (Chapman).

cocoon breakers, cocoon cutters, q.v. (T-B).

cocoon cutters, in certain pupal Lepidoptera, structures or processes often on the head, by means of which the pupa works its way out of the cocoon (T-B; Common, in CSIRO).

cocoonase, in Bombycidae and Saturniidae (Lepidoptera), a proteolytic enzyme secreted on the surface of the galea, by a newly emerged adult which moistens and softens the silk of the cocoon allowing the adult insect to emerge (Chapman; Common).

Code, International Code of Zoological Nomenclature, q.v. (T-B; ICZN).

Code of Ethics, a set of recommendations on the propriety of taxonomic actions, to guide the taxonomist, formulated as Appendix A of the International Code of Zoological Nomenclature (Mayr).

codlelure, synthetic sex pheromone of the ♀ codling moth, *Cydia pomonella* (Lepidoptera: Tortricidae), (*E,E*)-8,10-dodecadien-1-ol (Pfadt).

coecal, ending blindly, or in a closed tube or pouch (T-B).

coecum (pl., **coeca**), a blind sac or tube; applied to a series of appendages opening into the alimentary canal at the junction of the gizzard
and chylific ventricle; see caecum (T-B).

coecum penis, in ♂ Lepidoptera, the hollow, blind cephaloventrad
extension of the aedoeagus beyond the point where the ductus ejaculatorius enters (Tuxen, after Kusnezov).

coefficient of difference (CD), difference of means divided by sum of
standard deviations, (Mayr).

$$CD = \frac{|M_b M_a|}{SD_a + SD_b}$$

coefficient of relationship (r), the average fraction of genes shared by
common ancestry (Matthews and Matthews).

coefficient of variability (CV), the standard deviation as percentage of
the mean, (Mayr).

$$CV = \frac{SD \times 100}{M}$$

coeloblast, the endoderm in the narrow sense (T-B).

coeloconic sensillum, sensillum consisting of a conical sensory peg
sunk in a pit in the body wall, involved in olfaction, humidity perception, and temperature perception (T-B; Chapman).

coelom, in Arthropoda, hemocoel, q.v. (T-B).

coelomere, coelomic sacs, q.v. (Boudreaux).

coelomic cavity, in Arthropoda, hemocoel, q.v. (T-B).

coelomic sacs, in the embryo, paired sacs arising from the mesoderm
of each segment, consisting of a ventral somatic layer and a dorsal
splanchnic or visceral layer, which later fuse with the epineural sinus
to form the hemocoel (T-B; Hinton and Mackerras, in CSIRO).

Coenagrionoidea, superfamily within the suborder Zygoptera (Odonata), including the families Coenagrionidae, Platystictidae, Proto-
neuridae, Platycnemididae, Lestoideidae, Pseudostigmatidae, and
Megapodagrionidae, characterized by adults with 2 (or 3) antenodal
crossveins in the wing, postnodal crossveins mostly aligned with
crossveins behind them, and posterior cubitus (CuP) not arching
forward as it leaves the distal end of the quadrilateral (O'Farrell, in
CSIRO).

coenobiosis, a definite consociation of animals and plants of different
species (Tulloch, after Gaul).

coenocyte, an enlarged protoplast, the nuclear divisions of which have
not been followed by cytoplasmic cleavage (T-B, after Daubenmire).

coenogenous, oviparous at one season of the year, ovoviviparous at
another, as in Aphididae (Hemiptera: Sternorrhyncha)(T-B).

coeruleous, coeruleus, sky-blue; see caeruleus (T-B).

coevolution, when 2 or more populations interact so closely that each
serves as a strong selective force on the evolution of the other resulting in reciprocal stepwise adjustments (Matthews and Matthews).

coila, condyle, q.v. (T-B, after MacGillivray).

coiled accessory gland, in ♀ Gerridae (Hemiptera: Heteroptera), spermathecal tube, q.v. (Andersen).

coiled duct, in Gerromorpha (Hemiptera: Heteroptera), fecundation canal, q.v. (Andersen).

coiled tubular gland, in ♀ Ranatrinae (Hemiptera: Heteroptera: Nepidae), receptaculum seminis, q.v. (Tuxen, after Marshall and Severin).

coincident, coinciding; running together or lying in continuation of the other so as to appear like one, as veins (T-B).

coition, coitus, the mating act; copulation (T-B).

col-, Latin prefix; with (T-B).

colacobiosis, calobiosis, q.v. (T-B).

Coleoptera, endopterygote order of Neoptera (Insecta), comprising the beetles, characterized by adults with sclerotized forewings that normally meet edge to edge down the middle of the back and by oligopod or apodous larvae (T-B; Mackerras, in CSIRO).

Coleopterida, Coleopteroidea, q.v. (Boudreaux).

coleopteroid, beetlelike in form (T-B).

Coleopteroidea, group of Holometabola, including the Coleoptera and Strepsiptera (Boudreaux, after Handlirsch); see Neuropteroidea.

Coleorrhyncha, suborder within the Hemiptera, including only the superfamily Peloridioidea, characterized by adults with forewings with many closed cells formed by raised veins, well-developed pronotal expansions, and tarsi with fewer than 3 tarsomeres (Woodward et al., in CSIRO); see Sternorrhyncha, Auchenorrhyncha, and Heteroptera.

collagen, component of connective tissues of vertebrates and of the basement membrane in some insects (Chapman).

collagenase, a proteolytic digestive enzyme (T-B), produced by larval *Hypoderma* (Oestridae) and some blow flies (Calliphoridae) (Diptera) and acting on the collagen of animal tissues (Chapman).

collar, a circular or semicircular strip or band at the back of the head or front of the trunk or thorax, the morphological makeup varying with the taxon (Harbach and Knight); in Entomobryidae (Collembola), the characteristic group of macrochaetae along the anterior mesothoracic margin (Christiansen and Bellinger); in Heteroptera (Hemiptera), rounded or flattened collarlike anterior margin of the prothorax (Štys); in Siphonaptera, applied to that portion of any segment fitting directly over the anterior portion of the succeeding segment (Lewis, pers. comm.); in adult Lepidoptera, patagia, q.v. (T-B; Common, pers. comm.); see cervix.

collare (pl., **collaria**), in ♂ *Cricula* (Lepidoptera: Saturniidae), a strongly enlarged juxta (Tuxen, after Roepke).

collateral, a lateral branch of an axon (T-B, after Snodgrass).

collaterial, colleterial, q.v. (T-B).

collatoria, mouth of duct of colleterial glands in ♀ and of accessory genital glands in ♂ (T-B, after MacGillivray).

collecting basket, an arrangement of hairs, bristles and spines on the forelegs of certain insects, in which they collect or hold food while devouring it (T-B, after Needham).

collective group, an assemblage of nominal species that cannot be placed with certainty in known genera, with names proposed for collective groups to be subsequently treated as generic names (ICZN).

collective-group name, a name established expressly for a collective group, without a type species and, therefore not competing with other genus-group names for priority but competing with them for homonymy; a name established for a nominal genus or subgenus and later used for a collective group, with a type species and, therefore, competing with other genus group names for priority and for homonymy (ICZN).

Collembola, entognathous class or order within the superclass Hexapoda, comprising the springtails, possessing gradual metamorphosis, four-segmented legs (the last segment being a tibiotarsus), antenna with 4 or 6 articles, and abdomen with 6 or fewer segments even in the embryo (T-B; Mackerras, in CSIRO).

collenchyma, in galls of Cynipidae (Hymenoptera), the layer lying directly below the epidermis, in which the cells have thickened walls and, usually, crystalline contents, appearing hard, compact and crystalline to the eye (T-B, after Kinsey).

colleterial glands, in ♀ insects, accessory glands secreting a substance to fasten eggs to a support (Tuxen); in ♂ insects, accessory genital glands, q.v. (Tuxen); in ♀ Lepidoptera, glandulae sebaceae, q.v. (Tuxen).

colleterium, in ♀ Lepidoptera, glandulae sebaceae, q.v. (Tuxen).

colliculate, continuously covered with low, rounded elevations, not as pronounced as acinose (Harris, after R. W. Brown, and Stearn); see acinose, granulate, and papillate.

colliculum, in ♀ Lepidoptera, sclerotization of proximal part of ductus bursae, often tubular or funicular, more or less forming a continuation of ostium bursae (Tuxen, after Diakonoff); see antrum and cone.

Collifera, group within the Myriapoda, including the Pauropoda and Diplopoda (Boudreaux); see Atelopoda.

colligate, colligatus, attached to any part but not moveable (T-B).

colloid, gluelike; a condition of matter in which it is amorphous and without crystalline structure (T-B).

collophore, in Collembola, ventral tube, q.v. (T-B, after Snodgrass; Borror et al.).

collum (Latin, meaning: neck) (pl., **colla**), in Heteroptera (Hemiptera), collar, q.v., of prothorax (Štys), or incorrectly, cephalic neck (Štys, pers. comm., after Gross); in ♂ Siphonaptera, neck, q.v. (Tuxen, after Peus); in Pauropoda and Diplopoda, the legless segment immediately behind the head (Boudreaux).

collum bursae, in ♀ Lepidoptera, ductus bursae, q.v. (Tuxen, after de Graaf).

collum spermatophori, in Lepidoptera, a tubular neck which connects the aperture and frenum with the corpus of the spermatophore (Callahan and Chapin).

Colobognatha, former superorder of Diplopoda, including the orders Polyzoniida and Polydesmida (Borror et al.); see Helminthomorpha.

Colocasia bobone disease, disease of taro plants (*Colocasia*) caused by a rhabdovirus transmitted propagatively by *Laodelphax* (Hemiptera: Auchenorrhyncha: Delphacidae) (Nault and Ammar).

colon, that part of the hind gut between the ileum and the rectum (T-B); in Lepidoptera, tuba analis, q.v. (Tuxen, after Philpott).

colonial, living in colonies (CSIRO).

colonici, insects that live in colonies (Leftwich); in Aphididae (Hemiptera: Sternorrhyncha), first generation of aliencolae (Leftwich).

colonizing flight, in Isoptera, dispersal flight, q.v. (Krishna, pers. comm.).

colony, a group of individuals, other than a single mated pair, which constructs nests and rears offspring in a cooperative manner (Wilson); see aggregation.

colony fission, the multiplication of colonies by the departure of one or more reproductive forms, accompanied by groups of workers, from the parental nest, leaving behind comparable units to perpetuate the "parental" colony (Wilson); see swarming.

colony odor, the odor found on the bodies of social insects which is peculiar to a given colony; by smelling the colony odor of another member of the same species, an insect is able to determine whether it is a nestmate (Wilson); see nest odor and species odor.

Colopyga, Schizomida, q.v. (Borror et al.).

color, in insects, a single hue (T-B).

Colorado tick fever, viral disease of man in the western United States, transmitted by various ticks (Acari: Ixodidae) (Borror et al.).

coloration, in insects, an arrangement of colors (T-B).

colpus (pl., **colpi**), in ♀ Hymenoptera, groove in overhang of annulus, demarcating membrane between individual segments of gonapophysis (Tuxen, after E. L. Smith).

colulus, in spiders (Arachnida: Araneae), a slender pointed structure lying just anterior to the spinnerets (Borror et al.).

columella, in anopheline larvae (Diptera: Culicidae), the basal stalk of Nuttall and Shipley's organ supporting the more membranous bilobed part (Harbach and Knight, after Iyengar).

columna, in ♂ *Polystoechotes* (Planipennia: Polystoechotidae), hypovalva, q.v. (Tuxen, after Crampton); in ♂ *Panorpa* (Mecoptera: Panorpidae), median ventral projection from base of aedeagus (Byers, pers. comm, after Crampton).

com-, Latin prefix; a form of con- or co-, q.v. (T-B).

comate, comatus, hairy on the upper part of the head or the vertex only; hairy in general, with long, flexible hairs on the upper surface (T-B, after Kirby and Spence).

comb, a layer of brood cells or cocoons crowded together in a regular arrangment, characteristic of nests of many species of social wasps and bees (Hymenoptera) (T-B; Wilson); in Macrotermitinae (Isoptera: Termitidae) fungus comb, q.v. (T-B); in adult Siphonaptera, ctenidium, q.v. (Lewis, pers. comm.); in ♂ Lycaenidae (Lepidoptera), the serrate distal margin of the rostellum of the valva (Tuxen, after Nabokov); in most culicine and first instar anopheline larvae (Diptera: Culicidae), a row or patch of specialized spicules centered on each side of abdominal segment VIII (Peterson; Harbach and Knight, after Dyar); see antenna comb and honey comb.

comb plate, in certain culicine larvae (Diptera: Culicidae), a lateral sclerite on abdominal segment VIII which bears the comb scales (Harbach and Knight, after Belkin).

comb scale, in most culicine and first instar anopheline larvae (Diptera: Culicidae), one of the specialized spicules forming the comb on abdominal segment VIII (Harbach and Knight, after Felt).

combination, the association of a generic name and a specific name to form the name of a species; or of a generic name with a specific and a subspecific name to form the name of a subspecies (ICZN).

combination colors, in insects, colors arising from a combination of pigmentary and structural colors; more common than purely structural colors (T-B, after Imms).

combinations, in genetics, a reshuffling of characters (T-B).

combs, in larval Culicidae (Diptera), certain hairs on the upper surface of the maxillae, with which the brushes are cleaned (T-B); in adult Hymenoptera, strigilis, q.v. (T-B); see ctenidia.

comes (pl., **comiti**), in some ♂ Chrysopidae (Planipennia), keellike organ proximad of, and membranously connected to, hypandrium internum (Tuxen, after Tjeder).

commensal, a species that benefits through commensalism (T-B; Wilson).

commensalism, symbiosis in which members of one species are benefited while those of the other species are neither benefited nor harmed (T-B; Tulloch; Wilson).

comminute, to grind up fine; to reduce to minute particles (T-B).

comminuted, broken up into extremely small fragments (T-B).

Commission, International Commission on Zoological Nomenclature, q.v. (ICZN).

commissura, commissure, the joint in the costal nerve of the wings of Coleoptera where they bend at the transverse fold; the nerve cord connecting 2 ganglia; the point of meeting or union of 2 bodies; a bridge connecting any 2 bodies or structures, e.g., the tracheal tubes.

commissura (pl., **commissurae**), in ♂ Lepidoptera, articulation of each pedunculus with the vinculum (Tuxen, after Schroeder).

commisural, of or pertaining to a commissure (T-B).

commissural tracheal trunks, cross tracheal trunks continuous from one side of the body to the other, formed by anastomosis of the dorsal and ventral tracheae on each side (T-B, after Snodgrass); see dorsal tracheal commissure and ventral tracheal commissure.

common, of frequent occurrence; occurring on 2 adjacent parts; a band or fascia when it crosses both the anterior and posterior wings (T-B).

common name, vernacular name, q.v. (Mayr).

common oviduct, in ♀ insects, oviductus communis, q.v. (Tuxen).

common salivary duct, in many Diptera, the common median part of the salivary ducts opening into the salivary pump.

communal, condition or type of group in which members of the same generation cooperate in nest building but not in brood care (T-B; Wilson).

communalism, the association of insects of various castes in a colony, e.g., of bees (Leftwich).

communicable disease, in invertebrate pathology, contagious disease, q.v. (Steinhaus and Martignoni).

communication, action on the part of one organism (or cell) that alters the probability pattern of behavior in another organism (or cell) in an adaptive fashion (Matthews and Matthews).

communicatory activities, activities concerned with conveying information to, and influencing the mood and activities of, others of the same species (Matthews and Matthews).

community, in ecology, the animals or plants of a given habitat (T-B).

comose, comate; terminating in a hair-tuft or brush (T-B).

compacted, consolidated or closely united (T-B).

competitive exclusion, the principle that no 2 species can coexist at the same locality if they have identical ecological requirements (Mayr).

complanate, complanatus, compressed; flattened above and below; deplanate (T-B).

complemental reproductive, complementary reproductive, special sexual forms in the Termitidae (Isoptera), which in case of loss or death, replace the king (reproductive ♂) and queen (reproductive ♀) of the colony; produced from the nymphs by special feeding.

complete metamorphosis, metamorphosis in holometabolous insects which in general has 4 stages—egg, larva, pupa, and adult—each entirely different from the others (T-B); see incomplete metamorphosis.

complex, as an adjective, consisting of a number of differentiated parts (T-B); in ecology, a grouping or association of organisms (T-B); in taxonomy, a neutral term for a number of related taxonomic units, most commonly involving units in which the taxonomy is difficult or confusing (Mayr); see group and neutral term.

complex behavior, behavior involving more than orientation or movement with respect to a particular stimulus (Borror et al.).

complicant, when one elytron extends over the other and partly covers it (T-B).

complicate, complicatus (Latin), longitudinally laid in folds; intricate as opposed to simple (T-B).

complicating disease, in invertebrate pathology, a disease supervening during the course of an already existing infection (Steinhaus and Martignoni); see complication.

complication, in invertebrate pathology, a morbid process or event occurring during a disease which is not an essential part of the disease itself, though it may result from it or from other independent causes (Steinhaus and Martignoni).

component, any one part of a combined whole (T-B).

composite, compositus (Latin), compound (T-B).

compound, made up of many similar or dissimilar parts (T-B).

compound antenna, capitate antenna formed by several joints (T-B).

compound eye, in adult insects, nymphs of Exopterygota, and larvae of Mecoptera, an aggregation of separate visual elements known as ommatidia, each of which correponds with a single facet of the cornea (T-B, after Imms; Peterson; Hinton and Mackerras, in CSIRO); see ocellus and stemma.

compound ocellus, an ocellate spot in which the color is in 3 or more circles (T-B).

compound nest, a nest containing colonies of 2 or more species of social insects, up to the point where the galleries of the nests anastamose and the adults sometimes intermingle but where the broods of the species are still kept separate (Tulloch, after Gaul; Wilson); see mixed nest.

compound wax pores, in Aleyrodidae (Hemiptera: Sternorrhyncha), large cylindrical pores with many openings, producing long cylindrical rods of wax on dorsal submargin of pupa (Gill).

compressed, compressus (Latin), flattened by lateral pressure (T-B); flattened laterally as against flattened vertically of depressed (T-B).

compressor of labrum, a single or paired median muscle, attached on the anterior and posterior walls within the labrum (T-B, after Snodgrass).

Comstock-Kellog glands, in Acrididae (Orthoptera), glandular pouches, q.v. (Uvarov).

Comstock-Needham system, the most widely used system of nomenclature for the veins of the wing, intended by its authors to be applicable to insects of all orders, and to be a "natural" sytem related to the mode of formation of the principal veins from tracheae (Leftwich).

con-, Latin prefix; with (T-B).

concatenate, concatenatus, linked together in a chainlike series (T-B).

concave, concavus, hollowed out; the interior of a sphere as opposed to the outer or convex surface (T-B).

concave vein, major longitudinal wing vein running along a trough (T-B, after Snodgrass, Imms; Leftwich); see convex vein.

concavoconvex, hollowed out or concave on one surface, rounded or convex on the other; like a small segment of a hollow sphere (T-B).

concealed, applied to any part which is withdrawn or hidden in some manner (T-B).

concealing coloration, cryptic coloration, q.v. (CSIRO).

concentrated, gathered together at one point; intensified or strengthened by evaporation (T-B).

conceptaculum seminis (pl., **conceptacula seminis**), in ♀ Cimicidae (Hemiptera: Heteroptera), mesodermal organs of sperm storage, being a differentiation of the mesodermal oviducts (Tuxen, after Carayon).

conchate, conchatus, shelllike; applied to the shelllike inflation of the auricle in the cephalic tibia of Orthoptera (T-B).

Conchostraca, order of Branchiopoda (Crustacea), including the clam shrimps (Borror et al.).

concinne, neat; fine (T-B).

concolor, concolorous, of a uniform color, one part with another (T-B).

concolores, applied to the wings of Lepidoptera when their upper and lower surfaces are of the same color (T-B).

concretion, a massing together of parts or particles (T-B).

concurrent, running together; applied to a vein which arises separately, runs into another and does not again separate (T-B).

conditioned reflex, the action in the nervous system arising from external conditions (T-B).

conducting chamber, in ♂ Heteroptera (Hemiptera), ejaculatory reservoir, q.v. (Tuxen, after Kumar).

conductivity, the property of nervous or other protoplasmic tissue to convey through itself changes in metabolic activity (T-B).

conduplicate, conduplicatus (Latin), doubled or folded together (T-B).

condylar, of or pertaining to a condyle (T-B).

condyle, any process by means of which an appendage is articulated into a pan or cavity (T-B, after J. B. Smith); a process which articulates the base of the mandible to the head (T-B, after Tillyard) (see dorsal condyle and ventral condyle); in ♂ *Melitaea* (Lepidoptera: Nymphalidae), small process formed by the laterocaudad production of the lateral or dorsal margins of the anellus (Tuxen, after Higgins).

condylic, of or relating to a condyle or joint surface (T-B).

condylite, in ♂ Staphylinidae (Coleoptera), the smaller part of a divided paramere, articulating with the base of the penis (Tuxen, after Brundin).

Condylognatha, group within the Paraneoptera (Insecta), including the Thysanoptera and Hemiptera, possessing maxillary lever, styletlike laciniae and mandibles ensheathed in a rostrum, and with cubitus posterior (CuP) uniting with first anal vein in forewing (Hennig; Boudreaux).

Condylognathida, Condylognatha, q.v. (Boudreaux).

condylus of lamina media, in ♂ Siphonaptera, lobus fulcri medialis, q.v. (Tuxen, after Jordan).

cone, in the compound eye of insects, crystalline cone, q.v. (T-B); in Thysanoptera, the cone-shaped head structure containing the mouthparts, formed by the labrum and clypeus above and the labium below; the mouth cone (T-B); in ♀ *Melitaea* (Lepidoptera: Nymphalidae), a conical, cephalic extension of the antrum (Tuxen, after Higgins); in adult Culicidae (Diptera), one of the specialized spicules comprising the cibarial teeth (Harbach and Knight, after Annett et al.); see ostial cone.

cone gall, on witch-hazel, spiny witch-hazel gall, q.v. (Borror et al.); on spruce, spruce cone-gall, q.v. (O'Brien, pers. comm.).

confer (Latin), compare; abbrev., cf., cfr (T-B).

confertus (Latin), pressed together, crowded, thick, dense (T-B; R. W. Brown).

conflect, conflected, q.v. (T-B; Harris).

conflected, crowded; thickly clustered (T-B; Harris); see sparse.

confluent, confluens (Latin), running together; as of 2 macula when united in one outline (T-B).

confused, of markings, having indefinite outlines or running together as lines or spots without definite pattern (T-B; Harris); see intricate and obscure.

congener, a species belonging to the same genus as another (T-B).

congeneric, agreeing in all characters of generic value with other species compared (T-B); belonging to the same genus (Mayr)

congenital disease, in invertebrate pathology, one that is present in the animal at birth, but not necessarily inherited (Steinhaus and Martignoni).

congested, heaped together; crowded; distended (T-B).

conglobate, conglobatus (Latin), gathered together in a ball or sphere (T-B).

conglobate gland, in ♂ Blattaria, a median gland of unknown function opening into the ejaculatory duct between the phallomeres (T-B; Mackerras, in CSIRO; Leftwich).

conglomerate, conglomeratus (Latin), congregated; massed together (T-B).

congruence, in taxonomy, the degree of correspondence between different classifications, or the degree to which a character corresponds to a given classification.

congruency hypothesis, hypothesis that congruency, or appropriateness between plant as food source and insect as feeder, occurs whenever these 2 independently mutating systems interact in such a way that formerly nonattracting chemicals produced by the plant now stimulate feeding (Matthews and Matthews, after Dethier).

conic, conical, cylindrical, with a flat base, tapering to a point (T-B).

conical peg of gonostylus, in ♀ Pamphiliidae (Hymenoptera), lamnium, q.v. (Tuxen, after Middlekauff).

conicoacuminate, in the form of a long, pointed cone (T-B).

conidia, asexual fungus spores (T-B).

coniferous, coniferus, bearing conelike processes (T-B).

coniform larva, cone-shaped larva, pointed at the head end and enlarged, obtuse or truncate at the caudal end (Peterson).

Coniopterygoidea, superfamily within the Planipennia, including only the family Coniopterygidae, characterized by small adults with reduced wing venation, no pterostigma, wings and most parts of body covered with a waxy, mealy secretion, and wings coupled by 2 sets of hamuli-like curved bristles (Riek, in CSIRO).

conjoined, joined together (T-B).

conjugate, to bring together in pairs; consisting of a single pair (T-B).

conjugation, the union of pairs; applied to the merging of the ♂ and ♀ elements; sexual reproduction involving fusion of equal-sized gametes (T-B).

conjunctiva (pl., **conjunctivae**), intersegmental membrane, q.v., (T-B, after Comstock); in ♂ Heteroptera (Hemiptera), an intermediate membranous portion of the phallus when the proximal phallosoma and the distal endosoma are both sclerotized (Tuxen, after Singh-Pruthi); in tympanal organ of Noctuoidea (Lepidoptera), a soft white membrane separated from the tympanum by a sclerotized ridge, the epaulette, q.v. (Chapman, after Roeder and Treat); see corium.

conjunctiva appendages, in ♂ Heteroptera (Hemiptera), processus conjunctivae, q.v. (Tuxen, after Singh-Pruthi).

conjunctiva processes, in ♂ Heteroptera (Hemiptera), processus conjunctivae, q.v. (Tuxen, after Dupuis and Carvalho).

conjunctival appendages, in ♂ Auchenorrhyncha (Hemiptera), moveable appendages on theca (Tuxen, after China).

conjunctival membrane, intersegmental membrane, q.v. (Mackerras, in CSIRO; McAlpine).

conjunctivitis, an infectous bacterial disease of the conjunctival membrane of the eye, transmitted by *Musca domestica* L. (Diptera: Muscidae) (Borror et al.).

conjunctivus, a mandibular sclerite between the molar and the basalis (T-B).

conjunctura, the articulation of a wing to the thorax (T-B).

connate, connatus (Latin), united at base, or along the entire length (T-B); on wing veins, arising at one point (Common, pers. comm.).

connecting filament, in Psocoptera and Amblycera (Phthiraptera), one of a pair of filaments or a Y-branched filament running from the sitophore sclerite to the lingual sclerites (T-B, after Snodgrass).

connecting membranes, in ♂ Coleoptera, first and second connecting membranes, q.v. (Tuxen).

connecting piece, in ♀ Heteroptera (Hemiptera), sclerotization connecting anterior fibulae with posterior margin of abdominal segment VIII (transl. "Verbindungsstück" Verhoeff, after Tuxen).

connecting rod, in ♂ Diptera, processus longus, q.v. (Tuxen, after Crampton).

connective, anything connecting one thing with another (T-B); the longitudinal cords of nerve fibers connecting one ganglion of a nervous system with another next to it (T-B); in ♂ Psyllidae (Hemiptera: Sternorrhyncha), a sclerotized structure belonging to the phallobase and connecting the aedeagus with the base of the forceps (Tuxen); in ♂ Auchenorrhyncha (Hemiptera), a sclerotized structure belonging to the phallobase and connecting the aedeagus with the base of the genital styles (Tuxen).

connective tissue, any tissue binding together other tissues (T-B).

connective VIII A, (abbrev.) in ♀ Heteroptera (Hemiptera), anterior connecting leaf of gonapophysis VIII, q.v. (transl. "connectif VIII A" Dupuis, after Tuxen).

connexivum, in Heteroptera (Hemiptera), sharp lateral margin of abdomen, being a line of contact between dorsal and ventral laterotergites (T-B; Štys, pers. comm.).

connivent, converging; approaching together; wings so folded in repose that they unite perfectly at their corresponding margins (T-B).

conoid, in adult Culicidae (Diptera), a line of thickening which occurs from a point anterior to the calypter and proximal to the alula at the axillary incision when the wing is extended (Harbach and Knight, after Prashad, Christophers).

Conopoidea, superfamily within the Schizophora of the Muscomorpha (Diptera: Brachycera), including only the family Conopidae, characterized by adults with M_1 of wings approximated to or fused with R_5 distally and with δ postabdomen symmetrical (Colless and McAlpine, in CSIRO) (McAlpine).

conserve, to preserve the use of a name as a valid name, by removing the obstacles to such use, or to declare that a work is deemed published, in each case by a decision of the Commission using its plenary power (ICZN).

conserved name, a name previously unavailable or invalid that the Commission, by the use of its plenary power, has enabled to be used as a valid name by removal of the known obstacles to the use of the name as a valid name (ICZN).

conserved work, a work that the Commission has ruled to be available (ICZN).

consistency index (CI), for each character or for all the characters on a cladogram, the observed number of character state changes (L) relative to the minimum number theoretically possible (R) if there were no homoplasy, i.e., a measure of the degree of homoplasy, perfect consistency being 1.0; (Kluge and Farris).

$$ci = \frac{R}{L}$$

consolidated, coalescent into one part with any neighboring, and usually detached, part (T-B).

conspecific, belonging to the same species (Mayr).

consperse, conspersus, thickly sprinkled with minute irregular dots (T-B).

conspicuous, striking; easily seen at a glance (T-B).

conspurcate, conspurcatus, confusedly sprinkled with discolored or dark spots (T-B).

constancy, invariability in time (T-B).

constant, in genetics, any unvarying quantity (T-B); in mathematics, an invariable or fixed quantity (T-B).

constricted, constrictus (Latin), drawn in (T-B); narrowed (T-B; Borror et al.).

consute, consutus (Latin), with very minute elevations in series, some distance apart, and of a different color from the general surface, which somewhat resemble stitching (T-B; Harris); see catenate.

contact chemoreception, chemoreception resulting from direct contact with a chemical present in the liquid state or in solution at relatively high concentrations (Chapman); see olfaction.

contagious disease, in invertebrate pathology, a disease which is naturally transmitted by contact (Steinhaus and Martignoni).

contamination, in invertebrate pathology, harboring of or contact with microorganisms (or other organisms such as insect parasites) in the absence of a relationship which may be considered commensalistic, mutualistic, or parasitic (Steinhaus and Martignoni).

continental drift, movement of continental blocks composed of lighter, harder sial over a denser, more viscous sima (Mackerras, in CSIRO).

contiguous, so near together as to touch (T-B).

continuity, in nomenclature, the principle that continuity of usage should take precedence over priority of publication in determining which of 2 or more competing scientific names should be adopted for a particular taxon (Mayr); see priority.

continuous variation, variation in which individuals differ from each other by infinitely small steps, as variations in quality of expression of a character or group of characters (T-B; Mayr); see discontinuous variation and polymorphism.

contorted, twisted; obliquely incumbent upon each other (T-B).

contour, the outline or periphery (T-B).

contract, contracted, contractus (Latin), to draw, or drawn, together (T-B); to reduce, or reduced, in size by contraction (T-B).

contractile, capable of being drawn together or contracted or having the power of contracting (T-B).

contrasting, appearing in sharp relief or contrast, as one color or marking against another (T-B).

control, something that affords a standard of comparison or means of verification (Steinhaus and Martignoni); maintenance of or the effort to maintain a population density of insects or other undesirable animals below the point where injury to man's interests occurs (Steinhaus and Martignoni).

conus (pl., **coni**), in ♂ *Zonosoma* (= *Cyclophora*) (Lepidoptera: Geometridae), clavate process of caudal portion of valvula (Tuxen, after Bastelberger); in ♂ *Leucanitis* (Lepidoptera: Noctuidae), short process arising from sacculus or harpe (Tuxen, after John).

convergence, resemblance between 2 forms (either the animals themselves or their structures) derived from widely distant ancestries or origins, the resemblances having been brought about either by the adoption of similar habits or through reduction or elimination of original differences (T-B, after Tillyard); see divergence and parallelism.

convergent, converging, becoming closer distally (T-B; Borror et al.).

convex, the outer curved surface of a segment of a sphere, as opposed to concave (T-B).

convex vein, major longitudinal wing vein running along a ridge (T-B, after Snodgrass, Imms; Leftwich); see concave vein.

convolute, convoluted, convolutus, rolled or twisted spirally (T-B); also applied to wings when they are wrapped around the body (T-B).

convolution, a winding or fold, as of something rolled or folded on itself (T-B).

coordinate, in nomenclature, of the same value (ICZN).

copal, a transparent amberlike resin from various tropical trees (T-B).

Copeognatha, Pscoptera, q.v. (T-B, after Imms).

Copepoda, group within the Crustacea, including free-swimming and parasitic forms, characterized by an elongate, distinctly segmented body, 5 pairs of head appendages, and 4–6 pairs of thoracic legs (Borror et al.).

Cope's Rule, generalization that there is a steady increase in size in phyletic lines (Mayr).

Copromorphoidea, Alucitoidea, q.v. (Common, in CSIRO).

coprophagous, coprophagus, feeding on excrement or on decaying vegetable matter of an excrementitious character (T-B).

coprophagy, feeding on dung (T-B).

copula, copulation, q.v. (T-B).

copularium, in termites (Isoptera), the chamber housing the colony-founding couple (Wilson; Thorne, pers. comm.).

copulate, to unite in sexual intercourse (T-B).

copulation, linking of ♂ and ♀ genitalia, during which the ♂ transfers sperm to, or inseminates, the ♀ (Chapman).

copulation chamber, in certain Scolytidae (Coleoptera), an excavated chamber or cell in their burrows in which copulation takes place (T-B).

copulation hooks, in ♂ Heteroptera (Hemiptera), parameres, q.v. (Tuxen, after Ekblom).

copulatory, of or pertaining to copulation or pairing (T-B).

copulatory bursa, bursa copulatrix, q.v. (Leftwich).

copulatory hook, in ♂ Plecoptera, the terminal hook-shaped part of, or process on, the subanal plates (Tuxen, after Walker).

copulatory opening, vulva, q.v. (Chapman).

copulatory organ, in ♂ Phasmida, intromittent organ consisting of membranous lobes and a median sclerite (Tuxen); in ♂ Heteroptera (Hemiptera), phallus, q.v. (Tuxen); in Diptera, aedeagus, q.v. (McAlpine).

copulatory ossicule, in ♂ Hymenoptera, digitus, q.v. (Tuxen, after Crampton).

copulatory position, relative positions of ♂ and ♀ during copulation (McAlpine).

copulatory pouch, in ♀ Orthoptera, genital chamber, q.v. (Tuxen, after Snodgrass); in ♀ Coleoptera, bursa copulatrix, q.v. (Tuxen); in ♀ Lepidoptera, corpus bursae or bursa copulatrix, q.v. (Tuxen).

copulatory processes, in ♂ Grylloblattodea, accessory copulatory processes and principal copulatory process, q.v. (Tuxen).

copulatory rods, in ♂ Siphonaptera, virga penis, q.v. (Tuxen, after Shariff).

copulatory sac, in ♀ Lepidoptera, corpus bursae or bursa copulatrix (Tuxen).

copulatory shaft, in ♂ Corixidae (Hemiptera: Heteroptera), lamina ventralis, q.v. (Tuxen, after Griffith).

copulatory valves, in Phthiraptera, first gonapophyes, second gonapophyses, or gonoplacs, q.v. (Lyal, pers. comm.).

copulo (Latin), to couple; correct form for the act of mating is "in copulo," not "in copula" (T-B).

copulobi, (copulalobi), in ♂ Bittacidae (Mecoptera), epiandrium, q.v. (Tuxen, after Crampton).

copyist's error, an incorrect spelling made in copying (ICZN).

coracoid, in adult Culicidae (Diptera), a prolongation of the proximal margin of the second axillary sclerite which articulates with the third axillary sclerite (Harbach and Knight, after Prashad).

coralline, corallinus, a pale pinkish red (T-B).

corbel, an ovate area at the distal end of the tibia in Coleoptera, surrounded by a fringe of minute bristles; when the articular cavity is on the side, above the tip, the corbel is closed; when the cavity is at the extreme tip, the corbel is open (T-B).

corbicula (pl., **corbiculae**), in bees (Hymenoptera: Apoidea), pollen basket, q.v. (T-B; Leftwich).

corbiculate, corbiculatus, furnished with a brush of strong hairs; having corbiculae (T-B).

corcula, the reservoirs of the dorsal channel through which the insect blood flows; the chambers of the dorsal vessel (T-B).

cord, in adult Tipulidae (Diptera), a distinctive region near the apical third of the wing where the branching of the radial sector (R_s), media (M), and cubitus anterior (CuA) frequently occurs in an almost linear transverse line (Alexander and Byers, in McAlpine); in adult Trichoptera, the arrangement of the crossveins and of parts of the longitudinal veins into a more or less complete transverse line of anastomosis (Betten).

cordate, cordatus (Latin), **cordiform,** heart-shaped; triangular, with the corners of the base rounded; not necessarily emarginate at the middle of the base (T-B).

Cordulegastroidea, superfamily within the Anisoptera (Odonata), including the family Cordulegastridae, but sometimes included within the Aeshnoidea (Borror et al.; O'Farrell, in CSIRO).

corema (pl., **coremata**), in ♂ Arctiidae (Lepidoptera), one of a pair eversible sacs of ventrolateral regions of abdominal segments VII, VIII, or IX, typically containing long pencils or brushes of modified hairs or scales, sometimes spiniferous, presumably for scent distribution (Tuxen, after Pierce).

Coreoidea, superfamily within the infraorder Pentatomomorpha (Hemiptera: Heteroptera) usually diagnosed to include the families Coreidae, Alydidae, Rhopalidae, Hyocephalidae, and Stenocephalidae (Woodward et al., in CSIRO).

corethogyne, in many ♀ Tortricidae (Lepidoptera), area around papillae anales covered with dense, modified scales used to protect the egg mass (Tuxen, after Diakonoff).

coreum, exocuticle, q.v. (T-B).

coriaceo-reticulate, with impressed reticulations giving a leatherlike appearance (T-B); see coriarious.

coriaceous, coriaceus (Latin), leatherlike in texture, with minute cracks like human skin (T-B; Harris); see alutaceous and coriarious.

corial, of or pertaining to a corium; specifically, of the wing in Heteroptera (T-B).

corial glands, in wings of Plokiophilidae (Heteroptera: Cimicoidea), numerous, large, unicellular glands with low conical openings on the dorsal surface of the corium (Carayon).

coriarious, leatherlike in texture, with minute cracks like human skin (T-B; Harris); see alutaceous and coriaceous.

coriopruina, in Corixidae (Hemiptera: Heteroptera), a white frosted area between the anterior apex of the corium and the clavopruina (Lauck, in Menke).

corium (pl., **coria**), the flexible membrane between the body segments or appendage segments (T-B, after MacGillivray) (see conjunctiva and intersegmental membrane); in Heteroptera (Hemiptera), the proximal coriaceous or otherwise differentiated part of forewing exclusive of the clavus and distinct from the membrane, often being subdivided into the anterior (lateral) exocorium and posterior (interior) endocorium (Štys, pers. comm.); see cuneus and embolium.

Corixoidea, superfamily within the infraorder Nepomorpha of the Heteroptera (Hemiptera), including aquatic bugs of the family Corixidae, characterized by usually scooplike foretarsi (palae) (Woodward et al., in CSIRO).

corn stunt, disease of corn caused by a spiroplasma transmitted propagatively by leafhoppers (Hemiptera: Auchenorrhyncha: Cicadellidae) (Borror et al.).

cornea, cuticle covering the compound eye or ocellus (T-B).

corneagen cells, epidermal cells producing corneal lens of ommatidium and later becoming the primary pigment cells (Chapman); see corneagen layer.

corneagen layer, a layer of colorless, transparent cells over the insect eye beneath the cornea, which secretes and provides support to, the lens (T-B, after Imms).

corneagenous cells, corneagen cells, q.v. (T-B, after Snodgrass).

corneal, of or pertaining to the cornea (T-B).

corneal facet, one of the lenslike divisions of the cornea of the compound eye (T-B); see cornea, corneal lens, and ommatidium.

corneal hypodermis, corneagen layer, q.v. (T-B, after Comstock).

corneal layer, in the insect ocellus, a continuation of the cuticle over the ocellus (T-B, after Comstock); see corneal lens.

corneal lens, cuticular lens of ommatidium, ocellus, or stemma (Chapman).

corneal nipples, in some adult Lepidoptera, minute protuberances on the surface of the cornea in the ommatidia of compound eyes, which reduce light reflection from the cornea, thus increasing visual acuity (Common, after Bernhard et al.).

corneous, corneus, of a horny or chitinous substance; resembling horn in texture (T-B).

corner tooth, in Collembola, an angle, usually forming an acute projection, on the margin of the unguiculus which faces the unguis (Christiansen and Bellinger).

cornicle(s), in Aphididae (Hemiptera: Sternorrhyncha), tubular structure on each side of abdominal tergum V or VI, from which various alarm pheromones are expelled (T-B; Stoetzel, in Stehr).

corniculae, in Diptera, sclerotized flaps arising from the sides of, and projecting over, the cavity formed by the depressed portion of the cervical organ sclerite (sella), and bulging lateral cervicalia (Speight, after Lowne).

corniculus (pl., **corniculi**), in ♀ Orthoptera, hardened tips of first valvulae and second valvulae which dig holes in the ground for the deposition of eggs (T-B; Tulloch; Tuxen); in Aphididae (Hemiptera: Sternorrhyncha), cornicles, honey-tubes, q.v. (T-B; Tulloch); in larval Coleoptera, urogomphi, q.v. (Borror et al.).

corniform, like the horn of an ox (T-B); a long mucronate or pointed process (T-B).

cornu (pl., **cornua**), in ♂ Anisoptera (Odonata), flagella, q.v. (Tuxen, after Kennedy); in ♂ Orthoptera, ancora, q.v. (Tuxen, after Ramme); in ♂ Cicadidae (Hemiptera: Auchenorrhyncha), hornlike process terminating vesica (Tuxen, after Orian); in adult Chironomidae (Diptera), projections at dorsal end of cibarial pump considered homologous with cornua or oral arm of hypopharyngeal suspensorium (Saether); in larval Muscomorpha (Diptera), paired arms of tentoropharyngeal sclerite, including the dorsal and ventral cornua (Teskey, in McAlpine), or, wings, q.v. (Ferrar); in ♂ Apis (Hymenoptera: Apidae), projection from bursa of endophallus (Tuxen, after Snodgrass).

cornua (pl., **cornuae**), in larval Muscomorpha (Diptera), 2 hornlike processes pointed backward in the cephalopharyngeal skeleton (T-B); the prominently extended lateral angles of the posterior end of the basipharynx (T-B, after MacGillivray).

cornua of paramere, in ♂ Orthoptera, titillators, q.v. (Tuxen, after Walker).

cornua tegminis, in ♂ Coleoptera, parameres, q.v. (Tuxen).

cornute, cornutus, having horns or hornlike processes (T-B).

cornuti decidui (sing., **cornutus deciduus**), in ♂ Lepidoptera, cornuti of vesica of ♂ broken off and remaining in ♀ bursa copulatrix (Tuxen).

cornutus (pl., **cornuti**), in ♂ Lepidoptera, sclerotized armature of vesica, ranging in form from slender, single spines to rasplike teeth (Tuxen, after Pierce); in ♂ Mnesarchaeidae (Lepidoptera), spines and processes of sclerotized part of aedoeagus, not of vesica (Tuxen, after Philpott); in ♀ Pyralidae (Lepidoptera), scobinations or minute spines composing signum (Tuxen, after Agenjo); see cornuti decidui.

corona (pl., **coronae**), a crown or crownlike process (T-B); in ♂ Noctuidae (Lepidoptera), marginal armament of strong setae, spines or teeth, usually in linear arrangement, on cucullus (Tuxen, after Pierce).

coronal branch, coronal ecdysial line, q.v. (Peterson).

coronal ecdysial line, in immature insects, the median unpaired posterior part of the ecdysial cleavage line (Harbach and Knight); see coronal suture.

coronal gap, in many larval Nematocera (Diptera), the narrow or broad emargination in the posterolateral edge of the cranium to which the ecdysial cleavage lines extend (Harbach and Knight).

coronal lobes, in larval Chironomini (Diptera: Chironomidae), dorsal sclerotized lobes extending caudad of postoccipital margin (Saether).

coronal pores, in larval Chironomidae (Diptera), pores near coronal suture and coronal seta (S12) of head capsule (Saether).

coronal ridge, in adult Culicidae (Diptera), the cuticular ingrowth marked externally by the coronal suture (Harbach and Knight, after Schiemenz).

coronal setae, in adult Chironomidae (Diptera), setae on coronal triangle (Saether); in larval Chironomidae (Diptera), cephalic setae S11–S12 near posterodorsal margin of head capsule at coronal suture (Saether).

coronal suture, in adult insects, the median unpaired part of the epicranial suture (T-B); see epicranial arms.

coronal triangle, in adult Chironomidae (Diptera), region between dorsal arms of coronal suture (Saether).

coronate, coronatus, with a crownlike tip or termination (T-B).

coronate egg, one in which the upper end is surrounded by a circlet of spines (T-B).

coronatus (pl., **coronati**), in adult Lycaenidae (Lepidoptera), lateral sclerotized structures of anal region (Tuxen, after van Eecke).

coronet, a small crown or corona (T-B).

coronula, a cricle or semicircle of spines at the apex of the tibia (T-B); in adult Formicinae (Hymenoptera: Formicidae), a funnel-shaped circlet of setae around the edge of the acidopore (Brown, pers. comm., after Hung and Brown).

coronula aedoeagi, (pl., **coronulae aedoeagi**), in ♂ *Zygeana* (Lepidoptera: Zygaenidae), wreath of large spines on lamina dorsalis of aedoeagus (Tuxen, after Loritz).

corpora, pl. of corpus, q.v. (T-B).

corpora incerta, corpora allata, q.v. (T-B).

corpora optica, the dorsal optic parts of the brain in certain of the lower insects (T-B, after Snodgrass).

corpora pedunculata (sing., **corpus pedunculatum**), paired pedunculate masses in the protocerebrum (T-B), involved in visual integration in social Hymenoptera and also probably concerned with the selection and sequential organization of behavior patterns (Chapman, after Howse).

corpora ventralia (sing., **corpus ventrale**), the ventral bodies of the protocerebrum in the ventrolateral parts of the brain (T-B, after Snodgrass).

corporotentorium, the tentorium when in the form of a broad plate (T-B).

corpotendons, the tendons borne by the corpotentorium (T-B, after McGillivray); see tentorial arms.

corpotentorium, the prominent bridge which divides the foramen into 2 parts, on one side of which the alimentary canal passes and on the other the nervous system (T-B, after McGillivray); in more primitive insects, a median plate formed between the 2 sides of the tentorium (McAlpine); in adult Culicidae (Diptera), a slender process extending from the dorsal surface near the posterior end of each posterior tentorial arm to the postoccipital ridge (Harbach and Knight, after Schiemenz); see tentorial bridge.

corpus (pl., **corpora**), the whole body of the insect, including the head, thorax and abdomen (T-B, after Kirby and Spence); in Collembola, the median basal part of the tentaculum, attached to the body wall and bearing the projecting rami (Christiansen and Bellinger); in ♂ Siphonaptera, basimeres, q.v. (Tuxen, after Dampf).

corpus adiposum, fat body, q.v. (T-B).

corpus allatum (pl., **corpora allata**), a pair of small ovoid endocrine glands of ectodermal origin associated with the stomodeal ganglia behind the brain, being the source of juvenile hormone (T-B; Tulloch; Wilson; Chapman).

corpus allatum hormone, juvenile hormone, q.v. (Borror et al.).

corpus bursae, in ♀ Lepidoptera, the enlarged, saclike, distal part of the bursa copulatrix (Tuxen, after Stitz).

corpus cardiacum (pl., **corpora cardiaca**), pair of organs, often closely associated with the aorta and forming part of its wall, which store and release hormones from the neurosecretory cells of the brain and which intrinsically produce hormones that are concerned with regulation of the heartbeat and have other physiological effects (Tulloch; Chapman).

corpus forcipis, in ♂ Protura, basiperiphallus, q.v. (Tuxen, after Prell).

corpus luteum, the mass of degenerating follicle cells left in egg chamber after the discharge of egg (T-B, after Snodgrass).

corpus of clasper, in ♂ Siphonaptera, basimere, q.v. (Tuxen).

corpus scolopale, a sense rod; a scolopale, q.v. (T-B).

corpus seminalis, in ♀ Cimex (Heteroptera: Cimicidae), enlargement at base of each ovariole, derived from the follicular cells, in which sperm are stored (Chapman, after Davis).

corpus spermatophori, in Lepidoptera, saclike body of a spermatophorum (Tuxen, after Petersen).

corpuscle, a small cell (T-B); hemocyte, q.v. (T-B).

correct original spelling, the spelling of an available name when first published unless it is demonstrably incorrect under the Code (ICZN).

corrected type locality, a published statement of a type locality made to replace an erroneous statement of a type locality (ICZN).

correlated, derived from the same ancestral form; said of 2 or more features or qualities which bear a direct or an inverse relation to each other, but without implying a relation of cause and effect (T-B).

correlated characters, characters that are associated either as manifestations of a well-integrated ancestral gene complex or because they are functionally correlated (Mayr).

correlative, of a correlated nature; see correlated (T-B).

corrode, to eat away gradually, as by rust or decay (T-B).

corrodent, any one of the Psocoptera (T-B).

Corrodentia, Psocoptera, q.v. (T-B; Hennig).

corrugated, wrinkled with furrows; with alternate ridges and channels (T-B; Harris, after Emery and Brewster).

corselet, in Coleoptera, prothorax, q.v. (T-B).

cortex, the outer or superficial layer of the insect brain or of the ganglia (T-B).

cortical, relating to the cortex or outer skin or layer (T-B).

cortical cells, the cells of the cortex of the insect brain (T-B).

cortical cytoplasm, periplasm, q.v. (T-B, after Snodgrass).

cortical layer, periplasm, q.v. (Tulloch).

corticinus, barklike in sculpturing or texture (T-B; Harris); see fatiscent, fissate, and rumose.

corticolous, living in or on the bark of plants (T-B).

corvinus, crow black; deep, shining black with a greenish lustre (T-B).

corypha (pl., **coryphae**), in larval Scarabaeoidea (Coleoptera), the unpaired anterior region of the epipharynx between the clithra, bearing a small number of setae, often merged with the acropariae into a common apical region when the clithra is absent (T-B, after Böving).

coryphate, coryphatus, capillatus, q.v. (T-B).

corysterium, in ♀ insects, accessory genital glands, q.v. (T-B).

cosmopolitan, occurring throughout most of the world (T-B).

Cossoidea, superfamily within the suborder Ditrysia (Lepidoptera), including the families Cossidae, Metarbelidae, and Dudgeoneidae, including small to very large moths lacking chaetosemata and possessing a reduced proboscis and maxillary palpi, complete or nearly complete heteroneuan venation, forewing with media (M) strong within the discal cell, and hind wings shorter than the forewings; larvae are wood boring (Common, in CSIRO; Munroe, in Parker).

costa (pl., **costae**), any elevated ridge that is rounded at its crest (T-B); the first longitudinal vein (C) of the wing, running along the costal margin and terminating before the wing apex, often being reduced or absent in the hind wing (T-B, after Comstock; Common, pers. comm.); in ♂ Lepidoptera, dorsal, marginal part of valva, variously sclerotized, bearing a great variety of structures and processes (Tuxen, after Pierce); in ♂ Lepidoptera, dorsoproximal part of valva, thus only the proximal part of the costa (Tuxen, after Sibatani et al.).

costa of sacculus, in ♂ Lepidoptera, dorsal margin of sacculus (Tuxen, after Pierce).

costagial break, in adult Diptera, costal break slightly proximal to humeral crossvein (McAlpine); see humeral break.

costagium, in adult Diptera, costagial break, q.v. (McAlpine, after Séguy).

costal, of or relating to the costa (T-B).

costal area, the portion of the wing immediately behind the costal margin (T-B; Borror et al.).

costal arm, in ♂ Geometridae (Lepidoptera), branching armlike process in the middle of the costa of the valva (Tuxen, after Pierce).

costal brace, in wings of Ephemeroptera, a thick veinlet running from costa (C) to first branch of radius (R_1) at the base (T-B); see humeral crossvein.

costal break, in adult Diptera, esp. Schizophora, a point on the costa (C) where the sclerotization is weak or lacking or the vein appears to be broken (Borror et al.; McAlpine); see costagial break, humeral break, and subcostal break.

costal cell, the wing area between the costa (C) and subcosta (Sc) (T-B; Borror et al.).

costal crossveins, in many-veined insect wings, those that extend between the costa and the subcosta (T-B, after Comstock).

costal field, in Orthoptera, that region of the tegmina adjacent to the anterior margin or costa (T-B).

costal fold, in ♂ Lepidoptera, an expanded costal area folded over or under the forewing, often covering special pheromone-disseminating scales or hairs, e.g., certain Tortricidae, Hesperiidae, and Pyralidae (T-B, after Comstock; Common).

costal fracture, in many Heteroptera, a short, usually transverse line of weakness in the forewing separating the sometimes well-differentiated cuneus from the rest of the corium (Woodward et al., in CSIRO; Štys).

costal hinge, in adult Odonata, nodal furrow, q.v. (T-B).

costal hook of harpe, in ♂ Olethreutinae (Lepidoptera: Tortricidae), dorsocephalad extended costa of valva, often articulating with tegumen or parts thereof, fultura superior, or the generalized diaphragma (Tuxen, after Heinrich).

costal lobe, in ♀ Helotrephidae (Hemiptera: Heteroptera), asymmetrical expansion of the anterior margin of the right forewing (Papáček, Tonner, and Štys, after Esaki and China).

costal margin, the anterior margin of the wing whether costate or not (T-B).

costal membrane, in ♂ Olethreutinae (Lepidoptera: Tortricidae), membranous connective of proximal edge of valva with tegumen and vinculum (Tuxen, after Heinrich).

costal nervure, costa, q.v., of wing (T-B, after Jardine).

costal plate, in adult Diptera, tegula, q.v. (McAlpine).

costal region, in the wings of insects, term applied loosely to the area of the wing near the costa (C) (T-B).

costal sclerite, humeral plate, q.v. (T-B, after Comstock).

costal spines, in the wings of some Lepidoptera, a series of slightly curved spinelike setae on the costa of the hind wing near the base, which aid in holding the wings together (T-B, after Comstock); see pseudofrenulum.

costal vein, costa, q.v. (T-B).

costalis, the venella on the cephalic margin of the rotaxis (T-B, after MacGillivray).

costalization, the concentration of the development of the anterior wing veins toward the costal margin (Davis, pers. comm.).

costalla (pl., **costallae**), the funditae associated with the costal vein (T-B, after MacGillivray).

costate, costatus (Latin), furnished with longitudinal raised ribs or ridges (costae), much coarser than carinae (carinate) (T-B; Harris); see carinate, cristate, and porcate.

costiform, in the form of costae or raised ribs (T-B).

costoradial, of or pertaining to the radius and the costa of the insect wing (T-B).

costula, in Hymenoptera, a small ridge separating the externomedian metathoracic area into 2 parts (T-B); see costule.

costulate, costulatus (Latin), with less prominent ribs or ridges than costate (T-B; Harris).

cotton stainer, species of Heteroptera (Hemiptera) which cause discoloration of the cotton fibers by piercing the unripe bolls for their sap, e.g., *Dysdercus* spp. (Pyrrhocoridae) (T-B).

cotyla, cotyle, articular pan, q.v. (T-B).

cotyloid cavity, coxal cavity, (T-B).

cotype, a term not recognized by the Code, formerly used for either a syntype or paratype (ICZN).

coumaphos, $C_{14}H_{16}ClO_5PS$, an animal systematic insecticide; a synthetic organophosphate, O-(3-chloro-4-methyl-2-oxo-2H-1-benzopyran-7-yl) O,O-diethyl phosphorothioate; moderately toxic to mammals, oral LD_{50} for rats 56 to 230 mg/kg (Pfadt).

Counter (trade name), terbufos, q.v. (Pfadt).

countershading, crypsis in which there is a compensatory deepening or lightening of body color to counteract for apparent changes due to light intensity (Matthews and Matthews).

counter tympanic cavity, in adult Noctuoidea (Lepidoptera), a cavity at the base of the abdomen posterior to the tympanic cavity (Chapman, after Roeder and Treat).

counter tympanic hood, in adult Noctuoidea (Lepidoptera), an evaginated area of the lateral part of abdominal segment I extending anteriorly to partially cover the tympanic cavity (Common, in CSIRO).

counter tympanic membrane, in the tympanal organs of adult Noctuoidea (Lepidoptera), a secondary membrane resembling the tympanic membrane but without a sense organ, probably functioning as an accessory resonating structure (Chapman, after Roeder and Treat).

couplet(s), in a taxonomic key, paired, alternative diagnoses permitting one to choose between one of 2 directions or solutions.

coupling, engaging ♂ and ♀ genitalia, preceeding copulation (Mc-Alpine); see wing coupling.

courtship, exchange of signals which indicate the appropriateness of species, sex and, on the part of the ♀, readiness to mate (Chapman).

courtship feeding, offering of food by ♂ to ♀ preceeding mating (Matthews and Matthews).

cover, in ♂ Blattopteroidea, hypophallus, q.v. (Tuxen, after Wesche).

coverlet, in ♀ Lepidoptera, lodix, q.v. (Tuxen, after Pierce).

cowl, in ♂ Plecoptera, deep, membranous groove or pocket, in certain genera containing the supraanal lobe, usually supported on sclerotized lateral ribs (paragenital plates), formed by invagination of the epiproct (Tuxen, after Ricker); in ♀ Culicidae (Diptera), area between postgenital plate and postatrial sclerite (Tuxen, after Christophers).

cowpea mosaic, disease of bean plants caused by an isometric virus transmitted by various beetles (Coleoptera) (Borror et al.).

coxa (pl., **coxae**), the basal segment of the leg, by means of which it is articulated to the body (T-B); see coxopodite.

coxa genuina, in certain orders, the apparent anterior piece of a much enlarged meron (T-B, after Snodgrass); coxa vera, q.v. (T-B, after Imms)

coxa rotatoria, coxa with a monocondylic joint (T-B).

coxa scrobiculata, coxa with a dicondylic joint (T-B).

coxa vera, the anterior part of the meso- and metathoracic coxae in many insects (T-B, after Imms).

coxacava, coxal cavity, q.v. (T-B, after MacGillivray).

coxafossa, coxal cavity, q.v. (T-B, after MacGillivray).

coxal, of or pertaining to the coxa (T-B).

coxal bridge, precoxal bridge or postcoxal bridge, q.v. (Chapman).

coxal cavity, the opening or space in which the coxa articulates (T-B).

coxal corium, the articular membrane surrounding the base of the coxa (T-B, after Snodgrass).

coxal condyle, in acalyptrate Muscomorpha (Diptera), a pleural projection articulating with the coxa (Speight).

coxal epipodite, epipodite, q.v. (Chapman).

coxal file, in some aquatic Coleoptera, a series of striations just above the hind coxa of the ♂; possibly a stridulatory structure (T-B).

coxal gills, in nymphs of Ephemeroptera, membranous outgrowths that occur at or near base of coxae of some taxa (Peters, pers. comm., after Edmunds, Jensen, and Berner).

coxal gland, excretory gland at the base of the leg in Onychophora and many Chelicerata (von Kéler); in Thysanura, labial glands, q.v. (T-B; Leftwich; von Kéler).

coxal lobe, in larval Coleoptera, an abdominal, usually triangular, area extending from the hypopleurum toward the meson of the sternum (Peterson, after Böving and Craighead); parasternum.

coxal lobes, in ♂ aeolothripid Thysanoptera, hook- or spinelike appendages of sternum IX (Tuxen, after de Gryse and Treherne).

coxal organ, in Psocoptera, Pearman's organ, q.v. (Smithers, in CSIRO).

coxal plate, in Archaeognatha and Zygentoma, coxite, q.v. (Watson, in CSIRO); in adult Haliplidae (Coleoptera), a platelike extension of the hind coxa (T-B; Leftwich).

coxal process, coxifer, q.v. (T-B); in some ♂ Mycetophilidae (Diptera), special process on coxa (McAlpine).

coxal stylets, in many Archaeognatha, stylets of the thoracic coxae II or II and III (Sturm, pers. comm., after Janetschek); in Zygentoma, styli, q.v. (T-B).

coxal vesicles, exsertile vesicles, q.v. (T-B).

coxale, in ♂ Ephemeroptera, styliger, q.v. (Tuxen, after Walker).

coxapodeme, in adult Chironomidae (Diptera), apodeme formed by sclerotized dorsal and lateral borders of the basal foramen or the large opening of the gonocoxite into the body cavity (Saether).

coxifer, the pleural pivot of the coxa (T-B, after Crampton; McAlpine).

coxite(s), in adult insects, coxopodite, q.v. (Tuxen); in Archaeognatha and Zygentoma, flat appendages on the abdominal sterna, often bearing styli and exsertile vesicles (Tuxen; Sturm, pers. comm.); in ♂ Grylloblattodea, gonocoxae, q.v. (Tuxen, after Walker); in ♂ Thysanoptera, lateral parts of sternum IX (Tuxen, after de Gryse and Treherne); in ♂ Diptera, basistylus, q.v. (Tuxen, after de Meijere); in ♂ Chironomidae (Diptera), gonocoxite, q.v. (Saether); in ♂ *Sarcophaga* (Diptera: Sarcophagidae), surstyli, q.v. (Tuxen, after Rohdendorf); in ♂ Siphonaptera, basimere, q.v. (Tuxen); in ♂ Hymenoptera, gonocoxite, q.v. (Tuxen); in ♀ Neuroptera, gonapophyses laterales, q.v (Tuxen, after Tjeder); in ♀ Coleoptera, hemisternites, q.v. (Tuxen, after Tanner).

coxomarginale, basicoxite, q.v. (T-B, after Snodgrass).

coxopleural, of or pertaining to the coxa and the pleura (T-B).

coxopleural streak, in some adult Sarcophagidae, Calliphoridae, Muscidae, and Tachinidae (Diptera), a suturelike depression separating the katepimeron from the meron (McAlpine).

coxopleure, see antepleuron (T-B, after MacGillivray).

coxopleurite, the sclerite of a generalized thoracic pleuron adjacent to the dorsal margin of the coxa, bearing the dorsal coxal articulation, its anterior part becoming the definitive trochantin (T-B, after Snodgrass; Chapman).

coxopodal arch, in ♂ *Plega* and *Climaciella* (Planipennia: Mantispidae), gonarcus, q.v. (Tuxen, after Ferris).

coxopodite, in Arthropoda, the basal segment of the leg, being homologous with the coxa (T-B; Boudreaux); basal segment of gonopod (Tuxen); in Archaeognatha and Zygentoma, coxite, q.v. (Tuxen, after Snodgrass); in ♂ Grylloblattodea, gonocoxae, q.v. (Tuxen, after Walker); in ♂ *Agulla* (Raphidioptera: Raphidiidae), gonocoxites, q.v. (Tuxen, after Ferris and Pennebaker; Friedrich); in ♂ Corydalidae (Megaloptera), epiproct, q.v. (Tuxen, after Friedrich); in ♂ Mecoptera, gonocoxites, q.v. (Tuxen, after Snodgrass); in ♂ Trichoptera, the basal segment of an inferior appendage (Tuxen); in ♂ Diptera, basistylus, q.v. (Tuxen, after Snodgrass) or gonocoxite, q.v. (Saether); in ♂ Hymenoptera, gonocoxite, q.v. (Tuxen, after Beck).

coxopodite of cercus, in Orthoptera, cercal basipodite, q.v. (Tuxen, after Snodgrass).

coxopodite of segment VIII, in ♀ Neuroptera, gonapophyses posteriores, q.v. (Tuxen, after Ferris).

coxopodite of segment IX, in ♂ *Plega* and *Climaciella* (Planipennia: Mantispidae), gonarcus, q.v. (Tuxen, after Ferris); in ♂ *Dysmicohermes* (Megaloptera: Corydalidae), catoprocessus, q.v. (Tuxen, after Acker); in ♂ Mecoptera, gonocoxites, q.v. (Tuxen, after Ferris and Rees); in ♀ Neuroptera, gonapophyses laterales, q.v. (Tuxen, after Ferris).

coxosternal, of or pertaining to the coxosternum (T-B).

coxosternal plate, coxosternum, q.v. (T-B, after Folsom and Wardle).

coxosternapodeme, in ♀ Chironomidae (Diptera), apodeme of coxosternite IX nearly or weakly connected to ramus of gonapophysis IX anteriorly and caudolaterally attached to gonocoxite IX (Saether).

coxosternite, the limbbase element (or elements) of a coxo- or pleurosternum (T-B, after Snodgrass); in ♂ Symphyta (Hymenoptera), the apparent sternum IX forming a subgenital plate ventrally enclosing the genital capsule (Tuxen, after E. L. Smith); in ♀ Symphyta (Hymenoptera), remnants of sternum VIII and IX between gonocoxites VIII and IX (Tuxen, after E. L. Smith).

coxosternum, morphologically, a definitive sternal plate that includes the areas of the limb bases (T-B).

coxotrochanteral, of or pertaining both to the coxa and the trochanter (T-B).

coxotrochanteral joint, one of the 2 primary bendings of the arthropodan leg, between the coxa and the trochanter (T-B, after Snodgrass); see femorotibial joint.

crag, cervix, q.v. (T-B).

cranial, of or pertaining to the cranium (T-B).

cranium, the sclerotized skulllike part of the head (T-B; Harbach and Knight, after Snodgrass); see epicranium.

craspedum (pl., **caspeda**), in Thysanoptera, a posterior extension or flange of the abdominal tergites and/or sternites of certain grass inhabiting Thripidae (Mound et al.).

crassa (pl., **crassae**), the linear thickenings on each postgena; the mandibular apodemes (T-B, after MacGillivray).

crassus, thick; tumid (T-B).

crateriform, like a shallow funnel or deep bowl; applied to depressions (T-B).

crawler, in Coccoidea and Aleyrodoidea (Hemiptera: Sternorrhyncha), active first instar (Borror et al.).

creber, closely set (T-B).

creeping eruption, rare condition due to infestation of human skin by young larvae of Gasterophilidae (Diptera) (Colless and McAlpine, in CSIRO).

creeping welts, in Diptera larvae, esp. Schizophora, transverse swollen ridges on the anterior ventral margins and sometimes the anterior dorsal margins usually of abdominal segments I–VII, which have rows of minute, sclerotized hooks (Colless and McAlpine, in CSIRO; Teskey, in McAlpine).

cremaster, typically hooked spines on either the dorsal or ventral posterior tip of a pupa in Lepidoptera, used to attach it to the substrate attach or inside of a cocoon, or to help in liberating the pupa from the soil or other surroundings just before emergence (T-B; Leftwich).

cremastral, of or peratining to the cremaster (T-B).

crenate, crenatus (Latin), having the margin evenly notched with rounded teeth (T-B; Harris, after R. W. Brown); see crenulate.

crenulate, crenulatus (Latin), having the margin finely notched with small, rounded teeth (T-B; Harris, after R. W. Brown, and Munz); see crenate.

crenulations, small, evenly rounded, rather deeply curved scallops; transverse ridges or plicae (Peterson).

crepera, a gleam of paler color on a dark ground (T-B).

crepidium, in adult Hymenoptera, ventral ptyche, q.v. (Tuxen, after Ross).

crepis (pl., **crepides**), in larval Scarabaeoidea (Coleoptera), the thinly sclerotized, anteriorly concave, median cross bar pertaining to the region haptolachus, q.v., usually asymmetrical and only indicated by a fine line, or completely absent (T-B, after Böving).

crepitation, a crackling or creaking (T-B); in bombardier beetles (Coleoptera: Carabidae: Brachinini), a crackling sound produced by the discharge of defensive secretions (T-B).

crepuscular, active or flying at dusk (T-B); see matinal.

crescent sclerite, in ♂ Siphonaptera, tectum, q.v. (Tuxen, after Traub).

crescentic, crescent-shaped or crescentlike (T-B).

crescentiform, like a lunule or crescent (T-B).

crest, crista, q.v. (T-B); in adult Culicidae (Diptera), the posterior part of the pediment of a cone extending between the bases of adjacent rods and bearing spiculate processes (Harbach and Knight, after Christophers); in adult Lepidoptera, a raised ridge of one or more tufts of scales on the thorax and abdomen (Common, pers. comm.).

crested, cristate, q.v. (T-B).

cretaceous, chalky white (T-B); of the Cretaceous Period, q.v. (T-B).

Cretaceous Period, most recent of the 3 periods within the Mezozoic Era, extending between about 135 to 70 million years ago (Riek, in CSIRO).

cribellum, a sievelike plate opening near the upper surface of the mandible and forming part of the spinneret in some insects (T-B; Leftwich); in spiders (Arachnida: Araneae), a sievelike structure lying just anterior to the spinnerets (Borror et al.).

cribrate, cribratus (Latin), punctate, q.v. (T-B; Harris).

cribriform, with perforations like those of a sieve (T-B).

cribriform plates, in Cerococcidae and Lecanodiaspididae (Hemiptera: Sternorrhyncha: Coccoidea), normally circular, rarely irregular, plates with areolate surface, located in 2 (rarely 4) longitudinal rows or in clusters on abdominal dorsum (T-B, after MacGillivray; Kosztarab and Kozár).

cricket, a member of the superfamily Grylloidea (Orthoptera) (Key, in CSIRO).

cricoid sclerite, in ♂ *Oncopeltus* (Lygaeidae) and other Heteroptera (Hemiptera), a parietal differentiation of endosoma delimiting conjunctiva (disticonjunctiva) from distal vesica (Tuxen, after Bonhag and Wick).

crineous, crineus, crinosus, dark-brown, with a slight admixture of yellow and gray (T-B).

crinite, crinitus (Latin), thinly covered with very long flexible hairs (T-B).

crispate, crispatus, with a wrinkled or fluted margin (T-B).

crispus (Latin), curly (R. W. Brown); of a surface, with the edge disproportionately larger than the disc, causing the margin to have an irregular undulation (T-B).

crista (pl., **cristae**), a prominent, longitudinal carina on the upper surface of any part of the head or body (T-B); in *Blatta* (Blattaria: Blattidae), a cordlike ridge running the full length of the dorsal surface of the egg capsule (T-B, after W. M. Wheeler); in ♂ Lepidoptera, subbasal tuft of hairs on inner surface of each sacculus (Tuxen, after Meixner); in adult Lepidoptera, specialized vestiture of hairs or scales (Tuxen, after Kusnezov); in ♂ Geometridae (Lepidoptera), hairy or scaly process of juxta, on either side of aedoeagus (Tuxen, after Pierce).

crista acoustica, in Tettigoniidae (Orthoptera), the main chordotonal organ associated with the tympanal organ in the anterior hemocoelic space of the tibia (Chapman).

crista dorsalis, in ♂ Chironomidae (esp. Orthocladiinae) (Diptera), apicodorsal sclerotized lamella of gonostylus (Saether).

crista obliqua (pl., **cristae obliquae**), in ♂ *Argynnis* (Lepidoptera: Nymphalidae), oblique, dentate process of median, basal region of valva (Tuxen, after Petersen).

cristae, in adult Lepidoptera, specialized vestiture of hairs or scales (Tuxen, after Kusnezov); see crista.

cristate, cristatus (Latin), with a prominent carina or crest on the upper surface (T-B; Harris); see carinate, cristulate, costate, and porcate.

cristiform, in the form of a sharp ridge or crest (T-B).

cristula, a small crest (T-B).

cristulate, with several, small, crescentlike ridges or crests (T-B; Harris); see cristate and carinulate.

croceous, croceus (Latin), saffron yellow (T-B); yellow with an admixture of red (T-B).

crochet(s), any small hooklike organ (Leftwich); in Lepidoptera larvae, curved spines or hooks on the planta of the prolegs (T-B); in ♂

Ephemeroptera, genostyles, q.v. (Tuxen, after de Geer); in ♂ Siphonaptera, paired, frequently hook-shaped sclerites arising within the inner walls of the aedeagus, usually flanking the inner tube, variable in both size and shape, being rotated during copulation and pushed into the membranous slit of abdominal sternum IX of the ♀ (Tuxen, after Snodgrass; Rothschild and Traub); in larval *Atrichopogon* (Ceratopogonidae), Chironomidae, *Atherix* (Athericeridae), and Thaumaleidae (Diptera), relatively large, strongly hooked spinules on prolegs (Teskey, in McAlpine); in ♂ Hymenoptera, parameres, q.v. (Tuxen, after Radoszkowski).

crook, in adult Hesperiidae (Lepidoptera), the recurved tip of the antenna (T-B).

crop, the dilated portion of the alimentary canal behind the oesophagus, which serves to receive and hold food, previous to its slower passage through the digestive tract, being a simple dilation, as in Blattaria, or a lateral diverticulum joined to the oesophagus by a narrow tube, as in adult Diptera and in most adult Lepidoptera (T-B; Leftwich).

cross, offspring of 2 intraspecific forms (T-B); see hybrid.

cross-bar, in ♂ Nepidae (Hemiptera: Heteroptera), ponticulus transversalis, q.v. (Tuxen, after Hamilton).

cross nerve, suboesophageal commissure (T-B).

cross pieces, in ♀ Blaberoidea (Blattaria),a pair of composite sclerites lateral to the second valvifers composed of median expansions of the ninth paratergites, the ninth laterosternites and a pair of small sclerites derived from the ninth laterosternal area (Alsop, pers. comm., after McKittrick).

cross rib, in adult Lepidoptera, prominent struts or braces arranged transversely between the longitudinal ridges of a scale (Downey and Allyn).

crossveins, transverse veins linking the principal longitudinal veins in the insect wing and giving it greater strength, being numerous and variable in Ephemeroptera and Odonata but becoming fewer and located in fixed positions in many Neoptera (T-B, after Snodgrass; Leftwich).

crotchets, crochets, q.v. (T-B).

crotchet plates, in ♂ Siphonaptera, hamuli, q.v. (Tuxen, after Jordan).

crotoxyphos, $C_{14}H_{19}O_6P$, a synthetic insecticide; an organophosphate, α-methylbenzyl 3-hydroxycrotonate dimethyl phosphate; moderately toxic to mammals; acute oral LD_{50} for rats 125 mg/kg (Pfadt).

crown, the top of the head in Lepidoptera; coronet, corona, vertex, q.v. (T-B).

cruciate, cruciatus (Latin), crossing (Borror et al.); shaped like a cross (T-B).

cruciate bristles, usually in Diptera, any pair of bristles that point mediad and whose ends cross (T-B, after Comstock).

cruciato-complicatus, folded crosswise, incumbent when the inner margins overlap; not well distinguished from cruciate (T-B).

cruciform, cross-shaped (T-B).

cruciform pore, in nymphs and ♀ Eriococcidae (Hemiptera: Sternorrhyncha: Coccoidea), small oval structure with cross-shaped, central orifice, usually located on venter near margin of thorax and head (Miller, in Stehr; Kosztarab and Kozár).

crufomate, $C_{12}H_{19}ClNO_3P$, a synthetic, animal systemic; an organophosphate, 4-*tert*-butyl-2-chlorophenyl methyl methylphosphoramidate; moderately toxic to mammals, acute oral LD_{50} for rats 750 mg/kg (Pfadt).

crumena, in certain Hemiptera with mandibular and maxillary bristles much longer than the beak or rostrum, a long internal pouch in the head, in some extending backward into the thorax, to contain such bristles when retracted (T-B), e.g., in Coccoidea (Hemiptera: Sternorrhyncha).

crura, the legs or, more specifically, the thighs (T-B).

crura cerebri, circumoesophageal connectives, q.v. (T-B).

crural, of or pertaining to a crura (T-B).

crus, a leg or leglike structure (T-B).

Crustacea, subclass within the phylum Arthropoda containing the crabs, lobsters, etc. (T-B; Borror et al.).

crustaceous, hard, like the shell of a crab (T-B).

cryolite, an inorganic insecticide, sodium fluoaluminate; useful in controlling larvae of the codling moth, *Cydia pomonella,* orange tortrix, *Argyrotaenia citrana* (Lepidoptera: Tortricidae), and some other insects; low acute mammalian toxicity (Pfadt).

crypsis, camouflage by imitating certain environmental background features (Matthews and Matthews); see procrypsis and anticrypsis.

cryptic, hidden or concealed (T-B).

cryptic coloration, coloration affording crypsis (T-B).

cryptic species, sexually isolated populations with few or no tangible recognition characters to set them apart from the general species population (Mayr).

cryptically, in a hidden or concealed manner (T-B).

crypto-, Greek prefix; hidden (T-B).

cryptobiosis, the stage of an organism when it shows no visible signs of life and metabolic activity is brought reversibly to a standstill, e.g., larval *Polypedilum* (Diptera: Chironomidae) in dried up pools (Chapman).

cryptobiotic, living beneath cover, such as leaf litter, stones, and dead bark (Wilson).

cryptocephalic substage, in Muscomorpha (Diptera), the earliest form of the pupa in which the legs and wing buds are everted but the head is still inverted within the thorax, the form of the abdomen resembling that of larval instar IV (Peterson, after Snodgrass, Wahl).

Cryptocerata, Nepomorpha, q.v. (T-B; Woodward et al., in CSIRO).

cryptogastra, with the venter or belly covered or concealed (T-B).

cryptogastrous abdomen, in adult Coleoptera, an abdomen in which sternite II is membranous and hidden from view in the hind coxal cavity , e.g., in Curculionidae (Britton, after Jeannel and Paulian, in CSIRO).

cryptogyne, in ants (Hymenoptera: Formicidae), a term applied to queens which are indistinguishable from workers (Tulloch).

cryptonephridial system, in many Coleoptera and larval Lepidoptera, a condition in which the Malpighian tubules are closely associated with the rectum, forming a convoluted layer over its surface (Chapman).

cryptonephridial tubes, Malpighian tubules whose distal ends do not lie freely in the body cavity but are attached to various intestinal regions (Tulloch).

cryptonephry, cryptonephridial system, q.v. (CSIRO).

cryptopentamera, the tarsus with 5 articles, article 4 small and concealed (T-B).

cryptopleury, in some adult Hymenoptera, the condition in which the propleuron is extensively or entirely concealed by the lateral part of the pronotum (Gauld and Bolton).

cryptotetramera, with the tarsus 4 jointed, one of them small and concealed (T-B).

cryptothorax, a supposed thoracic ring between meso- and metathorax (T-B).

cryptozoic, living in concealed places, e.g., under bark, in leaf litter, beneath stones (CSIRO).

cryptozoite, a stage of the malarial protozoan *Plasmodium* spp. (Plasmodiidae) arising from the injected sporozoite which is found in the fixed tissues of man or other vertebrate host (Tulloch).

crypts, regenerative crypts, q.v. (T-B).

crystal cell, a type of hemocyte in *Drosophila* (Diptera: Drosphilidae) larvae which contains tyrosinase; possibly being a kind of oenocytoid (Tulloch, after Rizki, Jones).

crystalliferous, producing or bearing crystals, being applied to a number of bacteria of the genus *Bacillus,* e.g., *Bacillus thurengensis* (Steinhaus and Martignoni).

crystalline, transparent, like crystal (T-B).

crystalline body, a transparent subcorneal part of the dioptric apparatus of an eye, formed of cells or cell products, having an oval or conical shape (T-B, after Snodgrass); see crystalline cone and crystalline lens.

crystalline cone, in the insect eye, a hard transparent refractive body in eucone eyes, secreted by a group of 4 cells beneath the corneagen layer or the cornea, as the case may be (T-B, after Imms); see crystalline body.

crystalline humor, crystalline body, q.v. (T-B).

crystalline lens, in stemmata of some larval insects, an oval lens located beneath the cuticle (Chapman); see crystalline body and crystaline cone.

crystalline tract, in acone and exocone eyes, slender refractile strands of Semper cells extending inward to the retinula cells (Chapman).

crystalloid leucocyte, cystocyte, q.v. (Tulloch).

C-shaped, semicircular or cresent shaped; U-shaped (Peterson).

ctenidial spine, in adult Diptera, relatively large bristle among those comprising the ctenidium of the forefemur (McAlpine); in adult Siphonaptera, the modified spines which make up the helmet, genal, pronotal, and abdominal combs (Rothschild and Traub).

ctenidiobothria (sing., **ctenidiobothrium**), in Psocoptera, setae with comb-edged scales at their bases on hind tibiae and tarsi (transl. of "Ctenidiobothrien," Enderlein).

ctenidium (pl., **ctenidia**), comblike structure on any part of an insect (T-B); in Psocoptera, cteniobothria, q.v. (Borror et al.); in Polyctenidae (Hemiptera: Heteroptera: Cimicoidea), comblike rows of flattened spines on the body (Woodward et al., in CSIRO); in adult Diptera, comblike row of spinules at the distal end of the anteroventral surface of the forefemur (McAlpine); in adult Siphonaptera, combs of backward directed setae on body (T-B; Dunnet, in CSIRO; Lewis, pers. comm.); in ♀ Hymenoptera, spines on annuli of gonapophyses (Tuxen, after Ross).

cteniophore, in some ♂ Notodontidae (Lepidoptera), a projection on each anterolateral corner of abdominal sternite IV, bearing a set of thick, spinelike setae distally (Jordan).

Cu, cubitus, q.v. (Mackerras, in CSIRO).

CuA, cubitus anterior, q.v. (Mackerras, in CSIRO).

cubé powder, the finely ground roots of certain *Lonchocarpus* spp. (Legumosae), which contain rotenone (Pfadt).

cubital, referring or belonging to the cubitus (T-B).

cubital area, that area of the insect wing which lies between the main stem of the cubitus and the anal vein, bounded proximally by the anal crossing (T-B, after Comstock).

cubital cell(s), wing cell bounded anteriorly by the cubitus or one of its branches (T-B, after Comstock).

cubital cellule, in the insect wing, the cell between the radial cellule and the vein originating near the extremity of the cubitus (T-B, after Jardine).

cubital fork, branching or point of separation of the branches of the cubitus (T-B); in adult Diptera, branching of CuA into CuA_1 and CuA_2 (McAlpine).

cubital furrow, in Heteroptera (Hemiptera), simple or forked furrow or plica on the remigium of hind wing posterior to Cu (Štys, after Davis); see claval furrow.

cubital nerve, cubitus, q.v., of wing (T-B)

cubital nervure, cubitus, q.v., of wing (T-B).

cubital pecten, in the hind wings of certain Gelechioidea and Pyraloidea (Lepidoptera), a comb of stiff straight hairs on the upper side, directed upward and slightly backward on cubitus posterior (T-B, after Tillyard; Common, pers. comm.).

cubital plate, in Odonata and Neoptera, the basal wing sclerite from which cubitus, plical vein, and empusal vein originate (Ross et al., after Hamilton).

cubital supplement, in wings of Odonata, a midrib-like vein which divides the cubitoanal loop longitudinally (T-B, after Tillyard).

cubital vein, cubitus (Cu), q.v., of wing (T-B); in adult Diptera, branch R_{4+5} of radius (Colless and McAlpine, in CSIRO, after Schiner).

cubitoanal, pertaining to the cubitus and the anal vein of the insect wing (T-B).

cubitoanal crossvein, a crossvein between the cubitus and an anal vein (Borror et al.).

cubitoanal excision, in many insects, a notch in the margin of the wing at the point where the anal and preanal areas join (T-B, after Comstock).

cubitoanal fold, in insect wings, the continuation of the cubitoanal sulcus, which usually extends to the margin of the wing (T-B, after Comstock).

cubitoanal loop, in the wings of some Odonata, a loop developed between veins A_2 and Cu_2; the foot-shaped loop of Needham (T-B, after Comstock).

cubitoanal sulcus, the deep channel between the anterior and posterior tuberosities of the insect wing (T-B, after Comstock).

cubitomarginal ridge, in adult Culicidae (Diptera), a faint ridge or convex fold of the wing membrane running parallel to the wing margin across the apex of the cubitus anterior (CuA), extending anteriorly at least halfway to M_{3+4} and posteriorly fading away near the anal vein (Harbach and Knight, after Colless).

cubitus (Cu), the sixth longitudinal vein of the wing immediately posterior to the media (M), with 2 primary branches, cubitus anterior (CuA), which usually has 2 branches, CuA_1 and CuA_2, and a weaker, unbranched cubitus posterior (CuP) (T-B; Borror et al.; Common, pers. comm.); foretibia, q.v. (T-B).

cubitus anterior (CuA), anterior banch of cubitus (Mackerras, in CSIRO; Harbach and Knight).

cubitus posterior (CuP), posterior branch of cubitus (Mackerras, in CSIRO; Harbach and Knight).

cubitus posterior scale, in adult Culicidae (Diptera), one of the scales occurring in a group on the ventral surface of the wing at the base of the cubitus posterior and extending to the base of the anal vein (Harbach and Knight).

cuboidal, somewhat cube-shaped, or resembling a cube (T-B).

cuckoo spit, in Cercopidae (Hemiptera: Auchenorrhyncha), spittle, q.v. (T-B; Woodward et al., in CSIRO).

Cucujiformia, group within the Polyphaga (Coleoptera), including the superfamilies Cucujoidea, Cleroidea, Lymexyloidea, Chrysomeloidea, and Curculionoidea (Britton, in CSIRO).

Cucujoidea, superfamily within the Polyphaga (Coleoptera), including the family Cucujidae and many other families, characterized by adults with hind coxae without a transverse concavity or steep face against which the hind femora can be retracted, and $\male$ aedeagus of the vaginate type (Britton, in CSIRO).

cucullate, cucullated, cucullatus, hood-shaped; hoodlike; having a hood (T-B).

cucullus, a hood; a hood-shaped covering or structure (T-B); see capillitium; in the genitalia of ♂ Lepidoptera, the terminal part of the harpe, q.v. (T-B, after Klots), particularly, the distal or dorsodistal part of the valva, usually hairy or setose (Tuxen, after Pierce).

cucumber mosaic, disease of cucumber and tobacco plants caused by a rhabdovirus transmitted nonpersistently by aphids (Hemiptera: Sternorrhyncha: Aphididae) (Borror et al.).

cucumiform, cucumber-shaped (T-B).

cucurbit wilt, bacterial disease of cucumber plants and other curcubits caused by *Erwinia tracheiphila* transmitted by leaf beetles, *Acalymma vittata* and *Diabrotica unidecimpunctata howardi* (Coleoptera: Chrysomelidae) (Borror et al.).

cue-lure, a synthetic attractant of the ♂ melon fly, *Daucus cucurbitae* (Diptera: Tephritidae); 4-(*p*-hydroxyphenyl)-2-butanone acetate (Pfadt).

cuilleron, alula, q.v. (T-B).

Culicoidea, superfamily within the infraorder Culicimorpha (Diptera: Nematocera), including the families Culicidae, Chaoboridae, and Dixidae, possessing adult flies with a radial sector (R_s) and media (M) each with 3 branches (Colless and McAlpine, in CSIRO; McAlpine).

Culicomorpha, division within the suborder Nematocera (Diptera), including the superfamilies Culicoidea and Chironomoidea, possessing adults that lack the V-shaped mesonotal suture, discal cell on wing, and ocelli, and in which the radial sector (R_s) and media (M) each possess 3 or fewer branches (Colless and McAlpine, in CSIRO; McAlpine).

culmen, the longitudinal carina of a caterpillar (Lepidoptera) (T-B).

cultellate, knifelike (T-B).

cultellus (pl., **cultelli**), the sharp knifelike proboscis of some blood sucking flies (Diptera), or one of its bladelike lancets (T-B; Leftwich).

cultrate, cultriform, shaped like a pruning knife (T-B).

culus (Latin), anus, q.v. (T-B; Tuxen).

cumulate, in groups or heaps (T-B).

cumuliform swarm, a form of a locust swarm in flight in which the swarm extends upward in a towering form to over 1000 meters above the ground and in which the insects are relatively widely dispersed (0.001–0.100 locusts/cubic meter) (Chapman, after Waloff); see stratiform swarm.

cumulus, a heap (R. W. Brown); as of cells in a developing ovum (T-B).

cuneal incisure, in Heteroptera (Hemiptera), costal fracture, q.v.

cuneate, cuneatus (Latin), **cuneiform,** wedge-shaped (T-B; R. W. Brown).

cuneiform aedeagal apodeme, in ♂ Diptera, free, wedge- or Y-shaped, aedeagal apodeme (McAlpine).

cuneus (pl., **cunei**), in some Heteroptera, usually triangular posterolateral area of the corium, separated from the latter by the costal fracture (T-B; Štys, pers. comm.); in ♂ Lepidoptera, sclerotized structures of vesica (Tuxen, after Stitz).

CuP, cubitus posterior, q.v. (Mackerras, in CSIRO).

Cupediformia, a group within the Archostemata (Coleoptera) that includes the single superfamily Cupedoidea (Crowson).

Cupedoidea, single superfamily within the suborder Archostemata (Coleoptera), including the Ommatidae, Cupedidae, and Micromalthidae (Britton, in CSIRO).

cupola organ, campaniform sensillum, q.v. (T-B).

cupping disc, in primitive ♂ Symphyta (Hymenoptera), suction pad at tip of gonostylus (Tuxen, after Snodgrass).

cupreous, cupreus (Latin), copper-colored (T-B).

cuprophilic cell, midgut cells that absorb copper ions (Chapman).

cups, in wings of Nymphalidae (Lepidoptera), odoriferous openings provided with a covering membrane pierced in the center by a minute pore (T-B, after Imms).

cupule, a cup-shaped organ (T-B); in ♂ Hymenoptera, basal ring, q.v. (Tuxen, after Audouin); in ♀ Lithosiinae (Lepidoptera: Arctiidae), pouches in sternum VII at either side of lamella (Tuxen, after Field).

cupules, the suckerlike processes covering the under surface of the tarsi in ♂ Dytiscidae (Coleoptera).

cupuliferous, bearing cupules or little cups (T-B).

cupuliform, cup-shaped; like a little cup; cyathiform (T-B).

Curculionoidea, superfamily within the Polyphaga (Coleoptera), including the Curculionidae and other families, characterized by adults with pseudotetramerous tarsi, a head produced foward into a rostrum, abdomen with 5 visible sternites, and metasternum with a transverse suture near posterior edge, and by larvae with one or two-segmented antennae, and lacking urogomphi (Britton, in CSIRO).

curcumbitate, shaped like a melon, generally applied to insect eggs (Peterson).

curl grub, scarabaeiform larva, q.v. (CSIRO).

curly top, beet curly top, q.v. (Borror et al.).

Cursoria, Blattaria + Mantodea (T-B; Boudreaux).

cursorial, adapted for running (T-B); running in habit (Borror et al.).

Cursorida, name for hypothesized monophyletic group of Polyneoptera (Insecta), including the orders Zoraptera, Isoptera, Blattaria, and Mantodea (Boudreaux).

cursory, cursorial, q.v. (T-B).

curvate, curvatus (Latin), curved (T-B).

curved scales, in larval Chironomidae (Diptera), paraligula, q.v. (Saether).

Curvipalpia, infraorder within the Annulipalpia (Trichoptera), including the Philopotamoidea and Hydropsychoidea, characterized by adults with a flexible annulated maxillary palp segment, loss of ♂ parameres; and larva with reduced abdominal tergite X (Weaver); see Spicipalpia.

cusp, a pointed process (T-B); in mosquito larvae (Diptera: Culicidae), one of the pointed projections located at or near the apex of the dorsal teeth and the auxiliary ventral tooth of the mandible (Harbach and Knight).

cuspidal, ending in a point; pointed.

cuspidate, cuspidatus (Latin), pointed (T-B; R. W. Brown); see acuminate.

cuspis (pl., **cuspides**), cusp, q.v. (T-B); in ♂ Chironomidae (Diptera), outer, apical, nonmoveable finger of inferior and superior volsella (Saether); in ♂ Hymenoptera, outer, apical nonmoveable finger of volsella (Tuxen, after Michener).

cuspis volsellaris, in ♂ Hymenoptera, cuspis, q.v. (Tuxen, after Snodgrass).

custodite, custoditus, guarded; a body in an envelope (T-B).

cutaneous, of or pertaining to the exposed integument (T-B).

cutaneous respiration, respiration through the body surface, together with transport to the tissues by the hemolymph, e.g., Protura, most Collebola, insect eggs, aquatic insects (coupled with an apneustic respiratory system), and endoparastic insects (Chapman).

cutex, integument, q.v. (T-B).

cuticle, a secretion of the epidermis, covering the entire body of the insect as well as lining ectodermal invaginations such as the stomodaeum, proctodaeum, and tracheae (T-B, after Tillyard; Chapman); see endocuticle, epicuticle, exocuticle, and procuticle.

cuticula, cuticle, q.v. (T-B).

cuticula exterior (pl., **cuticulae exteriores**), in ♂ Sphingidae (Lepidoptera), outer layer of aedoeagus (Tuxen, after Oiticica).

cuticula interior (pl., **cuticulae interiores**), in ♂ Sphingidae (Lepidoptera), inner layer of aedoeagus (Tuxen, after Oiticica).

cuticular, of or pertaining to the cuticle (T-B).

cuticular appendages, outgrowths of the cuticle connected by a membranous joint, e.g., setae and spurs (T-B, after Imms); see cuticular processes.

cuticular colors, colors contained mostly in the epidermis, being permanent browns, blacks and yellows (T-B, after Imms).

cuticular lens, corneal lens, q.v. (Chapman).

cuticular nodules, small nodular more or less conical outgrowths of the cuticule (T-B, after Comstock).

cuticular outgrowth, outgrowths of the body surface, including cuticular appendages and cuticular processes (Teskey, in McAlpine).

cuticular projection, cuticular outgrowth, q.v. (Harbach and Knight).

cuticular processes, outgrowths which are integral parts of the substance of the cuticle, rigidly connected with it, without a membranous articulation, e.g., a spine (T-B, after Imms); see cuticular appendages.

cuticular wing, in anopheline larvae (Diptera: Culicidae), the expanded more membranous part of each lobe of Nuttall and Shipley's organ (Harbach and Knight, after Iyengar).

cuticularization, formation of cuticle; change into cuticle (T-B).

cuticulin, material making up the thicker inner portion of the epicuticle (T-B; Tulloch); complex consisting primarily of tanned lipoproteins, forming thin outer epicuticle (Chapman, after Locke).

cuticulin layer, inner and outer epicuticles, excluding wax and cement layers (Tulloch; Chapman, after Weis-Fogh); outer epicuticle, q.v. (Chapman, after Locke).

cutworm, name given to a larva of those Noctuidae (Lepidoptera) that typically cut off plants at the surface of the ground when feeding (Borror et al.).

cyaneous, cyaneus, dark-blue (T-B; R. W. Brown).

cyanescent, with a deep bluish tinge or shading (T-B).

cyanogen, C_2N_2, a colorless, poisonous, inflammable gas with a strong odor resembling that of peach blossoms.

cyanogenic, producing hydrocyanic acid (T-B).

cyathiform, obconical and concave; cup-shaped (T-B); see cupuliform.

cyatotheca, the cover of the thorax in the pupa (T-B).

cycle, a round or circle, e.g., of development; a life cycle (T-B).

cyclic, in chemistry, atoms linked together to form a ring structure (Pfadt).

cyclic-reflex hypothesis, hypothesis that feedback from a behavioral act itself is sufficient to cause the act to be repeated (Matthews and Matthews).

cyclical polymorphism, different forms appearing successively in different generations as the annual cycle proceeds, e.g., many species of Aphididae (Hemiptera: Sternorrhyncha) (Norris, in CSIRO); see alternation of generations.

cyclodevelopmental transmission, disease transmission in which the causal organisms undergo cyclical change but do not multiply, e.g., filarial worm transmission by Culicidae (Diptera) (Adkins, pers. comm.); see cyclopropagative transmission and circulative transmission.

cyclodienes, cyclic hydrocarbons belong to the cyclodiene group (Pfadt).

cyclolabia, the shorter forceps of earwigs, when of variable length within the species (T-B).

cyclomerism, a variation of the enterocoel theory, q.v., of the origin of metamerism that assumes that the enteric pouches closed off in an originally radially symmetrical coelenteratelike ancestor and became bilaterally symmetrical (Boudreaux).

cyclomorphosis, cyclical polymorphism, q.v. (Norris, in CSIRO).

cyclopiform larva, cyclopoid larva, q.v. (Gauld and Bolton).

cyclopoid larva, in Hymenoptera with hypermetamorphosis (e.g., some Platygasteridae), a larva characterized by a large swollen cephalothorax, very long sicklelike mandibles and a pair of bifurcate processes of various forms, resembling the nauplius larva of crustaceans (T-B, after Imms).

cyclopropagative transmission, disease transmission in which the causal organisms undergo changes and multiply in the body of the arthropod, e.g., malaria plasmodis transmitted by anopheline Culicidae (Diptera) (Adkins, pers. comm.); see cyclodevelopmental transmission and propagative transmission.

cyclops, a heretitary deformity of honey bees (Hymenoptera: Apidae), consisting of a fusion of both compound eyes at the vertex of the head (Steinhaus and Martignoni).

Cyclorrhapha, division within the Brachycera (Diptera), characterized by the circumverted ♂ genitalia and by the puparium from which the adult emerges by pushing off a circular lid or covering (T-B; Colless and McAlpine, in CSIRO originally from Brauer, 1863); Muscomorpha, q.v. (McAlpine); see Orthorrhapha.

cyclorrhaphous, circularly seamed (T-B).

cyclorrhaphous Brachycera, Muscomorpha, q.v. (McAlpine); see Cyclorrhapha.

cyclostome mouth, in Hymenoptera, hypoclypeal depression, q.v. (Gauld and Bolton).

cydariform, globose, but truncated at 2 opposite sides (T-B).

cyhexatin, a specific miticide; an organotin, tricyclohexyltin hydroxide; slightly toxic to mammals, acute oral LD_{50} for rats 540 mg/kg (Pfadt).

cylindraceous, cylindraceus, cylindrate, cylindrical, shaped like a cylinder (T-B).

cymbiform, boat-shaped; a concave disc with elevated margin; navicular (T-B).

Cynipoidea, superfamily within the Apocrita (Hymenoptera), including the families Cynipidae, Charipidae, Eucoilidae, Liopteridae, Ibaliidae, and Figitidae, characterized by adults in which the lateral pronotum is not vertically grooved for reception of the forefemur, the spiracular lobe of pronotum is not margined with close fine hairs, there is no subantennal groove, and none of the spurs of the hind tibia are modified for preening (Riek, in CSIRO; Gauld and Bolton).

Cynodon chlorotic streak, disease of bermudagrass (*Cynodon*) caused by a rhabdovirus transmitted propagatively by *Toya* (Hemiptera: Auchenorrhyncha: Delphacidae) (Nault and Ammar).

cyphosomatic larva, larva with dorsal and ventral surfaces of body distinctly nonparallel, i.e., the dorsal surface being curved (humped, elevated or convex) and ventral surface being straight or flat, e.g., many larval Galerucinae and Criocerinae (Coleoptera: Chrysomelidae) (Peterson).

cypsella (pl., **cypsellae**), in ♀ Hymenoptera, emargination between teeth of gonapophyses; the ventral or dorsal termination of the colpus (Tuxen, after E. L. Smith).

cyst, a sac or vesicle (T-B); sperm cyst, q.v. (Chapman).

cyst stage, in Margarodidae (Hemiptera: Sternorrhyncha: Coccoidea), intermediate instar that is shaped like a pearl, and lacks legs and has reduced antennae (Miller, in Stehr); see ground pearls.

cysteine, in larvae of the clothes moth *Tineola bisselliela* (Lepidoptera: Tineidae), reduced form of cystine catalyzed by the enzyme cystine reductase in the midgut (Gilmour, in CSIRO).

cysteine desulphydrase, in larvae of clothes moth *Tineola bisselliela* (Lepidoptera: Tineidae), enzyme in the midgut which splits hydrogen disulfide from cysteine (Gilmour, in CSIRO).

cysticercoid, a form of larval tapeworm (Pfadt).

cystine, in larvae of clothes moth *Tineola bisselliella* (Lepidoptera: Tineidae), unreduced form of cysteine released from wool in the midgut during digestion (Gilmour, in CSIRO).

cystine reductase, in larvae of clothes moth *Tineola bisselliela* (Lepidoptera: Tineidae), enzyme in the midgut catalyzing the reduction of cystine to cysteine (Gilmour, in CSIRO).

cystocyte, hemocyte with a defined nucleus and a pale, hyaline cytoplasm containing scattered black granules, being involved in coagulation or wound healing (Tulloch; Chapman); in ♀ insects, follicle cells, q.v. (T-B, after Snodgrass); in ♂ insects, cyst cells, q.v. (T-B, after Snodgrass).

cystocyte of Yeager, granular hemocyte, q.v. (Tulloch).

cytochrome, an intracellular respiratory pigment found in especially high concentrations in insect flight muscle (T-B, after Keilin; Gilmour, in CSIRO).

cytocidal, in invertebarte pathology, that which kills cells (Steinhaus and Martignoni).

cytogenetics, the comparative study of chromosomal mechansims and behavior in populations and taxa, and their effect on inheritance and evolution (Mayr); analytical study of chromosomal mechanisms regarded as the physical basis of genetic systems (White, in CSIRO); see chromosome cytology.

cytology, the study of the structure and physiology of the cell and its parts (T-B; Mayr).

cytoplasm, the protoplasm of the cell exclusive of the nucleus (T-B), usually a slightly viscous fluid with inclusions of various size and differentiated externally as a plasma membrane.

cytoplasmic polyhedrosis, a viral disease of insects, mainly the larvae of certain Lepidoptera, characterized by the formation of polyhedral inclusion bodies (polyhedra) in the cytoplasm of the midgut epithelial cells (Steinhaus and Martignoni); see polyhedrosis.

cytoplasmic polyhedrosis viruses, insect viruses that are occluded in a polyhedral protein crystal and multiply in the cell cytoplasm; virus particles are nearly spherical; majority occur in larvae of the Lepidoptera (Pfadt).

cyton, perikaryon, q.v. (T-B, after Snodgrass).

cytospecies, a species recognized soley on the basis of cytological criteria (Carlberg, pers. comm.).

cytotaxonomy, use of cytology and cytogenetics in elucidating the relationships of higher taxa and comparison of the chromosome sets of related species (White, in CSIRO).

D

Dacnonypha, infraorder of the suborder Glossata (Lepidoptera), including the superfamilies Catapterigoidea and Eriocranoidea (Sinev).

dactylopodite, a simple, clawlike segment at the end of the legs in some

Arthropoda, e.g., Protura; the clawlike segment at the end of the leg in Crustacea; pretarsus, q.v. (T-B, after Snodgrass).

dactyl, dactylus (Latin), a finger or toe (T-B); tarsomere, q.v. (T-B).

dactyls, in Gryllotalpidae (Orthoptera: Grylloidea), greatly enlarged terminal teeth of broad, compressed foretibia (Key, in CSIRO).

dagger mark, a marking in the form of a Greek psi (Ψ) (T-B).

Dalton's Law, the rule that the rate of evaporation from a water surface is proportional to the saturation deficiency of the air; applicable to rate of water loss in many insects (Tulloch).

damselfly, member of the suborder Zygoptera (Odonata) (Borror et al.).

dances, stereotyped movements of honeybee (Hymenoptera: Apidae) foragers on the vertical face of the honeycomb inside the hive which communicate sources of food, e.g., round dance, waggle dance (Matthews and Matthews).

dark-adapted eye, a compound eye adapted for low light intensities (Chapman); see light-adapted eye.

dart(s), in ♀ Hymenoptera, sting, q.v. (T-B) or first gonapophyses, q.v. (Tuxen, after Snodgrass).

Darwin principle, principle that important taxonomic characters are not the result of a specific ad hoc adapation (Mayr).

Dascilliformia, Dascilloidea + Elateriformia (Crowson); Dascilloidea (Hennig, after Crowson).

Dascilloidea, superfamily within the Polyphaga (Coleoptera), including the families Dascillidae and Rhipiceridae, possessing adults with a 5-5-5 tarsal formula, open procoxal cavities, 5 or 6 visible abdominal sternites, and a ♂ aedeagus of the trilobate type (Britton, in CSIRO; Lawrence, in Parker).

dash, a short disconnected streak or mark (T-B).

Dasanit (trade name), fensulfaothion, q.v. (Pfadt).

Dasygastres, bees (Hymenoptera: Apoidea), with pollen-carrying structures on the abdomen (T-B); see ventral scopa.

data matrix, a presentation of the attributes of species (or other taxa) in rows and columns (Mayr).

daubing, a process in which an intruder into a colony is soaked with liquids from the mouth; a defensive action of bumble bees (Hymenoptera: Apoidea) when rejecting an intruder of superior fighting ability (Tulloch, after Gaul).

daughter cell, a cell produced through mitosis from any antecedent cell (T-B).

day-eye, light-adapted eye, q.v. (T-B, after Comstock).

Day's organ, in some Pompilidae (Hymenoptera), an organ with a sculptured surface, located in the intersegmental membrane or on the anterior margin of abdominal tergite IV (and sometimes V) (Gauld and Bolton).

D-D (trade name), a soil fumigant for controlling nematodes and garden symphylan; heavy liquid with odor of chloroform; a mixture of 1,3-dichloropropene and 1,2-dichloropropane; moderately toxic to mammals by ingestion or by inhalation, acute oral LD_{50} for rats 140 mg/kg, inhalation LC_{50} for rats 1000 ppm (Pfadt).

DDT, $C_{14}H_9Cl_5$, a synthetic insecticide; a chlorinated hydrocarbon, 1,1,1-trichloro-2,2-bis(*p*-chlorophenyl)ethane; moderately toxic to mammals, acute oral LD_{50} for rats about 250 mg/kg (Pfadt).

dead end host, a vertebrate (usually) that may harbor a pathogen, may be severely affected by it, yet the level of pathogen in the blood and other peripheral tissues may be too low for a bloodsucking arthropod to become infective after feeding on the host (Adkins, pers. comm.).

dealate, an individual that has shed its wings, usually after mating; used as an adjective and a noun (Wilson).

dealation, the loss of wings in certain groups by casting or breaking off done by the insect itself (T-B); in ants (Hymenoptera: Formicidae) and other insects, the removal of the wings by the queens during or immediately following the nuptial flight and prior to colony foundation (Wilson; Leftwich); in termites (Isoptera), the shedding of the wings of ♂ and ♀ reproductive along the basal suture after the dispersal flight (Krishna, pers. comm.).

deamination, the splitting off of ammonia from amino acids to produce keto acids through the action of a deaminase (Chapman).

deaminase, an enzyme catalyzing the splitting off of ammonia from amino acids to produce keto acids, including either amino acid oxidases or glutamate dehydrogenase (Gilmur, in CSIRO; Chapman).

death feigning, in stick insects (Phasmida), many beetles (Coleoptera), larval and adult Lepidoptera, and other insects; thanatosis, q.v. (Tulloch; Leftwich)

deaurate, deauratus, a rubbed or worn gold color (T-B).

decaectopophysis, in ♂ Chironomidae (Diptera), inferior volsella, q.v. (Saether).

decalatecoria, in Isoptera, flexible membrane between sternum and tergum X (Tuxen, after Geyer).

Decapoda, order within the class Malacostraca (Crustacea), including lobsters, crayfish, crabs, and shrimps (Borror et al.).

decapophysis, a special apophysis of the structures of the tenth abdominal segment in ♀ insects (T-B, after MacGillivray).

decapygidium (pl., **decapygydia**), in Isoptera, pygydium when formed by abdominal segment X (Tuxen, after Crampton).

decasternal coria, in Isoptera, flexible membrane between sternum IX and sternum X (Tuxen, after Geyer).

decaton, the tenth segment of insects (T-B).

decavalvae, in ♀ insects, second gonapophyses, q.v. (T-B, after MacGillivray).

decavalvifer, in Orthoptera, second gonocoxa, q.v. (T-B, after MacGillivray).

decenal, an unsaturated aldehyde produced by the metathoracic scent glands of many bugs (Hemiptera: Heteroptera) (Gilmour, in CSIRO).

decephalic, with a prognathous head having the foramen divided into 2 parts by other structures (T-B, after MacGillivray).

deciduous, falling off at maturity or at certain periods (T-B).

deciduous cornuti, cornuti decidui, q.v. (Tuxen, after Pierce).

declinate, declinatus (Latin), somewhat bent; with the apex downward (T-B).

declivent, declivous, declivus (Latin), sloping downward (T-B; R. W. Brown).

decolorate, faded; of a faded-appearing color (T-B).

decrepitans, decrepitant, crackling (T-B).

decticous pupa, exarate pupa in which the mandibles are articulated, e.g., Megaloptera, Raphidioptera, Planipennia, Trichoptera, and some Lepidoptera, being used to help the insect to escape its cell or cocoon (Leftwich; Chapman); see adecticous pupa.

decumbent, bent downward (T-B; Borror et al.); bending down at tip from an upright base (T-B).

decurrent, closely attached to and running down another body (T-B).

decurved, bowed or curved downward (T-B).

decussate, crossing at an angle; X-like; in cross pairs; as when bristles alternately cross each other, in some Diptera (e.g. cruciate bristles) (T-B).

decussation, a crossing (T-B); see decussate.

defaunate, in invertebrate pathology, to remove from an organism its commensalistic and mutualistic microfauna, for which the organism ordinarily serves as a host, e.g., removing the flagellates from the alimentary tract of termites (Isoptera) (Steinhaus and Martignoni).

defaunated, deprived of fauna (T-B); see defaunate.

defecation, defaecation, excretion of feces (T-B; Chapman).

defecatory, of or pertaining to defecation (T-B).

defense autotomy, see autotomy.

defensive behavior, usually divided into a primary defense, including cryptic coloration and resting behavior, and secondary defense, including chemical defense, defense autotomy, flight, stridulation, and active fighting (Carlberg, pers. comm.).

defensive glands, in Phasmida, a pair of glands located on the prothorax and which emit a defensive secretion (Happ et al.; Strong); see defensive secretion.

defensive mechanisms, mechanisms for avoiding or misleading predators, e.g., warning or concealment coloration, autotomy, defensive secretions, urticating hairs (Norris, in CSIRO).

defensive secretion(s), caustic, irritant, or foul-smelling fluids which are discharged as a means of defense (Leftwich); in Phasmida, monoterpenes and actinidines produced by the defensive glands (Carlberg).

deficiency disease, in invertebrate pathology, a disease resulting from lack of carbohydrates, proteins, amino acids, fatty acids, vitamins, trace minerals, or other essential constituents and elements of the diet (Steinhaus and Martignoni).

definition, a statement in words that purports to give characters differentiating a taxon (ICZN); see delimitation, description, diagnosis, and differential diagnosis.

definitive accessory veins, accessory veins which have attained a position comparable in stability to that of the primitive branches of the principal veins (T-B, after Comstock).

definitive accessory host, the host, insect or otherwise, in which the sexual life of a parasite is passed (T-B, after Matheson).

definitive accessory reservoir, in medical entomology, a host, insect or otherwise, in which a natural supply of the sexual stage of a parasite occurs (T-B, after Matheson).

deflected, bent downward; of wings, having the inner margins lapping and the outer edges declining toward the sides (T-B).

deflexed, deflexus (Latin), abruptly bent downward (T-B).

deflexus capsulae, in ♂ Siphonaptera, inwardly deflected ventral end of lateral wall of capsula, with a tendon running cephalad (Tuxen, after Smit).

defoliators, insects that strip trees and other plants of leaves, either by direct feeding on the leaves or by spreading virus and fungus diseases which cause the leaves to curl up and eventually die (T-B; Leftwich).

deformed, twisted or set in an unusual form; specifically, in Coleoptera applied to knotted or twisted antennae as in ♂ Meloidae (T-B).

degenerate, deteriorate (T-B); to become of a lower type (T-B).

degenerate slave makers, slave making ants (Hymenoptera: Formicidae) that permit the host ♀ to live and continue egg production, thus forming mixed colonies (Tulloch, after Gaul).

degenerating hemocyte, senescent blood cells of different kinds in various stages of dissolution (Yeager); includes vacuolar leucocytes (Arvy, Gabe and Lhoste), isolated nuclei (Millara), free nuclei (Paillot), cytoplasmic free cells (Glaser) (Tulloch, after Jones).

degeneration, a progressive deterioration or loss of function of any part or organ (T-B); a passing from a higher to a lower form (T-B).

dehisce, to open for the discharge of contents, as a pod or a pupa (T-B).

dehiscence, the splitting of the pupal integument in the emergence of the adult in Lepidoptera (T-B).

dehiscent, open or standing open (T-B); separating toward the tip (T-B).

dehydrogenase, an enzyme that catalyzes dehydrogenation (Tulloch).

dehydrogenation, the removal of hydrogen from a molecule, see oxidation (Tulloch).

dejectamenta, excreta, q.v. (T-B).

delamination, a splitting or division into layers (T-B).

delayed dormant spray, an orchard spray applied during the period from swollen bud to late green tip of bud development (Pfadt).

Delhi boil, oriental sore, q.v. (Allaby).

delimitation, in taxonomy, a formal statement of the characters of a taxon which sets its limits (Mayr); see definition, diagnosis, differential diagnosis, and description.

Delnav (trade name), dioxathion, q.v. (Pfadt).

deltoid, elongate triangular; resembling a Greek Δ with apex extended (T-B).

delusory parasitosis, nervous disorder which causes victim to see and experience attacks by imaginary arthropods (Adkins, pers. comm.); see entomophobia.

demarcated, bounded or set off (T-B).

demarcation, a bounding, laying out or limiting (T-B).

deme, a local population of a species, i.e., the community of potentially interbreeding individuals at a given locality (Mayr).

demeton, $C_8H_{12}O_3PS_2$, a contact and plant systemic insecticide and acaricide; an organophosphate, mixture of *O,O*-diethyl *O*(and *S*)-2-[(ethylthio)ethyl] phosphorothioates; extremely toxic to mammals, acute oral LD_{50} for rats 12 mg/kg (Pfadt).

demi-, Latin prefix; half (T-B).

demidiate, half-round (T-B).

dendriform, dendritic, branched lake a tree; arborescent (T-B).

dendrite, a spicule branched to resemble a tree in form, having a basal stem bearing irregular or dichotomous branches which may be repeatedly branched in turn (Harbach and Knight).

dendrites, dendrons, finely ramifying branches given off from a nerve cell (T-B).

dendrogram, a drawing in the form of a tree designed to indicate degrees of relationship (Mayr); see cladogram, phenogram, and phylogenetic tree.

dendroid, with markings having the appearance of a shrub or small tree; branched (T-B).

dendrophagous, dendrophagus, feeding on woody tissues (T-B).

dendrophilous, living in woody tissue, or on trees (T-B).

dengue, viral disease of man in tropical and subtropical regions of America and Africa transmitted *Aedes* mosquitoes, esp. *A. aegypti* and *A. albopictus* (Diptera: Culicidae) (Borror et al.).

dengue fever, dengue, q.v. (Colless and McAlpine, in CSIRO).

dens (pl., **dentes**), a tooth or toothlike process (T-B); in Collembola, the long proximal segment of the distal arms of the forks of the manubrium bearing the mucro apically (T-B; Christiansen and Bellinger); in the plural, the teeth or pointed processes on the inner side of the mandible (T-B, after Smith).

dense, conflected, q.v. (T-B).

density-dependent factors, factors whose effects on a population are dependent upon the density of that particular population, being either directly or inversely related (Steinhaus and Martignoni).

densonucleosis, a fatal disease of the wax moth, *Galleria mellonella* (Lepidoptera: Pyralidae), caused by a virus (Steinhaus and Martignoni).

dentacerores, in Coccoidea (Hemiptera: Sternorrhyncha), the elongated cerores of the mesal row of orbacerores which produce irregularities in the membrane surrounding the anus (T-B, after MacGillivray).

dental papilla, in some Collembola, a basal dorsal projection of the dens (Christiansen and Bellinger).

dental sac, in some Collembola, an apical protrusion, thin-walled, and perhaps retractile, of the dens (Snider).

dental sclerite, in larval Muscomorpha (Diptera), a small toothlike sclerite located below the base of the mandible (T-B; McAlpine); dentate sclerite, ectostomal sclerite, q.v. (Ferrar)

dental spine, in some Collembola, one of a series of enlarged, modified setae, usually along the inner dorsal base of the dens (Christiansen and Bellinger).

dentate, dentatus (Latin), toothed (T-B); with toothlike prominences (T-B); with acute teeth, the sides of which are equal and the tip is above the middle of base (T-B).

dentate sclerite, in larval Muscomorpha (Diptera), dental sclerite, q.v (Ferrar).

dentate-serrate, toothed, with the dentations themselves serrated on their edges (T-B).

dens tentaculiformis (pl. **dentes tentaculiformes**), in ♂ *Zygaena* (Lepidoptera: Zygaenidae), single spines of the lamina dorsalis of the aedoeagus (Tuxen, after Loritz).

denticle, denticulus (Latin), a small tooth (T-B); in Coccoidea (Hemiptera: Sternorrhyncha), a single tooth near the middle of the ventral aspect of the claw (T-B, after Ferris).

denticulate, denticulated, denticulatus (Latin), set with little teeth or notches (T-B).

denticulate pads, in ♂ Dermaptera, indurated areas of the distal lobe bearing small teeth (Tuxen, after Burr).

denticulate pores, dentacerores, q.v. (T-B, after MacGillivray).

denticulus (pl., **denticuli**), in ♂ Siphonaptera, small toothlike protuberance at anterior margin of the telomere corresponding with a notch (fovea) on the inner side of the basimere (sometimes vice versa) (Tuxen, after Smit).

dentiform, formed or appearing like a tooth (T-B).

dentigerous plate, in ♀ Aeshnidae (Odonata), sternum X coated with small spines or bordered with fewer more robust ones or projecting as a two-pronged fork (Tuxen).

dentigerous process, dentigerous plate, q.v. (Tuxen, after Tillyard).

dentigerous tubercle, dentigerous plate, q.v. (Tuxen, after Tillyard).

denudate, denudated, denuded, without hairs or scales; without vesti-ture of any kind (T-B; Harris, after R. W. Brown, and Marchant and Charles); see glabrous, immaculate, investutus, and nude.

denude, to free from covering; to rub so as to remove the surface covering of scales, hair or other vestiture (T-B).

deorse, deorsum (Latin), downward (T-B).

deoxyribonucleic acid (**DNA**), nucleic acid providing the genetic template of chromosomes (White, in CSIRO).

depauperate colony, in ants (Hymenoptera: Formicidae), an impover-ished or dying colony (T-B).

dependent, hanging down (T-B).

deplanate, deplanatus, complanate, q.v. (T-B).

deportation, in social insects, the carrying of adults to a new nest, or the carrying of young inexperienced workers to the old nest from the field (Tulloch, after Gaul).

deposit excretion, the deposition of metabolic end products as intracellular granules or in other structures of the body, rather than their elimination from the body as feces.

depressed, depressus (Latin), flattened down as if pressed (T-B); see compressed.

depressor, depressor muscle, any muscle employed to lower or depress any appendage (T-B).

depuratory, cleansing (T-B).

Deratoptera, Orthoptera, q.v. (T-B).

derived character, a character that differs materially from the ancestral condition (Mayr); a character modified relative to the ancestral or primitive condition; see apomorphy.

derma, dermis, the inner and usually thicker layer of the cuticle, laminated in structure and nonpigmented, situated beneath the epidermis (T-B).

dermal, relating to the epidermis (T-B).

dermal glands, unicelluar epidermal glands which secrete wax, setae, pheromones, silk, irritant poisons, etc. (T-B; Leftwich); epidermal glands that secrete moulting fluid containing enzymes which liquefy the endocuticle prior to moulting (Leftwich); see exocrine glands.

dermal light sense, sensitivity to light by epidermal cells other than visual receptors, e.g., in larval *Tenebrio* (Coleoptera: Tenebrionidae) (Chapman).

dermal papillae, numerous small projections on surface of body, e.g., Phoenicoccidae (Hemiptera: Sternorrhyncha: Coccoidea) (Miller, in Stehr).

Dermaptera, order with the Polyneoptera (Insecta: Pterygota), comprising the earwigs, possessing tarsi with 3 tarsomeres, small forewings in the form of tegmina lacking definite veins, semicircular hind wings (when present) with radiating venation, and a flexible abdomen almost always terminated by a pair of forcepslike cerci (T-B; Mackerras, in CSIRO).

Dermapterida, Dermapteroidea, q.v. (Boudreaux).

Dermapteroidea, group within the Polyneoptera (Insecta), including the recent order Dermaptera and the extinct order Protelytroptera (Boudreaux, after Martynov).

dermatitis, inflammation of the skin (Pfadt).

dermatoblasts, in the insect embryo, a thin outer layer of cells, segregated from the ectoderm cells which form the ventral body wall (T-B, after Imms); see neuroblasts.

Dermatoptera, Dermaptera, q.v. (T-B).

Dermestoidea, superfamily within the Bostrychiformia (Coleoptera: Polyphaga), including the families Dermestidae, Derodontidae, Thorictidae, and Sarothriidae, possessing small, ovoid, compact adults with a 3 to five-segmented club, a 5-5-5 tarsal formula, 5 visible abdominal sternites, mesepimeron forming part of midcoxal cavity, and posterior edge of pronotum obtusely angled in the middle (Britton, in CSIRO).

dermomuscular, pertaining to both the skin or dermis and the muscles (T-B).

derris powder, the finely ground roots of the shrub *Derris elliptica* (Leguminosae), which contains rotenone (Pfadt).

desclerotization, loss of sclerotin in normally sclerotized parts or structures (T-B).

description, a more or less complete formal statement of the characters of a taxon without special emphasis on those which set limits to the taxon or distinguish it from coordinate taxa (Mayr); a statement in words of taxonomic characters of a specimen or taxon (ICZN); see diagnosis and original description.

descriptive entomology, alpha taxonomy, q.v. (T-B).

deserticolous, inhabiting deserts (T-B).

desiccate, to dry (T-B).

desiccation, drying (T-B).

desideratum (pl., **desiderata**), some thing or things needed or desired (T-B).

designated priority, in cases of simultaneous publication of several names, the priority established by the first reviser (Mayr).

designation, the nomenclatural act of an author or the Commission in fixing, by an express statement, the name-bearing type of a previously or a newly established nominal genus, subgenus, species, or subspecies (ICZN); see fixation, indication, nomenclatural act, original designation, and subsequent designation.

desmergate, an ant (Hymenoptera: Formicidae) intermediate between a soldier and a worker (T-B; Leftwich).

desquamation, the process of scaling or coming off in scales (T-B).

destitute, destitutus (Latin), lacking or destitute of something specified; being entirely without (used in contrast) (T-B; Harris, after Emery and Brewster).

detached notum, in ♀ Aculeata (Hymenoptera), detached proximal extension of notum of gonapophyses IX (Tuxen, after E. L. Smith).

detached rhaches (sing., **rhachis**), in ♂ Hymenoptera, the rhachies from either ventral ramus in the gonapophyseal midsection which are detached from the rami and fused to form a single sclerite, independent of the gonopod, forming the floor of the gonapophyses of Siricidae and Cephidae (Tuxen, after E. L. Smith).

determinate, determinatus, with well-defined outlines or distinct limits; fixed; marked out (T-B).

detonans, detonant, exploding; emitting a sudden noise or a puff like an explosion (T-B); see crepitation.

detritivorous, feeding on organic detritus (T-B).

detritovore, a heterotrophic animal that feeds on organic detritus, being of either plant or animal origin; see saprophage.

detritus, worn away (T-B; R. W. Brown); any disintegrated or broken up matter (T-B).

Deuteropolyphaga, Elateriformia, q.v. (Hennig, after Schilder).
Deuterophlebioidea, superfamily within the infraorder Blephariceromorpha (Diptera: Nematocera), including the family Blephariceridae (McAlpine).
deuterotoky, amphitoky, q.v. (T-B).
deutocerebral, of or pertaining to the deutocerebrum, q.v. (T-B).
deutocerebral commissure, the connection between the antennal
glomeruli of opposite sides, traversing the lower part of the brain
(T-B, after Snodgrass).
deutocerebral region, deutocerebrum, q.v. (T-B, after Snodgrass).
deutocerebral segment, antennal segment, q.v. (T-B).
deutocerebrum, the middle section of the insect brain, formed by the
ganglion of the second primary segment, and consisting of antennal
and olfactory lobes (T-B).
deutonymph, the third instar of a mite (Acari) (Borror et al.); second
stage nymph.
deutoplasm, yolk, q.v., of egg (T-B).
deutotergite, the secondary dorsal segment of the abdomen (T-B).
deutovum, the quiescent, undeveloped larval stage which hatches from
the egg of certain mites (Acari) and from which, after 6 or 7 days, the
active, six-legged larva emerges (Tulloch).
developmental cycle, the period from the fertilization of the egg to
eclosion of the adult insect (Wilson).
developmental polymorphism, differences of growth rate and of
numbers of moults within a population (Albrecht and Blackith).
deviation rule, rule stating that one sister species will be more different
from the common ancestor than the other sister species (Wiley, after
Hennig).
Devonian Period, one of 6 periods within the Paleozoic Era, between
the Silurian and Carboniferous, extending between about 400 and
350 million years before the present (Riek, in CSIRO).
dexitorma (pl., **dexitormae**), in larval Scarabaeoidea (Coleoptera), a
usually slender sclerome extending inward from the right hand angle of the epipharynx, sometimes provided with a heelshaped pternotorma (T-B, after Böving).
dextrad, extending or directed toward the right (T-B).
dextral, to the right side of the median line (T-B).
dextrocaudad, extending obliquely between dextrad and caudad
(T-B).
dextrocephalad, extending obliquely between dextrad and cephalad
(T-B).
dextron, the right side of the body (T-B).
dextrose, $C_6H_{12}O_6$; a monosaccharide, being an isomer of fructose,
found with the latter in sweet fruits and honey.
di-, Greek prefix; double; 2 (T-B).
dia-, Greek prefix; through (T-B).
diacammatogyne, worker ants of the genus *Diacamma* (Hymenoptera:
Formicidae) which take the place of normal females (Tulloch); see
cryptogyne.

diadenian type, in Heteroptera (Hemiptera), omphalian or diastomian type of metathoracic scent gland with gland cells concentrated within the paired glandular components of the system, and with scent reservoir(s) differentiated (transl. from French "type diadenien" Carayon) (Štys).

diagnosis, in taxonomy, a formal statement of the characters (or most important characters) which distinguishes a taxon from other or closely related coordinate taxa (T-B; Mayr); in invertebrate pathology, to distinguish one disease from another or the determination of a disease from its signs, symptoms, etiology, pathogenesis, physiopathology, morphopathology, etc., or the decison reached (Steinhaus and Martignoni); see definition, delimitation, description, and differential diagnosis.

dialysis, separation of the constituents of solutions through permeable membranes (T-B); the differentiatial diffusion of substances in solution through a suitable membrane thereby leading to their separation (Tulloch).

dialyzing, separating by dialysis (T-B).

Diandria, in Dermaptera, a term formerly used for those members of the Forficulina with 2 penis lobes in contrast to those with only one, the Monandria (Popham); see Catadermaptera.

diapause, a delay in development that is not the direct result of prevailing conditions (T-B; Chapman); see quiescence.

Diaphanopterodea, extinct order of Pterygota (Insecta), possessing adults with fore- and hind wings similar, radius (R) bent back at the base, and many veins closely aligned in the basal part of the wing (Riek, in CSIRO), sometimes included within the Megasecoptera (Boudreaux).

diaphanous, diaphanus, clear, semitransparent, but not like glass (T-B, after Kirby and Spence).

diaphragm, any thin dividing membrane (T-B); in ♂ Auchenorrhyncha (Hemiptera), genital phragm, q.v. (Ossiannilsson et al., in Tuxen); in ♂ Heteroptera (Hemiptera), the internal wall of the pygophore, separating the general body cavity from genital chamber (Tuxen, after Sharp).

diaphragm of the spermatheca, in some ♀ Siphonaptera, a diaphragm, perforated by a circular aperture dividing the bulga from the hilla (Rothschild and Traub).

diaphragma (pl., **diaphragmata**), in ♂ Lepidoptera, the more or less transverse sheet of membrane that closes the body cavity caudally (Tuxen, after Cholodkowsky); in ♂ Heteroptera (Hemiptera), diaphragm, q.v. (Tuxen, after Kahlow); in ♂ Rhopalidae (Hemiptera: Heteroptera), inferior process, q.v. (Tuxen, after Seidenstücker).

diarthrosis, any articulation that permits motion (T-B).

diaspicera, in Coccoidea (Hemiptera: Sternorrhyncha), a group of 3 cells of the ceratuba (T-B, after MacGillivray).

diastase, amylase, q.v. (T-B).

diastatic, of or pertaining to the diastase (T-B).

diastole, the relaxation phase of the heartbeat, resulting from relaxation of muscles in the heart wall assisted by elastic filaments supporting the heart, and, in some cases, by contraction of the aliform muscles (T-B; Chapman); see systole.

diastolic, of or pertaining to the diastole (T-B).

diastomian type, in adult Heteroptera, metathoracic scent gland apparatus opening by paired, widely spaced orifices associated with metacoxal cavities on metapleuron (transl. from French "type diastomien" Carayon) (Štys).

diataxy, in biosynthesis, ordering of building blocks (e.g., amino acids, nucleic bases) into specific sequences (e.g., proteins, nucleic acids) with RNA serving as a template (Steinhaus and Martignoni).

diathesis, in invertebrate pathology, an inherited constitutional state whereby an individual is especially liable to a certain disease (Steinhaus and Martignoni).

diatom rake, in nymphal Ephemeroptera, a structure of the galea composed of hairs, bristles, or pectinate spines used in scraping diatoms from stones or other objects (T-B, after Needham).

diatone, in Heteroptera (Hemiptera), maximum width of head across eyes (Štys).

diazinon, $C_{12}H_{21}N_2O_3PS$, a synthetic insecticide and acaricide; an organophosphate, O,O-diethyl O-(2-isopropyl-4-methyl-6-pyrimidyl) phosphorothioate; moderately toxic to mammals, acute oral LD_{50} for rats about 33 mg/kg (Pfadt).

Dibrom (trade name), naled, q.v. (Pfadt).

dibromo-chloropropane (DBCP), a soil fumigant, nematocidal and lethal to garden symphylans; heavy liquid, with odor of chloroform, 1,2-dibromo-3-chloropropane; moderatley toxic to mammals (Pfadt).

dicerous, dicerus, having 2 antennae (T-B, after Kirby and Spence).

dichaetae, those Muscomorpha (Diptera), with a proboscis consisting of 2 parts (T-B).

dichlorvos, $C_4H_7C_{12}O_4P$, a synthetic insecticide and space fumigant; an organophosphate, 2,2-dichlorovinyl dimethyl phosphate; moderatley toxic to mammals, acute oral LD_{50} for rats 50–80 mg/kg (Pfadt).

dichloropropenes mixture (DCP), soil fumigant, nematocidal fumigant; liquid with odor of chloroform, 1,3-dichloropropene and related hydrocarbons; moderately toxic to mammals (Pfadt).

dichoptic, in adult Diptera, having the eyes markedly separated medially (T-B; McAlpine); see holoptic.

dichotomizing, dichotomous, q.v. (T-B).

dichotomous, forked (T-B); divided or dividing into 2 parts (T-B; Mayr); of taxonomic keys, arranged into couplets, q.v. (T-B).

dichotomy, a branching of a single stem into 2 equal and diverging branches, used in phylogeny of ancestral lines of descent, and in venation of main veins or their branches; also, a table or key for determining species or higher groups, in which they are separated by contrasting characters arranged in couplets, 2 by 2 (T-B, after Tillyard).

dichromatism, the possession of 2 color varieties (T-B).

dichthadiiform ergatogyne, in army ants (Hymenoptera: Formicidae), a member of an aberrant reproductive caste, characterized by possession of a wingless alitrunk, a huge gaster, and an expanded postpetiole (Wilson).

dichthadiiform queen, dichthadiiform ergatogyne, q.v. (Brown and Taylor, in CSIRO).

dichthadiigyne, dichthadiiform ergatogyne, q.v. (Brown and Taylor, in CSIRO); an ant without eyes, ocelli or wings, with an exceedingly large gaster and ovaries, peculiar to the Dorylinae (Hymenoptera: Formicidae) (T-B).

Dicloacia, Integripalpia, q.v. (Weaver).

dicofol, a synthetic acaricide, a chlorinated hydrocarbon and relative of DDT; chemically, 4,4'-dichloro-*a*-(trichloromethyl)benzhydrol; moderately toxic to warm-blooded animals, acute oral LD_{50} for rats 809 mg/kg (Pfadt).

Dicondylata, Dicondylia, q.v. (Boudreaux).

Dicondylia, group within the Insecta including Zygentoma and Pterygota, possessing mandibles with a secondary anteroventral condyle (Hennig; Boudreaux); see Archaeognatha.

dicondylic, having 2 condyles (T-B).

dicondylic joint, in the insect leg, a joint with 2 points of articulation between the adjacent segments (T-B).

dicrotophos, a synthetic insecticide, plant systemic; an organophosphate, 3-hydroxy-*N,N*-dimethyl-*cis*-crotonamide, dimethyl phosphate; highly toxic to mammals; acute oral LD_{50} for rats 22 mg/kg (Pfadt).

Dictuoptera, Blattopteroidea, q.v. (Alsop, pers. comm., after Leach).

Dictyoptera, Blattaria, q.v. (T-B); Blattaria and Mantodea (Alsop, pers. comm., after Chopard); Blattaria, Mantodea, and Isoptera (Alsop, pers. comm., after Wille); see Blattopteroidea.

Dictyopterida, group within the Polyneoptera (Insecta), including the recent orders Zoraptera, Blattaria, Isoptera, and Mantodea, and the extinct order Protoblattoidea (Boudreaux).

dictyosomes, frequently crescent-shaped, ordered groupings of membranes, often associated with small vesicles, within a perikaryon, possibly concerned with the elaboration of cellular materials and secretions (Chapman).

didactyle, didactylus, two-toed (T-B); with 2 tarsi of equal length (T-B).

didymous, didymus, twin; double; geminate (T-B); of spots, touching or confluent (T-B).

diecious, dioecious, q.v.

dieldrin, $C_{12}H_8Cl_6O$, a highly residual insecticide; a chlorinated hydrocarbon of not less than 85% of 1,2,3,4,10,10-hexachloro-6,7-epoxy-1,4,4*a*,5,6,7,8,8*a*-octahydro-1,4-*endo-exo*-5,8-dimethanonaphthalene; acute oral LD_{50} for rats 100 mg/kg (Pfadt).

differentia, Linnaeus' polynomial species diagnosis (Mayr).

differential diagnosis, a formal statement of the characters which distinguish a given taxon from other specifically mentioned equivalent taxa (Mayr).

differentiation center, in the embryo, controlling center in the position of the future thorax which operates when the germ band reaches that area and determines its subsequent differentiation (Hinton and Mackerras, in CSIRO); see activation center.

difformis, irregular in form or outline; not comparable; anomalous (T-B).

diffracted, bending in different directions (T-B).

Diffraction Theory of Vision, theory of image formation in the compound eye by which the confluence of light reflected from a small object and passing through a group of facets produces a series of diffraction images at different depths in the retina (Gilmour, after Burtt and Catton, in CSIRO); see mosaic image.

diffuse, diffusus (Latin), spread out; extended; dispersed (T-B; R. W. Brown).

diffusion, a gradual mixing of 2 adjacent gases, 2 liquids, or a gas and a liquid (T-B).

diffusion tracheae, cylindrical tracheae having noncollapsible walls (T-B, after Snodgrass); see ventilation tracheae.

diflubenzuron, a synthetic insect growth regulator; 1-(4-chlorophenyl)-3-(2,6-difluorobezoyl)-urea; relatively nontoxic to mammals, acute oral LD_{50} for rats greater that 10,000 mg/kg (Pfadt).

digestion, the breakdown of larger food molecules by the action of enzymes either within the alimentary canal or extraorally (Gilmour, in CSIRO); see extraoral digestion.

digestive cells, the secretory and absorbtive cells of the ventricular epithelium as distinguished from the regenerative cells (T-B, after Snodgrass).

digestive system, alimentary canal, q.v. (CSIRO).

digestive tract, alimentary canal, q.v. (T-B); portion of alimentary canal behind the crop where assimilation takes place (T-B).

digit, digitus (Latin), a finger (T-B; R. W. Brown); a fingerlike structure (T-B); see digitus.

Digitaria striate, disease of grass (*Digitaria*) caused by a rhabdovirus transmitted propagatively by *Sogatella* (Hemiptera: Auchenorrhyncha: Delphacidae) (Nault and Ammar).

digitate, digitatus, fingerlike or divided into fingerlike processes (T-B).

digitiform, formed, shaped like or having the function of a finger (T-B).

digitoid appendage, in ♂ Siphonaptera, telomere, q.v. (Tuxen).

digitoid process, in ♂ Siphonaptera, telomere, q.v. (Tuxen).

digitule(s), in Coccoidea (Hemiptera: Sternorrhyncha), a pair of normally capitate setae at the inner base of the tarsal claws and at the outer distal margin of the tarsus (T-B, after MacGillivray; Kosztarab and Kozár).

digitulus, in ♀ Orthoptera, egg guide, q.v. (Tuxen, after Boldyrev).

digitus (pl., **digiti**), the terminal joint of the tarsus, bearing the claws;

a small appendage attached to the lacinia of the maxilla, rarely present and probably tactile; distitarsus, q.v. (T-B); in ♂ Noctuidae (Lepidoptera), small papilla from inner face of cucullus near anal angle of valva (T-B, after Klots; Tuxen, after Pierce) or, a fingerlike lobe arising from the costa of the harpe (Klots); in ♂ Chironomidae (Diptera), inner, apical moveable finger of superior volsella (Saether); in Drosophilidae, the lateral plates of the oviscapt (Grimaldi); in ♂ Hymenoptera, inner, apical, moveable finger of volsella (Tuxen); see digit.

digitus volsellaris, in ♂ Hymenoptera, digitus, q.v. (Tuxen, after Snodgrass).

diglycerides, predominant lipids within the hemolymph, being esters of glycerol and 2 fatty acids (Gilmour, in CSIRO; Chapman).

Dignatha, name for a group including the Paruropoda and Diplopoda (Hennig, after Tiegs, Manton).

digoneutic, in insects, two-brooded (T-B).

digoneutism, the power to produce 2 broods in one season (T-B).

5, 6-dihydroxyindole, intermediate metabolite in the formation of melanin from dopaquinone (Chapman).

dihydroxyphenylalanine (DOPA), intermediate metabolite in the formation of melanin from tyrosine (Chapman).

dilate, dilatutus, disproportionately broad (T-B).

dilated, widened (T-B); expanded (T-B).

dilation, an expansion or widening (T-B).

dilator (pl., **dilatores**), any muscle that functions to enlarge or open a structure (T-B); in ♂ *Pediculus humanus* (Phthiraptera: Anoplura), mesomeral arch, q.v. (Clay, in Tuxen).

dilator buccalis, a muscle which opens or dilates the insect mouth; mouth dilator (T-B).

dilator cibarii, one of a pair of muscles within the clypeus arising from its anterior wall and inserted in the epipharyngeal surface of the cibarium (T-B, after Snodgrass).

dilator muscle of spiracle, a muscle serving to open either the external or the internal closing apparatus of the spiracular atrium (T-B, after Snodgrass).

dilator muscles of alimentary canal, muscles extending from the body wall to the alimentary canal (T-B, after Snodgrass).

dilator pharyngealis, the dilator muscle of the pharynx (T-B).

dilator postpharyngealis, postpharyngeal dilator, q.v. (T-B).

dilatores pharyngis frontales, frontal dilators of the pharynx, q.v. (T-B).

dilatores pharyngis postfrontales, postfrontal pharyngeal dilators, q.v. (T-B).

dilute, dilutus, of a pale or paling color, thinned out (T-B).

dilutior, much thinned out or diluted (T-B).

Dimalata, Labiata, q.v. (Mackerras, after Sharov, in CSIRO).

dimera, forms with tarsi with 2 tarsomeres, being specifically applied to some groups of Hemiptera (T-B); once used for a superfamily of Psocoptera (T-B).

dimerous, composed of 2 pieces (T-B); in parts arranged in pairs (T-B); having tarsi with 2 tarsomeres (T-B).

dimethoate, $C_5H_{12}NO_3PS_2$, a synthetic insecticide and acaricide, plant systemic; an organophosphate, O,O-dimethyl S-(N-methyl-carbamoylmethyl) phosphorodithioate; moderately toxic to mammals, acute oral LD_{50} for rats 250 to 500 mg/kg (Pfadt).

dimidiate, dimidiatus (Latin), halved (T-B; R. W. Brown); extending half-way around or across (T-B); of elytra, when they cover only half the abdomen (T-B); see abbreviate.

dimidiate fascia, abbreviate fascia, q.v. (T-B).

dimidius, of half length (T-B).

Dimilin (trade name), diflubenzuron, q.v. (Pfadt).

Dimite (trade name), chlorfenethol, q.v. (Pfadt).

dimorph, an individual belonging to one of the 2 forms of the same species (T-B); in *Periphyllis* (Hemiptera: Sternorrhyncha: Aphididae), aestivating immature (O'Brien, pers. comm.).

dimorphic, dimorphous, occurring in 2 distinct forms (T-B).

dimorphism, a difference in form, color, etc., between individuals of the same species, characterizing 2 distinct types, e.g., seasonal, sexual or geographic dimorphism (T-B); occurrence of 2 distinct morphological types (morphs, phena) in a single population (Mayr); in caste systems, the existence in the same colony of 2 different forms, including 2 size classes, not connected by intermediates (Wilson); see polymorphism and sexual dimorphism.

dinergate, in ants (Hymenoptera: Formicidae), soldier, q.v., being a caste with the head and jaws greatly enlarged (T-B; Leftwich).

dinergatogyne, in ants (Hymenoptera: Formicidae), a mosaic form combining the charcteristics of a soldier (dinergate) and ergatogyne (Tulloch).

dinergatogynomorph, an individual ant (Hymenoptera: Formicidae) in which ♀ characteristics alternate with worker and soldier characteristics (Tulloch, after Gaul).

dinitrocresol, a synthetic insecticide; a nitrophenyl compound, 4,6-dinitro-o-cresol, sodium salt; highly toxic to man, acute oral LD_{50} for rats 30 mg/kg (Pfadt).

dinocap, $C_{18}H_{24}N_2O_6$, a synthetic insecticide and fungicide; a nitrophenol derivative, 2-(1-methylheptyl)-4,6-dinitrophenyl crotonate; slightly toxic to mammals; acute oral LD_{50} for rats 980 to 1190 mg/kg (Pfadt).

dinopthisergate, in ants (Hymenoptera: Formicidae), a soldier-worker pupal mosaic which, because of parasitism or other causes, fails to transform to the adult stage (Tulloch).

dioecious, with distinct sexes; unisexual, ♂ and ♀ gametes produced in separate individuals (T-B); having the ♂ and ♀ organs in different individuals, any one individual being either ♂ or ♀ (Borror et al.); see bisexual.

Diopsoidea, superfamily within the Schizophora-Acalyptratae within the infraorder Muscomorpha (Diptera: Brachycera), including the families Diopsidae, Psilidae, Tanypezidae, and Strongylophthalmyiidae, including adult flies without vibrissae, ♂ postabdomen with a well-developed segment VI, and ♀ ovipositor without a distinct sheath or piercing organ (McAlpine); see Tanypezoidea.

dioptrate, in an ocellate spot, having the pupil crossed or divided by a transverse line (T-B).

dioptric, refractive; causing vision by means of the refraction of light (T-B).

dioptric apparatus, the outer transparent part of an optic organ, consisting of the cornea and usually of a subcorneal crystalline body (T-B, after Snodgrass).

dioptric layer, a refractive layer of the insect eye (T-B); see tapetum.

dioxathion, $C_{12}H_{26}O_6P_2S_4$, a synthetic insecticide and acaricide; an organophosphate, *S,S'-p*-dioxane-2,3-diyl *O,O*-diethyl phosphorodithioate (cis and trans isomers); moderately toxic to mammals, acute oral LD_{50} for rats 110 mg/kg (Pfadt).

diphagous parasitoid, in Aphelinidae (Hymenoptera), a species in which the ♂ is a parasitoid of the same host species as the ♀, but feeds in a different way, e.g., *Coccophagus hemera*, of Great Britain (Gauld and Bolton, after Flanders); see heterotrophic parasitoid and heteronomous hyperparasitoid.

diphasic allometry, polymorphism in which the allometric regression line, when plotted on a double logarithmic scale, "breaks" and consists of 2 segments of different slopes whose ends meet at an intersection point (Wilson); see allometry.

diphenyol, a phenol with a second hydroxyl group attached to the aromatic ring, e.g., dopa, N-acetyldopamine, etc. (Gilmour, in CSIRO).

diphtheria, a highly contagious bacterial disease of humans caused by presence of *Corynebacterium diphtheriae*, characterized by fever, heart weakness, anemia, and great prostration; often fatal (Pfadt).

diploergate, in ants (Hymenoptera: Formicidae), a mosaic individual embracing characteristics of both major and media workers (Tulloch, after Gaul).

Diplogangliata, Arthropoda, q.v. (T-B).

Diploglossata, Hemimerina, q.v. (Borror et al.; Popham, pers. comm.).

diploid, double (T-B); having a double set of chromosomes (2n), being the normal number for cells except for mature germ cells (Tulloch; Mayr); see haploid and polyploid.

diplopod, a member of the Diplopoda (T-B).

Diplopoda, class within the Myriapoda (Arthropoda), including the millipedes, characterized by having most body segments with 2 pairs of legs (Borror et al.).

Diploptera, Diplopteryga, q.v. (T-B).

Diplopteryga, in Hymenoptera, wasps in which the wings are longitudinally folded when at rest, i.e., Vespidae (T-B; Carpenter, pers. comm.).

Diplura, primitively flightless, entognathous class or order within the Hexapoda, possessing long filiform antennae, five-segmented legs, and 10-segmented abdomen (Tulloch; Mackerras, in CSIRO).

dipneumones, having 2 lungs, as in certain spiders (Arachnida: Araneae) (T-B).

Dipsocoromorpha, infraorder of Heteroptera (Hemiptera), including the families Cryptostemmatidae, Dipsocoridae, Hypsipterygidae, Schizopteridae, and Stemmocryptidae (Schuh).

Diptera, order of endopterygote insects, consisting of the two-winged flies, possessing adults with the hind wings reduced to form a pair of clubbed halters and enlarged mesothorax; apodous larvae (T-B; Mackerras, in CSIRO).

Dipterex (trade name), trichlorfon, q.v. (Pfadt).

dipterocecidium, a gall formed by a fly (Diptera) (T-B).

dipterous, belonging to or having the characters of Diptera (T-B).

direct causes, in invertebrate pathology, those factors or agents which cause disease directly, including poisons, microorganisms, entomophagous parasites, physical or mechanical agents, glandular disturbances and nutritional deficiencies (Steinhaus and Martignoni); see predisposing factors.

direct flight, in the Odonata, flight in which the downstroke of the wing is controlled directly by the basalare muscle, external to the pleural wing process (Chapman); see indirect flight.

direct metamorphosis, incomplete metamorphosis, q.v. (T-B).

direct wing muscles, the axillary and dorsal muscles of the wings (T-B).

directed response, response to a stimulus consisting of orientation relative to (tropism) or movement toward or away from (taxis) the stimulus (Borror et al.); see complex behavior.

directing tube, in larval Lepidoptera, the anterior division of the silk-spinning apparatus lying within the spinneret (T-B).

direction finding, sense of direction mediated by light-compass reaction, dances, pheromones, or "memorized" landmarks (Leftwich).

directive coloration, directive marks or colors which tend to divert the attention of an enemy from more vital parts (T-B).

director penis (pl., **directores penis**), in *Cyrestis* (Lepidoptera: Nymphalidae), vertical, lip-shaped, sclerotized process cephalad from ostium bursae (Tuxen, after de Graaf).

dirigo (pl., **dirigones**), in ♂ Odonata, various processes in the neighborhood of base of abdomen enabling orientation of the accessory genitalia on abdominal segment II (Tuxen, after Fraser).

dis-, Latin prefix; separation; a parting from (T-B).

disc (**disk**), the central upper surface of any part (T-B); all the area within a margin (T-B); the central area of a wing (T-B); in Orthoptera, the obliquely ridged outer surface of the hind femur (T-B); imaginal disc, q.v. (Wilson).

disc of valva, in ♂ Lepidoptera, valvula, q.v. (Tuxen, after Pierce).

disca, the place of attachment to the body of a large muscle, showing as a disc or ring on the outer surface (T-B, after MacGillivray).

discal, on or relating to the disc of any surface or structure (T-B).

discal area, in wings, the more central part, or that area covered by the discal cell (T-B).

discal bristles, in adult Diptera, discal setae, q.v. (T-B, after Comstock).

discal cell, in adult Lepidoptera, large median cell of wing extending from the base toward or beyond the center, resulting from the loss of the chorda and the basal portion of the media (T-B; Common, in CSIRO); in some adult Diptera, closed cell near middle of wing bounded proximally by the base of the third branch of media (M_3), posteriorly by a long free vein (probably M_3), and distally by medial crossvein (McAlpine); in adult Hymenoptera, first discoidal cell (DC1), q.v. (Borror et al.).

discal crossvein, discoidal crossvein, q.v. (T-B, after Curran).

discal elevation, in Tingidae (Hemiptera: Heteroptera), the central area of the forewing raised above the surrounding level (T-B).

discal medial cell, in adult Muscomorpha (Diptera: Brachycera), between media (M) and first branch of cubitus anterior (CuA_1), being closed distally by discal medial-cubital crossvein (McAlpine); see discal cell.

discal medial-cubital crossvein (dm-cu), in some Nematocera, some orthorrhaphous Brachycera, and all Muscomorpha (Diptera), union of third branch of media (M_3) and medial crossvein (McAlpine).

discal patch, in some ♂ Hesperiidae (Lepidoptera), the oblique streak of specialized black scales on the disc of the anterior wings.

discal sclerite, in some Muscomorpha (Diptera), plate of labella bearing presomal teeth (Colless and McAlpine, in CSIRO).

discal scutellar bristles, in adult Diptera, discal scutellar setae, q.v. (T-B).

discal scutellar setae, in adult Diptera, setae on the disc of the mesoscutellum (McAlpine).

discal scutellars, in adult Diptera, discal scutellar setae, q.v. (T-B, after Curran).

discal seta, in certain Coccoidea (Hemiptera: Sternorrhyncha), a single large seta on the caudal half of the dorsal surface of the operculum (T-B, after MacGillivray).

discal setae, in adult Diptera, one or more pairs of stiff setae inserted near the middle of the dorsum of the abdominal segments before the hind margin (McAlpine).

discal vein, in Lepidoptera, the crossvein closing the discal or median cell, extending from R_5 to M_1 (T-B).

discaloca, in Coccoidea (Hemiptera: Sternorrhyncha), a small round projecting area in the middle of the ventral aspect of the caudal end of the body (T-B, after MacGillivray).

disciform, formed or shaped like a disc (T-B).

discleritous, condition in which tergites and sternites are distinct and separate (Tuxen); see synscleritous.

discocellular nervure or **veins,** in adult Lepidoptera, discal vein, q.v. (T-B).

discocellulars, in adult Lepidoptera, the collective term applied to all short, more or less transverse veins closing the cell of the wing distally (T-B, after Tillyard).

discoid, discoidal, relating to the disc, or middle (T-B); shaped like a round plate (T-B).

discoidal area, the middle area or field of an organ, especially the wings (T-B); in Orthoptera, that area of the tegmina between the posterior, or anal, and the anterior, or costal, areas (T-B); in Tingidae (Hemiptera: Heteroptera), area of forewing posterior to subcostal area (Drake and Ruhoff).

discoidal areolet, in Odonata, one of the cells occuring in rows on the outer side of the triangle between the short sector (M_4 of Comstock) and the upper sector of the triangle (Cu_1 of Comstock) (T-B).

discoidal cell (DC), a term applied to some outstanding cells of an insect wing, e.g., in adult Psocoptera, cell of forewing formed when the cubital crossvein (cu) meets the media (M), being bounded elsewhere by the medial crossvein (m) and the cubital crossvein (cu) (Badonnel); the quadrilateral in Odonata or the median cell in Diptera (T-B, after Tillyard); in Trichoptera, opened or closed cell in the wings formed by the furcation of sector radii (R_{2+3} and R_{4+5}) (Schmid); in adult Hymenoptera, first discoidal cell, located near the middle of the wing (T-B; Riek, in CSIRO; Gauld and Bolton) or, one or more median cells in distal half of wing, including first discoidal cell (Gauld and Bolton).

discoidal crossvein, in adult Diptera, the vein separating the discal and basal medial cell (M_3 of Comstock-Needham system) (T-B, after Curran; McAlpine).

discoidal field, discoidal area, q.v. (T-B).

discoidal field with trichobothria, in Psocoptera, sclerotized area of paraprocts with trichobothria (transl. "champ discoïdal à trichobothries" Badonnel, after Tuxen).

discoidal nervule, in Lepidoptera, M_1 (Comstock).

discoidal pores, in Coccoidea (Hemiptera: Sternorrhyncha), very small pores close to the eyes (Kosztarab and Kozár); in Aleyrodidae (Hemiptera: Sternorrhyncha), small pores randomly dispersed over dorsal and sometimes ventral abdominal surfaces of adults (Gill).

discoidal triangle, in adult Odonata, triangle, q.v. (T-B).

discoidal vein, in adult Hymenoptera, anterior cubitus (CuA), extending along the posterior margin of the first median cell (T-B; Riek, in CSIRO).

discoideous, discoideus, discoidal, q.v. (T-B).

discolor, discolorate, discolored, discolorous, of different colors; variegated (T-B; R. W. Brown).

discontinuous variation, variation in which the individuals of a sample fall into classes which do not grade into one other (Mayr); see continuous variation and polymorphism.

Discota, Holometabola, q.v. (T-B); see Adiscota.

discrete, discretus (Latin), separated (T-B; R. W. Brown); applied to parts definitely marked off from others (T-B).

discrimen, in some Insecta, e.g., adult Coleoptera, a median longitudinal sulcus of the pterothorax, marking an invagination of the sternum (Chapman).

dicriminal line, in adult Coleoptera (Insecta: Neoptera), discrimen, q.v. (Britton, after Ferris, in CSIRO).

discriminant function, the sum of numerical values of certain diagnostic characters multipled by calculated constants (Mayr).

discs, the abdominal motor processes of larval Coleoptera (T-B).

discus (Latin), a flat, circular plate (T-B; R. W. Brown); a somewhat flat circular part or area (T-B).

discus of maxilla, the disc or stalk of the maxilla; the second part of the maxilla adjoining the insertion (T-B).

disease, in invertebrate pathology, departure from the state of health; condition or process that represents the response of an animal's body to injury or insult; a disturbance of function or structure of a tissue or organ of the body, or of the body in general (Steinhaus and Martignoni); see syndrome.

disease of the clear heads, in invertebrate pathology, gattine, q.v. (Steinhaus and Martignoni).

disease transmission, spread of disease to humans, other animals, and to plants by insects which either serve as a transport host or as an intermediate host for the disease causing pathogen (Leftwich); see viral transmission.

disharmonic growth, allometric growth, q.v. (Tulloch).

disjoined, disjointed, disjunct, q.v. (T-B).

disjunct, disjunctus (Latin), disunited (T-B; R. W. Brown).

disk, disc, q.v. (T-B).

dislocated, of a stria, band or line, being interrupted, with the various parts out of alignment (T-B).

disparlure, synthetic ♀ gypsy moth *Lymantria dispar* (Lepidoptera: Lymantriidae) sex pheromone; *cis*-7,8-epoxy-2-methyloctadecane (Pfadt).

dispersal flight, in Isoptera, seasonal mass exodus from the nest of winged reproductives, for the purposes of colonization (Krishna, pers. comm.); see nuptial flight and mating flight.

dispersed, dispersus (Latin), with scattered markings or small sculptures (T-B; Harris); see sparse.

displacement activity, an apparently nonfunctional stereotyped response to a stimulus (Matthews and Matthews).

display, structure or behavior pattern that evolved as a communicative visual signal to other conspecific animals (Matthews and Matthews).

disposed, arranged or laid out (T-B).

disruptive coloration, crypsis in which there is a visual breaking of the insect's outline so that parts of it appear to fade separately into the background (Matthews and Matthews).

dissepiment, a partition wall; applied to the forming septa separating the coelom sacs in the embryo (T-B); also the thin envelope about the members in obtect pupae (T-B).

dissilient, bursting open elastically (T-B).

distacalypteron, the antosquama (sic), squama, antitegula (T-B, after MacGillivray).

distad, toward the distal end (T-B).

distadentis (pl., **distadentes**), the dentes of the distal end of the mandible (T-B, after MacGillivray); in larval Chironominae (Diptera: Chironomidae), dorsal, outer subapical tooth of mandible (Saether).

distagalea, distigalea, q.v. (T-B, after MacGillivray).

distal, near or toward the free end of any appendage (T-B); that part of a segment farthest from the body (T-B).

distal arm (of sternum IX), in ♂ Siphonaptera, posterior arm of abdominal sternum IX (Tuxen, after Smit).

distal brustia, in larval Chironomidae (Diptera), pecten mandibularis, q.v. (Saether).

distal cell, in the wings, the cell bounded by the branches of the cross-veins (T-B).

distal lobe, in ♂ Dermaptera, distal portion of penis, mesad to parameres (Tuxen, after Snodgrass).

distal lobe of harpagones, in ♂ Neuropteroidea, stylus, q.v. (Tuxen, after Carpenter).

distal meatus, in ♂ Anisoptera (Odonata), distal opening of seminal duct (Tuxen, after Borror).

distal median plate, in adult Diptera, plate in the median area of the wing base separated from proximal median plate by basal fold (McAlpine); in adult Chironomidae (Diptera), plate of wing base posterior to brachiolum and distal to proximal median plate (Saether); see second median plate.

distal process, the peripheral branch or one of several distal branches of a sensory nerve cell (T-B, after Snodgrass).

distal process of harpe, in ♂ Pieridae (Lepidoptera), part of harpe (Tuxen, after Klots).

distal process of sternum X, in ♂ Neuroptera, mediuncus, q.v. (Tuxen, after Killington).

distal retinula cells, iris pigment cells; densely pigmented cells surrounding the crystalline cone-cells and the corneal hypodermis (T-B, after Comstock).

distal rhachis, in ♂ Hymenoptera, portion of rhachies at tips of gonapophyses, not fused to each other but may form projecting, sculptured sclerites pointing proximally and distally (Tuxen, after E. L. Smith).

distal segment of gonostyli, in ♂ Mecoptera, stylus, q.v. (Tuxen, after Issiki).

distal segment of penis, in ♂ Zygoptera (Odonata), glans, q.v. (Tuxen, after Kennedy).

distal sensory area, in larval Scarabaeoidea (Coleoptera), haptomerum, q.v. (T-B, after Hayes).

distal tubular gland, in ♀ Heteroptera (Hemiptera), glandula apicalis (in a vermiform gland), q.v. (Tuxen, after Davis).

distalia, flagellum, q.v., of antenna (T-B, after Tillyard).

distant, widely separated; remote from; indicating the separation of parts from each other by sutures or incisures (T-B).

disticalypter, in adult Diptera, upper calypter, q.v. (McAlpine).

disticardo, the distal region of the cardo (T-B, after Crampton).

disticercus, in some ♀ Diptera, second segment of cercus (Tuxen, after Gerry).

distichous, distichus, bipartite; separated into 2 parts (T-B).

distichous antennae, pectinate antennae in which the processes originate from the apex of a segment and bend forward at acute angles (T-B).

disticonjunctiva (pl., **disticonjunctivae**), in ♂ Heteroptera (Hemiptera), proximal part of endosoma extending from and proximally including ejaculatory reservoir (Tuxen, after Bonhag and Wick).

disticoxa, in adult Mycetophilidae (Diptera), distal portion of midcoxa (McAlpine); see basicoxa.

distigalea, the distal segment of the galea (T-B).

distimentum, in larval Chironomidae (Diptera), usually toothed, dorsal plate of double-walled mentum (Saether).

distimere, in ♂ insects, telomere, q.v. (Tuxen, after Snodgrass); in ♂ Diptera, dististylus, q.v. (Tuxen) or gonostylus, q.v. (McAlpine); in ♂ Siphonaptera, telomere, q.v. (Tuxen).

distiphallus (pl., **distiphalli**), in ♂ Diptera, distal part of aedeagus (Tuxen, after Hennig and van Emden; McAlpine); see basiphallus.

distiproboscis, in adult Diptera, prementum, q.v., bearing the labella (T-B; McAlpine).

distipulvillus, in Heteroptera (Hemiptera), distal membranous or setaceous part of the pulvillus (Goel and Schaefer).

dististipes, the distal portion of the maxillary stipes (Peterson).

dististyle, gonostyle, q.v. (Mackerras, in CSIRO); in ♂ Diptera, gonostylus, q.v. (McAlpine); in ♂ Chironomidae (Diptera) and Mecoptera, dististylus, q.v. (Saether; Byers, pers. comm.).

dististylus (pl., **dististyli**), in ♂ Mecoptera, stylus, q.v. (Tuxen, after Crampton); in ♂ Diptera, distal segment of gonopods (Tuxen); see gonostylus.

distitarsal, of or pertaining to the distitarsus (T-B).

distitarsus, the distal tarsomere (T-B).

distivolsella (pl., **distivolsellae**), in ♂ Hymenoptera, cuspis, q.v. (Tuxen, after Peck).

distivolsellar apodeme, in ♂ Hymenoptera, apodeme of cuspis (Tuxen, after Peck).

distolateral lobes, in ♂ Siphonaptera, paired lobes, ovate in shape, which flank either the apical portion of the median dorsal lobe or Ford's sclerite (Rothschild and Traub).

disulfoton, a synthetic insecticide and acaricide, plant systemic absorbed through the roots; an organophosphate, O,O-diethyl S-2-[(ethylthio)ethyl] phosphorodithioate; extremely toxic to mammals, acute oral LD$_{50}$ for rats 2 to 12 mg/kg (Pfadt).

Di-Syston (trade name), disulfoton, q.v. (Pfadt).

Ditrocha, old name for Hymenoptera in which the adult possesses a trochantellus, e.g., some Apocrita (T-B).

Ditrysia, division of the Lepidoptera, in which there are 2 genital openings in the ♀, the ostium bursae on abdominal sternum VIII and the genital aperture on abdominal sternum IX–X (Common, after Börner, in CSIRO).

ditrysian type of genitalia, referring to ♀ genitalia with 2 sexual openings, one for copulation, the other for egg deposition, e.g., Nogodinidae and some Delphacidae (Hemiptera: Auchenorrhyncha: Fulgoroidea) (Asche); ♀ genitalia of Lepidoptera in which opening of vagina and bursa copulatrix are widely separate (Tuxen); see monotrysian and exoporian types.

diuresis, hormonally induced enhancement of secretion of fluid by the Malpighian tubules soon after feeding (Chapman); see diuretic hormone.

diuretic hormone, hormone initiating diuresis; in *Rhodnius* (Hemiptera: Heteroptera: Reduviidae), produced by the neurosecretory cells in the posterior part of the fused ventral ganglionic mass and released into the hemolymph from the neurohemal organs; in locusts (Orthoptera; Caelifera), produced in the cerebral neurosecretory cells and released into the hemolymph from the corpora cardiaca (Chapman).

diurnae, day fliers; applied to butterflies (T-B).

diurnal, active or habitually flying by day (T-B).

diurnal rhythm, a daily rhythm of activity (Leftwich).

divaricable, able to spread apart or divaricate (T-B).

divaricate, divaricatus (Latin), forked or divided into 2 branches (T-B); straddling or spreading apart (T-B); of wings, lapped at the base and diverging behind (T-B); extending outward and then curving inward towards each other, e.g., divaricate tarsal claws (Borror et al., in CSIRO).

divergence, differentiation of a species through the acquisition of novel features; see anagenesis and convergence.

divergent, spreading out from a common base (T-B).

diverse, unequal; differing in size or shape; of various kinds (T-B).

diverticulum (pl., **diverticula**), any off-shoot from a vessel, being usually blind or saclike, e.g., midgut caecum (T-B); in ♀ Pentatomoidea (Hemiptera: Heteroptera), diverticulum ductus, q.v. (Tuxen, after McDonald).

diverticulum ductus, in ♀ Heteroptera (Hemiptera), tubular or sacciform diverticulum of ductus receptaculi (Tuxen, after Dupuis).

dividens (vena), in Orthoptera, vena dividens, q.v. (T-B, after Comstock).

division, a rank, that if treated as a division of a genus or subgenus, is deemed to be of subgeneric rank for the purposes of nomenclature; a taxon at the rank of division (ICZN).

division of labor, polyethism, q.v. (Wilson).

DNA, deoxyribonucleic acid, q.v. (White, in CSIRO).

dog-ear marks, in bees (Hymenoptera: Apoidea), small, subtriangular marks of light color, just below the antennae (T-B, after Cockerell).

dolabrate, dolabratus, hatchet-shaped (T-B).

dolabriform, hatchet-shaped; compressed, with a prominent dilated keel and cylindrical base (T-B).

dolichaster, in larval Ascalaphidae (Planipennia), one of the modified setae fringing the lateral segmental processes of the mandible (T-B, after Imms).

dolioloides, obtect or coarctate pupae (T-B).

Dollo's Rule, principle that evolution is irreversible to the extent that structures or functions once lost cannot be regained (Mayr).

dome organ, campaniform sensillum, q.v. (T-B).

dominance, a ranking of individuals on the basis of real or apparent authority, strength, influence, etc. (Matthews and Matthews).

dominance hierarchy, the physical domination of some members of a group by other members, in relatively orderly and long-lasting patterns. Except for the highest and lowest ranking individuals, a given member will dominate one or more of its companions and be dominated in turn by one or more of the others. The hierarchy is initiated and sustained by hostile behavior, albeit sometimes of a subtle and indirect nature (Wilson).

dominant, a character more constant and conspicuous than any other (T-B); a type or series occurring in large numbers both as to genera, species and individuals and in which differentiation is yet active (T-B); an allele which determines the phenotype of a heterozygote (Mayr); see heterozygous, homozygous, and recessive.

Donnan equilibrium, relative concentration of potassium ions inside and chloride ions outside an axon, producing a negative charge within the axon and a membrane (resting) potential across the plasma membrane (Chapman).

DOPA, dihydroxyphenylalanine, q.v. (Chapman).

dopamine, intermediate metabolite in the production of N-acetyldopamine from dihydroxyphenylalanine (Chapman).

dopaquinone, intermediate metabolite in the production of melanin from dihydroxyphenylalanine (Chapman).

dormancy, quiescence, q.v. (Borror et al.) or diapause, q.v. (Leftwich).

dormant, sleeping; or inactive as if asleep; aestivating, q.v. (T-B).

dormant spray, a spray applied to trees in true dormancy, before the buds begin to swell (Pfadt).

dorsad, in the direction of the dorsum or back of an insect (T-B).

dorsal, on or of the functionally upper surface (that opposite the surface bearing the trunk appendages); of appendages, the upper surface when the appendage is fully extended horizontally from the body (T-B; Christiansen and Bellinger).

dorsal abdominal scent gland, in nymphal Heteroptera (Hemiptera), paired on unpaired abdominal scent gland with paired on unpaired orifices situated intersegmentally or intrasegmentally on pregenital mediotergites, structure and function sometimes persisting to the adult stage, occurrence often sex-dependant (Štys, pers. comm.); see metathoracic scent gland.

dorsal aedeagal bridge, in ♂ Culicidae (Diptera), the transverse sclerotization connecting the aedeagal sclerites nearest the anus (Harbach and Knight, after Knight and Laffoon).

dorsal aedeagal sclerites, in ♂ Cyrtacanthacridinae (Orthoptera:

Acrididae), dorsal, solidly sclerotized structures in phallotreme membrane (Tuxen, after Eades).

dorsal aedeagal valves, see aedeagal valves (Tuxen); in Cyrtacanthacridinae (Orthoptera: Acrididae), anterior (dorsal) apical processes or lobes of aedeagus (Tuxen, after Eades).

dorsal amnioserosal sac, the dorsal organ at a later stage in certain insect embryos, formed from the ruptured and contracted amnion and serosa (T-B, after Imms).

dorsal anal lobe, in Siphonaptera, the dorsal lobe of the proctiger (Lewis, pers. comm.).

dorsal anal plate, in Aphidoidea (Hemiptera: Sternorrhyncha), variously shaped plate, bearing setae, located caudad of anal aperture (Ilharco and Van Harten).

dorsal aorta, aorta, q.v. (CSIRO).

dorsal aperture of median flap, in some ♂ *Dihybocerus* (Embiidina: Embiidae), a small opening on the dorsal surface of the median flap, representing the aperture of a fingerlike membranous pouch (Ross, in Tuxen).

dorsal apodeme, in adult Culicidae (Diptera), a small prominence borne on the dorsal (internal) surface of the posterior hard plate (Harbach and Knight, after Barraud and Covell).

dorsal apodeme of aedeagus, in ♂ Auchenorrhyncha (Hemiptera), dorsal part of socle (Tuxen, after Young).

dorsal apotome, in immature insects, the cranial area bounded laterally by the frontal ecdysial lines and apically by an imaginary line between the most apical parts of the frontal ecdysial lines (Harbach and Knight, after Laffoon and Knight); see frontal apotome.

dorsal appendices, in ♂ Caelifera (Orthoptera), a pair of moveable sclerites attached to apical valves of the penis (Tuxen, after Dirsh).

dorsal arm, in ♂ *Culex* (Diptera: Culicidae), the dorsal process (in the normal resting position) of the outer division of the lateral plate (Harbach and Knight, after Sundararaman) (see ampulla); in ♂ Siphonaptera, an upright sclerite extending from the inner tube, to and beyond the dorsocaudal angle of the end chamber (Lewis, pers. comm., after Traub).

dorsal arms of the tentorium, apparent secondary outgrowths of the anterior arms of the tentorium, extending to near the bases of the antennae (T-B, after Snodgrass).

dorsal axillar surface, in adult Apocrita (Hymenoptera), region of axilla median to the axillar carina (Gibson).

dorsal base, in ♂ Siphonaptera, dorsal wall of palliolum when inflated (transl. "Dorsalbase" Wagner, after Tuxen).

dorsal blastoderm, serosa, q.v. (T-B, after Snodgrass).

dorsal blood vessel, dorsal vessel, q.v. (T-B).

dorsal bridge of dorsal phallotreme sclerites, in ♂ Orthoptera, ponticulus, q.v. (Tuxen, after Snodgrass).

dorsal bridge of ovipositor, in ♀ Hymenoptera, notum, q.v. (Tuxen).

dorsal bridge of penis valves, in ♂ Hymenoptera, dorsal sclerotic bridge between bases of penis valves (Tuxen, after Michener).

dorsal bristles, in adult Diptera, dorsocentrals, q.v. (T-B).

dorsal brush, in larval Culicidae (Diptera), setae arising as a group from the dorsocaudal angle of abdominal segment X (Harbach and Knight, after Wesenberg-Lund).

dorsal cavity, in ♂ Grylloidea (Orthoptera), a large pouch ventrad of the pseudepiphallus and dorsad of the gonopore (Tuxen, after Snodgrass); in ♂ Tettigonioidea (Orthoptera), titillator cavity, q.v. (Tuxen, after Snodgrass).

dorsal chitin rods, in ♂ Nepidae (Hemiptera: Heteroptera), basal plates, q.v. (Tuxen, after Hamilton).

dorsal closure, formation of the dorsal wall of the embryo, thus surrounding the yolk, involving first the formation of a provisional dorsal closure by extra-embryonic membranes as a result of katatrepsis, followed by replacement with embryonic endoderm which grows upward to form the definitive dorsal closure (Chapman).

dorsal condyle, in mandibulate insecta, the dorsal condyle of the mandible which articulates within an articular pan on the pleurostoma (T-B, after MacGillivray); see ventral condyle.

dorsal connectives, in ♂ Heteroptera (Hemiptera), the apodemes of the basal plates ending in a capitate process on which are inserted the protractor muscles of the phallus (Tuxen, after Baker).

dorsal cornua, in larval Muscomorpha (Diptera: Brachycera), dorsal arms of the tentoropharyngeal sclerite (Teskey, in McAlpine).

dorsal crest, in some Collembola, a vertical, longitudinal lamella on the dorsum of the sixth abdominal segment (Christiansen and Bellinger); in ♂ Lepidoptera, tegumen + uncus, q.v. (Tuxen, after Scudder and Burgess).

dorsal diaphragm, the principal septum of the hemocoele which extends across the abdominal cavity above the alimentary canal (T-B, after Imms); aliform muscles and associated membrane that separate the pericardial sinus from the perivisceral sinus (Chapman).

dorsal disk, in Aleyrodidae (Hemiptera: Sternorrhyncha), oval disk covering medial area of pupal dorsum (Russell).

dorsal ecdysial line, any dorsal preformed line of weakness along which the cuticle spits (usually) or bends during ecdysis (Harbach and Knight).

dorsal evagination of bursa copulatrix, in ♀ *Hydrometra* (Heteroptera: Hydrometridae), vaginal pouch, q.v. (Tuxen, after Sprague).

dorsal field, in Orthoptera, the horizontal area of the closed forewings (Otte, pers. comm.).

dorsal flap, in ♂ Culicidae (Diptera), part of the basistylus (coxite) when this is divided by a median strip of membrane (Tuxen).

dorsal fringe, in many larval Culicidae (Diptera), one of the pharyngeal fringes borne dorsal to the laterodorsal pharyngeal sclerite in the lateral margin of the pharynx (Harbach and Knight); see primary dorsal fringe and secondary dorsal fringes.

dorsal gland, in larval Lycaenidae (Lepidoptera), an eversible glandular organ, situated middorsally on abdominal segment VII (Common and Waterhouse).

dorsal gland orifices, in Diaspididae (Hemiptera: Sternorrhyncha): Coccoidea), dorsal pores, q.v. (T-B, after MacGillivray).

dorsal glands, in Coccoidea (Hemiptera: Sternorrhyncha), dorsal pores, q.v. (T-B, after MacGillivray).

dorsal gonapophyses, in ♀ Psocoptera, valvae dorsales, q.v. (Tuxen, after Chapman); in ♀ Aleyrodidae (Hemiptera: Sternorrhyncha), the unpaired gonapophysis of abdominal segment IX (Tuxen).

dorsal gonocoxal bridge, in ♂ Hymenoptera, basal sclerotic bridge between gonocoxites on the dorsum (Tuxen, after Michener).

dorsal groove, in adult social wasps (Hymenoptera: Vespidae), groove running from the epicranium to the episternal scrobe on the mesepisternum (Carpenter, pers. comm., after Richards).

dorsal group of setae, in larval Lepidoptera, primary setae D1 and D2 of thorax and abdomen (Stehr, after Hinton).

dorsal hair tuft, in larval Culicidae (Diptera), a tuft of long setae located on the caudo-dorsomeson of abdominal segment IX (Peterson).

dorsal hooks, in ♂ Auchenorrhyncha (Hemiptera), anal hooks, q.v. (Tuxen, after Lower).

dorsal labral sclerite, in Diptera larvae, e.g., Culicidae, median labral plate, q.v. (Teskey, in McAlpine; Harbach and Knight, after Christophers).

dorsal laterotergite(s), in Heteroptera (Hemiptera), dorsal plate of an abdominal laterotergite, q.v., often subdivided into dorsal external and dorsal inner laterotergites (Štys, pers. comm.).

dorsal light reaction, transverse orientation in which the dorsal surface the of body is kept perpendicular to a directed source of light at all times, e.g., in dragonflies (Odonata) (Matthews and Matthews).

dorsal light reflex, dorsal light reaction, q.v. (Tulloch).

dorsal lip, in Coccoidea (Hemiptera: Sternorrhyncha), a transverse, strongly chitinized plate which supports the caudal end of the anal tube on the dorsal side (T-B, after MacGillivray).

dorsal line, in larval Lepidoptera, a medial, dorsal, longitudinal line (T-B).

dorsal lobe, in ♂ Argynninae (Lepidoptera: Nymphalidae), ampulla (Tuxen, after dos Passos and Grey).

dorsal lobe of aedeagus, in ♂ Siphonaptera, single or subdivided lobe on the dorsal margin of the aedeagus (Tuxen, after Traub); in ♂ Chironomidae (Diptera), median volsella, q.v. (Saether).

dorsal lobe of apodemal strut, in ♂ Siphonaptera, lobus fulcri medialis, q.v. (Tuxen, after Traub).

dorsal lobe of fulcrum, in ♂ Siphonaptera, lobus fulcri medialis, q.v. (Tuxen, after Traub).

dorsal lobe of paramere, in ♂ Neuroptera, superprocessus, q.v. (Tuxen, after Tjeder).

dorsal lobe of penis, in ♂ Orthoptera, dorsal aedeagal valve, q.v. (Tuxen, after Walker).

dorsal lobe of segment IX, in ♂ Plecoptera, hemitergal processes, q.v. (Tuxen, after Frison).

dorsal lobes, in ♂ *Zorotypus snyderi* Caudell (Zoraptera), part of complicated genital structure (Tuxen).

dorsal mandibular spine, in many larval Culicidae (Diptera), a small spine arising immediately dorsal to the base of the dorsal mandibular seta (Harbach and Knight).

dorsal maxillary suture, in larval Culicidae (Diptera), the variably developed seam occurring on the dorsal surface of the maxilla, extending from the brush to the base where it is continuous with the stipital arm, serving as the boundary between the laciniastipes and galeastipes (Harbach and Knight).

dorsal muscles, in insects, the ordinary longitudinal muscles of the dorsum, in which the fibers are typically longitudinal and attached on the intersegmental folds or on the antecostae of successive terga (T-B, after Snodgrass).

dorsal ocelli, when present, the usual simple eyes of adult insects, normally 3 in number, in some orders 2 (T-B).

dorsal oral brush, in many larval Culicidae (Diptera), a fringe or covering of filaments located on or near the dorsal oral sclerite (Harbach and Knight).

dorsal oral sclerite, in many larval Culicidae (Diptera), a small crescentic plate located just inside the mouth on the midline of the dorsal wall of the pharynx (Harbach and Knight).

dorsal organ, in the insect embryo, primary dorsal organ, q.v., or secondary dorsal organ, q.v. (T-B, after Imms); primary dorsal organ, q.v. (T-B, after Snodgrass).

dorsal ostioles, in Pseudococcidae (Hemiptera: Sternorrhyncha: Coccoidea), ostioles, q.v. (T-B, after Ferris and Murdock).

dorsal parameres, in ♂ Aeolothripidae (Thysanoptera), dorsal pair of parameres (Tuxen); in ♂ *Neopanorpa* (Mecoptera: Panorpidae), paired dorsal processes of the aedeagus (Tuxen, after Byers), penunci (Tjeder, in Tuxen).

dorsal paratergite, in Heteroptera (Hemiptera), dorsal laterotergite, q.v. (Štys, pers. comm.).

dorsal phallic lobes, in ♂ Ensifera (Orthoptera), paired dorsal lobes of phallus (Tuxen).

dorsal phallic valves, in ♂ Mecoptera, dorsal valves, q.v. (Crampton).

dorsal pharyngeal sclerite, in many larval Culicidae (Diptera), one of a pair of laterally symmetrical, roughly lunate plates of the dorsal wall of the pharynx (Harbach and Knight).

dorsal plate(s), in ♀ Psyllidae (Hemiptera: Sternorrhyncha), the dorsal one of the genital plates, the apical tergum, bearing the anus (Tuxen); in ♀ Nepidae (Hemiptera: Heteroptera), gonapophyses of abdominal segment IX, q.v. (Tuxen, after Hamilton); in larval Buprestidae (Coleoptera), the plate or disk on the dorsal surface of the enlarged segment behind the head (Peterson); in ♀ Hydropsychidae (Trichoptera), broad posterior corners of abdominal tergite VIII (Nielsen); in larval Trichoptera, the dorsal sclerite bridging the flexible membranous connection between the lateral sclerite and the anal claw of an anal proleg (Wiggins).

dorsal pores, in Coccoidea (Hemiptera: Sternorrhyncha), wax-producing disk pores (T-B, after MacGillivray; Kosztarab, pers. comm.).

dorsal pouch, in ♀ Heteroptera (Hemiptera), vaginal pouch, q.v. (Tuxen, after Bonhag and Wick).

dorsal premental teeth, in some larval Culicidae and Dixidae (Diptera), a row or series of teeth located on each side of the midline of the labiohypopharynx immediately ventral to the salivary meatus (Harbach and Knight).

dorsal process, in ♂ Trichoptera, unpaired dorsoanal projection from abdominal segment IX or dorsooral projection from abdominal segment X or paired or unpaired structure arising by the fusion of these processes (Tuxen).

dorsal process (of corpus of clasper) in ♂ Siphonaptera, processus basimeris, q.v. (Tuxen, after Peus).

dorsal process of tergum IX, in ♂ Mecoptera, epiandrium, q.v. (Tuxen, after Ferris and Rees).

dorsal processes, in ♂ Leuctridae (Plecoptera), sclerotic modifications of terga V–X (Tuxen, after Hynes).

dorsal ptyche, in ♂ and ♀ Symphyta, ♀ Parasitica, and most ♂ Hymenoptera, longitudinal mesal fold in corium of each gonapophysis IX, being a dorsal limit of egg canal and a continuation of ejaculatory duct (Tuxen, after E. L. Smith).

dorsal ramus, in ♂ Hymenoptera, dorsal ramus of gonapophysis IX (Tuxen, after E. L. Smith); in ♀ Hymenoptera, dorsal apodeme running length of a gonopod and connecting it basally to the gonocoxite, most commonly applied to gonapophyses (Tuxen, after E. L. Smith); in larval Anophelinae (Culicidae) and Dixidae (Diptera), a rodlike structure joining the cibarial bars immediately dorsal to the hypopharynx (Harbach and Knight).

dorsal ridge of sacculus, in ♂ Coleophoridae (Lepidoptera), dorsal ridge of the more or less caudad projecting, mesal part of valva (Tuxen, after Toll).

dorsal rod, in ♂ Heteroptera (Hemiptera), ponticulus transversalis, q.v. (Tuxen, after Akbar).

dorsal sac, in ♀ Cantacaderinae (Hemiptera: Heteroptera: Tingidae), vaginal pouch, q.v. (Tuxen, after Drake and Davis).

dorsal scale, that part of the covering scale of the Diaspididae (Hemiptera: Sternorrhyncha) that lies above the insect, as opposed to the ventral scale, which lies below (T-B).

dorsal sclerite, in larval Trichoptera, sclerite on the dorsum of segment IX (Wiggins).

dorsal sclerite of capsule, in ♂ Siphonaptera, central sclerite, q.v. (Tuxen, after Jordan).

dorsal sclerite of pumping bulb, in ♂ Siphonaptera, tectum, q.v. (Tuxen, after Shariff).

dorsal sensory organs, in larval Muscomorpha (Diptera), sensory lobes on the head segment, sometimes called the antennae, but possibly not homologous with true antennae (Ferrar).

dorsal setae, in pupal Chironomidae (Diptera), dorsocentrals, q.v. (Saether); in adult Culicidae (Diptera), cibarial setae borne lateral and/ or posterior to the anterior hard palate of the clypeopalatum (Harbach and Knight).

dorsal sinus, pericardial sinus, q.v. (T-B, after Imms).

dorsal space, in larval Limacodidae (Lepidoptera), the area between the subdorsal ridges (T-B).

dorsal spine of harpe, in ♂ Pieridae (Lepidoptera), (Tuxen, after Klots).

dorsal spur, in larval Syrphidae (Diptera), a sharply pointed spine or a ridgelike elevation of the posterior spiracular plate and mesal to the circular plate (Peterson, after Heiss).

dorsal stapes, in ♂ Heteroptera (Hemiptera), ponticulus transversalis, q.v. (Tuxen, after Ahmad and Southwood).

dorsal stylet, in Phthiraptera, the upper paired stylet of the trophi (T-B).

dorsal supports, in ♀ Nepidae (Hemiptera: Heteroptera), gonocoxites of abdominal segment IX, q.v. (Tuxen, after Hamilton).

dorsal talon, in ♂ Embiidina, talonlike projection of apex of left or right tergal processes, comprising bulk of left tergal process in most cases (Ross, in Tuxen).

dorsal tentorial arm, process arising dorsally from anterior tentorial arm (Chapman, after Snodgrass).

dorsal tooth, in ♂ Siphonaptera, armature of tubus inferior (Tuxen).

dorsal tracheae, the dorsal segmental tracheae originating at a spiracle (T-B).

dorsal tracheal commissure, one that crosses above the dorsal blood vessel (T-B).

dorsal tracheal trunk, a longitudinal dorsal trunk uniting the series of dorsal tracheae (T-B).

dorsal triangle, in adult Trichoptera, a diamond-shaped dorsal portion of the frons above the closely approximate antennae, q.v. (Ross).

dorsal tubercle, in certain Coccoidea, e.g., Coccidae (Hemiptera: Sternorrhyncha), submarginal dorsal tubercle, q.v. (T-B, after MacGillivray); in ♂ Siphonaptera, dorsobasal incrassation of tubus interior (Tuxen, after Hopkins and Rothschild)

dorsal tubular spinnerets, in Coccoidea (Hemiptera: Sternorrhyncha), dorsal pores, q.v. (T-B, after MacGillivray).

dorsal valve(s), in ♂ Orthoptera, dorsal aedeagal valve, q.v. (Tuxen, after Roberts); in ♀ Grylloblattodea, second valvulae, q.v. (Tuxen, after Crampton); in ♀ Isoptera, dorsal pair of valves arising from sternum IX (Tuxen); in ♀ Psyllidae (Hemiptera: Sternorrhyncha), dorsal plate, q.v. (Tuxen); in ♀ Aleyrodidae (Hemiptera: Sternorrhyncha), lateral parts of unpaired dorsal gonapophyses directed caudally at end of abdomen; in ♂ Mecoptera, paired dorsal lobes of aedeagus (Tuxen, after Byers).

dorsal valvulae, in ♀ Odonata, lateral gonapophyses, q.v. (Tuxen, after Crampton); in ♀ Isoptera, dorsal valves, q.v. (Tuxen); in ♀ Orthoptera, posterior valvulae, q.v. (Tuxen, after Walker); in ♀ Psyllidae (Hemiptera: Sternorrhyncha), posterior pair of valves of sternum IX (Tuxen); in ♀ Auchenorrhyncha (Hemiptera), sawcase, q.v. (Tuxen).

dorsal vessel, contractile longitudinal vessel which opens into the hemocoel and which usually lies in a dorsal pericardial sinus (Chapman); see aorta and heart.

dorsally arched middle plate, in ♂ Siphonaptera, velum, q.v. (Tuxen, after Traub).

dorsiferous, carrying or bearing on the back, especially eggs or young (T-B).

dorsellum, in adult Hymenoptera, central part of the metanotum (Gauld and Bolton).

dorsoalar region, in Diptera, an area bounded by 2 imaginary lines drawn from the scutellar bridges forward, and coinciding with a space free from bristles that exists on the outer side of the dorsal rows and is often occupied by a dorsal thoracic stripe (T-B).

dorsocaudal, toward the back and tail end (T-B).

dorsocaudal angle of sacculus, in ♂ Coleophoridae (Lepidoptera), dorsocaudal angle of the more or less caudal projecting, mesal part of valva (Tuxen, after Toll).

dorsocentral area, in many adult Nematocera (Diptera), a longitudinal area of the scutum on each side of the acrostichal area extending from the post pronotal lobe (humeral lobe) to the prescutellar area, and bearing the dorsocentral scales (in Culicidae), setae and setulae.

dorsocentral bristles, dorsocentral setae, q.v. (T-B).

dorsocentral setae, in adult Diptera, sublateral row of setae on scutum; in adult Culicidae (Diptera), setae occurring on the dorsocentral area, being divided into anterior and posterior rows near the median posterior corner of the scutal fossa at about the level of the antealar area (Harbach and Knight); in pupal Chironomidae (Diptera), sublateral rows of setae (2–4) on cephalothorax, corresponding to dorsocentrals in adults (Saether); see acrostichal setae.

dorsocentrals, dorsocentral setae, q.v. (Saether).

dorsoflexion, in ♂ Diptera, dorsal flexion of the apical portion of the abdomen (McAlpine).

dorsohumeral region, in Diptera, a space bounded by the anterior end of the thorax and transverse suture on 2 sides and by the dorsopleural suture and dorsocentral region on the 2 others (T-B).

dorsolateral, at the top and to the side (Borror et al.).

dorsolateral organs, in larval Lycaenidae (Lepidoptera), a pair of eversible, tubular organs situated dorsolaterally on abdominal segment VIII (Common and Waterhouse).

dorsolateral suture, in larval Coleoptera, a frequently rather indistinct groove immediately below the spiracle-bearing parascutal area, being in the abdomen parallel with the ventrolateral suture, but in the thorax being more oblique (Peterson, after Böving and Craighead).

dorsolum, mesoscutum, q.v. (T-B).

dorsomedials, in adult Diptera, acrostichal setae, q.v. (Saether).

dorsomedian spine of spermatophore, in ♂ Gryllidae (Orthoptera), guiding rod, q.v. (Tuxen, after Walker).

dorsomesal, at the top and along the midline (Borror et al.).

dorsomesal lobe, in ♀ Chironomidae (Diptera), central inner lobe of gonapophysis VIII surrounding the vagina (Saether).

dorsomeson, the intersection of the meson with the dorsum of the body (T-B, after Garman).

dorsope, in adult Zelinae (Hymenoptera: Braconidae), an anterodorsal depression of the first metasomal tergite, more-or-less pit-shaped, situated between the more-or-less developed dorslateral carina and the dorsal carina (van Achterberg).

dorsopleural line, the line of separation between the dorsum and the pleural region of the body, often marked by a fold or groove (T-B, after Snodgrass).

dorsopleural suture, in adult Diptera, the lateral suture between the dorsum and pleuron from the humeri (postpronotal lobes) through the base of the wing; separates the mesonotum from the pleuron (T-B, after J. B. Smith).

dorsoposterior pouch, in ♀ Cydnidae, Scutelleridae, and Pyrrhocoridae (Hemiptera: Heteroptera), vaginal pouch, q.v. (Tuxen, after Scudder).

dorsoprocessus, in some ♂ Neuroptera, single median dorsal process of tergum IX (Tuxen, after Tjeder).

dorsoscutellar bristles, in adult Diptera, discal scutellar setae, q.v. (Borror et al.).

dorsotentoria, dorsal arms of tentorium, q.v. (T-B).

dorsovaginal glands, in ♀ Heteroptera (Hemiptera), ringed glands, q.v. (Tuxen, after Carayon, Usinger, and Wygodzinsky).

dorsovalvae, in ♂ Mecoptera, dorsal valves, q.v. (Tuxen, after Crampton).

dorsovalvulae, in ♀ insects, gonoplacs, q.v. (Tuxen, after Crampton).

dorsoventral, in a line from the upper to lower surface (T-B).

dorsulum, the mesonotum before the scutellum, with the wing sockets (T-B); also, specifically, the mesoscutellum (T-B).

dorsum, in general, the upper surface (T-B).

dorylaner, unusually large ♂ ants in the Dorylini (Hymenoptera: Formicidae), characterized by long and peculiar mandibles, long cylindrical abdomen, and peculiar genitalia (T-B).

dorylophile, an obigate guest of one of the army ants belonging to the Dorylini (Hymenoptera: Formicidae) (Wilson).

double ocellus, an ocellate spot made up of 2 such spots (T-B).

double apodeme, in ♂ Diptera, phallapodeme, q.v. (Tuxen, after Wesché).

doublure, in some Diapriidae (Hymenoptera: Proctotrupoidea), overfolding of tergites alongside of the gaster (Riek, in CSIRO).

downy mildew, any plant disease caused by species of fungi in the family Peronosporaceae and characterized by the downy growth on the host lesions (Pfadt).

Doyere's cone, the final termination of a nerve fiber on or within a muscle cell (Tulloch).

dragonfly, member of the suborder Anisoptera (Odonata) (O'Farrell, in CSIRO).

draw-thread, the silk-producing gland in Lepidoptera (T-B).

Drepanoidea, superfamily of the infraorder Ditrysia (Lepidoptera) containing the family Drepanidae; adults small to medium-sized, usually with broad wings and falcate forewings, frenulum usually clubbed, two-chambered tympanal organs at base of abdomen; larvae with crochets in mesoseries, usually biordinal, anal prolegs reduced or absent; pupae without dorsal spines, not protruded at ecdysis (Common).

driver ants, African army ants belonging to the genus *Anomma* and, less frequently, other members of the Dorylini (Hymenoptera: Formicidae) (Wilson).

drone, in social Apoidea (Hymenoptera), the ♂ bee, especially a ♂ honey bee or bumble bee, that develops from unfertilized eggs (T-B; Wilson).

drone broodiness, morbid drone-laying, q.v. (Steinhaus and Martignoni).

drone laying, morbid drone-laying, q.v. (Steinhaus and Martignoni).

Drosophiloidea, Ephydroidea, q.v. (Colless and McAlpine, in CSIRO).

drum, in Cicadidae (Hemiptera: Auchenorrhyncha), tymbal, q.v. (Woodward et al., in CSIRO).

dry wax, in Coccoidea (Hemitpera: Sternorrhyncha) wax with a mealy texture that does not contain an aqueous substance (Miller, in Stehr).

Dryopoidea, superfamily within the Polyphaga (Coleoptera), including the families Eulichadidae, Callirhipidae, Ptilodactylidae, Chelonariidae, Heteroceridae, Limnichidae, Dryopidae, Lutrochidae, Elminthidae, and Psephenidae, possessing adults with forecoxae open behind, head usually with a distinct frontoclypeal suture, and the abdomen with 5 or 6 visible sternites (Britton, after Hinton, in CSIRO; Lawrence, in Parker).

duaspiracle, a spiracle of the second abdominal segment of an insect (T-B, after MacGillivray).

duct, a channel, tube or canal for carrying a secretion from a gland to the point of discharge (T-B).

ducteole, ductule, a ductlet or small duct (T-B).

ductifer, in ♂ Heteroptera (Hemiptera), small sclerotized arch or rod surrounding ductus seminis where it enters phallus at foramen ductus (Tuxen, after Bonhag and Wick).

ductless gland, endocrine gland, q.v. (Tulloch).

ductus bullae, in ♀ Lepidoptera, the duct from ductus seminalis to bulla seminalis; or the part of ductus seminalis from ductus bursae to bulla seminalis or to ductus bullae (as defined above) (Tuxen).

ductus bursae, in ♀ Lepidoptera, a tube of varying length connecting ostium bursae with corpus bursae (Tuxen, after Petersen), incorrectly applied to ductus seminalis, q.v. (Tuxen, after Weber); in ♀

Siphonaptera, distal part of bursa copulatrix (Tuxen, after Snodgrass); in ♀ Coleoptera, bursal duct, q.v. (Tuxen).

ductus bursae copulatricis, in ♀ Siphonaptera, ductus bursae, q.v. (Tuxen, after Oudemans).

ductus communis (pl., **ducti communes**), in ♀ Siphonaptera, part of ductus spermatheca between mouth of ductus obturatus and bursa copulatrix (Tuxen, after Peus).

ductus ejaculatorius (pl., **ducti ejaculatorii**), in ♂ insects, the ectodermal, mostly median, and unpaired exit tube of efferent system, opening by gonopore at tip of penis or into endophallus (vesica in Lepidoptera, in Thysanoptera pseudovirga) (Tuxen); in ♂ Heteroptera (Hemiptera), the median ectodermal efferent duct proximal to phallus, merging into ductus seminis at foramen ductus (Tuxen, after Meyer); incorrectly applied in ♂ Lepidoptera to vesica, q.v. (Tuxen), in ♂ Hymenoptera to penis, q.v. (Tuxen, after Kluge), and in ♂ Heteroptera to ductus seminis proximalis, q.v. (Tuxen, after Ashlock).

ductus ejaculatorius duplex, in ♂ Lepidoptera, vasa deferentia, q.v. (Tuxen).

ductus ejaculatorius partim, in ♂ Heteroptera (Hemiptera), vesica, q.v. (Tuxen, after Ekblom).

ductus ejaculatorius simplex, in ♂ Lepidoptera, ductus ejaculatorius, q.v. (Tuxen, after Hering).

ductus inferior, in ♂ Lepidoptera, fultura inferior (Tuxen, after Wehrli).

ductus inferior penis, in ♂ *Eupithecia* (Lepidoptera: Geometridae), fultura inferior (Tuxen, after Schroeder).

ductus intrabursalis (pl., **ducti intrabursales**), in ♀ Zygaenidae (Lepidoptera), duct connecting prebursa and the reduced corpus bursae (Tuxen, after Alberti).

ductus obturatorius, in ♀ Siphonaptera, ductus obturatus, q.v. (Tuxen, after Lass).

ductus obturatus, in ♀ Siphonaptera, blind duct, q.v. (Tuxen, after Snodgrass).

ductus odoriferus (pl., **ducti odoriferi**), in ♀ Lepidoptera, duct connecting a glandula odorifera with oviductus communis (Tuxen, after Stitz).

ductus receptaculi, in ♀ Heteroptera (Hemiptera), ductus spermathecae, q.v. (Dupuis, in Tuxen); in ♀ Lepidoptera, the single vessel connecting receptaculum seminis with vestibulum (Tuxen, after Stitz); in ♀ Coleoptera, ductus spermathecae, q.v. (Tuxen).

ductus receptaculi seminis, in ♀ Siphonaptera, ductus spermathecae (Tuxen, after Lass).

ductus sebaceus (pl., **ducti sebacei**), in ♀ Lepidoptera, the single duct connecting glandulae sebaceae with vestibulum (Tuxen, after Stitz).

ductus seminalis, in ♀ Heteroptera (Hemiptera), ductus receptaculi, q.v. (Tuxen, after von Siebold); in ♀ Coleoptera, seminal canal, q.v (Tuxen); in ♀ ditrysian Lepidoptera, the duct connecting bursa copulatrix with vestibulum of oviductus communis, communicating en route with bulla seminalis (if present) and sometimes with receptaculum seminis (Tuxen, after Petersen); in ♂ Lepidoptera, ductus ejaculatorius + vesica, q.v. (Tuxen, after Pierce); in ♀ Siphonaptera, ductus spermathecae, q.v. (Tuxen, after Dampf).

ductus seminalis communis, in ♀ Siphonaptera, ductus communis, q.v. (Tuxen, after Snodgrass).

ductus seminis, in ♂ Heteroptera (Hemiptera), the median ectodermal duct in phallus, from foramen ductus to secondary gonopore, frequently differentiated into d. s. proximalis and d. s. distalis (Tuxen, after Kullenberg).

ductus seminis conjunctivae, in ♂ Heteroptera (Hemiptera), ductus seminis proximalis, q.v. (Tuxen, after Ashlock).

ductus seminis distalis, in ♂ Heteroptera (Hemiptera), the median ectodermal duct in distal segment (endosoma) of phallus (Tuxen, after Dupuis).

ductus seminis proximalis, in ♂ Heteroptera (Hemiptera), the median ectodermal duct in proximal segment (phallosoma) of phallus (Tuxen, after Dupuis).

ductus seminis vesicae, in ♂ Heteroptera (Hemiptera), ductus seminis distalis, q.v. (Tuxen, after Ashlock).

ductus spermathecae, in ♀ insects, the primary canal through which the sperm enter the spermatheca (receptaculum seminis) from vagina or bursa copulatrix (Tuxen), or through a homologue of spermatheca (e.g., vermiform gland in some Heteroptera) connected with vagina or bursa copulatrix.

ductus spermatici, in ♂ Lepidoptera, ductus ejaculatorius + vasa deferentia (Tuxen, after Burmeister).

ductus superior, in ♂ Lepidoptera, transtilla (Tuxen, after Dampf).

ductus superior penis, in ♂ *Eupithecia* (Lepidoptera: Geometridae), fultura superior (Tuxen, after Schroeder).

Dufour's gland, in aculeate Hymenoptera, a small, simple sac with thin glandular walls and a delicate muscular sheath, secreting the alkaline element of the poison or various pheromones, opening into the poison duct near the base of the sting (T-B; Wilson; Chapman, after W. M. Wheeler).

dulosis, relation in which workers of a parasitic (dulotic) ant species (Hymenoptera: Formicidae) raid the nests of another species, capture brood (usually in the form of pupae), and rear then as enslaved nestmates (T-B; Wilson).

dumdum fever, kala-azar, q.v. (Adkins, pers. comm.).

duodenum, the chylific ventricle; also applied to the first section of the digestive tract just behind the entrance of the Malpighian tubules (T-B).

dun, in Ephemeroptera, subimago, q.v. (Leftwich).

dupion, a cocoon spun by 2 silk worms together or the coarse silk from such a cocoon (T-B).

duplicate, duplicatus (Latin), double (T-B).

duplicated cilia, in Thysanoptera, accessory cilia, q.v. (Mound et al.).

duplication, in adult Hymenoptera, internal lamina of posterior margin of a tergum or a sternum (Tuxen, after Michener).

duplicatopectinate, having the branches of a bipectinated antenna alternately long and short (T-B).

duplicatura vaginalis (pl., **duplicaturae vaginales**), in ♀ Siphonaptera, fingerlike diverticulum (in some cases several) in the roof of the vagina proximad of the orifice of the duct of the bursa copulatrix (Tuxen, after Lass; Rothschild and Traub).

Dursban (trade name), chlorpyrifos, q.v. (Pfadt).

durus, hard (T-B).

dusky, somewhat darkened, pale fuscous (T-B).

Dutch elm disease, fungal disease of elm trees caused by *Ceratocystus ulmi* transmitted externally by *Scolytus multistriatus* (Coleoptera: Scolytidae) (Borror et al.).

Dutch shell disease, maladie du pied, q.v. (Steinhaus and Martignoni).

Dyar's Rule, an observational rule which shows that in larval Lepidoptera the increase in head width shows a regular geometrical progression in successive instars (T-B; Leftwich); see Przibram's rule.

Dyfonate (trade name), fonofos, q.v. (Pfadt).

Dylox (trade name), trichlorfon, q.v. (Pfadt).

dynamic, pertaining to motion; active, as opposed to static (T-B).

dysentery, in invertebrate pathology, a number of disorders marked by lesions of the alimentary canal and often attended by abnormal frequency of fecal discharges (Steinhaus and Martignoni); amoebic dysentery, q.v., or bacillary dysentery, q.v. (Borror et al.); see flacherie.

Dzierzon's Rule, the supposed rule for sex determination among social Hymenoptera wherein all fertilized eggs become females and all unfertilized eggs become males (T-B, after Gaul); see haplodiploidy.

E

e-, Latin prefix; without (T-B; Harris).

EAG, electroantennogram, q.v. (Matthews and Matthews).

ear, in Orthoptera, tympanal organ, q.v., on foretibia or first abdominal segment (T-B).

eardrum, tympanum, q.v. (Borror et al.).

earwig, member of the order Dermaptera, and particulary those with conspicuous forcepslike cerci (Giles, in CSIRO).

eastern spruce gall, spruce cone-gall, q.v. (Borror et al.).

eau de Labarraque, a solution of sodium hypochlorite used in bleaching insect structures (T-B).

ebenine, black like ebony (T-B).

eburneous, eburneus, ivory white (T-B).

ecalcarate, ecalcaratus, without spurs, or calcaria (T-B).

ecarinate, ecarinatus (Latin), without or deprived of a keel or a carina (T-B; Harris); see carinate.

ecaudate, without a cauda or taillike process or structure (T-B).

ecaudate wing, wing without taillike processes (T-B).

ecdysial cleavage line, in immature insects, a line of weakness in the form of an inverted Y on the dorsal midline of the head and continuing on the thorax, along which the cuticle splits when the insect moults (Chapman); see epicranial suture.

ecdysial fluid, moulting fluid, q.v. (Tulloch; Leftwich).

ecdysial line, ecdysial cleavage line, q.v. (Chapman).

ecdysial membrane, a thin membrane found between the old and new cuticles at the time of moulting in certain insects; its origin is uncertain but it seems to arise by modification of the innermost layer of the old cuticle (Tulloch, after Richards).

ecdysial scar, in some insects, a scar in new cuticle representing a former spiracle (Gilmour, in CSIRO).

ecdysial suture, in larval Lepidoptera, ecdysial cleavage line, q.v. (Stehr, after Hinton).

ecdysis, the process of casting the skin (T-B; Chapman); see moulting.

ecdyson, ecdysone, q.v. (Leftwich).

ecdysone, steroid hormone, probably derived from cholesterol, secreted by the prothoracic glands and stimulating the secretion of moulting fluid from glands in the epidermis (Chapman).

Echinocloa ragged stunt, disease of grass (*Echinacloa*) caused by a reovirus (*Fijivirus*) transmitted propagatively by *Sogatella* (Hemiptera: Auchenorrhyncha: Delphacidae) (Nault and Ammar).

echinate, echinatus (Latin), thickly set or armed with short, stout spines or prickles; spiny like a hedgehog (T-B; Harris, after Funk); see echinulate.

echinulate, with very small prickles; minutely echinate (Harris, after Marchant and Charles).

echinulations, in ♂ Embiidina, peglike modified setae on the inner surface (usually on a lobe) of the basal segment of the left cercus (Tuxen, after Davis).

ecitophile, an obligate guest of one of the army ants belonging to the tribe Ecitonini, especially the genus *Eciton* (Hymenoptera: Formicidae) itself (Wilson).

eclipse period, in the development cycle of viruses, a phase or period, occurring immediately after infection (i.e., immediately after the virus enters the host cell), in which infective particles cannot be detected; the phase during which the infected host cell contains no material capable of infecting another cell or another host (Steinhaus and Martignoni).

eclosion, escape of the adult insect from the cuticle of the pupa, the cocoon, or the puparium, or, in hemimetabolous insects, from the cuticle of the last nymphal instar (T-B; Leftwich; Chapman); see hatching.

ecological, of or pertaining to the interactions of organisms and their environment (T-B).

ecological isolation, a condition in which interbreeding between 2 or more otherwise sympatric populations is believed to be prevented by factors (Mayr); see geographic isolation and reproductive isolation.

ecological race, a local race that owes its most conspicuous attributes to the selective effect of a specific environment (Mayr).

ecological subspecies, ecological race, q.v. (T-B, after Ferris).

ecology, the study of the interactions between organisms and their environment (T-B; Mayr); see autecology and synecology.

ecomone, communicative signal which originated either from an organism or the abiotic environment (Matthews and Matthews, after Pasteels).

ecomorph, in Collembola, a structurally modified form, commonly with reduced mouthparts and cuticular modifications such as abdominal spines, in certain Hypogastruridae and Isotomidae, and believed to be associated with diapause and unfavorable conditions (Christiansen and Bellinger).

ecomorphosis, environmentally induced variation in form (Borror et al.).

economic injury level, the lowest pest density that will cause economic damage; or the pest density that causes damage equal to the cost of preventing the damage (Pfadt).

economic threshold, the pest density at which control measures should be applied to prevent an increasing pest population from reaching the economic injury level (Pfadt).

ecophenotypic variation, a nongenetic modification of the phenotype by specific ecological conditions, particularly those of habitat (Mayr).

ecospecies, a group of populations so related that they are able to exchange genes freely without loss of fertility or vigor in the offspring (Mayr, after Turesson).

ecosystem, a biome or community and its abiotic environment (Allaby).

ectad, from within toward the outer surface of the insect body (T-B).

ectadenia, in ♂ insects, accessory glands of ectodermal origin, opening into the ductus ejaculatorius (T-B, after Imms; Tuxen).

ectal, outward, or without (T-B); pertaining to the outer surface of the insect body (T-B).

ectoblast, the outer wall of a cell; the ectoderm or epiblast (T-B).

ectoderm, in embryonic development, the germ layer giving rise to the nervous system and the integument (T-B); see endoderm and mesoderm.

ectodermal, of or pertaining to the ectoderm; arising from the ectoderm (T-B).

Ectognatha, hypothesized monophyletic group, sometimes considered as equivalent to the Insecta, including the Archaeognatha and the Dicondylia (Jacobs and Seidel, after Hennig); see Entognatha.

Ectognathata, Ectognatha, q.v. (Boudreaux).

ectognathous, with exserted mouthparts (T-B); with primitively exposed mouthparts, e.g., true insects, i.e., Insecta (Macherras, in CSIRO); see entognathous.

ectohormone, pheromone, q.v. (Tulloch).

ectolabium, labium, q.v. (T-B).

ectoparameres, in ♂ Grylloidea (Orthoptera), lateral or ventrolateral outqrowths of pseudepiphallus (Tuxen, after Walker); in ♂ Chironomidae (Diptera), aedeagal lobe, q.v. (Saether).

ectoparasite, an external parasite of insects or vertebrates, e.g., fleas (Siphonaptera), lice (Phthiraptera), louse flies (Diptera: Hippoboscidae), and bed bugs (Heteroptera: Cimicidae) (T-B; Norris, in CSIRO); see endoparasite.

ectoparasitic, of the nature of or pertaining to an ectoparasite (T-B).

ectoparsitoid, idiobiont that develops externally on a concealed host, and feeds through an integumentary lesion (Gauld and Bolton).

ectophagous, feeding externally outside the body of victim or host (T-B; Gauld and Bolton); see endophagous.

ectophallic membrane, in ♂ Caelifera (Orthoptera), the outer integument of the phallus (Tuxen).

ectophallic valves, in ♂ Eumastacidae (Orthoptera), a pair of sclerotized valves representing a continuation of the ectophallic membrane and forming the apex of the aedeagus (Tuxen, after Dirsh).

ectophallus, in ♂ insects, outer phallic wall in distinction to the endophallus (Tuxen, after Snodgrass); in ♂ Hymenoptera, penis, q.v. (Tuxen).

ectoplasm, an external layer of protoplasm in a cell (T-B).

ectoproct(s), in adult Neuropteroidea, one of a pair of plates of tergum X (sometimes fused dorsally) surrounding the anus and usually bearing trichobothria, in some Planipennia fused with tergite IX (Tuxen, after Tjeder), in Raphidioptera, possibly also containing elements of tergite XI (Aspöck et al.).

ectoptygma, in the embryo, serosa, q.v. (T-B, after Graber).

ectoskeletal, exoskeletal, q.v. (T-B).

ectospermalege (pl. **ectospermalegia**), in some Cimicoidea (Hemiptera: Heteroptera), external pouchlike ectodermal part of the spermalege, q.v. (Carayon, in Usinger).

ectostomal sclerite, in larval Muscomorpha (Diptera), dental sclerite, q.v. (Ferrar).

ectosymbiont, a symbiont that associates with the host colonies during at least part of its life cycle in some relationship other than internal parasitism (Wilson).

ectotheca, in ♂ Corixidae (Hemiptera: Heteroptera), lamina ventralis, q.v. (Tuxen, after Hungerford).

ectotrachea, the outer surface or layer of the trachea (T-B).

Ectotrophi, Ectognatha, q.v. (Jacobs and Seidel).

ectotrophous, ectognathous, q.v. (T-B).

Ectropoda, Strophandria, q.v. (Hennig, after Börner).

edaphic, relating to the soil (T-B).

edaphic factor, the influence of soil properties on organisms (especially plants) (Mayr).

ED$_{50}$, median effective dose, q.v. (Steinhaus and Martignoni).

EDB, ethylene dibromide, q.v. (Pfadt).

edeagus, aedeagus or aedoeagus, q.v. (Tuxen).

edematus, dull translucent white (T-B).

edentate, edentatus, edentulous, without teeth; toothless (T-B).

edentula, those having no teeth (T-B).

edge, the margin; acies, q.v. (T-B).

editum (pl., **edita**), in ♂ Calyptrata, e.g., *Glossina* (Diptera: Glossinidae), surstyli, q.v. (Tuxen); in ♂ Noctuidae (Lepidoptera), small, rounded, hairy prominence of inner face of valva ventrad of ampulla and costad of central area (Tuxen, after Pierce).

edoeagus, aedeagus or aedoeagus, q.v. (Tuxen).

E. E. stage, extraerythrocytic stage, q.v. (Tulloch).

effaced, obliterated; rubbed out; not visible (T-B).

effector, one of the organs of the body, principally a muscle or a gland, activated by nerve stimuli (T-B, after Snodgrass).

efferent, carrying outward or away from the center (T-B).

efferent canal, in ♀ Lepidoptera, the more sclerotized, helically coiled of 2 closely intertwined ducts that together comprise the ductus spermathecae; the efferent, internal or fertilization canal serves to transport sperm from the utriculus through the vesicle down to the vagina (Mitter); see afferent canal.

efferent neuron or **neurone,** one that conveys impulses from ganglia outward to muscles or glands; a motor nerve cell (T-B).

efferent nerve, a nerve that conducts from a nerve center toward the periphery; the axon of a motor nerve cell (T-B, after Snodgrass).

efferent system, in ♂ Coleoptera, collective term for efferent ducts, accessory glands, vesiculae seminales and ductus ejaculatorius (Tuxen).

efflected, somewhat angularly bent outward (T-B).

effluvium, a foul or unpleasant smell or emanation (T-B).

effractor (pl., **effractores**), in ♂ Phthiraptera, posteriad projection from mesomeral arch (Lyal).

egest, evacuate, q.v. (T-B).

egestion, evacuation, q.v. (T-B).

egg, a simple cell, capable of being fertilized, containing the germ, the food-yolk necessary for its nutriment, and a covering membrane (T-B); a single ovum or cell from an ovary (T-B); the first stage of the insect (T-B).

egg burster, a projecting point, hard spines, or ridges on the head or other part of an embryo, used in breaking the shell when hatching (T-B; Leftwich).

egg cap, in some Heteroptera, *Carausius* (Phasmida), Embiidina, and Phthiraptera, a lid joined to the body of the egg along a line of weakness, which is forced off by the hatching insect (Tulloch; Chapman).

egg case, the case or covering prepared or secreted by an insect to contain or hold together the egg mass as a whole (T-B); ootheca, q.v. (T-B).

egg calyx, calyx, q.v. (T-B).

egg chamber, one of the follicles of an ovariole containing an oocyte (T-B, after Snodgrass).

egg guide, in ♀ Caelifera (Orthoptera), median caudal process of the subgenital plate (T-B; Tuxen); in ♀ Leptophlebiidae (Ephemeroptera), prominent, sclerotization of sternum VII and sometimes VIII (Tuxen, after Morrison).

egg guides, in ♀ Diptera, hypogynial valves, q.v. (Tuxen); in ♀ Chironomidae (Diptera), gonapophyses VIII, q.v. (Saether).

egg passage, in ♀ Coleoptera, median oviduct, q.v. (Tuxen).

egg plate, in in ♀ Plecoptera, subgenital plate, q.v. (Tuxen, after Brekke).

egg pod, in Acrididae (Orthoptera), a mass of eggs under the ground held together by a frothy secretion (T-B; Chapman).

egg pouch, ootheca, q.v. (T-B).

egg raft, in some culicine genera (Diptera: Culicidae), for example, a group of vertically oriented eggs that lies flat on the surface of the water (Chapman).

egg shell, chorion, q.v. (CSIRO).

egg tooth, egg burster, q.v. (T-B).

egg tube, ovariole, q.v. (T-B).

egg valve, in ♀ Ephemeroptera, egg guide, q.v. (Tuxen, after Berner) or subgenital plate, q.v. (Tuxen, after Morgan).

eight-shaped pores, (8-shaped pores) flat, oval structure composed of 2 adjacent circles giving the appearance of an "8", e.g., in nymphs and ♀ Asterolecaniidae, Cerococcidae, Lecanodiaspididae (Hemiptera: Sternorrhyncha: Coccoidea) (Miller, in Stehr).

eight-shaped tubular duct, (8-shaped tubular duct) cylindrical structure with a central septum giving the appearance of an "8", e.g., Phoeniococcidae (Hemiptera: Sternorrhyncha: Coccoidea) (Miller, in Stehr).

eighth gonocoxites, in ♀ Berothidae (Planipennia), postgenitale, q.v. (Tuxen, after Adams and MacLeod).

eighth hemitergites, in ♀ Apoidea (Hymenoptera), lateral remnants of abdominal tergum VIII (Tuxen, after Michener).

eighth parasternites, in ♀ Heteroptera (Hemiptera), incorrectly, gonocoxites of abdominal segment VIII (Tuxen, after Ekblom).

eighth sternite, in Heteroptera (Hemiptera), incorrectly, gonocoxites of abdominal segment VIII (Tuxen, after Christophers and Cragg); in ♀ Neuroptera, subgenitale, q.v. (Tuxen, after Tjeder).

ejaculator (pl., **ejaculatores**), in ♂ Diptera, sperm pump, q.v. (Tuxen).

ejaculator apodeme, in ♂ Diptera, aedeagal apodeme, q.v. (Tuxen).

ejaculator sac, in ♂ Diptera, ejaculator, q.v. (Tuxen).

ejaculatory apodeme, aedeagal apodeme, q.v. (Tuxen; McAlpine) or in ♂ Muscomorpha (Diptera: Brachycera), median unpaired process of sperm pump independent of aedeagal apodeme (McAlpine).

ejaculatory bulb, in ♂ Isoptera, swollen bulbous termination of ejaculatory duct, receiving right and left vasa deferentia (Tuxen, after Weesner); in ♂ Diptera, bulbus ejaculatorius, q.v. (T-B, after Snodgrass; Tuxen) or sperm pump, q.v. (McAlpine) ; in ♂ Siphonaptera, a muscular, almost spherical, bulblike organ in which sperm is mixed with a secretion from the accessory glands before passing into the penis (Rothschild and Traub).

ejaculatory canal, in ♂ Coleoptera, ductus ejaculatorius, q.v. (Tuxen).

ejaculatory duct, in ♂ insects, ductus ejaculatorius, q.v. (T-B; Tuxen); in ♂ Reduviidae (Hemiptera: Heteroptera), ductus seminis proximalis, q.v. (Tuxen, after Davis); in ♂ Diptera, sperm duct, q.v. (McAlpine); in ♂ Siphonaptera, tubus interior, q.v. (Tuxen, after Jordan).

ejaculatory pump, in adult Diptera, sperm pump, q.v. (McAlpine).

ejaculatory reservoir, in ♂ Pentatomomorpha (incl. Aradidae and Piesmatidae), Dipsocoromorpha and Nepidae (Hemiptera: Heteroptera), complex differentiation of proximal end of ductus seminis distalis in endosoma, lying at distal end of ligamentary processes (Tuxen, after Singh-Pruthi).

ejaculatory sac, in ♂ Caelifera (Orthoptera), a distal dilatation of ductus ejaculatorius (Tuxen); in ♂ Phthiraptera, endophallus, q.v. (Clay, in Tuxen); in ♂ Diptera, sperm sac, q.v. (McAlpine).

ejaculatory vesicles, in ♂ Ensifera (Orthoptera), a pair of lateral, generally oval vesicles near outlet of ductus ejaculatorius (Tuxen, after Snodgrass).

elabrate, elabratus (Latin), without a labrum (T-B).

elaiophores, special glands within flowers that secrete oils that are collected by some bees (Hymenoptera: Apoidea) (Gauld and Bolton).

elastes, in *Machilis* (Archaeognatha: Machilidae), the elastic organs of the ventral segments which assist in the act of leaping (T-B).

elastic, flexible throughout (T-B).

elate, elatus (Latin), high (T-B; R. W. Brown); see elevated.

elater, in Collembola, furcula, q.v. (T-B); a beetle belonging to the family Elateridae (Coleoptera) (Leftwich).

elateriform larva, larva resembling larval Elateridae (Coleoptera), i.e., elongated, cylindrical, orthosomatic and possessing a firm exoskeleton, e.g., larval Elateridae, Tenebrionidae and several other beetle families (Peterson; Leftwich).

Elateriformia, group within the Polyphaga (Coleoptera), including the superfamilies Byrrhoidea, Dryopoidea, Buprestoidea, Rhipiceroidea, Elateroidea, and Cantharoidea (Britton, in CSIRO).

elaterium (pl., **elateria**), in ♀ Hymenoptera, cuticular hinge between united dorsal rami of gonapophyses IX (Tuxen, after E. L. Smith).

Elateroidea, superfamily within the Polyphaga (Coleoptera), including the families Artematopidae, Elateridae, Eucnemidae, Cebrionidae, Cerophytidae, Perothopidae, and Throscidae, possessing adults with globular forecoxae, penultimate tarsomere lobed or bilobed beneath, trochantins concealed, tarsi with 5-5-5 tarsal formula, abdomen with 5 visible sternites, basal and second sternites separated by a distinct suture, metasternum without a transverse suture, and abdominal tergites much less strongly sclerotized than the exposed parts (Britton, in CSIRO; Lawrence, in Parker).

elbowed antenna, geniculate antenna, q.v. (T-B).

electroantennogram (**EAG**), a record of the summed receptor potentials of a number of olfactory receptors responding to a stimulus (Matthews and Matthews).

electrophoresis, a process of separating molecules, particularly polypeptides, owing to their differential rates of migration in an electric field (Mayr).

electroretinogram, a record of the sum of potentials arising in the eye and optic lobe as a whole (Chapman).

elephant lice, members of the suborder Rhyncophthirina (Phthiraptera) (Calaby, in CSIRO).

elephantiasis, in humans, enlargement of the limbs or scrotum, often extreme, as a result of the obstruction of lymphatic channels by filiarial worms (Nematoda: Filariidae), especially *Wucheria bancrofti,* which is carried and transmitted by females of the mosquito *Culex fatigans* (Diptera: Culicidae) (Allaby).

Eleutherata, all forms with free separated maxillae (T-B); later, Co-leoptera, q.v. (T-B).

eleutherotogony, in embryonic development, when the back of the insect is formed without participation of the membranes (T-B, after Henneguy).

elevated, elevatus (Latin), raised (R. W. Brown); of a part, higher than its surroundings (T-B).

elevator, a muscle which is employed to raise any moveable part (T-B).

eleventh sternite, in ♂ *Inocellia* (Raphidioptera: Inocelliidae), gonarcus, q.v. (Tuxen, after Acker).

elimination, the physiological discharge of any waste or useless substances from the body tissues (T-B).

elinguata, without a tongue (T-B); forms in which the maxillae are connate with the labium (T-B); see synista.

elite, referring to a colony member displaying greater than average initiative and activity.

ellipsoidal, elliptical, q.v. (T-B).

elliptical, ellipticum (Latin), oblong-oval; the ends equally rounded, together forming an even ellipsoid (T-B).

Ellipura, hypothesized monophyletic group including the Collembola and Protura (Boudreaux, after Börner).

Ellipurata, Eppipura, q.v. (Boudreaux).

elongate, elongatus (Latin), prolonged (R. W. Brown); much longer than wide (T-B).

elongated plasmatocyte, plasmatocyte with very fine spindle ends (Tulloch, after Jones).

elute, elutus (Latin), with scarcely distinct markings (T-B; Harris).

elytral, of or pertaining to the elytron.

elytral hypomeron, in adult Coleoptera, epipleural fold, q.v. (T-B).

elytral interval, convex longitudinal area situated between elytrl striae or interneurs of Coleoptera (Erwin).

elytral ligula, in adult Coleoptera, e.g., Dytiscidae, a tonguelike process on the inner face of the side margin of the elytron that perfects the union of the elytron with the abdominal sterna (T-B).

elytriform, shaped or appearing like an elytron (T-B).

elytriform wings, in Strepsiptera, pseudoelytra, q.v. (Riek, in CSIRO).

elytrin, chitin, q.v. (T-B).

elytron (pl., **elytra**), the leathery forewing of beetles (Coleoptera), serving as a covering for the hind wings, commonly meeting opposite elytron in a straight line down the middle of the dorsum in repose (T-B); see hemelytron and tegmen.

Elytroptera, Coleoptera, q.v. (T-B).

emandibulata, those insects in which there are no functional mandibles in any stage (T-B).

emandibulate, emandibulatus, lacking functional mandibles, e.g., most Lepidoptera; applied in any stage (T-B).

emarginate, emarginatus (Latin), notched at the margin (T-B).

emarginate collar, in ♂ Lepidoptera, sternum VIII (transl. "collier échancré" Réaumur, after Tuxen).

emargination, a cut-out place in an edge or margin (T-B).

embiid, a member of the order Embiidina (Ross, in CSIRO).

Embiidina, order within the Neoptera (Insecta), comprising the web spinners, the members of which possess a greatly swollen basitarsus of the foreleg containing a silk gland, and narrow wings with reduced venation (Tulloch; Mackerras, in CSIRO; Ross, pers. comm.).

Embiodida, Embiidina, q.v. (Boudreaux).

Embioidea, Embiidina, q.v. (Boudreaux, after Handlirsch).

Embioptera, Embiidina, q.v. (T-B; Borror et al.).

embolar, of or pertaining to the embolium (T-B).

embolar groove, in Heteroptera (Hemiptera), variously distinct trough-shaped groove of forewing running parallel with the costal margin anterior to the medial fracture and often delimiting the embolium (Štys); see median furrow.

embolium, in the forewing of some Heteroptera (Hemiptera), variously delimited or differentiated submarginal part of the corium (exocorium, q.v., or a part of it) situated basal to the costal fracture (Štys, pers. comm.).

embossed, ornamented with raised sculpturing (T-B; Harris); see sculptured.

embryo, the young animal before leaving the body of the parent or before emerging from the egg (T-B).

embryo chains, in polyembryonic endoparasites, chains of embryos (Hinton and Mackerras, in CSIRO).

embryology, the study of embryonic development (Hinton and Mackerras, in CSIRO).

embryonic, found in, or relating to the embryo (T-B); see atrophied and rudimentary.

embryonic period, the part of the life cycle of an insect between fertilization and hatching of the egg (T-B, after Folsom and Wardle).

emendation, any demonstrably intentional change in the original spelling of an available name, other than a mandatory change (ICZN); an available name formed by intentionally changing the original spelling of an available name unless the change is mandatory (ICZN); see justified emendation and unjustified emendation.

emendatus (Latin), amended; abbrev., emend. (T-B).

emergence, eclosion, q.v., of the adult insect (T-B).

Emery's Rule, the rule that species of social parasites are very similar to their host species and therefore presumably closely related to them phylogenetically (Wilson).

emigration, the movement of a colony from one nest site to another (Wilson).

emitted energy orientation, reading of other's or one's own energy patterns for clues as to the topography of the immediate environment, e.g., groups of whirligig beetles (Gyrinidae) (Matthews and Matthews).

emmet, an ant (Hymenoptera: Formicidae) (T-B).

Empidiformia, Empidoidea, q.v. (Hennig).

Empidoidea, superfamily within the division Orthorrhapha of the suborder Brachycera (Diptera), including the families Empididae and Dolichopodidae, characterized by adults with the anterior cubitus (CuA) of the wing shortened (Colless and McAlpine, in CSIRO; McAlpine).

empodial appendage, in Collembola, unguiculus, q.v. (Christiansen and Bellinger).

empodial hair, in Coccoidea (Hemiptera: Sternorrhyncha), digitule, q.v. (T-B, after MacGillivray).

empodium (pl., **empodia**), a spine- or lobelike process of the unguitractor (T-B, after Crampton; Chapman); in Heteroptera (Hemiptera), distal extension of the unguitractor plate, (Goel and Schaefer) or, inaccurately, any single structure between the claws (Štys, pers. comm., after Gross); in adult Diptera, an unpaired median process arising from the ventral or plantar region of the arolium (McAlpine); see arolium, euplantulae, and pulvillus.

empty spherule cell, spherule cell, q.v. (Tulloch, after Métalnikov).

empusal vein, in winged insects, the generally convex, unbranched eighth longitudinal vein system, originating on the cubital plate and lying just before the claval furrow of Neoptera (Ross et al., after Hamilton); first anal vein (1A) of Comstock and Needham; postcubitus or second postcubitus (PCu) of Snodgrass (Morse, pers. comm.).

emulsifiable concentrate, a liquid formulation of insecticide containing an emulsifier so water may be added to form an emulsion (Pfadt).

emulsion, a suspension of fine droplets of one liquid in another, such as oil in water (Pfadt).

enarthrosis, an articulation like a ball and socket joint (T-B).

encased pupa, a pupa in a case or cocoon.

encephalitis (pl., **encephalitides**), any viral disease of the brain, but usually referring to the ones in man and horses that are caused by several different viruses and transmitted by mosquitoes in the genera *Culex* and *Aedes* (Diptera: Culicidae) (Borror et al.).

encephalon, the part of the head containing the brain (T-B).

encircled, ringed; margined round about (T-B); in ♂ Geometridae (Lepidoptera), descriptive of an ostium bursae the lateral structures of which are connected by sclerotized processes to apophyses anteriores which are united dorsally by a sclerotized band of tergum VIII (Tuxen, after Pierce).

end apparatus, in a class-3 dermal gland, a perforated, relatively electron-dense structure, continuous with ductule, lying within cavity of gland cell (Chapman, after Noirot and Quennedey).

end chamber, the germarium of a gonadial tube (T-B, after Snodgrass); in ♂ Siphonaptera, a spaceous, hollow end chamber of the aedeagus, usually wide open or expanded dorsally and open to a lesser degree ventrally (Tuxen, after Snodgrass); in ♀ Siphonaptera, camera genitalis, q.v. (Tuxen, after Sharif).

end chamber hook, in Anisoptera (Odonata), a tooth borne on the inner border of the lateral lobe (T-B).

end organ, of a nerve, the peripheral receptors for external stimuli, at the end of a nerve fiber (T-B).

endapophyses, in ♂ Orthoptera, apodemes q.v., of cingulum (Tuxen, after Walker).

endemic, of a taxonomic group, restricted to a given geographical region (T-B, after Tillyard; Mackerras, in CSIRO).

endemic typhus, disease of man and rodents caused by *Rickettsia mooseri* Monteiro (Rickettsiae) and transmitted to man by the rat flea, *Xenopsylla cheopis* (Rothschild) (Siphonaptera); to rodents by various other fleas, lice (Phthiraptera), and mites and ticks (Acari) (Borror et al.).

endemicity, percentage of local members of a taxon (usually species of a genus) that is limited to that geographical region (MacKerras, in CSIRO).

endemism, the occurrence of taxonomic groups restricted to a given region (MacKerras, in CSIRO).

endite, a mesal lobe of any limb segment (T-B, after Snodgrass); in spiders (Arachnida: Araneae), the basal segment of the pedipalp, which is enlarged and functions as a crushing jaw (Borror et al.).

endite lobes, galea and lacinia of maxilla (Teskey, in McAlpine).

endite processes, in ♂ Embiidina, cercus-basipodites, q.v. (Tuxen, after Snodgrass).

endo-, Greek prefix; within (T-B).

endoapophysis, in ♂ Chironomidae (Diptera), apodemes of ♂ hypopygium, q.v. (Saether); in ♀ Chironomidae (Diptera), gonapophysis IX, q.v. (Saether).

endoblast, an inner layer formed by the invagination of the blastoderm (T-B).

endocardium, the inner lining membrane of the heart (T-B).

endochorion, the inner layer of the chorion of the insect egg (T-B, after Packard).

endocorium, in Heteroptera (Hemiptera), posterior (mesal in repose) part of the corium between the exocorium and clavus (Štys, pers. comm.).

endocranium, the inner surface of the cranium (T-B).

endocrine glands, specialized glands outside the central nervous system that produce hormones which are released directly into the hemolymph, or indirectly via storage organs, e.g., corpora cardiaca, corpoara allata, and prothoracic glands (Tulloch; Chapman); see endocrine organs and neurosecretory cells.

endocrine organs, neurosecretory cells of the central nervous system or endocrine glands which produce hormones (Chapman).

endocrine system, system of endocrine organs (Borror et al.).

endocuticle, soft, transparent, flexible portion of chitinous cuticle, located between tanned exocuticle and Schmidt's layer (Tulloch; Chapman); see exocuticle.

endocuticula, endocuticle, q.v. (T-B).

endoderm, germ layer resulting from invagination of the blastoderm during gastrulation which gives rise to the midgut (T-B; Tulloch; Chapman); see ectoderm and mesoderm.

endodermal, of or pertaining to endoderm (T-B).

endodulfan, $C_9H_6Cl_6O_3S$, a synthetic insecticide and acaricide; a chlorinated hydrocarbon, 6,7,8,9,10,10-hexachloro-1,5,5a,6,9,9ahexahydro-6,9-methano-2,4,3-benzodioxathiepin 3-oxide; moderately toxic to mammals, acute oral LD_{50} for rats 30 to 110 mg/kg (Pfadt).

endoecie, in Isoptera, the central part of the subterranean nest, containing the eggs and young (Noirot, in Krishna and Weesner).

endomeral plate, in ♂ Mallophaga (Phthiraptera), mesomeral arch, q.v. (Clay, in Tuxen).

endomeres, in ♂ Phthiraptera, mesomeres, q.v. (Clay, in Tuxen; Lyal); in ♂ Culicidae (Diptera), parameres, q.v. (Tuxen, after Crampton); some in ♂ Chironomidae (Diptera), appendages or lobes of ♂ hypopygium when these are derived from gonapophysis IX only and do not include parts of gonocoxite (Saether) or inferior volsella, q.v. (Saether).

endomesoderm, the inner layer formed by an invagination of the middle portion of the primitive band of the embryo, and from which the endoderm and mesoderm are subsequently differentiated (T-B).

endomitosis, chromosomal replication without cell division (White, in CSIRO).

endoparamere(s), the lateral end of the peronea produced internally as a stout paramere (T-B, after MacGillivray); in ♂ Orthoptera, laminae phalli, q.v. (Tuxen, after Walker); in ♂ Chironomidae (Diptera), phallapodeme, q.v. (Saether); in ♀ Chironomidae (Diptera), coxosternapodeme, q.v. (Saether).

endoparasites, internal parasites, that usually leave the host before pupation, e.g., larvae of Chalcididae and Ichneumonidae (Hymenoptera) and Tachinidae (Diptera) that parasitize insects, or certain flies (Diptera) that cause myiasis in humans and other vertebrates (T-B; Leftwich); see ectoparasites and endoparasitoid.

endoparasitoid, idiobiont whose larvae feed internally within the host (Gauld and Bolton).

endophagous, feeding internally on the host (T-B); see ectophagous.

endophallic apodeme, in ♂ Cyrtacanthacridinae (Orthoptera: Acrididae), anterior portion of endophallic plate (Tuxen, after Eades).

endophallic cavity, in ♂ Ensifera (Orthoptera), the cavity into which the gonopore opens (Tuxen, after Snodgrass); in ♂ Caelifera (Orthoptera), spermatophore sac, q.v. (Ander, in Tuxen).

endophallic chamber, in ♂ Coleoptera, internal sac, q.v. (Tuxen, after Snodgrass).

endophallic diverticulum (pl., **endophallic diverticula**), in ♂ Heteroptera (Hemiptera), 2 (Tingidae) or one (Vianaididae) alleged diverticula of the ductus seminis (Tuxen, after Drake and Davis).

endophallic duct, in ♂ Heteroptera (Hemiptera), ductus seminis proximalis, q.v. (Tuxen, after Khanna); in ♂ Pentatomoidea (Hemiptera: Heteroptera), ductus seminis distalis, q.v. (Tuxen, after McDonald).

endophallic hilt, in ♂ Tabanoidea (Diptera), basiphallus, q.v. (McAlpine).

endophallic membrane, in ♂ Caelifera (Orthoptera), the membrane covering the cavities in phallus (Ander, in Tuxen).

endophallic plates, in ♂ Orthoptera, laminae phalli, q.v. (Tuxen, after Snodgrass).

endophallic sac, in ♂ Orthoptera, sac of endophallus consisting of ejaculatory sac, spermatophore sac, and phallotreme (Tuxen, after Dirsh).

endophallic sclerites, in ♂ Orthoptera, sclerites in endophallic membrane (Ander, in Tuxen).

endophallic sperm reservoir, in ♂ Lygaeidae and Malcidae (Hemiptera: Heteroptera), ejaculatory reservoir, q.v. (Tuxen, after Bonhag and Wick).

endophallic tines, in ♂ Tabanoidea (Diptera), aedeagal tines, q.v. (McAlpine).

endophallic tube, in ♂ Diptera, one or more membranous internal tubes comprising endophallus (McAlpine).

endophallus (pl., **endophalli**), in ♂ insects, the internal sac or tube of the phallus invaginated at the end of the aedeagus, receiving ductus ejaculatorius at anterior end (primary gonopore) and opening apically through the phallotreme (secondary gonopore), typically eversible, but sometimes a permanently internal phallic structure (Tuxen, after Snodgrass); in ♂ Blattopteroidea, hypophallus + phallus (Tuxen, after Snodgrass); in ♂ Psocoptera, radula, q.v. (Tuxen, after Mockford); in ♂ Heteroptera (Hemiptera), ductus seminis distalis, q.v. (Tuxen, after Ashlock) or ductus seminis (as a whole), q.v. (Tuxen, after Bonhag and Wick); in Diptera, one of 3 membranous internal tubes of the aedeagus (McAlpine); in ♂ Chironomidae (Diptera), eversible portion of ♂ intromittent organ sometimes carrying spines, virga, at apex (Saether); in ♂ Siphonaptera, a long, sacklike continuation cephalad of the tubus interior enclosing the true penis (Tuxen, after Snodgrass).

endophytic, living and feeding within plant or tree tissue, as borers or miners (T-B; Gauld and Bolton); see exophytic.

endophytic oviposition, a form of oviposition in Anisoptera (Odonata), where elongated eggs are inserted by means of an ovipositor into leaves or stems of water plants (T-B, after Imms).

endoplasm, the inner or central part of the cytoplasm (T-B).

endopleural ridge, pleural ridge, q.v. (T-B).

endopleurite, Y-shaped ingrowth of cuticle from the sides of the thorax, consisting of pleural ridge, q.v., and pleural apophysis, q.v. (T-B; Leftwich).

endopodite, the mesal branch of a biramous appendage (T-B).

endopolyploidy, polploidy in which somatic cells have undergone one or more cycles of endomitosis, e.g., salivary gland cells in *Gerris* (Hemiptera: Heteroptera: Gerridae) (White, in CSIRO).

endoprocess, in ♂ Heteroptera (Hemiptera), suspensorial apodemes, q.v. (Tuxen, after Yang).

Endopterygota, Holometabola, q.v. (T-B).

endopterygote, having endopterygote wing development (Borror et al.); see exopterygote.

endopterygote orders, Holometabola, q.v. (Mackerras, in CSIRO).

endopterygote wing developement, in Holometabola, the development of wings within pockets in the integument which are everted after the larval-pupal apolysis (Hinton and Mackerras, in CSIRO).

Endopterygotida, Holometabola, q.v. (Boudreaux).

endoskeletal, relating or referring to the endoskeleton (T-B).

endoskeletal rod, apodeme, q.v. (T-B).

endoskeleton, those sclerotized processes extending inward into the body cavity from the body wall and serving for the attachment of muscles (T-B); in ♂ Chironomidae, apodemes of ♂ hypopygium, q.v. (Saether); see apodeme, phragma, and tentorium.

endosmosis, osmosis from the outside in (T-B).

endosoma (pl., **endosomata**), in ♂ Auchenorrhyncha (Hemiptera), aedeagus, q.v. (Tuxen, after China); in ♂ Heteroptera (Hemiptera), distal segment of phallus, free of ligamentary processes and surrounding the ductus seminis distalis from the ejaculatory reservoir or homologous level (included) down to the secondary gonopore (Tuxen, after Singh-Pruthi).

endosomal diverticula, in ♂ Tingidae, endophallic diverticula, q.v. (Tuxen, after Singh-Pruthi).

endosomal sperm reservoir, in ♂ Colobathristidae (Hemiptera: Heteroptera), ejaculatory reservoir, q.v. (Tuxen, after Štys).

endosternal, of or within the endosternum (T-B).

endosternal ridge, the Y-shaped union of the convergent ridges from the bases of the apophyses (T-B, after Snodgrass).

endosternite, a cuticular invagination of a thoracic sternum, being a site of muscle attachment; see furca and sternal apophysis.

endosternum, the inner part of the sternum (T-B); in Chelicerata, plate wintin the prosoma on which the ventral muscles of all the legs originate (Boudreaux).

endostracum, endocuticle, q.v. (Tulloch).

endotendons, in ♂ Siphonaptera, virga penis, q.v. (Tuxen, after Peus).

endotergite, phragma, q.v. (T-B).

endotheca, in ♂ insects, the inner wall of the phallotheca (T-B, after Snodgrass); in ♂ Phthiraptera, endophallus, q.v. (Tuxen, after Schmutz; Lyal); in ♂ Heteroptera (Hemiptera), conjunctiva, q.v.

(Tuxen, after Larsén); in ♂ Trichoptera, membranous depression of distal end of phallobase from which aedeagus and parameres, if any, arise (Tuxen, after Nielsen).

endothermy, the ability to increase body temperature beyond that of the environment (Matthews and Matthews).

endothorax, the internal framework or processes of the thorax (T-B).

endotoky, ovovivipary, q.v. (T-B).

endotoxins, in invertebrate pathology, substances produced by micro-organisms which are not secreted into the surrounding medium but are confined within the microbial cell, being released after autolysis (Steinhaus and Martignoni).

endotrachea, intima, q.v., of trachea (T-B).

Endotropha, Diplura, q.v. (Boudreaux, after Grassi).

endrin, $C_{12}H_8Cl_6O$, a highly residual insecticide, particularly effective against lepidopterous larvae; chlorinated hydrocarbon, the *endo-endo* isomer of dieldrin; highly toxic to mammals, acute oral LD_{50} for rats 10–12 mg/kg (Pfadt).

enervis, without veins of any kind; applied to wings (T-B).

engraved, exsculptate, q.v. (T-B; Harris).

Enicocephaloidea, Enicocephalomorpha, q.v.

Enicocephalomorpha, infraorder within the Heteroptera, including only the family Enicocephalidae, characterized by undifferentiated forewings, the distinctive structure of the head and foretarsi and tibiae, and the highly modified and often greatly reduced ♂ and ♀ enternal genitalia (Štys); see Euheteroptera.

enlarged portion of spermathecal duct, in ♀ Siphonaptera, pars dilatata, q.v. (Tuxen).

ennaton, the ninth abdominal segment in insects (T-B).

ensate, ensatus, ensiform, sword-shaped; two-edged, large at base and tapering to the point (T-B); see anceps.

ensheathe, to cover or enclose, as with a sheathe (T-B).

Ensifera, suborder within the Orthoptera, including the superfamilies Gryllacridoidea, Tettigonoidea, and Grylloidea, characterized by antennae with more than 30 articles (Key, in CSIRO).

entad, extending inwardly from without (T-B).

ental, inward from the external surface of the insect body, applied to structures within the body (T-B).

entelechy (in metaphysics), a cause leading to an end as a purpose; a condition in which actuality follows on potentiality; an expression met with in philosophical biology to indicate a cause which leads to an effect predetermined by the inner constitution of the cause; in effect, an immanent principle in nature which conditions, leads to and carries out its purposive ends (T-B).

enteric, relating to the enteron, i.e., alimentary canal (T-B).

enteric caeca, midgut caeca, q.v. (Gilmour, in CSIRO).

enteric coeca, midgut caeca, q.v. (T-B).

enteric discharge, defensive response consisting of regurgitating or defecating, e.g., "tobacco juice" regurgitated by grasshoppers (Orthoptera: Caelifera) (Matthews and Matthews).

enteric epithelium, a layer of cells of the wall of the digestive tract resting on a basement membrane (T-B, after Snodgrass).

enteric valve, in Isoptera, the valve connecting the first segment of the hind gut with the second segment, or paunch (Noirot et al., in Krishna and Weesner).

enterokinase, an enzyme produced in the lining cells of the insect duodenum, which activates trypsin (T-B).

enterolith, in invertebrate pathology, a concretion formed in the intestinal tract (Steinhaus and Martignoni).

enterolithiasis, the presence of enteroliths in the intestinal tract of an animal, e.g., single or agglomerated spherical or polymorphous enteroliths in the rectum of the adult queen honeybee (Hymenoptera: Apidae) (Steinhaus and Martignoni).

enteromyiasis, infection of the intestines of vertebrates by the larvae of flies (Diptera) (Steinhaus and Martignoni).

enteron, alimentary canal, q.v. (T-B).

Entex (trade name), fenthion, q.v. (Pfadt).

entire, without marginal teeth or notches (T-B; Borror et al.).

entocranium, tentorium, q.v. (T-B).

entocuticle, endocuticle, q.v. (T-B, after MacGillivray).

entoderm, endoderm, q.v. (T-B).

entodorsum, entotergum, q.v. (T-B).

Entognatha, hypothesized monophyletic group within the Hexapoda, including the Collembola, Protura, and Diplura, possessing entognathous mouthparts (Hennig).

Entognathata, Entognatha, q.v. (Boudreaux).

entognathous, with mouthparts in pockets, resulting from the growth of the facial integument over the mandibles and maxillae, fusing with edges of the labium, e.g., in Diplura, Protura, and Collembola (T-B); see ectognathous.

entoleter, a centrifugal force machine to kill insects infesting grain (Pfadt).

entoloma, anal margin, q.v., of wings (T-B).

entomic, relating to insects (Steinhaus and Martignoni).

entomiasis, lesions produced by insects in general on the tissues of living animals (T-B).

Entomobryoidea, superfamily within the suborder Arthropleona (Collembola), including the Entomobryidae and Isotomidae, characterized by a prothorax completely without setae (Wallace and Mackerras, in CSIRO).

entomogenous, refering to organisms growing in or on the bodies of insects, connoting a parasitic or other intimate symbiotic relationship (T-B; Steinhaus and Martignoni).

entomography, the description of an insect or of its life history (T-B).

entomolin, entomoline, chitin, q.v. (T-B).

entomologist, one who collects and studies insects (T-B).

entomology, that branch of zoology that deals with insects only; restricted by common consent to the Hexapoda (T-B).

Entomophaga, group proposed for the entomophagous Coleoptera + Strepsiptera (Kinzelbach, in Hennig, after Abdullah).

entomophagous, consuming chiefly insects or their parts (T-B; Steinhaus and Martignoni; Leftwich); see insectivorous.

entomophilic, insect-loving, describing close association between bacteria, fungi, protozoa, and nematodes, and insects (Steinhaus and Martignoni); see entomophilous.

entomophilous, insect-loving, being applied to plants especially adapted for pollination by insects (T-B); see entomophilic.

entomophily, pollination of flowers by insects (Leftwich).

entomophobia, abnormal fear of insects (Tulloch); see delusory parasitosis.

Entomophthorales, an order of Zycomycetes (fungi) which contain about 150 insect pathogens (Soper, in Nault).

entomophytic, referring to almost any relationship between plant microorganisms (bacteria and fungi) and insects (Steinhaus and Martignoni); see entomophytous.

entomophytous, referring to plants produced in or on an insect (T-B); see entomogenous and entomophytic.

entomopox virus (EPV), insect virus that resembles vertebrate pox viruses in having a beaded lipoprotein envelope, a platelike core, and either one or 2 lateral bodies, differing in being occluded in large proteinaceous bodies, having been found in Coleoptera, Lepidoptera, and Diptera (Pfadt).

entomosis, a disease caused by a parasitic insect (T-B).

entomotaxy, the preservation and preparation of insects for study (T-B).

entomotomist, a student of insect structure (T-B); insect morphologist.

entomotomy, that science which deals with internal structure of insects; insect anatomy (T-B).

entomurochrome, the coloring matter of the Malpighian tubes (T-B).

entoparasite, endoparasite, q.v. (T-B).

entopleuron, pleural apophysis, q.v. (T-B, after MacGillivray).

entoprocessus, in ♂ Neuroptera, one of a pair of lateral processes of the gonarcus, q.v. (Tuxen, after Tjeder).

Entopteraria, Endopterygota, q.v. (T-B).

entoptygma, in the embryo, amnion, q.v. (T-B, after Graber).

entosternum, furca, q.v., or sternal apophyses, q.v. (T-B).

entotergum, a large V-shaped ridge on the undersurface of the notum having its apex forward (T-B, after Snodgrass).

entothorax, entosternum, q.v. (T-B).

Entotrophi, Diplura, q.v. (Tulloch; Boudreaux, after Grassi); Entognatha, q.v. (Borror et al.).

entotrophous, entognathous, q.v. (T-B).

entozoa, those animals that live within the body of others (T-B).

envelope, a sheath of carton or wax surrounding the nest of a social insect, especially that of a social wasp (Hymenoptera: Vespidae) (Wilson).

enveloping cell, the intermediate cell of a sense organ, or of one of the component sensory units of the organ, probably corresponding to the trichogen of a seta (T-B, after Snodgrass); trichogen cell, q.v. (T-B, after Snodgrass).

environment, the totality of physical, chemical, and biotic conditions affecting an organism (T-B; Mayr); see habitat and niche.

enzootic disease, in invertebrate pathology, a disease (usually of low prevalence) which is constantly present in a population (Steinhaus and Martignoni); see epizootic.

enzyme, naturally occurring organic catalyst, being usually a protein (T-B; Tulloch, after Rockstein); see -ase.

Eoblattodea, extinct group of Polyneoptera (Insecta), resembling the Blattaria but possessing a long ovipositor (Hennig, after Laurentiaux).

Eocene Epoch, one of 5 epochs within the Tertiary Period, between Paleocene and the Oligocene, extending between about 60 and 40 million years before the present (Riek, in CSIRO).

Eonura, extinct group based upon Australian Triassic *Eoses*, originally placed in Lepidoptera, later transferred to the Mecoptera (Riek, after Tindale, in CSIRO).

eonymph, in Symphyta (Hymenoptera), the last larval instar (Hinton and Mackerras, in CSIRO); see prepupa.

eonymphal stage, eonymph, q.v. (Gauld and Bolton).

eoplasmatocyte, a variety of plasmotocyte with very conspicuous acidophilic nucleus and light basophilic cytoplasm (Tulloch, after Jones).

eoplasmatocytoid, a variety of plasmatocyte intermediate between the eoplasmatocyte and microplasmatocyte (Tulloch, after Jones).

Eopolyneuridea, an extinct group of Nematocera (Diptera), from the Upper Triassic (Hennig, after Rodendorf).

Eoptychopteridea, an extinct group of Culicomorpha (Diptera: Nematocera) (Hennig, after Rodendorf).

Eosentomidea, a suborder of Protura consisting of the family Eosentomidae, having spiracles on the meso- and metathorax, and lacking any pectinated structure (Nosek).

-eous, -eus, a suffix which indicates the possession of the quality of the stem word, e.g., membranaceous, like a membrane in texture.

epalpate, having no palpi (T-B).

epandrial lobes, in ♂ Mecoptera, dorsal abdominal tergum IX (Penny, pers. comm., after Byers).

epandrium (pl., **epandria**), the ninth abdominal tergite in the ♂ insect, especially in Diptera (T-B; McAlpine).

epaulet, in adult Diptera, tegula, q.v. (T-B); see humeral plate.

epaulette, in adult Noctuoidea (Lepidoptera), a sclerotized ridge separating the tympanum from the conjunctiva (Chapman, after Roeder and Treat).

Epermenioidea, superfamily of the infraorder Ditrysia (Lepidoptera) containing the family Epermeniidae, including very small moths with pecten on scape, naked proboscis, narrow wings with projecting tufts of scales on inner margin of forewings, and dense, stiff bristles on hind tibiae; larvae with 2 prespiracular (L) setae on prothorax; pupae without dorsal spines, not protruded from cocoon at ecdysis (Common).

ephebic, relating to the winged, adult stage (T-B).

eperythrozoonosis, a disease in swine caused by the *Eperythrozoa suis* (Protozoa); symptoms are fever and anemia, may be fatal; transmitted by hog louse, *Haematopinus suis* (Phthiraptera: Anoplura: Haematopinidae) (Pfadt).

Ephemerata, Ephemeroptera, q.v. (Boudreaux).

Ephemerelloidea, superfamily of Ephemeroptera, including the families Ephemerellidae, Leptohyphidae, and Tricorythidae (Landa and Soldán).

Ephemerida, Ephemeroptera, q.v. (T-B, after Comstock; Boudreaux, after Leach).

Ephemeridae, family within the Ephemeroptera, formerly used as a name for the entire order (T-B; Riek, in CSIRO).

Ephemerina, Ephemeroptera, q.v. (T-B).

Ephemeroidea, superfamily of Ephemeroptera, including the families Behningiidae, Potamanthidae, Euthyplociidae, Polymitarcyidae, Ephemeridae, and Palingeniidae (Landa and Soldán); Ephemeroptera, q.v. (Boudreaux, after Handlirsch).

Ephemeroptera, order within the Paleoptera (Insecta), comprising the mayflies, possessing adults in which the hind wing is much smaller than forewing, the anterior media (MA) of the forewing is branched, and the radial sector is not pectinately branched; immature stages (naiads) aquatic; unique among Recent insects in that nonfeeding adults undergo an additional moult before attaining sexual maturity (T-B; Mackerras, in CSIRO).

Ephydroidea, superfamily of the Schizophora-Acalyptratae within the infraorder Muscomorpha (Diptera: Brachycera), including the families Drosophilidae, Ephydridae, Curtonotidae, Diastatidae, Camillidae, Chloropidae, Cryptochetidae, Tethinidae, and Canacidae, including adult flies with the costa broken at the end of the subcosta, ♂ postabdomen symmetrical with reduced segmentation, and ♀ postabdominal segments short (McAlpine).

epi-, Greek prefix; on or upon (T-B).

epiandrial lobes, in ♂ Mecoptera, dorsal abdominal appendages of abdominal tergum IX (Penny, pers. comm., after Byers).

epiandrium (pl., **epiandria**), in ♂ Mecoptera, posteriorly produced part, often paired, of tergum IX (Tuxen) (see epiandrial lobes); in ♂ Diptera, periandrium, q.v. (Boudreaux).

epiandropodites, in ♂ Diptera, dististylus, q.v. (Tuxen, after Christophers).

epiblast, the outer germ layer of the embryo (T-B).

epicephalon, in most adult orthorrhaphous Brachycera and all Muscomorpha (Diptera), a distinct median sclerite on the occiput (Mc Alpine).

epicnemis, in certain Arachnida, an accessory joint at the base of the tibia, apparently without motion (T-B).

epicnemial carina, in many adult Apocrita (Hymenoptera), a ridge that more or less parallels the anterior margin of the mesepisternum (Gauld and Bolton).

epicnemium, in many adult Apocrita (Hymenoptera), portion of mesepisternum anterior to epicnemial carina (Gibson; Gauld and Bolton).

epicondyle, dorsal condyle, q.v., of mandible (T-B, after MacGillivray).

epicranial, relating or pertaining to the epicranium (T-B).

epicranial arm(s), in adult insects, one of the divarications of the Y-shaped epicranial suture (T-B, after MacGillivray); see frontal suture.

epicranial notch, in larval Lepidoptera, V-shaped dorsomedial space delimited laterally by the caudal projections of the head capsule (Stehr).

epicranial lobe, in larval Lepidoptera, the lateral, superior convex lobe of the head (T-B).

epicranial plates, 2 cuticular plates covering the dorsal surface of the insect's head (Leftwich); see epicranium.

epicranial stem, in adult insects, coronal suture, q.v. (T-B).

epicranial suture, in adult insects, a Y-shaped suture on the head, above the antennae, with the arms (frontal sutures) diverging anteriorly (T-B, after Imms, J. B. Smith); see coronal suture and ecdysial cleavage line.

epicranium, the upper part of the head from the frons to the neck, including frons, vertex and genae (T-B; Mackerras, in CSIRO); in adult Diptera, vertex, q.v. (McAlpine).

epicuticle, the thin outer layer of cuticle, covering the exocuticle, consisting of the inner epicuticle, outer epicuticle, wax layer, and cement layer (Tulloch; Chapman).

epicuticula, epicuticle, q.v. (T-B).

epicuticular filaments, terminal ramifications of the pore canals within the epicuticle (Chapman).

epideme, articulatory epideme, q.v. (T-B).

epidemic typhus, disease of man and rodents caused by *Rickettsia mooseri* (Rickettsiacce) transmitted to man by the body louse, *Pediculus humanus humanus* (Phthiraptera: Anoplura), rat flea, *Xenopsylla cheopis* (Siphonaptera), and rat mite, *Liponyssus bacoti* (Acari) (Borror et al.); see endemic typhus.

epidermal, of, pertaining to, or like the epidermis (T-B).

epidermal layer, in galls of Cynipidae (Hymenoptera), the outer covering of the gall, including the fairly normal epidermis and all the abnormal developments from it; largely naked or at most with stellate hairs (T-B, after Kinsey).

epidermata, abnormal excrescences or outgrowths from the skin (T-B).

epidermis, the ectodermal cell layer of the integument which is one cell thick and which secretes the cuticle (T-B; Tulloch; Chapman).

epididymis (pl., **epididymides**), compact, coiled part of a vas deferens (Tuxen); the convoluted efferent ducts, massed at the posterior part of the testes (T-B).

epigaeic, living on the surface of the earth (T-B, after W. M. Wheeler); living, or at least foraging, primarily above ground (Wilson); see hypogaeic.

epigamic, serving to attract the other sex in the breeding season.

epigamic behavior, courtship, q.v. (Tulloch).

epigamic coloration, colors displayed by animals in courtship (T-B).

epigamic selection, sexual selection, q.v., involving choices between the sexes (Matthews and Matthews).

epigastric furrow, in spiders (Arachnida: Araneae), a transverse ventral suture near the base of the abdomen, along which lie the openings of the book lungs and the reproductive organs (Borror et al.).

epigastrium, the first entire ventral sclerite of the abdomen (T-B).

epigenesis, hypothesis that an organism develops by the appearance of new structures and functions (T-B; Allaby); see preformation.

epigenetic period, the time after the union of the ♂ and ♀ elements, during which organs are forming (T-B).

epiglossa, epipharynx, q.v. (T-B).

epiglottis, epipharynx, q.v. (T-B).

epignathous, having mouthparts directed cephalad, prognathous (Peterson).

epigusta, the part of the propharynx posterior to the epipharynx and the tormae (T-B, after MacGillivray).

epigynium (pl., **epigynia**), in ♀ Diptera, tergum IX (Tuxen, after Crampton); in ♀ Diptera, tergite of abdominal segment VIII (McAlpine).

epigynum, in ♀ spiders (Arachnida: Araneae), external genitalia (Borror et al.).

epilabium, in larval Chironomidae (Diptera), ligula, q.v. (Saether).

epilabrum, in Myriapoda, a sclerite at each side of the labrum (T-B).

Epilamproidea, superfamily proposed for certain groups recently placed within both the Blattellidae and Blaberidae (Blattaria) (Hennig, after Princis).

epilimnion, the upper of 3 strata (others are the thermocline and hypolimnion) of water found in deep lakes, characterized by high oxygen levels and abundance of life (Tulloch).

epilobe, of the mentum in Carabidae (Coleoptera), corresponding to a partially divided ligula (T-B); a lateral appendage of a bilobed mentum (T-B).

epimegetic, applied to the largest in a series of insects exhibiting polymorphism, q.v., and major (Tulloch).

epimeral parapterum, subalare, q.v. (T-B).

epimeral suture, the caudal part of the sternopleural suture of authors (T-B, after MacGillivray).

epimere(s), in ♂ *Megalomus* (Plenipennia: Hemerobiidae), entoprocessus, q.v. (Tuxen, after Carpenter); in ♂ Mecoptera, dorsal valves, q.v. (Tuxen, after Ferris and Rees); in ♂ Lepidoptera, a dorsal process of phallobase (T-B, after Snodgrass; Tuxen).

epimeron (pl., **epimera**), the posterior division of a thoracic pleuron, marked anteriorly by the pleural sulcus (T-B, after Tillyard; Chapman, after Snodgrass).

epimeron II, in adult Chironomidae (Diptera), sclerite above second coxa and behind anepisternum II and preepisternum II, occasionally carrying setae (Saether).

Epimorpha, subclass of Chilopoda, including the orders Scolopendromorpha and Geophilomorpha, characterized by adults and newly hatched young with 21 or more pairs of legs (Borror et al.); see Anamorpha.

epimorphic development, epimorphosis, q.v. (Chapman).

epimorphosis, development in which all of the segments are differentiated in the embryo before hatching (Chapman); see anamorphosis.

epineural sinus, in the insect embryo, the space produced mainly by the separation of the yolk from the embryo, over the region of the ventral nerve cord, being the beginning of the permanent body cavity (T-B, after Imms).

epineurium, the membrane which invests a nerve ganglion (T-B, after Imms).

epinotal spines, in adult Myrmecinae (Hymenoptera: Formicidae), spines on epinotum which protect the pedicel (T-B, after W. M. Wheeler).

epinotum, in adult Hymenoptera, propodeum, q.v. (T-B, after Comstock; Gauld and Bolton); the dorsal aspect of the pronotum (T-B, after MacGillivray).

epiopticon, medulla externa, q.v. (T-B, after Hickson; Leftwich).

epiphallic spine, in some ♂ Enicocephalidae (Hemiptera: Heteroptera), supradistal plate forming a distinct medial part of the pseudosternite (Štys, after Jeannel).

epiphallus (pl., **epiphalli**), in ♂ Blattopteroidea, a pair of valves situated dorsal to the phallus (Tuxen); in ♂ Caelifera (Orthoptera), separate sclerite above dorsocephalic part of phallus (Tuxen, after Snodgrass); in ♂ Grylloidea (Orthoptera: Ensifera), pseudepiphallus, q.v. (Tuxen, after Snodgrass); in ♂ Rhaphidophoridae (Orthoptera: Ensifera), pseudosternite, q.v. (Tuxen, after Snodgrass); in most ♂ Ensifera (Orthoptera), titillator, q.v. (Tuxen, after Snodgrass); in ♂ Thysanoptera, incorrectly applied to membranous vesicle (= endophallus) issuing from periandrium (= phallobase) and bearing genital orifice (Tuxen, after de Gryse and Treherne; Heming; Lyal); in ♂ Diptera, esp. Brachycera, external process of basiphallus arising from its posteromedial surface (Tuxen; McAlpine).

epipharyngeal, belonging or relating to the epipharynx (T-B).

epipharyngeal armature, in predatory adult Dolichopodidae (Diptera), blade- or toothlike processes on the sides of the labrum (McAlpine).

epipharyngeal bar, in larvae of many Nematocera (Diptera), median sclerite on the epipharynx with an associated brush of setae, lying between the premandibles and behind the median ends of the tormae (Teskey, after Matsuda, in McAlpine).

epipharyngeal comb, in larval Chironomidae (Diptera), pecten epipharyngis, q.v. (Saether).

epipharyngeal process, in Heteroptera (Hemiptera), epipharyngeal projection, q.v. (Štys, after Spooner).

epipharyngeal projection, in some Heteroptera, narrow continuation of epipharynx beyond the apex of labrum covering the proximal sector of the stylet groove (Štys; Andersen).

epipharyngeal sclerite, in larval Muscomorpha (Diptera: Brachycera), fenestrated sclerite lying above the anterior margin of the hypopharyngeal sclerite (Teskey, in McAlpine); in bees (Hymenoptera: Apoidea), a pair of straplike pieces extending backward from the 2 sides of the base of the epipharynx (T-B); see hypopharyngeal sclerite.

epipharyngeal sense organ, in Heteroptera (Hemiptera), anterior (x) and posterior (y) groups of sensilla located in the epipharynx, apparently with some sensory function related to feeding (Cobben; Andersen).

epipharyngeal wall, the membranous inner surfaces of the clypeus and labrum (T-B, after Snodgrass).

epipharynx, the membranous roof of the mouth of an insect, provided with taste receptors and sometimes elongated to form part of the proboscis, being associated with the labrum (T-B; Leftwich); in larval Scarabaeoidea (Coleoptera), the complex buccal area forming the inner or under lining of the labrum and extending below the clypeus (T-B, after Böving).

epiphysis, in many families of Lepidoptera, a leaflike, or spurlike, basally-articulating process on the inner aspect of the foretibia used to clean antennae (T-B, after Comstock; Common, in CSIRO); see antenna cleaner, q.v.

epiphyte, a plant growing nonparasitically upon others, especially in the upper branches of trees, e.g., ferns, orchids, bromeliads, etc. (T-B, ater Tillyard).

epipleural fold, in adult Coleoptera, the raised lower edge of the epipleuron (T-B).

epipleural rod, in ♂ Diptera, processus longus, q.v. (Tuxen, after Graham-Smith).

epipleurite, the upper pleural plate when a pleuron is horizontally divided into 2 parts, e.g., anepisternum and anepimeron, q.v. (T-B); the basalar and subalar sclerites of a wing-bearing segment differentiated from the upper ends of the episternum and epimeron (T-B, after Snodgrass).

epipleuron, (pl., **epipleura**), in adult Coleoptera, the deflexed or inflexed portion of the elytron, laterally when the elytra are closed (T-B, after J. B. Smith).

epipleurum, in larval Coleoptera, the lateral area immediately above the ventrolateral suture and below the alar area; dorsally limited in thoracic segments by a normally oblique, in abdominal segment always horizontal, dorsolateral suture (Peterson, after Böving and Craighead).

epiploon, fat body, q.v. (T-B); see caul.

epipodite, an outer lobe of the coxopodite, often being a gill-bearing organ (T-B, after Snodgrass).

epiprocessi, processes of epiandrium, q.v. (Tuxen, after Crampton).

epiproct, the dorsal part of the eleventh abdominal segment in insects (T-B, after Snodgrass); in Plecoptera, supraanal lobe, q.v. (Tuxen); in adult Raphidiidae (Raphidioptera), ectoproct, q.v. (Tuxen, after Crampton); in ♂ Ascalaphidae and Myrmeleontidae (Planipennia), abdominal sternum IX (Tuxen, after Crampton); in ♂ *Nymphes* (Planipennia: Nymphidae), mediuncus, q.v. (Tuxen, after Crampton); in adult Mecoptera, supraanale, q.v. (Tuxen, after Crampton); in larval Lepidoptera, supraanal plate, q.v. (Peterson); in ♀ Diptera, supraanal plate, q.v. (Tuxen).

Epipsocetae, group within the suborder Psocomorpha (Psocoptera), including the families Epipsocidae, Neurostigmatidae, Dolabellopsocidae, Ptiloneuridae, and Cladiopsocidae, the members of which possess a radial-medial crossvein in the forewing, valva externa more or less reduced, and a linear sclerite running lengthwise in each lateral half of the anterior surface of the labrum (Mockford and Garcia Aldrete).

epipygium (pl., **epipygia**), in adult Hymenoptera, the tergite of the last abdominal segment (T-B; Gauld and Bolton); see epiproct and hypopygium.

episematic colors, in the theory of mimicry, recognition colors (T-B).

episite, predator, q.v. (T-B; Leftwich); see parasite.

episitic, predaceous, q.v.

episome, in insect pathology, an element of genetic material capable of transmitting heritable traits and alternating between autonomous (extrachromosomal) or integrated (physically attached to a chromosome) states in the host cell (Steinhaus and Martignoni).

episternal, of or pertaining to the episternum (T-B).

episternal fissure, in adult Diptera, anepisternal cleft, q.v. (McAlpine).

episternal lateral, preepisternum, q.v. (T-B, after MacGillivray).

episternal paraptera, basalar sclerites, q.v. (T-B).

episternal scrobe, in virtually all adult Apocrita (Hymenoptera), a small pit on mesepisternum, slightly before the epimeron and about one-third of its length down (Gauld and Bolton).

episternal sulcus, in adult Vespidae (Hymenoptera), dorsal part of scrobal sulcus (Carpenter, pers. comm., after Bohert and Merke).

episternal suture, the anterior part of the sternopleural suture of authors (T-B, after MacGillivray).

episternites, the upper pair of appendages forming the ovipositor in grasshoppers (T-B); posterior valvulae, q.v.

episterno-precoxal, of or pertaining to the episternum and the precoxa together (T-B).

episternum (pl., **episterna**), the anterior sclerite on the pleuron, marked posteriorly by the pleural sulcus (T-B, after Imms; Chapman, after Snodgrass); in Acridoidea (Orthoptera), a small sclerite protruding from beneath the lower anterior part of the pronotal lobes (Otte, pers. comm.); in adult Chironomidae (Diptera), pre-episternum, q.v. (Saether).

epistoma, the oral margin or sclerite directly behind the labrum, e.g., anteclypeus, clypeus or frontoclypeus (T-B); specifically, in adult Diptera, lower facial margin, q.v. (T-B; Colless and McAlpine, in CSIRO; McAlpine).

epistomal plate, in larval Muscomorpha (Diptera), a rounded or angular sclerite anterodorsal to, and between, the anterior arms of the intermediate sclerite; epistomal sclerite, q.v. (Ferrar).

epistomal ridge, the internal projection of the epistomal suture (T-B).

epistomal sclerite, in larval Muscomorpha (Diptera: Brachycera), epipharyngeal sclerite, q.v. (Teskey, in McAlpine); epistomal plate, q.v. (Ferrar).

epistomal sulcus, epistomal suture, q.v. (Chapman).

epistomal suture, a groove uniting the anterior ends of the subgenal sutures across the face forming internally a strong epistomal ridge, typically straight, but often arched upward, sometimes absent (T-B, after Snodgrass); frontoclypeal suture, q.v. (T-B; McAlpine).

epistome, epistoma, q.v. (Borror et al.).

epistomis, epistoma, q.v. (T-B).

epistomum, epistoma, q.v. (T-B).

epitendon, in ♂ Siphonaptera, slender appendage attached to anterior tip of aedeagal apodeme (Tuxen, after Peus).

epithelial, of or pertaining to the epithelium (T-B).

epithelial layer, any layer of cells, one surface of which bounds a space, e.g., epithelial layer of the gut, the cellular lining of the gut bounding the enteron (T-B, after Klots).

epithelial sheath, in certain insects, an outside covering of flat cells of the tunica intima; the wall of a testicular tubule, sometimes two-layered (T-B, after Snodgrass).

epithelium, the layer of cells which covers a surface or lines a cavity (T-B).

epitorma (pl., **epitormae**), in some larval Scarabaeoidea (Coleoptera), a rod extending from the inner end of the laeotorma (T-B, after Böving).

epitorma anterior, in larval Coleoptera, epitorma directed toward apex of epipharynx (T-B, after Böving).

epitorma posterior, in larval Coleoptera, epitorma directed toward base of epipharynx (T-B, after Böving).

epizoon (pl., **epizoa**), ectoparsite, q.v. (T-B).

epizootic, in invertebrate pathology, an outbreak of disease in which there is an unsually large number of cases; a disease or a phase of a disease of high morbidity and one that is only irregularly present in recognizable form (Tulloch, after Philip; Steinhaus and Martignoni) (see panzootic); living or parasitic on animals from the outside or on the surface.

epizootic wave, in invertebrate pathology, a disease phenomenon in animal populations characterized by important attributes, as the number of individual organisms afflicted by a given disease in a certain area, and the manner in which this number increases and decreases in a given period of time (Steinhaus and Martignoni).

epizootiology, the study of diseases of animals on the basis of mass phenomena, i.e., diseases as they occur in groups of animals rather than in the individual animal (Tulloch, after Philip; Steinhaus and Martignoni).

epizygum, (pl., **epizyga**), in some larval Scarabaeoidea (Coleoptera), the elongate plate or bar extending from the zygum toward the cithrum on the right side of the epipharyx (T-B, after Böving).

EPN, $C_{14}H_{14}NO_4PS$, a synthetic insecticide and acaricide; an organo-phosphate, O-ethyl O-p-nitrophenyl phenylphosphonothioate; highly toxic to mammals, acute oral LD_{50} for rats 33 mg/kg (Pfadt).

epoch, in the geological time scale, a subdivision of a period.

epomia, in some adult Hymenoptera, keel located laterally along transverse furrow of pronotum, receiving the front femur (T-B; Gauld and Bolton).

Eproboscidea, Pupipara, q.v. (Grimaldi, pers. comm., after Latreille).

epupillate, destitute of a pupil or central spot; applied to ocellate spots (T-B).

equal, of the same length, size or shape; without superficial inequalities (T-B).

equate, without larger partial elevations or depressions (T-B).

equidistant, the same distance from any 2 or more points (T-B).

equilibrium, in chemistry, the state reached when a reversible reaction is completed and no further reaction takes place (T-B).

equitant, laminated; folding one upon the other (T-B).

EPV, entomopox virus, q.v. (Pfadt).

era, major subdivision of the geological time scale, e.g., Paleozoic Era, Mesozoic Era, and Cenozoic Era.

eradication, in invertebrate pathology, the removal of all recognizable units of the infecting agent from the host; the complete removal, destruction, or extirpation of a living organism from its environment (Steinhaus and Martignoni).

erect, erectus (Latin), upright (T-B; R. W. Brown).

erectile, capable of being erected; applied to an appendage, a hair or other process, or to any tissue which may be distended and made rigid (T-B).

erecto-patent, in the wings of Hesperiidae (Lepidoptera), when at rest, having the forewings erect and the hind wings horizontal (T-B).

ereisma, in Sminthuridae (Collembola), furcula, q.v. (T-B, after Kirby and Spence).

eremochaetus, in Diptera, with a general absence of bristles (T-B).

eremophilous, desert-loving; applied to animals that live in deserts or arid regions (T-B); see xerophilous.

eremosymbiont, a species living in an ant (Hymenoptera: Formicidae) nest, neither taking nor receiving nor contributing to the society, but living in it for protection (Tulloch).

ergatandromorph, an ant (Hymenoptera: Formicidae) which combines some of the characteristics of both ♂ and worker (T-B; Leftwich).

ergatandrous, in ants (Hymenoptera: Formicidae), having workerlike males (T-B).

ergataner, a ♂ ant (Hymenoptera: Formicidae) resembling a worker, because it has lost its wings (T-B; Leftwich).

ergate, in ants (Hymenoptera: Formicidae), worker, q.v. (T-B; Leftwich).

ergatogynandromorph, in ants (Hymenoptera: Formicidae), a mosaic form combining qualities of the ♂ and worker (Tulloch).

ergatogyne, in ants (Hymenoptera: Formicidae), any form morphologically intermediate between the worker and the queen (T-B; Wilson).

ergatogynous, in ants (Hymenoptera: Formicidae), having ergatogynes (T-B).

ergatoid, in Isoptera, ergatoid reproductive, q.v. (Krishna, pers. comm.); in Formicidae (Hymenoptera), ergatogyne, q.v. (T-B; Brown and Taylor, in CSIRO).

ergatoid male, in ants (Hymenoptera: Formicidae), ergatomorphic male, q.v. (Wilson).

ergatoid reproductive, in Isoptera, a supplementary reproductive without a trace of wing buds, usually larval in external form, and with a distinctively rounded head, derived in one or 2 moults from the worker (Miller; Noirot; Wilson).

ergatomorphic male, in ants (Hymenoptera: Formicidae), an individual with normal ♂ genitalia, and a workerlike body (Wilson).

ergatotelic type, in social insects, a group in which only the secondary instincts are manifested in the queen, while the worker retains the primary series in full vigor (T-B, after W. M. Wheeler).

ergonomics, the quantitative study of work, performance, and efficiency (Wilson).

ergosterol, dietary sterol, functioning similarly to cholesterol (Chapman).

ericeticolous, living in poor, sandy or gravelly places (T-B).

Eriocranioidea, single superfamily within the suborder Dacnonypha (Lepidoptera), including the families Acanthopteroctetidae, Eriocraniidae, and Lophocoronidae; larvae leaf mining (Davis; Common, in CSIRO; Borror et al.).

eroded, erose, erosus, gnawed (T-B); of a margin or edge, having irregular teeth and emarginations (T-B).

eruca, a larva, especially a caterpillar (Lepidoptera) (T-B).

eruciform larva, larva resembling a caterpillar or polypod larva in form or appearance, i.e., having a fleshy body, a thin skin, and prolegs or cushion-feet on the abdomen, e.g., larvae of Symphyta (Hymenoptera) (T-B; Leftwich; Gauld and Bolton).

erucina, eruciform larva, q.v. (T-B).

erucivorous, a feeder on caterpillars, as a parasite (T-B).

eruptive cell, spherule cell, q.v. (Tulloch, after Yeager).

erythraeous, erythraeus, red; nearly arterial blood-red (T-B).

erythrine, erythrinus, deep brick-red, tending to blood-red (T-B).

erythroic, erythrous, reddish (T-B).

erythropsin, a coloring substance found in the eyes of night-flying insects impregnating the retinular elements (T-B, after Imms).

erythropterin, red pterine pigment, e.g., in orange-tip butterfly *Anthocharis cardamines* (Lepidoptera: Pieridae) (Chapman).

erythropterine, pterine pigment producing a red color (Tulloch).

escutcheon, in adult Coleoptera, scutellum, q.v. (T-B; Leftwich); a shieldlike covering over the thorax (Leftwich).

escutellate, escutellatus, exscutellate, exscutellatus, having no scutellum (T-B).

esoderma, endocuticle, q.v. (T-B).

esophagus, oesophagus, q.v. (Harbach and Knight).

espundia, dermal disease of man in the New World, caused by *Leishmania brasiliensis* Vianna (Protozoa) transmitted by sand flies, *Lutzomyia* spp. (Diptera: Psychodidae) (Borror et al.; Adkins, pers. comm.).

essential character, specific character, q.v. (T-B).

essentialism, a school of philosophy, originating with Plato and Aristotle, later maintained by the Thomists and so-called realists among the philosophers who believed in the reality of underlying universals or essences; (Mayr); see typological thinking.

establish, to make available under the provisions of the Code (ICZN).

ester, an organic compound formed when an alcohol and an organic acid react (T-B).

estivation, aestivation, q.v. (Leftwich).

ethanol, ethyl alcohol, q.v.

ether, organic compound in which 2 hydrocarbon radicals are joined through an atom of oxygen (Pfadt).

ethion, $C_9H_{22}O_4P_2S_4$, a synthetic insecticide and acaricide; an organophosphate, O,O,O',O'-tetraethyl S,S'-methylene biphosphorodithioate; moderately toxic to mammals, acute oral LD_{50} for rats 96 mg/kg (Pfadt).

Ethiopian Realm, Ethiopian Region, q.v. (Mackerras, after Wallace).

Ethiopian Region, faunal region including Africa south of the Sahara, southern Arabia, and Madagascar (T-B).

ethocline, a series of different behaviors observed among related species and representing stages in a single evolutionary trend (Wilson).

ethology, the study of animal behavior (Matthews and Matthews).

ethoprop, a synthetic, soil insecticide and nematicide; an organophosphate, O-ethyl S,S-dipropyl phosphorodithioate; moderately toxic to mammals, acute oral LD_{50} for rats 62 mg/kg (Pfadt).

ethyl alcohol, C_2H_5OH; grain alcohol; a product of fermentation of sugars; a clear white liquid readily miscible with water in any proportion; used in hardening and preserving animal tissues and to remove water from them for microscopic preparations (T-B); see alcohol.

ethylene dibromide (EDB), a soil and commodity fumigant, insecticidal and nematocidal; heavy liquid with odor of chloroform; 1,2-dibromoethane; moderately toxic to mammals (Pfadt).

Ethyl Guthion (trade name), anizophosethyl, q.v. (Pfadt).

ethylene glycol, $C_2H_6O_2$; a polyhydric alcohol used in automobile antifreeze and in collection fluids used in various insect traps.

etiolated, whitened or bleached from lack of sunlight or from disease (T-B).

etiological agent, the cause of disease in plants and animals (T-B); see pathogen.

etiology, the study of the causes of disease (Steinhaus and Martignoni).

etymology, the origin and development of a word; the study of origin and development of words.

ET$_{50}$, median effective time, q.v. (Steinhaus and Martignoni).

eucaryotes, organisms with well-developed nucleus and meiosis (Mayr); see procaryotes.

eucephalic head capsule, in most larvae of Nematocera (Diptera), a well-developed, fully exposed head capsule with mandibles usually bearing teeth and operating in a horizontal or oblique plane (Teskey, after Brauer, in McAlpine).

eucephalous larva, an apodous larva with a well-developed head capsule, e.g., Nematocera (Diptera), Coleoptera (Buprestidae and Cerambycidae), and Aculeata (Hymenoptera) (T-B; Chapman); see acephalous larva and hemicephalous larva.

Eucinetiformia, a group within the Polyphaga (Coleoptera) that includes the single superfamily Eucinetoidea (Crowson).

Eucinetoidea, a superfamily within the Eucinetiformia that includes Clambidae, Eucinetidae, and Scirtidae (Crowson).

eucoiliform larva, in Hymenoptera with a hypermetamorphosis, e.g., Eucoilidae, a primary larva with 3 pairs of long thoracic appendages and without the cephalic process and girdle of setae of the teleaform larva (T-B, after Imms); a stage in which a fairly advanced protopod larva emerges from the egg (T-B, after Wardle; Gauld and Bolton).

eucone eyes, eucone ommatidia, q.v. (T-B, after Snodgrass).

eucone ommatidia, ommatidia in which a crystalline cone is present, produced by 4 Semper cells (Chapman).

eucoxa, the anterior division of the insect coxa (T-B, after Crampton); in adult Diptera, anterior region of midcoxa excluding the meron (McAlpine).

Eudermaptera, suborder of Dermaptera, containing the families Spongiphoridae (Labiidae), Chelisochidae, and Forficulidae (Steinmann; Sakai, pers. comm.); see Catadermaptera.

eudextral, in ♂ Coleoptera, morphologically belonging to the right side (Lindroth and Palmén).

Eudiptera, the living two-winged Diptera (Rohdendorf).

eudorsal, in ♂ Coleoptera, morphologically dorsal (Tuxen, after Lindroth and Palmén).

Eugnatha, Helminthomorpha, q.v. (Borror et al.).

Euheteroptera, subdivision of the Heteroptera including the Dipsocoromorpha, Neoheteroptera, and Panheteroptera; see Enicocephalomorpha (Schuh, after Štys).

Euholognatha, infraorder of Plecoptera, within the suborder Arctoperlaria, including the Nemouroidea and the family Scopuridae (Zwick, in Hennig).

eulabium, prementum, q.v. (T-B).

Eumecoptera, a suborder sometimes recognized within the Mecoptera, including the recent families Boreidae, Notiothaumidae, Panorpidae, Panorpodidae, Choristidae, Nannochoristidae, Apteropanorpidae, and Bittacidae, and the extinct families Permopanorpidae, Mesopanorpodidae, Mesochoristidae, and Permotipulidae, possessing adults with the cubitus anterior (CuA) simple (not forked) in the fore- and hind wing (Riek, in CSIRO; Penny, pers. comm.).

Eumegasecoptera, suborder of the extinct order Megasccoptera, including the families Brodiidae, Aspidothoracidae, Bardohymenidae, Foririidae, Protohymenidae, Scytohymenidae, Sphecopteridae, Mischopteridae, Ischnoptilidae, and Corydaloididae, possessing wings that could not be flexed backward over the abdomen (Brues et al.); see Paramegasecoptera.

eumegetic, applied to the intermediate forms in a series of insects exhibiting polymorphism (Tulloch).

Eumetabola, hypothesized monophyletic group including the Paraneoptera and Holometabola (Hennig).

eunotum, the wing-bearing plate of the notum, anterior to the postnotum (T-B, after Crampton); in adult Diptera, larger anterior, wing-bearing plate of mesonotum (Colless and McAlpine, in CSIRO).

Euorthoptera, the orthopteroid orders, excluding Dermaptera (T-B).

Eupaleodictyoptera, suborder of Paleodictyoptera, possessing mandibulate mouthparts (Riek, in CSIRO).

euphallic organs, in ♂ insects, embryologically homogenous entity different from pseudophallic organs and derived from larval penis lobes situated ventrally between abdominal segments IX and X, in Paraneoptera (Acercaria, q.v.) and Holometabola divided into 4 lobes, the 2 median combining to form the phallus, the 2 lateral forming parameres (transl. "organes euphalliques" Dupuis, after Tuxen).

euplantula (pl., **euplantulae**), padlike structures on the ventral surface of the tarsal subsegments (T-B, after Snodgrass).

eupleuron (pl., **eupleura**), anapleurite, q.v. (T-B, after Crampton).

Euplexoptera, Dermaptera, q.v. (T-B).

Euprotodonata, name proposed for a group including the extinct families Protagriidae and Calvertiellidae, more recently included within the Paleodictyoptera (Hennig, after Carpenter).

Eupsocida, Psocomorpha, q.v. (Borror et al., after Roesler).

eurazygos, in ♂ Coleoptera, the enlarged distal part of the azygos containing the internal sac (if present) and outer wall of the genital tube, from the ostium of the penis (orifice of ductus ejaculatorius) to the base of the tube ("second connecting membrane") (Tuxen).

eurazygotic portion, eurazygos, q.v. (Tuxen).

European foulbrood, a disease of larval honey bees caused by *Strepto-*

coccus pluton (White), with mortality being high among four- and five-day-old larvae (Steinhaus and Martignoni).

European wheat striate mosaic, disease of wheat caused by a tenuivirus transmitted propagatively by *Javesella* (Hemiptera: Auchenorrhyncha: Delphacidae) (Nault and Ammar).

eury-, prefix; wide range of tolerance (Tulloch).

eurygamous, as applied to Culicidae (Diptera), those requiring large cages for mating, i.e., the swarming flight of the males a necessity; see stenogamous (Tulloch, after Roubaud).

eurygamy, being unable to mate in a confined space, e.g., many Diptera that must swarm (Leftwich).

euryhaline, able to tolerate a wide range of degrees of salinity (Allaby).

Eurypterida, extinct subclass of Merostomata from the Cambrian Period to the Carboniferous Periods within the Paleozoic Era, including aquatic forms with 5 pairs of leglike appendages; a pair each of simple and compound eyes; 12-segmented opisthosoma; platelike appendages concealing gills on the first 5 segments; and lacking an elongate telson (Borror et al.).

eurythermal, capable of living throughout a wide range of temperatures (Tulloch).

euryvalent organism, one that because of its adaptations is able to meet a wide variety of environmental conditions (Tulloch).

eusinistral, in ♂ Coleoptera, morphologically belonging to the left side (Tuxen, after Lindroth and Palmén).

eusocial, applied to the condition or to the group possessing it in which individuals display all of the following traits: cooperation in caring for the young; reproductive division of labor, with more or less sterile individuals working on behalf of individuals engaged in reproduction; and overlap of at least 2 generations of life stages capable of contributing to colony labor (Wilson).

eusternum, the intrasegmental ventral plate of a thoracic segment exclusive of the spinasternum, but usually including the sternopleurites (T-B, after Snodgrass); a large sclerite of variable shape frequently extending laterally and upward into the pleural region (T-B, after Imms); the anterior sternite of the sternum (T-B, after Wardle); in larval Coleoptera, the anterior sternal area in front of the suture between the furcal pits (Böving and Craighead).

Eusthenioidea, superfamily of Plecoptera, including the Eustheniidae and Diamphipnoidae, in which the marginal contour of the anojugal fan of the hind wing is continuous with the rest of the wing and in which crossveins are present all over the anojugal fan (Zwick, pers. comm.).

eustipes, basistipes, stipes, q.v. (T-B, after MacGillivray).

Eutracheata, applied to those Arthropoda, including the Insecta, which have a well-developed tracheal system (T-B); see Tracheata.

eutrochantin, coxopleurite, q.v. (T-B, after Crampton).

eutrophapsis, in social insects, the habit in which the ♀ brings prey or food to the young in a previously prepared nest (Tulloch, after Gaul).

eutrophication, the process of enrichment of a body of water in dissolved nutrients either naturally or artificially (Pfadt).

euventral, in ♂ Coleoptera, morphologically ventral (Tuxen, after Lindroth and Palmén).

evacuate, to illiminate waste products of digestion, per anus (T-B).

evacuating fluid, in ampulla of spermatophore in *Acheta* (Orthoptera: Gryllidae), fluid with a low osmotic pressure in an outer reservoir, functioning to force sperm out of the ampulla (Chapman, after Khalifa).

evacuation, the act of eliminating waste products from the digestive system (T-B).

evaginable, eversible, q.v. (T-B).

evaginate, evert, q.v. (T-B).

evagination, an outpocketing, or a saclike structure on the outside (T-B; Borror et al.); see invagination.

evanescent, disappearing; becoming gradually less, fading (T-B).

Evanioidea, superfamily within the suborder Apocrita (Hymenoptera), including the families Evaniidae, Aulacidae, and Gasteruptiidae, including adult flies with a hind wing lacking closed cells, pronotum without a dorsal surface in median area extending back above tegulae, no subantennal groove, and spurs on hind tibia not modified for preening (Riek, in CSIRO).

evaporative area, in Heteroptera (Hemiptera), evaporatorium, q.v. (Štys, pers. comm.).

evaporatorium, in Heteroptera (Hemiptera), the part of cuticle associated with the orifice (and/or ostiolar groove, auricle), modified for assistance in rapid evaporation of scent gland products, provided with a specialized microsculpture, and, in the case of adult metathoracic scent glands, occupying a varying portion of thoracic pleuron (Štys, pers. comm.).

eversible, capable of being turned outward or inside out (T-B).

eversible gland, in adult Saldidae (Hemiptera: Heteroptera), a gland located in the intersegmental membrane at the posterolateral margin of sternum VII (Cobben).

eversible membrane, in ♂ Lepidoptera, vesica, q.v. (Tuxen, after Chapman).

eversible sac, in Hypogastruridae (Collembola), bilobed, saclike structure appearing ventrally between antennal segments 3 and 4 (Maynard); in ♂ Grylloblattodea, sac connected with or forming part of left phallomere (Tuxen, after Walker); in some ♂ Megaloptera, utriculi, q.v. (Tuxen, after Acker).

eversible vesicles, in Collembola, a pair of sacs at the tip of the ventral tube that are everted by blood pressure from within the body and are withdrawn by retractor muscles (Chapman); see exsertile vesicles.

evident, easily seen or recognized (T-B).

evolutionary biology, branch of organismal biology focusing on patterns and mechanisms of evolutionary change, e.g., population genetics; see ecology and taxonomy.

evolutionary classification, a form of natural classification which recognizes both paraphyletic and monophyletic taxa (Mayr).

evolutionary success, relative success (measured as number of species or some other variable) between sister groups which began their evolutionary development with the same holomorphological and ecological endowment of their common stem species and which subsequently continue to have the same opportunities available for their development (Hennig).

evolutionary taxonomy, natural classification, q.v. (T-B).

ex-, Latin prefix; out of; proceeding from (T-B; Harris).

ex larva, from or out of the larva, being usually applied to specimens that have been bred from larvae (T-B).

ex ovum (pl., **ex ova**), from or out of the egg; applied to specimens that have been bred from the egg stage (T-B).

ex parte (Latin), in part (T-B).

examinium, in adult Hymenoptera, ventral ptyche, q.v. (Tuxen, after Ross).

exarate, exaratus (Latin), ploughed; sculpted; furrowed; sulcated; an excavated surface in general (T-B; Harris, after R. W. Brown, and Funk); see impressed.

exarate pupa, a type of pupa in which the legs and wings are free from the body and the abdomen is moveable, such that the pupa is capable of limited locomotion (T-B; Leftwich).

exarticulate, exarticulatus (Latin), without distinct joints (T-B).

exarticulate antenna, a one-segmented antenna (T-B).

exasperate, exasperatus (Latin), asperate, q.v. (T-B; Harris).

excalcarate, excalcaratus, without spurs (T-B).

excaudate, ecaudate, q.v. (T-B).

excavate, excavatus (Latin), excavated, q.v. (T-B; Harris).

excavated, with a scooped out depression; superficially, with a hollowed out area (Harris, after Funk, and Marchant and Charles); see lacunose.

excentric, not in the center; revolving or arranged about a point that is not central (T-B).

excind, excindate, having an angular notch on an end (T-B).

excised, with a deep cut or notch (T-B); cut out of (T-B).

excision, a deep cut (T-B); a notch or other cut-out part (T-B).

excluded name, a scientific name that under the Code cannot be an avaiable name (ICZN).

excrementaceous, excrementitious, excrementous, made up of or resembling excrement or feces (T-B).

excrescence, an outgrowth or elevation; usually abnormal (T-B).

excreta, the waste products eliminated by an insect, principally from digestion (T-B); feces, q.v.

excretion, the act of getting rid of products of metabolism by storing them in an insoluble form or by removing them from the body (T-B; Tulloch); see storage excretion.

excretory organs, those structures concerned with ridding the body of waste products, including the ileum, labial glands, Malpighian tubules, midgut, nephrocytes, and rectum (T-B; Chapman).

excretory system, excretory organs, q.v. (Gilmour, in CSIRO).

excurrent, attenuate, narrowly prolonged (T-B).

excurved, excurvus, curved outward (T-B).

exflagellation, the protrusion of threadlike daughter cells from the microgametocyte of the protozoan *Plasmodium* (Plasmodiidae) (Tulloch).

exite, an outer lobe of any limb segment (T-B, after Snodgrass).

exo-, Greek prefix; on the outside of; without, in the same sense (T-B).

exochorion, thick outer, ectodermal layer of the shell or chorion of an insects egg, variously shaped and sculptured and having a small hole or micropyle at one end (T-B; Leftwich).

exocone eye, compound eye composed of exocone ommatidia (T-B, after Imms; Leftwich).

exocone ommatidia, ommatidia in which the corneal lens is biconcave with a long cone-shaped projection on the inside and the Semper cells do not form a crystalline cone, but extend inwards to the retinula cells as slender refractile strands, e.g., in Elateridae and Lampyridae (Coleoptera) (Chapman); see acone and eucone ommatidia.

exocorium, in Heteroptera (Hemiptera), that part of the corium anterior to the radius (T-B; Štys); see embolium and cuneus.

exocrine gland, gland whose secretions are discharged through a duct or tube (Tulloch); cluster of secretory cells whose products are discharged outside of the body (Matthews and Matthews; Chapman); see endocrine gland.

exocuticle, outer, melanized and sclerotized portion of cuticle that is absent at points of articulation or flexion (Tulloch; Chapman).

exocuticula, exocuticle, q.v. (T-B).

exocytosis, hormone released from the axon ending when the membrane of a neurosecretory vesicle fuses with the axon membrane (Chapman).

exoderm, exoderma, exocuticle, q.v. (T-B).

exodont mandibles, in some adult Apocrita (Hymenoptera), e.g., Mymarommatidae, Vanhoriidae, and some Braconidae, spatulate and outcurved mandibles (Gauld and Bolton).

exoloma, apical margin, q.v., of the wing (T-B).

exophytic, relating to the outside of plant tissue (T-B); feeding on living plant tissues externally, from outside the plant (Gauld and Bolton); see endophytic.

exophytic oviposition, a form of oviposition in Anisoptera (Odonata), in which the rounded eggs are either dropped freely into the water or attached superficially to water plants (T-B, after Imms).

exopodite, the outer branch of a biramous appendage (Borror et al.); the segment on the outer aspect of the basipodite in Crustacea (T-B); the third segment of a maxillary palp (T-B).

Exoporia, an infraorder of Glossata (Lepidoptera), comprising the superfamilies of Mnesarchaeoidea and Hepialoidea, possessing ♀ genitalia of the exoporian type and ♂ without a sclerotized aedoeagus (Kristensen; Common).

exoporian type of genitalia, in ♀ Hepialoidea and Mnesarchaeoidea (Lepidoptera: Exoporia), vagina and ductus bursae open separately, and are connected by an external groove along which spermatozoa pass (Tuxen, after Bourgogne; Common, in CSIRO); see monotrysian and ditrysian types of genitalia.

Exopteraria, Exopterygota, q.v. (T-B).

Exopterygota, exopterygote orders, q.v. (Borror et al.), but occasionally excluding the Paleoptera (Mackerras, in CSIRO).

exopterygote, having exopterygote wing development (Borror et al.); see endopterygote.

exopterygote orders, orders within the Pterygota, including the Paleoptera, Polyneoptera, and Paraneoptera possessing exopterygote wing development and incomplete metamorphosis (Mackerras, in CSIRO).

exopterygote wing development, type of wing growth in Paleoptera, Polyneoptera, and Paraneoptera, in which the wings develop, usually progressively, in external sheaths that lie on the dorsal surface of the body of the nymph (Hinton and Mackerras, in CSIRO).

exopterygotous, of or pertaining to the Exopterygota (T-B); having wings develop externally (T-B).

exoskeletal plates, sclerites, q.v. (T-B).

exoskeleton, the external skeleton consisting of hard cuticle, to the inner side of which muscles are attached (T-B; Leftwich).

exosoma, in ♂ Heteroptera (Hemiptera), phallotheca, q.v. (Tuxen, after Leston).

exotic, not a native of the place where found (T-B); an introduced species (T-B); also, any species occurring in any country outside of the limits of the country whose fauna is under consideration (T-B).

exotoky, ovipary, q.v. (T-B).

exotoxins, in invertebrate pathology, poisonous substances produced by the microbial cell and liberated into the surrounding environment, without destruction of the cell (Steinhaus and Martignoni); see endotoxins.

expalpate, expalpatus (Latin), without palpi (T-B).

expanded, spread or flattened out; applied to Lepidoptera when set for the cabinet, with the wings spread; also to any other insect so set (T-B).

expanse, the distance between the apices or other widest point of the wings when fully spread (T-B).

expansion skating, in Gerroidea (Hemiptera: Heteroptera), the dispersing of fluid (probably saliva) onto the water surface, which lowers the surface tension causing the insect to move much more rapidly than is otherwise possible (Andersen).

expiratory, relating to the act of expiration, when the abdomen is contracted and the air contained in the abdominal tracheae is presumably forced out (T-B).

explanate, explanatus, spread out and flattened; applied to a margin (T-B).

explant, an excised fragment of a tissue or an organ used to initiate an *in vitro* culture (Steinhaus and Martignoni).

explicate, unfolded or open; without folds or plicae (T-B; Harris); see plicate.

exploratory learning, latent learning, q.v. (Matthews and Matthews).

exploratory trail, an odor trail laid more or less continuously by the advance workers of a foraging group, being a kind of communication used regularly by army ants (Hymenoptera: Formicidae) (Wilson); see recruitment trail.

explosive cell, spherule cell, q.v. (Tulloch, after Hardy).

exposed, visible; the opposite of concealed (T-B).

exsculptate, exsculptus (Latin), with irregular, more or less longitudinal depressions, as if carved or scooped out (T-B; Harris, after Marchant and Charles).

exscutellate, exscutellatus (Latin), having no scutellum (T-B).

exserted, exsertus (Latin), projecting; thrust forth (T-B; R. W. Brown).

exsertile, possible to exsert or extrude (T-B).

exsertile vesicles, paired vesicles inside of bases of legs on most segments in Symphyla (Myriapoda) and on venter of abdominal segments in Protura, Diplura, Archaeognatha, and Zygentoma, capable of absorbing water from the substrate (Mackerras; Wallace and Mackerras; Watson, all in CSIRO; Sturm, after Bitsch); see eversible vesicles.

exsertion, a protrusion (T-B); an extension of a line or other ornamentation beyond its ordinary course (T-B).

extant, of a taxon having living representatives (ICZN); of a specimen still in existence (ICZN).

extended, spread out (T-B); not lying one upon the other (T-B).

extending, reaching or attaining to (T-B).

extense, extensus, extended; expanded (T-B).

extensile, extensible, capable of being stretched or drawn out (T-B).

extension of sacculus, in ♂ Noctuidae (Lepidoptera), apical process of sacculus (Tuxen, after Pierce).

extension plate, unguitractor, q.v. (T-B).

extension sole, pulvillus, q.v. (T-B).

extenso-tendon, the tendon to which the extensor tendons are attached (T-B, after MacGillivray).

extensor muscle, one which extends or straightens out an appendage or structure (T-B).

extensor row, in adult Diptera, a row of bristles on the upper surface of the femur (T-B, after Comstock).

extenuate, to make or to become weak, thin or slender (T-B).

exterior edge, costal margin, q.v., of wing (T-B).

exterior margin, apical margin, q.v., or costal margin, q.v., of wing (T-B).

exterior palpi, maxillary palpi, q.v. (T-B).

exterior paramere, in ♂ Hymenoptera, gonostylus, q.v. (Tuxen, after Priesner).

external, belonging to or on the outside (T-B).

external apodeme, in ♂ Culicidae (Diptera), an apodematous basal continuation of the external or lateral sclerotization of the gonocoxite (Harbach and Knight, after Barraud).

external area, in adult Apocrita (Hymenoptera), the upper of the 3 areas of the propodeum, between the median and lateral longitudinal carinae (T-B); see area.

external chiasma, outer chiasma, q.v. (T-B, after Needham).

external genitalia, genitalia, q.v. (T-B, after Snodgrass); in Muscomorpha (Diptera), the genital segment (andrium) and its associated structures (Griffiths).

external lobe of posterior gonopod, in ♀ Psocoptera, valvae externae, q.v. (Tuxen, after Pearman).

external lobes, in ♂ Coleoptera, basal piece, q.v. (Tuxen).

external median area, in Hymenoptera, the median of the 3 areas between the median and lateral longitudinal carinae; the second lateral area (T-B).

external medullary mass, epiopticon, q.v. (T-B).

external paramera, all the genital appendages (except the internal) of the ♂ (T-B).

external parameres, in ♂ Psocoptera, parameres, q.v. (Tuxen, after Badonnel).

external process, in some ♂ *Culex* (Diptera: Culicidae), main part of the lateral plate where an internal process is distinguishable (Harbach and Knight, after Sirivanakarn).

external respiration, the process of transferring the respiratory gases through the body wall; taking place in insects through thin areas of the ectoderm, either at the body surface or in the walls of evaginations (gills) or invaginations (tracheae) (T-B, after Snodgrass).

external wall, in ♂ Heteroptera (Hemiptera), external wall of phallus surrounding ductus seminis, (transl. "Aussenwand" Kullenberg, after Tuxen).

externomedian nerve, the humeral and discoidal veins together (T-B).

exteroceptor, a sense organ located externally for the perception of external stimuli (T-B).

extinct, of a taxon having no living representatives (ICZN).

extrachorion, the outer coating of the egg secreted in the common oviduct of Acrididae (Orthoptera) and in other insects (Cobben, after Hartley); see suprachorionic layers.

extraembryonic, lying outside of the embryo (T-B).

extraembryonic field, see serosa, dorsal blastoderm (T-B).

extraerythrocytic stage, cryptozoite, q.v. (Tulloch).

extraepicardial, without, or outside of, the epicardium (T-B).

extrafloral nectaries, in plants, any structure outside of a flower that secretes nectar (T-B).

extragenital insemination, in many Cimicoidea (Hemiptera: Heteroptera), traumatic insemination, q.v., occurring outside the genital region (Carayon, in Usinger).

extraintestinal, outside of the intestine (T-B).

extranidal, outside the nest or hive (Tulloch).

extraocular, remote from or beyond the eyes (T-B).

extraocular antennae, those inserted on the outside of the eyes, or set very distant from the eyes (T-B).

extraoral, outside of or beyond the mouth (T-B).

extraoral cavity, preoral cavity, q.v. (T-B).

extraoral digestion, external digestion in which saliva containing digestive enzymes is either placed on or injected into food, followed by sucking up of soluble products (Gilmour, in CSIRO).

extremity, the point most removed from the base (T-B).

extrinsic, extraneous; external; not in or of a body (T-B).

extrinsic articulation, a type of articulation in which the articulating surfaces are areas of contact on the outside of the skeletal parts (T-B; Snodgrass).

extrorse, extrorsum, toward the outside (T-B).

extrude, to turn or force out (T-B).

extrusion, the act of pushing or forcing out (T-B).

exudate, exudation, q.v. (T-B).

exudation, secretion or modified excretory product from exocrine glands (Leftwich).

exudatoria, in Pseudomyrminae among ants (Hymenoptera: Formicidae), and in certain termites (Isoptera), special papillae or appendages in the larva which exude a secretion highly acceptable to their adult worker nurses (T-B, after Imms); fingerlike appendages found on the larvae of certain ant species (Hymenoptera: Formicidae), and on a variety of termitophiles, presumably producing secretions attractive to ant or termite (Isoptera) workers (Wilson).

exude, to ooze or flow slowly through minute openings (T-B).

exuviae, (sing. and pl.), the caste skin of larvae or nymphs at ecdysis (T-B, after Tillyard; Leftwich); in the Diaspididae (Hemiptera: Sternorrhyncha), the larval skin when caste and incorporated into the scale (T-B, after J. B. Smith); in some Diptera, puparium, q.v. (Leftwich).

exuvial droplets, in larval *Calpodes* (Lepidoptera: Hesperiidae), electron-dense droplets secreted during the production of the procuticle, probably containing inactive precursors of the moulting enzymes (Chapman, after Locke and Krishnan).

exuvial fluid, moulting fluid, q.v. (Leftwich).

exuvial glands, moulting glands, q.v. (T-B).

exuvial space, space between epidermis and cuticle after apolysis (Chapman).

exuviate, to undergo ecdysis (T-B); see moulting.

exuviation, ecdysis, q.v. (T-B).

eye, compound eye, q.v., or ocellus, q.v. (T-B).

eye bridge, in some adult Nematocera, e.g., Sciaridae and Cecidomyiidae (Diptera), narrow row of facets above the antennae connecting the 2 compound eyes (Colless and McAlpine, in CSIRO; McAlpine).

eye cap, in some adult Lepidoptera, laterally expanded and curved scape of antenna (T-B, after Comstock; Common, in CSIRO).

eye index, in adult Lepidoptera, a relative measurement of the vertical diameter of the compound eye divided by the height of the frons (Powell).

eye of color, an ocellate spot, q.v. (T-B).

eye patch, in Collembola, laterodorsal pigmented area on the head surrounding the group of eyes (Christiansen and Bellinger).

eye spots, eyelike markings commonly found on the wings of Lepidoptera, some Fulgoridae (Hemiptera: Auchenorrhyncha), and other insects (Matthews and Matthews; O'Brien, pers. comm.); a rudimentary ocellus (T-B).

eyelike glands, in Coccoidea (Hemiptera: Sternorrhyncha), cicatrices, q.v. (T-B).

eyepiece micrometer, a linear scale in the field of vision of the eyepiece (or one of a pair of eyepieces) of a microscope for use as a measuring device (Mayr).

eyes, the organs of sight; in insects composed of numerous facets, set one on each side of the head; the term is properly applied to compound eyes only, but is sometimes used to designate the simple eyes or ocelli also (T-B).

F

face, in adult Diptera, anterior frons below the antennae, bounded laterally by the compound eyes and ventrally by the frontoclypeal suture, or if this is absent, by the level of the anterior tentorial pits (T-B or anterior margin of the oral cavity, after Curran; Colless and McAlpine, in CSIRO; McAlpine); the upper or outer surface of any part or appendage; the front of the head between the compound eyes about the mouth to the vertex, usually being applied to insects in which the head is vertical (T-B); in Ephemeroptera, a fusion of the front and the vertex; in adult Hymenoptera, the area between the mouth margin and the median ocellus (T-B; Gauld and Bolton).

facet, corneal facet, q.v., of compound eye (T-B).

facetted eye, compound eye, q.v. (T-B).

facial, of the vertical anterior surface of the head (Christiansen and Bellinger).

facial angle, the angles formed by the junctions of the face and vertex (T-B).

facial bristles, in adult Diptera, supravibrissal setae, q.v. (T-B).

facial carina, in adult Diptera, especially Schizophora, median ridge separating antennal grooves (T-B; McAlpine).

facial depression, antennal groove, q.v. (T-B).

facial fovea, in adult bees (Hymenoptera: Apoidea), a depressed area lateral of torulus in the perocular area (Eickwort, pers. comm., after Michener).

facial impression, in adult Diptera, genal groove, q.v. (McAlpine).

facial mask, in larval Muscomorpha (Diptera), a simple or complex pattern of grooves on the ventral surface of the head segment that channel food toward the mouth (Ferrar).

facial orbits, in adult Hymenoptera, the lateral margins of the lower face adjacent to the eyes (T-B, after MacGillivray; Gauld and Bolton); see frontal orbits.

facial plate, in adult Diptera, central portion of face between the frontogenal sutures (T-B, after Curran; McAlpine).

facial quadrangle, in bees (Hymenoptera: Apoidea), the quadrangle bounded laterally by the eyes, above by a line between their summits and below by a similar line between their lower points (T-B).

facial ridge, in adult Schizophora (Diptera: Brachycera), often convex and usually narrow strip between the inner margin of each parafacial and the corresponding frontogenal suture (T-B, after J. B. Smith; McAlpine).

facial tubercle, in adult Diptera, facial carina, q.v. (T-B).

facial warp, in adult Diptera, genal groove, q.v. (McAlpine).

facialium (pl. **facialia**), in adult Diptera, facial ridge, q.v. (T-B, after Comstock).

facies, general appearance of a species, genus or group of insects (T-B).

facilitation, social facilitation, q.v. (Wilson); the passage of nerve impulses over a specific channel of synaptic connections once a given reflex has been established (Tulloch).

facioorbital bristles, in adult Diptera, frontoorbital setae, q.v. (T-B, after Comstock).

facultative diapause, a diapause in multivoltine insects usually induced by decreasing photoperiod and temperature and terminated by increasing photoperiod and temperature (Common).

facultative parasite, a parasite that changes its host (T-B); an organism which normally exists as a free-living form but which under certain conditions may adopt a parasitic mode of life (Tulloch).

facultative slavery, the making of slaves by ants who can survive without slaves (Tulloch).

fade time, the interval between release of a pheromone and disappearance from the active space (Matthews and Matthews).

faeces, feces, q.v. (Chapman).

fairy shrimp, a member of the Anostraca (Crustacea: Branchiopoda) (Borror et al.).

falcate, falcatus (Latin), sickle-shaped, hooked (T-B; R. W. Brown); of a wing, when deeply excavated below the apex so as to have the latter acute and a little curved (T-B).

falciform, falcate, q.v. (T-B).

falciform setae, in ♂ Chironomidae (Diptera), lamellate setae of median volsella gradually narrowed to a point and curved scythelike (Saether).

falling reflex, a reflex action by which a falling insect will, in a short distance, right itself so that it will land on its feet or adopt a suitable position for flying (Leftwich).

fallopian tubes, oviduct, q.v. (T-B; Snodgrass).

falsadentes, in adult Diptera, prestomal teeth, q.v. (T-B, after MacGillivray).

false claspers, in ♂ Lepidoptera, ramus, q.v. (Tuxen, after Burgess).

false comb, in adult Siphonaptera, spiniform, innervated, spinelike bristles, arranged in a comblike row (Rothschild and Traub).

false head, among larval Syrphidae (Diptera), a broad globose or hood-like cephalic segment or segments with a visible constriction behind them (Peterson, after Heiss).

false legs, prolegs, q.v., or pseudopodia, q.v. (T-B; Leftwich).

false ovipositor, in ♀ Trichoptera, abdominal segment IX when slender and retractile (Tuxen).

false spiracles, in Nepidae (Hemiptera: Heteroptera), 3 pairs of sievelike structures on the connexiva of abdominal sterna III–V near the spiracles but unconnected with the tracheal system (T-B).

false stem mothers, in Adelgidae (Hemiptera: Sternorrhyncha), sistentes, q.v. (Stoetzel, pers. comm.).

false vein, in adult Diptera, esp. Nematocera, foldlike thickenings (usually concave) in the wing membrane between the main veins (McAlpine); in adult Leptoceridae (Trichoptera), an apparent posterior branch of media (MP) close to the stem of cubitus (Cu) in the hind wings (Morse, pers. comm.).

falx (pl. **falces**), in adult Siphonaptera, an internal thickening of the body wall, extending over the vertex from one antennal groove to the other (T-B, after Comstock); in ♂ Lycaenidae (Lepidoptera), one of a pair of heavily sclerotized, curved or angulate arms, articulated with caudal margin of tegumen ventrad of base of uncus (if present) and extending ventrocaudad, probably homologous with a gnathos in which the arms remain separate, and, therefore, derived from sternum X (Tuxen, after Bethune-Baker).

fambresia, yaws, q.v. (Adkins, pers. comm.).

family (pl., **families**), a rank within the family group between superfamily and subfamily (ICZN); a taxon at the rank of family (ICZN).

family group, in the hierachy of classification, the highest ranking group of taxa whose names are regulated by the Code, including taxa at the ranks of superfamily, family, subfamily, tribe, and any other rank below superfamily and above the genus group that may be required, such as subtribe (ICZN).

family-group name, a scientific name of any taxon of the family group (ICZN).

family name, a scientific name of a taxon of the rank of family (ICZN); ending in -idae.

famphur, $C_{10}H_{16}NO_2PS_2$, a synthetic insecticide, animal systemic; an organophosphate, O-[p-(dimethylsulfamoyl)phenyl] O,O-dimethyl phosphorothioate; acute oral LD_{50} for rats 35 to 62 mg/kg (Pfadt).

farctus, fully filled (T-B).

farinaceous, farinaceus (Latin), mealy or powdery looking; applied to surfaces of wings (T-B; Harris, after Marchant and Charles); see farinose, pollinose, pruinose, pulverulent, and rorulent.

farinose, farinosus (Latin), dotted with many single flourlike spots; mealy (T-B; Harris); see farinaceous, pollinose, pruinose, pulverulent, and rorulent.

farnesol, terpene showing juvenile hormone activity (Borror et al.).

fascia, a transverse band or broad line; termed common when it crosses both wings or wing covers (T-B).

fasciate, fasciatus (Latin), with a broad transverse stripe or band (T-B).

fascicle, in adult Culicidae (Diptera), the closely appressed bundle of 6 needlelike mouthparts (stylets), including the labrum, 2 mandibles, 2 laciniae, and the hypopharynx, which form the piercing-siphoning apparatus (Harbach and Knight, in Robinson).

facicula (pl., **fasciculae**), a bundle of muscle fibers (T-B).

fasciculate, fasciculatus, bundled; clustered as in a bundle; tufted; superficially covered with bundles of long hair (T-B).

fasciculate antenna, one in which every joint has a distinct pencil or fascicule of long hairs (T-B).

fasciculus, in ♂ *Aedia* (Lepidoptera: Ethmiidae), type of cornuti (Tuxen, after Roepke).

fastigial, of or pertaining to, or of the nature of, a fastigium (T-B).

fastigiate, fastigiatus (Latin), flat-topped and of equal height (T-B); of elytra, extending a little beyond the abdomen (T-B).

fastigium, in many Orthoptera, anterior part of vertex projecting anteriorly beyond eyes (T-B; Key, in CSIRO); a prominent angle between the vertex and face (T-B, after Imms).

fat, any of numerous esters composed of fatty acids, e.g., triglycerides and phospholipids (Gilmour, in CSIRO).

fat body, loosely aggregated or compact masses of cells, being primarily trophocytes, enclosed in a membranous sheath and freely suspended in the hemocoel so that they are intimately bathed by the blood, functioning in food storage, general metabolism, and in storage excretion (T-B; Leftwich; Chapman).

fat cell, trophocyte, q.v. (T-B).

fatigue, exhaustion from stimuli following each other too rapidly to permit complete recovery of nerve-tone or irritability (T-B).

fatiscent, with superficial cracks, crevices, or similar openings (T-B; Harris, after Marchant and Charles); see corticinus, fissate, and rimose.

fatty acids, acids combined to form a fat (Gilmour, in CSIRO).

fauna, the animal life of a region (T-B; Mayr); see biota and flora.

faveolate, alveolate, q.v. (Harris).

favose, favosus (Latin), **favous,** alveolate, q.v. (T-B; Harris).

favus (Latin), honeycomb, q.v. (R. W. Brown); a cell like that of a honeycomb (T-B).

feature, character, q.v.

fecal, of or pertaiing to the feces or excrement (T-B).

fecal pellets, in Kalotermitidae and Termopsidae (Isoptera), dessicated feces in the form of hexagonal prisms, which correspond to the shape of the rectum (Krishna, pers. comm.).

feces, excrement; waste expelled from the anus (T-B); see frass.

fecifork, in certain larval Coleoptera and Lepidoptera, anal comb, q.v. (Leftwich).

fecula, the excrement of insects (T-B).

fecundation, fertilization, q.v. (T-B).

fecundation canal, in ♀ Heteroptera (Hemiptera), a slender, usually weakly sclerotized, tube running along the dorsal wall of the common oviduct from the gynatrial sac to point of entrance into the common oviduct; divided into the basal thickening and the fecundation pump; coiled duct, diverticulum ductus, q.v. (Tuxen, after Scudder; Andersen).

fecundation pump, in some ♀ Gerromorpha (Hemiptera: Heteroptera), a widened area of the fecundation canal provided with a pair of plate like flanges.

fecundity, the average number of eggs laid by an insect (Leftwich).

feeble, feebly, not strongly; not markedly; slightly; scarcely noticeable (T-B).

feeler, a tactile organ (T-B); see antenna and palpus.

feet, legs, q.v. (T-B); see foot.

felt chamber, in Diptera larvae, a spongy structure within the spiracular chamber which seemingly acts as an air filter (Tulloch, after Richards; Teskey, in McAlpine); in pupal Chironomidae (Diptera), that part of the respiratory atrium which is a tubular continuation of the tracheal trunk (Saether).

felt line, in most adult Mutillidae and Bradynobaenidae (Hymenoptera), a narrow longitudinal band of relatively dense, closely appressed hairs, close to and parallel with the lateral margin of abdominal tergum 3 (Borror et al.; Gauld and Bolton).

female, the sex in which the ova are developed, designated by ♀, the astronomical sign for Venus (T-B).

female clasping organ, in ♀ *Bourletiella* spp. (Collembola: Sminthuridae), modification of dorsal anal valve and its setae, forming a crest with opercular, hook-shaped, setiform and tendriliform setae (Richards).

female pronucleus, the nucleus of the egg cell (T-B).

female reproductive system, reproductive system of the ♀ insect, consisting of paired ovaries, lateral and median oviducts, vagina, accessory glands, and usually a spermatheca (Leftwich).

female squama genitalis, in ♀ Protura, the external genitalia, consisting of the perigynium, carrying 2 long basal apodemes and opening dorsally, and the distal paired styli (Tuxen).

female subanal appendages, in ♀ Symphypleona (Collembola), 2 highly modified setae occurring on ventral surface of each lateral anal lobe (Richards).

femina, the female; belonging to the female sex (T-B).

femoral armament, in Blattaria, armament on forefemora classified as: Type A—strong or large spines which gradually decrease in size towards the apex of the femur, terminating in 2 or more longer spines (e.g., Type A_2, Type A_3, or Type A_4); Type B—one or more large proximal spines followed by a row of short, slender, piliform spinules, terminating in 2 or 3 large terminal spines (Type B_2, Type B_3); Type C—a row of piliform spinules only (large proximal spines absent), terminating in 1–3 large spines (Type C_1, C_2, or C_3) (Bruijning).

femoral lines, in adult Biphyllidae (Coleoptera: Cucujoidea), fine ridges on the basal abdominal sternite which run backwards and outwards from the inner ends of the hind coxae (Britton, in CSIRO).

femorate, femoratus, with abnormal or unusually developed femora or thighs (T-B).

femoroalary organs, the sound-producing apparatus of certain Orthoptera, in which the hind femora are rubbed against the tegmina (T-B, after Folsom and Wardle).

femorotibial, pertaining to both femur and tibia or to the articulation between them (T-B).

femorotibial joint, one of the 2 primary articulations of the arthropod leg, between the femur and the tibia (T-B, after Snodgrass).

femorotrochanteric, of or pertaining to the femur and the trochanter (T-B).

femur (pl., **femora**), the third, and usually the stoutest segment of the leg, articulated to the body through the trochanter and coxa and bearing the tibia at its distal end (T-B).

fenbutatin-oxide, a specific miticide; an orhanotin, hexakis (β,β-dimethylphenethyl) distannoxane; slightly toxic to mammals, acute oral LD_{50} for rats 2631 mg/kg (Pfadt).

fenestra (pl., **fenestrae**), a window (T-B; R. W. Brown); a transparent glassy spot or mark (T-B); windowlike perforations in a membrane (T-B); a pellucid mark in a wing vein, commonly marking a wing fold (T-B; Gauld and Bolton); in ♂ Odonata, the genital opening on the ventral surface of abdominal segment II (Tuxen); in Blattaria, a small, pale, membranous area at the base of the antennae (T-B); in Isoptera, fontanelle, q.v. (T-B).

fenestrate, fenestrated, fenestratus (Latin), with transparent areas or windowlike openings (fenestrae) as in the wings of some Lepidoptera (T-B; Harris, after Munz).

fenestrate membrane, of the compound eye, the membrane at the base of the ommatidia, at their junction with the optic nerve (T-B); see retina.

fenestrate ocellus, an ocellate spot (T-B).

fenestrella, in certain Orthoptera, a transparent eyelike spot in the anal area of the tegmina (T-B, after Kirby and Spence).

fenson, $C_{12}H_9ClO_3S$, a synthetic acaricide; asulfonate, p-chlorophenyl benzene sulfonate; slightly toxic to mammals, acute oral LD_{50} for rats 1560 to 1740 mg/kg (Pfadt).

fensulfothion, a synthetic, soil insecticide and nematocide; an organophosphate, O,O-diethyl O-p-[(methylsulfinyl)phenyl] phosphorothioate; highly toxic to mammals; acute oral LD_{50} for rats 2 to 11 mg/kg (Pfadt).

fenthion, $C_{10}H_{15}O_3PS_2$, a synthetic insecticide, animal systemic; an organophosphate, O,O-dimethyl O-[4-(methylthio)-m-tolyl] phosphorothioate; moderately toxic to mammals; acute oral LD_{50} for rats 178 to 310 mg/kg (Pfadt).

feral, wild; in the wild state (T-B).

ferbam, a protective fungicide used for foliage application; ferric dimethyldithiocarbamate; of low acute mammalian toxicity, acute oral LD_{50} for rats greater than 17,000 mg/kg (Pfadt).

fermentation chamber, dilated portion of hind gut of certain insects in which food materials are broken down by various bacteria (Tulloch); in larval Scarabaeoidea (Coleoptera), modified ileum in which the intima is produced into spines and in which microorganisms digest cellulose (Chapman).

ferreous, ferreus, the metallic gray of polished iron (T-B).

ferrugineous, ferrugineus, ferruginosus, ferruginous, rusty red-brown (T-B).

ferrugino-testaceous, a rusty yellow-brown (T-B).

fertility, ability to reproduce (T-B).

fertilization, the penetration of the sperm through the micropyle of an ovum and the union with its cell nucleus (T-B; Tulloch; Chapman); see copulation and insemination.

fertilize, to inseminate; to introduce the spermatozoa (T-B).

festivus, variegated with bright colors (T-B).

festooned, arranged in loops as if hung from nails (T-B).

fetid, having a disagreeable smell; malodorous (T-B).

fetid glands, in Orthoptera, certain glands which secrete a malodorous fluid (T-B).

fiber, threadlike structure of any tissue (T-B).

fibril, fibrilla (pl., **fibrillae**), a muscle sarcostyle, q.v.; the finer fibrous structure of a muscle or nerve (T-B).

fibrillated, formed or consisting of fibrillae (T-B).

fibrin, a protein compound making up a large part of the muscular tissue; also found in blood and other body liquids (T-B).

fibrinogen, a protein substance of the blood and other body fluids, concerned in the production of fibrin (T-B); in larval *Bombyx* (Lepidoptera: Bombycidae), precursor of fibroin, secreted in the posterior part of the silk gland, denatured to fibroin on extrusion (Chapman).

fibroin, tough inner protein of silk (T-B; Chapman).

fibula (pl., **fibulae**), in adult Trichoptera and some Lepidoptera, jugal lobe, q.v. (T-B); in ♂ *Zonosoma* (Lepidoptera: Geometridae), process of caudomedian part of inner face of valva (Tuxen, after Bastelberger); in ♂ *Leucanitis* (Lepidoptera: Noctuidae), clavate, hairy, digitoid process of dorsomedian region of valvula (Tuxen, after John); in ♂ *Kallima* (Lepidoptera: Nymphalidae), long, rodlike structure, furcate dorsally, ventrad of aedoeagus, being part of fultura inferior (Tuxen, after Roepke); in ♂ Riodinidae (Lepidoptera), specialized form of sclerotized, outer, proximal sheath of aedoeagus (Tuxen, after Stichel); in ♀ Lycaenidae (Lepidoptera), sterigma, q.v. (Tuxen, after Chapman).

fibula vaginalis (pl., **fibulae vaginales**), in ♀ Siphonaptera, sclerotized area of dorsal wall of vagina immediately anterior to duplicatura vaginalis (Tuxen, after Lass).

fibulae anteriores, in ♀ Heteroptera (Hemiptera), posterior connecting leaf of gonapophysis VIII, q.v. (Tuxen, after Verhoeff).

fibulae posteriores, in ♀ Heteroptera (Hemiptera), anterior connecting leaf of gonapophysis IX, q.v. (Tuxen, after Verhoeff).

fide (Latin), on the authority of; employed to indicate that an author has not seen a work or a specimen cited (T-B).

fifth longitudinal vein, in Diptera (Williston), the M_3 and Cu_{1+2} of Comstock (T-B).

Fiji disease, disease of sugarcane caused by a reovirus (*Fijivirus*), transmitted propagatively by *Perkinsiella* (Hemiptera: Auchenorrhyncha: Delphacidae) (Nault and Ammar).

fila, pl. filum, q.v. (T-B).

fila ovipositorius (pl.), in ♀ Phasmida, the inferior valvulae when exceeding end of abdomen (Tuxen, after Brunner v. Wattenwyl).

filaceous, having fila or threads (T-B).

filament, a thread (T-B); a long slender process of equal diameter throughout (T-B); an elongated appendage (T-B); in ♂ *Protonemura* and *Siphonoperla* (Plecoptera), long filiform process emitted from copulatory organ (penis or supaanal lobe) (Tuxen, after Kimmins; Zwick, pers. comm.).

filament plate, in an early stage of the insect embryo, a differentiated sheet of cells which connects the genital rudiment with the heart rudiment of the same side of the body (T-B, after Imms).

filamento di sostegno (Italian), support filament, q.v. (Tuxen, after Berlese).

filamentous, filament- or threadlike (T-B).

filaria (pl., **filariae**), round worm (Nematoda) which invades the lymphatic system of man and other animals, causing filariasis (T-B).

filarial worm, filaria, q.v. (Borror et al.).

filariasis, disease of man in tropical and subtropical regions of the world caused by the presence of minute worms or filariae, *Wuchereia bancrofti* (Cobbold) and *Brugia malayi* (Brug) (Nematoda), transmitted by Culicidae (esp. *Aedes, Culex, Anopheles,* and *Mansonia*) and Ceratopogonidae (*Culicoides*) (Diptera) (T-B; Colless and McAlpine, in CSIRO; Borror et al.); see loaiasis.

filate, filiate, filiform, threadlike; thin like a thread; of an edge, separated from the disc by a channel, which produces a very slender threadlike margin (T-B).

filate antenna, in Diptera, simple antenna, without lateral hair or dilation (T-B).

filator, the silk-spinning structure of caterpillars (Lepidoptera) (T-B); see silk press.

file, ridged structure functioning in stridulation (T-B); in some Poduromorpha (Collembola), a group of similar, usually short, setae on the ventral surface of the fourth antennal segment (Christiansen and Bellinger); in crickets (Orthoptera: Grylloidea) and long-horned grasshoppers (Orthoptera: Tettigonioidea), a filelike ridge on the ventral side of the tegmen, near the base, forming part of the stridulating mechanism (T-B; Borror et al.); see stridulitrum.

filiform, threadlike, i.e., slender and of equal diameter, being commonly applied to antennae (T-B).

Filipalpia, old taxon for Plecoptera, including Peltoperlidae, Nemouridae, Pteronarcidae, and other families, characterized by glossae and paraglossae being about equal size (Riek, after Ricker, in CSIRO; Borror et al.; Zwick, pers. comm.); see Setipalpia.

Filippi's gland, in most larval Lepidoptera, paired accessory glands associated with the silk glands (T-B); see Lyonnet's gland.

fillet, a transverse raised band between the antennae in Lepidoptera.

filose, ending in a threadlike process (T-B).

filter apparatus, finely branched processes of the atrial wall of some spiracles, often forming 2 thick but air-pervious mats just within the atrial orifice (T-B, after Snodgrass).

filter chamber, in Cicadoidea, Cercopoidea, many Cicadelloidea, and Sternorrhyncha (Hemiptera), a part of the alimentary canal in which the 2 ends of the midgut and the beginning of the hind gut are bound together in a membranous and muscular sheath (T-B, after Snodgrass; Chapman; L. O'Brien, pers. comm.).

filtering apparatus, in larvae of some Nematocera (Diptera), pharyngeal filter, q.v. (Teskey, in McAlpine).

filum (pl., **fila**), a thread (T-B); in *Machilis* (Archaeognatha: Machilidae), cercus, q.v. (T-B).

filum terminale (pl., **fila terminalia**), in Archaeognatha, Zygentoma, and Ephemeroptera, tergum XI prolonged into a median appendage (Tuxen; von Kéler).

fimbria, thick, ciliated hairs at the termination of any part (T-B); in adult Lepidoptera, marginal scales, q.v.; see cilia.

fimbriate, fimbriatus, fringed with hairs of irregular length; terminated by nonparallel hairs or bristles; applied to a part or structure (T-B, after Kirby and Spence).

fimbriate antenna, a setaceous antenna, each joint of which bears a single lateral hair (T-B).

fimbriate plates, in Coccoidea (Hemiptera: Sternorrhyncha), pectinae, q.v. (T-B, after MacGillivray).

finger, in ♂ Siphonaptera, telomere, q.v. (Tuxen, after Rothschild); in the maxilla, the digitus, q.v. (T-B).

finger millet mosaic, disease of millet caused by a rhabdovirus transmitted propagatively by *Sogatella* and *Peregrinus* (Hemiptera: Auchenorrhyncha: Delphacidae) (Nault and Ammar).

fire blight, disease of pear, apple, and quince trees caused by the bacterium *Erwinia amylovora* transmitted externally by various insects, especially flies, bees, and leafhoppers (Borror et al.).

first anal vein (1A), the wing vein just posterior to the cubitus (T-B, after Comstock).

first axillary plate, first axillary sclerite, q.v. (McAlpine).

first axillary sclerite, sclerite articulating proximally with the anterior notal process and distally with the subcostal vein and the second axillary sclerite (T-B, after Imms; Chapman, after Snodgrass); see second axillary sclerite and third axillary sclerite.

first basal cell, in adult Diptera, basal radial cell, q.v., of wing (T-B, after Curran; McAlpine).

first clypeus, postclypeus, q.v. (T-B).

first connecting membrane, in ♂ Coleoptera, tubular membrane (non-sclerotized part of genital tube) connecting penis to tegmen (Tuxen).

first discoidal cell (DC1), in adult Hymenoptera, closed cell in middle of wing behind $R_s + M$ (Gauld and Bolton).

first fibula(e), in ♀ Heteroptera (Hemiptera), posterior connecting leaf of gonapophysis VIII, q.v. (Tuxen, after Štys).

first-form reproductive, in Isoptera, primary reproductive, q.v. (Miller; Wilson).

first genital sclerite, in ♂ Muscomorpha (Diptera: Brachycera), syntergosternite, q.v. (McAlpine).

first gonapophyses, in ♀ insects, gonapophyses of abdominal segment VIII, forming the anterior or ventral blades of ovipositor (Tuxen; Gauld and Bolton).

first gonapophysis, in ♂ Hymenoptera, volsella, q.v. (Tuxen, after Rohwer).

first gonocoxae, gonocoxae of abdominal segment VIII (Tuxen, after Snodgrass; Gauld and Bolton); in ♀ of some orders, gonangulum, q.v. (Tuxen); in ♀ Heteroptera (Hemiptera), gonocoxites of abdominal segment VIII, q.v. (Tuxen, after Scudder).

first gonocoxopodites, in ♀ Heteroptera (Hemiptera), gonocoxites of abdominal segment VIII, q.v. (Tuxen, after Davis).

first incisura, in Coccidea (Hemiptera: Sternorrhyncha), the distinct indentation or notch of the margin of the pygidium on the meson between the median pair of lobes (T-B, after MacGillivray).

first inner apical nervure, in adult Hymenoptera, short second branch of cubitus anterior (Cu_2), extending to first anal vein (1A) (T-B, after Norton).

first inner ramus, in ♀ Heteroptera (Hemiptera), posterior connecting leaf of gonapophysis VIII, q.v. (Tuxen, after Ahmad and Southwood).

first jugal vein, jugal bar, q.v. (T-B).

first lateral suture, in Odonata, the suture which starts from beneath the base of the front wing behind the humeral suture and meets it behind the second coxa (T-B, after Smith).

first longitudinal vein, in adult Diptera, first branch of radius (R_1) (T-B, after Williston, Meigen; Colless and McAlpine, in CSIRO).

first maxillae, in Arthropoda, the second pair of appendages of the gnathal region of the head; in insects, maxillae, q.v. (T-B, after Snodgrass).

first median plate, a small sclerite of variable shape lying in the angle between the second axillary and the distal arm of the third axillary at the base of the mediocubital field of the wing; accessory to the third axillary in function, and usually attached to it (T-B, after Snodgrass).

first outer ramus, in ♀ Heteroptera (Hemiptera), anterior connecting leaf of gonapophysis VIII, q.v. (Tuxen, after Ahmad and Southwood).

first pair of hamules, in ♂ Odonata, hamuli anteriores, q.v. (Tuxen, after Thompson).

first phragma, in adult Culicidae (Diptera), a transverse apodeme just under the overhanging anterior promontory and internally connecting the antepronota, extending posteriorly from each antepronotum as a thin rod-shaped apodeme (Harbach and Knight, after Christophers).

first radio-medial crossvein, in certain neuropterous insects, the vein in the hind wing, arising from R_s and extending toward the base of the wing, joining the media (M) near its base (T-B, after Comstock).

first ramus, in ♀ Heteroptera (Hemiptera), posterior connecting leaf of gonapophysis VIII, q.v. (Tuxen, after Scudder) or anterior connecting leaf of gonapophysis VIII, q.v. (Tuxen, after Southwood).

first reviser, the first author to subsequently cite names (including different original spellings of the same name) or nomenclatural acts published on the same date and to choose one of them to have precedence over the other(s), with exceptions stated in the Code (ICZN).

first segment, in any segmented appendage, the one nearest the body (T-B).

first segment of penis, in ♂ Odonata, stem, q.v. (Tuxen, after Selys-Longchamps) or vesicula spermalis, q.v. (Tuxen, after Borror).

first species rule, a practice of some authors of deeming the first species named in a new genus to be the type of that genus (T-B, after ICZN); applied in general to the works of the older authors where no generic type was named (T-B).

first submarginal cross-nervure, in adult Hymenoptera, part of the media (M) and the radio-medial cross vein (T-B, after Comstock).

first thoracic spiracle, the spiracle of the mesothorax, often displaced into the posterior part of the prothorax (T-B, after Snodgrass).

first trochanter, trochanter, q.v. (T-B, after Snodgrass).

first valves, in ♀ Thysanoptera, ventral blades of ovipositor (Tuxen); first gonapophyses q.v. (Tuxen); in Isoptera, ventral valves, q.v. (Tuxen).

first valvifer(s), gonangulum, q.v. (Tuxen, after Snodgrass).

first valvulae, first gonapophyses, q.v. (Tuxen, after Snodgrass).

first vein, in adult Diptera, radius (R) and first branch of radius (R_1) (T-B, after Curran).

fissate, fissus (Latin), with fissures or cracks; divided or cleft (T-B; Harris, after Marchant and Charles); see corticinus, fatiscent, and rimose.

fissile, fissilis (Latin), cleft or divided, as the wings in plume moths (T-B); also used for lamellate (T-B).

fissiparous, reproducing by fission; having that form of asexual generation in which the parent divides, each part becoming a new individual (T-B).

fissure, fissura (Latin), a crevice; a narrow longitudinal opening; a slit (T-B).

fissus (Latin), fissate, q.v. (T-B).

fistula (pl., **fistulae**), a slender tube (T-B); in Lepidoptera, the channel formed by the union of the parts of the proboscis (T-B); in ♂ Siphonaptera, long, slender, semimembranous, external part of tubus interior distad of its sclerotized sheath (Tuxen, after Peus).

fistular, like a slender, cylindrical tube (T-B).

fistulose, fistulosus (Latin), **fistulous,** porous (R.W. Brown); shaped like a pipe (T-B).

five-day fever, trench fever, q.v. (Adkins, pers. comm.).

fixation, a general term for the determination of a name-bearing type whether by original designation, by indication, or by subsequent desigation (ICZN); see fixation by elimination.

fixation by elimination, the supposed fixation of a type species by transfer of all but one of the originally included species from a genus, but not in itself an available method of type fixation according to the Code; however a published statement such as "A-us x-us, type by elimination" may be considered a designation providing the requirements of the Code are satisfied (ICZN).

fixed action pattern, a species-specific motor pattern requiring few or no external stimuli or additional sensory cues for its maintenance or completion, once initiated (Matthews and Matthews).

fixed hairs, microtrichia, q.v. (T-B, after Kellogg).

fixed process, in ♂ Siphonaptera, processus basimeris, q.v. (Tuxen).

flabellae, in Coccoidea (Hemiptera: Sternorrhyncha), flabelliform marginal hairs, q.v.

flabellate, fan-shaped, i.e., with long thin processes lying flat on each other like the folds of a fan, e.g., flabellate antennae of ♂ Rhipiceridae (Coleoptera) (T-B; Borror et al.).

flabelliform, flabellate, q.v. (T-B).

flabelliform marginal hairs, in Coccoidea (Hemiptera: Sternorrhyncha), the flattened, scalelike marginal setae in certain genera, broad oval in outline.

flabellum, a fanlike or leaflike process (T-B; Borror et al.); in bees (Hymenoptera: Apoidea), a spoonlike lobe at the tip of the ligula (T-B; Leftwich).

flabs, labellar lobes, q.v. (T-B).

flaccid, feeble; limber; lax (T-B).

flacherie, disease of the silkworm, *Bombyx mori* (Lepidoptera: Bombycidae), which is apparently caused by a virus (Allaby); see gattine and touffe flacherie.

flagellar segment, flagellomere, q.v. (Gauld and Bolton).

flagellar whorl, in some adult Nematocera (Diptera), a ring of long curved setae borne by each flagellomere of the antenna (Harbach and Knight, after Belkin).

flagellate, flagellatus (Latin), whiplike (T-B); having a flagellum or whiplike structure (T-B).

flagelliform, whiplike; whipshaped (T-B).

flagellomere, one part of a multiannulated flagellum of an antenna (McAlpine).

flagellosis, in invertebrate pathology, infection with a flagellate protozoan (Steinhaus and Martignoni).

flagellum (pl., **flagella**), a small whip or whiplike process (T-B); the third part of the antenna beyond the pedicel (T-B; Harbach and Knight); the taillike process of a spermatozoan (T-B); in ♂ Cixiidae and Derbidae (Hemiptera: Auchenorrhyncha: Fulgoroidea), distal articulated part of aedeagus, usually dorsally reflexed, often with spines or distinctly shaped lobes as opposed to proximal shaft (O'Brien, pers. comm.); in ♂ Heteroptera (Hemiptera), processus gonopori, q.v. (Tuxen, after Leston); in ♂ Pentatomoidea (Hemiptera: Heteroptera), bifid process, q.v. (Tuxen, after Handlirsch); in ♂ Coleoptera, sclerotized terminal prolongation of the ductus ejaculatorius, usually concealed within the internal sac when in repose, but sometimes very long and constantly protruding through the ostium of the penis (Lindroth and Palmén, in Tuxen).

flammate, flammeus, fiery-red (T-B; R. W. Brown).

flange, a projecting rim or edge (T-B); in ♂ Crambinae (Lepidoptera: Pyralidae), sclerotized, projecting edge or rim of the costa of valva (Tuxen, after Philpott).

flank, the side of the thorax; the pleuron (T-B).

flap of clasper, in ♂ Siphonaptera, processus basimeris, q.v. (Tuxen, after Jordan).

flaps, in ♀ Lepidoptera, papillae anales, q.v. (Tuxen, after Burgess).

flaring, widening out like the mouth of a trumpet (T-B).

flash coloration, hidden colors and/or patterns that are suddenly exposed when an organism is threatened, e.g., brilliant red or orange hind wings of some moths (Lepidoptera) or grasshoppers (Orthoptera) exposed when the insect is disturbed (Matthews and Matthews; Leftwich).

flasklike sense organ, coeloconic sensillum, q.v. (T-B).

flat egg, in Lepidoptera, an egg, when deposited, that is asymmetrical in horizontal section with a horizontal micropylar axis and the micropyle at one end (Common, after Chapman).

flavanoid, plant pigment, sometimes incorporated as noncuticular pigment in insects (Gilmour, in CSIRO).

flavescent, of a somewhat yellow color; verging on yellow; in Odonata, slightly smoky (an incorrect usage) (T-B).

flavid, yellowed; sulphur yellow (T-B).

flavone, yellow plant pigment sometimes used unaltered as an insect pigment, e.g., in the marbled white butterfly, *Melanargia galathea* (Lepidoptera: Satyridae) (Tulloch; Chapman); see carotinoids.

flavotestaceous, light yellow-brown (T-B).

flavous, flavus (Latin), yellow (T-B; R. W. Brown).

flavovirens, green verging upon yellow (T-B).

flaxseed, the puparium of the Hessian fly, *Mayetiola destructor* (Diptera: Cecidomyiidae) (Pfadt).

flea, a member of the order Siphonaptera (Dunnet, in CSIRO).

fleshy filament, in some larval Rhopalocera (Lepidoptera), a flexible, attenuate external process of the body wall (Peterson).

fleshy mound, in ♂ *Vanessa atalanta* (Lepidoptera: Nymphalidae), internal, longitudinal process of inner face of valva caudad of sacculus, being part of harpe (transl. "monticule charnu" Réaumur, after Tuxen).

flex, to bend; to curve back (T-B).

flexible, pliable; with elastic properties (T-B).

flexile, flexilis, capable of being bent at an angle without breaking; flexible (T-B).

flexion, in ♂ Diptera, bending of the apical portion of the abdomen, including ventroflexion, dorsoflexion, and lateroflexion (Mc Alpine).

flexion line, line along which bending of the wings occurs in flight (Chapman, after Wootton); see fold line.

flexor, flexor muscle, q.v. (T-B).

flexor membranes, membranous areas between the pretarsal claws which apparently serve to transfer the tension of the apodeme on the unguitractor to the claws, forcing them upward (T-B).

flexor muscle, a muscle which bends any jointed structure (T-B).

flexor row, in adult Diptera, one or more rows of bristles along the lower surface of the femur (T-B, after Comstock).

flexuose, flexuosus (Latin), **flexuous,** with many bends; winding (T-B; R. W. Brown).

flexure, in ♂ Caelifera (Orthoptera), flexible sclerotized part of penis connecting its basal and apical valves (Tuxen, after Roberts).

flicker fusion frequency, the rate of flickering light that an eye is just unable to distinguish from continuous light (Matthews and Matthews).

flicker vision, vision relying on an object's real or apparent motion rather than its static form (Matthews and Matthews).

flightless, either apterous or with wings that are reduced and nonfunctional (Leftwich).

fling mechanism, flight mechanism producing thrust, in which the wings are clapped together at the top of the upstroke followed by rapid promotion of the leading edges of the wings, separating which the posterior parts remain in contact, sucking air into the increasing gap between the upper surfaces of the wings creating bound vortices around the edges, e.g., in the chalcid wasp *Encarsia* (Hymenoptera) (Chapman, after Weis-Fogh).

flocculent, consisting of soft flakes (T-B).

flocculus (pl., **flocculi**), a hairy or bristly appendage on the posterior coxa of some Hymenoptera (T-B).

floccus (Latin), a tuft of wool or woollike hair (T-B; R. W. Brown).

floor, in insect anatomy, the lower interior wall of any cavity (T-B).

floor of genital cavity, in ♂ Lepidoptera, diaphragma, q.v. (Tuxen, after Chapman).

floor pouches, in ♀ Acridoidea (Orthoptera), forwardly directed pockets in the membranous floor of the genital chamber (Agarwala).

flora, the plant life of a region (T-B; Mayr); see biota and fauna.

floricomous, in ♀ Geometridae and Tortricidae (Lepidoptera), adjective descriptive of papillae anales elaborately decorated with long thickened hairs and scales (Tuxen, after Pierce).

flosculiferous, bearing a flosculus (T-B).

flosculus, in some Fulgoroidea (Hemiptera: Auchenorrhyncha), a small, tubular, lunulate anal organ with a central style (T-B).

flowable, a pesticide formulation in which finely divided particles are suspended in a water or oil base (Pfadt).

fluctuating variations, the neo-Darwinian concept of unstable changes in the characteristics of a species, which seem to disappear from generation to generation, or which depend on genetic or somatic influences conditioned by known or unknown factors, which eventually, by natural selection, tend to crystallize and become permanent; a characteristic of nascent species in plastic aggregates (T-B, after Kinsey).

fluke, a parasitic flatworm of the class Trematoda (Pfadt).

fluted, having parallel grooves or flutes; channeled (T-B; Harris, after Funk); see canaliculate and channeled.

fluting, alternating ridges and valleys in the wings of Pterygota (Insecta), used as the principle basis for homologizing wing veins, the anterior branch being convex (desigated by a " + ") and the posterior branch being concave (designated by a "−").

fluting ribs, in ♂ Siphonaptera, a series of longitudinal, often parallel ribs, producing a fluted effect to the lateral lobes of the aedeagus, and sometimes the more distal portions of the aedeagal pouch (Rothschild and Traub).

fluviatile, inhabiting the margins of running streams (T-B).

fly (pl. **flies**), member of the order Diptera (Colless and McAlpine, in CSIRO).

fly blow, eggs or maggots of flesh flies (Diptera: Calliphoridae, Sarcophagidae) (T-B).

fly belt, the restricted area infested by tsetse flies in Africa (T-B).

fly blown, covered with fly blow (T-B).

fold, flexion line, q.v., or fold line, q.v., of wing (Gauld and Bolton).

fold line, line along which wings fold at rest (Chapman, after Wootton); see flexion line.

folded membrane, in first abdominal segment of Cicadidae (Hemiptera: Auchenorrhyncha), the membrane in the anterior wall of the ventral cavity of the chordotonal organ (T-B, after Comstock; Chapman, after Pringle).

foleaceous, foleaceus, foliaceous, q.v. (T-B).

foleate, foliaceous, q.v. (T-B).

foleate setae, in ♂ Chironomidae (Diptera), lamellate setae of the median volsella basally broad, leaf-shaped, with or without hairlike point (Saether).

foliaceous, foliaceus (Latin), resembling a leaf (T-B).

foliate, foliaceous, q.v. (T-B).

folic acid, essential water-soluble vitamin in insects (Glimour, in CSIRO).

folioles, foliolae, leaflike processes from a margin or protuberance (T-B).

follicle, a cellular sac or tube (T-B); a minute cavity, sac, or tube (Borror et al.); oocyte with its surrounding follicular epithelium (Chapman); see egg chamber and testis follicle.

follicle cells, cells of follicular epithelium (T-B, after Snodgrass; Chapman).

follicular, made up of, or having, follicles (T-B).

follicular epithelium, layer of cells enveloping developing oocyte, derived from prefollicular cells within the germarium (Chapman); see egg chamber and follicle.

folliculate, enclosed in a case, cocoon, or follicle (T-B); having follicles (T-B).

folliculus, cocoon, q.v. (T-B).

fonofos, a synthetic insecticide and acaricide; an organophosphate, O-ethyl S-phenyl ethylphosphonodithioate; highly toxic to mammals, acute oral LD_{50} for rats 8 to 18 mg/kg (Pfadt).

fontanel, fontanelle, q.v. (T-B).

fontanelle, in soldier Termitidae and Rhinotermitidae (Isoptera), pore on the frontal region of the head though which exude secretions of the frontal gland (T-B; Gay, in CSIRO); in some Zoraptera, the frontal opening of the fontanelle gland or cephalic gland (Paulian).

fontannelle plate, in Termitidae (Isoptera) a raised area on top of the head where the fontanelle is located (Weesner, in Krishna and Weesner).

food canal, canal anterior to the cibarium in insects with sucking mouthparts, through which fluid food is ingested (McAlpine); see food meatus.

food meatus, in adult Culicidae (Diptera), the channel formed by the juxtaposition of the mouthparts anterior to the cibarium (Harbach and Knight, after Knight and Laffoon).

food plant, host plant, q.v. (T-B).

food pump, in adult Diptera, cibarial pump, q.v. (McAlpine).

food reservoir, in adult Lepidoptera, crop, q.v. (T-B).

foot, tarsus, q.v. (T-B) or pretarsus, q.v. (Leftwich); in ♂ Auchenorrhyncha (Hemiptera), apical more or less footlike extension of the style (Tuxen, after Young); see feet.

foot-shaped loop, in wings of Odonata, cubitoanal loop, q.v. (T-B).

foot-shaped piece, in ♀ *Apatania* (Trichoptera: Limnephilidae), ridge on ventral surface of processus spermathecae (Nielsen; Tuxen, after Morton).

foot spinners, web spinners, q.v. (Ross, in CSIRO).

foot shield, in larval Lepidoptera, the chitinous plate on the outer side of the proleg (T-B).

footstalk, of the maxilla, stipes, q.v. (T-B); in ♂ *Halpe* (Lepidoptera: Hesperiidae), lateroproximal process of the valva (Tuxen, after Evans); in ♂ Geometridae, the rodlike proximal part of the labis (Tuxen, after Pierce).

forager, in social insects, a member of the worker caste that gathers food and brings it back to the colony (Chapman).

foramen (Latin), an opening in the body wall for the passage of a vessel or nerve (T-B); any opening at an apex (T-B); the opening of a cocoon (T-B).

foramen basal, in ♂ Heteroptera (Hemiptera), basal foramen, q.v. (Tuxen, after Davis).

foramen ductus (pl., **foramina ductus**), in ♂ Heteroptera (Hemiptera), small aperture in septum (if any) closing basal foramen (Tuxen, after Dupuis).

foramen magnum, occipital foramen, q.v. (T-B).

foramen occipitale, occipital foramen, q.v. (T-B).

foramina, small openings in the body wall (T-B); in Orthoptera, subgenual organs, q.v. (T-B).

foraminal, of or pertaining to a foramen (T-B).

forb, any herbaceous plant other than a grass (Gramineae) (Pfadt).

forceps (pl., **forcipes**), pincers or claspers at the apex of the abdomen of certain insects, either for clasping by ♂ in copulation or in defense (T-B; Leftwich); in ♂ Protura, periphallus, q.v. (Tuxen, after Prell); in ♂ Ephemeroptera, gonostyles, q.v. (Tuxen, after Palmén); in Dermaptera, (pincerlike) cerci, q.v. (T-B; Tuxen); in ♂ Blattopteroidea, phallus, q.v. (Tuxen); in ♂ Psyllidae (Hemiptera: Sternorrhyncha), a pair of appendages on posterior part of hypandrium (Tuxen); in ♂ Auchenorrhyncha (Hemiptera), styles, q.v. (Tuxen, after Caldwell); in ♂ Heteroptera (Hemiptera), parameres, q.v. (Tuxen, after Strawinski); in ♂ Pentatomoidea (*Eusthenes*) (Hemiptera: Heteroptera: Tessaratomidae), secondary processes of the various phallic segments (Tuxen, after Handlirsch), i.e. processus phallothecae and processus conjunctivae, q.v.; in ♂ Coleoptera, aedeagus, q.v. (Tuxen); in ♂ Lepidoptera, process of sacculus (Tuxen, after Bastelberger) or valvae, q.v. (Tuxen, after Cholodkowsky); in ♂ Diptera, surstyli (claspers) gonopods, q.v. (Tuxen) or cerci, q.v. (Tuxen, after Böttcher); in ♂ Hymenoptera, gonocoxites + penis valves (Tuxen, after Konow); in ♂ Hymenoptera, gonocoxite, q.v. (Tuxen, after Dufour), distal parts of gonocoxites + gonostyli (Tuxen, after Hartig), gonocoxites + gonostyli + volsellae (Tuxen, after Radoszkowski), or gonobase + gonocoxite + gonostylus (Tuxen, after Rohwer); see forcipes.

forceps base, in ♂ Ephemeroptera, styliger, q.v. (Tuxen, after Kimmins).

forceps basis, in ♂ Ephemeroptera, styliger, q.v. (Tuxen, after Eaton).

forceps copulatrix, in ♂ Psyllidae (Hemiptera: Sternorrhyncha), forceps, q.v. (Tuxen, after Sulc).

forceps limbs, in ♂ Ephemeroptera, genostyles, q.v. (Tuxen, after Eaton).

forceps superior, in ♂ Asilidae (Diptera), epandrium with surstyli, q.v. (Tuxen).

forcipate, forcipated, forcipatus, bearing forceps or similar structures (T-B).

forcipate claspers, in ♂ Diptera, gonopods, q.v. (McAlpine).

forcipes exteriores, in ♂ Blattopteroidea, hypophallus, q.v. (Tuxen, after Wesché); in ♂ Pentatomoidea (*Eusthenes*) (Hemiptera: Heteroptera: Tessaratomidae), processus phallothecae, q.v. (Tuxen, after Handlirsch).

forcipes inferiores, in ♂ Blattopteroidea, epiphallus, q.v. (Tuxen, after Wesché); in ♂ Muscomorpha (Diptera), surstyli, q.v. (Tuxen, after Wesché).

forcipes interiores, in ♂ Pentatomoidea (*Eusthenes*) (Hemiptera: Heteroptera: Tessaratomidae), processus conjunctivae 2, q.v. (Tuxen, after Handlirsh).

forcipes intermediae, in ♂ Pentatomoidea (*Eusthenes*) (Hemiptera: Heteroptera: Tessaratomidae), processus conjunctivae 1, q.v. (Tuxen, after Handlirsch).

forcipes superiores, in ♂ Muscomorpha (Diptera), cerci, q.v. (Tuxen, after Wesché); in ♂ Siphonaptera, parameres, q.v. (Tuxen, after Wesché)

forcipula (pl., **forcipulae**), in ♂ Diptera, gonopods, q.v. (Tuxen).

forcipiform, having the form of forceps or pincers (T-B).

Ford's sclerites, in ♂ Siphonaptera, a pair of variable sclerites, often at least partly fused, dorsad, and usually near apex of tubus interior (Tuxen, after Rothschild and Traub).

fore, anterior (T-B).

forebrain, protocerebrum, q.v. (T-B).

forecoxa, coxa of the foreleg (McAlpine).

forefemur, femur of the foreleg (McAlpine).

foregut, the ectodermal part of the insect alimentary canal which extends from the mouth to the end of the gizzard (proventriculus) (T-B; Gilmour, in CSIRO); see stomodaeum.

foregut-borne transmission, viral transmission in which the viral particles are attached to the cuticular lining of the anterior alimentary canal of aphids (Sternorrhyncha: Aphididae) and leafhoppers (Auchenorrhyncha: Cicadellidae) (Hemiptera), but are not found within the hemolymph of these vectors (Nault and Ammar); see viral transmission.

forehead, in Imblycera and Ischnocera (Phthiraptera), the head in front of the mandibles and antennae (T-B).

foreintestine, foregut, q.v. (T-B).

foreleg, prothoracic leg (McAlpine).

forensic entomology, any courtroom or legal activity involving insects (Adkins, pers. comm.); see medicolegal entomology.

foretarsus, the tarsus of one of the forelegs (Harbach and Knight).

foretibia, tibia of the foreleg (McAlpine).

foretrochanter, the trochanter of one of the forelegs (Harbach and Knight).

foretrochantin, in larval Trichoptera, prothoracic episternum, usually projecting and variously shaped (Wiggins).

foreunguis, claw, q.v., of foreleg (Harbach and Knight).

forewing, the first pair of wings, arising from the mesothorax (Leftwich); see hind wing.

forfex (Latin), a paired anal structure which opens and shuts transversely, like a pair of scissors (T-B).

forficate, forficatus, forcipate, q.v. (T-B).

forficulid neck, in Dermaptera contriction between posterior ventral cervical sclerite and anterior ventral cervical sclerite (Steinmann; Popham).

Forficulidea, Eudermaptera, q.v. (Popham).

Forficulina, Catadermaptera + Eudermaptera, q.v. (Giles, in CSIRO; Borror et al.).

Forficuloidea, Eudermaptera, q.v. (Hincks and Popham, in Tuxen; Giles, in CSIRO; Steinmann).

fork, in ♂ Coleoptera, paired processes (apophyses, apodemes) of tegmen or penis (Tuxen); in ♂ Coleoptera, spicules, q.v. (Tuxen, after Hopkins); in winged Trichoptera, apical cell, q.v. (McLachlan).

fork organ, in ♀ Micropterygidae (Lepidoptera), a peculiar, trifurcate signum (Tuxen, after Philpott).

forked sclerite, in ♀ Hymenoptera, detached notum, q.v. (Tuxen, after Richards).

form, forma (Latin), a term that if published after 1961 is deemed to denote infraspecific rank but that if published before 1960 is to be interpreted according to the Code (ICZN); those individuals of a species differing, in a stated way, from other individuals within the species (e.g., larval and adult forms, ♂ and ♀ forms, ecological forms, and seasonal forms) (ICZN).

formaldehyde, CH_2O; a colorless, pungent gas, used in solution as a perservative or for hardening tissues (T-B).

formalin, a 40 percent solution of formaldehyde in water.

formatendon, the tendinous apodeme of the tentorium (T-B, after MacGillivray).

formative cell, trichogen cell, q.v. (T-B).

Formenkreis (German), a collective category of allopatric subspecies or species (Mayr, after Kleinschmidt); in paleontology, a group of related species or subspecies (Mayr).

formentanate, $C_{11}H_{16}ClN_3O_2$, a synthetic insecticide and acaricide; a carbamate, [3-dimethylamino-(methylene-iminophenyl)]-N-methyl-carbamate; highly toxic to mammals; acute oral LD_{50} for rats 24 mg/kg (Pfadt).

formic, of, pertaining to or derived from ants (Hymenoptera: Formicidae) (T-B).

formic acid, simple aliphatic acid, HCO_2H, used in defense, produced in the venom glands of ants of the subfamily Formicinae (Hymenoptera: Formicidae) (T-B; Gilmour, in CSIRO).

formica (Latin), ant (R. W. Brown).

formicarium, formicary, q.v. (Tulloch).

formicary, an ant nest (Hymenoptera: Formicidae) (T-B); an artificial nest used in the laboratory to house ants (Wilson).

formicinus (Latin), of ants (R. W. Brown).

Formicoidea, superfamily within the Aculeata (Hymenoptera: Apocrita), including only the family Formicidae (ants), social species characterized by a wingless worker caste, often possessing a metapleural gland, and with one or 2 segments of abdomen nodiform or scalelike (pedicel) and sharply marked off from remainder (gaster) (Brown and Taylor, in CSIRO); included within the Vespoidea (*sensu* Gauld and Bolton, after Brothers).

formicula (Latin), small ant (R. W. Brown).

fornicate, fornicatus (Latin), arched or vaulted; concave within, convex without (T-B).

fossa (pl., **fossae**), a pit or deep sulcus, q.v. (T-B).

fossa spongiosa, in Heteroptera (Hemiptera), fossula spongiosa, q.v.

fossil, remains or traces of plants or animals of some previous geological period, e.g., impressions in rocks or amber inclusions.

fossoria, burrowers; in Orthoptera, the mole crickets and allies (Gryllotalpidae); in Hymenoptera, the digging wasps (T-B).

fossorial, formed for or with the habit of digging or burrowing (T-B).

fossula (pl. **fossulae**), a small fossa (R. W. Brown); a somewhat long and narrow depression or gutter (T-B); an elongated shallow groove (T-B, after Kirby and Spence); grooves on the head or sides of prothorax in which antennae are concealed (T-B, after J. B. Smith); see scrobe.

fossula spongiosa, in many Reduviidae and some Nabidae and Anthocoridae (Hemiptera: Heteroptera), apically on one or more pairs of tibiae, a vesicular hemolymph-filled structure beset with adhesive glandular setae and shorter sensory pegs (Lent and Wygodzinsky).

fossulate, fossulatus (Latin), with oblong depressions (fossulae) more elongate or furrowlike than scrobiculate (T-B; Harris, after R. W. Brown); see exsculptate, lacunose, and scrobiculate.

fossulet, fossula, q.v. (T-B).

foulbrood, American foulbrood, q.v., or European foulbrood, q.v. (Steinhaus and Martignoni).

fourth axillary, fourth axillary plate, q.v. (T-B, after Imms).

fourth axillary plate, sclerite at wing base articulating distally with the third axillary sclerite, being the apical portion of posterior notal wing process that has become detached (McAlpine, after Bonhag).

fourth longitudinal vein, in adult Diptera, part of media posterior (T-B, after Williston).

fovea (pl., **foveae**), a pit (T-B; R. W. Brown); in Poduromorpha (Collembola, a region of cuticle with fine granulations in contrast to adjacent areas (Christiansen and Bellinger); in ♂ Pieridae (Lepidoptera), a pit sometimes covered by a sclerotized flap, in central region of valva (Tuxen, after Klots); in ♂ Siphonaptera, notch on inner side of basimere corresponding with denticle (denticulus) at anterior margin of telomere (sometimes vice versa) (Tuxen, after Jordan and Rothschild); see foveola.

foveate, foveatus (Latin), pitted with numerous, regular, depressions or pits (foveae) (T-B; Harris, after R. W. Brown, and Marchant and Charles); see foveolate, lacunose, and punctate.

foveola (pl., **foviolae**), small deep pit or fovea (T-B; Harris); see fovea.

foveolate, foveolatus (Latin), with small deep pits; finely pitted (Harris, after R. W. Brown, and Marchant and Charles); see foveate and punctate.

foveolet, foveola, q.v. (T-B).

fowl spirochaetosis, disease of chickens, turkeys, and geese, caused by the spirochaete *Borrelia anserine* and transmitted by the fowl tick, *Argus persicus* (Acari: Argasidae) (Borror et al.).

fractate, geniculate, q.v. (T-B).

fractate antenna, geniculate antenna, q.v. (T-B).

fracticipit, in adult Siphonaptera, possessing a complete transverse interantennal groove connecting antennal fossae, dividing frons from occiput (Dunnet, in CSIRO); see integricipit.

fracture, in wings of Heteroptera (Hemiptera), costal fracture, q.v. (T-B).

fractus (Latin), broken (T-B; R. W. Brown); see geniculate (T-B).

fragile, easily breakable; thin and brittle (T-B).

fragmentum of coxopodite, in ♂ Planipennia, paramere, q.v. (Tuxen, after Ferris).

frass, solid larval insect excrement (T-B); plant fragments made by a wood-boring insects, usually mixed with excrement (Borror et al.); see feces.

frayed setae, in Coccoidea (Hemiptera: Sternorrhyncha), clavate setae in which the margin of the distal part is indented or toothed (T-B, after MacGillivray).

free, unrestricted in movement; detached; not firmly joined with or united to any other part (T-B); said of pupae when all the parts and appendages are separately encased as in Coleoptera (T-B).

free mesodermal cell, hemocyte, q.v. (T-B).

free pupa, exarate pupa, q.v. (T-B; Leftwich).

free water, in any chemical compound, such as protoplasm, water that may be evaporated out without changing the composition or formula of the compound (T-B); see bound water.

free wax cell, in the hemolymph of Aphidoidea and Coccoidea (Hemiptera: Sternorrhyncha), oenocyte, q.v. (Tulloch).

frenal area, in adult Chalcididae (Hymenoptera), sclerite behind the mesoscutellum (Gauld and Bolton); see mesopostnotum.

Frenatae, collective term for those Lepidoptera with a more or less well-marked frenulum in the adult, including the Ditrysia and Heteroneura (T-B; Borror et al.).

frenate, having a frenulum (T-B).

frenelum, in ♂ *Zygaena* (Lepidoptera: Zygaenidae), proximal strongly sclerotized lamellae of lamina ventralis of aedoeagus (Tuxen, after Loritz).

frenular bristles, in many ♀ Lepidoptera, bristles composing frenulum (Chapman).

frenulum, in many adult Lepidoptera, the spine, in males, and the bristles, in females, arising from the base of the costa of the hind wings, projecting beneath the forewing, whose function is to unite the wings in flight (T-B); in Cicadidae (Hemiptera: Auchenorrhyncha), the triangular lateral piece on the mesonotum which connects with the trochlea (T-B);

frenulum hook, in many ♂ Lepidoptera, retinaculum, q.v. (T-B).

frenum (pl., **frena**), that which holds things together; a lunate or triangular posterobasal portion of the wing in Odonata and Trichoptera; see tendo; in Heteroptera (Hemiptera), the lateral groove in the upper margin of the scutellum into which fits or catches the channeled locking device on the lower edge of the clavus of the hemelytron; in ♂ Riodinidae (Lepidoptera), heavily sclerotized strap, firmly attached to the aedoeagus, which it attaches to the bases of the valvae (Tuxen, after Clench).

fringe, an edging of hair, scales, or other processes extending well beyond a margin and usually of even length (T-B); in Asterolecaniidae (Hemiptera: Sternorrhyncha), the marginal band of glassy threads of wax excreted from the multilocular pores (T-B; Kosztarab and Kozár); in adult Lepidoptera, scales or hairs projecting beyond the margins of the wing membrane (T-B) (see marginal scales); in pupal Chironomidae (Diptera), hairlike or filamentous setae at extreme lateral margins of anal lobe (Saether).

fringe cilium (pl. **cilia**), in macropterous Thysanoptera, long straight or wavy hairs or setae borne in single or double rows by the wing margins; in Terebrantia (Thysanoptera), inserted in 8-shaped sockets and capable of being flipped from one side of the 8 the to other, being unsocketed in Tubulifera (Mound et al.).

fringe scale, in many winged insects, any scale in the wing fringe (Harbach and Knight); in adult Culicidae (Diptera), one of the long fusiform scales occurring in a longitudinal row along the posterior margin of the wing (Harbach and Knight, after Theobald).

fringe setae, in Coccoidea (Hemiptera: Sternorrhyncha), the transverse row of setae apically on the venter of the anal tube (T-B, after MacGillivray).

fringed plates, in Coccoidea (Hemiptera: Sternorrhyncha), pectinae, q.v. (T-B, after MacGillivray).

frog, articular pan, q.v. (T-B).

froghopper, a member of the superfamily Cercopoidea (Hemiptera: Auchenorrhyncha) (Woodward et al., in CSIRO).

frons, the unpaired sclerite of the head lying between the epicranial arms, bearing the median ocellus (T-B, after Imms); the upper anterior portion of the head capsule, usually a distinct sclerite between the epicranium and clypeus (T-B, after Tillyard); in Siphonaptera, that part of the anterior dorsal wall of the head in front of the antennal groove and the falx (T-B, after Comstock); in Diptera, that part of the vertex which extends from the base of the antennae to the upper base of the head (T-B, after Comstock); in larval Chironomidae (Diptera), frontal apotome, q.v. (Saether).

frons basalis, in ♂ Hymenoptera, ventral gonocoxal bridge, q.v. (Tuxen, after Beck).

front, frons, q.v. (T-B).

frontal, of or pertaining to the frons (T-B); see anterior.

frontal apotome, in pupal Chironomidae (Diptera), plate in front of and between covering case of pedicel, usually carrying frontal setae and often cephalic tubercles (Saether); in some larval Chironomidae (Diptera), dorsal sclerite of head carrying frontal setae (S4 and S5) (Saether); see frontoclypeal apotome.

frontal area, in Hymenoptera, the region of the head located between the antennal furrows, the frontal crest and the ocellar furrow (T-B); in ants, a small demarcated usually triangular space in the midline just above or back of the clypeus (T-B, after Wheeler).

frontal bristles, in adult Diptera, frontals, q.v. (T-B).

frontal carina (pl., **frontal carinae**), a longitudinal ridge on the frons, mesad of the antennae in some adult Hymenoptera (e.g., Formicidae), ridgelike posterior extension of frontal lobe onto frons (Gauld and Bolton; Borror et al.); see frontal ridge.

frontal costa, in Orthoptera, frontal ridge, q.v. (T-B); see median carina and lateral carina.

frontal crest, in some adult Hymenoptera, an elevation extending across the head just above the toruli, usually being limited on each side by the antennal furrows, but sometimes extending across the antennal furrows nearly to the margin of the compound eyes; frequently interrupted by the median fovea, when it is said to be broken (T-B).

frontal dilators of the pharynx, one or more pairs of slender muscles arising on the frons and inserted on the anterior part of the pharynx (T-B, after Snodgrass).

frontal disc, in larval Muscomorpha (Diptera), a prominent histoblast upon which the rudiment of an antenna is developed (T-B, after Comstock).

frontal fastigium, in Tetrigidae (Orthoptera), a process of the face extending dorsad between the antennae and meeting or nearly meeting the fastigium of the vertex (T-B).

frontal fissure, in adult Diptera, ptilinal fissure, q.v. (T-B).

frontal ganglion, small ganglion of the stomatogastric nervous system, lying above the oesophagus in front of the brain, acting as a motor relay center, coordinating local sensory input with premotor excitation from the brain (T-B; Chapman).

frontal ganglion connectives, the connectives between the tritocerebral ganglia and the frontal ganglion (T-B, after Snodgrass).

frontal gland, in soldier termites of the Rhinotermitidae and Termitidae (esp. Nasutitermitinae) (Isoptera), a large median gland beneath the integument of the head, opening by a median pore, which produces a milky defense secretion and an alarm pheromone (T-B; Chapman); see nasute soldier.

frontal lobe(s), in Psyllidae (Hemiptera: Sternorrhyncha), 2 lobes or swellings more or less completely divided by a suture in which an ocellus is situated; in some adult Hymenoptera (e.g., Formicidae), a cuticular outgrowth, projecting over torulus, partially or entirely shielding the antennal articulation (Gauld and Bolton).

frontal lunule, in adults Schizophora (Diptera: Brachycera: Muscomorpha), a small oval or crescentic space above the bases of the antennae formed by and below the transverse ptilinal fissure (Colless and McAlpine, in CSIRO).

frontal nerve, a nerve arising anteriorly from the frontal ganglion (T-B; Chapman).

frontal ocellus, in Isoptera, fontanelle, q.v. (T-B).

frontal orbits, in adult Diptera, fronto-orbital plates, q.v. (T-B, after Curran); in adult Hymenoptera, lateral margins of frons adjacent to the compound eyes (T-B, after MacGillivray; Gauld and Bolton); see facial orbits.

frontal organ, in Lepismatidae (Zygentoma), a median structure on the frons representing reduced median and lateral ocelli (Watson, in CSIRO); in Isoptera, fontanelle, q.v. (Gay, in CSIRO).

frontal pits, anterior tentorial pits, q.v. (T-B, after Crampton).

frontal plate, in pupal Chironomidae (Diptera), frontal apotome, q.v. (Saether); in some adult Schizophora (Diptera: Brachycera: Muscomorpha), differentiated lower portion of fronto-orbital plates (McAlpine).

frontal plate of the tentorium, in Blattaria, the basally fused anterior arms of the tentorium which form a broad plate (T-B, after Imms).

frontal pore, in Isoptera, fontanelle, q.v. (Leftwich).

frontal process, in larval Agromyzidae (Diptera: Muscomorpha), a cuticular projection on the head that may be straight or curved, sometimes expanded apically like a club (Ferrar).

frontal processes, in adult Diptera, antennal processes, q.v. (T-B).

frontal ridge, in Orthoptera, a raised area on the face (Otte, pers. comm.); in adult Coleoptera, a sharp ridge on the dorsal margin of the eye, extending forward (T-B); see median carina.

frontal sac, in adult Diptera, ptilinum, q.v. (Leftwich).

frontal setae, in larval Lepidoptera, 2 setae (F1, F2) borne on the frons or frontoclypeus (Peterson; Stehr); in some adult Schizophora (Diptera: Brachycera), setae on frontal plate (McAlpine); in pupal Chironomidae (Diptera), pair of setae usually situated on frontal apotome, but occasionally below on prefrons (Saether); in larval Chironomidae (Diptera), cephalic setae S4 and S5 situated on frontal apotome (Saether); in adult Diptera, frontals, q.v. (Saether).

frontal stripe, in adult Diptera, frontal vitta, q.v. (T-B; Colless and McAlpine, in CSIRO).

frontal suture, the suture formed by the epicranial arms (T-B, after Crampton); in adult Diptera, ptilinal fissure, q.v. (T-B); in Coleoptera, frontoclypeal suture, q.v. (T-B).

frontal triangle, in ♂ Diptera, the triangular space, between the eyes, and below limited by a line drawn through base of antennae; the triangle in holoptic flies bounded above by the eyes and below by the antennae (Curran).

frontal tubercle(s), in Isoptera, nasus, q.v. (T-B); in certain Aphididae (Hemiptera: Sternorrhyncha), the raised structure upon which the antennae are placed (T-B, after J. B. Smith); in adult Chironomidae (Diptera), pair of small lobes just above the antennae probably representing remains of reduced ocelli (Saether).

frontal tuft, in adult Culicidae (Diptera), a specialized name applied to a group of erect elongate simple setae and fusiform scales on interocular space and adjacent vertex, being applied particularly to anophelines (Harbach and Knight, after Kirkpatrick).

frontal vesicle, in Aeshnidae and other Odonata, a swelling between the compound eyes, bearing the ocelli (T-B, after Garman).

frontal vitta, in adult Schizophora (Diptera: Brachycera), relatively elastic median area of frons between fronto-orbital plates, q.v. (T-B, after Curran; McAlpine).

frontal warts, in pupal Chironomidae (Diptera), wartlike tubercles on frontal apotome in addition to cephalic tubercles (Saether).

frontalia, in adult Diptera, interfrons, q.v. (T-B).

frontalin, sex pheromone in ♂ Scolytidae (Coleoptera), i.e., 1,5-dimethyl-6,8-dioxabicyclo (3.2.1) octane (Chapman).

frontals, in adult Diptera, bristles situated along the inner edge of the parafrontals (T-B, after Curran); in adult Chironomidae (Diptera), group of setae occasionally present ventral to inner verticals (Saether).

frontoclypeal, of or pertaining to the frontoclypeus (T-B).

frontoclypeal apotome, in larval Diptera, fused clypeus and frontal apotome (Teskey, in McAlpine); in larval Trichoptera, frontoclypeus, q.v. (Wiggins).

frontoclypeal area, that part of the insect head between the antennae or the frontal sutures (when present) and the base of the labrum (T-B, after Snodgrass); see frontoclypeus.

frontoclypeal membrane, in adult Muscomorpha (Diptera: Brachycera), broad flexible membrane separating clypeus from face (McAlpine).

frontoclypeal sulcus, frontoclypeal suture, q.v. (Chapman).

frontoclypeal suture, the suture between the frons and the clypeus (T-B); in larval Chironomidae (Diptera), interantennal sulcus, q.v. (Saether); see epistomal suture.

frontoclypeolabral apotome, in some larval Chironomidae (Diptera), dorsal sclerite consisting of fused labral sclerites, clypeus and frontal apotome, carrying cephalic setae S1–S5 or S2–S5, e.g., some Tanypodinae and a few Orthocladiinae (Saether).

frontoclypeus, the combined frons and clypeus when the suture between them is obsolete (T-B, after Comstock); in larval Diptera, frontoclypeal apotome, q.v. (Teskey, in McAlpine); see epistoma.

frontogenal suture, subantennal suture, q.v. (T-B), or epicranial arm (T-B, after MacGillivray); in adult Diptera, suture running dorsally from the anterior tentorial pit toward the base of the antenna (McAlpine, after Matsuda).

fronto-orbital area, in adult Diptera, fronto-orbital plate, q.v. (Colless and McAlpine, in CSIRO).

fronto-orbital bristles, in adult Diptera, fronto-orbital setae, q.v. (T-B, after J. B. Smith; Borror et al.).

fronto-orbital plate, in adult Schizophora (Diptera: Brachycera), lateral plate between frontal vitta and compound eye (McAlpine).

fronto-orbital setae, in adult Schizophora (Diptera: Brachycera), setae arising on fronto-orbital plate (McAlpine).

fronto-orbital setulae, in adult Schizophora (Diptera: Brachycera), setulae arising from fronto-orbital plate (McAlpine).

frontoparietal region, in larval Symphyta (Hymenoptera), dorsal region of epicranium lateral to the frontal sutures (Gauld and Bolton).

froth glands, in nymphs of Cercopidae (Hemiptera: Auchenorrhyncha), glands of Batelli, q.v. (T-B, after Comstock).

fructose, $C_6H_{12}O_6$; a monosaccharide, being an isomer of dextrose, found in sweet fruits and honey.

fulcral, of or pertaining to a fulcrum of a lever or similar mechanism (T-B).

fulcral plate, in ♀ Hymenoptera, gonangulum, q.v. (T-B; Tuxen).

fulcral strut, in ♂ Siphonaptera, fulcrum, q.v. (Tuxen, after Snodgrass).

fulcrant trochanter, continued along the femur but not intervening between it and the coxa, as in carabids (Coleoptera: Carabidae) (T-B).

fulcrum (pl., **fulcra**), a prop or support (T-B); in entognathous hexapods (Protura, Collembola, and Diplura), a Y-shaped sclerite within the head, corresponding to the posterior tentorial arms of the Ectognatha (Wallace and Mackerras, after Manton, in CSIRO); in ♂ Lycaenidae (Lepidoptera), sclerotized medioventral support for aedoeagus and part of fultura inferior (Tuxen, after Bethune-Baker); in ♂ Siphonaptera, apodemal strut, q.v. (Tuxen, after Snodgrass); in adult Muscomorpha (Diptera), U-shaped clypeus and skeleton of cibarial pump (McAlpine); in ♀ Chironomidae (Diptera), pivot of gonocoxite IX against knob on gonocoxapodeme (Saether); in adult Chironomidae (Diptera), cibarial pump, q.v. (Saether); in larval Chironomidae (Diptera), supporting apodemes of premento-hypopharyngeal complex (Saether); in ♀ Hymenoptera, tergite IX (Symphyta) or combined gonocoxites IX (Aculeata); in ♂ Lepidoptera, juxta, q.v (Tuxen, after Snodgrass).

fulcrum penis, in ♂ Anthomyiidae (Diptera), the complex formed by the hypandrium, pre- and postgonites and intromittent organ, with its appendages (Tuxen, after Schnabl and Dziedzicki).

fulgid, fulgidus (Latin), shining; gleaming (T-B; R. W. Brown).

Fulgoriformes, Fulgoroidea, q.v. (Hennig).

Fulgoroidea, superfamily within the Auchenorrhyncha (Hemiptera), including the Fulgoridae and many other families, the members of which possess elongate, widely-separated midcoxae and an enlarged pedicel of the antenna with numerous wartlike sensilla (Woodward et al., in CSIRO).

Fulgoromorpha, Fulgoroidea, q.v. (Hennig).

fuliginous, fuliginosus (Latin), sooty black (T-B; R. W. Brown)

full bibliographical synonymy, a reasonably complete list of references to a given taxon arranged so as simultaneously to serve the need of nomenclature (chronology of names) and zoology (pertinent taxonomic and biological sources) (Mayr); see synonymy.

fultella, in ♂ Tephritoidea (Diptera), aedeagal apodeme, q.v., when it is furnished with a pair of lateral processes extending to the hypandrium (Tulloch, after Munro).

fultura (pl., **fulturae**), suspensory sclerite, q.v. (T-B); in ♂ Hepialidae (Lepidoptera), one of a pair of rectangular sclerites extending into abdomen from sternum IX (Tuxen, after Stekolnikov).

fultura inferior (pl., **fulturae inferiores**), in ♂ Lepidoptera, sclerotized structures of the ventral part of the diaphragma, ventrad of the aedoeagus, thus including the structures of the ventral part of the anellus and of the juxta (Tuxen, after Petersen); in ♂ Lycaenidae (Lepidoptera), forked penis support, q.v. (Tuxen, after Stempffer).

fultura penis, in ♂ Lepidoptera, inclusive term for all the sclerotized structures of the diaphragma, viz. fultura inferior and fultura superior, including anellus, transtilla and juxta (Tuxen, after Petersen).

fultura superior (pl., **fulturae superiores**), in ♂ Lepidoptera, sclerotized structures of the dorsal part of the diaphragma, dorsad of the aedoeagus, and thus including the structures of the dorsal part of the anellus and of the transtilla (Tuxen, after Petersen).

fulvescent, with a reddish-yellow (T-B).

fulvid, fulvous, fulvus (Latin), reddish-yellow (T-B; R. W. Brown).

fulvo-aeneous, brass-colored (T-B; R. W. Brown).

fumate, fumatus, fumeus, q.v. (T-B).

fumeus (Latin), smoke-colored (T-B).

fumigant, a substance or mixture of substances which produces gas, vapor, fume, or smoke inteneded to destroy insect and other pests (Pfadt).

fumose, fumeus, q.v. (T-B).

function, the work or duty which a given part or organ normally performs (T-B).

functional, of or pertaining to function (T-B); functioning or acting (T-B).

Fundal (trade name), chlordimeform, q.v. (Pfadt).

fundament, the beginning or foundation of a structure in the embryo (T-B, after Folsom and Wardle).

fundarima, the fissure, line or furrow marking the line of fusion of the stipulae (T-B, after MacGillivray).

fundatrigenia (pl., **fundatrigeniae**), in Aphididae (Hemiptera: Sternorrhyncha), daughter of fundatrix living on the primary host (T-B, after Imms).

fundatrix (pl., **fundatrices**), in Aphididae (Hemiptera: Sternorrhyncha), apterous viviparous parthenogenetic ♀ which emerges in the spring from overwintering eggs (T-B, after Imms).

fundatrix spuria, in Aphididae (Hemiptera: Sternorrhyncha), migrantes, q.v. (T-B).

fundus, bottom; base (T-B; R. W. Brown).

fundus bursae (pl., **fundi bursae**), in ♀ Lepidoptera, the cephalad extremity of corpus bursae (Tuxen, after Petersen).

funeral pheromone, among social insects a chemical cue that indicates that a nestmate is dead (Matthews and Matthews).

fungicide, any substance that kills fungi or inhibits the growth of the spores or hyphae (Pfadt).

fungicolous, living in or on fungi (T-B).

fungivorous, fungus-feeding (T-B).

fungus comb, in nests of Macrotermitinae (Isoptera: Termitidae), a spongy, dark reddish-brown material made by the workers from the excreta, on which they make their fungus beds (Thorne, pers. comm.).

fungus cultivation, cultivation of fungi as food by ants (Hymenoptera: Formicidae) and termites (Isoptera) (Leftwich).

fungus garden, a special chamber in the nest in which certain ants (Hymenoptera: Formicidae: Myrmecinae: Attini) cultivate fungi for food (T-B; Brown, in Parker); in Macrotermitinae (Isoptera: Termitidae), fungus comb, q.v. (T-B).

funicle, that part of the flagellum of the antenna proximal to the club (T-B, after Comstock; Riek, in CSIRO), in insects with geniculate antennae, e.g. Curculionidae (Coleoptera) and ants (Hymenoptera: Formicidae), funicle + pedicel (Britton, Riek, in CSIRO; Borror et al.).

funicular joint, in Hymenoptera, any joint of the funicle, q.v. (T-B).

funiculate, funiculatus, whiplike; long, slender, composed of many flexible joints (T-B).

funicule, funiculus (Latin), funicle, q.v. (T-B).

funiculus, funicle, q.v. (T-B).

funis (Latin), line; cord (R. W. Brown); in adult Diptera, the bar on which the pseudotracheae terminate (T-B, after MacGillivray).

funnel, peritrophic membrane, q.v. (T-B).

funnel-shaped appendages, in ♀ Phasmida, appendages posteriorly on abdominal segment VIII (Tuxen).

Furadan (trade name), carbofuran, q.v. (Pfadt).

furca (pl., **furcae**), a fork (T-B; R. W. Brown); in a thoracic segment of higher insects, Y-shaped internal apodeme formed through the approximation and fusion of the paired sternal apophyses, serving as a site for muscle attachment (T-B; Chapman); in Collembola, furcula, q.v. (T-B); in ♂ *Lycaenesthes* (Lepidoptera: Lycaenidae) and *Ennomos* (Lepidoptera: Geometridae), sclerotized structure of juxta, either a median, furcate process or a pair of diverging arms, sometimes asymmetrical (Tuxen, after Bethune-Baker, Pierce), in other ♂ Geometridae, part of sacculus (Tuxen, after Pierce); in ♂ Siphonaptera, Ford's sclerites, q.v. (Tuxen, after Günther); in ♀ Nematocera and orthorrhaphous Brachycera (Diptera), genital fork, q.v. (Tuxen; McAlpine).

furcae maxillares, in Psocoptera, laciniae, q.v. (T-B, after Comstock; Mockford, pers. comm.).

furcal arms, arms of furca within thorax (T-B).

furcal orifice, furcal pit, q.v. (T-B).

furcal pit, external pit on thoracic sternum marking the invaginated furca.

furcasternal suture, in adult Culicidae (Diptera), discrimen, q.v. (Harbach and Knight, after Owen).

furcasternum, a distinct part of the sternum of some insects bearing the furca (T-B); see sternuellum.

furcate, fucated, furcatus (Latin), forked (T-B).

furcate setae, in Coccoidea (Hemiptera: Sternorrhyncha), frayed setae, q.v.; in ♂ *Tanytarsus heusdensis* (Diptera: Chironomidae), lamellate setae of median volsella basally slender, straplike, apically spilt into long points (Saether).

furcella, spina, q.v., of thoracic sternum (T-B, after MacGillivray).

furcellina, the pit or thickening on the outer surface of the spinasternum marking the invagination of the spina (T-B, after MacGillivray).

furcina, sternal apophyseal pit, q.v. (T-B, after MacGillivray).

furcula (Latin), a forked process (T-B); in Collembola, the more or less forked spring or leaping appendage borne on the fourth abdominal segment (T-B; Wallace and Mackerras, in CSIRO); in Orthoptera, a pair of backwardly directed appendages which overlie in a more or less forked position the base of the supraanal plate (T-B); in larval Papilionidae (Lepidoptera), osmeterium, q.v. (T-B); in ♀ Hymenoptera, detached notum, q.v. (Tuxen, after Snodgrass).

furcula supraanalis, in Orthoptera, suranal fork, q.v. (T-B).

furcular, of or pertaining to a furcula (T-B).

furred, covered with short, dense decumbent hair resembling fur (T-B).

furuncular, boillike.

fuscescent, becoming brown; with a brown shading (T-B).

fuscoferruginous, brownish rust red (T-B).

fuscopiceous, pitch black with a brown tinge or admixture (T-B).

fuscorufous, red-brown, approaching liver brown (T-B).

fuscotestaceous, dull reddish brown (T-B).

fuscous, fuscus, dark brown, approaching black; a plain mixture of black and red (T-B).

fused, run together; as when 2 normally separated markings or sclerites become confluent and have a common outline (T-B).

fusi (sing., **fusus**), the spinners; organs consisting of 2 retractile pieces, issuing from the mammulae and rendering threads (T-B, after Jardine).

fusi piliformis, in Coccoidea (Hemiptera: Sternorrhyncha), plates, q.v. (T-B, after MacGillivray).

fusi spiniformis, in Coccoidea (Hemiptera: Sternorrhyncha), the plates, q.v. (T-B, after MacGillivray).

fusiform, fusiformate, spindle-shaped, i.e., broad at the middle and narrowing toward the ends (T-B).

fusiform leucocyte, plasmatocyte, q.v. (Tulloch).

fusion, a joining and welding together of adjacent, ordinarily discrete parts of sclerites of the insect body (T-B).

fusion plate, in ♂ Capniidae (Plecoptera), internal plate joining sub-anal plates (Tuxen, after Hanson).

fustis (pl., **fustes**), a club (R. W. Brown); in ♀ Phlaeothripidae (Thysanoptera), unpaired sclerotized thickening in roof of vagina appearing in macerated whole mounts as a rod in abdominal segment IX (Tuxen, after Priesner; Heming).

fusulus, spinneret, q.v. (T-B).

G

gaead, young of ametabolous, insects (Leftwich); see nymph and larva.

galactose, $C_6H_{12}O_6$, a sugar differing slightly from glucose in its molecular arrangement, formed by hydrolysis of lactose (T-B).

galarastra, the rastra on the galea of the maxilla (T-B, after MacGillivray).

galea (pl., **galeae**), the outer lobe of the maxilla, usually two-jointed, often hoodlike, subject to great modifications in Hymenoptera and Diptera, and joined to form the proboscis in adult Glossata (Lepidoptera) (T-B, after J. B. Smith, Tillyard); in adult Diptera, maxillary blade, q.v. (McAlpine, after authors).

galeafimbrium, galarastra, q.v. (T-B, after MacGillivray).

galearia, in adult Hymenoptera, the setiferous lobe of the basigalea (T-B, after MacGillivray).

galearis, in adult Lepidoptera, proboscis, q.v. (T-B, after MacGillvray).

galeate, furnished with a galea (T-B).

Galecron (trade name), chlordimeform, q.v. (Pfadt).

galeotheca, that part of the pupal case that covers the galea (T-B).

gall, an abnormal growth of plant tissues caused by various organisms which irritate the plant and possibly lead to the production of some type of growth hormone (T-B; Leftwich).

gall nuts, any galls of the hard, round, woody type (Leftwich).

gall wasp, a member of the family Cynipidae (Hymenoptera: Cynipoidea) which causes gall formation in plants (T-B; Leftwich).

galla, gall, q.v. (T-B).

galleries, in Embiidina, tunnels and chambers composed of silk and debris, usually fecal (Ross, in CSIRO).

gallicola (pl., **gallicolae**), any insect that produces and lives in a gall, but more particularly the ground dwelling stages of Phylloxeridae and Adelgidae) (Hemiptera: Sternorrhyncha) (T-B; Leftwich).

gallicolae migrantes, winged gall-making forms which fly to an intermediate host, e.g., *Chermes* (Hemiptera: Sternorrhyncha: Adelgidae) of spruce, and diapause as first instar nymphs (T-B, after Imms).

gallicolous, dwelling in galls, whether as producers or inquilines (T-B).

galliphagous, feeding upon galls or gall tissue (T-B).

gallivorous, galliphagous, q.v. (T-B).

galvanotropism, movement in response to electric currents (T-B).

gamergate, in many Ponerinae (Hymenoptera: Formicidae), fertilized, ovipositing worker that assumes the reproductive function of the queen caste (Brown, pers. comm., after Peters); see gynecoid.

gamete, a reproductive cell, sperm or egg, having the haploid number of chromosomes (T-B; Tulloch).

gametocyte, a gamete-producing cell (Tulloch); the cell of the malaria-causing protozoan *Plasmodium* found in the red blood cells of man, and which when taken into the stomach of a mosquito gives rise to gametes (Tulloch) (see microgametocyte and macrogametocyte).

gametogenetic egg, in Aphididae (Hemiptera: Sternorrhyncha), the egg of true sexual forms (T-B, after Comstock); see pseudovum.

gamma taxonomy, evolutionary biology, q.v. (Mayr).

gamogenesis, reproduction through fertilization (T-B); see parthenogenesis.

ganglia allata, corpora allata, q.v. (T-B).

gangliform, ganglioform, ganglioniform, of the form of a ganglion (T-B).

ganglion (pl., **ganglia**), a nerve center composed of a cell mass and fibers; the white disclike bodies connected by a double cord, lying just above the ventral surface within the body (T-B); see brain, frontal ganglion, ingluvial ganglion, and suboesophageal ganglion.

ganglion ventriculare, hypocerebral ganglion, q.v. (T-B).

ganglionate, furnished with or consisting of ganglia (T-B).

ganglionic cells, nerve cells of the ganglia (T-B).

ganglionic center, a coalescence of 2 or more ganglia of adjoining segments (T-B).

ganglionic commissure, the short nerve cord connecting any 2 adjacent ganglia in series (T-B, after Wardle).

ganglionic layer, lamina ganglionaris, q.v. (T-B).

ganglionic plate, lamina ganglionaris, q.v. (T-B, after Needham).

Gardona (trade name), stirofos, q.v. (Pfadt).

Garvox (trade name), bendiocarb, q.v. (Pfadt).

gaseous plastron, in aquatic insects, plastron, q.v. (Tulloch).

gaster, in adult Apocrita (Hymenoptera), the swollen part of the abdomen behind the waist, including abdominal segments III (or IV) through X and always excluding the propodeum (Chapman; Brown, pers. comm.); see metasoma.

gasterotheca, that part of the theca or pupal case which encloses the abdomen (T-B).

gastral groove, a groovelike invagination in the middle of the ventral plate of the insect egg (T-B, after Imms).

gastric, belonging to the midgut (T-B); in adult Apocrita (Hymenoptera), of or pertaining to the gaster (T-B).

gastric caecum, midgut caecum, q.v. (T-B).

gastrilegous, having pollen baskets under the abdomen (Tulloch, after Gaul).

gastrocoele, the gastrulation cavity; archenteron (T-B, after Snodgrass).

gastrocoeli, in some adult Hymenoptera, thyrdida, q.v. (T-B; Riek, in CSIRO).

gastroileal folds, in insects, the boundary between the intestine and the chylific stomach or ventricle, which forms a valve (T-B).

gastrula, in the insect embryo, the stage resembling a sac, with an outer layer of epiblastic cells and an inner layer of hypoblastic cells; the embryo after gastrulation (T-B).

gastrulation, the process of forming a gastrula (T-B); in embryonic development, formation of mesoderm and endoderm by invagination, overgrowth or proliferation of the blastoderm (Chapman).

gated rhythm, periodical behavior of a population that occurs only once in an individual's life, e.g., mass emergence of cicadas (Hemiptera: Anchenorrhyncha: Cicadidae) (Matthews and Matthews).

gathering hairs, the soft, flattened, often hooked hairs on the tongue of bees (Apoidea) and other Hymenoptera (T-B).

gattine, type of flacherie of the silkworm, *Bombyx mori* (Lepidoptera: Bombycidae), said to be caused by a virus and concomitant infection by enterococci closely related to *Streptococcus faecalis,* in which the affected frequently becomes swollen and almost translucent (Steinhaus and Martignoni).

Gause's Rule, theory that no 2 species with identical ecological requirements can coexist in the same place (Mayr); see competitive exclusion.

Geadephaga, a purely descriptive group, consisting of the terrestrial families of the suborder Adephaga (Coleoptera), including Carabidae, Rhysodidae, Paussidae, Cicindelidae, and Trachypachidae (Crowson); see Caraboidea and Hyradephaga.

Gelastocoroidea, Ochteroidea, q.v.

gelatinous, of a jellylike texture or consistency; viscid (T-B).

Gelechioidea, superfamily within the Ditrysia (Lepidoptera), including the Gelichiidae, Oecophoridae, Coleophoridae, and many other families of very small to medium-sized moths, lacking chaetosemata and possessing an epiphysis and a 0-2-4 tibial spur formula; larvae concealed feeders (Common, in CSIRO).

geminate, geminatus (Latin), arranged in pairs composed of 2 similar parts; double; twinned (T-B).

geminate pores, in ♀ Coccoidea (Hemiptera: Sternorrhyncha), paired pores (Woodward et al., after Russell, in CSIRO).

geminivirus, plant viruses with isometeric inclusion bodies transmitted circulatively by various insects, e.g., certain Auchenorrhyncha (Hemiptera).

geminous, geminus (Latin), geminate, q.v. (T-B).

gemma, a bud or budlike organic growth (T-B).

gemmate, gemmatus, marked with metallic or bright colored spots (T-B).

gemmation, budding; reproduction by budding (T-B).

gemmiparous, having a form of asexual reproduction where new individuals arise as buds from the germ body of the parent (T-B).

gena (pl., **genae**), cheek, q.v. (R. W. Brown); the part of the cranium on each side below the eye (T-B); in Odonata, the area between the eyes and clypeus and mouthparts (T-B); in Orthoptera, the area below the eye and bounded by the subocular sulcus (anteriorly), the subgenal sulcus (ventrally), and the occipital sulcus (posteriorly) (Chapman); in adult Diptera, the space between the lower front of the eye and the subcranial cavity (T-B; McAlpine); in adult Culicidae (Diptera), the anterolateral area of the cranium extending posteroventrally from the anterior tentorial pit behind the clypeus and united ventrally with its mate between the compound eyes (Harbach and Knight, after Giles); in larval Chironomidae (Diptera), sclerite on each side of the head making up the larger portion of the head capsule (except frontal apotome and postmentum), meeting dorsally at the coronal suture when frontal apotome not reaching postoccipital margin (Saether).

genacerores, in Diaspididae (Hemiptera: Sternorrhyncha: Coccoidea), circumgenital pores, q.v. (T-B, after MacGillivray).

genal bridge, in some adult Hymenoptera, bridge formed posterior to labium by the fusion of the genae (Gauld and Bolton); see hypostomal bridge and postgenal bridge.

genal bristles, in adult Diptera, bristles on gena near the lower corner of the eye (T-B; McAlpine); see vibrissae.

genal carina, in adult Hymenoptera, carina delimiting postgena posterior to base of mandible (Gauld and Bolton).

genal comb, in adult Siphonaptera, a row of strong spines borne anteroventrally on the gena (T-B; Borror et al.); see ctenidia.

genal dilation, in many adult muscoid flies (Diptera), hairy, strongly sclerotized portion of gena lying below the genal groove and extending foward towards the vibrissal angle (McAlpine).

genal groove, in adult Schizophora (Diptera: Brachycera), a weakened, often depressed and groovelike area near the ventral limits of the ptilinal suture and the juncture of the gena and the parafacial (McAlpine).

genal lobe, in adult Siphonaptera, genal process, q.v. (Lewis, pers. comm.).

genal orbit, the part of gena adjacent to the compound eye (T-B, after MacGillivray; Gauld and Bolton).

genal plate, in Helotrephidae (Hemiptera: Heteroptera), ventral part of gena situated in front of lateral pronotal plate, q.v. (Papáček, Tonner, and Štys, from Esaki and China).

genal process, in adult Siphonaptera, the posterior extension of the gena, frequently terminating in a sharp point (Lewis, pers. comm.).

genal setae, in adult Chironomidae (Diptera), cephalic setae (S9 and S10) situated laterally on the head capsule posterior to larval eyes (Saether); in larval Lepidoptera, 2 setae (G1 and G2) on the gena of the head capsule, posteroventral of the stemmata (Common, after Hinton), setae MG1 and MG2 (Stehr).

genal sulcus, in adult Hymenoptera, molar sulcus, q.v. (Gauld and Bolton).

genaponta, hypostomal bridge, q.v. (T-B, after MacGillivray).

genatasinus, in ♂ Muscomorpha (Diptera), genital pouch, q.v. (T-B, after MacGillivray; Tuxen).

gene, unit of inheritance, carried in a chromosome, transmitted from generation to generation by the gametes, and controlling the development of the individual (T-B; Mayr); a certain length of a chromosome recognizable only in operational terms which in the classical genetic sense seems to act as a unit in (a) cell control and regulation, (b) inheritance and genetic recombination and (c) mutation (Tulloch).

gene flow, the exchange of genetic factors between populations owing to dispersal of zygotes or gametes (Mayr).

gene frequency, the percentage of a given gene in a population (Mayr).

gene pool, the totality of the genes of a given population existing at a given time (Mayr).

generalized, in biology, the comparative term used in contrast with specialized or cenogenetic to indicate an ancient or long-standing character as compared with one more recently evolved; an archaic, primitive or generalized type is one in which such ancient characters predominate (T-B, after Tillyard).

generation, from any given stage in the life cycle to the same stage in the offspring (T-B; Borror et al.); see brood.

generic name, a scientific name of a taxon at the rank of genus (ICZN); the first name of a binomen or a trinomen (ICZN).

Gene's organ, in ticks (Acari), an organ connected with egg-laying, glandular in structure, present only in the females and functional only at oviposition (T-B, after Matheson).

genetic drift, genetic changes in populations caused by random phenomena rather than by selection (Mayr).

genetic hermaphrodite, hermaphrodite, q.v. (T-B).

genetic load, in bisexual species, biologically inferior homozygotes produced in each generation by segregation (White, in CSIRO).

genetic recombination, a reshuffling of genetic material during meiosis (White, in CSIRO).

genicular arc, in Orthoptera, semilunar process, q.v. (T-B).

genicular lunette, in Caelifera (Orthoptera), an area of the genicular region of the hind femur immediately below the genicular arc (Key).

geniculate, geniculatus (Latin), knee-jointed, i.e., abruptly bent in an obtuse angle, e.g., as in the antennae of an ant (Hymenoptera: Formicidae) (T-B; Leftwich).

geniculum, a little knee or bend (T-B).

geniculus (penis), in ♂ Sphingidae (Lepidoptera), coecum penis (Tuxen, after Baltzer).

genital aperture, genital opening, q.v. (Tuxen).

genital apodeme, in ♂ Phthiraptera, basal apodeme. q.v. (Tuxen).

genital arch, in ♂ Diptera, epandrium, q.v. (McAlpine).

genital armature, armatura genitalis, q.v. (Tuxen).

genital atrium, in ♂ Auchenorrhyncha (Hemiptera), basal opening of aedeagus (Tuxen, after Young); in ♂ Heteroptera (Hemiptera), genital chamber, q.v. (Tuxen, after Leston).

genital block, in ♂ Auchenorrhyncha (Hemiptera), genital chamber with styles and phallic organs (transl. "bloc génital" Ribaut, after Tuxen).

genital canals, in ♀ Strepsiptera, unpaired tubes leading from hemocoele to brood canal (Tuxen; Chapman, after Clausen).

genital capsule, in ♂ Auchenorrhyncha (Hemiptera), abdominal segment IX (Tuxen); in ♂ Heteroptera (Hemiptera), pygophore, q.v. (Tuxen, after Usinger).

genital cavity, in ♀ and ♂ Plecoptera, genital chamber, q.v. (Tuxen, after Brinck); in ♀ Isoptera, vestibulum, q.v. (Tuxen, after Walker); in ♂ Heteroptera (Hemiptera), genital chamber, q.v. (Tuxen, after Christophers and Cragg; in ♂ Lepidoptera, the cavity enclosed by the valvae (Tuxen, after Gosse).

genital chamber, in some ♂ insects, ventral invagination between abdominal sterna IX and X containing phallic organs (Tuxen, after Snodgrass); in ♂ Protura, invagination between abdominal sterna XI and XII containing phallic organs (Tuxen); in ♂ Caelifera (Orthoptera), cavity formed by paraprocts, pallium, and subgenital plate (Tuxen; Chapman, after Uvarov); in ♂ Heteroptera (Hemiptera), the concavity of the pygophore, separated from the general body cavity by the diaphragm, and including the anal tube, phallus and parameres (Tuxen, after Snodgrass); in some ♀ insects, copulatory invagination cavity caudad of or above sternum VIII containing the gonopore and orifice of the spermatheca, often narrowed to form a tubular or pouchlike vagina (Tuxen, after Snodgrass); in ♀ Isoptera, vestibulum, q.v. (Tuxen); in ♀ Orthoptera, cavity between the subgenital plate, ventral body wall and anterior valvulae (Tuxen); in ♀ Dermaptera, chamber into which the common oviduct as well as the spermatheca and rectum open, formed by sterna VIII and IX dorsally (Tuxen, after Nel); in ♀ Heteroptera (Hemiptera), vagina, q.v. (Tuxen, after Bonhag and Wick); in ♀ Lepidoptera, sinus vaginalis, q.v. (Tuxen); in ♀ Siphonaptera, camera genitalis, q.v. (Tuxen, after Snodgrass); in ♀ Diptera, pouchlike or tubular chamber within the genital opening between abdominal segments VIII and IX (McAlpine); in ♀ Chironomidae (Diptera), vagina, q.v. (Saether).

genital cover, in ♂ Hymenoptera, abdominal sterna VIII and IX (transl. "couvercle génital" Radoszkowski, after Tuxen).

genital duct, gonoduct, q.v. (Tulloch); in ♂ Coleoptera, ductus ejaculatorius, q.v. (Tuxen).

genital ducts, in ♀ Strepsiptera, genital canals, q.v. (Reik, in CSIRO).

genital embracer, in ♂ Urostylidae (Hemiptera: Heteroptera), inferior process, q.v. (Tuxen, after Yang).

genital foramen, in ♂ Hymenoptera, opening in gonobase by which lumen of genitalia communicates with body cavity (Tuxen, after Michener).

genital fork, in many ♀ Nematocera and orthorrhaphous Brachycera

(Diptera), forked sclerite in the dorsal wall of the ♀ genital chamber, being a modification of abdominal sternite IX (McAlpine).

genital fossa, in ♂ Odonata, fenestra, q.v. (Tuxen, after Walker; O'Farrell, in CSIRO).

genital hamule(s), in ♂ insects, a little hook or plate covering the anal cavity (T-B); in ♂ Odonata, hamuli, q.v. (Tuxen); in ♂ Plecoptera, supraanal hook, q.v., or copulatory hook, q.v. (T-B); in ♂ Lepidoptera, uncus, q.v. (T-B).

genital hook(s), in ♂ Plecoptera, copulatory hook, q.v. (Tuxen, after Walker) or, hemitergal processes, q.v. (Tuxen, after Ricker); in ♂ Embiidina, dorsal talon, subventral flange, and tergal processes, q.v. (transl. "Genitalhaken" Verhoeff, after Tuxen).

genital lamella, in ♀ Chironomidae (Diptera), cercus, q.v. (Saether).

genital lobe(s), in ♂ Corduliidae and Libellulidae (Odonata), the produced end of the posterolateral angles of tergum II (Tuxen); in ♂ Plecoptera, hemitergal processes, q.v. (Tuxen, after Frison); in ♂ Zoraptera, clasping organs, q.v. (Tuxen, after Snodgrass); in ♀ Chironomidae (Diptera), cercus, q.v. (Saether).

genital meatus, in ♂ Odonata, the opening of the genital duct on the ventral surface of abdominal segment IX (Tuxen).

genital membrane, in ♀ Hymenoptera, remnant of the gonosternite forming a fold into which the ovipositor or sting is withdrawn (Tuxen, after E. L. Smith).

genital opening, the opening of the ductus ejaculatorius (♂) or ductus communis (♀) on the ventral surface (Tuxen); in ♂ Plecoptera, external orifice of the genital cavity (Tuxen, after Brinck); see primary gonopore.

genital orifice, in ♀ Diptera, genital opening, q.v. (McAlpine).

genital palps, in ♀ Coleoptera, styli, q.v. (Tuxen).

genital papilla(e), primary genital papillae, q.v. (Mackerras, in CSIRO); in ♂ Collembola, papilla genitalis, q.v. (Tuxen).

genital phragm, in ♂ Delphacidae (Hemiptera: Auchenorrhyncha), transverse wall in pygofer (Tuxen).

genital plate(s), in ♂ Collembola, papilla genitalis, q.v. (Tuxen, after K. Christiansen); in ♀ Collembola, abdominal sternum V, anterior to genital opening (Tuxen); in ♀ Plecoptera, subgenital plate, q.v. (Tuxen, after Needham and Claassen); in ♀ Isoptera, hypogynium, q.v. (Tuxen, after Fuller); in Phthiraptera, subgenital plate, q.v. (Tuxen); in ♂ Psyllidae (Hemiptera: Sternorrhyncha), hypandrium, q.v. (Tuxen) or proctiger (Tuxen, after Edwards); in ♀ Psyllidae (Hemiptera: Sternorrhyncha), ventral plate, q.v., or dorsal plate, q.v. (Tuxen); in ♀ Aphididae (Hemiptera: Sternorrhyncha), sternum VIII (Tuxen); in ♂ Cicadomorpha (Auchenorrhyncha) and some ♂ Enicocephalidae (Hemiptera: Heteroptera) (Hemiptera), a pair of usually horizontal, sometimes two-segmented plates posteroventral to abdominal sternum IX (Tuxen; Štys); in ♂ Pentatomoidea (Hemiptera: Heteroptera), superior lateral process, q.v. (Tuxen, after Baker); in ♂ Sialis (Megaloptera: Sialidae), gonarcus, q.v. (Tuxen, after Ross); in ♀ Coleoptera, hemisternites, q.v. (Tuxen, after Wilson); in ♀ Lepidoptera, sterigma, q.v. (Tuxen, after Pierce); in ♀ Mecoptera, medigynium, q.v. (Tuxen, after Byers); in ♂ Hymenoptera, abdominal sternum VIII (transl. "Genitalplatte" Enslin, after Tuxen).

genital pore, in ♂ Odonata, genital meatus, q.v. (Tuxen, after Tillyard); in ♂ Coleoptera, gonopore, q.v. (Tuxen).

genital pores, in ♂ Ephemeroptera, the openings of the sperm ducts at the end of the penis (T-B, after Needham); in ♀ Strepsiptera, openings of the genital canals into the brood canal (Tuxen).

genital pouch, in ♂ immature insects, median anterior invagination of the body wall between sterna IX and X, containing primary phallic lobes (transl. "Genitaltasche" Zander, after Tuxen); in ♂ Muscomorpha (Diptera), a pouch below (morphologically above) the hypandrium receiving tips of the surstyli and cerci (Tuxen); in ♂ Muscomorpha (Diptera: Brachycera), ventral pouch in the membrane adjoining the posterior margin of abdominal sternite V into which more posterior segments are telescoped (McAlpine).

genital ridges, in the insect embryo, thickenings of the splanchnic wall of the mesoderm in the abdominal region of the body, the cell groups of which are the rudiments of the testes or of the ovaries (T-B, after Snodgrass).

genital ring, in many ♂ Nematocera (Diptera), basal ring, q.v. (McAlpine).

genital sac, in ♂ Phthiraptera, endophallus, q.v. (Clay, in Tuxen; Lyal).

genital scale, in ♀ Auchenorrhyncha (Hemiptera), a sclerotized median process of abdominal sternum VII (Tuxen).

genital segment(s), the segments principally (but not exclusively) involved in the formation of copulatory organs, viz., in ♂ abdominal segment IX, in ♀ abdominal segments VIII and IX (Tuxen); in ♂ Psyllidae (Heteroptera: Sternorrhyncha), hypandrium, q.v. (Tuxen); in ♂ Heteroptera (Hemiptera), pygophore, q.v. (Tuxen, after Baker).

genital sheath, in ♂ Strepsiptera, aedeagus, q.v. (Tuxen, after Pierce).

genital space, in ♀ Scarabaeidae (Coleoptera), the vulvar part of the cloaca (as contrasted with the anal or rectal part) (transl. "Genitalraum" Heymons, in Tuxen).

genital spike, in ♂ Coccoidea (Hemiptera: Sternorrhyncha), penis sheath, q.v. (Tuxen).

genital styles, in ♂ Ephemeroptera, genostyles, q.v. (Tuxen, after Crass); in nymphs and most ♂ of Blattaria and Isoptera, styli, q.v., of abdominal segment IX (T-B; Alsop, pers. comm., after McKittrick); in ♂ Auchenorrhyncha (Hemiptera), styles, q.v. (Tuxen, after China).

genital tube(s), in ♂ Coleoptera, penis + tegmen + connecting membranes (Tuxen); in ♀ Strepsiptera, genital canals, q.v. (Tuxen, after Bohart); in ♀ Lepidoptera, ductus bursae, q.v. (Tuxen, after Pierce).

genital tubercles, in ♀ Coleoptera, styli, q.v. (Tuxen, after Wilson).

genital tuft, in ♂ Lepidoptera, a hair pencil, q.v., arising from a corema (T-B).

genital valve(s), in ♀ Odonata, lateral gonapophyses, q.v. (Tuxen); in ♂ Cicadoidea (Hemiptera: Auchenorrhyncha), abdominal sternum IX bearing a triangular or semilunar, ventral, horizontal plate (Tuxen); in ♀ Psyllidae (Hemiptera: Sternorrhyncha), ventral plate, q.v. (Tuxen) or, genital plates, q.v. (Tuxen, after Edwards); in ♂ *Sialis* (Megaloptera: Sialidae), sternum IX (transl. "Genitalklappe" Scitz, after Tuxen); in ♀ Coleoptera, hemisternites, q.v. (Tuxen, after Böving); in ♂ Mecoptera, gonocoxites, q.v. (Esben-Petersen).

genitalia, ectodermal structures of ♂ and ♀ insects involved in copulation, fertilization, and oviposition (T-B; Leftwich; Gauld and Bolton).

genitoanal chamber, in Aculeata (Hymenoptera), the chamber in which lie the ovipositor or the ♂ genitalia and the anal tube or proctiger (Tuxen, after Michener).

genitoanal cone, in some ♂ Phthiraptera, particularly Ischnocera, dorsal cone formed by abdominal segments IX–XI, which bears the genital and anal openings (transl. "Genitoanalkonus" von Kéler, in Tuxen).

genoholotype, orthotype, q.v. (T-B).

genolectotype, logotype, q.v. (T-B).

genome, the genetic material of an organism, i.e., a set of chromosomes with the genes that they contain (Steinhaus and Martignoni).

genostyles, in ♂ Ephemeroptera, one to multisegmented projections from posterior corners of sternum IX functioning during copulation (Tulloch; Tuxen).

genosyntype, one of a series of species upon which a genus is founded, no one species being mentioned as type (T-B); see type species.

genotype, type species, q.v. (T-B; ICZN); the genetic constitution of an individual or taxon (Mayr); see phenotype.

genovertical plate, in adult Diptera, fronto-orbital area, q.v. (T-B; Borror et al.).

genu, femorotibial joint, q.v. (T-B).

genus (pl., **genera**), an assemblage of species agreeing in some one character or series of characters (T-B); a category for a taxon including one species or a group of species, presumably of common phylogenetic origin (Mayr); a set of similar species of relatively recent common ancestry (Wilson); the rank within a genus group next below the family group and the species group (ICZN); a taxon of the rank of genus (ICZN).

genus group, in the hierarchy of classification the group of taxa between the family group and the species group, including taxa at the ranks of genus and subgenus (ICZN).

genus-group name, a scientific name of any genus or subgenus, including names for collective groups and for ichnotaxa at the genus-group level (ICZN).

genus name, generic name, q.v. (ICZN).

genus novum (Latin), new genus, hitherto undescribed, abbreviated "gen. nov." or "g. n." (T-B).

Geocorisae, a group formerly recognized within the Heteroptera, including the terrestrial bugs (Woodward et al., in CSIRO).

Geocorizae, Geocorisae, q.v. (Borror et al.).

Geodephaga, Geadephaga, q.v. (Hennig).

Geodromica, a grouping formerly recognized for the terrestrial Heteroptera in which the antennae are not concealed (T-B).

geographic isolate, a population that is separated by geographical barriers from the main body of the species (Mayr).

geographic isolation, the separation of a gene pool by geographic barriers (T-B; Mayr); the prevention of gene exchange between populations by geographical barriers (Mayr).

geographic orientation, object orientation exhibiting a lengthening of search (straight run) phase, grading into dispersal and migration (Matthews and Matthews, after Jander).

geographic subspecies, subspecies, q.v. (T-B, after Ferris).

geographical barriers, geographical features that serve to isolate populations and impede gene flow (Mackerras, in CSIRO).

geographical race, subspecies, q.v. (Mayr).

Geometroidea, a large, worldwide complex within the division Ditrysia (Lepidoptera), containing only the Geometridae, possessing broad winged, slender bodied adults with chaetosema, naked proboscis, basal abdominal typana, and wings often held erect over body at rest; larva crawl in a looping motion, usually with only last 2 pairs of abdominal prolegs present (Ferguson); Drepanoidea + Uranioidea + Geometroidea (Common, in CSIRO).

geophagous, feeding on earth (containing organic matter) (T-B).

Geophilomorpha, order within the subclass Epimorpha (Chilopoda), characterized by 14-segmented antennae, 29 or more pairs of legs, and lacking ocelli (Borror et al.).

geophilous, living on the ground (T-B).

geotaxis, orientation in relation to the earth or ground, including a tendency to move or crawl towards or into the earth (positive geotaxis) or away from the earth (negative geotaxis) (T-B; Leftwich).

geotropism, response to gravity (T-B).

geraniol, an alcohol formed from geranial, being a constituent of oil of orange-rind, cheap oil of lemon grass, and oil of citron (T-B); pheromone deposited by honey bees (Hymenoptera: Apidae), to mark an abundant source of nectar (Gilmour, in CSIRO).

germ ball, reproductive cells in larvae from which, exceptionally, young may develop as buds (T-B).

germ band, the area of thickened cells on the ventral side of the blastoderm which beomes the embryo (T-B, after Snodgrass).

germ cells, reproductive cells destined to become ova or spermatozoa, differentiated from the somatic cells during cell cleavage (T-B, after Snodgrass).

germ disc, germ band, q.v. (T-B).

germ plasm, that part of the germ cell which carries the hereditary characters (T-B); see somatoplasm.

germ tract, the cytoplasmic area of the blastula containing the germ cells; posterior polar plasm (T-B, after Snodgrass).

germarium (pl., **germaria**), in ♂ insects, portion of testis follicle, in which the germ cells divide to produce spermatogonia, usually located apically (apical germarium) but sometimes, e.g., in some Collembola, located laterally (parietal germarium) (T-B; Mackerras, in CSIRO; Chapman); in ♀ insects, portion of ovariole in which oocytes are produced from oogonia (T-B; Chapman); see ovary and testis.

germinal band, germ band, q.v. (T-B).

germinal disc, germ band, q.v. (T-B).

germinal epithelium, epithelial tissue which develops into the gametes (sex cells) (T-B); see also epithelium (T-B, after Klots).

germinal layers, in the early development of the embryo, the 3 layers of cells (T-B, after Tillyard); see ectoderm, mesoderm, and endoderm.

germinal vesicle, the nucleus of the insect egg (T-B, after Imms; Chapman).

gerontogeic, belonging to the Old World (T-B); see neogeic.

Gerroidea, superfamily with the infraorder Gerromorpha (Hemiptera: Heteroptera), including Hermatobatidae, Veliidae, and Gerridae (formerly including all families of Gerromorpha sensu Andersen), mostly with the pretarsus subapical and various other modifications for life on the water surface; predaceous, mostly pleustonic (sometimes marine), rarely epigeic, riparial, or hygropetric (Andersen).

Gerromorpha, infraorder within the Heteroptera, including members of the predatory, water-surface dwelling families, Mesoveliidae, Macroveliidae, Hydrometridae, Hebridae, Paraphrynoveliidae, Hermatobatidae, Gerridae, and Veliidae, characterized by recessed cephalic trichobothria and other attributes (Andersen).

gestation, the period during which the embryo or ovum is maturing in the body of the ♀ parent (T-B).

giant cell, teratocyte, q.v. (Tulloch).

giant chromosome, polytene chromosome, q.v. (Gilmour, in CSIRO).

giant fiber, axon of a giant nerve cell (Chapman).

giant neuron, nerve cell with axon of large diameter facilitating rapid transmission of an impulse (Matthews and Matthews); interneurone within the ventral nerve cord with much greater diameter than other interneurones, providing direct fast link between sensilla and effectors and considered to play an important role in evasive behaviour (Chapman).

gibba, a rounded protuberance or prominence (T-B); in Pyralidae (Lepidoptera), a protuberance on abdominal tergum IX of the pupa (Davis, pers. comm.).

gibbose, gibbosus (Latin), very crooked; twisted; protuberant (T-B; R. W. Brown); see gibbous.

gibbous, gibbus (Latin), humped; hump-backed; protuberant; bent; (T-B; R. W. Brown); see gibbose.

gill, a special, variously formed respiratory organ in the aquatic immature stages of many insects, by means of which they get dissolved oxygen from the water (T-B; Tulloch); see physical gill, plastron, rectal gill, spiracular gill, and tracheal gill.

gill tuft, a group of filamentous gills, generally lateral (T-B).

Gilson's gland, in larval Trichoptera, certain metameric thoracic glands regarded functionally as organs of excretion (T-B; Imms), on the prothorax opening at the tip of the prosternal horn (Nielsen).

gilvous, gilvus, flavous, q.v. (T-B)

gin traps, in pupal Coleoptera, defense organs formed by local sclerotization of opposable edges of adjacent abdominal segments (Britton, in CSIRO).

ginglymus, hinge joint permitting flexion in only one plane, e.g., mandibular articulation with gena in insects other than Archaeognatha (T-B; Mackerras, in CSIRO).

girdle, in ♂ Lepidoptera, silk band used to support pupa in many Papilionoidea and some Geometridae (Tuxen, after Bethune-Baker); in ♂ Siphonaptera, cingulum, q.v. (Tuxen, after Traub).

gizzard, part of the alimentary canal immediately behind the crop but anterior to the midgut, varying greatly in different insects but having as its main function the sifting of food before digestion and absorbtion in the midgut, frequently being equipped with hard plates or teeth and powerful circular muscles in insects that ingest solid food (T-B; Leftwich).

glaber (Latin), **glabrous,** smooth, devoid of pubescence; devoid of any sculpturing (T-B; Harris, after Funk, and Marchant and Charles); see denudate, immaculate, investitus, and nude.

glabrate, almost glabrous (Harris, after Munz, and Funk).

gladium, in ♀ Blattopteroidea, valvulae internae, q.v. (Tuxen, after Berlese).

glairy, having the aspect of or resembling glair or white of egg (T-B).

gland, an organ or structure, usually multicellular but occasionally unicellular, whose function is to synthesize specific chemical compounds (T-B; Tulloch); see endocrine gland and exocrine gland.

gland-bearing prominence, in Diaspididae (Hemiptera: Sternorrhyncha: Coccoidea), gland tubercle, q.v. (T-B).

gland orifice, in Coccoidea (Hemiptera: Sternorrhyncha), the external opening through which a gland pours its secretions (T-B).

gland spine, in nymphal and ♀ Coccoidea (Hemiptera: Sternorrhyncha), sclerotized spine with an internal tubular duct (T-B; Kosztarab and Kozár).

gland tubercle(s), in Diaspididae (Hemiptera: Sternorrhyncha: Coccoidea), short, sclerotized tubercles with tubular ducts and swollen base, located in groups along ventral thoracic and abdominal margin (Kosztarab and Kozár).

glandiferous spines, in Coccoidea (Hemiptera: Sternorrhyncha), gland spine, q.v. (T-B, after MacGillivray).

gland of Filippi, in larval Lepidoptera, Lyonnet's gland, q.v. (T-B, after Snodgrass).

glands of Batelli, in nymphs of Cercopidae (Hemiptera: Auchenorrhyncha), large hypodermal glands in the pleural regions of abdominal segments VII and VIII (T-B).

glandubae, in larval Symphyta (Hymenoptera), cutaneous glands, sessil or stalked, provided with sclerotized rings about their external opening (Peterson, after Yuasa).

glandula apicalis (pl., **glandulae apicales**), in some ♀ Heteroptera (Hemiptera), gland attached to the capsula seminalis of the spermatheca (Tuxen, after Dupuis).

glandula appendicularis, in ♀ Heteroptera (Hemiptera), either diverticulum ductus or glandula apicalis, q.v. (Tuxen, after von Siebold).

glandula receptaculi, in ♀ Lepidoptera, single, filiform gland connected with the distal part of the receptaculum seminis (Tuxen, after Petersen).

glandula vaginalis (pl., **glandulae vaginales**), in ♀ Siphonaptera, gland opening into the vestibulum vaginae (Tuxen, after Lass).

glandulae accessoriae (sing., **glandula accessoriae**), accessory glands of reproductive organs (Tuxen).

glandulae appendiculares (sing., **glandula appendicularis**), in ♂ Lepidoptera, paired glands opening into the vasa deferentia (Tuxen, after Cholodkowsky), glandulae sebaceae, q.v. (Tuxen, after Cholodkowsky).

glandulae mucosae, the accessory glands at the base of the vasa deferentia, whose secretion mixes with the semen and forms the seminal packets (T-B, after Packard).

glandulae odoriferae (sing., **glandula odorifera**), in ♀ Lepidoptera, paired glands opening into the oviductus communis near the ostium oviductus, presumably to secrete odoriferous substances (Tuxen, after Petersen).

glandulae sebaceae (sing., **glandula sebacea**), in Lepidoptera, paired, sometimes united glands connected with the vestibulum or ductus ejaculatorius; in ♂, secreting the spermatophores, in ♀ secreting an adhesive for fastening the eggs to a substrate and/or to each other (Tuxen, after Petersen).

glandular, having the character or function of a gland, being used to describe specialized hairs, spines, and other processes (T-B).

glandular bristle, stout and rigid glandular seta (T-B).

glandular chaeta, glandular bristle, q.v. (T-B, after Wardle).

glandular hairs, urticating hairs, q.v. (T-B).

glandular pore, in Coccoidea (Hemiptera: Sternorrhyncha), wax pore, q.v. (T-B, after MacGillivray).

glandular pouches, in ♀ Caelifera (Orthoptera), a pair of pouches opening into the genital chamber (Tuxen).

glandular setae, tubular setae which function as the outlet for the secretions of dermal glands (T-B).

glandular tube, in ♀ Gerromorpha (Hemiptera: Heteroptera), diverticulum ductus, q.v. (Tuxen, after Pendergrast).

glandular vesicles, in ♀ Orthoptera, glandular pouches, q.v. (Tuxen, after Snodgrass).

glans (pl., **glandes**), in ♂ Odonata, apex or terminal segment of the prophallus (Tuxen); in ♂ Tephritoidea (Diptera), swollen structure at the end of a long, coiled, or convoluted basiphallus, being a differentiation of the distiphallus (Tuxen; McAlpine).

glans penis, in ♂ Lepidoptera, vesica, q.v. (Tuxen, after Malpighi).

glassy, transparent; glasslike in appearance (T-B).

glaucous, glaucus (Latin), sea-green; pale bluish green (T-B; Kirby and Spence).

glia tissue, the cellular supporting tissue of the nervous system (T-B, after Snodgrass); see glial cells.

glial cells, cells forming an insulating, protective sheath around a nerve cell (Chapman); see glia tissue.

globate, globose, q.v. (T-B).

globose, globosus (Latin), spherical or nearly so (T-B; Borror et al.).

globular, globose, q.v. (T-B).

globular appendix, in ♂ Plecoptera, vesicle, q.v. (Tuxen, after Frison).

globuli cells, specialized association cells of the brain, usually distinguished by their small size, poverty of cytoplasm, and richly chromatic nuclei (T-B, after Snodgrass).

globulin, an albumenoid protein in the blood of insects (T-B); proteins which are soluble in dilute solutions of NaCl, $MgSO_4$, etc.; found in milk (lactoglobulin), blood (serumglobulin), etc. (Tulloch).

glochis, a barbed point (T-B); in Heteroptera (Hemiptera), the spur or short vein associated with Cu on hind wing and caudad to the latter (Štys, from Stål).

glomerate, glomeratus (Latin), formed into a ball (T-B; R. W. Brown).

glomerule, glomerulus (pl., **glomeruli**), a small compact mass of intermingled terminal arborizations of nerve fibers within a nerve center (T-B, after Snodgrass).

glomerulous, of or formed by glomerules (T-B).

glossa (pl., **glossae**), tongue (T-B; R. W. Brown); inner pair of lobes at apex of prementum of labium (T-B, after Tillyard; Chapman, after Snodgrass); in adult Lepidoptera, proboscis, q.v. (T-B); in larval Chironomidae (Diptera), ligula, q.v. (Saether); in adult Hymenoptera, median lobe at the apex of the prementum (Gauld and Bolton); see ligula and paraglossa.

glossaria, a distinctly chitinized area of the latarima of the glossae (T-B, after MacGillivray).

glossarium, in adult Diptera, labrum-epipharynx, q.v. (T-B).

Glossata, a suborder comprising most of the of Lepidoptera, characterized by possession of a proboscis (Kristensen).

glossate, furnished with a coiled proboscis, e.g., most adult Lepidoptera (T-B).

Glosselytrodea, extinct order of pterygote insects, from the Permian to the Jurassic, characterized by a well-marked basal expansion enclosing rows of cellules in the costal area of the tegminous forewing in most species (Riek, in CSIRO).

glossinid, tsetse fly, q.v. (T-B).

glossotheca, that part of the pupa which covers the tongue (T-B).

glucosamine, a chemical constituent of chitin (T-B; Chapman).

glucose, monosaccharide, being a major constituent of disaccharides (e.g., trehalose) and polysaccharides (e.g., glycogen) (T-B; Chapman).

glucose-1-phosphate, intermediate metabolite in the production of glycogen or trehalose in the fat body from glucose-6-phosphate (Gilmour, in CSIRO).

glucose-6-phosphate, intermediate metabolite in the production of trehalose and glycogen in the fat body from glucose (Gilour, in CSIRO).

glucosidase, an enzyme attacking the linkage between glucose molecules or a glucose molecule and another substance (T-B; Chapman).

glucoside, any compound which, on hydrolysis, yields glucose together with one other substance with the latter sometimes being toxic, e.g., salicin, arbutin, and cellobiose which occur naturally in plants (T-B; Gilmour, in CSIRO; Chapman).

glume(s), in adults of many Chalcidoidea, Cynipoidea, and Proctotrupoidea (Hymenoptera), longitudinal ridges on flagellar segments of antenna (Riek, in CSIRO); see tyloid.

glutamic acid, $C_5H_9O_4N$; an amino acid, functioning as the most effective donor of amino groups in transamination reactions producing other amino acids (Gilmour, in CSIRO).

glutamic acid dehydrogenase, enzyme in the fat body which oxidatively deaminates glutamic acid (Gilmour, in CSIRO).

glutinose, glutinosus (Latin), **glutinous,** viscous; sticky (T-B; R. W. Brown).

gluttony principle, the concept that it is better to live in an area where predators have full stomachs rather than where their stomachs are empty (Matthews and Matthews, after Brown).

glycerin, glycerine, $C_3H_5(OH)_3$; a colorless dense liquid obtained from the saponification of animal fats; miscible with water, oils and alcohol; used in dissecting and for mounting for the microscope; also added to alcohol for the preservation of biological specimens to prevent them from drying out (T-B).

glycerol, glycerin, q.v.; component together with fatty acids forming fats, functioning at high concentrations in the hemolymph to prevent freezing (Gilmour, in CSIRO; Chapman).

glycine, $NH_2CH_2CO_2H$; a simple amino acid that is essential in the diet of some Diptera (Chapman).

glycogen, polysaccharide forming the major energy reserve in many insects and stored mainly in the fat body (T-B; Chapman).

glycolysis, anaerobic breakdown of glucose to pyruvate within the cytoplasm outside of the mitochondria (Chapman).

glycosidase, an enzyme attacking linkages between sugar molecules, e.g., glucosidase (Chapman).

glymmae, in some adult Ichneumonidae (Hymenoptera: Apocrita), lateral foveae between the base and spiracles of the petiole (abdominal segment II) (Riek, in CSIRO; Gauld and Bolton).

glyoxylic acid, additional product in the formation of urea from allantoic acid (Gilmour, in CSIRO).

gnat, a small nematocerous fly (Diptera: Nematocera), especially males in mating swarms (Leftwich; Adkins, pers. comm.).

gnath, in ♂ Lepidoptera, gnathos, q.v. (Tuxen, after Chapman).

gnathal, relating to or pertaining to the jaws, or to a gnathos (T-B).

gnathal pouch, in Protura and Collembola, the chamber in the oral fold containing the recessed mandible or maxilla (Bellinger, pers. comm.).

gnathal region, the first of the 3 regions into which the embryonic trunk segments become segregated, the appendages of which are destined to become the mandibles, first maxillae, and second maxillae (T-B, after Snodgrass); see gnathocephalon.

gnathal segment, one of the 3 segments of the insect embryo, bearing either the rudimentary mandibles, maxillae, and labium (T-B, after Snodgrass; Hinton and Mackerras, in CSIRO).

gnathite, a jaw or jawlike appendage (T-B); see mouthparts.

gnathobase, in Arthropoda, endite, q.v., of one of the basal segments of an appendage situated near the mouth, used in the process of feeding (T-B, after Tillyard); in Hexapoda, lacinia or galea, q.v. (T-B, after Tillyard).

gnathocephalon, the part of the head formed by the gnathal segments, bearing the mandibles and the first and second maxillae (T-B, after Snodgrass).

gnathochilarium, in Diplopoda and Pauropoda, a platelike mouthpart structure, representing the fused maxillae and labium (T-B; Tulloch; Borror et al.; Boudreaux).

Gnathomorpha, hypothesized monophyletic group within the Arthropoda, including the Trilobitomorpha and the Mandibulata (Boudreaux).

gnathopoda, the arthropods; the first pair of legs in insects; especially applied in crustaceans; mouth feet (T-B).

gnathos (pl., **gnathi**), a jaw (R. W. Brown); in ♂ Lepidoptera, a pair of arms articulated with the caudal margin of the tegumen ventrolaterad of the articulation of the uncus and the socii (if present), extending ventrad and mesad, usually fusing together distally, forming a V or Y around the tuba analis laterally and ventrally (T-B, after Klots; Tuxen, after Pierce); also applied to the subscaphium, q.v. (Tuxen, after Zerny and Beier).

gnathothoracic, in the insect embryo, pertaining to the combined gnathal and thoracic regions (T-B, after Snodgrass).

gnathus, gnathos, q.v. (Tuxen, after Chapman).

gnotobiotic, of or relating to gnotobiotics (Steinhaus and Martignoni).

gnotobiotics, field of biology concerned with breeding or culturing of organisms by themselves or in association with other completely known kinds of organisms (Steinhaus and Martignoni).

goblet cells, in Ephemeroptera, Plecoptera, and larval Lepidoptera, midgut cells, distributed between the columnar cells, that have their apical border deeply invaginated into the cell, forming a large cavity connected with the gut lumen that is bounded by irregular microvilli containing elongate mitochondria, possibly involved in removing excess potassium from the hemolymph or in deposit excretion (T-B; Chapman).

Godman and Salvin organ, in ♂ *Ageronia* (Lepidoptera: Nymphalidae), ramus, q.v. (Tuxen, after Reverdin).

goffered, with regular impressions, closely set, and separated by narrow ridges; waffling or honeycombs (T-B; Harris, after Emery and Brewster); see alveolate, areolate, cancellate, clathrate, and reticulate.

golden rod gall, spherical stem gall produced on golden rod (*Solidago,* Compositae) by the larva of *Eurosta* spp. (Diptera: Tephritidae) (Leftwich; Borror et al.); elongate, spindle-shaped gall produced on the stems of golden rod (*Solidago*) by *Gnorimoschema* spp. (Lepidoptera: Gelechiidae) (Leftwich; Borror et al.).

gonacanthus, in ♂ Diptera, epiphallus, q.v. (Tuxen).

gonad, the ovary or testis, or the embryonic rudiment of either, formed by splanchnic mesoderm cells enveloping the germ cells (T-B, after Snodgrass).

gonadal gonopore, (primary) gonopore, q.v. (Tuxen, after E. L. Smith).

gonadial, of or pertaining to the gonads (T-B).

gonadial tube, any one of the fine tubes lined with germinal epithelium, that constitutes the gamete-forming part of a gonad or sex organ (T-B, after Klots).

gonadotrophic hormone, any hormone that stimulates previtellogenic development of oocytes and vitellogeneis (Chapman).

gonadotropin, gonadothrophic hormone, q.v. (Gilmour, in CSIRO).

gonangulum (pl., **gonangula**), in ♀ insects, sclerite attached ventrally to the base of the first gonapophysis and dorsally articulating with the second gonacoxa and abdominal tergum IX, and probably homologous to the anterodorsal corner of coxa IX (Tuxen, after Scudder).

gonapophysis (pl., **gonapophyses**), genitalia, q.v. (T-B, after Comstock); the appendages surrounding the gonopore (T-B, after Tillyard); in ♂ Archaeognatha and Zygentoma, median proximal processes of the coxopodites of gonopods present on abdominal segment VIII + IX, forming the ♀ ovipositor, or on abdominal segments VIII + X, forming ♂ parameres (Tuxen, after Snodgrass; von Kéler); in ♂ Odonata, appendages surrounding the genital meatus (Tuxen); in ♂ Aphidoidea (Hemiptera: Sternorrhyncha), claspers, q.v. (Tuxen, after Hottes); in ♂ Pentatomoidea (Hemiptera: Heteroptera), parameres, q.v. (Tuxen, after Whitfield); in ♂ Coleoptera, aedeagus, q.v. (Tuxen); in ♂ Lepidoptera, a pair of lateral appendages of abdominal segment VIII (which may form the rami) and 2 pairs of abdominal segment IX (Tuxen, after Poljanec); in ♂ Tipuliidae (Diptera), parameres, q.v. (Tuxen, after de Meijere); in ♀ insects, median proximal processes of the gonocoxae, including the first and second gonapophyses together forming the ovipositor, q.v.; in most insect orders (Tuxen, after Snodgrass; Gauld and Bolton, after Scudder); in ♀ Phthiraptera, first gonapophyses, q.v. (Clay, in

Tuxen; Lyal); in ♀ Aphididae (Hemiptera: Sternorrhyncha), a few pilose generally small protuberances behind the vulva (Tuxen); in ♀ *Ithone* (Planipennia: Ithonidae), pseudostylus, q.v. (Tuxen, after Tillyard).

gonapophyses anteriores (sing., **gonapophysis anterior**), in ♀ insects, first gonapophyses, q.v. (Tuxen); in *Wesmaelius* (Planipennia: Hemerobiidae), second gonapophyses, q.v. (Tuxen, after Tjeder); in ♀ Coleophoridae (Lepidoptera), second gonapophyses, q.v. (Tuxen, after Toll).

gonapophyses laterales (sing., **gonapophysis lateralis**), in ♀ Plenipennia, lateral valves of the ovipositor, a pair of processes from sternum IX (Tuxen); in ♀ Boreidae (Mecoptera), lower valves of ovipositor, arising from sternum VIII (Byers).

gonapophyses of abdominal segment VIII, first gonapophyses, q.v. (Tuxen).

gonapophyses of abdominal segment IX, second gonapophyses, q.v. (Tuxen).

gonapophyses posteriores (sing., **gonapophysis posterior**), in ♀ insects, second gonapophyses, q.v. (Tuxen); in ♀ Coleophoridae (Lepidoptera), apophyses anteriores, q.v. (Tuxen, after Toll).

gonapophysis VIII, in ♀ Hymenoptera, first gonapophyses, q.v., forming the moving component of the ovipositor or sting (Tuxen, after E. L. Smith; Gauld and Bolton); in ♀ Chironomidae (Diptera), hypogynial valves, q.v. (Saether).

gonapophysis IX, in ♂ Hymenoptera, mesal appendage (endite or exite) on gonocoxite IX forming the intromittent organ, rotated and primitively fused with gonapophysis IX on the opposite side (Tuxen, after E. L. Smith); in ♀ Hymenoptera, segmented mesal appendage (endite or exite) on gonocoxite IX, rotated 180° laterally on the long axis and fused with the opposite one along the new dorsal margin (notum) (Tuxen, after E. L. Smith); in ♀ Chironomidae (Diptera), vaginal apodeme, q.v. (Saether).

gonapsis (pl., **gonapsides**), in some ♂ Chrysopidae (Planipennia), a largely internal structure with projecting apex situated in dorsal membrane of sternum IX (Tuxen, after Tjeder).

gonarcus, in ♂ Megaloptera, Planipennia, and Raphidioptera, generally arch-shaped structure below anal segment and above aedeagus (Tuxen, after Tjeder).

Gondwanaland, during much of the Mesozoic Era, a southern supercontinent consisting of continental blocks of South America, Africa, Madagascar, India, Antarctica, and Australia (Mackerras, in CSIRO); see Laurasia.

gongylidium (pl., **gongylidia**), swollen hyphal tips of symbiotic fungi cultivated and fed upon by Attini (Hymenoptera: Formicidae) (Wilson).

gonites, in ♂ Diptera, parameres, q.v. (Tuxen, after Crampton); pregonites, q.v. (Griffiths).

gonobase, in *Climaciella* (Planipennia: Mantispidae), gonarcus, q.v.

(Tuxen, after Michener); in ♂ Hymenoptera, basal ring, q.v. (Tuxen, after E. L. Smith).

gonobasis, in ♂ Simuliidae (Diptera), basal ring, q.v. (Tuxen).

gonobasite, in Zygentoma, coxite, q.v. (Tuxen, after Börner).

gonocardo, in ♂ Hymenoptera, basal ring, q.v. (Tuxen, after Crampton).

gonochaeta (pl., **gonochaetae**), in ♀ Aphididae (Hemiptera: Sternorrhyncha), hairs on gonapophyses (transl. "Gonochaeten" Iglisch, in Tuxen).

gonoclavi (sing., **gonoclavus**), in ♀ Mecoptera, axis, q.v. (Tjeder, in Tuxen).

gonocondyle, in ♂ Hymenoptera, apodeme of gonobase, q.v. (Tuxen, after Crampton).

gonocoxae (sing., **gonocoxa**), in ♀ insects, coxae of genital segments (VIII and IX) (Tuxen, after Scudder); in ♂ Grylloblattodea, stylus-bearing sclerites on abdominal segment IX (Tuxen).

gonocoxal apodeme, in ♂ Hymenoptera, anterior, often fused, apodeme of gonocoxites, extending into concavity of the gonobase (Tuxen, after Rozen); in ♂ Nematocera and orthorrhaphous Diptera, conspicuous internal process of the gonocoxite (McAlpine).

gonocoxal arms, in ♂ Hymenoptera, ventrobasal prolongations of gonocoxites which, if fused, form the ventral gonocoxal bridge (Tuxen, after Peck).

gonocoxal bridges, in ♂ Hymenoptera, basal sclerotic bridges between gonocoxites, a ventral and a dorsal one (Tuxen, after Michener).

gonocoxal process, in Zygentoma, process on the coxite turned caudad (transl. "Gonocoxit-Fortsatz" Escherich, in Tuxen).

gonocoxapodeme, in ♀ Chironomidae (Diptera), internally thickened ridge or apodeme along the caudolateral margin of gonosternite VIII representing reduced gonocoxite VIII (Saether).

gonocoxite(s), the coxites of the gonopods (Tuxen); in ♂ Archaeognatha, Zygentoma, and Grylloblattodea, gonocoxae, q.v. (Tuxen); in ♂ Coleoptera, basal piece, q.v. (Tuxen, after Michener); in ♂ Neuroptera and Mecoptera, basal segment of gonapophyses of abdominal segment IX (Tuxen); in ♂ *Climaciella* (Planipennia: Mantispidae), paramere, q.v. (Tuxen, after Michener); in ♂ Diptera, basistylus, q.v. (Tuxen); in ♂ Hymenoptera, basal segment of outer clasper, i.e., gonocoxopodite minus gonobase, volsella and penis valve (Tuxen); in ♂ Hymenoptera, gonoforceps, q.v. (Tuxen, after Michener); in ♀ Heteroptera (Hemiptera), 4 plates or blades, 2 from abdominal segment VIII, 2 from abdominal segment IX, articulating on corresponding laterotergites and bearing gonapophyses (Tuxen, after Rawat); in ♀ Chrysopidae (Planipennia), gonapophyses laterales, q.v. (Tuxen, after Adams).

gonocoxite VIII, in ♀ insects, coxite of abdominal segment VIII, derived from union of the subcoxa, coxa and part of the coxosternite (Tuxen, after E. L. Smith); in ♀ Chironomidae (Diptera), gonocoxapodeme, q.v. (Saether).

gonocoxite IX, in ♂ insects, coxite of abdominal segment IX, detached from tergum, rearticulated to sternum IX, uniting mesally and separating transversely forming the gonobase (Section 1), gonocoxite (Section 2) and volsella (Section 3), the latter attached to each other basally (Tuxen, after E. L. Smith); in ♀ insects, coxite of abdominal segment IX, derived from union of subcoxa, coxa, and part of coxosternite, primitively articulated to tergum IX, but shifted to the ventral margin of gonocoxite VIII in Hymenoptera (Tuxen, after E. L. Smith); in ♀ Heteroptera (Hemiptera), gonocoxite of abdominal segment IX, frequently provided with styloids (Tuxen, after Rawat); in ♂ Diptera, basistylus, q.v. (McAlpine); in ♀ Chironomidae (Diptera), sclerite on segment IX, articulating along dorsal edge with ninth tergum and connected dorsoventrally to coxosternapodeme, sometimes being fused with tergum IX to form gonotergite IX, q.v. (Saether).

gonocoxopodite(s), coxopodite of abdominal segment IX, consisting of a coxite (the gonocoxite), a stylus (the gonostylus), and an inner process (the volsella) (Harbach and Knight); in ♀ Heteroptera (Hemiptera), gonocoxites VIII and IX, q.v. (Tuxen, after Davis); in adult Hymenoptera, coxal portions of gonopods, in ♂ including gonobase, gonocoxite, volsella and penis valve (Tuxen, after Michener).

gonocrista (pl., **gonocristae**), in some ♂ Chrysopidae (Planipennia), single or paired, toothed plates on the dorsal membrane of sternum IX (Tuxen, after Tjeder).

gonoduct, the duct leading from a gonad to the genital opening; in the ♀, the oviduct; in the ♂, the vasa deferentia (T-B, after Tillyard).

gonoforceps (pl., **gonoforcipes**), in ♂ Heteroptera (Hemiptera), parameres, q.v. (Tuxen, after Michener); in ♂ Hymenoptera, a morphologically noncommital term meaning gonocoxite alone or indistinguishably fused with gonostylus (Tuxen, after Michener).

gonofurca (pl., **gonofurcae**), in ♂ Diptera, sclerite on base of paramere, connected with gonostern (Tuxen, after Rubzov).

gonolacinia, in ♂ Hymenoptera, digitus, q.v. (Tuxen, after Peck).

gonolatus (pl., **gonolati**), in ♂ Nemopteridae (Planipennia), platelike, sometimes concave sclerotized central part of gonosaccus (Tuxen, after Tjeder).

gonomacula, in ♂ Hymenoptera, cupping disk, q.v. (Tuxen, after Crampton).

gonoplac(s), in some ♀ insects, posteroexternal process of second gonocoxa, sometimes developed into an ovipositor sheath (Tuxen, after Scudder; Gauld and Bolton).

gonopod(s), the appendages of the genital segments, i.e., abdominal segment IX (rarely VIII) in ♂ and abdominal segments VIII and IX in ♀ (T-B, after Snodgrass; Tuxen); a gonapophysis or gonostylus borne on a gonocoxite (Tuxen, after E. L. Smith); in Ephemeroptera, gonostyles, q.v. (Tuxen); in ♂ Blattopteroidea, styli, q.v. (Tuxen); in ♀ Phthiraptera, gonapophyses, q.v. (Tuxen); in ♂ Aphididae (Hemiptera: Sternorrhyncha), claspers, q.v. (Tuxen); in ♂ Heteroptera (Hemiptera), parameres, q.v. (Tuxen, after Leston);

in ♂ *Corydalus* (Megaloptera: Corydalidae), anoprocessus + catoprocessus (Tuxen, after Crampton); in ♂ *Raphidia* (Raphidioptera: Raphidiidae), stylus, q.v. (Tuxen, after Crampton); in ♂ Mecoptera, gonocoxites, q.v. (Tuxen, after Tillyard); in ♂ Trichoptera, inferior appendages, q.v. (Tuxen, after Nielsen); in ♂ Muscomorpha (Diptera), surstyli, q.v. (Tuxen) or, paired lobes lateral to the parameres (McAlpine); in ♂ Culicidae (Diptera), claspettes, q.v. (Tuxen, after Brolemann).

gonopodium, gonopod, q.v. (Leftwich).

gonoporal process, in ♂ Heteroptera (Hemiptera), processus gonopori, q.v. (Tuxen, after Ashlock).

gonopore, the external opening of a genital duct, i.e., ductus ejaculatorius (♂) or oviductus communis (♀), or primitively one of the paired apertures of the vasa deferentia (♂) or the lateral oviducts (♀); (T-B, after Snodgrass; Tuxen); in ♂ Orthoptera, Auchenorrhyncha (Hemiptera), and Hymenoptera, phallotrema, q.v. (Tuxen); in ♂ Heteroptera (Hemiptera), secondary gonopore, q.v. (Tuxen); in ♀ Coleoptera, vulva, q.v. (Tuxen).

gonopore of spermatheca, in ♀ Psocoptera, spermapore, q.v. (Tuxen, after Pearman).

gonopore plate, in ♀ Psocoptera, the sclerite of abdominal sternum IX on which the ductus spermathecae opens (Tuxen, after Pearman).

gonopore process, in ♂ Caelifera (Orthoptera), a lower ventrocaudad process of the laminae phalli near the gonopore (Tuxen).

gonoporus, in ♀ Orthoptera, gonopore, q.v. (Tuxen); in ♀ Psocoptera, gonopore of spermatheca, q.v. (Tuxen, after Roesler); in ♀ Lepidoptera, ostium bursae, q.v. (Tuxen, after Weber).

gonoporus externus, in ♂ Heteroptera (Hemiptera), secondary gonopore, q.v. (Tuxen, after Piotrowski).

gonoporus internus, in ♂ Heteroptera (Hemiptera), primary gonopore, q.v. (Tuxen, after Piotrowski).

gonosaccus (pl., **gonosacci**), in ♂ Neuroptera, simple or paired saclike invaginated, but usually eversible, widening of membranous tissue forming hind bodywall of abdomen (Tuxen, after Tjeder).

gonosetae (sing., **gonoseta**), in ♂ Neuroptera, strong setae, ususally one or 2 groups, on the gonosaccus (Tuxen, after Tjeder).

gonosiculus, in ♂ Hymenoptera, digitus, q.v. (Tuxen, after Crampton).

gonosomite, in ♂ insects, genital segment, q.v. (Tuxen, after Snodgrass).

gonosquama, in ♂ Hymenoptera, paramere, q.v. (Tuxen, after Peck).

gonostatumen (pl., **gonostatum ina**), in ♂ Nymphalidae (Lepidoptera), modification of sternum VIII (Tuxen, after Dillon).

gonostern, in ♂ Diptera, unpaired slcerite on basis of parameres and gonostyli and part of hypandrium (Tuxen, after Rubzov).

gonosternite, subgenital sclerite resulting from fusion of the coxosternite with gonocoxites (Tuxen, after E. L. Smith).

gonostipes, in ♂ Mecoptera, gonocoxite or basal segment of genital style, q.v. (Tuxen, after Crampton); in ♂ Diptera, basistylus, q.v.

(Tuxen, after Cole), or gonocoxite, q.v. (McAlpine); in ♂ Hymenoptera, gonocoxite, q.v. (Tuxen, after Crampton).

gonostipital arms, in ♂ Hymenoptera, gonocoxal arms, q.v. (Tuxen, after Crampton).

gonostylar claw, in some ♂ Culicidae (Diptera), the differentiated, more or less spiniform seta(e) at or near the apex of the gonostylus (Harbach and Knight, after Knight and Laffoon).

gonostyle, in ♂ Odonata, style, q.v. (Tuxen, after Asahina); in Mecoptera, stylus, q.v. (Tuxen, after Wood).

gonostyloids, in ♀ Heteroptera (Hemiptera), gonoplacs, q.v. (Tuxen, after Štys).

gonostylus (pl., **gonostyli**), stylus of a genital segment (Tuxen); in ♂ insects, stylus of the ninth segment, generally modified to form the clasping organ (T-B, after Snodgrass); in ♂ Auchenorrhyncha (Hemiptera), styles, q.v. (Tuxen); in ♂ Heteroptera (Hemiptera), paramere(s), q.v. (Tuxen, after Bonhag and Wick); in ♂ *Agulla* (Raphidioptera: Raphidiidae), stylus, q.v. (Tuxen, after Michener); in ♂ Mecoptera, stylus, q.v. (Tuxen, after Crampton); in ♂ Diptera, dististylus, q.v. (Tuxen); in ♂ Coleoptera, paramere, q.v. (Tuxen, after Michener); in ♂ Hymenoptera, paramere, q.v. (Tuxen, after E. L. Smith); in ♀ Telmatogetoninae (Diptera: Chironomidae), long, tapering appendage with narrow apodeme of reduced gonocoxite IX, forming an antovipositor together with the cerci, gonapophyses VIII and posterior extensions of tergite IX (Saether); in ♀ Hymenoptera, gonoplac (Tuxen, after Michener).

gonotergite, in ♀ Tanypodinae, Aphroteniinae, and Podonominae (Diptera: Chironomidae), sclerite resulting from fusion of abdominal tergite IX with gonocoxites to either side, usually being reduced in Tanypodinae to a narrow strip (Saether).

gonotrema, in ♀ Diptera, genital opening, q.v. (McAlpine); see gonotreme.

gonotreme, in ♂ and ♀ Protura, the opening of the genital chamber, located between abdominal sterna XI and XII (Tuxen); in ♀ Coleoptera, vulva, q.v. (Tuxen); in ♀ Culicidae (Diptera), genital opening, q.v. (Harbach and Knight, after Snodgrass); in ♀ Siphonaptera, external opening of the genital chamber (Tuxen).

gonotrophic concordance, in hibernating Culicidae (Diptera), the utilization of occasional blood meals for the formation of fat rather than development of eggs (Tulloch, after Swellengrebel).

gonotrophic dissociation, in Culicidae (Diptera), the utilization of prehibernating blood meals for the formation of fat rather than the development of eggs (Tulloch, after Swellengrebel).

gonyodon, in some Noctuidae (Lepidoptera), a toothlike articulated process at the apex of the femur (T-B).

gonytheca, the articulating surface of the femur to which the tibia is joined (T-B).

gossyplure, synthetic sex pheromone of ♀ pink bollworm moth, *Pectinophora gossypiella* (Lepidoptera: Gelechiidae); a mixture of 4 isomers of 7,11-hexadecadien-1-ol acetate (Pfadt).

Graber's organ, in larval Tabanidae (Diptera), an elaborate pyriform structure located posteriorly in the abdomen, opening through a fine tube on the dorsum between the last 2 abdominal terga (T-B, after Imms).

gracile, slender; graceful (T-B).

gradate, arranged in a series; blending so as to merge one into the other, e.g., colors (T-B).

gradate crossvein(s), in adult Megaloptera, Planipennia, and Raphidioptera, a crossvein of a gradate series (Oswald, pers. comm.).

gradate series, in adult Megaloptera, Planipennia, and Raphidioptera, a series of crossveins which form a more or less continuous oblique, transverse or arcuate path across some of the longitudinal veins of a wing (Oswald, pers. comm.).

gradate veins, in adult Planipennia, Megaloptera, and Raphidioptera, gradate crossveins, q.v. (T-B, after Comstock).

gradation, the time interval between the lowest point of the density of animal population and the next, thus including one full wave of the numerical fluctuation of the population (Steinhaus and Martignoni).

grade, a group of animals similar in level of organization, that is not necessarily monophyletic (Mayr; Mackerras, in CSIRO).

graded diplay, a behavioral continuum communicating slight changes in motivation (Matthews and Matthews).

gradient, a regular ascent or descent either actually or an arithmetical or other graphic rise and fall (T-B).

gradual metamorphosis, simple metamorphosis of paurometabolous insects (Borror et al.).

graminivorous, feeding or subsisting on grasses (Gramineae) (T-B); see granivorous.

grandlure, synthetic aggregating and sex pheromone produced by the ♂ boll weevil, *Anthonomus grandis grandis* (Coleoptera: Curculionidae); consists of 4 compounds, approximately 50% of ($+$)-*cis*-2-iso-prpenyl-1-methylcyclobutaneethanol, (*Z*)-3,3-dimethyl-Δ_1, β-cyclohexaneethanol and 50% of (*Z*)- and (*E*)-3,3-dimethyl-Δ_1, α-cyclohexaneacetaldehyde (Pfadt).

granicula (sing., **grandiculum**), in Lithosiinae (Lepidoptera: Arctiidae), small clustered sclerotizations in the walls of the vesica (♂) and bursa copulatrix (♀) ranging from very minute thickenings to scobinations or small spines (Tuxen, after Birket-Smith).

granivorous, feeding on grain; feeding on seeds of grasses (Gauld and Bolton); see graminivorous.

granose, moniliform, q.v. (T-B).

granular, granulate, q.v. (T-B),

granular eosinophilic cell, granular hemocyte, q.v. (Tulloch).

granular hemocyte, phagocytic hemocyte characterized by the possession of acidophilic granules and abundant rough endoplasmic reticulum (Tulloch, after Jones; Chapman).

granular leucocyte, granular hemocyte, q.v. (T-B, after Snodgrass; Tulloch).

granular spheres, granular hemocyte, q.v. (T-B, after Imms).

granulate, granulatus (Latin), covered with or made up of very small grains or granules; minutely and densely verrucose or minutely farinose (T-B; Harris, after Munz, and Stearn); see acinose and farinose.

granule(s), granulum (Latin), a little grain or a minute grainlike elevation (T-B); in Collembola, small separate concentrations of pigment giving the surface a dotted appearance (Christiansen and Bellinger); an insecticidal formulation in which the insecticide is impregnated on small particles of clay, the size of the particles being expressed in terms of mesh size of 2 limiting screens, e.g., 8/15, 15/30, 24/48, 30/60 (Pfadt).

granulocyte, granular hemocyte, q.v. (Tulloch).

granulose, granulate, q.v. (T-B; Harris).

granulosis, a virus disease of certain insects, especially larval Lepidoptera, characterized by the presence of minute granular inclusions (capsules) in infected cells (Steinhaus and Martignoni; Pfadt).

granulosis inclusion virus, insect viruses characterized by the presence in large numbers of very small but microscopically discernible granular inclusions in infected cells, and particularly visible in the cytoplasm of the host, the granules consisting of proteinaceous material within which the virus particle is located (Pfadt).

grasserie, nucleopolyhedrosis of the silkworm, *Bombyx mori* (Lepidoptera: Bombycidae) (Steinhaus and Martignoni); see jaundice.

grasshopper, a member of the superfamily Acridoidea or Eumastacoidea (short-horned grasshoppers) or the superfamily Tettigonioidea (long-horned grasshoppers) (Orthoptera) (Key, in CSIRO).

gravid, heavy with fully-developed eggs (T-B).

greater abdomen, in Sminthuridae (Collembola), the fused anterior 4 abdominal segments (Christiansen and Bellinger).

greater ampulla, in adult Calyptratae (Diptera: Muscomorpha), a bulbus swelling in the basal portion of the pleural wing process (McAlpine).

greater ocellars, in Diptera, ocellar setae, q.v. (T-B, after Comstock).

green glands, the highly modified nephridia in Crustacea (T-B).

green muscardine, a mycosis of various larval, pupal, and adult insects, caused by the hypomycetous fungus *Metarrhizium anisopliae* Sorokin, infection occurring principally through mycelial penetration through the insect's integument and producing olive green, mature spores from hyphae that emerge through the integument following death of the insect (Steinhaus and Martignoni).

gregarious, commonly found in aggregations (T-B; Norris, in CSIRO); see social.

gregarious parasitism, development of 2 or more parasitoid larvae on a single host (Gauld and Bolton).

gregarious phase, a form or phase of certain Phasmatida, locusts (Orthoptera: Acrididae), larval Lepidoptera and a few other insects, characteristic of high-density populations (Norris, in CSIRO); see kentromorphism and solitary phase.

grège (French), raw silk, including the sericin (T-B).

grès (French), sericin, q.v. (T-B).

gressorial, gressorious, gressorius, having legs fitted for walking (T-B); in adult Nymphalidae (Lepidoptera), with the anterior legs aborted, the others fitted for walking (T-B).

grinding teeth, mola, q.v. (T-B).

Gripopterygoidea, superfamily within the suborder Antarctoperlaria (Plecoptera), including the families Austroperlidae and Gripopterygidae (Zwick, in Hennig).

griscent, ashen gray (T-B).

griseous, griseus (Latin), gray (T-B; R. W. Brown).

grooming, use of the legs or mandibles to remove particles of detritus from parts of the body (Chapman); in social insects, the licking of the body surfaces of nestmates (Wilson); see self-grooming.

groove of anellus, in ♂ Lepidoptera, midventral, internal furrow of the anellus, in and dorsad of which the aedoeagus lies (transl. "Rinne des Ringwalles" Zander, after Tuxen).

gross pathology, in insect pathology, the study of macroscopic lesions (Steinhaus and Martignoni); see histopathology.

grossus (Latin), big; coarse; thick (T-B; R. W. Brown).

ground pearls, encysted immatures of Margarodidae, e.g., *Eumargarodes* and *Promargarodes* (Hemiptera: Sternorrhyncha: Coccoidea), capable of long periods of quiescence during unfavorable conditions, used as beads, particularly in South Africa and in the Bahamas (T-B; Woodward et al., in CSIRO).

ground speed, the speed of an insect in flight measured in terms of its movement relative to the ground (Chapman); see air speed.

group, an assemblage of taxa (ICZN); see collective group, family group, genus group, species group, and taxonomic group.

group effect, an alteration in behavior or physiology within a species brought about by signals that are directed in neither space nor time, being simple example is social facilitation (Wilson); in *Eurycantha calcarata* (Phasmida), the phenomenon of individuals reared in a group growing faster and having fewer nymphal instars than those reared alone (Carlberg, pers. comm.).

group predation, the hunting and retreiving of living prey by groups of cooperating animals, a behavior best developed in army ants (Hymenoptera: Formicidae) (Wilson).

group selection, where natural selection is operating on the level of the colony, or family group, rather than on the single organism (Matthews and Matthews).

group shagreen, in pupal Chironomidae (Diptera), groups of small spinules arranged in short, distinct rows (Saether).

grouped glands, in Diaspididae (Hemiptera: Sternorrhyncha: Coccoidea), circumgenital pores, q.v. (T-B, after MacGillivray).

grouped orifices of spiracles, in Coccoidea (Hemiptera: Sternorrhyncha), spiracular pore band, q.v. (T-B, after MacGillivray).

grouse-locust, member of the family Tetrigidae (Orthoptera: Tetrigoidea) (Key, in CSIRO); see locust.

growth regulator, synthetic compound that promotes, inhibits, or otherwise modifies normal growth (Allaby).

grub, larva, q.v. (T-B); scarabaeiform larva, q.v. (Borror et al.); an apodous larva having a tiny head, few sense organs, and a fleshy, rounded body, e.g., larvae of bees (Hymenoptera: Apoidea) and some Coleoptera (T-B; Peterson; Leftwich); see maggot.

Gryllacridoidea, superfamily within the suborder Ensifera (Orthoptera), including Gryllacrididae, Stenopelmatidae, Rhaphidophoridae, Cooloolidae, and Schizodactylidae, possessing tarsi with 4 tarsomeres, forewings not tegminized when present, no stridulatory specializations, and fore- and midtibiae usually with ventral articulated spines (Key, in CSIRO).

Grylliformida, hypothesied monophyletic group within the Polyneoptera (Insecta), including the Protorthopterida and the Orthopterida (Boudreaux).

Grylloblattaria, Grylloblattodea, q.v. (Boudreaux).

Grylloblattodea, order of apterous, mandibulate, exopterygote Neoptera, having all legs cursorial, with large coxae, pronotum without descending lateral lobes, auditory organs lacking, long slender, segmented cerci, sternum IX in ♂ bearing articulated coxites, ovipositor strongly projecting, eggs free, and immatures terrestrial (Key, in CSIRO).

Grylloidea, superfamily within the suborder Ensifera (Orthoptera), including the Gryllidae, Myrmecophilidae, and Gryllotalpidae, the members of which possess tarsi with 3 tarsomeres (Key, in CSIRO).

guanine, $C_5H_5N_5O$; a purine, being white in purified form, metabolized to produce uric acid, and also one of the base constituents of nucleic acids (T-B; Chapman).

guard setae, in Collembola, one of a number (usually 2) of simple or modified setae just basal to, and projecting over, the third antennal segment sense organ (Christiansen and Bellinger); in Miridae, (Hemiptera: Heteroptera), one of conspicuous setae situated at the dorsal apex of tarsus (Schuh).

guarded pupa, a pupa in a partly open cocoon (T-B).

guest, an insect which lives in nests or dwelling places of other species not necessarily at the expense of the host (T-B); a social symbiont (Wilson).

guide, in some ♂ Enicocephalidae (Hemiptera: Heteroptera), reduced remnants of external genitalia arising from the posteroventral margin of the pygophore (Štys, after Jeannel).

guiding rod, in ♂ Gryllidae (Orthoptera), a grooved rod or lobe serving to guide the spermatophore duct, situated in the dorsal wall of the dorsal cavity, extending to the underside of the pseudepiphallus (Tuxen, after Alexander and Otte).

gula, in prognathous insects, the fused lower ends of the postocciput forming a ventral plate (T-B; Chapman).

gulacavae, posterior tentorial pits, q.v. (Tulloch).

gulamental plate, gulamentum, q.v. (T-B, after Crampton).

gulamentum, the gula and submentum fused together into one sclerite (T-B, after Crampton).

gular, of or pertaining to the gula (T-B).

gular area, gula, q.v. (Peterson).

gular peduncle, in Coleoptera, gulamentum, q.v. (T-B).

gular pit, posterior tentorial pit, q.v. (T-B, after Crampton).

gular plate, gula, q.v. (T-B).

gular suture, the line of division between the gula or throat and the genae (T-B); in prognathous insects, the ventroanterior extension of the postoccipital suture, q.v. (Chapman).

Gularostria, Sternorrhyncha, q.v. (Borror et al.).

gullet, oesophagus, q.v. (T-B).

gulomental, referring or pertaining to the region covered by the gula and mentum (T-B).

gustatory, relating to the sense of taste (T-B).

gustatory nerves, the nerves of the organs of taste (T-B).

gustatory organ, in nymphal Ephemeroptera, a row of sensillae on the underside of the triangular labrum (T-B, after Needham); in Heteroptera (Hemiptera), epipharyngeal sense organ, q.v. (Štys, pers. comm.).

gustatory sense, taste, q.v. (T-B).

gutta (Latin), drop; a spot (T-B; R. W. Brown).

guttate, guttatus (Latin), dappled; speckled; spotted (T-B; R. W. Brown).

guttiform, drop-shaped; droplike in form (T-B).

gyandrarchy, a social organization founded by both ♂ and ♀, usually with the fertile forms living together for some time (Tulloch, after Gaul).

Gymnocerata, a grade group of the Heteroptera (Hemiptera) with freely movable, conspicuous antennae (Schuh); see Cryptocerata.

gymnodomous, in social wasps (Hymenoptera: Vespidae), having a nest with exposed or uncovered combs, e.g., *Polistes* or *Miscocyttarus* (Tulloch, after Bequaert); see calyptodomous.

gymnogastra, in Hymenoptera, species in which the venter is visible (T-B); see cryptogastra.

gymnoparia (pl., **gymnopariae**), in some larval Scarabaeoidea (Coleoptera), the naked part of the paria between the acanthoparia and the chaetoparia and behind the acroparia (T-B, after Böving).

gymnoptera, species with membranous wings not covered with scales (T-B).

gynaecaner, a ♂ ant (Hymenoptera: Formicidae), which resembles the ♀ and has the same number of antennal articles (T-B).

gynaecoid, in gregarious, polymorphic Tubulifera (Thysanoptera), the normal, minor, femalelike form of males (Stannard).

gynaecotelix type, in the social insects, a group in which the ♀ is the complete prototype of the sex, with all the primary instincts of the sex, including those of the worker cast (T-B, after W. M. Wheeler).

gynandromorph, in general, any insect combining the secondary ♂ or ♀ characters in the same individual, not necessarily an hermaphrodite, although sometimes such (T-B); see bilateral gynandromorph, hermaphrodite, and intersex.

gynandromorphic, exhibiting gynandromorphism (T-B).

gynadromorphism, the condition of being a gynandromorph (T-B).

gynarchy, a social organization in which the ♀ is the foundress and dominant figure (Tulloch, after Gaul).

gynatrial complex, in ♀ Gerromorpha and other Heteroptera (Hemiptera), a term referring to that portion of internal ectodermalia composed of the gynatrial sac, spermathecal tube, and fecundation canal (Andersen).

gynatrial glands, in ♀ Heteroptera (Hemiptera), ringed glands, q.v. (Tuxen, after Štys).

gynatrial sac, in ♀ Heteroptera (Hemiptera), vaginal pouch, q.v. (Tuxen, after Štys).

gynatrium, in ♀ Orthoptera, genital chamber, q.v. (Tuxen); in Heteroptera (Hemiptera), vagina, q.v. (Tuxen, after Gupta).

gyne, in Hymenoptera, queen, q.v. (T-B; Michener).

gynecoid, in ants (Hymenoptera: Formicidae), gamergate, q.v. (T-B).

gynephore, in Cynipidae (Hymenoptera), a parthenogenetic ♀ that lays only ♀ eggs (Gauld and Bolton); see androphore.

gynergate, in ants (Hymenoptera: Formicidae), a mosaic form combining worker and queen characteristics (Tulloch); a ♀ containing patches of tissue of both the queen and worker castes (Wilson).

gynetype, a ♀ type (T-B, after Banks and Caudell); see type.

gynium, in ♀ Diptera, abdominal segment VIII, the tergum being called the epigynium and the sternum being called the hypogynium (McAlpine).

gynogenesis, unusual type of thelytoky, in which the development of eggs in triploid females is triggered by healthy sperm, e.g., *mobilis* form of *Ptinus clavipes* (Coleoptera: Ptinidae) (Chapman, after Sanderson).

gynopara (pl., **gynoparae**), in host-alternative species of Aphididae (Hemiptera: Sternorrhyncha), the autumn migrants that fly back to the primary host where they produce oviparae (Stoetzel, pers. comm.).

gyri cerebrales, corpora pedunculata, q.v. (T-B).

gyroscopic organ, in adult Diptera, halters, q.v. (T-B).

H

H-shaped sclerite, in larval Muscomorpha (Diptera: Brachycera), hypopharyngeal sclerite, q.v. (Teskey, in McAlpine).

habena (Latin), a strap (T-B; R. W. Brown).

habit, habitus, q.v. (T-B).

habitacle, in Isoptera, the distinct, central part of the epigeous nest, also referred to as the nursery or hive (Noirot, in Krishna and Weesner).

habitat, living place of an organism or community characterized by its physical or biotic properties (Allaby); see environment and niche.

habituation, the gradual lessening of responsiveness to a stimulus as experience finds it to be harmless or at least unavoidable (Matthews and Matthews).

habitus, general form and appearance (T-B; Christiansen and Bellinger).

hackberry gall, small galls on the surface of the leaves of hackberry trees (*Celtis* spp.) produced by *Pachypsylla* spp. (Hemiptera: Sternorrhyncha: Psyllidae) (Borror et al.).

haem-, see hem-.

hair, a slender flexible filament of equal diameter throughout, being either a macrotrichium or a microtrichium (T-B; McAlpine).

hair bed, hair plate, q.v. (Chapman).

hair-fields, hair-scales, spinules (T-B, after Jardine).

hair pencil, in ♂ Lepidoptera, scent brush contained within a corema, q.v., or alar pocket, q.v. (Chapman); in larval Lepidoptera, a group of long parallel setae arising from a verricule.

hair plate, group of delicate tactile hairs, commonly located near points of articulation, functioning in proprioreception (Tulloch; Chapman).

hair sack, in ♂ Plutellidae (Lepidoptera), corema, q.v., on sternum IX (Tuxen, after Philpott).

hair sensillum, trichoid sensillum, q.v. (Borror et al.).

hairworm, a member of the class Nematomorpha.

hairy, covered or clothed with hairs (T-B).

hairy eye, in adult Chironomidae (Diptera), compound eye in which the macrotrichia between the corneal lenses are longer than the height of the lens (Saether); see pubescent eyes.

hairy lobes, in ♂ Lepidoptera, anellus lobes (Tuxen, after Eyer).

halberd-shaped, triangular and hollowed out at the sides and base (T-B).

Haller's organ, in ticks (Acari), a small vesicle containing sensory hairs on the tarsus of the first pair of legs, established to be olfactory in function (T-B, after Matheson).

halophilous, inhabiting areas with relatively high concentrations of salt ions (T-B; Norris, in CSIRO); see estuarine, intertidal, and marine.

Halterata, Diptera, q.v. (T-B).

Halteriptera, Diptera, q.v. (T-B).

halter(es), in adult Diptera, modified hind wing, which are sense organs concerned with the maintenance of stability in flight (T-B; Chapman).

hamadens, a peculiar toothlike projection of the lacinia proximad of the maxadentes (T-B, after MacGillivray).

hamate, hamatus (Latin), hooked (T-B; R. W. Brown).

hammer, in ♂ Acroneuriinae (Plecoptera: Perlidae), a rounded or squarish, raised tubercle or finger-naillike appendix on the posterior part of sternum IX (subgenital plate) (Tuxen, after Needham and Claassen); in ♂ Heteroptera (Hemiptera), ductifer, q.v. (Tuxen, after Ludwig).

hammer-shaped sclerites, in ♂ Siphonaptera, subhamuli, q.v. (Tuxen, after Sharif).

hamula, in Collembola, tenaculum, q.v. (T-B; Leftwich).

hamular hook, in ♂ Libellulidae (Odonata), robust curved hook in which the basal lobe of the posterior hamulus (Tuxen).

hamular process, in ♂ Odonata, a fork of the hamulus, q.v. (T-B, after Garman); see hamular hook.

hamules, hamuli, q.v.

hamuli (sing., **hamulus**), in ♂ Odonata, hamuli anteriores and hamuli posteriores, q.v. (Tuxen) or hamular hook, q.v. (Tuxen, after Asahina); in tree crickets (Orthoptera: Gryllidae: Oecanthinae), hook-like processes of the genitalia (T-B, after J. B. Smith); in ♂ Siphonaptera, crochets, q.v. (Tuxen, after Barrera); in adult Hymenoptera, hooks in a row along the costal margin of the hind wing which catch into a fold of the forewing to couple wings in flight (T-B; Chapman); in ♂ Hymenoptera, parameres, q.v. (Tuxen, after Radoszkowski) or gonocoxites + gonostyli + volsellae (Tuxen, after Radoszkowski); see hamulus.

hamuli anteriores (sing., **hamulus anterior**), in ♂ Odonata, a pair of clasps situated anteriorly in fenestra, used in grasping ♀ (Tuxen).

hamuli posteriores (sing., **hamulus posterior**), in ♂ Odonata, a pair of clasps situated posteriorly in fenestra, used in grasping ♀ (Tuxen).

hamulohalteres, in ♂ Coccoidea (Hemiptera: Sternorrhyncha), reduced metathoracic wings (Kosztarab and Kozár).

hamulus (pl., **hamuli**), a small hook (T-B); see hamuli.

hamus (pl., **hami**), a hook (T-B); in Tubulifera (Thysanoptera), a small distal hook of each tarsomere (Heming); in Heteroptera (Hemiptera), the spur or short vein, sometimes pointed, projecting into the middle cell of the hind wing (T-B); in ♂ frenate Lepidoptera, retinaculum, q.v. (T-B; Tulloch); in ♂ Chlidanotini and Schoenotenini (Lepidoptera: Tortricidae), paired processes of the ventral surface of the tegumen, articulating dorsad of or beside the socii, mostly slender, long, with hooked or hamulate tops, directed caudad or caudolaterad, dorsad of the gnathos (Tuxen, after Diakonoff).

Hancock's glands, in some ♂ tree crickets (Orthoptera: Ensifera: Oecanthinae), metanotal glands of which secrete fluid on which the ♀ feeds while copulating (Tulloch).

hand, see manus (T-B).

handbook, in taxonomy, a publication designed primarily as an aid to field and laboratory identification rather than the presentation of new taxonomic conclusions (Mayr); see manual and monograph.

hangingfly, a member of the family Bittacidae (Mecoptera) (Setty); see scorpionfly.

hapantotype, one or more preparations of directly related individuals representing different stages in the life cycle together forming a name-bearing type in an extant species of protozoa (ICZN).

haplodiploidy, the mode of sex determination in which males are derived from haploid eggs and females from diploid eggs, characteristic of Hymenoptera, many Thysanoptera, Acari and some other groups, e.g., *Micromalthus* (Coleoptera: Micromalthidae) (Wilson; Chapman; Eickwort, pers. comm.).

Haplogastra, group sometimes recognized within the suborder Polyphaga (Coleoptera), including the Staphylinoidea, Histeroidea, Hydrophiloidea, and Scarabaeoidea, characterized by adults in which abdominal sternum II is only visible as a lateral rudiment (Britton, after Jeannel and Paulian, in CSIRO); see Heterogastra.

haplogastrous abdomen, in some adult Coleoptera (e.g., Scarabeidae), abdomen in which sternite 2 is reduced to a small triangular plate on each side (Britton, after Jeannel and Paulian, in CSIRO); see adephagous abdomen, cryptogastrous abdomen, and hologastrous abdomen.

haploid, having only a single set of chromosomes, e.g., most gametes (Mayr); see diploid and polyploid.

haplometrosis, in ants (Hymenoptera: Formicidae), the founding of a new colony by a single fertile ♀ (Tulloch).

haplotype, type species, q.v., of a genus, being a single species included at the time of founding the genus, but not specifically stated to be the type of the genus (O'Brien, pers. comm., after Metcalf and VanDuzee); see logotype and orthotype.

haptolachus, in larval Scarabaeoidea (Coleoptera), the medioposterior region of the epipharynx, located behind the pedium, below the clypeus in many species, consisting of the nesia, a number of sensillae, and the crepis (T-B, after Böving).

haptomerum, in larval Scarabaeoidea (Coleoptera), the medioanterior region of the epipharynx, in front of the pedium and behind the corypha, or behind the apical region consisting of the united acropariae and corypha, and consisting of the zygum, various sensillae and a series of crepis (T-B, after Böving).

hard tick, a tick of the family Ixodidae (Acari) (Borror et al.); see soft tick.

harmonic growth, see Przibram's Rule (Tulloch).

harp, in Grylloidea (Orthoptera), the area of the forewing lying between the mirror and the stridulum (Otte, pers. comm.).

harpactophagous, predaceous, q.v. (T-B).

harpago (pl., **harpagones**), in ♂ insects, moveable phallic or periphallic processes of abdominal segment IX, derivatives of gonostyli (styli) or parameres, usually having a clasping function (Tuxen, after Snodgrass); in ♂ Ephemeroptera, genostyles, q.v. (Tuxen, after Snodgrass); in ♂ Auchenorrhyncha (Hemiptera), styles, q.v. (Tuxen, after Snodgrass); in ♂ Aleyrodidae (Hemiptera: Sternorrhyncha), claspers, q.v. (Tuxen, after Pesson); in ♂ Heteroptera (Hemiptera), parameres, q.v. (Tuxen, after Snodgrass); in ♂ Raphidioptera, gonocoxite, q.v. (Tuxen, after Carpenter); in ♂ Mecoptera, stylus, q.v. (Tuxen, after Snodgrass); in ♂ Trichoptera, the distal segment of an inferior appendage (Tuxen, after Nielsen), or inferior appendage, q.v. (T-B, after Snodgrass); in ♂ Lepidoptera, valvae, q.v. (Tuxen, after Buchanan White); in ♂ Diptera, gonopod, q.v. (McAlpine), dististylus, q.v. (Tuxen) or sclerotized parts of aedeagus (Tuxen, after Lindner); in ♂ Culicidae (Diptera), claspettes, q.v. (Tuxen, after

Howard, Dyar and Knab); in ♂ Siphonaptera, telomere, q.v. (Tuxen, after Barrera) or hamuli, q.v. (Tuxen, after Sharif).

harpagoger, in ♂ Diptera, basistylus, q.v. (Tuxen).

harpagon, in ♂ Megaloptera, catoprocessus, q.v. (Tuxen, after Friedrich).

harpe(s), in ♂ Lepidoptera, distinct part of valva bearing one or more processes (Tuxen, after Sibatani et al.); in ♂ Noctuidae and Geometridae (Lepidoptera) the ventrocaudal part of the valva, caudad of the sacculus (Tuxen); in Rhopalocera (Lepidoptera), the cucullus and valvula having been lost, the ventrodistal, sometimes nearly the whole distal, part of the valva (Tuxen), also applied to total armature of the inner face of the valva (Tuxen, after Rothschild and Jordan) or to the entire valva, q.v. (Tuxen, after J. B. Smith); in ♂ Diptera, dististylus, q.v. (Tuxen; Saether), postgonites, q.v. (Tuxen), gonopods, q.v. (Tuxen, after Lindner), or parameres, q.v. (McAlpine); in ♂ Culicidae (Diptera), processes of tergum X (Tuxen, after Howard, Dyar and Knab); in ♂ Muscomorpha (Diptera), surstyli, q.v. (Tuxen); in ♂ Calliphoridae (Diptera), paraphallus, q.v. (Tuxen, after Zumpt and Heinz); in ♂ Hymenoptera, gonostylus, q.v. (Tuxen, after Crampton); see harpago.

harvesting ants, ants (Hymenoptera: Formicidae) that store seeds in their nests (Wilson).

harvestman, certain long-legged members of the order Opiliones (Arachnida) (Borror et al.).

hastate, hastatus, halberd-shaped; excavated at the base and sides but with spreading lobes or angles (T-B).

hastate pupil, in an ocellate spot, when the pupil is hastate, i.e., halberd shaped (T-B).

hastiform, hastate, q.v. (T-B).

hastisetae, hastisetal tufts, spear-headed setae frequently found in tufts arising from the tergites, especially the caudal segments of larvae of Anthreninae (Coleoptera: Dermestidae) (Peterson).

hatched, closely marked with numerous short transverse lines (T-B; Harris); see strigate.

hatching, the breaking of the eggshell by an insect in the process of emergence (T-B); see eclosion.

hatching membrane, a membranous sheath investing the young insect at the time of hatching, probably an embryonic exuvial cuticula, shed during hatching or shortly thereafter (not the amnion) (T-B, after Snodgrass).

hatching spine(s), egg burster, q.v. (T-B).

Haustellata, group proposed for insects with mouthparts modified into a sucking tube, including Hemiptera, Siphonaptera, Diptera, and Lepidoptera (Boudreaux, after Clairville).

haustellate, formed for sucking, being applied chiefly to mouthpart structures (T-B); see mandibulate.

haustellate insects, insects whose mouthparts are adapted for sucking (Leftwich).

Haustellodea, hypothesized monophyletic group including the orders Siphonaptera and Diptera (Boudreaux).

haustellum, in general, proboscis, q.v. (T-B); in adult Diptera, distal portion of the proboscis representing the prementum (Borror et al.).

Hayes' plate, in larval Scarabaeoidea (Coleoptera), nesium, q.v. (Tulloch).

Hayes' sense cone, in larval Scarabaeoidea (Coleoptera), nesium, q.v. (Tulloch).

head, the first or anterior region of the insect body, articulated at its base to the thorax, bearing the mouth structures and antennae, and believed by some authors to be composed of 7 primitive segments: (1) the ocular or protocerebral; (2) the antennal or deutocerebral; (3) intercalary or tritocerebral; (4) mandibular; (5) superlingual; (6) maxillary; and (7) labial or second maxillary (T-B, after J. B. Smith).

head capsule, the fused sclerites of the head which form a hard compact case, including the epicranium, frons, clypeus, genae, and gula (T-B, after Imms; Leftwich); cranium.

head of clasp, in ♂ Lepidoptera, apical part of valva, i.e., cucullus or harpe (Tuxen, after Warren).

head of harpe, in ♂ Argynninae (Lepidoptera: Nymphalidae), ampulla (Tuxen, after Warren).

head of spermatheca, in ♀ Siphonaptera, bulga, q.v. (Tuxen).

head skeleton, in larval Muscomorpha (Diptera), cephalopharyngeal skeleton, q.v. (Ferrar).

head vesicle, in adult Diptera, ptilinum, q.v. (T-B).

hearing, mechanoreception of vibrations borne through the air, water, or substratum (Chapman).

hearing organ, tympanal organ, q.v. (Leftwich).

heart, posterior portion of dorsal vessel, in abdomen or as far anteriorly as prothorax, possessing ostia (Chapman); see aorta.

heart chamber, one of the segmental swellings of the heart (T-B, after Snodgrass); see ampulla.

heautotype, autotype, q.v. (T-B, after Banks and Caudell).

Hebroidea, superfamily of Heteroptera within the infraorder Gerromorpha including the minute, predatory, water-surface dwelling bugs of the family Hebridae (Andersen).

Hedyloidea, superfamily within the Rhopalocera (Lepidoptera), containing only the family Hedylidae, whose members were formerly placed in the Geometridae (Scoble).

heel, in ♂ Auchenorrhyncha (Hemiptera), angular median corner of the foot of the style (Tuxen, after Young); in certain larval Coleoptera, a padlike prolongation of the base of the tarsungulus, opposing the claw (Peterson); in ♂ Siphonaptera, calx, q.v. (Tuxen, after Jordan); in adult Hymenoptera, tibial spur, q.v. (T-B).

Heidenreich's disease, a lethal disease of larvae of rhinoceros beetles, *Oryctes* spp. (Coleoptera: Scarabaeidae) in which the infected larvae fail to retain lipids and the fat body and muscles atrophy and eventually become necrotic (Steinhaus and Martignoni).

Heitler's lump, in Orthoptera, a process beneath the articulation of the hind femur at the femorotibial joint, over which the apodeme of the flexor tibiae slides (Chapman).

helcodermatus, cariose, q.v. (T-B; Harris).

helcodermatus spines, in pupae, boring or tearing spines (T-B).

Heleomyzoidea, superfamily of Schizophora (Diptera: Brachycera: Cyclorrhapha), including the Heleomyzidae and other families, adults possessing vibrissae or a group of bristles or hairs on vibrissal angle, prosternum without precoxal bridges, and ♀ postabdomen not forming an elongate ovipositor (Colless and McAlpine, in CSIRO).

heliciform, in the form of a spiral snail shell; applied to the cases of some Trichoptera (T-B).

helicoid process, in some ♂ Lygaeidae and Coreidae (Hemiptera: Heteroptera), cricoid sclerite of helical shape (Tuxen, after Ashlock).

heliconome, a spiraled shape, serpentine leaf mine or ophionome (Hering).

heliophobic, negatively heliotropic (T-B).

heliotactic, positively heliotropic (T-B); see diurnal.

heliotropism, movement of insects relative to the sun, being a special case of phototropism (T-B; Leftwich).

helmet comb, in Siphonaptera, the vertical comb extending along the posterior margin of the helmet in members of the family Stephanocircidae (Lewis, pers. comm.).

Helminthomorpha, superorder within the subclass Chilognatha (Diplopoda), including the orders Callipodida, Chordeumatida, Julida, Platydesmida, Polydesmida, Polyzoniida, Siphoniulida, Siphonophorida, Spirobolida, Spirostreptida, and Stemmiulida, possessing 18 or more body segments and 7 pairs of legs anterior to the ♂ gonopods on seventh segment (Borror et al.; Hoffman, in Parker).

helminths, including roundworms and flatworms, commonly parasites of insects and sometimes causing disease in vertebrates (Norris, in CSIRO; Borror, et. al.).

helocerous, with clavate antennae (T-B).

helus (pl., **heli**), in larval Scarabaeoidea (Coleoptera), a coarse fixed spine without a cup, belonging to the region of the haptomerum (T-B, after Böving).

helvolus, pale-yellow (R. W. Brown).

helvus, bay-yellow (R. W. Brown); honey-colored (T-B).

hemal, of, pertaining to or connected with the circulatory system (T-B).

hematocyte, hemocyte, q.v. (Tulloch).

hematophagous, feeding on blood (Adkins, pers. comm.).

hematophagy, blood feeding (Norris, in CSIRO).

hemelytron (pl., **hemelytra**), anterior wing of Heteroptera (Hemiptera), the basal portion of which is thickened and the apical portion membranous in most members of the group (T-B); see elytron and tegmen.

Hemerobioidea, superfamily within the Planipennia, including the Hemerobiidae, Chrysopidae, and Psychopsidae, possessing terrestrial larvae with mandible and maxilla curved inward, tarsi with 2 claws and an empodium, palpi present, and tibia and tarsus separated (Riek, in CSIRO).

hemi-, Greek prefix; half (T-B).

hemicephalic head capsule, in larval Diptera, mainly orthorrhaphous taxa, a head capsule more or less reduced posteriorly and partially retracted into the thorax, with sickle-shaped mandibles operating in a vertical plane (Teskey, in McAlpine).

hemicephalous larva, in Tipulidae and Brachycera (Diptera), a larva with a reduced head capsule which can be retracted within the thorax (T-B); see acephalous larva and eucephalous larva.

hemielytron, hemelytron, q.v. (T-B).

hemimacropterous, short winged forms of certain, wing-polymorphic Thysanoptera with wing length about half that of macropterae (Mound and Walker); see brachypterous.

Hemimerina, suborder of Dermaptera, including ectoparasites of *Cricetomys* (Rodentia) of southern Africa belonging to the family Hemimeridae, possessing a single penis lobe in the ♂, mandible lacking proximal molar area, ♀ exhibiting pseudoplacental viviparity, tarsomeres with large pads for gripping hairs, and lacking eyes and hind wings (Giles, in CSIRO); see Arixeniina, Catadermaptera, and Eudermaptera.

Hemimeroptera, Hemiptera, q.v. (T-B).

Hemimetabola, a former division of the Pterygota including forms with incomplete metamorphosis and in which the immature stages are aquatic, i.e., Odonata, Plecoptera, and Ephemeroptera (T-B, after Imms); see Ametabola, Exopterygota, Paurometabola, and Holometabola.

hemimetabolous, having an incomplete metamorphosis, but with aquatic immatures (naiads) differing significantly from adults, e.g., Odonata, Plecoptera, and Ephemeroptera (T-B; Borror et al.); see ametabolous, heterometabolous, paurometabolous, and holometabolous.

Hemiphlebioidea, superfamily within the suborder Zygoptera (Odonata), including the single family Hemiphlebiidae, adults possessing fewer than 3 antenodal crossveins and postnodal crossveins that are not in line with crossveins behind them, and nymphs with median and lateral gills lamellate and labium with paraglossae (O'Farrell, in CSIRO).

hemipneusitic respiration, a type of respiration in which one or more pairs of spiracles are closed, especially among larvae (T-B); respiration with 8 pairs of functional spiracles, one mesothoracic and 7 abdominal, e.g., larval Mycetophilidae (Diptera) (Chapman, after Keilin); see holopneustic respiration and peripneustic respiration.

Hemiptera, order of exopterygote (paurometabolous) Neoptera (Insecta), including the suborders Sternorrhyncha, Auchenorrhyncha, Coleorrhyncha, and Heteroptera, characterized by sucking mouthparts consisting of hinged stylets (mandibles and maxillae) resting in a dorsally grooved rostrate labium, suction canal and salivary canal within maxillary stylets, maxillary and labial palps absent (Hennig);

sometimes restricted to just the Heteroptera by North American authors (Borror et al.).

hemipteroid orders, Paraneoptera, q.v. (Mackerras, Riek, in CSIRO).

Hemipteroidea, Acercaria, q.v. (Boudreaux, after Handlirsch).

hemipupa, in some paedogenetic Cecidomyiidae (Diptera), a rounded pupal form with or without vestiges of wings and legs that gives birth to larvae (Chapman); see pupal paedogenesis.

hemispheric, hemispherical, hemisphaericum, shaped like the half of a globe or sphere (T-B).

hemisternites, in Ephemeroptera, paraprocts, q.v. (Tuxen); in ♀ Coleoptera, the 2 sclerites of abdominal sternum IX surrounding vulva, sometimes fused (Tuxen).

hemitergal processes, in ♂ Plecoptera, fingerlike or otherwise modified processes of hemitergites of tergum X (Tuxen, after Brinck).

hemitergites, divided halves of abdominal tergum IX or X in some adult insects (Mackerras, in CSIRO); in ♂ Embiidina, the 2 parts into which abdominal tergum X is divided (T-B, after Tillyard; Tuxen); in adult Hymenoptera, lateral remnants of abdominal terga (Tuxen, after Michener).

hemizygous, applied to individual with only a haploid chromosome number, e.g., most ♂ Hymenoptera (Gauld and Bolton); see haploid.

hemocoel, the body cavity or cavities of the embryo between the mesoderm and the other germ layers, probably a remnant of the blastocoel (T-B, after Snodgrass); the general body cavity in which the blood flows in insects and arthropods as well as in a number of other invertebrates (T-B; Leftwich).

hemocoelic, of or pertaining to the hemocoel (T-B).

hemocoelic insemination, in some Cimicoidea and Nabidae (Hemiptera: Heteroptera) and Strepsiptera, deposition of sperm into the body cavity rather than in the reproductive tract (Chapman); see traumatic insemination.

hemocoelous viviparity, viviparity in which development occurs in the hemocoel of the parent ♀, e.g., Strepsiptera and in some larval Cecidomyiidae (Diptera) which reproduce paedogenetically (Chapman).

hemocyanin, an oxygen-carrier found in the blood of arthropods, analogous to the hemoglobin of animals in function and chemical structure, but containing copper instead of iron (T-B).

hemocyte, blood cells suspended in fluid plasma of hemolymph (Chapman); see adipohemocyte, cystocyte, granular hemocyte, oenocytoid, plasmatocyte, prohemocyte, and spherule cell.

hemocytoblast, prohemocyte, q.v. (Tulloch).

hemocytopoietic organ, hemopoietic organ, q.v. (Tulloch).

hemoglobin, respiratory pigment found in the hemolymph of relatively few insects, e.g., some larval Chironomidae (Diptera), the aquatic bugs of the subfamily Anisopinae (Hemiptera: Heteroptera: Notonectidae), and the endoparasitic larvae of *Gasterophilus* (Diptera: Gasterophilidae) (Chapman).

hemolymph, the watery blood or lymphlike nutrient fluid of the lower invertebrates (T-B); the blood of insects, consisting of fluid plasma in which nucleated cells (hemocytes) are suspended (Chapman).

hemolytic, causing breaking down or destruction of red blood cells (T-B, after Matheson).

hemophagous, hematophagous, q.v. (T-B).

hemopoiesis, production of new hemocytes (Chapman).

hemopoietic organ, any group of cells thought to produce new hemocytes (Chapman); in larval Lepidoptera, 4 organs behind the prothoracic spiracles, consisting of a mass of rounded cells connected together by an intracellular reticulum and enclosed in a capsule (Chapman).

hemorrhage, any discharge of blood from a ruptured vessel (T-B).

hemostatic diaphragm, in Orthoptera and Phasmida, an occlusive diaphragm between the femur and trochanter limiting the loss of hemolymph following autotomy of the leg (Key, in CSIRO).

hemostatic membrane, hemostatic diaphragm, q.v. (Tulloch).

hemoxanthine, a dissolved albuminoid in the insect blood, which has both a respiratory and a nutritive function (T-B).

hemozoin granules, melanin granules of the *Plasmodium* sporozoite (T-B, after Comstock); pigment granules resulting from the breakdown of hemoglobin found in malarial organisms (Tulloch).

henia (pl., **heniae**), in ♀ Plebeiinae (Lepidoptera: Lycaenidae), distal, membranous, tubular part of an erectile everting apparatus by means of which the ostium bursae can be extruded to contact ♂ in copulo (Tuxen, after Chapman).

henion (pl., **henia**), in ♂ Olethreutini (Lepidoptera: Tortricidae), bandlike vertical connection between middle of gnathos and dorsal part of anellus, representing an element of the diaphragma (Tuxen, after Diakonoff).

hepatic, hepaticus (Latin), pertaining to the liver (T-B; R. W. Brown); liver-colored, i.e., reddish brown (T-B); pertaining to exeretion (T-B).

hepatic caecum, midgut caecum, q.v. (T-B).

hepatic cells, nephrocytes, q.v. (T-B, after Snodgrass).

hepatic pouch, midgut caecum, q.v. (T-B).

hepaticolor, reddish-brown (T-B); see hepatic.

Hepialoidea, superfamily of the infrorder Exoporia (Lepidoptera), including the Paleosetidae, Neotheoridae, Anomosetidae, Prototheoridae, and Hepialidae, small to very large moths without ocelli and chaetosemata, with short antennae, small, nonfunctional mandibles, proboscis small or absent, wing venation homoneurous, wing scales with secondary ridges, and exoporian ♀ genitalia; larvae elongate, slender, hypognathous, with normal thoracic legs and prolegs; pupae adecticous, with dorsal spines and plates, protruded at ecdysis (Common).

heptachlor, $C_{10}H_5Cl_7$, a synthetic insecticide; a chlorinated hydrocarbon, 1,4,5,6,7,8,8-heptachloro-3a,4,7,7,7a-tetrahydro-4,7-methanoindene; moderately toxic to mammals, acute oral LD_{50} for rats 40 to 188 mg/kg (Pfadt).

Heptagenioidea, superfamily of Ephemeroptera, including Oligoneu-riidae, Heptageniidae, and the extinct Epeoromimidae (Landa and Soldán).

herbicide, a chemical for killing plants (Pfadt).

herbiphagy, herbivory, q.v. (Wood).

herbivore, an animal feeding on nonwoody plant tissue (T-B).

herbivorous, feeding on nonwoody plant tissue (T-B); see xylophagous and phytophagous.

herbivory, feeding on nonwoody plant tissue (Matthews and Matthews).

heritability (h^2), the degree of genetic determination of the variability that is present in a sample population; h^2 = R/S where R is the magnitude of response, i.e., the difference between the mean value of the parental and filial populations, and S is the selection differential, i.e., the deviation of the chosen patterns from the whole population in their mean value for the trait under selection (Matthews and Matthews).

hereditary, inherited; handed down from parent to offspring (T-B).

hereditary transmission, transovarian transmission, q.v. (Tulloch).

heredity, inheritance from progenitors; organic resemblance based on descent (T-B, after Conklin).

hermaphrodite, an individual possessing both ovaries and testes, e.g., cottony cushion scale, *Icerya purchasi* (Hemiptera: Sternorrhyncha: Margarodidae) and a few Phoridae (Diptera) (T-B; White, in CSIRO; Chapman); see gynandromorph and intersex.

hermaphroditic, of the nature of a hermaphrodite (T-B).

hermaphroditism, the condition of being a hermaphrodite (T-B).

hesmosis, in ants (Hymenoptera: Formicidae), colony fission, q.v. (Wilson).

Hesperioidea, superfamily within the division Ditrysia (Lepidoptera), commonly called skippers, including the Hesperiidae and Megathymidae, possessing adults with the bases of the antennae widely separated, veins arising separately from discal cell in fore- and hind wing, antennae clubbed, and wings broad (Common, in CSIRO).

hetero-, Greek prefix; unequal; different from (T-B).

Heterobathmiina, a primitive suborder of Lepidoptera from Patagonia, including the single superfamily Heterobathmioidea, possess monotrysian, mandibulate adults, homoneurous venation, and leaf mining larvae (Kristensen and Nielsen).

Heterobathmioidea, only superfamily of suborder Heterobathmiina (Lepidoptera), including the family Heterobathmiidae, adults being small, narrow-winged moths, with unspecialized galea, functional mandibles, homoneurous wing venation, and primitive, solid scales; larvae leaf-mining, with 7 stemmata each side of head and thoracic legs with bipartite trochanger; pupae decticous, with coarse apical teeth on hypertrophied mandibles (Kristensen).

heterobathmy, mosaiclike distribution of primitive and derived characters among related species (Hennig); see mosaic evolution.

Heterocera, moths, i.e., Lepidoptera in which the antennae are of any form other than clubbed at the tip, including the suborders Zeugloptera, Exoporia, Monotrysia, and most of the Ditrysia (T-B; Leftwich; Munroe, in Parker); see Rhopalocera.

heterochrome, of different color; applied to species in which there are 2 color forms of one sex, one of which is like (homoeochrome) the opposite sex, as in certain Odonata and Lepidoptera (T-B).

heterochrony, dissociation, during development, of the factors of shape, size, and maturity, so that organisms mature in these respects at earlier or later growth stages (T-B; Allaby).

Heterodactyla, name proposed for all the Brachycera (Diptera), excluding the Tabanomorpha (Hennig).

heterodynamic life cycle, a life cycle in which there is a period of diapause (Tulloch; Borror et al.); see holodynamic life cycle.

heteroecy, in Aphidoidea (Hemiptera: Sternorrhyncha), heteroecism, q.v. (Blackman and Eastop).

heteroecism, a condition in which a parasite preys upon two, usually widely different, hosts which are attacked alternately either by successive generations or in sequence during the development of a single individual parasite (Tulloch).

heterogametic sex, sex with a pair of dissimilar sex chromosomes (XY) (White, in CSIRO).

heterogamy, alternation of bisexual and parthenogenetic reproduction (T-B; Borror et al.); see alternation of generations.

Heterogastra, a grouping within the Polyphaga (Coleoptera), possessing a hologastrous or cryptogastrous abdomen, including the Elateriformia, Bostrychiformia, Cucujiformia, and the Dascilloidea (Scarabaeiformia) (Britton, after Jeannel and Paulian, in CSIRO); see Haplogastra.

heterogeneous, differing in kind; unlike in quality (T-B).

heterogenesis, heterogeny, q.v. (T-B).

heterogeny, the form of reproduction in certain insects which has sexual and asexual or parthenogenetic forms, or some cyclic form of alternation of generations (T-B).

heterogonic growth, allometric growth, q.v. (Tulloch; Leftwich).

heterogony, allometric growth, q.v. (Leftwich).

Heterogyna, the ants (Hymenoptera: Formicidae); referring to the different kinds of females (queens and workers), as distinguished from males.

heteroideus chrochets, in larval Arctiidae (Lepidoptera), a mesoseries of crochets possessing a median, well-developed series of hooks flanked by smaller or rudimentary crochets (Peterson).

Heteromera, Tenebrionoidea, q.v. (T-B; Britton, in CSIRO; Lawrence, in Parker).

heteromerous, with the 3 pairs of tarsi differing in the number of tarsomeres, e.g., Heteromera (Coleoptera) (T-B; Borror et al.).

Heterometabola, Exopterygota, q.v. (T-B).

heterometabolous, paurometabolous or hemimetabolous, including those insects with exopterygote wing development.

Heteromorpha, Endopterygota, q.v. (T-B).

heteromorphic, holometabolous, q.v. (T-B).

heteromorphosis, hypermetamorphosis, q.v. (Chapman; Gauld and Bolton); the replacement of one organ or part by another of a different kind following mutilation (T-B).

heteromorphous, holometabolous, q.v. (T-B).

heteromorphs, adult ♀ Odonata unlike ♂ in color (O'Farrell, in CSIRO); see andromorphs.

Heteroneura, Monotrysia, q.v. (Borror et al.; Kristensen).

heteroneurous venation, in the Monotrysia and Ditrysia (Lepidoptera), wing venation in which hind wing venation is reduced: subcosta (Sc) and R_1 are fused, at least distally, and radial sector (R_s) is unbranched (Common, in CSIRO).

heteronomous, having 2 parts which when compared with each other, are of different quality; differing in development or function (T-B).

heteronomous hyperparastioid, in Aphelinidae (Hymenoptera), species in which the ♂ develops as a hyperparasitoid of one host while the ♀ develops as a normal parasitoid on another host (Gauld and Bolton, after Walter); see diphagous parasitoid and heterotrophic parasitoid.

heteronomous parasitoid, in Aphelinidae (Hymenoptera), a species of parasitoid exhibiting heteronomy (Gauld and Bolton); see diphagous parasitoid, heterotrophic parasitoid, and heteronomous hyperparasitoid.

heteronomy, in Aphelinidae (Hymenoptera), the condition of having ♂ host relationships that differ from ♀ host relationships within the same species (Gauld and Bolton, after Flanders).

heteropalpi, palpi with a different number of joints in the ♂ and the ♀, as in some Trichoptera (T-B).

heteroparthenogenesis, heterogamy, q.v. (T-B).

Heterophaga, name proposed for a group including the suborders Myxophaga and Polyphaga (Coleoptera) (Baehr, in Hennig, after Klausnitzer).

Heteroptera, suborder of the Hemiptera (often given ordinal ranking by North American workers), characterized by adults with forewings (when present) folded flat over the body, often in the form of hemelytra (except Enicocephalomorpha, Gerromorpha, some Dipsocoromorpha) with basally thickened corium, apical membranes usually broadly overlapping, gula present, dorsal abdominal scent glands in nymphs, and metathoracic scent glands in adults (T-B; Woodward et al., in CSIRO).

Heteropteroidea, an ordinal-level taxon including Coleorrhyncha and Heteroptera (Hemiptera) (Hennig).

heteropterous, with forewings developed as hemelytra (T-B); pertaining to the Heteroptera (T-B).

heterosis, higher fitness among heterozygotes (White, in CSIRO).

heterotroph, applied to any organism which requires a supply of organic material from the environment; all animals and fungi (Tulloch).

heterotrophic parasitoid, in Aphelinidae (Hymenoptera), a species in

which the ♂ is a parasitoid of a different host species than the famale,
e.g., *Encarsia lutea* (Gauld and Bolton, after Stoner and Butler); see
diphagous parasitoid and heteronomous hyperparasitoid.

heterotypical, of a genus, described from more than one species, these
differing in structure (T-B).

heterozygous, having different alleles at homologous loci of 2 parental
chromosomes (Mayr); see homozygous.

HETP, a synthetic insecticide and acaricide; an organophosphate mixture of ethyl polyphosphates containing 12 to 20% of tetraethyl py-
rophosphate (tepp); extremely toxic to mammals, acute oral LD_{50} for
rate 7 mg/kg (Pfadt).

hexachaetous, in some adult Diptera, with the mouthparts including 6
piercing stylets, e.g., ♀ mosquitoes (Culicidae) (T-B).

Hexagenitoidea, extinct superfamily of Ephemeroptera, from the
Middle Jurassic and Upper Miocene, including Hexagenitidae,
Aenigmephemeridae, and Aphelophlebodidae (Landa and Soldán).

hexalure, synthetic attractant for ♂ pink bollworm moth, *Pectinophora
gossypiella* (Lepidoptera: Gelechiidae); cis-7-hexadecen-1-ol acetate
(Pfadt).

hexanephric, with 6 Malpighian tubules (T-B).

hexapod, a six-legged arthropod (T-B); a member of the Hexapoda
(Mackerras, in CSIRO); see insect.

Hexapoda, superclass within the phylum Arthropoda, including Collembola, Protura, Diplura, and class Insecta, characterized by
mouthparts consisting of mandibles, maxillae, and labium, head with
anterior and posterior tentorial arms; three-segmented thorax, normally with 3 pairs of legs in the adult, and abdomen with 6–12
segments, with at most rudimentary limbs (T-B; Mackerras, in
CSIRO).

hexapodal, hexapodous, q.v. (T-B).

hexapodous, hexapodus (Latin), six-legged (T-B).

hibernaculum, a tent or sheath made out of a leaf or other material, in
which a larva hides or lies dormant (T-B).

hibernate, to pass the winter in a quiescent condition (T-B).

hibernation, quiescence, q.v., during seasonal low temperatures (T-B;
Leftwich); see aestivation and diapause.

Hick's bottles, on antennae of bees and ants (Hymenoptera: Aculeata),
campaniform sensilla, q.v. (T-B).

Hick's papillae, in adult Diptera, minute peglike processes at the base
of the halter (McAlpine); see organ of Hicks.

hierarchy, in classification, the system of ranks which indicates the
categorical level of various taxa (Mayr); see taxonomic category.

higher category, a taxonomic category of rank higher than species
(Mayr); see supraspecific.

highly eusocial, living in a eusocial colony in which the castes are
morphologically dissimilar and food exchange among adults is extensive (Michener).

hill, the dome-shaped mound or crater surmounting a formicary, which is perforated with cavities serving as incubators for the various immature stages of ants (T-B, after W. M. Wheeler).

hilla (pl., **hillae**), in ♀ Siphonaptera, small, terminal part of spermatheca (Tuxen, after Peus).

hill topping, behaviour exhibited by certain insects whereby they fly to hill-tops or elevated points (Common and Waterhouse).

hind angle, in forewing of Lepidoptera, anal angle, q.v. (T-B).

hind coxa, coxa of the hind leg (Harbach and Knight).

hind body, abdomen, q.v. (T-B).

hind coxa, coxa of the hind leg (McAlpine).

hind femur, femur of the hind leg (McAlpine).

hind gut, posterior, ectodermal portion of the alimentary canal from the end of the midgut to the anus, including the Malpighian tubules and rectal glands (T-B; Gilmour, in CSIRO); see foregut and midgut.

hind intestine, hind gut, q.v. (T-B).

hind leg, metathoracic leg (McAlpine).

hind tarsus, the tarsus of one of the hind legs (Harbach and Knight).

hind tibia, tibia of the hind leg (McAlpine).

hind trochanter, the trochanter of one of the hind legs (Harbach and Knight).

hind unguis, claw, q.v., of hind leg (Harbach and Knight).

hind wing(s), wing arising from the metathorax (Leftwich); see forewing.

hinge, articulation, q.v. (T-B); in ♂ Dermaptera, point of attachment of parameres to penis (Tuxen, after Burr); in ♂ Pentatomidae (Hemiptera: Heteroptera), short membrane between articulatory apparatus and phallotheca (Tuxen, after Baker); in ♀ Culicidae (Diptera), the point of articulation between the upper and lower vaginal lips (Harbach and Knight, after Coher).

hinged flaps, in ♂ Podopinae (Hemiptera: Heteroptera: Pentatomidae), parandria, q.v. (Tuxen, after Leston).

Hippoboscoidea, superfamily of Schizophora (Diptera: Brachycera: Muscomorpha), including mammalian ectoparasites in the families Hippoboscidae, Nycteribiidae, and Streblidae (McAlpine); see Pupipara.

hirsute, hirsutus (Latin), hairy; rough; shaggy; clothed with long, dense setae (T-B; R. W. Brown).

hirsutiusculus, somewhat hairy (T-B).

hispid, hispidus, bristly; sparsely set with short, stiff bristles (T-B).

histamine, an amine, $C_5H_9N_3$, produced by the decomposition of histidine and found in all organic matter; toxic compound in venoms associated with insect stings (Gilmour, in CSIRO).

Histeroidea, superfamily within the Polyphaga (Coleoptera), including the Histeridae, Sphaeritidae, and Synteliidae, possessing adults with a haplogastrous abdomen, elbowed antenna with terminal club consisting of 3 articles, short compact body, simple claws on tarsus, abdomen with 5 visible sternites, and at least last abdominal tergum exposed (Britton, in CSIRO).

histidine, $C_6H_9N_3O_2$, an essential amino acid in the diet of insects (Gilmour, in CSIRO).

histoblast, imaginal disc, q.v. (T-B, after Comstock).

histoblastic, of or pertaining to histoblasts (T-B).

histochemistry, the microscopic study of the chemical characteristics of tissues, through the use of substances (dyes, etc.) providing identifying chemical reactions (Steinhaus and Martignoni).

histogenesis, in Holometabola, the process of developing adult structures from the products of histolysis (T-B, after Wardle; Borror et al.).

histogenetic, of or pertaining to histogenesis (Borror et al.).

histogram, a set of rectangles in which the midpoints of class intervals are plotted on the abscissa and the frequencies on the ordinate (Mayr).

histological, of or pertaining to histology (T-B).

histology, the study of the tissues of organisms (T-B).

histolysis, a breaking down, degeneration and dissolution of organic tissue (T-B); in holometabolous insects, a process whereby larval structures are broken down into material that can be used in the development of adult structures (Borror et al.).

histolytic, of or pertaining to histolysis (T-B); of the nature of histolysis (T-B).

histolytic disease, Heidenreich's disease, q.v. (Steinhaus and Martignoni).

histopathology, in invertebrate pathology, a study of abnormal microscopic changes in the tissue structure (Steinhaus and Martignoni).

histosiphon, stylostome, q.v. (Pfadt).

histriobdellid larva, in some Mymaridae (Hymenoptera), cylindrical second instar larva divided into 6 segments, the first and last being the largest, and often bearing paired fleshy processes (Gauld and Bolton, after Jackson).

hiva aura, hive odor, q.v. (Wilson).

hive odor, nest odor of honey bees (Hymenoptera: Apoidea) (Wilson).

H-melanosis, melanosis caused by yeastlike microorganisms (Steinhaus and Martigoni).

hoary, greyish-white (T-B); see incanus.

holarctic, distributed within the Holarctic Region (T-B).

Holarctic Region, faunal region combining the Nearctic and Palaearctic Regions (Mackerras, in CSIRO).

holidic, pertaining to a medium (used for growing organisms) whose intended constituents, other than purified inert materials, have exactly known chemical structure before the medium is compounded (Steinhaus and Martignoni); see meridic and oligidic.

holistic, looking at wholes as more than the sums of their parts (Mayr).

holoblastic cleavage, the type of cleavage in which the entire egg is divided (T-B, after Snodgrass).

holocephalous larva, larva with a fully developed head capsule (Leftwich); see acephalous and hemicephalous.

holocrine, of or pertaining to holocrine secretion (T-B).

holocrine secretion, release of enzymes into the lumen of the midgut or salivary duct by disintegration of the secretory cells (Borror et al.).

holocriny, holocrine secretion, q.v. (T-B, after Wardle).

holocyclic species, in Aphididae (Hemiptera: Sternorrhyncha), those species in which the winter host plants are relatively few, reproduction always sexual and with no migration to summer host plants (T-B, after Wardle).

holodynamic life cycle, a life cycle in which there is continuous development without a period of diapause (Borror et al.); see heterodynamic life cycle.

hologastrous abdomen, in adult Coleoptera, e.g., some Cantharoidea (*Chauliognathus* [Cantharidae] and *Metriorrhynchus* [Lycidae]), an abdomen with sternite II complete and fully sclerotized, like segment III (Britton, after Jeannel and Paulian, in CSIRO).

Holognatha, Filipalpia, q.v. (T-B, after Enderlein; Borror et al.).

Holometabola, insects which pass through a complete metamorphosis in which the larva is very different from the adult and does not become more like the adult, but transforms dramatically by means of a pupal stage, being equivalent to Endopterygota or endopterygote orders, including Megaloptera, Raphidioptera, Planipennia, Mecoptera, Trichoptera, Lepidoptera, Coleoptera, Strepsiptera, Hymenoptera, Diptera, and Siphonaptera (T-B, after Imms; Leftwich; Mackerras, in CSIRO); see Ametabola, Hemimetabola and Paurometabola.

holometabolan, a holometabolous insect (T-B).

holometabolous, pertaining to the Holometabola (T-B); see ametabolous and heterometabolous.

holomorphology, totality of an individual's characteristics from fertilization to death (Hennig).

holoparalectotype, a specimen from the original material, later established as a paratype, that belongs to the sex described by the author (Tulloch).

Holopeltidia, Uropygi, q.v. (Borror et al.).

holopneustic respiration, respiration with all the spiracles open and functional, i.e., with the primitive type of insect respiratory system (T-B); respiration with 10 functional spiracles: 1 mesothoracic, 1 metathoracic, and 8 abdominal, e.g., larval Bibionidae (Diptera) (Chapman, after Keilin).

holophyletic, monophyletic, q.v. (sensu Hennig).

holophyly, monophyly, q.v. (sensu Hennig).

holoptic eyes, in Anisoptera (Odonata) and many ♂ Diptera, especially Nematocera and orthorrhaphous Brachycera, compound eyes that extend dorsally and are contiguous along the midline (T-B; Chapman; McAlpine); see dichoptic.

holosericeous, holosericeus, with short, dense, decumbent, silky hair, giving a satiny luster (T-B).

holotype, a single specimen designated as the name-bearing type of a species or subspecies when it was established, or the single specimen on which the taxon was based when no type was specified (T-B, after Banks and Caudell; ICZN).

homelytron (pl., **homelytra**), elytron, q.v. (T-B).

home range, the range over which an animal normally wanders in search of food, shelter, and/or mates (Matthews and Matthews).

homeochromatism, tending to regional color variation, as when over a given region many butterflies tend to vary similarly as regards color (T-B).

homeochrome, of the same color (T-B); see heterochrome.

homeomerous, isomerous, q.v. (T-B).

homeonomous, of the same substance or texture (T-B).

homeosis, the replacement of a damaged appendage by a different one (Leftwich).

homeostasis, the maintenance of a steady state, especially a physiological or social steady state, by means of self-regulation through internal feedback responses (Wilson).

homeotype, homoeotype, homotype, a specimen compared with the type by one other than the author and determined by him as conspecific with the type (T-B, after Banks and Caudell).

Homilopsocidea, heterogeneous group within the suborder Psocomorpha (Psocoptera), including the families Peripsocidae, Lachesillidae, Pseudocaeciliidae, Archipsocidae, and other families, the members of which possess a well developed valva externa bearing numerous setae (Mockford and Garcia Aldrete).

homo-, Greek prefix, the same; similar to (T-B).

homochromy, change of color to resemble the environment (Chapman).

homochronic heredity, homochronous heredity, the appearance of a variation in offspring at whatever age it first appeared in the parent (T-B).

homochronous, occurring at the same time, as changes in an organism which appear in the offspring at the same age at which they did in the parent (T-B).

homodynamic life cycle, holodynamic life cycle, q.v. (Tulloch).

homodynamous, serially homologous; homology of the metameres (T-B).

Homoeodactyla, Tabanomorpha, q.v. (Hennig).

homogametic sex, sex in which there is a pair of similar sex chromosomes (XX) (White, in CSIRO); see heterogametic sex.

homogeneous, of the same kind or nature; similar in texture or parts (T-B).

homogenous, similar in structure due to community of descent (T-B).

homoideus crochets, in larval Lepidoptera, e.g., most Noctuidae, crochets arranged in a mesoseries, all of equal length (Peterson; Stehr); see heteroideus crochets.

homoiothermal, with regard to animals, warm-blooded (T-B).

homolog, a homologous character state; a homologous chromosome.

homologization, the act of homologizing or of being identical in origin (T-B).

homologous, of a pair of features occurring in different organisms, one being derived from the another, i.e., being states of a single character; of a pair of chromosomes, pairing during meiosis; see analogous.

homology, a correspondence in type of structure between parts or organs of different organisms, due to evolutionary differentiation from the same or a corresponding part or organ of some remote ancestor (T-B, after Tillyard); see serial homology.

Homomorpha, insects in which the immatures resemble the adults (T-B).

homomorphous, having a similar external appearance or form (T-B).

Homoneura, a collective term for those Lepidoptera with homoneurous venation (Borror et al.).

homoneurous venation, in adult Zeugloptera, Aglossata, Heterobathmiina, Dacnonypha, and Exoporia (Lepidoptera), wing venation in which fore- and hind wings are similar with both wings possessing a humeral vein, a radial sector (R_s) with 4 branches, a media with 3 branches, and the 3 anal veins fused distally (Common, in CSIRO).

homonomous, pertaining to homology of parts arranged on a transverse axis; similarly developed and of equal function (T-B).

homonym, in the family group: each of 2 or more available names having the same spelling, or differing only in suffix, and denoting different nominal taxa (ICZN); in the genus group: each of 2 or more available names having the same spelling, and denoting different nominal taxa (ICZN); in the species group: each of 2 or more available names having the same spelling, or spellings deemed under the Code to be the same, and established for different nominal taxa (ICZN); see junior homonym, primary homonym, secondary homonym, and senior homonym.

homonymous, having the same name applying to different conceptions (T-B).

homonymy, the relationship among homonyms (ICZN); Principle of Homonymy, q.v. (ICZN).

homoosis, homoeosis, q.v. (Tulloch; Leftwich).

homoplastic, of characters, exhibiting convergence or parallelism.

homoplasy, the apparent independent evolution of characteristics that are indistinguishable based only on inspection; see convergence and parallelism.

Homoptera, a group of exopterygote insects, including the Coleorrhyncha (sometimes), Sternorrhyncha, and Auchenorrhyncha, all 3 of which are more recently treated as suborders of the Hemiptera (T-B; Woodward et al., in CSIRO).

homopteran, any one of the Homoptera (T-B); of or pertaining to the Homoptera (T-B).

Homorpha, Homomorpha, q.v. (Peterson).

homotenous, retaining the primitive form (T-B).

homozygous, having identical alleles at the 2 homologous loci of a diploid chromosome set (Mayr); see heterozygous.

honey, the thickened and partly digested nectar of flowers, containing a very high concentration of sugars, produced by various bees (Hymenoptera: Apoidea) and used as food for the larvae (T-B; Chapman); see poisoned honey.

honey bee, a member of the genus *Apis* (Hymenoptera: Apidae) or more particularly a member of the domestic species *A. mellifera,* being usually applied to the worker caste (Wilson).

honey pot, honeypot, an individual wax cell for the storage of honey, found in the nests of bumblebees (Hymenoptera: Apidae) (Tulloch, after Gaul); a container made by stingless bees or bumblebees (Hymenoptera: Apidae) from soft cerumen and used to store honey (Wilson).

honey stomach, in aculeate Hymenoptera, a dilation of the oesophagous into a thin-walled crop, serving as a reservoir for liquids (T-B, after Imms); in the honey bee (Hymenoptera: Apidae), the crop in which nectar is mixed with enzymes from the salivary glands and converted to honey before being disgorged (Leftwich).

honey stopper, a valve at the posterior end of a bee's (Hymenoptera: Apidea), crop, specialized for preventing the passage of nectar into the stomach (Leftwich); see stomodaeal valve.

honey tubes, in Aphididae (Hemiptera: Sternorrhyncha), cornicles, q.v. (T-B).

honey yellow, a clear light golden yellow (T-B).

honeycomb, aggregation of hexagonal cells made of beeswax, in which honey is stored (T-B; Wilson; Chapman); see brood comb and comb.

honeydew, watery fluid, containing sugars, excreted from the anus of Aphidoidea and Coccoidea (Sternorrhyncha) and Membracidae and most Fulgoroidea (Auchenorrhyncha) (T-B; Chapman; L. O'Brien, pers. comm.); an exudate from the surface of galls (T-B).

honeydew glands, in Coccoidae (Hemiptera: Sternorrhyncha), rectal wax pores, q.v. (T-B, after MacGillivray).

hood, galea, q.v., of the maxilla; in Tingidae (Hemiptera: Heteroptera), the elevated anterior part of the prothorax, often covering the head; in Lepidoptera; see counter-tympanal hood, q.v.; in ♂ Siphonaptera, the cloaklike, cowel-shaped structure, draped over the apical end of the aedeagus representing the unmodified walls of the end chamber (Rothschild and Traub), or end chamber, q.v. (Tuxen; Jordan).

Hood's solution, preservation fluid consisting of 95 ml of 70–80% ethyl alcohol and 5 ml of glycerine (Borror et al.).

hook plates, in pupal Trichoptera, paired hook-bearing sclerites near the anterior and/or posterior margins of abdominal terga III–VIII, q.v. (Ross).

hooked hairs, in adult Hymenoptera, gathering hairs, q.v. (T-B).

hooklets, hamuli, q.v. (T-B); in pupal Chironomidae (Diptera), recurved spines posteriorly on abdominal tergite II and sometimes elsewhere (Saether).

hooklike dorsal process, in ♂ Siphonaptera, dorsal arm of tubus interior, q.v. (Tuxen, after Sharif).

hooks, sclerotized prongs with decurved ends (Peterson); in ♂ Lepidoptera, falces, q.v. (Tuxen, after Bethune-Baker); in ♂ *Nisoniades* (Lepidoptera: Hesperiidae), valvae, q.v. (Tuxen, after Scudder and Burgess); in ♂ Siphonaptera, lobes of aedeagus, q.v. (Tuxen).

Hopkins Bioclimatic Law, the observational principle that other conditions being equal, the variations in time of occurrence of a given periodic event in life activity in temperate North America is at the general average rate of 4 days to each degree of latitude, 5 degrees of longitude and 400 feet of altitude; later northward, eastward and upward in spring and early summer and the reverse in late summer and autumn (T-B, after Hopkins).

Hopkins Host Selection Principle, a theory which holds that the ♀ of an insect breeding on 2 or more hosts will prefer to lay eggs on the host on which said ♀ was reared (T-B, after Wardle).

Hopkin's organ, in ♀ Siphonaptera, a sclerite situated in the roof of the vagina distad of the opening of the duct of the bursa copulatrix and extending on either side of it (Rothschild and Traub).

hopperburn, a disease of potato, alfalfa, and other plants resulting from the feeding of the potato leafhopper, *Empoasca fabae* (Hemiptera: Auchenorrhyncha: Cicadellidae), a toxicogenic insect (Pfadt).

horizontal, parallel with the horizon, in either position or motion (T-B).

horizontal arm of sternum IX, in ♂ Siphonaptera, distal arm, q.v. (Tuxen).

horizontal classification, classification which stresses grouping together species in a similar stage of evolution, rather than location on the same phyletic line (Mayr); see vertical classification.

horizontal plane, plane parallel with horizon (McAlpine).

horizontal plate, in ♂ Micropterigidae (Lepidoptera), small sclerite between bases of valvae and abdominal sternum IX (Tuxen, after Philpott).

hormone, a catalytic agent produced by an endocrine organ, generally transported via the hemolymph and exhibiting an effect not confined to the site of secretion (T-B; Tulloch, after Rockstein; Chapman).

horn, a large, pointed process of the head (T-B); any process resembling a horn of a bovine (T-B); in the plural, sometimes applied to the antennae (T-B); a stiff, pointed, unbranched cuticular process (Peterson).

horn of plenty organ, in ♀ Lepidoptera, prolapsus vulvare, q.v. (Tuxen).

horn sac, in pupal Podonominae (Diptera: Chironomidae), long, apical diverticulum on respiratory atrium without connection to plastron plate (Saether).

hornet, a large wasp of the subfamily Vespinae (Hymenoptera: Vespidae), particularly a member of the genus *Vespa* or (in the United States) the bald-faced hornet *Vespula* (*Dolichovespula*) *maculata* (Wilson).

hornworm, a caterpillar (Lepidoptera: Sphingidae) with a dorsal spine or horn on the eighth abdominal segment (Borror et al.).

horny, thickened or hardened (Borror et al.).

horny ring, in ♂ Hymenoptera, basal ring, q.v. (Tuxen, after Newport).

horseshoe-shaped basal plate, in ♂ *Zorotypus snyderi* (Zoraptera), stirrup-shaped ventral plate at floor of abdomen to which are hinged the clasping organs (Tuxen, after Gurney).

horseshoe-shaped sclerite, in ♂ *Zorotypus zimmermani* (Zoraptera), horseshoe-shaped basal plate, q.v. (Tuxen, after Gurney).

host, the organism in or on which a parasite lives (T-B; Borror et al.); the plant on which an insect feeds (Borror et al.); maker of a cell or other structures in which guest insects take up their abode (T-B); see accidental host, natural host, normal host, and typical host.

host alternation, in Aphididae (Hemiptera: Sternorrhyncha), cyclic alternation between primary and secondary host plants associated with alternation of generations (Woodward et al., in CSIRO); see primary host and secondary host.

host plant, the plant species on which an insect species breeds and develops, in many predaceous and parasitic insects, fixed by the host plant of the preferred prey (T-B); see food plant.

host races, in oligophagous food specialists or parasites, genetically different races of the same species, occurring on different hosts.

host specificity, the degree to which a species specializes on one or more species of hosts (Norris, in CSIRO); see monophagous, oligophagous, and polyphagous.

hovering, maintaining a stationary position in flight (Chapman).

Hoyer's mounting medium, water-based mounting medium consisting of 50 ml of distilled water, 30 grams of gum arabic, 200 grams of chloral hydrate, and 20 ml of glycerine (Borror et al.).

Hudsonian Zone, that part of the Boreal Region comprising the northern part of the great transcontinental coniferous forests; in the eastern United States restricted to the cold summits of the highest mountains, from northern New England to western North Carolina; in the West it covering the higher slopes of the Rocky and Sierra-Cascade systems (T-B).

humeral, relating to the shoulder or humerus (T-B); located in the anterior basal portion of the wing (Borror et al.).

humeral angle, the angle at the base of the costal margin of the wing (T-B); in Orthoptera, the obtusely rounded angle formed by the deflection of the sides of the pronotum from the dorsum (T-B); in hind wing of adult Lepidoptera, humeral lobe, q.v. (T-B; Chapman); in elytron of Coleoptera, humerus, q.v. (T-B).

humeral break, in adult Diptera, costal break located slightly distal to humeral crossvein (McAlpine).

humeral bristle, in adult Diptera, postpronotal seta, q.v. (T-B, after Comstock; McAlpine).

humeral callus (pl. **calli**), in higher adult Diptera, postpronotal lobe, q.v. (T-B, after Comstock; Colless and McAlpine, in CSIRO; McAlpine).

humeral carina, in some adult Coleoptera, an elevated ridge or keel on the outer anterior angle of the elytron (T-B).

humeral crossvein, crossvein extending between the costa and subcosta close to the base of the wing (T-B, after Comstock).

humeral lobe, the area of contact between the hind wing and the forewing (T-B); in adult Lepidoptera and some Mecoptera, a lobe at the base of the costal margin of the hind wing (Chapman).

humeral nerve, humeral crossvein, q.v. (T-B).

humeral nervure, humeral crossvein, q.v. (T-B).

humeral pits, in some Nematocera (Diptera), prescutal pits, q.v. (T-B, after Curran; McAlpine).

humeral plate, basicosta, i.e., the anterior preaxillary sclerite of the wing base supporting the costal vein, being very large in Odonata (T-B, after Snodgrass); see tegula.

humeral scars, in some Nematocera, prescutal pits, q.v. (McAlpine).

humeral setae, in adult Chironomidae (Diptera), dorsocentrals in front of the parapsidal suture (Saether).

humeral stripe, in adult Odonata, a stripe which covers the humeral suture (T-B).

humeral suture, in Odonata, the suture running from just in front of the base of the forewing to the edge of the midcoxa, separating the mesepisternum from the mesepimeron (T-B); in termites (Isoptera), basal suture, q.v. (T-B).

humeral veinlet, humeral crossvein, q.v. (T-B, after Tillyard).

humeral veins, in wings of Neuroptera and some Lepidoptera, secondary branches of subcosta, developed to strengthen the humeral angle (T-B; Borror et al.); see recurrent vein.

humeralis, in adult Coleoptera, humerus, q.v. (T-B).

humerals, in adult Chironomidae (Diptera), humeral setae, q.v. (Saether).

humerulus (pl., **humeruli**), in ♂ Plebeiinae (Lepidoptera: Lycaenidae), distal part or limb of the bent, armlike falx (gnathos) (Tuxen, after Nabokov).

humerus (pl., **humeri**), shoulder (T-B; R. W. Brown); in Orthoptera, femur of the front leg (T-B); in Heteroptera (Hemiptera), the posterolateral angle of the pronotum (T-B; Borror et al.); in adult Coleoptera, the basal exterior angle of the elytra (T-B); in adult Diptera, postpronotal lobe, q.v. (T-B; McAlpine); in adult Hymenoptera, subcosta, q.v., of wing or anterolateral angle of the pronotum (T-B; Brown, pers. comm.).

humid, of atmosphere, containing much water vapor; moist (T-B).

hump, in larval Integripalpia (Trichoptera), retractile protuberance on the lateral and dorsal side of the first abdominal segment (Wiggins).

hyaline, hyalinus (Latin), of glass (R. W. Brown); transparent; glassy (T-B).

hyaline band, in ♂ Lygaeidae (Hemiptera: Heteroptera), the united ligamentary processes running into the phallosoma as far as the ejaculatory reservoir (Tuxen, after Bonhag and Wick).

hyaline cell, cystocyte, q.v. (Tulloch).

hyaline hemocyte, cystocyte, q.v. (Chapman).

hyaluronic acid, a mucopolysaccharide, being a component of the peritrophic membrane (Gilmour, in CSIRO).

hyaluronidase, in some predaceous insects, an enzyme injected into prey with the saliva that breaks down the polysaccharide ground substance of connective tissues, aids the penetration of the saliva, and assists in liquefying the tissues of the victim (Gilmour, in CSIRO).

Hyblaeoidea, superfamily of infraorder Ditrysia (Lepidoptera) containing one family Hyblaeidae; medium-sized moths with stout body, naked proboscis, three- or four-segmented maxillary palpi, without tympanal organs; larvae stout, without secondary setae, crochets in bi- or triordinal circle, 2 prespiracular (L) setae on prothorax; pupae stout, without dorsal spines, not protruded at ecdysis (Common).

hybrid, the progeny of 2 individuals belonging to different species (ICZN).

hybrid belt, a zone of interbreeding between 2 species, subspecies, or other unlike populations, i.e., a zone of secondary intergradation (Mayr).

hybridization, the crossing of individuals belonging to 2 unlike natural populations, principally species (Mayr); see allopatric hybridization.

Hydrachnoidea, superfamily within the Acarina, e.g., water mites of the family Hydrachnellidae, commonly parasitic on aquatic insects (Norris, Colless and McAlpine, Riek, in CSIRO).

Hydradephaga, group sometimes recognized to include the aquatic families of the suborder Adephaga (Coleoptera), including Amphizoidae, Dytiscidae, Gyrinidae, Haliplidae, Hygrobiidae, and Noteridae (T-B); see Caraboidea and Geodephaga.

hydradephagous, relating to or like Hydradephaga (T-B).

hydranapheuxis, in Gerromorpha and some other Heteroptera associated with the air-water interface, the process of deforming the meniscus to allow ascension to the adjacent substrate (Cobben, after Baudoin).

hydro-, prefix; relating to water (T-B).

hydrocarbon, a compound that contains only carbon and hydrogen (Pfadt).

hydrochloric acid, HCl; a colorless, fuming liquid when pure; commercially in about a 25% solution in distilled water, when it shows no fuming; acid, mixes with water in any proportion; used in histology as a tissue-hardener.

hydrocyanic acid, (HCN), highly poisonous acid, produced by combination of hydrogen and cyanogen, and existing as a colorless liquid with the smell of peach blossoms or bitter almonds, produced by the defense glands of some Diplopoda and Insecta; in larval *Paropsis* (Coleoptera: Chrysomelidae), defensive secretion emitted from paired eversible gland on abdominal segment VIII (Britton, in CSIRO).

Hydrocorisae, Nepomorpha, q.v. (Borror et al.).

hydrofuge, water repelling (Chapman).

hydrofuge hairs, water-repelling hairs, commonly found on aquatic insects and important for breaking the surface tension of the water in order to obtain oxygen (Chapman).

hydrofuge structures, devices such as hairs and glands on the cuticle of aquatic insects requiring atmospheric oxygen to permit the breaking of the surface film (Tulloch); see hydrophobe and hydrophile hair.

hydrogen peroxide, in bombardier beetles, *Brachinus* (Coleoptera: Carabidae), component, together with diphenols, of defensive secretion (Gilmour, in CSIRO).

hydrolysis, a chemical reaction in which a compound reacts with the ions of water (H^+ and OH^-) to produce a weak acid, a weak base, or both.

hydrolyze, to undergo or cause to undergo hydrolysis.

Hydrometroidea, superfamily of Heteroptera within the infraorder Gerromorpha including the predatory Paraphyrnoveliidae, Macroveliidae, and Hydrometridae (Andersen).

hydrophile hair, a water-attracting hair, i.e., one which makes an angle of contact approaching zero with the water surface (Tulloch); see hydrophobe hair.

Hydrophiloidea, superfamily within the Polyphaga (Coleoptera), including aquatic and semiaquatic beetles of the Limnebiidae, Hydraenidae, Spercheidae, Georyssidae, and Limnebiidae, characterized by relatively short antennae with the apical 3–5 articles forming a strongly pubescent club

hydrophilous, water-loving, i.e., living at least in part in water; see hygrophilous.

hydrophobic hairs, hydrofuge hairs, q.v. (Teskey, in McAlpine).

hydropic egg, a lecithal egg, q.v. (Gauld and Bolton).

hydropyle, a specialized structure, consisting of a thickened region of the serosal epicuticle over a layer of endocuticle which is thinner than elsewhere with the area of contact between the 2 layers greatly increased by interdigitation, appearing to have a dominant role in the uptake of water, e.g., eggs of Acrididae (Orthoptera) (Tulloch; Chapman).

hydroquinone, adiphenol, being a major constituent of the defense secretions of bombardier beetles, *Brachinus* (Coleoptera: Carabidae) (Gilmour, in CSIRO).

hydrostatic, of or pertaining to water pressure (T-B).

hydrostatic organs, in a few genera of larval Chaoboridae (Diptera), crescent-shaped pigmented organs found on the lateral aspects of the thorax and near the caudal end (Peterson).

hydrotropism, the reaction of an organism to water (T-B).

hydroxyl ion, the OH_- group in solution carrying a negative electric charge (Tulloch).

hygrokinesis, orientation to a difference in humidity (Tulloch).

hygrometabolism, the dependence of metabolism on humidity (T-B).

hygropetric, pertaining to life on a thin film of water, as in some Gerromorpha (Hemiptera: Heteroptera) (Andersen).

hygrophilous, moisture-loving, i.e., living in damp, wet places.

hygroreceptor, receptor that responds to changes in relative humidity (Chapman).

hymen, a thin flat membrane serving as a partition (T-B).

Hymenoptera, holometabolous order of Neoptera (Insecta), including sawflies, wasps, ants, bees, and others, with adults characterized by mandibulate mouthparts, 2 pairs of membranous wings (in alate forms), the larger forewings and the smaller hind wings linked by one or more hamuli, appendiculate ovipositor in ♀, and prominent antennae with generally more than 9 articles (Riek, in CSIRO); see Apocrita and Symphyta.

Hymenopterida, Hymenopteroidea, q.v. (Boudreaux).

hymenopteriform larva, in Apocrita (Hymenoptera), eucephalous larva, q.v., (Gauld and Bolton).

Hymenopteroidea, supraordinal group within the Holometabola, including only the Hymenoptera (Mackerras, in CSIRO).

hyoid, having the form of the Greek upsilon (Y) (T-B).

hyoid sclerite, in some adult Diptera, esp. Muscomorpha, a crescentic or U-shaped sclerite associated with the cibarial pump at the base of the food canal (T-B, after Imms; McAlpine).

hypandrial apodeme, in ♂ Diptera, proximal process of hypandrium (Tuxen).

hypandrial arms, in Muscomorpha (Diptera), posterior divisions of the hypandrium (Griffiths).

hypandrial sclerite, in ♂ Phthiraptera, sclerite in dorsal wall of subgenital lobe (Tuxen, after Schmutz).

hypandrial valves, in ♂ Auchenorrhyncha (Hemiptera), genital plates, q.v. (Tuxen).

hypandrium (pl., **hypandria**), in ♂ insects, subgenital plate, q.v. (T-B, after Crampton; Tuxen); in ♂ Ephemeroptera, styliger, q.v. (Tuxen, after Crampton); in ♂ Isoptera, subgenital plate, q.v. (Tuxen, after Crampton); in ♂ Plecoptera, subgenital plate, q.v. (Tuxen, after Crampton); in ♂ Embiidina, subgenital plate, q.v. (Ross, in Tuxen); in ♂ Zoraptera, subgenital plate, q.v. (Tuxen, after Crampton); in ♂ Psocoptera, abdominal sternum IX, in some cases also abdominal sternum VIII, enclosing atrium genitale (Tuxen); in ♂ Thysanoptera, median part of abdominal sternum IX (Tuxen, after de Gryse and Treherne); in ♂ Psyllidae (Hemiptera: Sternorrhyncha), subgenital plate, q.v. (Tuxen); in most ♂ Cicadelloidea (Hemiptera: Auchenorrhyncha), genital valves + genital plates (Tuxen; L. O'Brien pers. comm.); in ♂ Cicadidae (Hemiptera: Auchenorrhyncha), boat-shaped abdominal sternite VIII below pygofer (Tuxen; L. O'Brien, pers. comm.); in ♂ Heteroptera (Hemiptera), ventro-posterior margin of pygophore (abdominal segment IX) when protruded (Tuxen, after Crampton); in ♂ Veliidae (Hemiptera: Heteroptera), pygophore, q.v. (Tuxen, after Gould); in ♂ Megaloptera and some Planipennia, abdominal sternum IX (Tuxen); in some ♂

Coniopterygidae (Planipennia), fused gonocoxites (Tuxen, after Tjeder); in ♂ Mecoptera, abdominal sternum IX (Tuxen, after Crampton); in ♂ Diptera, abdominal sternum IX (Tuxen, McAlpine); in ♂ Hymenoptera, any of last abdominal sterna VII, VIII or IX (Tuxen); in ♂ Hymenoptera, abdominal sternum IX (Tuxen, after Crampton).

hypandrium internum (pl., **hypandria interna**), in ♂ Neuroptera, internal sclerotized organ at base of ductus ejaculatorius (Tuxen, after Tjeder).

hypandrium process, in ♂ Embiidina, distal process on hypandrium beneath ejaculatory duct (Ross, in Tuxen).

hypandropodites, in ♂ Diptera, claspette, q.v. (Tuxen, after Christophers).

hyper-, Greek prefix; over and beyond; excess (T-B).

hyperaminoacidemia, presence of amino acids in the hemolymph in excess of the normal amount, e.g., silk retention in silkworms (Lepidoptera: Bombycidae), producing a lethal increase of amino acids in the hemolymph (Steinhaus and Martignoni); see silk toxicity.

hypergamesis, in Cimicoidea (Hemiptera: Heteroptera), hypothesis on nutritive contribution of superabundant spermatozoa injected into ♀ abdomen during traumatic insemination (Carayon in Usinger, after Berlese).

hyperglycemic hormone, a hormone that activates the phosphorylase catalysing the production of trehalose from glycogen in the fat body; in locusts (Orthoptera), there are 2 hyperglycemic hormones, one produced by the neurosecretory cells and one produced by the corpora cardiaca (Chapman).

hypermetamorphosis, development with successive larval forms having quite different forms, e.g., Strepsiptera, Mantispidae (Planipennia), Meloidae and some Staphylinidae (Coleoptera), Acroceridae, Bombyliidae, and Nemestrinidae (Diptera), Perilampidae and Eucharitidae (Hymenoptera), Epipyropidae and Gracillariidae (Lepidoptera), as well as in some other endoparasitic forms of Diptera and Hymenoptera (T-B, after Peterson; Chapman).

hyperparasite, a parasite that lives on or in another parasite, e.g., the minute *Hemiteles* (Hymenoptera: Ichneumonidae) which is parasitic in the larger *Apanteles* (Hymenoptera: Braconidae), the latter itself being a parasite in caterpillars (T-B; Leftwich).

hyperparasitism, feeding by parasitoids on other parasitoids, e.g., many Chalcidoidea, Cynipoidea, Ichnenmonidae, Ceraphronoidea, and Trigonalyoidea (Hymenoptera) (Gauld and Bolton).

hyperparasitoid, hyperparasite, q.v. (Gauld and Bolton).

hyperparasitoidism, hyperparasitism, q.v. (T-B).

hyperplasia, an increase in the number of functional units of an organ (organelles, cells, tissues), excluding tumor formation, whereby the bulk of an organ is increased in response to increased functional demands (Steinhaus and Martignoni, after Goss); see hyperplasia.

hyperpneustic, with supernumerary spiracles in the same segment, as in the thorax of some Diplura (T-B, after Snodgrass; von Kéler).

hypertrigonal space, in adult Anisoptera (Odonata), supratriangular space, q.v. (T-B).

hypertrophy, an increase in size (weight) and functional capacity of an organ or tissue, without an increase in the number of structural units upon which their functions depend, stimulated by increased functional demands (T-B; Steinhaus and Martignoni, after Goss); see hyperplasia.

hypha (pl., **hyphae**), any of the threadlike parts making up the mycelium of a fungus (T-B).

Hyphomycetes, a catchall taxon for imperfect fungi that reproduce asexually, including many entomopathogenic species (Soper, in Nault).

hypistoma, hypopharynx, q.v. (T-B).

hypnody, quiescence, q.v. (T-B); hypermetamorphosis, q.v. (T-B, after Künckel).

hypnosis, the condition in which all reflexes are immobilized, due to excessive mechanical stimuli; see stereokinesis (Tulloch).

hypnotheca, in Meloidae (Coleoptera), semipupa, q.v. (T-B, after Künckel).

hypo-, Greek prefix; under or beneath (T-B).

hypoblast, endoderm, q.v. (T-B).

hypocauda (pl., **hypocaudae**), in ♀ Berothidae (Planipennia), long fingerlike process from the lower margin of each gonapophysis lateralis (Tuxen, after Tjeder).

hypocerebral ganglion, part of the stomatogastric nervous system, being an expansion of the recurrent nerve behind the brain, connected laterally to the corpora cardiaca and posteriorly to the ingluvial ganglia (T-B, after Imms; Chapman).

hypochilan comb, in larval Chironomidae (Diptera), dorsomentum, q.v., or mentum, q.v. (Saether).

hypochilum, in larval Nematocera (Diptera), hypostoma, q.v. (Teskey, in McAlpine); in larval Chironomidae (Diptera), mentum, q.v. (Saether).

hypoclypeal depression, in some adult Braconidae (Hymenoptera), semicircular emargination of clypeus (Gauld and Bolton).

hypochondria, 2 partial segments which come between the first entire ventral segment and the posterior part of the postpectus in certain Coleoptera (T-B, after Linn.).

hypocondyle, ventral condyle, q.v., of mandible (T-B, after McAlpine).

hypocostal lamina, in Heteroptera (Hemiptera), ventrally deflected proximal part of costal forewing margin (Štys).

hypocostal ridge, in Heteroptera (Hemiptera), hypocostal lamina, q.v. (Polhemus).

hypocular suture, in Corixidae (Hemiptera: Heteroptera), short paired sulcus of the head capsule posteroventral to the eyes (Hungerford; Nieser).

hypocrateriform, salver-shaped (T-B); tubular below, but suddenly expanding into a flat border at the top.

hypocuspis (pl., **hypocuspides**), in ♂ Nymphes (Planipennia: Nymphidae), downward directed unpaired immoveable process from the under side of the mediuncus (Tuxen, after Tjeder).

hypodactyle, in Hemiptera, labium, q.v. (T-B).

hypoderm, epidermis, q.v. (T-B).

hypodermal, hypodermatic, hypodermic, epidermal, q.v. (T-B).

hypodermal colors, colors lodged in the cells of the insect hypodermis in the form of granules or drops of fat, being evanescent after death (T-B, after Imms).

hypodermic envelope, peripodial membrane, q.v. (T-B).

hypodermis, epidermis, q.v. (T-B; Tulloch, after Richards).

hypodigm, the entire material of a species that is available to a taxonomist (Mayr).

hypoepimeral area, in most adult Apocrita (Hymenoptera), area on mesepisternum above the scrobal suture (Gauld and Bolton); see speculum.

hypogaeic, subterranean, q.v. (T-B, Tulloch); subterranean or cryptobiotic, q.v. (Wilson); see epigaeic.

hypogenum, in ♀ Isoptera, hypogynium, q.v. (Tuxen, after Crampton).

hypoglottis, in many adult Coleoptera, a sclerite or cuticular element sometimes present beween the mentum and the prementum (T-B; Leftwich).

hypognathous, having the head vertical and the mouth directed ventrad, e.g., most exophagous Lepidoptera and Hymenoptera larvae (T-B; Peterson; Gauld and Bolton); see prognathous and hypognathous.

hypographous, shaded; applied to a fascia that becomes gradually darker (T-B).

hypogynial plate, in ♀ Blephariceridae, a single, median plate in the same position as the hypogynial valves (McAlpine).

hypogynial valves, in ♀ Diptera, appendages of abdominal sternum VIII possibly homologous with gonapophyses (Tuxen; McAlpine).

hypogynium (pl., **hypogynia**), in ♀ insects, sternum VIII (Tuxen, after Crampton; McAlpine); in ♀ Isoptera, subgenital plate, q.v. (Tuxen, after Crampton).

hypolimnion, the bottom stratum in deep lakes characterized by low oxygen levels and nearly a complete absence of living organisms, see epilimnion and thermocline (Tulloch).

hypomegetic, applied to the smallest in a series of insects exhibiting polymorphism (Tulloch); see minor.

hypomere(s), in ♂ insects, ventral process of the phallobase (Tuxen, after Snodgrass); in ♂ Phthiraptera, parameres, q.v. (Clay, in Tuxen; Lyal); in ♂ Neuroptera, ventral, paired processes of the aedeagus (Tuxen); in ♂ Mecoptera, ventral parameres, q.v. (Tuxen, after Ferris and Rees).

hypomeron, (pl., **hypomera**), in adult Coleoptera, pronotal hypomeron, q.v. (T-B; Britton, in CSIRO) or epipleural fold, q.v. (T-B).

hyponome, mine, q.v. (Hering).

hypophallus, in ♂ Blattopteroidea, valve situated on left side ventral to the phallus, carrying the phallotreme (Tuxen); also applied in ♂ Blattopteroidea to the epiphallus, q.v. (Tuxen, after Wesché); in ♂ Thysanoptera, parameres, q.v. (Tuxen, after de Gryse and Treherne); in ♂ Calyptratae (Diptera), sclerotizations of the distiphallus (Tuxen).

hypopharyngeal, relating to the hypopharynx (T-B).

hypopharyngeal bracon, in larval Coleoptera, a transverse brace between the hypopharynx and the anterior part of the hypostomal margin (Peterson, after Hopkins).

hypopharyngeal gland, in adult Hymenoptera, paired glands in the head with ducts opening at the base of the hypopharynx, being particularly well developed in worker honey bees (Apidae) in which they produce brood food and an invertase (Chapman, after Snodgrass).

hypopharyngeal pecten, in larval Chironomidae (Diptera), pecten hypopharyngis, q.v. (Saether).

hypopharyngeal sclerite(s), in larval Muscomorpha (Diptera: Brachycera), main part of the cephalopharyngeal skeleton lying between the mandibles and the tentoropharyngeal sclerite (Teskey, in McAlpine); in bees (Hymenoptera: Apoidea), a pair of straplike pieces along the hypopharynx to the mentum (T-B); see epipharyngeal sclerites.

hypopharyngeal sclerome, in larval insects, a basal sclerite of the hypopharynx (Peterson).

hypopharyngeal suspensorium, suspensory sclerites, q.v. (T-B).

hypopharynx, a median lobe immediately behind the mouth, possessing chemoreceptors (T-B; Chapman) (see superlinguae); in adult Chironomidae, labial lonchus, q.v. (Saether); in larval Chironomidae (Diptera), dorsal part of the prementohypopharyngeal complex separated from the prementum by the salivary outlet, usually carrying several rows of hypopharyngeal scales or, in Tanypodinae, well-defined rows of teeth to each side forming the pecten hypopharyngis (Saether).

hypophysis, in ♂ Heteroptera (Hemiptera), paired or unpaired processes of the external wall of the pygophore such as hypandrium or parandria (Tuxen, after Dupuis).

hypoplasia, a defective or incomplete development of an organ system, organ, or tissue, such that the organ or tissue never reaches normal size (Steinhaus and Martignoni); an atrophy caused by the destruction of some of the elements (e.g., cell) rather than a general reduction in size (quantitative atrophy) (Steinhaus and Martignoni).

hypopleural bristles, in Diptera, bristles on the hypopleuron, usually in a vertical row (T-B, after Curran).

hypopleural organ, in ♀ larvae of many Siricoidea (Hymenoptera: Symphyla), mycargium positioned laterally in the fold between abdominal segments I and II (Gauld and Bolton).

hypopleural row, in Diptera, see hypopleural bristles (T-B).

hypopleurite, the lower pleural plate when a pleuron is divided horizontally into 2 parts (T-B); in sawfly larvae (Hymenoptera: Symphyta), an enlarged area of a proleg immediately ventrad of the postepipleurite (Peterson).

hypopleuron (pl., **hypopleura**), in adult Diptera, katepimeron, q.v. (T-B, after Comstock, J. B. Smith) or meron, q.v. (McAlpine).

hypopleurum, in larval Coleoptera, the lateral area immediately below the ventrolateral suture; in thorax usually carrying 2 scleromes: the episternum, anterior to the articulation of the coxa, and the epimeron, posterior to this articulation (Peterson, after Hopkins).

hypopneustic respiration, hemipneustic respiration, q.v. (T-B) or oligopneustic respiration, q.v. (Leftwich).

hypoprocessus, in ♂ Heteroptera (Hemiptera), inferior process, q.v. (Tuxen, after Crampton).

hypoproct, ventral plate of proctiger (McAlpine); in ♀ Diptera, subanal plate, q.v. (Tuxen, after Crampton).

hypoptera, hypoptere, tegula, q.v. (T-B).

hypopus (pl., **hypopi**), a nymphal stage in the development of certain mites, e.g., Saproglyphidae (Acari), in which the organism is small and has developed suckers or claspers for grasping insects and thereby effecting dispersal (Riek, in CSIRO; Pfadt).

hypopyge, in ♂ Heteroptera (Hemiptera), pygophore, q.v. (Tuxen, after Wygodzinsky).

hypopygeal appendages, in ♂ Heteroptera (Hemiptera), superior lateral process, q.v. (Tuxen, after Leston).

hypopygial appendages, in ♂ Podopinae (Hemiptera: Heteroptera), parandria, q.v. (Tuxen, after Barber and Sailer).

hypopygial process, in ♂ Emesinae (Hemiptera: Heteroptera), hypandrium, q.v. (Tuxen, after Wygodzinsky).

hypopygial setae, in certain Coccoidea (Hemiptera: Sternorrhyncha), the 2 longitudinal rows of setae on the ventral aspect of the outer wall of the anal tube (T-B, after MacGillivray).

hypopygial spine, in the genus *Cynips* (Hymenoptera: Cynipidae), a spinous structure of the hypopygium (T-B).

hypopygidium, in ♂ Hymenoptera, sternum IX (Tuxen, after Enslin).

hypopygium (pl., **hypopygia**), in adult insects, hind part of abdomen (Tuxen); in ♂ Auchenorrhyncha (Hemiptera), pygofer, q.v. (Tuxen); in ♂ Heteroptera (Hemiptera), pygophore, q.v. (Tuxen, after Sailer); in ♂ Lepidoptera, the most posterior sternum or fused sterna (Tuxen, after Kirby and Spence); in Strepsiptera, abdominal sternum IX (Tuxen, after Brues); in ♂ Diptera, abdominal segment IX, or more loosely used to include attached segments of postabdomen (Tuxen); in ♀ Diptera, genital segments, q.v. (Tuxen) or terminalia, q.v. (McAlpine); in adult Hymenoptera, last visible abdominal sternum, being sternum IX in ♂ and sternum VII in ♀ (Tuxen, after André; Gauld and Bolton).

hypopygium circumversum (pl., **hypopygia circumversa**), in ♂ Cyclorrhapha (Diptera), hypopygium twisted by 360° (Tuxen).

hypopygium inversum (pl., **hypopygia inversa**), in certain ♂ Nematocera and orthorrhaphous Brachycera (Diptera), hypopygium twisted by 180° (Tuxen).

hypopygium retoversum, in ♂ Diptera, hypopygium inversum, q.v. (Tuxen, after Gleichauf).

hypostema (pl., **hypostemata**), in ♀ Plebeiinae (Lepidoptera: Lycaenidae), proximal, sclerotized part of an erectile everting apparatus (Tuxen, after Chapman).

hyposternum, preepisternum, q.v. (T-B, after MacGillivray).

hypostigmal area, in adult Culicidae (Diptera), the weakly sclerotized membranous area of the anterior mesanepisternum immediately below the mesothoracic spiracle (Harbach and Knight, after Wood et al.).

hypostigmal cell, in adult Myrmeleontidae (Planipennia), hypostigmatic cell, q.v. (T-B).

hypostigmal scale, in adult Culicidae (Diptera), one of the scales occurring in a small cluster on the hypostigmal area of the anterior mesanepisternum (Harbach and Knight).

hypostigmatic cell, in adult Myrmeleontoidea (Planipennia), the cell immediately behind the point of fusion of subcosta (Sc) and radius (R), being sometimes greatly elongated (Borror et al.).

hypostigmatic space, hypostigmatic cell, q.v. (T-B, after Tillyard).

hypostoma (pl., **hypostomata**), the region of the subgena behind the mandible (Chapman) (see pleurostoma); in adult Culicidae (Diptera), the membranous basal part of the proboscis lying ventrally between the genae (Harbach and Knight, after Schiemenz); in larval Nematocera (Diptera), sclerotized, anteriorly toothed plate situated below the mouthparts (Teskey, in McAlpine); in larval Chironomidae (Diptera), anterior, more ventral part of subgenal margin against the maxilla, probably being partly fused with the cardo of the maxilla (Saether); see submentum.

hypostomal apodemes, in adult Masarinae (Hymenoptera: Vespidae), projections from hypostoma into oral fossa (Carpenter, pers. comm., after Richards).

hypostomal areas, sclerites set off by the hypostomal sutures (T-B).

hypostomal bridge, the union or approximation of the hypostomal lobes of the cranial wall closing the ventral end of the occipital foramen behind and above the true base of the labium, being particularly well developed in Diptera (T-B, after Snodgrass; Chapman).

hypostomal carina, in adult Hymenoptera, ridge delimiting hypostoma laterally (Gauld and Bolton).

hypostomal groove, in larval Chironomidae (Diptera), median suture, q.v. (Saether).

hypostomal margin, in larval Coleoptera, the ventral marginal thickening of each of the epicranial halves between the ventral mandibular condyle and the ventral tentorial pit (Peterson, after Böving and Craighead).

hypostomal plate, in larval Chironomidae (Diptera), mentum, q.v. (Saether).

hypostomal sclerite, in larval Muscomorpha (Diptera; Brachycera), hypopharyngeal sclerite, q.v. (T-B; Teskey, in McAlpine).

hypostomal spur, in larval Ichneumonoidea (Hymenoptera: Apocrita), sclerotize rod projecting ventrally from the hypostoma across the stipes (Gauld and Bolton, after Short).

hypostomal sulcus, hypostomal suture, q.v. (Chapman).

hypostomal suture, the part of the subgenal suture posterior to the mandible, being often obsolete or suppressed (T-B, after Snodgrass).

hypostome, in ticks (Acari), a dartlike structure arising from the median ventral surface of the basis capituli (T-B, after Matheson); the upper lip or labrum of the Crustacea (T-B).

hypostomium, in larval Nematocera (Diptera), hypostoma, q.v. (Colless and McAlpine, after Crosskey; Tesky, in McAlpine); in larval Chironomidae (Diptera: Nematocera), mentum, q.v. (Saether).

hypostylus (pl., **hypostyli**), in ♂ *Nymphes* (Planipennia: Nymphidae), paramere, q.v. (Tuxen, after Tjeder; Oswald, pers. comm.).

hypotendon, in ♂ Siphonaptera, apophysis, q.v. (Tuxen, after Peus).

hypotenusis, in adult Odonata, the simple or broken crossvein between M_4 and Cu_1, forming the outer boundary of the triangle (T-B).

hypotome, a structure in bumble bees (Hymenoptera: Apidae), between the volsella and penis (T-B, after Dufour); in ♂ Hymenoptera, abdominal sternum IX (Tuxen).

hypotype, a specimen, not the type, upon which a subsequent or supplementary description is based (T-B).

hypovalva (pl., **hypovalvae**), in ♂ Auchenorrhyncha (Hemiptera), genital plates, q.v. (Tuxen, after Crampton); in ♂ Raphidioptera and some Planipennia, distal, produced portion of abdominal sternum IX (Tuxen, after Tjeder); in ♂ Mecoptera, distal, produced, often paired part of abdominal sternum IX (Tuxen); in ♀ Diptera, hypogynial valves, q.v. (Tuxen, after Crampton; McAlpine).

hypoxanthine, intermediate meabolite in the production of xanthine from inosine-5'-phosphate in the fat body (Gilmour, in CSIRO).

hypoxia, a high level of carbon dioxide and a low level of oxygen in the tissues (Chapman).

I

ibid., ibidem, in the same place; same reference (T-B).

-iceous, -icius, Latin suffix; a likeness or the possession of a character; see aceus (T-B).

Ichneumonoidea, superfamily within the suborder Apocrita (Hymenoptera), including the Ichneumonidae, Apozygidae, Aphidiidae, Braconidae, Paxylommatidae and Agriotypidae, adults exhibiting fusion of veins C and Sc + R + R_s in the proximal part of the forewing with vertual obliteration of the costal cell and division of sternum I of the gaster (Gauld and Bolton, after Mason).

ichnotaxon, a taxon based on the fossilized work of an animal, including fossilized trails, tracks and burrows (trace fossils), made by an animal (ICZN).

ichthyophagous, fish-eating (T-B).

icotype, a typical specimen which serves the purpose of identification, but has not been mentioned in the literature (T-B, after J. B. Smith).

ICZN, International Commission of Zoological Nomenclature, q.v.

idem (Latin), the same; abbrev., id.

identification, the determination of the taxonomic identity of an individual (T-B, after Ferris; Mayr); see classification.

ideotype, a specimen named by the author after examination with the type, but not also a topotype (T-B); see homeotype.

idiobiont, a parasitoid that prevents further development of the host by paralyzing or killing it (Gauld and Bolton, after Asker and Shaw); see koinobiont.

Idiogastra, suborder once proposed for the family Orussidae (Hymenoptera) (Gauld and Bolton, after Rohwer and Cushman); see Orussoidea.

Idiostoloidea, superfamily of Heteroptera within the Pentatomomorpha recognized to contain the family Idiostolidae (Schuh).

ignitus (Latin), glowing (T-B; R. W. Brown).

ileocolon, the anterior portion of the hind gut, extending from the midgut to the rectum, when not distinctly differentiated into ileum and colon (T-B).

ileum, an undifferentiated part of the hind gut between the pylorus and the colon or rectum (T-B; Chapman).

imaginal, pertaining to the adult or imago (T-B).

imaginal bud, imaginal disc, q.v. (T-B).

imaginal cells, imaginal disc, q.v. (T-B).

imaginal disc, a relatively undifferentiated tissue mass occurring in the body of a larva which is destined to develop later into an adult organ (T-B; Wilson).

imaginal moulting, in Entognatha, Archaeognatha, and Zygentoma, moulting by sexually mature adults (Boudreaux).

imagination, the process of becoming an imago or adult insect (T-B, after Packard).

imagine, imago, q.v. (T-B).

imago (pl., **imagines, imagos,** or **imagoes**), the adult and sexually developed insect (T-B); in termites (Isoptera), pigmented, winged form which develops into a primary reproductive (Wilson; Thorne, pers. comm.).

imbricate, imbricatus (Latin), partly overlapping and appearing like shingles on a roof or scales on a fish (T-B; Harris, after Munz, and Harrington and Durrell); see cataphracted, scutate, and squamate.

Imidan (trade name), phosmet, q.v. (Pfadt).

immaculate, immaculatus (Latin), destitute of spots, marks, or sculpturing (T-B; Harris, after Stearn); see denudate, glabrous, investutus, maculate, and nude.

immarginate, immarginatus (Latin), without an elevated rim or margin (T-B).

immature, belonging to a life stage preceding the imago; a life stage preceding the imago, e.g., a nymph or larva.

immersed, immersus (Latin), inserted, imbedded or hidden in (T-B).

immobile, not having motion (T-B).

Immoidea, superfamily of the infraorder Ditrysia (Lepidoptera) containing one family Immidae, including small moths without ocelli but possessing chaetosemata, filiform antennae, naked proboscis, minute maxillary palpi, hind wing broad, abdomen with tortricoid apodemes; larvae with 3 prespiracular (L) setae or spines, not protruded at ecdysis (Common).

immoveable finger, in ♂ Siphonaptera, processus basimeris, q.v. (Tuxen).

immunity, resistence by plants to insect attacks (T-B); resistence of insects to attack by pathogenic microorganisms and disease that could result, usually being considered an acquired state (Tulloch; Steinhaus and Martignoni; Chapman).

immunization, in invertebrate pathology, the process of increasing the resistence of the host (Steinhaus and Martignoni).

immunogen, antigenlike substance providing a stimulus to an immune response by an insect (Steinhaus and Martignoni, after Chadwick); see antigen.

imperfect, imperfectus, not perfect; immature, q.v. (T-B).

imperforate, not perforated (T-B).

implicate, infolded (T-B).

impregnate, to make fertile or pregnant; to fertilize (T-B).

impressed, impressus (Latin), having shallow, depressed areas or markings (T-B; Harris); see cicatrose, lacunose, and variolate.

impression, an indentation or depression on a surface (T-B).

impubis, without hair (T-B).

impunctate, impunctatus (Latin), not punctate or marked with punctures (T-B; Harris); see punctate.

in situ (Latin), in its natural place or normal position (T-B).

in vitro, in invertebrate pathology, in an artifical environment outside of a living organism (Steinhaus and Martignoni).

in vivo, in invertebrate pathology, in the living organism (Steinhaus and Martignoni).

inadvertent error, an incorrect spelling, such as a *lapsus calami,* or a copyist's error or a printer's error, not intended by the original author (ICZN).

inaequalis, uneven; rough; unequal; different (T-B; R. W. Brown).

Inaequipalpia, former suborder of Trichoptera, including species with adults with heteropalpi (Riek, in CSIRO; Mey, pers. comm., after Kolenati); see Aequipalpia.

inanition, exhaustion from lack of nutrients; the physical condition resulting from the complete lack of nutrients (Steinhaus and Martignoni).

inapparent infection, in invertebrate pathology, attenuated infection, q.v. (Steinhaus and Martignoni).

inappropriate name, a name that denotes a character, a quality, or an origin not possessed by the taxon bearing the name (ICZN).

inarticulate, not jointed or segmented (T-B).

inaurate, inauratus, golden yellow (T-B).

inborn disease, inherited disease, q.v. (Steihaus and Martignoni).

incanus (Latin), hoary, q.v. (T-B, after Kirby and Spence).

incased pupa, encased pupa, q.v. (T-B).

incertae sedis, of uncertain taxonomic position (ICZN).

inch, the former English and American standard of length in insect measurement; = 12 lines, roughly, 25mm; usually expressed in units and hundredths, as 1.01; see millimeter, centimeter.

inchworm, looper, q.v. (Borror et al.).

incidence, in invertebrate patholgy, the number of new cases of particular disease within a given period of time, in a population being studied (Steinhaus and Martignoni).

incipient, beginning to be or to appear (T-B); of species, in the process of arising (T-B).

incised, incisus (Latin), notched or cut into (T-B).

incised notches, in Coccoidea (Hemiptera: Sternorrhyncha), incisurae, q.v. (T-B, after MacGillivray).

incision, any cut into a margin or through a surface (T-B).

incisor, a structure which produces an incision; a cutting tooth or mandible (T-B).

incisor lobe, in larval Nematocera, toothed distal lobe of mandible (Teskey, in McAlpine).

incisura axillaris, axillary incision, q.v., of wing (T-B).

incisurae, in Coccoidea (Hemiptera: Sternorrhyncha), the incisions in the margin of the pygidium (T-B, after MacGillivray, Comstock).

incisure, incisura, an impressed line marking the junction of 2 segments; an incision (T-B).

incitant, in invertebrate pathology, a factor that incites or activates occult pathogens (Steinhaus and Martignoni).

inclinate, inclinatus (Latin), leaning or inclined (T-B); bent toward the midline of the body, being commonly applied to the setae of adult Diptera (Borror et al.; McAlpine); see lateroclinate, proclinate, and reclinate.

inclivous vein, in adult Zelinae (Hymenoptera: Braconidae), a transverse vein of which the anterior end is nearer to the wing base than its posterior end (van Achterberg); see reclivous vein.

inclusive fitness, the sum of personal fitness and a kinship component (Matthews and Matthews).

inclusus, wholly or partly hidden (T-B).

incomplete metamorphosis, development in which there is no pupa (T-B); see complete metamorphosis.

inconspicuous, not attracting attention or quickly noticeable (T-B).

in copula, in the process of mating (Matthews and Matthews).

incorrect original spelling, an original spelling of a scientific name that is incorrect under the Code (ICZN).

incorrect subsequent spelling, any change in the spelling of an available scientific name other than a mandatory change or an emendation (ICZN).

incrassate, incrassated, incrassatus (Latin), thickened; rather suddenly swollen at some one point, especially near tip (T-B).

incubate, to brood; to cause to develop, as an egg (T-B).

incubation, embryonal or hatching period of an egg (T-B).

incubation period, in invertebrate pathology, the period of time elapsing between entrance or introduction of microorganisms in the animal body and the development of symptoms and signs of an infectious disease (Steinhaus and Martignoni).

incumbent, incumbens (Latin), lying one over another (T-B); of wings, when they cover the dorsum horizontally (T-B).

incumbent wings, those which lie horizontally on the dorsum when the insect is at rest (T-B).

incunabulum, cocoon, q.v. (T-B).

Incurvariiformes, Incurvarioidea, q.v. (Munroe, in Parker).

Incurvariina, Incurvarioidea, q.v. (Hennig).

Incurvarioidea, superfamily within the subdivision Monotrysia (Lepidoptera), including the Cesidosidae, Incurvariidae, Heliozelidae, Adelidae, Crinopterigidae, and Prodoxidae, including small or very small moths, sometimes with very long antennae; antennal scape not expanded, proboscis usually scaled near base, labial palpi with lateral bristles, wing ventation heteroneurous, ♂ valvae often with pectinifers, ♀ with piercing ovipositor and monotrysian genitalia; larvae apodous or with short ventral prolegs and without anal prolegs; pupae with dorsal spines on abdomen, protuded at ecdysis (Nielson and Davis; Common).

incurvate, incurvatus (Latin), **incurved,** bowed or curved inwards (T-B).

indentation, a dent or dimple (T-B).

independent vein, in adult Lepidoptera, first median vein (M_1) in outer portion of wing which arising from the discal cell (T-B, after J. B. Smith).

indeterminate, indeterminatus (Latin), not defined nor well marked; obscure; of no constant form or shape (T-B).

indication, a published act or information that in the absence of a definition or description allows a name proposed before 1931, and that otherwise satisfies the relevant provosions of the Code (ICZN); a method of fixing the type species of a nominal genus (ICZN); see designation and fixation.

indicum (Latin), indigo, q.v. (R. W. Brown).

indigenous, native, q.v. (T-B).

indigo, a deep violet-blue (T-B).

indirect flight, in adult Ephemeroptera and Neoptera, flight in which the downstroke of the wing is controlled indirectly by dorsoventral muscles of the pterothorax (Chapman).

indirect metamorphosis, complete metamorphosis, q.v. (T-B).

indirect wing muscles, the dorsal and tergosternal muscles of the meso- and metathorax (T-B).

individual variation, variation within a population (Mayr).

Indo-Malayan Region, Oriental Region, q.v. (Mackerras, in CSIRO).

induction, in embryonic developement, the activation of a particular gene (Boudreaux); in invertebrate pathology, the activation of an occult pathogen, leading to progressive infection and disease, e.g., the provoked transformation of a provirus into a virulent (cytocidal) virus (Steinhaus and Martignoni).

indumentum, a covering of hairs, scales or tufts (T-B).

indurated, induratus (Latin), hardened (T-B).

indusium, in embryo of Tettigoniidae (Orthoptera), a third envelope which appears as a disclike thickening of the serosa in front of the head (T-B, after Imms; Chapman); the case made by the insect larva (T-B, after J. B. Smith).

industrial melanism, populational color change due to natural selection, involving the increase in the proportion of melanic forms which are more cryptic on substrates blackened from industrial pollution, e.g., peppered moth, *Bistonia betularia* (Lepidoptera: Geometridae), in United Kingdom (Mayr; Chapman); see melanism.

induvia, in Ephemeroptera, a chitinous concentrically layered structure symmetrically placed between the compound eyes and a little posterior to the brain above the oesophagus; also found in the ventral side of abdominal segments VIII and IX (T-B, after Needham); see Palmer's organ.

inermis (Latin), **inermous,** unarmed, q.v.; without striae, spines, or any other sharp processes (T-B; Harris, after R. W. Brown); see munite and mutic.

infaunate, to introduce a commensal or mutualistic microfauna into an organism that is capable of serving as a host, e.g., the introduction of certain flagellates or ciliates into a defaunated termite (Steinhaus and Martignoni); see defaunate.

infection, in invertebrate pathology, the introduction or entry of a pathogenic microorganism into a susceptible host, resulting in the presence of the microorganism within the body of the host, whether or not this causes detactable pathologic effects (or overt disease); see attenuated infection, autoinfection, mixed infection, progressive infection, reinfection, secondary infection, and superinfection.

infectious disease, in invertebrate pathology, disease caused by the actions of a living organism (Steinhaus and Martignoni).

infective phase, in invertebrate pathology, the last phase in the developmental cycle of a virus, in which the virus acquires infectivity (Steinhaus and Martignoni); see maturation phase.

infectivity, the quality of being infective; the abilty to produce infection (Steinhaus and Martignoni).

Infericornia, formerly used for those Heteroptera (Hemiptera), in which the antennae appear to be inserted well down on the sides of head, e.g., Lygaeidae (T-B).

inferior, beneath, below or behind (T-B).

inferior anal appendages, in ♂ Zygoptera (Odonata), cerci, q.v. (Tuxen).

inferior apophyses, in ♀ Ensifera (Orthoptera), short processes from lower basal part of posterior valvulae (Tuxen).

inferior appendage(s), in ♂ Anisoptera (Odonata), appendix dorsalis, q.v. (T-B); in ♂ Zygoptera (Odonata), inferior anal appendages, q.v. (Borror et al.); in ♂ Plecoptera, abdominal sternum X (Tuxen, after

Helson); in ♂ Megaloptera, Raphidioptera, and Planipennia, ento-processus, q.v. (Tuxen, after Tjeder); in ♂ Trichoptera, appendages attached ventrally and anally to abdominal segment IX, i.e., gonopods, q.v. (Tuxen, after Nielsen), parameres, q.v. (T-B, after Snodgrass); in ♂ Chironomidae (Diptera), inferior volsella, q.v. (Saether).

inferior intervalvula, in ♀ Orthoptera, transverse sclerite uniting inferior (Ensifera) or superior (Caelifera) apophyses at base of posterior valvulae (Tuxen); in ♀ Psyllidae (Hemiptera: Sternorrhyncha), a median dorsal process articulating with a pair of processes from the dorsal valvulae and with the dorsal plate (Tuxen, after Brittain).

inferior lobe, lacinia, q.v., of maxilla (T-B).

inferior orbit, see genal orbit (T-B, after MacGillivray).

inferior orbital setae, in adult Diptera, frontal setae, q.v. (McAlpine).

inferior orbital setulae, in adult Diptera, frontal setulae, q.v. (McAlpine).

inferior process, in ♂ Heteroptera (Hemiptera), median apical process of the floor of genital chamber below the phallus, an expansion of the edges of the median groove (Tuxen, after Sharp).

inferior region, the costal region of the wing (T-B).

inferior rest, in ♂ Tessaratomidae (Hemiptera: Heteroptera), inferior process, q.v. (Tuxen, after Leston).

inferior ridge, in ♂ Heteroptera (Hemiptera), inferior process, q.v. (Tuxen, after Baker).

inferior valvulae, in ♂ Phasmida, gonapophyses of gonopods of abdominal segment VIII (Tuxen).

inferior volsella, in ♂ Chironomidae (Diptera), apparent mesodorsal inferior appendage, lobe or field of gonocoxite (Saether).

inferior wings, hind wings, q.v. (T-B).

inferiors, in ♂ Zygoptera (Odonata), cerci, q.v. (T-B, after Garman).

inferoposterior, below and behind (T-B).

infertility, inability to reproduce (T-B).

infestation, the living in or on a host by metazoan parasites, e.g., the infestation of flies (Diptera) by mites (Acari) (Steinhaus and Martignoni).

infiltration, the process of filtering into or permeating (T-B).

inflatable sacs, in ♂ Aleyrodidae (Hemiptera: Sternorrhyncha), saclike lobes located laterally to aedeagus (Gill).

inflated, inflatus (Latin), blown up; distended; bladderlike; see tumid, bullate (T-B).

inflected, inflexus (Latin), bent inward at an angle (T-B).

inflected skeleton, endoskeleton, q.v. (Mackerras, in CSIRO).

inflection, an inward bending or flexion (T-B).

infra-, Latin prefix; below or beneath (T-B); see sub- and supra-.

infraalar bulla, in adult Diptera, greater ampulla, q.v. (McAlpine).

infraanal flaps, paraprocts, q.v. (T-B; Tuxen).

infraanal lobe, a thick, conical fleshy lobe, often ending in a chitinous point, situated beneath the vent in caterpillars (Lepidoptera) (T-B).

infraanal plates, paraprocts, q.v. (T-B; Tuxen).

infrabrustia, brustia (q.v.) limited to the ventral or caudal aspect of the mandible (T-B, after MacGillivray).

infrabuccal cavity, infrabuccal chamber, q.v. (T-B).

infrabuccal chamber, in adult Formicidae (Hymenoptera), a sac below the floor of the mouth, opening into a short narrow canal, serving a variety of functions including food storage (T-B; Riek, in CSIRO).

infracercal plates, in Orthoptera, paraprocts, q.v. (T-B).

infraclypeus, anteclypeus, q.v. (T-B).

infracoxal, subcoxal, q.v. (T-B).

infracted, infractus (Latin), abruptly bent inward, as if broken (T-B).

infradistal plate, in some ♂ Enicocephalidae (Hemiptera: Heteroptera), fused apical segments of genital plates (Štys).

infraepimeron, katepimeron, q.v. (T-B).

infraepisternum, katepisternum, q.v. (T-B).

infragenital, subgenital, q.v. (T-B).

infrahypostomal sclerites, in larval Muscomorpha (Diptera), subhypostomal sclerites, q.v. (Farrar).

inframarginal, submarginal, q.v. (T-B).

inframedian vein, in Orthoptera, cubitus, q.v. (T-B).

infraocular, subocular, q.v. (T-B).

infraoesophageal, suboesophageal, q.v. (T-B).

infraorder, an optional category below the suborder (Mayr).

infrared, beyond the visible spectrum of light at the red end, responded to by some night-flying moths (Lepidoptera) (T-B; Gilmour, in CSIRO).

infrascutellum, in adult Diptera, subscutellum, q.v. (McAlpine).

infrasocial, leading a solitary existence (Tulloch); see social.

infraspecific, within the species; usually applied to categories (subspecies) and phena (varieties) (Mayr); see form, subspecies, and variety.

infraspecific name, a general term for any name used for a taxon or an individual form below the rank of species, including subspecific and infrasubspecific names (ICZN).

infraspiracular process, in larval Muscomorpha (Diptera), feathery processes projecting from the aperture of the perispiracular glands (Ferrar); spiracular hairs, q.v.

infrasquamal setulae, in adult Diptera, fine hairs below the point of attachment of the squamae (T-B, after Curran).

infrastigmatal, situated below the stigmata or spiracles (T-B).

infrasubspecific, of a rank, taxon, or name: one at a rank lower than that of subspecies (ICZN).

infrasubspecific form, in taxonomy, form, q.v. (Mayr).

infrasubspecific name, a name additional to a binomen (and not an interpolated name) that is not often deemed to be subspecific, or additional to a trinomen (ICZN).

infrasubspecific taxon, a taxon at lower rank than the subspecies, whose name is not regulated by the Code (ICZN).

infringing, encroaching upon (T-B).

infumated, infumatus (Latin), smoke-colored; clouded, as with smoke (T-B).

infunda, in Hemiptera, the salivary pump, q.v. (T-B, after MacGillivray); in Coccoidea (Hemiptera: Sternorrhyncha), the hypopharynx of Berlese and Green (T-B, after MacGillivray).

infundibulate, infundibuliform, shaped like a funnel (T-B).

infundibulum (Latin), funnel (R. W. Brown); any funnel-shaped organ or structure (T-B).

infuscate, infuscated, infuscatus (Latin), smoky gray-brown, with a blackish tinge (T-B).

ingens (Latin), unusually large or disproportionate in size (T-B; R. W. Brown).

ingest, to eat (T-B).

ingestion, taking in of food; eating (T-B).

ingestive, of or pertaining to ingestion or the swallowing of food (T-B).

ingestive infection, in medical entomology, that form in which the parasites are received at the time of feeding, the infective stage being taken through the mouth (T-B, after Matheson).

ingluvial, of or pertaining to the crop of insects (T-B).

ingluvial ganglia, paired ganglia of the stomatogastric nervous system, innervating the posterior portion of the foregut and the midgut (T-B, after Snodgrass).

ingluvies, crop, q.v. (T-B).

ingurgitation, the act of swallowing (T-B).

injury, damage, wound, or trauma (Steinhaus and Martignoni).

innate behavior, behavior that does not involve volition or learning (Borror et al.).

inner and upper pair of valves, in ♀ Aleyrodidae (Hemiptera: Sternorrhyncha), dorsal gonapophyses, q.v. (Tuxen, after Quaintance and Baker).

inner appendages of anal tergum, in ♂ Diptera, cerci, q.v. (Tuxen, after Graham-Smith).

inner chitinous press, in ♀ Aleyrodidae (Hemiptera: Sternorrhyncha), a system of sclerotized bars basally supporting the valves (Tuxen).

inner claspers, in ♂ Auchenorrhyncha (Hemiptera), styles, q.v. (Tuxen, after McAtee); in ♂ Hymenoptera, volsellae, q.v. (Tuxen, after Beck) or parameres, q.v. (Tuxen, after Michener).

inner copulatory organ, in ♂ Diptera, intromittent organ, parameres and hypandrium (Tuxen).

inner cuticula of bursa copulatrix, in ♀ Lepidoptera, spermatophorum, q.v. (Tuxen, after Verson).

inner division, in ♂ *Culex* (Diptera: Culicidae), the sternal and most mesal part of the lateral plate of the phallosome in the normal resting position (Harbach and Knight, after Belkin).

inner dorsocentral bristles, in adult Diptera, acrostichal setae, q.v. (T-B).

inner dorsocentral scale, in adult Culicidae (Diptera), one of the scales occurring in a more or less distinct longitudinal row located mesad of the dorsocentral setae on the scutum (Harbach and Knight).

inner female ectodermal genitalia, in ♀ Heteroptera (Hemiptera), complex of the ectodermal ♀ genital ducts and associated structures (Tuxen, after Štys).

inner genital chamber, in ♀ Isoptera, inner vestibulum, q.v. (Tuxen, after Weesner).

inner gonapophysis, in ♀ Aleyrodidae (Hemiptera: Sternorrhyncha), inner valve, q.v. (Tuxen).

inner internal rod, in adult Siphonaptera, a vertical, inner, strengthening rod on the mesal wall of the coxae (Lewis, pers. comm.).

inner lobe of maxilla, lacinia, q.v. (T-B).

inner lobe of posterior gonopod or gonapophysis, in ♀ Psocoptera, valvae dorsales, q.v. (Tuxen, after Pearman).

inner edge, anal margin, q.v., of wing (T-B).

inner margin, anal margin, q.v., of wing (T-B).

inner paramere, in ♂ Hymenoptera, volsella, q.v. (Tuxen, after Priesner).

inner parameres, in ♂ *Eusthenes* (Hemiptera: Heteroptera: Tessaratomidae), lateral parts of basiconjunctiva (transl. "innere Parameren" Handlirsch, in Tuxen).

inner plates, in ♂ Hymenoptera, second gonocoxae, q.v. (Tuxen).

inner processes, in ♂ Psocoptera, internal parameres, q.v. (Tuxen, after Pearman).

inner squama, in adult Diptera, the larger of 2 squamae arising from the posterior mesoscutellar margin, and forming a hoodlike canopy over the halter (T-B); lower calyter, q.v.

inner surface of the leg, the ventral surface of the insect leg when extended at right angles to the body (T-B, after Snodgrass).

inner ramus, in ♀ Heteroptera (Hemiptera), posterior connecting leaf of gonapophysis VIII, q.v. (Tuxen, after Snodgrass).

inner rhabdites, in ♂ Ephemeoptera, penis, q.v. (Tuxen, after Packard).

inner rods, in ♀ Lepidoptera, apophyses posteriores, q.v. (Tuxen).

inner sac, in ♂ Pieridae (Lepidoptera), spinulated, membranous sac in central cavity of valva between ectal and ental layers (Tuxen, after Klots).

inner surstylus, in ♂ Tephritoidea (Diptera), inner articulated lobes of epandrium (McAlpine).

inner tube, in ♂ Siphonaptera, tubus interior, q.v. (Tuxen, after Snodgrass).

inner unquis, in Collembola, the functionally ventral, usually concave, margin facing the unguiculus (if present) (Christiansen and Bellinger).

inner valve(s), in ♀ Isoptera, inner pair of valves borne on abdominal sternum IX (Tuxen); in ♀ Grylloblattodea, third valvulae, q.v. (Tuxen, after Crampton); in ♀ Auchenorrhyncha (Hemiptera), second gonapophyses, q.v. (Tuxen); in ♀ Aleyrodidae (Hemiptera: Sternorrhyncha), median part of unpaired dorsal gonapophysis (Tuxen, after Deshpande).

inner valvulae, in ♀ Phasmida, Orthoptera, and Hemiptera (Auchenorrhyncha), second gonapophyses, q.v. (Tuxen); in ♀ Isoptera, inner valves, q.v. (Tuxen).

inner vertical bristles, in adult Diptera, the large setae lying on the vertex of the head, mesal to the outer verticals, and usually in line with the ipsilateral orbitals (McAlpine); see inner vertical setae.

inner vertical setae, in adult Chironomidae (Diptera), verticals closest to coronal suture, set off from outer verticals by distance or size (Saether).

inner verticals, in adult Diptera, inner vertical setae, q.v. (Saether).

inner vestibulum, in ♀ Isoptera, inner (proximal or anterior) portion of vestibulum (genital chamber) where the latter is divided into inner and outer portions (Tuxen, after Roonwal).

innervate, to supply with nerves (T-B).

innotate, innotatus (Latin), without markings (T-B; Harris); see notate.

inocular antenna, antenna in which the base is partly or wholly surrounded by the compound eye (T-B).

inoculative, in medical entomology the manner of infection of the organism when it takes place through the act of biting by the carrier, the organism being inoculated through the feeding process (T-B, after Matheson).

inosculans, inosculating, settling into a cavity, as one part into the cavity of another (T-B).

inosine-5'-phosphate, in purine metabolism, purine ribotide produced from ribose-5-phosphate combined with carbon and nitrogen sources such as formate, glycine, and aspartate (Gilmour, after Waterhouse).

inquiline, an animal living in the home of another and sharing its food, especially a guest or lodger in the nests of termites (Isoptera) and bees, ants, and wasps (Hymenoptera) (T-B, after Tillyard; Leftwich); an organism that lives on or within the body of another, or in its nest or abode, without benefit or damage to either (Steinhaus and Martignoni); see inquilinism.

inquilinism, symbiotic relationship in which one of the 2 partners (the inquiline) lives habitually on or within the body of the other partner, or in its nest or abode, this relationship being nonobligate with neither of the 2 partners either benefiting or suffering harm (Steinhaus and Martignoni); the relation in which a socially parasitic species spends the entire life cycle in the nests of its host species, the former either lacking workers or, if present, usually scarce and degenerate in behavior (Wilson).

insect, a member of the class Insecta, but frequently used for other members of the Hexapoda (T-B); see hexapod.

insect immunogen, immunogen, q.v. (Steinhaus and Martignoni).

insect society, in the strict sense, a colony of eusocial insects (ants, eusocial wasps, bees [Hymenoptera], or termites [Isoptera]); in the broad sense, any group of presocial or eusocial insects (Wilson).

insect sociology (insect sociobiology), the study of social behavior and population characteristics related to social behavior in insects (Wilson).

Insecta, class within the superclass Hexapoda, including the Archaeognatha, Zygentoma and all Pterygota, characterized by ectognathous mouthparts, antennae with intrinsic muscles in scape only, no postantennal organ, and epimorphic larval development (T-B; Mackerras, in CSIRO).

insectan, pertaining to or characteristic of an insect (T-B).

insectary, a place or building where insects are bred and studied (T-B).

insectean, insectan, q.v. (T-B).

insecticide, a toxic chemical substance employed to kill and control insects (Pfadt).

insectivore, an insect eater (T-B).

insectivorous, subsisting by eating insects (T-B).

insectorubin, a brown pigment, usually incorporated with melanin, in the epidermis and cuticle of insects, formerly considered to be a mixture of a group of pigments called ommochromes, q.v. (Leftwich).

insectoverdin, a mixture of carotenoid (yellow) and bile pigments (e.g., blue-green biliverdin) derived from food, and producing a green color in hemolymph (Leftwich; Chapman).

inseminated, having received semen (containing sperm) (T-B; Chapman).

insemination, transfer of semen (containing sperm) from the ♂ to the ♀ (Chapman); see copulation and fertilization.

inserted, insertus (Latin), introduced into; placed in; placed between (R. W. Brown); having the base of one part set into another (T-B).

inserted head, one entirely or partly concealed within the thorax (T-B).

insertion, the point of attachment of moveable parts (T-B); of a muscle, its attachment to a moveable part (T-B).

insolation, exposure to the sun's rays (T-B).

inspiratory, of or pertaining to inspiration in breathing.

instar, stage between moults in the nymph or larva, numbered to designate the various stages, e.g., the first instar is the stage between the egg and first moult (T-B; Tulloch; Stehr); see stadium.

instinctive behavior, unlearned stereotyped behavior, in which the nerve pathways involved are hereditary (T-B, after Wardle; Borror et al.); see fixed action pattern and reflex arc.

instita (pl., **institae**), in ♀ Sterrhinae (Lepidoptera: Geometridae), loose apron, corresponding to mappa of ♂, which hangs over the ostium bursa and is part of the lamella antevaginalis (Tuxen, after Pierce).

institia, striae or furrows of equal width throughout (T-B; Harris).

instrate, in ♂ *Eupithecia pimpinellata* (Lepidoptera: Geometridae), adjective, descriptive of bursa copulatrix with its inner surface completely covered with short spines or points forming star-shaped folds (Tuxen, after Pierce).

insula (pl., **insulae**), in some ♀ Culicidae (Diptera), small, median sclerite on the lower vaginal lip (Tuxen, after Christophers; Harbach and Knight); see islet.

insula plate, in ♀ Culicidae (Diptera), insula, q.v. (Tuxen, after Gerry).

insular seta, in ♀ Culicidae (Diptera), one of the setae borne on the insula (Harbach and Knight).

integer (Latin), whole; entire (R. W. Brown); without incisions, as a margin (T-B); a whole number.

integrated control, integrated pest management, q.v. (Steinhaus and Martignoni; Pfadt).

integrated pest management (IPM), concept of employing the optimum combination of control methods, including biological, cultural, mechanical, physical, and/or chemical control measures, to reduce a pest insect population to below an economic threshold, with as few harmful effects as possible on the environment and nontarget organisms (Borror et al.).

integricipit, in adult Siphonatera, lacking a transverse interantennal groove (Dunnet, in CSIRO); see fracticipit.

Integricipita, former suborder of Siphonaptera, including integricipit fleas (Lewis, pers. comm.).

Integripalpia, suborder of Trichoptera, including the infraorders Plenitentoria and Brevitentoria, possessing females without a cloaca (the vulva and rectum with separate openings), with abdominal segments X and XI reduced, with abdominal segments VIII and IX without long internal apodemes, and lacking cerci; larvae with lateral and middorsal humps on abdominal segment I (Hennig, after Martynov; Weaver).

integument, the outer layer of the insect, comprising the epidermis and the cuticle, lying upon basement membrane (T-B; Tulloch, after Richards; Chapman); see cuticle and exoskeleton.

integumental scolophore, scolophore, q.v. (T-B; Comstock).

integumental vestiture or setae, in larval Syrphidae (Diptera), numerous minute spines or hairs which may cover the epidermis, not including the segmental spines (Peterson, after Heiss).

integumentary, of or pertaining to the integument (T-B).

intelligence, the capacity to modify behavior as a result of experience (Borror et al.).

inter-, Latin prefix; among or between (T-B).

interantennal, between the bases of the antennae (T-B).

interantennal groove, in adult Culicidae (Diptera), a median longitudinal groove produced by the approximation of the membranous antennal sockets over the narrow middle part of the frons (Harbach and Knight); in adult Siphonaptera, the suture extending over the top of the head from one antennal fossa to the other (Lewis, pers. comm.).

interantennal ridge, in adult Culicidae (Diptera), the apodeme marked externally by the interantennal suture (Harbach and Knight; transl. "Interantennalleiste" Schiemenz); in adult Siphonaptera, falx, q.v. (Lewis, pers. comm.).

interantennal setae, in Coccoidea (Hemiptera: Sternorrhyncha), setae ventrally on the head between, and caudad of, the articulation of the antennae (T-B, after MacGillivray).

interantennal sulcus, in larval Chironomidae (Diptera), suture separating frontal or frontoclypeal apotome from clyepus and labrum (Saether).

interantennal suture, in adult Culicidae (Diptera), the median longitudinal suture extending from the postfrontal sutures to a point near the epistomal suture where it may bear arms which diverge laterally (Harbach and Knight, after Robinson); in adult Siphonaptera, interantennal groove, q.v. (Lewis, pers. comm.).

interarticular, between articles or segments (T-B); between articulations.

interbases, in some ♂ Tipulidae (Diptera), e.g., Pediciini, appendages of the basistylus (Tuxen; Alexander and Byers, in McAlpine).

interbifid groove, in adult Diptera, pseudotrachea, q.v. (T-B, after Snodgrass).

intercalary, additional, interpolated, or inserted between, as a wing vein or other structure (T-B).

intercalary appendages, the rudimentary post antennal or premandibular appendages (T-B, after Snodgrass).

intercalary bristle, in adult Siphonaptera, the main row of bristles on each segment consisting of a series of long setae, alternating with short, hairlike intercalary bristles (Lewis, pers. comm.).

intercalary cell, in adult Lepidoptera, the secondary cell within the discal cell of either fore- or hind wing formed by the forking of the base of the medial vein (Common, pers. comm.).

intercalary piece, in ♂ Lepidoptera, distal part of a vas deferens, said to be histologically different from proximal part (transl. "Schaltstück" Stitz, after Tuxen).

intercalary plates, in certain species of Coccoidea (Hemiptera: Sternorrhyncha), the longitudinal row of plates on each side between the mesal plates and the lateral plates (T-B, after MacGillivray).

intercalary sclerite(s), in Gerromorpha, Nepomorpha, and a few other groups of Heteroptera (Hemiptera), 2 minute sclerotized plates dorsally between segments 3 and 4 of the labium (Cobben; Andersen); in adult Lepidoptera, a small sclerite in the membrane between the scape and pedicel of the antenna in certain primitive taxa (Kristensen).

intercalary segment, the last preoral segment of the insect head, anterior to the mandibular segment (T-B; McAlpine); see head.

intercalary vein, an added or supplementary wing vein in interspace between longitudinal veins, e.g., in Ephemeroptera and Orthoptera (T-B; Borror et al.; Chapman); see accessory vein and intercostula.

intercalate, to interpolate; to insert into any serial arrangement between any 2 members (T-B).

intercaste, in social insects such as termites (Isoptera) and bees and ants (Hymenoptera), caste that is intermediate between the recognized castes (Leftwich).

intercellular, between and among cells (T-B).

interclavicle, in acalyptrate Muscomorpha (Diptera), the prothoracic presternum (Speight, after Pandey and Agrawal).

intercostal, between veins or costae; usually in the narrow grooves between veins in the costal region of a wing (T-B).

intercostal vein, in adult Hymenoptera, subcosta, q.v. (Borror et al.).

intercostula, small, veinlike structures between the normal veins, visible on a wing margin but lost toward the disc (T-B); see intercalary vein.

intercoxal process, in Coleoptera, a median protrusion of the basal segment of the abdomen between the hind coxae (T-B).

interference colors, iridescent colors resulting from the reflection of light from a series of superimposed surfaces separated by distances comparable to the wavelenghts of light, being commonly produced by scales of Lepidoptera (Chapman).

interfollicular tissue, tissue separating successive follicles in an ovariole (Chapman).

interfrons, in adult Diptera, frontal vitta, q.v. (Colless and McAlpine, in CSIRO; McAlpine).

interfrontal bristles, in adult Diptera, interfrontal setae, q.v. (T-B, after Curran).

interfrontal hairs, in adult Diptera, interfrontal setae, q.v. (T-B, after Curran).

interfrontal setae, in adult Diptera, setae on frontal vitta (McAlpine).

interfrontalia, in adult Diptera, frontal vitta, q.v. (T-B, after Curran).

interganglionic, between ganglia (T-B).

interganglionic nerve cord, the fused commissures of the ganglia forming the ganglionic centers (T-B, after Wardle).

intergenital groove, in ♀ Exoporia (Lepidoptera), longitudinal, median furrow of intersegmental membrane caudad (ventrad) of ostium bursae (transl. "sillon intergénital" Bourgogne, in Tuxen).

intergenital zone, in ♀ Exoporia (Lepidoptera), region between papillae anales and lamella antevaginalis (transl. "zone intergénitale" Bourgogne, after Tuxen).

intergonocoxal connective, in ♀ Chironomidae (Diptera), weak, membranous strap connecting gonocoxites ventrally (Saether).

intergonocoxal membrane, in ♀ Heteroptera (Hemiptera), membrane uniting the ninth gonocoxites posteriorly (Tuxen, after Scudder).

interior, within; internal; the inside (T-B).

interior arms of genital embracer, in ♂ Heteroptera (Hemiptera), suspensorial apodemes, q.v. (Tuxen, after Yang).

interior edge, anal margin, q.v., of wing (T-B).

interior honeydew, in Coccoidea (Hemiptera: Sternorrhyncha), wet wax, q.v. (Miller, in Stehr, after Kawai and Tamaki).

interior palpi, labial palpi, q.v. (T-B).

interlobar space, in ♂ Culicidae (Diptera), the distance between the lobes of abdominal tergum IX (Harbach and Knight, after Belkin).

intermaxillaire, galea, q.v. (T-B).

intermedian endomere, in ♂ Chironomidae (Diptera), superior volsella, q.v.(Saether).

intermedian volsella, in ♂ Chironomidae (Diptera), superior volsella, q.v. (Saether).

intermediary, in adult Culicidae (Diptera), the line of thickening occurring where there are folds in the region of the alula and calypter when the wing is extended (Harbach and Knight, after Prashad).

intermediate, lying between others in position; or possessing characters between 2 other forms (T-B).

intermediate appendage(s), in ♂ Plecoptera, upper part of the cleft subanal plate (Tuxen, after Kimmins); in ♂ Trichoptera, various processes of composite abdominal segment X (Tuxen).

intermediate cell, chromophile, q.v (Tulloch, after Jones).

intermediate chamber, in ♀ Heteroptera (Hemiptera), pars intermedialis, q.v. (Tuxen, after Davis).

intermediate chordotonal organ, in Tettigoniidae and Grylloidea (Orthoptera), group of scolopidia proximal to the crista acustica within the subgenual organ of the tibia (Chapman).

intermediate field, in Orthoptera, discoidal area, q.v. (T-B).

intermediate host, in medical entomology, the host, insect or otherwise, in which the asexual stages of a parasite are passed (T-B, after Matheson).

intermediate host reservoir, in medical entomology, hosts, insect or otherwise, in which a natural supply of the asexual stages of a parasite occur (T-B, after Matheson).

intermediate mesenteron rudiment, a median strand of cells of the ventral endoderm remnant taking part in the regeneration of the mesenteron in some insects (T-B, after Snodgrass).

intermediate metabolism, all cellular reactions which are not immediately involved with the release of energy (Chapman).

intermediate moult, in Blattaria, Isoptera, Mantodea and Orthoptera, moult involving apolysis before hatching and the shedding of embryonic cuticle by the pharate first instar (pronymph) following hatching (Key, in CSIRO; Chapman; Alsop, pers. comm.).

intermediate piece, in ♂ Heteroptera (Hemiptera), pars intermedialis, q.v. (Tuxen, after Slater and Carayon).

intermicellar, found or occurring among the micellae of chitin (T-B).

intermediate process(es), in ♂ Plecoptera, intermediate appendage, q.v. (Tuxen, after Hynes); in ♂ Hydroptilidae (Trichoptera), lateral arms of subgenital plate, q.v. (Kelley), lateral processes, q.v. (Tuxen), in other ♂ Trichoptera, intermediate appendages, q.v. (Tuxen).

intermediate sclerite, in wing of Chironomidae (Diptera), arculus, q.v. (Saether); in larval Muscomorpha (Diptera: Brachycera), hypopharyngeal sclerite, q.v. (Teskey, in McAlpine).

intermediate valves, in ♀ Isoptera, second gonapophyses, q.v. (Tuxen).

intermediate valvulae, in ♀ Orthoptera, second gonapophyses, q.v. (Tuxen, after Snodgrass).

internal apodeme (of tergum IX), in ♂ Siphonaptera, apodeme of tergum IX, q.v. (Tuxen).

internal apparatus, in ♀ Neuroptera, bursa copulatrix, q.v. (Tuxen, after Tjeder); in ♀ Trichoptera, structures of unknown homology in genital chamber (Tuxen).

internal area, in adult Hymenoptera, the posterior of the 3 areas between median and lateral longitudinal carinae on the metanotum; third lateral area (T-B).

internal body, in ♀ Aschiphasminae (Phasmida: Bacunculidae), enigmatic sclerotization in hind part of bursa copulatrix, often visible outside as a large spur (transl. "Binnenkörper" Günther, in Tuxen).

internal cell, in adult Hymenoptera (Packard), the second anal of Comstock (T-B, after J. B. Smith).

internal chiasma, optic lobe, q.v. (T-B, after Packard).

internal fold, in ♀ Zygoptera (Odonata), a small process or flap projecting from the anterior surface of the second segment of the penis (Tuxen, after Kennedy).

internal genitalia, in ♀ insects, collectively the spermatheca and accessory glands, the genital chamber and the vagina (T-B, after Snodgrass).

internal hypandrium, in ♂ Neuroptera, hypandrium internum, q.v. (Tuxen, after Tjeder).

internal incrassation, in Siphonaptera, one or more thickenings along the margins of the head capsule (Lewis, pers. comm.); see preoral tuber.

internal lobe, in ♂ Anisoptera (Odonata), internal fold, q.v. (Tuxen, after Borror).

internal medullary mass, medulla interna, q.v. (T-B, after Hickson).

internal palpal hair, in ♂ *Anopheles* (Diptera: Culicidae), one of the very minute setae borne on the inner surface of the maxillary palpi (Harbach and Knight, after Christophers).

internal paramera, mesomeres, q.v. (T-B).

internal parameres, in ♂ Psocoptera, mesomeres, q.v. (Tuxen, after Badonnel; Lyal, pers. comm.).

internal parasite, endoparasite, q.v. (Leftwich).

internal plate, in ♂ Phthiraptera, basal apodeme, q.v. (Tuxen).

internal plate at base of sternum IX, in ♀ Neuroptera, bursa copulatrix, q.v. (Tuxen, after Killington).

internal process, in some ♂ *Culex* (Diptera: Culicidae), a prominent projection arising from the inner surface of the lateral plate when the latter is otherwise simple and undivided (Harbach and Knight, after Colless).

internal respiration, the process of oxidation accompanying metabolism in the cells of the body tissues (T-B, after Snodgrass).

internal sac, in ♂ Coleoptera, invaginated cavity at the distal end of the penis, into which opens the ductus ejaculatorius, and which is everted in copula (Tuxen).

internal skeleton, in ♀ Mecoptera, medigynium, q.v. (Tuxen, after Miyaké).

internal spine, in ♂ Culicidae (Diptera), spine at the center of the inner side of the basistylus (coxite) (Tuxen).

internal triangle, in adult Odonata, triangle, q.v. (T-B).

internal veins, in Lepidoptera, one to 3 unbranched veins running free from the base to the outer margin of the wing near the hind angle; 1a to 1c in the numerical series; the anal veins of Comstock (T-B, after J. B. Smith).

internal wing cell, in adult Odonata, the triangular wing cell behind and proximad of the triangle (T-B, after Garman).

International Code of Zoological Nomenclature (ICZN), the official set of regulations dealing with zoological nomenclature (Mayr); see Commission.

International Commission on Zoological Nomenclature, Commission on Zoological Nomenclature, q.v. (Key, in CSIRO).

interneur, in adult Coleoptera, longitudinal impression (stria) or row of serial punctures situated between elytral intervals (Erwin).

interneural, between the veins of the wings (T-B).

interneurone, association nerve cell, q.v. (Chapman).

internode, that part of a plant stem between 2 successive nodes (T-B).

internomandibular gland, in bees (Hymenoptera: Apoidea), mandibular gland, q.v. (T-B, after J. B. Smith).

internomedian vein, in Orthoptera, cubitus anterior, q.v., of wing (T-B).

internuncial neurone, association nerve cell, q.v. (T-B).

interocellar furrow, in Hymenoptera, a short depressed line or space extending from middle of ocellar furrow to median ocellus, flaring out adjacent to median ocellus and frequently forming a depressed area surrounding the ocellus (T-B).

interoceptor, proprioreceptor, q.v. (T-B).

interocular, between the compound eyes (T-B); in Collembola, between the 2 eye patches (Christiansen and Bellinger).

interocular antennae, those which are set between the eyes (T-B).

interocular setae, in adult Chironomidae (Diptera), orbitals, q.v. (Saether); in adult Culicidae (Diptera), setae arising on the interocular space (Harbach and Knight, after Knight).

interocular space, in adult Culicidae (Diptera), the narrow part of the vertex between the compound eyes and above the postfrontal sutures (Harbach and Knight, after Christophers).

interoculars, in adult Chironomidae (Diptera), orbitals, q.v. (Saether).

interparameral bridge, in ♂ Trichoptera, parameral bridge, q.v. (Tuxen, after Snodgrass).

interparameral sclerite, in ♂ Muscomorpha (Diptera: Brachycera), abdominal sternum X (McAlpine, after Griffiths); the sclerite linking the hypandrium and the telomeres in the upper wall of the periandrial fold (Griffiths).

interpleural suture, in Odonata, the suture between the meso- and metapleural regions (Garman).

interpleurite, one of the intersegmentalia between the pleurites (T-B, after Imms).

interplical, lying between folds, e.g., between the alternate ridges and grooves in the anal area of the hind wing of Orthoptera (T-B).

interpolated name, a name placed within parentheses after a generic name to denote a subgenus, after a genus-group name to denote an aggregate of species, or after a specific name to denote an aggregate of subspecies (ICZN).

interposed sectors, in Odonata, the shorter longitudinal veins occurring in the wings of some species between the chief veins; supplementary sectors (T-B).

interpseudotracheal pegs, in Diptera, contact chemoreceptors located on labella between the pseudotracheae (Chapman).

interradial nexus, in Myrmeleontidae (Planipennia), a conjunction of adjacent wing veins which joins the tip of the first and second branches of the radial sector (T-B, after Comstock).

interrupted, interruptus (Latin), broken in continuity, but with the tips of the broken parts in line with each other (T-B).

intersegmental, between segments (T-B); see interarticular.

intersegmental apodeme, in adult Culicidae (Diptera), an often well developed apodeme borne on the anterior margin of the intersegmental cleft and extending dorsad from the metapleural ridge (Harbach and Knight, after Owen).

intersegmental cleft, in adult Culicidae (Diptera), a fissure separating the metanotum and metapostnotum dorsally and extending ventrad between the metepimeron and metapostnotum at the level of the pleural apophysis (when present), bearing the dorsal part of the intersegmental suture along the caudal margin and the ventral part of the metapleural suture as well as the intersegmental apodeme along its anterior margin (Harbach and Knight, after Owen).

intersegmental groove, suture marking former primary segments in secondary segmentation (McAlpine).

intersegmental lobes, in ♂ Siphonaptera, lobes, often densely spiculose, formed from intersegmental membrane between abdominal sterna VIII and IX (Tuxen, after Wagner).

intersegmental membrane, the flexible infolded part of the cuticle or conjunctiva between 2 secondary adjacent segments which allows freedom of movement of the body, usually being the nonsclerotized posterior part of a primary segment (T-B); membrane connecting the segments of the body and the appendages (Harbach and Knight).

intersegmental plates, cervical sclerites, q.v. (T-B, after Chapman).

intersegmental ridge, the apodeme marked externally by the intersegmental suture (Harbach and Knight); in adult Culicidae (Diptera), an incomplete ridge between the pro- and mesothorax extending downward between the propleuron and the anterior mesanepisternum and continuing ventrally between the pleural and sternal apophyses along the anterior margin of the mesokatepisternum; between the meso- and metathorax, a well developed ridge separating the segments laterally and ventrally; between the metathorax and abdominal segment I, a weakly developed ridge extending dorsad along the posterior margin of the intersegmental cleft (Harbach and Knight, after Owen).

intersegmental sclerites, intersegmentalia, q.v. (Chapman).

intersegmental suture, a line or groove separating adjacent segments (Harbach and Knight); in the thorax of adult Culicidae (Diptera), a groove produced incidental to a ridge which marks the posterior limits of each segment; between the pro- and mesothorax, a line separating the mesepisternum from the prothorax which is discontinuous between the propleuron and the anterior mesanepisternum; between the meso- and metathorax, a groove arising in the midventral area at the anterior margin of the metabasisternum and extending dorsad, arising near the apex of the metameron and extending dorsad on the caudal edge of the intersegmental cleft (Harbach and Knight, after Owen).

intersegmentalia, small detached plates or sclerites between adjacent segments of the insect body, which belong partly to the segment in front and partly to that behind (T-B, after Imms); see cervical sclerites, interpleurites, postnotum, and intersternites.

intersex, an individual more or less intermediate in phenotype between ♂ and ♀ (Mayr); see gynandromorph and hermaphrodite.

intersexual selection, epigamic selection, q.v.

interspace, in adult Coleoptera, interval, q.v. (T-B); in some Orthoptera, a deep incision or sulcus on the posterior margin of the metasternum (T-B, after Walden); in adult Lepidoptera, spaces between wing veins not included in closed cells.

interspaceal, occurring in the interspaces between 2 wing veins or 2 elytral striae (T-B).

interspiracular nodule, seta, or **lamella,** in larval Syrphidae (Diptera), a rounded or roughened protuberance, hair, or lamella situated on the posterior spiracular plate in the angle formed by the spiracles (Peterson, after Heiss).

intersternal fold, in ♀ Isoptera, fold of intesegmental membrane between abdominal sterna VII and VIII near the beginning of the spermatic groove (Tuxen, after Imms).

intersternites, primary intersegmental sclerites of the venter, becoming the spinastera of the thorax (T-B, after Snodgrass).

intersternum, in Odonata, a large sclerite of the thoracic sternum just anterior to the abdomen (T-B, after Garman); the postpleurite or opisthopleurite (T-B, after MacGillivray).

interstice, interstitium (Latin), a space between 2 lines, whether striate or punctate (T-B; Harris); see interval.

interstitial, situated between 2 segments (Borror et al.); coincident, q.v. (Borror et al.).

interstititial line, the elevated ridge between 2 striae or series of punctures (T-B).

intertergite, one of the segmentalia between tergites (T-B, after Imms); see postnotum.

intertidal, between the mean high-water level and mean low-water level in a coastal region (Allaby); see littoral.

interval, the space between 2 structures or sculptures (T-B; Harris); see interstice.

intervalviferal membrane, in ♀ Heteroptera (Hemiptera), intergonocoxal membrane, q.v. (Tuxen, after Davis).

intervalvula, in ♀ Hymenoptera, detached notum, q.v. (Tuxen, after Richards).

intervalvula inferior, in ♀ Orthoptera, inferior intervalvula, q.v. (Tuxen, after Ander).

intervalvula posterior, in ♀ Orthoptera, superior intervalvula, q.v. (Tuxen, after Ander).

intervalvulae, in ♀ insects, second gonapophyses, q.v. (Tuxen, after Crampton).

intervalvular apodeme, in ♀ Caelifera (Orthoptera), a pair of long, cephalad directed rods articulating with both anterior and posterior valvulae (Tuxen).

intervalvular membrane, in ♀ Grylloblattodea, membrane connecting bases of second valvulae (Tuxen).

intervalvular space, in ♀ Heteroptera (Hemiptera), vestibulum, q.v. (Tuxen, after Bonhag and Wick).

interventricular valve, the inner opening between the chambers of the heart (T-B, after J. B. Smith).

interventricular valvule, a small valve of the heart, situated in front of the semilunar valve (T-B).

intervenular, between any 2 veins (T-B).

intestina parva, ileum, q.v. (T-B).

intestinal myiasis, disease of man or other vertebrates caused by the larvae of certain Diptera living as intestinal parasites (Leftwich).

intestine, hind gut, q.v. (T-B).

intima, the cuticular lining of the foregut, hind gut, and tracheae (T-B, after Matheson; Chapman).

intorted, intortus (Latin), turned or twisted inwardly (T-B).

intoxication, in invertebrate pathology, poisoning, including poisoning by toxins (Steinhaus and Martignoni).

intra-, Latin prefix; within; between (T-B).

intraalar bristles, in adult Diptera, intraalar setae, q.v. (T-B; Colless and McAlpine, in CSIRO).

intraalar setae, in adult Diptera, a longitudinal row of setae on the mesoscutum between the dorsocentral setae and the supraalar setae (McAlpine).

intracellular, occurring within the cell or in a cell (T-B).

intracranial, within the cranium (T-B).

intraepidermal, within or inside of the epidermis (T-B).

intraganglionic, within or inside a ganglion (T-B).

intrahemocoelic, within the hemocoel (Steinhaus and Martignoni).

intrahumeral bristles, in adult calyptrate Diptera, bristles found immediately in front of the thoracic suture, between the humeral callus and the presutural depression (T-B); see presutural bristles.

intralecithal cleavage, meroblastic cleavage, q.v. (Boudreaux).

intramural rods of endophallic sack, in ♂ Siphonaptera, virga doralis + virga ventralis (Tuxen, after Snodgrass).

intraocular, situated within the compound eye (T-B).

intrasegmental, the condition of being with a segment (T-B).

intrasexual selection, sexual selection based upon interactions between males or, less commonly, between females (Matthews and Matthews).

intrauterine, applied to development, when the young hatch within the vagina of the mother (T-B); see ovoviviparous and viviparous.

intricate, intricatus (Latin), confused; markings, whether elevated or depressed, so run into each other as to be difficult to see (T-B; Harris); see confused and obscure.

intrinsic articulation, a type of articulation in which the points making contact are sclerotic prolongations within the articular membrane (T-B, after Snodgrass).

intro-, Latin prefix; within (T-B).

introgressive hybridization, the spread of one or more genes of one species into the germ plasm of another species as a result of hybridization (Mayr).

introitus ductus, in ♂ Noctuidae (Lepidoptera), opening of aedoeagus for passage of the ductus ejaculatorius (Tuxen, after Boursin).

introitus vaginae, in ♀ Lepidoptera, ostium bursae, q.v. (Tuxen) or in ♀ Coleophoridae (Lepidoptera), colliculum (in part) + ostium bursae (in part) (Tuxen, after Toll).

intromittent, designed for entering or putting within (T-B).

intromittent organ, in ♂ insects, an organ for the transfer of seminal fluid from the ♂ into the ♀ (Tuxen), e.g., aedeagus, penis, or phallus, q.v.

introrse, introrsum, directed inward, or toward the body (T-B).

intrusus, intruded; opposite of protruded, q.v. (T-B).

intumescent, enlarged; swollen; expanded (T-B).

intussusception, deposition of new particles of formative material in a tissue or structure (T-B).

invaginate, to turn inward or to retract within the body wall (T-B).

invaginated tubular duct, in Eriococcidae and Lecanodiaspididae (Hemiptera: Sternorrhyncha: Coccoidea), cylindrical dermal structure with apex in form of a cup (Miller, in Stehr).

invagination, a pouch or sac formed by an infolding or indrawing of the outer surface (T-B); see evagination.

invagination of the embryo, the direct infolding of the embryo within the egg (T-B, after Snodgrass).

invalid name, any name that is not valid under the Code (ICZN).

invalid nomenclatural act, any available nomenclatural act that is not valid under provisions of the Code (ICZN).

invasion, in invertebrate pathology, the penetration by a microorganism through the integument and other epithelial barriers of the body of a host organism (Steinhaus and Martignoni).

inversion, in some ♂ Diptera, e.g., Culicidae, rotation of terminalia 180° resulting in true ventral structures coming to lie in a dorsal position (McAlpine).

invertase, a digestive emzyme that converts sucrose to glucose and fructose via hydrolysis, produced by hypopharyngeal glands or labial glands (T-B; Chapman).

invertebral, invertebrate, without a backbone or vertebral column (T-B).

Invertebrata, the animals without a backbone (T-B).

invest, to cover (T-B).

investitus, unclothed; without scales or hairs (T-B; Harris); see denudate, glabrous, immaculate, and nude.

investment, a covering (T-B).

involucrate, involucratus, involute, q.v. (T-B).

involucrum (Latin), case; envelope (R. W. Brown); a sheath of soft cerumen surrounding the brood chamber in a nest of stingless bees (Hymenoptera: Apidae: Meliponinae) (Wilson).

involucrum alarum, in Dermaptera, a flap of the metanotum (T-B).

involute, involuted, involutus (Latin), complex, intricate (R. W. Brown); rolled inward spirally (T-B).

involuti, butterflies whose larvae live in a folded leaf, e.g., Hesperiidae (Lepidoptera) (T-B).

involution of the embryo, invagination of the embryo accompanied by a revolution and final reversal of position in the egg (T-B, after Snodgrass).

ioterium, in adult Hymenoptera, poison gland or poison sac, q.v. (T-B, after Kirby and Spence).

IPM, integrated pest management, q.v. (Borror et al.).

Iranian maize mosaic, disease of corn caused by a rhabdovirus transmitted propogatively by *Ribautodelphax* (Hemiptera: Auchenorrhyncha: Delphacidae) (Nault and Ammar).

iridescence, in optics, producing different colors by diffraction (T-B, after Wardle); change of color with the angle of viewing characteristic of interference colors, e.g., the bodies of dragonflies (Odonata), the wings of some Lepidoptera, and the elytra of some beetles (Coleoptera) (Leftwich; Chapman).

iridescent, iricolor, iridicolor, iridicolorous, having or reflecting colors of the iris or rainbow (T-B).

iridescent virus disease, a disease of Diptera, Lepidoptera, and Coleoptera, caused by large (virions ca. 130 millimicrons in diameter) icosahedral viruses, for which the larval fat body appears to be the principal site of multiplication (Steinhaus and Martignoni).

iris, the dark pigment of the primary pigment cell, q.v., surrounding the dioptric apparatus of an ommatidium (T-B, after Snodgrass); the colored circle enclosing the pupil of an ocellate spot (T-B).

iris cells, primary pigment cells, q.v. (T-B, after Needham).

iris pigment, iris, q.v. (T-B, after J. B. Smith).

iris pigment cells, primary pigment cells, q.v. (T-B, after Snodgrass).

iris tapetum, iris, q.v. (T-B).

irised, with rainbow colors (T-B).

irregular, unequal, curved, bent or otherwise twisted or modified without order or symmetry, e.g., certain antennae (T-B).

irreversibility rule, Dollo's Rule, q.v. (Mayr).

irritability, in biology, response of an organism to stimuli, as of a nerve or muscle (T-B).

irrorate, irrorated, irroratus (Latin), freckled or speckled; covered with minute spots or granules (T-B; Harris, after R. W. Brown); see adsperse, atomarious, farinose, and maculate.

isabelline, brownish-yellow.

ischia, pleura, q.v. (T-B).

ischiopodite, in Arthropoda, the third segment of a generalized limb, being fused with the trochanter in Insecta (T-B, after Snodgrass).

Ischnocera, suborder within the Phtiraptera, including the Trichodectidae, Philopteridae, and Heptapsogasteridae, the members of which possess antennae that are not concealed in grooves, vertical mandibles, and maxillary palpi absent (Calaby, in CSIRO; Lyal, pers. comm.); see Amblycera, Anoplura, and Rhyncophthirina.

island, an isolated part within the boundaries of any structure or body (T-B).

Isle of Wight disease, in adult honeybees (Hymenoptera: Apidae), acarine disease, q.v., or disentery, q.v. (Steinhaus and Martignoni; Leftwich; Borror et al.).

islet, a spot of a different color included in a plaga or other large spot; an insula (T-B).

iso-, Greek prefix; equal (T-B).

isolate, to separate out from others (T-B).

isolating mechanisms, properties of individuals that prevent successful interbreeding with individuals that belong to different populations (Mayr).

isolation, complete separation from similar forms, in biology; may be geographic, climatic, etc. (T-B).

isoleucine, essential amino acid in the diet of insects (Glimour, in CSIRO).

isomer, any of 2 chemical compounds having like constituent atoms, but differing in physical or chemical properties because of differences in arrangement of the atoms (Pfadt).

Isomera, a collective term for those Coleoptera in which all tarsi have an equal number of tarsomeres, e.g., Carabidae, with a 5-5-5 tarsal formula (T-B); see Heteromera.

isomerous, with an equal number of tarsomeres on all tarsi (T-B).

isometric growth, growth in which the rate of growth of one part is the same as another part (Chapman); see isometry.

isometry, the condition in which the relative proportions of body parts remain constant with change in total body size; allometry, q.v., where $a = 1$ (Wilson); see negative allometry and positive allometry.

isomorphous, having the same form, appearance or construction (T-B).

isopalpi, palpi with the same number of joints in both sexes, e.g., in some Trichoptera (T-B).

isophene, a line connecting points of equal expression of a character (T-B; Mayr); lines at right angles to a cline on a map (Mayr).

isopneustic, term describing arrangement of spiracles, 2 thoracic and 8 abdominal pairs, all situated in the intersegmental membranes, an arrangement persisting only in some embryos (Leftwich); see holopneustic respiration.

Isopoda, order of Malacostraca (Crustacea), including marine forms and terrestrial sowbugs and pillbugs, characterized by being dorsoventrally flattened and lacking a thoracic carapace (Borror et al.).

isoprene (2-methyl butadiene), C_5H_8, a colorless, volatile liquid and structural component of terpenes (Allaby).

Isoptera, polymorphic, mandibulate, exopterygote order within the Neoptera, living in social units composed of a limited number of reproductive forms associated with numerous wingless sterile soldiers and workers, antennae filiform or moniliform, wings, when present, including 2, similar, elongate, membranous, net-veined pairs held flat over the body at rest, and capable of being shed by means of the basal sutures, cerci short, and external genitalia rudimentary or wanting (T-B; Gay, in CSIRO).

Isopterodea, Blattopteroidea, q.v. (Boudreaux).

iteroparous, a type of life history in which the animal reproduces 2 or more times during its lifetime (Borror et al.); see semelparous.

Ithonoidea, superfamily within the Planipennia, including the Ithonidae (Borror et al.), and sometimes also the Polystoechotidae (Henry, in Parker); sometimes included within the Osmyloidea, q.v. (Riek, in CSIRO).

-itus, Latin suffix; -atus, q.v. (T-B).

-ius, Latin suffix; having the power or ability to (T-B).

Ixodida, suborder within the Acari, including the ticks: Argasidae (soft ticks) and Ixodidae (hard ticks) (Borror et al.).

J

jail fever, epidemic typhus, q.v. (Adkins, pers. comm.).

janthine, violet colored (T-B).

Japanese gypsy-moth disease, a disease of larvae of *Lymantria dispar* (Lepidoptera: Lymantriidae) presumably caused by the bacterium *Streptococcus disparis,* in which the larvae cease to feed and become diarrheic (Steinhaus and Martignoni).

Jassidoidea, Cicadelloidea, q.v. (Hennig).

Jassidomorpha, Cicadelloidea + Cercopoidea (Hennig, after Heslop-Harrison).

jaundice, nucleopolyhedrosis of the silkworm, *Bombyx mori* (Lepidoptera: Bombycidae) (Steinahus and Martignoni); see grasserie.

Javelle water, a solution of potassium hypochlorite used in bleaching insect structures (T-B).

jaw, in insects with chewing mouthparts, mandible or maxilla (Leftwich).

jaw capsule, in larval Diptera, the case which contains the mouth structures in those taxa in which the head is differentiated (T-B).

jobet, crop, q.v. (T-B).

Johnstonian organ, Johnston's organ, q.v. (T-B).

Johnston's organ, a chordotonal organ lying in the second antennal segment with its insertion in the articulation between the second and third segments, functioning to perceive movements of the antennal flagellum and involved in flight control and sound perception (T-B; Chapman).

joint, articulation, q.v. (T-B).

jointed, articulate, q.v. (T-B).

jointlet, in Archaeognatha, intermediate article between the segments of the flagellum (Wygodzinsky).

Jordan's organ, in adult Lepidoptera, chaetosema, q.v. (Leftwich).

jowl, in adult Diptera, gena, q.v. (T-B, after Curran; McAlpine).

jubate, jubatus, fringed with long, pendent hairs (T-B).

jugal bar, in winged insects, one or 2 spurlike extensions ("jugal veins") of a basal sclerite near the posterior base of the wing (Ross et al., after Hamilton).

jugal bristles, bristles on the edge of the jugal lobe (T-B; Chapman).

jugal fold, in the forewing, and sometimes the hind wing, of most Neoptera, a fold located behind the last anal vein, setting off the jugum from the clavus (T-B, after Snodgrass; Chapman; Gauld and Bolton).

jugal lobe, in Hymenoptera, a lobe at the base of the hind wing, on the posterior side, proximal to the claval lobe (T-B; Borror et al.; Chapman; Gauld and Bolton); in adult Lepidoptera and Trichoptera, jugum, q.v. (T-B).

jugal region, jugum, q.v. (T-B, after Snodgrass).

jugal vein, jugal bar, q.v. (Ross et al.).

Jugatae, a collective term for those Lepidoptera in which there is a jugum instead of a frenulum to unite the wings in flight, including the Zeugloptera, Dacnonypha, and Exoporia (T-B; Borror et al.).

jugate, in Lepidoptera, having a jugum wing-coupling apparatus, e.g., Hepialidae (T-B); any Lepidoptera having a jugum (T-B).

jugular, of or pertaining to the throat (T-B).

jugular sclerites, cervical sclerites, q.v. (T-B).

jugulum, gula, q.v. (T-B); occipital foramen, q.v. (T-B); that sclerite just behind the submentum; the cavity of the posterior part of the head to which the neck is joined; the lateral and under parts of the prothorax (T-B, after J. B. Smith).

jugum (pl., **juga**), basal area of wing set off by jugal fold (Chapman; Gauld and Bolton); in certain adult Lepidoptera and Trichoptera, a lobe or process at the base of the forewings, overlapping the hind wings and holding the 2 together in flight (T-B; Tulloch; Chapman); in Heteroptera (Hemiptera), mandibular plate q.v. (T-B).

Jullien's organ, organ of Jullien, q.v. (T-B, after Klots).

jumping plant-louse, member of the superfamily Psylloidea (Hemiptera: Sternorrhyncha) (Hennig).

junctura, in ♂ Culicidae (Diptera), floor of the space between the base of the gonocoxite and the proctiger, being variously chitinized and in varying degrees of attachment with the gonocoxite, basal piece, paramere, aedeagus or proctiger (Harbach and Knight, after Christophers).

junior homonym, of 2 homonyms, the later established (ICZN).

junior synonym, of 2 synonyms, the later established (ICZN); see objective synonym, senior synonym, and subjective synonym.

Jurassic Period, one of the 3 periods within the Mesozoic Era, between the Triassic Period and the Cretaceous Period, extending between about 180 and 135 million years before the present (Riek, in CSIRO).

justa-, prefix, for juxta, Latin; near (T-B).

justified emendation, the correction of an incorrect original spelling (ICZN).

juvenile hormone (JH), a C-18 (JH-I), C-17 (JH-II), or C-16 (JH-III) sesquiterpene produced by the corpora allata that is released into the hemolymph, being involved in ♀ receptivity, color change, diapause, heartbeat, larval development, metamorphosis, migration, muscle autolysis, oogenesis, and polymorphism, and modifying the effects of ecdysone and prothoracotrophic hormone (Tulloch, after Rockstein; Chapman).

juvenile stage, any postembyonic stage in development preceding the sexually mature adult stage (Steinhaus and Martignoni); see larva, nymph, and pupa.

juxta, in ♂ Lepidoptera, sclerotized plate, often shield-shaped, ventral to the aedeagus, more or less strongly fastened to or fused with bases of the sacculi and ventral part of the vinculum, sometimes connected with the anellus by a median rodlike process, and which is often forked dorsally so as to more or less surround and support the aedeagus (Tuxen, after Pierce); in ♂ Noctuidae (Lepidoptera), juxta + anellus (Tuxen, after Pierce); in ♂ Diptera, distiphallus, q.v. (McAlpine); in ♂ Calliphoridae (Diptera), eversible membranous terminal section of the distiphallus (Tuxen, after Zumpt and Heinz).

juxtacardo, in larval Coleoptera, a separate part of the cardo extending from the cardo proper toward the submentum (Peterson, after Böving and Craighead).

juxtastipes, in larval Coleoptera, a separate part of the stipes extending from the stipes proper toward the mentum (Peterson, after Böving and Craighead).

K

K-selection, selection that acts to maintain population levels at just about their carrying capacity, K, the number of individuals that the environment can support (Matthews and Matthews).

K-strategist, K-selected species in relatively stable habitats without high reproductive potential but with relatively high survival of young (Matthews and Matthews).

KAAD mixture, (kerosene/alcohol/acetic acid/dioxane mixture), killing agent for insect larvae consisting of 10 ml of kerosene, 70–100 ml of 95% ethyl alcohol, 20 ml of glacial acetic acid, and 10 ml of dioxane (Borror et al.).

Kahle's solution, preservation fluid consisting of 30 ml of 95% ethyl alcohol, 12 ml of formaldehyde, 4 ml of glacial acetic acid, and 60 ml of distilled water (Borror et al.).

kairomone, allelochemical of adaptive value to the organism receiving it (Matthews and Matthews).

kala-azar, a type of leishmaniasis, being a disease of man caused by the flagellate protozoan, *Leishmania donovani* (Trypanosomatidae), and transmitted by the bite of sand flies (genera *Phlebotomus* and *Lutzomyia*; Diptera: Psychodidae) (Borror et al.); see espundia and oriental sore.

kappa, in adult Diptera, palpiger, q.v. (T-B, after MacGillivray).

kappa group, in larval Lepidoptera, lateral group, q.v. (Peterson, after Fracker); see prespiracular setae.

Karathane (trade name), dinocap, q.v. (Pfadt).

karyological character, a character involving chromosome structure or number (Mayr).

karyolymph, protoplasm within the cell nucleus (Chapman).

karyotype, chromosome set (White, in CSIRO).

katabolic, pertaining to, or of the nature of katabolism; see anabolic (T-B).

katabolism, catabolism, q.v. (T-B, after Tulloch).

katapleure, preepisternum, q.v. (T-B, after MacGillivray).

katatergite, in adult Diptera, ventral subdivision of laterotergite, q.v. (Colless and McAlpine, in CSIRO; McAlpine; see anatergite).

katatrepsis, the passage of the insect embryo in blastokinesis from the dorsal aspect of the ovum to its original position on the ventral aspect (T-B, after W. M. Wheeler).

katepimeron, lower portion of divided epimeron (T-B; Mackerras, in CSIRO).

katepisternal seta, in adult Diptera, seta on katepisternum (McAlpine).

katepisternal setula, in adult Diptera, setula on katepisternum (McAlpine).

katepisternal sulcus, in some adult Simuliidae (Diptera), a horizontal groove dividing the katepisternum into an upper and a lower part (McAlpine).

katepisternum, lower portion of divided episternum (T-B, after Comstock; Mackerras, in CSIRO).

katydid, a member of the superfamily Tettigonioidea (Orthoptera) (Key, pers. comm).

keel, an elevated ridge or carina (T-B); in ♂ Gelastocoridae (Hemiptera: Heteroptera), hypandrium, q.v. (Tuxen, after Martin); in ♂ Siphonaptera, in ♂ Siphonaptera, a sclerotization that sometimes marks the fusion of the ventral walls of the aedeagal pouch (Rothschild and Traub); in ♂ *Leucanitis* (Lepidoptera: Noctuidae), dorsal ridge or keel of uncus (transl. "Kiel" John, in Tuxen).

Kelthane (trade name), dicofol, q.v. (Pfadt).

kentromorphic phases, population-density induced morphological and pigementation differences in the Australian plague species of Phasmida, *Podocanthus wilkinsoni, Didymuria violscens,* and *Ctenomorphodes tessulata* (Key).

kentromorphism, changes in color, pattern, anatomical proportions, physiology and behavior of certain insects in response to stimuli received in high-density populations (Norris, in CSIRO); see gregarious phase and solitary phase.

Kenyon cells, a group of cell bodies over the calyx of the corpora pedunculata of the brain (Chapman).

keratin, inert animal protein found in wool, hair and feathers, akin to chitin of insects, that may be digested by Ischnocera and Amblycera (Phthiraptera) of birds and mammals, some larval Dermestidae (Coleoptera), and some larval Tineidae (Lepidoptera) (T-B; Chapman).

keratinase, enzyme capable of digesting keratin under anaerobic conditions (Chapman).

keratitis, inflammation of the cornea of the eyes of man or livestock (Pfadt).

kermes (Arabic), deep red; crimson (R. W. Brown); a red dye prepared from the dried females of the *Kermes ilicis* (Hemiptera: Sternorrhyncha), which lives on oak in the Mediterranean Region (T-B); a genus of scale insects (Hemiptera: Sternorrhyncha: Coccoidea).

kermesinus, dark red, with much blue (T-B).

9-ketodecenoic acid, queen substance, q.v. (Gilmour, in CSIRO).

key, a tabulation of characters of species, genera, etc., serving to identify taxa (T-B; Mayr); see dichotomous key.

key character, in taxonomy, a character of special utility in a key (Mayr).

kHz, abbrev. kilohertz, q.v. (Borror et al.).

kidney-shaped, reniform, q.v. (T-B).

kilocycle, 1000 cycles per second; used to express the frequency of electromagnetic waves.

kilohertz, kilocycles per second (Borror et al.).

kin groups, sets of individuals whose members are genetically more closely related than random because many have the same parents (Matthews and Matthews).

kin selection theory, theory advanced by Hamilton that individual inclusive fitness may be raised through altruism (Matthews and Matthews).

kinesis, locomotory activity of an organism in response to a stimulus (Tulloch); moving in a way that is related only to the intensity of a stimulus, disregarding any spatial properties which the stimulus might possess (Matthews and Matthews).

kinetopause, arrested activity without necessarily arrested development (Leftwich); see diapause.

king, in termites (Isoptera), ♂ primary reproductive, usually being dealate (T-B; Krishna, pers. comm.).

kingdom, the highest rank in the hierarchial classification, in zoology consisting of a single taxon, the Animalia (ICZN).

kinship component, an individual's effect on the gene pool of succeeding generations through effects on the reproduction of individuals possessing genes to varying degrees like its own; an individual's effects on the fitness of its neighbors multiplied by its respective fractional relatedness to them (Matthews and Matthews, after Hamilton).

klinokinesis, an avoidance action manifested by some insects that normally fly in a straight line when the environment is favorable but perform rapid turning movements as soon as there is any unfavorable stimulus (Leftwich).

klinotaxis, a movement of an insect in a definite direction in relation to a stimulus, e.g., toward or away from light (Leftwich); see phototaxis.

knee, femorotibial joint, q.v. (T-B; Harbach and Knight).

knee spot, in adult Culicidae (Diptera), a group of scales occurring at the terminations of the femur, tibia, and first tarsomere, being normally applied to a band of pale scales occurring at the apex of the femur (Harbach and Knight, after Christophers).

knife-blade, in ♀ Incurvariidae (Lepidoptera), modified sclerotized parts of abdominal segments IX and X forming a cutting apparatus or ovipositor (Tuxen, after Wood).

knob(s), in adult Diptera, enlarged head of halter (McAlpine); in ♂ *Dysdercus* (Hemiptera: Heteroptera: Pyrrhocoridae), capitate processes, q.v. (Tuxen, after Khanna).

koinobiont, parasitoid attacking exposed or weakly concealed active immature insects, allowing them to continue to develop for some time after oviposition by the parasite (Gauld and Bolton); see idiobiont.

Korlan (trade name), ronnel, q.v. (Pfadt).

Krause's membrane, a transverse septum in the middle of each clear band or zone (sarcomere) of the insect muscle, to which the sarcostyles are joined, consisting of a network of radially distributed threads which cut across the muscle fiber (T-B, after Imms).

kynurenine, an oxidation product of the amino acid tryptophan that gives rise to some of the red and brown pigments (ommochromes) in insects (Leftwich; Chapman).

L

L appendix, in larval Chironomidae (Diptera), ligula, q.v. (Saether).

L setae, in larval Chironomidae (Diptera), lateral setae L(1–4) of abdomen (Saether).

labella, in some adult Diptera, paired oral lobes or pads at the distal end of the proboscis derived from the labial palpi (T-B; McAlpine); see labellum.

labellar, in Diptera, of or pertaining to the labella (T-B).

labellar abductor apodeme, in adult Culicidae (Diptera), a small cuticular process located below the inner basal margin of each labellum, serving for attachment of the labellar abductor muscle (Harbach and Knight).

labellar basal sclerite, in adult Culicidae (Diptera), one of several small sclerites occurring ventrally in the membranous articulation between the prementum and the labella (Harbach and Knight, after Knight).

labellar mesial sclerite, in adult Culicidae (Diptera), one of the narrow sclerotized strips borne on the inner surface of each labellum (Harbach and Knight).

labellar sclerite, in adult Culicidae (Diptera), one of several cuticular plates borne on each labellum (Harbach and Knight); the prominent basal sclerite on each labellum (Harbach and Knight, after Patton and Evans).

labellum, in the honey bee (Hymenoptera: Apidae), flabellum, q.v. (T-B, after Imms); see labella.

labia (sing., **labium**), peritreme, q.v., of spiracle (T-B, after MacGillivray); in Coccoidea (Hemiptera: Sternorrhyncha), cicatrices, q.v. (T-B, after MacGillivray); in ♀ Hymenoptera, 2 papillae of abdominal segment IX originally bearing the separate gonopores, projecting as lobes paralleling mesal margin of gonapophyses IX from the ventral aspect of coxosternite IX in Symphyta (Tuxen, after E. L. Smith).

labiae, in ♀ Lepidoptera, papillae anales, q.v. (Tuxen).

labial, belonging or referring to the labium (T-B).

labial basal seta, in adult Culicidae (Diptera), one in a row of setae occurring ventrally near the base of the labium (Harbach and Knight, after Knight).

labial gills, in some nymphal Ephemeroptera, membranous outgrowths on venter of mentum near base of palps (Riek, in CSIRO).

labial glands, glands opening by a median duct between the base of the hypopharynx and the labium, or on the hypopharynx, usually functioning to produce saliva but also producing silk in larval Lepidoptera and Trichoptera (T-B, after Snodgrass; Chapman).

labial hooks, in Anisoptera (Odonata), hooks or spines on the labial palps of nymphs (Leftwich).

labial kidneys, in Collembola, Diplura, Archaeognatha, and Zygentoma, labial glands, q.v., functioning in excretion (T-B, after Wigglesworth; Watson, in CSIRO).

labial lobe, in larval Muscomorpha (Diptera: Brachycera), lobe at the hind margin of the mouth (Teskey, in McAlpine).

labial lonchus, in adult Chironomidae (Diptera), labial portion of hypopharynx, forming a small sclerotized plate appearing as a ventral, slender, triangular process of the cibarial pump (Saether).

labial mask, in Odonata, mask, q.v. (Chapman).

labial palp (pl., **palpi** or **palps**), the one- to four-segmented appendage of the insect labium, borne on the palpiger (T-B).

labial palpiger, palpiger, q.v. (Peterson).

labial plate, in larval Nematocera (Diptera), hypostoma, q.v. (Teskey, in McAlpine); reduced, sclerotized, usually serrate, labium present in larvae of many families of aquatic Diptera (Peterson); in larval Chironomidae (Diptera), mentum, q.v. (Saether).

labial sclerite, in adult Culicidae (Diptera), one of 2 small cuticular plates borne immediately proximal to the prementum, receiving the cardino-prementalis from the cardo (Harbach and Knight; transl. "Labialsklerit" Schiemenz); in larval Muscomorpha (Diptera: Brachycera), hypopharyngeal sclerite, q.v., or one of several small sclerites located anteriorly below the hypopharyngeal sclerite (Teskey, in McAlpine); in larval Ichneumonoidea (Hymenoptera), a more or less V-shaped sclerite bordering labium laterally and ventrally (Gauld and Bolton, after Short).

labial segment, the last gnathal segment of the head, being the labium (T-B; McAlpine); see head.

labial stipes, stipes, q.v. (Peterson).

labial stylets, in Coccoidea (Hemiptera: Sternorrhyncha), rostral filaments, q.v. (Kostarab and Kozár).

labial suture, the suture between the prementum and the postmentum (T-B; Borror et al.).

labial triangle, in Collembola, the ventral, external surface of one-half of the labium, bounded by the margins of the labial sclerite, the labial appendages, and the median ventral groove (Christiansen and Bellinger).

labial vesicles, in larval Tanypodinae (Diptera: Chironomidae), lateral vesicles on M appendage (Saether); mouthhooks, q.v. (Farrar).

Labiata, name of hypothesized monophyletic group consisting of Symphyla and Hexapoda (Mackerras, after Tiegs).

labiate, labiatus, liplike or having liplike sutures (T-B).

Labiduroidea, Cataderaptera, q.v. (Giles, in CSIRO).

labiella, hypopharynx, q.v. (T-B, after Packard).

labile, labilis (Latin), readily changing; unstable (T-B).

labiohypopharyngeal sclerite, in larval Muscomorpha (Diptera: Brachycera), hypopharyngeal sclerite, q.v. (Teskey, in McAlpine).

Labioidea, a superfamily sometimes recognized in the Dermaptera, including the families Carcinophoridae, Spongiphoridae (Labiidae), and Arixeniidae (Popham).

labiomaxillary, pertaining to the labium and the maxilla together (T-B).

labiopedia, genetic mutation in which labial palpi are replaced by fully formed legs, e.g., as observed in *Tribolium confusum* (Coleoptera: Tenebrionidae) (Boudreaux, after Daly and Sokoloff).

labiostipites, prementum, q.v., or that part of the labium formed by the stipites of the component labial (second maxillary) appendages (T-B, after Snodgrass).

labipalp(s), labipalpi (Latin) (sing., **labipalpus**), labial palpi, q.v. (T-B).

labis (pl., **labides**), in ♂ Lepidoptera, paired, hairy or dentate processes of dorsolateral parts of fultura superior or transtilla (Tuxen, after Pierce).

labium (Latin) (pl., **labia**), lip (R. W. Brown); the fused second maxillae, forming the floor of the mouth in mandibulate insects, behind the first maxillae and opposed to the labrum (T-B); in some ♀ Chironomidae (Diptera), membranous lobe at caudal end of gonapophysis IX (Saether); in larval Chironomidae (Diptera), mentum, q.v., or premento-hypopharygeal complex, q.v. (Saether).

labium superius, labrum, q.v. (T-B).

labral, of or pertaining to the labrum (T-B).

labral brush, in some larval Nematocera (Diptera), lateral palatal brush, q.v. (Teskey, in McAlpine).

labral fan, in larval Simuliidae (Diptera), paired, stalked, fanlike structures arising laterally from labrum (Peterson, in McAlpine).

labral lamella, in larval Chironomidae (Diptera), one to several, smooth to pectinate lamellae between setae anteriores on labrum and tormal bar (Saether).

labral lever, in adult Culicidae (Diptera), a hook-shaped apodeme arising dorsally from each side of the labrum with a muscle attached at its innermost end having its opposite attachment on the ventral wall of the labrum (Harbach and Knight, after Snodgrass).

labral margin, in larval Chironomidae (Diptera), sclerotized margin consisting of anterolateral triangular sclerite, posterolateral platelike torma, and sclerotized median margin fused with torma (tormal bar) (Saether).

labral nerve, nerve extending from tritocerebrum to the labrum (T-B; Chapman, after Albrecht).

labral papillae, in Collembola (esp., some Isotomidae and Entomobryidae), subapical projections on the dorsal surface of the labrum (Christiansen and Bellinger).

labral plate, in larval Diptera, dorsal labral plate, q.v. (Teskey, in McAlpine).

labral rod, in larval Chironomidae (Diptera), peglike sensillum of labrum between seta anteriores and seta premandibularis (Saether).

labral sclerites, in some larvae of Chironomidae (Diptera), distinct sclerites on dorsal side of labrum carrying labral setae (S1 and S2) (Saether).

labral sensillum, in larval Chironomidae (Diptera), larger, more prominent and mesal peg of bisensillum, occasionally pointed and on a tubercle, appearing three-segmented (Saether).

labral setae, in larval Chironomidae (Diptera), cephalic setae (S1 and S2), situated on labral sclerites or corresponding areas (Saether).

labral suture, suture between the labrum and the clypeus (T-B).

labralia, in larval Chironomidae (Diptera), tormal bar, q.v., or labral margin, q.v. (Saether).

labraria, in adult Hymenoptera, epipharynx, q.v. (T-B, after MacGillivray).

labraris, in Hymenoptera, the tube formed by the glossae (T-B, after MacGillivray).

labrecula, in adult Hymenoptera, the small transverse lip guarding the entrance to the basipharynx (T-B, after MacGillivray).

labrofrontal lobes, tritocerebrum, q.v. (T-B).

labrofrontal nerve, a short nerve trunk arising anteriorly from the tritocerebrum (T-B, after Snodgrass), giving rise to frontal and labral nerves.

labropalatum, in adult Culicidae (Diptera), the part of the palatum formed by the oral surface of the labrum (Harbach and Knight, after Laffoon and Knight).

labrum, the upper lip, abutting the clypeus in front of the mouth (T-B; Chapman).

labrum-epipharynx, in adult Diptera, labrum, q.v., formed into an unpaired central lancet (T-B; Colless and McAlpine, in CSIRO; McAlpine).

lac, the yellowish or reddish-brown resinous substance produced from the epidermal glands of ♀ *Laccifer lacca* (Hemiptera: Sternorrhyncha: Coccoidea: Kerridae), of many industrial and scientific uses (T-B); see shellac, seed lac, and stick lac.

lac dye, a red dye produced from the lac of ♀ *Laccifer lacca* (Hemiptera: Sternorrhyncha: Coccoidea: Kerridae) (T-B).

lac glands, in certain Kerridae (Hemiptera: Sternorrhyncha; Coccoidea), epidermal glands which secrete lac (T-B).

laccaic acid, one of the organic acids in lac (T-B).

lacer (Latin), torn; mangled; cut up (R. W. Brown); applied to a margin with irregular, broad and deep emarginations (T-B); see lacerated.

lacerate-flush feeding, in phytophagous Heteroptera (Hemiptera), the process of lacerating and macerating cells with the stylets and then flushing out the material with saliva and inbibing it (Cobben; after Miles); see sawing-clipping feeding.

lacerated, laceratus (Latin), ragged; torn in appearance (T-B); see lacer.

lacinella, the lateral lobe of the lacinia when it is two-lobed (T-B, after MacGillivray).

lacinia(e), a blade; the inner of the 2 gnathobases of the first maxilla (T-B, after Tillyard); the inner lobe of the maxilla, articulated to the stipes and bearing brushes of hairs or spines (T-B, after J. B. Smith); in adult Diptera, a flat lancetlike piercing structure which is never jointed (T-B; McAlpine); in Psocoptera, a hard elongated rod, slightly bifurcated or toothed at its free end and ensheathed by galea (T-B, after Imms); in ♂ Hymenoptera, digitus, q.v. (Tuxen, after Thomson); in larval Chironomidae (Diptera), posteriomesal projection or lobe of maxilla carrying several long bristlelike or short scalelike chaetae (Saether).

lacinia coriaria, a long, leathery and flexible lacinia (T-B).

lacinia costae, in ♂ Lepidoptera, sclerotized thickening, especially prominent in some Geometridae, on ventral edge of costa along ectal surface of valva (Tuxen, after Sabatini et al.).

lacinia exterioris, galea, q.v. (T-B).

lacinia falcata, one lacinia acute and bent toward the opposite one; sickle-shaped lacinia (T-B).

lacinia fusca, in ♀ Sphingidae (Lepidoptera), signum, q.v. (Tuxen, after Baltzer).

lacinia interioris, lacinia, q.v. (T-B).

lacinia mandibulae, in larval holometabolous insects, a fleshy or membranous process arising from the anterior or mesal face of the mandible (Peterson); see prostheca and lacinia mobilis.

lacinia mobilis, in *Campodea* and *Anajapyx* (Diplura) and in some mayfly nymphs (Ephemeroptera), platelike appendage near the extremity of the mandible (T-B, after Imms; Boudreaux); in some nymphal Ephemeroptera, a small appendage on the mandible, lying between the molar surfaces and the canines, often curved, sometimes blunt at the tip or minutely toothed, but more often frayed out into a long brush of fine hairs (T-B, after Needham); see prostheca.

lacinia obtusa, lacinia which is rounded and not produced or acute (T-B).

laciniafimbrium, laciniarastra, q.v. (T-B, after MacGillivray).

lacinial chaetae, in larval Chironomidae (Diptera), chaetae on lacinia (Saether).

laciniate, laciniated, laciniatus (Latin), cut into irregular unequal and deep segments; jagged (T-B).

laciniate ovipositor, in ♀ insects, ovipositor with elongate gonapophyses, often laterally compressed (Štys).

laciniarastra, rastra of the lacina (T-B, after MacGillivray).

lacinoidea, the mesal lobe of the lacinia when it is two-lobed (T-B, after MacGillivray).

lactase, a digestive enzyme, which hydrolyzes lactose to produce glucose and galactose (T-B).

lacte, milk-white (T-B).

lacteal, relating to milk; milky in appearance (T-B).

lacteous, lacteus, milky-color (T-B).

lactescent, secreting or yielding a milky fluid (T-B).

lactic acid, product of anaerobic respiration of glucose in insect tissues (Chapman); see lactic dehydrogenase.

lactic dehydrogenase, enzyme catalyzing production of lactic acid from glucose in insect tissues under anaerobic conditions (Chapman).

lactose, $C_{12}H_{22}O_{11}$, disaccharide found in milk, composed of a molecule of glucose and galactose.

lacuna (pl., **lacunae**), a pit; a gap; an empty space; irregular impressions or cavities, specifically, the nonwalled cavities of the body (T-B).

lacunate, lacunose, q.v. (Harris).

lacunose, lacunosus (Latin), full of hollows or cavities; with scattered and irregular broad shallow cavities (T-B; Harris, after Marchant and Charles, and R. W. Brown); see excavated, foveate, impressed, and variolate.

laemodipodiform, resembling the Laemodipoda (Crustacea) in form, e.g., the nymphs of Phasmida (T-B).

laeotorma, in larval Scarabaeoidea (Coleoptera), a transverse sclerome from the left hind angle of the epipharynx, usually provided with pternotorma, often with epitorma or part of the epitorma and, more rarely, the apotorma (T-B, after Böving).

laeotropic, turning to the left; or inclined to turn to the left (T-B).

laete, laetus (Latin), very bright in color (T-B).

laevis, levigate, q.v. (T-B; Harris).

laevigatus (Latin), levigate, q.v. (T-B; Harris).

lagena receptaculi (pl., **lagenae**), in ♀ Lepidoptera, a more or less offset dilation of basal portion of glandula receptaculi (Tuxen, after Stitz), or of spermathecal utriculus (Dugdale).

lageniform, lagenoid, bottle-shaped; bellying out and coming to a narrow neck (T-B).

lamella(e), small lamina (R. W. Brown); a thin plate or leaflike process (T-B); in Coccoidea (Hemiptera: Sternorrhyncha: Coccoidea), plates, q.v. (T-B, after MacGillivray); in ♂ Boreidae (Mecoptera), sclerotized part of the aedeagus (Tuxen); in ♀ Leptoceridae (Trichoptera), one of a pair of conspicuous vertical plates on either side of the posterior external opening of the genital chamber (Nielson); in ♂ Siphonaptera, laminae of aedeagal apodeme, q.v. (Tuxen).

lamella antevaginalis (pl., **lamellae antevaginales**), in ♀ Lepidoptera, the anterior portion of sterigma, derived from intersegmental membranes VII–VIII, perhaps also in part from sternum VII with which it may be joined (Tuxen, after Kusnezov).

lamella basalis infera, in ♂ Tipulidae (Diptera), abdominal sternum VIII (Tuxen, after Westhoff).

lamella basalis supera, in ♂ Tipulidae (Diptera), abdominal tergum VIII (Tuxen, after Westhoff).

lamella postvaginalis, in ♀ Lepidoptera, the posterior (often dorsal) portion of sterigma, derived from intersegmental membranes VII–VIII, perhaps also in part from abdominal sternum VIII with which it may be joined (Tuxen, after Kusnezov).

lamella terminalis infera, in ♂ Tipulidae (Diptera), hypandrium, q.v. (Tuxen, after Westhoff).

lamella terminalis supera, in ♂ Tipulidae (Diptera), epandrium, q.v. (Tuxen, after Westhoff).

lamellae of galea, in larval Chironomidae (Diptera), smooth or serrated lamellae on mesal margin of galea of maxilla (Saether).

lamellae of tergum X, in ♂ Embiidina, hemitergites, q.v. (Tuxen, after Melander).

lamellate, lamellatus (Latin), sheet or leaflike; composed of or covered with laminae or thin sheets (T-B).

lamellate antenna, clubbed antenna with closely opposed leaflike surfaces, the concealed surfaces with sensory pits, e.g., in adult Scarabaeidae (Coleoptera) (T-B; Borror et al.); see flabellate antenna.

lamelles, in Coccoidea (Hemiptera: Sternorrhyncha), lobes, q.v. (T-B, after MacGillivray).

Lamellicornia, those Coleoptera with lamellate antennae, i,e., Scarabaeoidea (T-B; Britton, in CSIRO).

lamelliform, made up of or resembling leaves, blades or lamellae (T-B).

lamellocytes, in larval *Drosophila* (Diptera: Drosophilidae), typically flattened hemocytes that function in encapsulation (Chapman).

lamina, in ♂ Odonata, lamina anterior, q.v. (Tuxen); in ♂ Lepidoptera, tegumen, q.v. (Tuxen, after LeDoux); in ♂ *Eupithecia* (Lepidoptera: Geometridae), median, shieldlike dilation of vinculum (Tuxen, after Schroeder).

lamina annularis, in ♂ Hymenoptera, basal ring, q.v. (Tuxen, after Verhoeff).

lamina anterior, in ♂ Odonata, anterior margin of fenestra often deeply notched or projecting as a hood (Tuxen).

lamina basalis, in larval Chironomidae (Diptera), ventromesal plates, q.v. (Saether).

lamina batilliformis, in ♂ Zygoptera (Odonata), the inconspicuous ligula (Tuxen, after Rathke).

lamina dentata, in ♀ Lepidoptera, signum, q.v. (Tuxen, after Petersen).

lamina dorsalis (pl., **laminae dorsales**), in ♂ Zygaenidae (Lepidoptera), together with lamina ventralis spiny membranes of distal part of aedoeagus (Tuxen, after Haaf).

lamina externa, paraglossa, q.v. (T-B).

lamina ganglionaris, outermost of 3 neuropile masses within the optic lobe (T-B; Chapman).

lamina infraanalis, in larval Anisoptera (Odonata), one of 2 lateroventral sclerites in the walls of the circular fold which contain the anus (T-B, after Snodgrass).

lamina interna, ligula, q.v. (T-B).

lamina labii, in Protura, anterior hyaline prolongation of the labium (Bellinger, pers. comm.).

lamina lateralis, in Chrysopidae (Planipennia), part of abdominal tergum IX (Tuxen, after Tjeder).

lamina lingualis (pl., **laminae linguales**), in Diplopoda, one of 2 median distal plates of gnathochilarium (Borror et al.).

lamina media, in ♂ Siphonaptera, median plate of aedeagal apodeme (Tuxen, after Peus).

lamina oblonga, in ♀ Hymenoptera, second gonocoxa, q.v. (Tuxen).

lamina of phallosome, in ♂ Siphonaptera, lamina media, q.v. (Tuxen, after Jordan).

lamina parameralis, in ♂ Hymenoptera, gonocoxite, q.v. (Tuxen, after Snodgrass).

lamina posterior, in ♂ Odonata, posterior margin of fenestra, only visible by dissection (Tuxen).

lamina preputialis, in ♂ Pyralidae, sclerotization of dorsal part of anellus (Tuxen, after Stitz).

lamina subgenitalis, plate below genitalia, with various morphological meanings, but often synonymous with subgenital plate (Tuxen); in ♂ Phasmida, poculum, q.v. (Key, pers. comm.); in ♀ Phasmida, operculum, q.v. (Tuxen; Key, pers. comm.); in ♂ Orthoptera, subgenital plate, q.v. (Tuxen); in ♂ Neuroptera, abdominal sternum IX (Tuxen, after Morton); in ♀ Plecoptera, subgenital plate, q.v. (Tuxen, after Klapálek); in ♀ Mecoptera, subgenitale, q.v. (Tuxen, after Tjeder).

lamina superior, in Chrysopidae (Planipennia), epiproct, q.v. (Tuxen, after Tjeder).

lamina supraanalis, in nymphal Anisoptera (Odonata), a small dorsal sclerite in the walls of the circular fold which contains the anus (T-B, after Snodgrass); in Phasmida, epiproct, q.v. (Tuxen); in Orthoptera, epiproct, q.v. (Tuxen, after Brunner v. Wattenwyl), or part of epiproct (Key, pers. comm.).

lamina ventralis (pl., **laminae ventrales**), in ♂ Nepomorpha (Hemiptera: Heteroptera), sclerotic blade issuing from fusion of ligamentary processes and running ventrally along phallosoma (Tuxen, after Dupuis); in ♂ Zygaenidae (Lepidoptera), together with lamina dorsalis spiny membranes of distal part of aedoeagus (Tuxen, after Haaf).

lamina volsellaris, in ♂ Hymenoptera, basivolsella, q.v. (Tuxen, after Snodgrass).

laminae abdominales, in ♀ Lepidoptera, papillae anales, q.v. (Tuxen, after Stitz).

laminae aedeagales, in ♂ Hymenoptera, parameres, q.v. (Tuxen, after Snodgrass).

laminae anales, in ♀ Lepidoptera, papillae anales, q.v. (Tuxen, after Dampf).

laminae anales inferiores, in Orthoptera, paraprocts, q.v. (Tuxen, after Brunner v. Wattenwyl).

laminae genitales, in ♂ Auchenorrhyncha (Hemiptera), genital plates, q.v. (Tuxen).

laminae inferiores, in ♀ Batteropteroidea, valvulae inferiores, q.v. (Tuxen, after Berlese).

laminae laterales (sing., **lamina lateralis**), in ♂ Siphonaptera, arched lateral plates of aedeagal apodeme, joined dorsally with lamina media (Tuxen, after Peus).

laminae laterales epiphalli, in ♂ Caelifera (Orthoptera), the lateral parts of epiphallus when this is medially incised (Tuxen).

laminae of aedeagal apodeme, in ♂ Siphonaptera, parts of aedeagal apodeme (Tuxen).

laminae penis, in ♂ Orthoptera, laminae phalli, q.v. (Tuxen, after Grassé and Hollande).

laminae phalli, in ♂ Caelifera (Orthoptera), sclerotizations in endophallic membrane limiting spermatophore sac (Tuxen).

laminae subanales, in Grylloblattodea and Orthoptera, paraprocts, q.v. (Tuxen).

laminae superiores, in ♀ Batteropteroidea, valvulae superiores, q.v. (Tuxen, after Berlese).

laminate, laminatus (Latin), lamellate, q.v. (T-B).

laminatocarinate, with an elevated ridge or keel, formed of thin plates (T-B).

laminiform, layerlike; having the appearance or made up of laminae (T-B).

Lammert's cycle, a daily cycle of temperature change observed in beehives in the winter, in which muscular activity is initiated when the temperature drops to 13°C and ceased when the temperature reaches 25°C (Leftwich).

lamnadens, in adult Diptera, discal sclerite, q.v., of labella (T-B, after MacGillivray).

lamnae (sing., **lamna**), in ♀ Mecoptera, lateral paired structures of the medigynium (Tuxen).

lamnium (pl., **lamnia**), in adult Hymenoptera, segments of gonopod beyond radix (Tuxen, after Ross).

lana, wool (T-B; R. W. Brown); in some adult Lepidoptera, the long hair on the abdomen (T-B).

lanate, lanatus (Latin), densely covered with long, very fine and somewhat curling hairs, like wool (T-B).

lance, in ♀ Hymenoptera, gonapophyses, q.v. (Tuxen, after Ross).

lanceolate, lanceolatus (Latin), lance- or spear-shaped; oblong and tapering to end (T-B).

lanceolate cell, in adult Hymenoptera, first or second anal cells (T-B, after Norton; Borror et al.).

lancet(s), stylet, q.v., being a modified mouthpart (T-B); in ♀ Aculeata (Hymenoptera), first gonapophyses, q.v., except rami (Tuxen, after Snodgrass).

Lannate (trade name), methomyl, q.v. (Pfadt).

lanuginose, lanuginosus, lanuginous, covered with longish very fine soft down or fine soft hair (T-B); see crinitus.

lanugo (Latin), down of fine hairs (T-B; R. W. Brown).

laparostict, in adult Scarabaeoidea (Coleoptera), having the spiracles situated in the pleural membrane, being covered by the elytra when the later are closed (T-B; Britton, in CSIRO); see pleurostict.

lapidicolous, living under deeply imbedded stones (T-B); see cryptobiotic.

lappets, in ♀ Lepidoptera, papillae anales, q.v. (Tuxen, after Scudder).

lapsus calami (sing. and pl.) (Latin), a slip (or slips) of the pen, i.e., an error (or errors) made by an author in writing a text, such as a misspelling of a name (ICZN); see copyist's error and printer's error.

large crossvein, in adult Diptera, discal medial-cubital crossvein, q.v. (T-B, after Curran).

large intestine, colon, q.v. (T-B).

larva(e), a young insect which quits the egg in an early stage of morphological development and differs fundamentally in form from the adult (T-B); the immature form of animals that undergo metamorphosis (T-B, after Imms); feeding and growing stage of holometabolous insects that undergo complete metamorphosis (Peterson); in termites (Isoptera), an immature individual without any trace of wing buds or soldier characteristics (Wilson); in Thysanoptera, 2 active feeding instars (larva I, larva II) (Heming); see nymph.

larva aculeata, one with dense, furlike hair (T-B).

larva cornuta, one with fleshy horns or processes (T-B).

larva furcifera, one with furcate processes (T-B).

larva ursina, a hairy caterpillar; a woolly bear (T-B).

larval, of or pertaining to a larva; in an immature stage called a larva; see nymphal.

larval eyes, in larval Nematocera and orthorrhaphous Brachycera (Diptera), stemmata, q.v. (Teskey, in McAlpine).

larval heteromorphosis, hypermetamorphosis, q.v. (Norris, in CSIRO).

larval organ, in many nymphal Saldidae (Hemiptera: Heteroptera), an apparently sensory structure, in the form of depression, located on abdominal sternum III just mesad of the spiracle (Cobben).

larval pellicle, in Coccoidea (Hemiptera: Sternorrhyncha), the first cast skin or exuviae of the larva (T-B).

larvapod, proleg, q.v. (T-B, after MacGillivary).

larvarium, a nest or shelter made by insect larvae, sometimes a silken hammock or tube but often pieces of leaf, pine-needles, soil particles, etc., woven together (Leftwich); see cocoon and hibernaculum.

larviform, shaped like or resembling a larva (T-B).

larvina, maggot, q.v. (T-B).

larviparous, giving birth to larvae instead of eggs, e.g., certain Diptera (T-B, after Tillyard; Leftwich); see viviparous.

larviposition, the deposition of larvae by adult females, in some Diptera (Chapman).

larvipositor, in larviparous Diptera, the modified ovipositor (T-B).

larvule, early larval mayfly (Ephemeroptera) that appears to have no developed respiratory, circulatory or nervous systems (T-B).

lashed, having a more or less complete fringe of stiff hairs or bristles along the orbit of the compound eye (T-B).

lasureus, the dark blue color of lapis lazuli (T-B).

latatergum, laterotergite, q.v. (T-B, after MacGillivray).

latent infection, in invertebrate pathology, an inapparent infection in which the pathogen is still present in the noninfective phase, and in which a certain pathogen-host equilibrium is established (Steinhaus and Martignoni); see occult virus.

latent learning, learning without apparent reinforcement, e.g., orientation flight of bees and wasps (Hymenoptera: Aculeata) (Matthews and Matthews).

laterad, toward the side and away from the median line (T-B).

lateral, relating, pertaining, or attached, to the side (T-B).

lateral abdominal gills, in some Calopterygidae (Anisoptera), filamentous gills attached toward the ventral surface of the second to seventh or eighth abdominal segments (T-B).

lateral anterior promontory scale, in adult Anophelinae (Diptera: Culicidae), one of the scales usually forming a tuft on the lateral corner of the anterior promontory (Harbach and Knight).

lateral anterior promontory seta, in adult Culicidae (Diptera), one of the setae occurring in a small cluster on the lateral corner of the anterior promontory at or near the anterior end of the dorsocentral setae (Harbach and Knight).

lateral antepronotals, in pupal Chironomidae (Diptera), lateral group of setae (or one seta) on each side of antepronotum (Saether).

lateral apical lobes, in ♂ Pentatomoidea (Hemiptera: Heteroptera), parandria, q.v. (Tuxen, after Ruckes).

lateral apodeme, pleural apophysis, q.v. (T-B, after Needham,

MacGillivray); in ♀ Orthoptera, intervalvular apodeme, q.v. (Tuxen, after Snodgrass).

lateral appendages, in ♂ Nemouridae (Plecoptera), one-segmented modified cercus (Tuxen, after Morton); in ♂ Aleyrodidae (Hemiptera: Sternorrhyncha), claspers, q.v. (Tuxen); in ♂ Heteroptera (Hemiptera), parameres, q.v. (Tuxen, after Sharp).

lateral areas, in adult Apocrita (Hymenoptera), the 3 spaces on the propodeum, between the median and lateral long carinae (T-B).

lateral arm, in ♂ *Culex* (Diptera: Culicidae), the variously developed lateral process (in the normal resting position), of the outer division of the lateral plate of the phallosome (Harbach and Knight, after Belkin); in larval Chironomidae (Diptera), premandible, q.v. (Saether).

lateral axillar surface, in adult Apocrita (Hymenoptera), region of the axilla lateral to the axillar carina (Gibson); see dorsal axillar surface.

lateral basal process, in ♂ *Culex* (Diptera: Culicidae), a lateral projection at the base of the outer division of the lateral plate (Harbach and Knight, after Sirivanakarn).

lateral basivalvular sclerite, in ♀ Caelifera (Orthoptera), lateral sclerite of ventral ovipositor valve (Ander, in Tuxen).

lateral blades, in ♀ *Apatania* (Trichoptera: Limnephilidae), a pair of dorsolateral sclerotized folds of the ductus bursae (Nielsen, after Morton).

lateral braces, in ♂ Plecoptera, paragenital plates, q.v. (Tuxen, after Smith).

lateral bristle, in adult Diptera, lateral marginal seta, q.v. (T-B, after Comstock).

lateral carinae, in Orthoptera, lateral facial carinae, q.v. (T-B); in Orthoptera, carinae on prothorax extending along each lateral margin of the dorsal field (T-B).

lateral caudal setae, in Ephemeroptera, cerci, q.v. (Tuxen, after Uéno).

lateral cerari, in Coccoidea (Hemiptera: Sternorrhyncha), all except the eighteenth pair or anal cerari (T-B, after MacGillivray).

lateral claspers, in ♂ Geometridae (Lepidoptera), valvae, q.v. (Tuxen, after Packard).

lateral comb, in larval Culicidae (Diptera), a group of spines or scales on the lateral aspects of abdominal segment VIII (Peterson).

lateral connectives, in ♂ Heteroptera (Hemiptera), suspensorial apodemes, q.v. (Tuxen, after Leston).

lateral endoapophysis, in ♂ Chironomidae (Diptera), lateral sternapodeme, q.v. (Saether).

lateral endomere, in ♂ Chironomidae (Diptera), inferior volsella, q.v. (Saether).

lateral facial bristles, in Diptera, one or 2 bristles sometimes present on the sides of the head below the eyes (T-B, after Comstock).

lateral facial carinae, in Orthoptera, carinae of the head extending downward from the anterior margin of the eyes (Key, pers. comm.).

lateral field, in Orthoptera, the vertical surfaces of the closed forewings (Otte, pers. comm.).

lateral filaments, long tapering appendages on the margins of the abdomen in certain aquatic larvae (T-B, after Comstock and Kellogg).

lateral filaments of aedeagus, in ♂ Chironomidae (Diptera), inferior volsella, q.v. (Saether).

lateral flange, in adult Culicidae (Diptera), the lateral expansion of the posterior part of the cibarium (Harbach and Knight, after Sinton and Covell).

lateral fovea, in adult bees (Hymenoptera: Apoidea), facial fovea, q.v. (T-B; Eickwort, pers. comm.).

lateral foveolae, in Orthoptera, temporal foveolae, q.v. (T-B).

lateral fringe, in larval Integripalpia (Trichoptera), a line of setae extending along each side of most segments, q.v. (Wiggins).

lateral frontal organs, in most Archaeognatha and Zygentoma, separate capsules containing median neurosecretory cells located on dorsal side of brain (Chapman).

lateral glandular pouches, in ♂ Orthoptera, ejaculatory vesicles, q.v. (Tuxen, after Walker).

lateral gonapophyses, in ♀ Odonata, a pair of processes arising from abdominal sternum IX and forming part of ovipositor (Tuxen); in ♀ Orthoptera, posterior valvulae, q.v. (Tuxen, after Walker); in ♀ Psocoptera, valvae externae, q.v. (Tuxen, after Chapman).

lateral gonopods, in ♀ Psocoptera, valvae externae, q.v. (Tuxen, after Pearman).

lateral group, in larval Lepidoptera, primary or subprimary setae L2 to L3 located laterally on thoracic and abdominal segments, usually near the spiracle (Stehr, after Hinton).

lateral hooks, in larval Muscomorpha (Diptera), mouth hooks, q.v (Ferrar).

lateral keel, in Odonata, a ridge on the side of the abdomen (T-B, after Garman).

lateral line, in larval Lepidoptera, a line at the margin of the dorsum between the subdorsal and parastigmatal lines (T-B, after J. B. Smith); in case-bearing larval Trichoptera, lateral fringe, q.v. (T-B, after Imms).

lateral lingual sclerite(s), lingual sclerites, q.v. (Chapman).

lateral lobe, in Odonata, the part of the labium which corresponds to the paraglossa with the palpiger and palpus (T-B, after Gerstaecker), or more probably, to the palpus alone (T-B, after Butler); also, an expansion borne by the squama at the side (T-B, after Garman); in many Orthoptera, the deflexed part of the pronotum which covers the sides of the prothorax (T-B); in certain adult Hymenoptera, parapsis, q.v. (T-B, after J. B. Smith).

lateral lobes, in some ♂ *Zorotypus* (Zoraptera), part of the complicated genital structure; in ♂ Psyllidae (Hemiptera: Sternorrhyncha), proctiger lobes, q.v. (Tuxen); in ♂ Auchenorrhyncha (Hemiptera), side lobes of pygofer, q.v. (Tuxen); in ♀ Auchenorrhyncha (Hemiptera), oblong plates belonging to sternum VIII flanking base of saw-case (Tuxen); in ♂ Coleoptera, parameres, q.v. (Tuxen) or the

appendages of a supposed single paramere (Tuxen, after Spilman);
in ♂ Rhyacophilidae (Trichoptera), dorsal process of abdominal segment X (Tuxen, after McLachlan).

lateral lobes of aedeagus, in ♂ Chironomidae, inferior volsella, q.v.
(Saether); in ♂ Siphonaptera, single lobes on each side on margin of
palliolum (Tuxen, after Traub).

lateral lobes of epiphallus, in ♂ Orthoptera, processus lateralis
epiphalli, q.v. (Tuxen, after Snodgrass).

lateral lobes of fulcrum, in ♂ Siphonaptera, lobi fulcri laterales, q.v.
(Tuxen).

lateral lobes of sternum VIII, in ♀ Polycentropodidae and Hydropsychidae (Trichoptera), ventral plates, q.v. (Tuxen).

lateral longitudinal area, in adult Hymenoptera, an area extending
between the median and pleural carinae of propodeum (T-B).

lateral marginal seta(e), in adult Diptera, one or more setae on or near
the lateral margin of an abdominal tergite (McAlpine).

lateral mesoscutal lobes, in adult Hymenoptera, parapsides, q.v. (Gibson).

lateral metanotal area, in most adult Siphonaptera, lateral sclerites
distinct from remainder of the metanotum (Lewis, pers. comm., after Snodgrass).

lateral muscles, in insects, those which are typically dorsoventral and
both intrasegmental and intersegmental (T-B, after Snodgrass).

lateral nerve cords, the lateral strands of nerve tissue produced from
the ventral neuroblasts (T-B, after Snodgrass).

lateral ocelli, stemmata, q.v. (T-B).

lateral oviducts, oviductus laterales, q.v. (Tuxen).

lateral parapsidal suture, in many adult Nematocera and orthorrhaphous Brachycera (Diptera), lateral suture delimiting a narrow lateral sclerite, the paratergite (McAlpine).

lateral penellipse, in larval Lepidoptera, e.g., Psychidae, an almost
complete circle of crochets open or incomplete toward the meson
(Peterson).

lateral penis lobes, in ♂ Heteroptera (Hemiptera), processus conjunctivae, q.v. (Tuxen, after Baker).

lateral phallic lobes, in ♂ Ensifera (Orthoptera), paired lateral lobes of
phallus (Tuxen).

lateral pharyngeal glands, hypopharyngeal glands, q.v. (T-B, after
Imms).

lateral pieces of cheliferous segment, in ♂ Mecoptera, gonocoxites,
q.v. (Tuxen, after McLachlan).

lateral plantar bristles, in adults Siphonaptera, pairs of stout bristles
arising along the margins of tarsomere 5 (Lewis, pers. comm.).

lateral plate(s), in ♀ Nepidae (Hemiptera: Heteroptera), gonapophyses of abdominal segment VIII, q.v. (Tuxen, after Hamilton); in ♂
Sialis (Megaloptera: Sialidae), parameres, q.v. (Tuxen, after Ross); in
♂ Siphonaptera, laminae laterales, q.v. (Tuxen); in larval Trichoptera, the principle lateral and dorsal sclerite of the distal portion
of an anal proleg, separated from the anal claw by a dorsal plate and

a ventral sole plate (Wiggins); in ♂ *Culex* (Diptera: Culicidae), one of the pair of variously developed lateral sclerotizations of the phallosome located between the aedeagus and proctiger (Harbach and Knight, after Christophers); in larval Muscomorpha (Diptera), tentoropharyngeal sclerite, q.v. (Farrar).

lateral plate of epiphallus, in ♂ Orthoptera, processus lateralis epiphalli, q.v. (Tuxen, after Roberts).

lateral prescutellar scale, in adult Culicidae (Diptera), one of the prescutellar scales occurring in line on each lateral margin of the prescutellar area of the scutum, being difficult to separate anteriorly from the dorsocentral scales (Harbach and Knight).

lateral process(es), in ♂ Plecoptera, stylets, q.v. (Tuxen, after Needham and Claassen); in ♂ Urostylidae and Coreidae (Hemiptera: Heteroptera), parandria, q.v. (Tuxen, after Yang, Brown); in ♂ *Neopanorpa* (Mecoptera: Panorpidae), lateral processes of aedeagus (Tuxen, after Byers); in some ♂ Hydroptilidae (Trichoptera), lateral projections from posterior margin of abdominal segment IX (Tuxen, after Nielsen).

lateral process of terebra, in ♀ insects, lateral gonapophyses, q.v. (Tuxen, after Tillyard).

lateral process of valva, in ♂ Lepidoptera, processus basalis (valvae), q.v. (Tuxen, after John).

lateral processes of tegumen, in ♂ Lepidoptera, socii (Tuxen, after Philpott).

lateral pronotal carina, in Helotrephidae (Hemiptera: Heteroptera), sharp lateral edge of cephalonotum (Papáček, Tonner, and Štys, after Esaki and China).

lateral pronotal plate, in Helotrephidae (Hemiptera: Heteroptera), ventrally deflected lateral part of pronotum (Papáček, Tonner, and Štys, after Esaki and China).

lateral ridge(s), in ♂ Siphonaptera, laminae laterales, q.v. (Tuxen, after Sharif); in slug caterpillars (Lepidoptera: Limacodidae), a raised line along the lateral series of abdominal tubercles (T-B).

lateral scale, one of the lateral processes of the ovipositor in Cynipidae (Hymenoptera), lying within and below the anal scale (T-B).

lateral sclerite(s), in ♂ Dermaptera, side wall of basal region of penis, carrying parameres (Tuxen); in larval Trichoptera, basal part of anal proleg (Ross; Wiggins).

lateral sclerite of ventral ovipositor valve, in ♀ Caelifera (Orthoptera), lateral basivalvular sclerite, q.v. (Agarwala).

lateral sclerites of epiphallus, in ♂ Caelifera (Orthoptera), small paired sclerites one on each side of epiphallus (Ander, in Tuxen); also called "oval sclerites" and "appendices" (Key, pers. comm.).

lateral scutal fossal scale, in adult Culicidae (Diptera), one of the scales occurring in a more or less distinct line on the lateral margin of the scutal fossa above the ante- and postpronotum, sometimes being continuous posteriorly with the antealar scales (Harbach and Knight).

lateral scutal fossal seta, in adult Culicidae (Diptera), one of the setae occurring in a small group on the lateral margin of the scutal fossa above the postnotum (Harbach and Knight).

lateral scutellar scale, in adult Culicidae (Diptera), one of the scales occurring in a small group on each lateral lobe of the scutellum (Harbach and Knight).

lateral scutellar seta, in adult Culicidae (Diptera), one of the setae occurring in a small group on each lateral lobe of the scutellum (Harbach and Knight).

lateral setae, in Odonata, setae of the proximal segment of the labial palpi (T-B, after Garman).

lateral setae of tergites, in adult Chironomidae (Diptera), caudolateral group of setae on abdominal terga, when anterior transverse row of setae (basal setae) are lacking (Saether).

lateral space, in slug caterpillars (Lepidoptera: Limacodidae), the area on each side between the subdorsal and lateral ridges (T-B).

lateral spines, in Odonata, spines at the caudal end of the lateral keel, q.v. (T-B, after Garman).

lateral spur of dilator, in ♂ Anoplura (Phthiraptera), parameres, q.v. (Tuxen).

lateral sternapodeme, in ♂ Chironomidae (Diptera), anterolateral projections of sternapodeme (Saether).

lateral styles, in ♂ Plecoptera, stylets, q.v. (Tuxen, after Frison).

lateral stylets, in ♂ Plecoptera, stylets, q.v. (Tuxen, after Hanson).

lateral tails, in Ephemeroptera, cerci, q.v. (Tuxen, after Needham, Traver and Hsu)

lateral thorns, in larval Syrphidae (Diptera), heavily sclerotized prominent curved hooks on the lateral margins of the dorsum of the false head (Peterson, after Heiss).

lateral tracheal trunk, the longitudinal tracheal trunk on each side of the body connected with the lateral spiracles (T-B, after Snodgrass).

lateral tubercle(s), in many larval Integripalpia (Trichoptera), tiny forked and sclerotized processes on the lateral side of certain abdominal segments (Wiggins); in larval Lepidoptera, a tubercle on the thoracic and abdominal segments (T-B).

lateral tubule, in larvae of some Chironomini (Diptera: Chironomidae), small tubule laterally on each side of abdominal segment X (Saether); see ventral tubules.

lateral valves, in ♀ Isoptera, dorsal valves, q.v. (Tuxen); in ♀ Aleyrodidae (Hemiptera: Sternorrhyncha), gonoplacs (Tuxen); in ♀ Auchenorrhyncha (Hemiptera), saw-case, q.v. (Tuxen).

lateral valvulae, in ♀ Odonata, lateral gonapophyses, q.v. (Tuxen, after Asahina); in ♀ Orthoptera, gonoplacs, q.v. (Tuxen, after Snodgrass); in ♀ Heteroptera (Hemiptera), gonoplacs, q.v. (Tuxen, after Rawat).

lateral volsella, in ♂ Chironomidae (Diptera), inferior volsella, q.v. (Saether).

lateral window, in ♂ Lycaenidae (Lepidoptera), lateral membranous area between tegumen and scaphium (Tuxen, after Shirozu and Yamamoto).

laterals, in ♂ Heteroptera (Hemiptera), parameres, q.v. (Tuxen).

laterals (of tegumen), in ♂ Lycaenidae (Lepidoptera), paired, subdorsal lobes of caudal margin of tegumen (Tuxen, after Bethune-Baker).

latericeous, latericius, lateritious, lateritius, brick-red (T-B).

laterocervicalia, cervical sclerites, q.v. (T-B, after Crampton).

lateroclinate, directed laterally, being applied to setae of adult Diptera (McAlpine); see proclinate and reclinate.

laterodorsal, lateral and above the median horizontal plane (Christiansen and Bellinger).

lateroflexion, in ♂ Diptera, bending and infolding of the apical portion of the abdomen (McAlpine).

laterope, in adult Zelinae (Hymenoptera: Braconidae), an anterodorsal depression of the first metasomal tergite, more or less pit-shaped, situated in the glymma below the more or less developed dorsolateral carina (van Achterberg).

lateropharyngeal, situated on the side of the pharynx (T-B).

lateropostnotum, postalar bridge, q.v. (T-B).

lateroprocessus, in some ♂ Neuropteroidea, a backward-directed lateral process on each side of abdominal tergum IX (Tuxen, after Tjeder).

lateroproximal ends of the ridge, in ♂ Heteroptera (Hemiptera), suspensorial apodemes, q.v. (Tuxen, after Schaefer).

laterosternal, to the side of the sternum (T-B); of or pertaining to a laterosternite (T-B).

laterosternal shelf, in ♀ Blattaria, lateral elements of abdominal sternum VIII twisted ventrally at medial ends and reversed from original position, forming the base of a dorsally invaginated anterior wall between the much enlarged abdominal sterna VII and VIII (Alsop, pers. comm., after McKittrick).

laterosternite(s), the lateral part of a definitive thoracic sternum, apparently derived from the sternopleurite of the subcoxa; a small sclerite occurring in the pleural region of the abdomen (actually a pleurite, in the sense that it lies in the pleural region) (T-B, after Snodgrass); in Isoptera and Dermaptera, separate lateral plates of the sides of the eusternum (T-B, after Imms); in ♀ Ensifera (Orthoptera), a small sclerite in the pleural wall above the subgenital plate (Tuxen); in Heteroptera (Hemiptera), lateral subdivisions of sterna of pregenital abdominal segments (e.g. in some aquatic bugs) (Štys, pers. comm.); in some adult Ichneumonidae (Hymenoptera), separate lateral piece of abdominal sternite (Gauld and Bolton).

laterosternite IX, in ♂ Chironomidae, lateral sclerite on each side of abdominal tergum IX (Saether); in ♀ Chironomidae (Diptera), gonocoxite IX, q.v. (Saether).

laterostigmatal, of or pertaining to the side, immediately above the spiracle (T-B).

laterotergal, to the side of the tergum (T-B).

laterotergite(s), a lateral sclerotization of the dorsum distinct from a principal median tergite (T-B, after Snodgrass); in Heteroptera

(Hemiptera), see dorsal and ventral laterotergites, q.v. (Tuxen, after Dupuis); in ♀ Panorpidae (Mecoptera), additional side plates on abdominal segments VII and VIII (Tuxen; Ferris and Rees); in adult Diptera, the lateral portion of the postnotum on each side of the mediotergite (McAlpine); in adult Culicidae (Diptera), the lateral part of abdominal tergum I when more or less distinctly separated from the median dorsal part (Harbach and Knight, after Belkin); see paratergite.

laterotergite IX, in ♂ Chironomidae (Diptera), laterosternite IX, q.v. (Saether).

lateroventral, lateral and below the median horizontal plane (T-B; Christiansen and Bellinger).

lateroventral ambulatory appendages, generalized or primitive legs, or any evaginations which function as structures for walking (T-B).

lateroventral curved lobes (of apodemal strut), in ♂ Siphonaptera, lobi fulcri laterales, q.v. (Tuxen, after Traub).

lateroventral metathoracic carina, in Odonata, the dividing line between the metepimera and the metasterna (T-B).

lateroventral sclerite, in Acridoidea (Orthoptera), ventral lobe, when sclerotised, q.v. (transl. "sclerites lateroventraux" from Amedegnato).

lateroverted, displaced toward the side of the body (T-B).

latescent, becoming obscure or hidden (T-B).

latex, a milky exudation; specifically, the milky sap of numerous plants, such as the Asclepiadaceae, Euphorbiaceae, and Moraceae (T-B).

Latreille's segment, in adult Apocrita (Hymenoptera), propodeum, q.v. (T-B).

latticed, clathrate, q.v. (T-B; Harris).

latus, the side of the insect body; broad (T-B).

latuscula, ommatidia, q.v. (T-B, after J. B. Smith); in adult Diptera, notopleuron, q.v. (T-B, after MacGillivray).

Laurasia, a formerly unified land mass, embracing what are now North America, Europe, and Asia (excluding the Indian subcontinent) (Allaby); see Gondwanaland.

Lauterborn organs, in larval Chironomidae (Diptera), compound organ at apex of second antennal segment, consisting of a peg sensillum and 2 series of digitiform, thin-walled extensions (Saether).

Lauxanioidea, superfamily within the Schizophora (Diptera: Brachycera), including the Lauxaniidae, Chamaemyiidae, and Periscelididae, being sometimes included within the Sciomyzoidea (Borror et al.); superfamily within the Schizophora-Acalyptratae within the infraorder Muscomorpha (Diptera: Brachycera), including the Lauxaniidae and Chamaemyiidae (McAlpine).

law of disharmony, allometry, q.v. (T-B).

law of priority, Principle of Priority, q.v. (T-B).

LC$_{50}$, median lethal concentration, q.v. (Pfadt).

LD$_{50}$, median lethal dose, q.v. (Steinhaus and Martignoni).

leaf insect, in Phasmida, members of the Phylloidea (Carlberg, pers. comm.).

leaf miner, an insect that lives in and feeds upon the mesophyll between the upper and lower surfaces of a leaf (Borror et al.).

leaf petiole gall, round gall of leaf petioles of poplar trees caused by *Pemphigus populitransversus* (Hemiptera: Sternorrhyncha: Aphidoidea) (Borror et al.); see vagabond gall.

leaf-shaped appendages, in ♀ Phasmida, funnel-shaped appendages, q.v. (Tuxen).

leaf-shaped ventral sclerite, in ♂ Siphonaptera, virga ventralis, q.v. (Tuxen, after Sharif).

leafhoppers, members of the families Cicadellidae and Eurymelidae (Hemiptera: Auchenorrhyncha: Cicadelloidea) (Woodward et al., in CSIRO; O'Brien, pers. comm.).

leaflet of aedeagus, in ♂ Anophelinae (Diptera: Culicidae), elongate leaflike structure at the apex of the aedeagus, being homologous with the ventral arms of *Culex* (Harbach and Knight, after Knight and Laffoon).

learning, acquisition of information or patterns of behavior other than by genetic inheritance, or the modification of genetically acquired information or behavior as the result of experience (Allaby); see conditioning, habituation, latent learning, time sense, and trial-and-error learning.

lecithal egg, relatively large, yolky eggs, being physiologically "expensive" for the ♀ (Gauld and Bolton); see alecithal egg.

lectoallotype, a specimen from the original material designated later than the original example, and of the opposite sex to that of the lectotype (Tulloch); see allotype.

lectotype, a syntype designated as the single name-bearing type specimen subsequent to the establishment of a nominal species or subspecies (T-B; ICZN).

leg, in Hexapoda, one of the paired appendages of the thorax, used for locomotion and support, usually consisting of the coxa, trochanter, femur, tibia and pretarsus (T-B; Harbach and Knight); see proleg.

legal control, control of pests through the enactment of legislation that enforces control measures or imposes regulations, such as quarantines, to prevent the introduction or spread of pests (Pfadt).

legion, a group of genera, subequal to a tribe (T-B).

legionary ant, army ant, q.v. (Wilson).

legnum, the margin of a squama (T-B).

legula(e), in adult Lepidoptera, the flexible straplike or tonguelike outgrowths bordering the food channel of the haustellum (Davis); in ♂ Tenthredinoidea (Hymenoptera), main body of distal portion of independent gonapophysis IX when distal rhachis is separated from gonopod (Tuxen, after E. L. Smith).

leishmaniasis, infection with or disease caused by protozoans of the genus *Leishmania*, commmonly transmitted by sand flies of the genus *Phlebotomus* (Diptera: Psychodidae) (Colless and McAlpine, in CSIRO; Allaby); see espundia, kala-azar, and oriental sore.

lek, a specific site where males display and compete for the attention of females, e.g., Hawaiian *Drosophila* (Diptera: Drosophilidae), euglossine bees (Hymenoptera: Apidae: Bombinae: Euglossini), Asian fireflies (Coleoptera: Lampyridae), and certain dragonflies (Odonata) (Matthews and Matthews).

lemniscate, ribbonlike (T-B); in the form of an "8" (T-B).

Lemurian Realm, in biogeography, Madagascar (T-B).

lens, corneal lens, q.v., or crystalline lens, q.v. (T-B, after Snodgrass; Chapman).

lenticular, lenticulate, lenticulatus (Latin), lens-shaped; resembling a lentil in shape; double-convex (T-B).

lentic, pertaining to or living in still water (lakes, ponds or swamps) (T-B, after Needham; Atkins).

lenticular organ, in Acridoidea (Orthoptera), a small organ situated at dorsodistal angle of one of the distal antennal articles (Key).

lentigen layer, corneagen layer, q.v. (T-B).

Lepidoptera, order within the Holometabola (Insecta), including moths and butterflies, characterized by adults with 2 pairs of membranous wings clothed on both surfaces with usually overlapping scales and possessing eruciform larvae (Common, in CSIRO).

lepidopteran, a member of the order Lepidoptera (T-B).

lepidopteric acid, a green pigment obtained from the wing scales of Lepidoptera, being a derivative of uric acid (T-B); see lepidotic acid.

lepidopterin, a protein decomposition product found in Lepidoptera (T-B).

lepidopterous, of or pertaining to the Lepidoptera (T-B).

lepidote, lepidotic, set with minute scales (T-B).

lepidotic acid, a yellow pigment obtained from scales of butterflies (Lepidoptera), a derivative of uric acid (T-B); see lepidopteric acid.

lepis, a scale (T-B).

lepismoid, having the shape or appearance of a silverfish or bristletail of the family Lepismatidae (Zygentoma), possessing filamentous caudal cerci, slender many-jointed antennae, and a subcylindrical or depressed body sometimes covered with shiny scales (Peterson).

Lepismoidea, Zygentoma, q.v. (Boudreaux, after Handlirsch).

leprosy, a chronic, transmissable disease caused by a specific bacterium, *Mycobacterium leprae* (Pfadt).

leprous leprosus (Latin), scaly (T-B; R. W. Brown).

leptiform, campodeiform, q.v. (T-B).

Leptophlebioidea, superfamily of Ephemeroptera, including only the family Leptophlebiidae (Landa and Soldán).

leptophragmata (sing., **leptophragma**), specialized cells attaching the cryptonephridial Malpighian tubules to the perinephric membrane within perinephric cavity (Chapman).

Leptopodoidea, superfamily of Heteroptera (Hemiptera) within the infraorder Leptopodomorpha including the intertidal Omaniidae and largely terrestrial Leptopodidae (Schuh); see Leptopodomorpha.

Leptopodomorpha, infraorder of Heteroptera (Hemiptera) including the littoral, intertidal, and sometimes terrestrial predators of the superfamilies Saldoidea and Leptopodoidea (Schuh).

leptos (Greek), fine; small; thin; delicate (T-B; R. W. Brown).

lerp, in nymphal Psyllidae (Hemiptera: Sternorrhyncha), a delicate and complex shelter produced from a carbohydrate secretion from the anus (Norris and Woodward et al., in CSIRO); see scale.

lesser ampulla, in certain adult Calyptratae (Diptera), e.g., Calliphoridae and Sarcophagidae, swollen anterior part of pleural wing process (McAlpine); see greater ampulla.

lesser ocellar bristles, in Diptera, 3 to 12 pairs of bristles, in 2, sometimes 4, parallel lines beginning very close to the greater ocellars, q.v.; post-ocellars (T-B, after Comstock).

lesion, in invertebrate pathology, a wound or injury (Steinhaus and Martignoni); any more or less circumscribed pathologic change in the tissues, including a change or loss of function (Steinhaus and Martignoni); see biochemical lesion.

Lestinoidea, superfamily within the suborder Zygoptera (Odonata), including the Lestidae and Chlorolestidae, characterized by adults with 3 or fewer antenodal crossveins, postnodal crossveins aligned with crossveins behind them, and first anal vein (1A) fully developed (O'Farrell, in CSIRO).

lestobiosis, in ants (Hymenoptera: Formicidae), the relation in which colonies of a small species nest in the walls of the nest of a larger species and enter the chambers of the larger species to prey on brood or rob the food stores (T-B, after Forel; Wilson).

Lestoidea, Lestinoidea, q.v. (Hennig).

lethal yellowing, a disease of coconut and other palms transmitted by *Myndus crudus* Van Duzee (Hemiptera: Auchenorrhyncha: Fulgoroidea: Cixiidae) (O'Brien, pers. comm.).

Lethane 384 (trade name), a synthetic insecticide; a thiocyanate, β-butoxy-β'-thiocyano-diethyl ether; moderately toxic to mammals, acute oral LD_{50} for rats 90 mg/kg (Pfadt).

lethargic, torpid; inactive (T-B).

letisimulation, thanatosis, q.v. (Tulloch).

lettuce necrotic yellows, disease of lettuce plants caused by rhabdovirus transmitted propagatively by the aphid *Hyperomyzus lactucae* (L.) (Hemiptera: Sternorrhyncha: Aphididae) (Borror et al.).

leucine, $C_6H_{13}NO_2$, an essential amino acid in the diet of insects (T-B; Gilmour, in CSIRO).

leucoblast, prohemocyte, q.v. (Tulloch).

leucocyte, plasmatocyte, q.v. (T-B; Tulloch).

leucodiscs, in ♂ Siphonaptera, circular cuticular structures with convex surfaces that superficially resemble placoids, and occur on the head and other parts of the body (Rothschild and Traub).

leucopoietic organ, hemopoietic organ, q.v. (Tulloch).

leucopterine, pterine pigment producing white coloration in the wing scales of Lepidoptera, esp. Pieridae, being a derivative of uric acid (Tulloch; Chapman).

levation, the raising of an appendage or part of an appendage (T-B; Chapman).

levator, levator muscle, any muscle used in raising an appendage (T-B).

leveling, in soil nesting species, the removal or dispersing of conspicuous mounds near the nest entry (Matthews and Matthews).

lever apparatus, in ♂ Heteroptera (Hemiptera), articulatory apparatus, q.v. (Tuxen, after Ekblom).

levers of penis, in ♂ Siphonaptera, virga penis, q.v. (Tuxen).

levigate, a smooth surface, sometimes somewhat shiny or polished; without elevations or depressions (T-B; Harris, after R. W. Brown, Marchant and Charles, and Funk); see glabrous, nitid, and politus.

levulose, fructose, q.v. (T-B).

Libelluloidea, superfamily within the suborder Anisoptera (Odonata), including the Libellulidae, Corduliidae, and Synthemidae, characterized by adults with triangles in fore- and hind wings dissimilar and eyes touching, and nymphs with a deeply concave, ladle-shaped labium (O'Farrell, in CSIRO).

liber (Latin), free (T-B).

lice (sing., **louse**), members of the order Phthiraptera (Calaby, in CSIRO).

life cycle, the series of developmental changes undergone by the individuals comprising a population, including fertilization, reproduction, and the death, and the replacement of those individuals by a new generation (Allaby).

life history, a detailed record of a life cycle.

life stage, any distinctive period in the life of an insect, e.g., egg, larva, pupa, or adult in holometabolous insects (T-B); see instar and stadium.

ligament(s), a band or sheet of tough fibrous tissue between 2 parts or segments (T-B); in ♂ Heteroptera (Hemiptera), ligamentary processes, q.v. (Tuxen, after Singh-Pruthi); in ♂ Zygaenidae (Lepidoptera), saccus, q.v. (Tuxen, after Haaf).

ligamentary processes, in ♂ Heteroptera (Hemiptera), sclerotized postero-ventral prolongations of basal plates, primitively paired, but often secondarily more or less coalescent (Tuxen, after Dupuis and Carvalho).

ligamentous processes, in ♂ Saldidae (Hemiptera: Heteroptera), ligamentary processes, q.v. (Tuxen, after Cobben).

light-adapted eye, a compound eye adapted for high intensities of light (Chapman); see dark-adapted eye.

light-compass reaction, orientation so locomotion occurs at a fixed angle relative to light rays (Matthews and Matthews); the ability to move in a straight line by keeping the sun in a definite position on the retina of the eye, e.g., in ants (Hymenoptera: Formicidae) (Leftwich).

light-producing organs, luminescent organs distributed over the entire body or concentrated in particular areas such as on the head or the tip of the abdomen (Leftwich; Chapman); see luminescence.

ligneous, ligneus (Latin), **ligniform,** woodlike; woody; made of wood (T-B).

lignicolous, living in wood (T-B).

lignin, complex corss-linked polymer comprising phenylpropanoid units found in many plant cell walls (Allaby).

lignivorous, xylophagous, q.v. (T-B).

ligula (pl., **ligulae),** collective name for glossae and paraglossae, whether fused or separate (Leftwich; Harbach and Knight; Chapman); in ♂ Odonata, strongly curved and channeled process arched over stem of prophallus (Tuxen); in Aleyrododae (Hemiptera: Sternorrhyncha), lingula, q.v. (Tuxen, after Pesson); in adult Coleoptera, elyral ligula, q.v. (T-B); in ♂ Coleoptera, flagellum, q.v. (Tuxen, after Holdhaus); in ♂ Papilionidae (Lepidoptera), scaphium, q.v. (Tuxen, after Berio); in adult Culicidae (Diptera), the sharp-pointed lobe occurring distally on the midline of the labium between the labella (Harbach and Knight, after Becher); in larval Chironomidae (Diptera), anterior mesodorsal appendage of prementum consisting of fused glossae and perhaps paraglossae, being a conspicuous sclerotized, toothed, internal plate in Tanypodinae, but mostly smaller, often much serrated or deeply divided in other subfamilies (Saether).

ligulate, ligulatus, strap-shaped; linear, much longer than broad (T-B).

ligulate sclerite, in larval Muscomorpha (Diptera), rod-shaped sclerites in the position of the subhypostomal sclerites, and possibly homologous with them (Ferrar).

liguloid arch, in larval *Calliphora* (Diptera: Calliphoridae), labial sclerite, q.v. (Teskey, after Miller, in McAlpine).

lilaceous, lilaceus, lilacinous, lilacinus, lilac-colored, i.e., pale violet-blue (T-B); see indigo.

limaciform, having the form of a *Limax* (Gastropoda) or slug (T-B); see limaciform larva.

limaciform larva, a legless larva having the form of a *Limax* or slug (Gastropoda), e.g., larva of some sawflies (Hymenoptera: Symphyta) and some moths such as Limacodidae (Lepidoptera) (T-B; Leftwich); see slug caterpillar.

limb, leg, q.v. (T-B).

limb basis, the primary basal segment of an appendage supporting the telopodite; sometimes subdivided into a proximal subcoxa (pleuropodite or pleuron), and a distal coxa; coxopodite (T-B, after Snodgrass).

limbate, limbatus, with a margin or limb of a different color (T-B).

limbus (Latin), border; fringe; hem; edge (T-B; R. W. Brown); in Cicadidae (Hemiptera: Sternorrhyncha), the area along the outer and posterior margin of the wing beyond the closed cells (T-B, after J. B. Smith).

lime-sulfur, an insecticide and fungicide made by boiling sulfur and lime together in water, which react to form both soluble and insoluble salts of calcium polysulfide; irritating to eyes, nose, and skin (Pfadt).

limnology, the study of the fauna of waters (T-B).

limophagous, mud-eating (T-B).

limpet, close-fitting to stones or other objects in the water, after the fashion of the small mollusk of that name (T-B).

limpid, clear and transparent; applied to wings and ornamentation (T-B).

limuloid, tear-drop shaped (Matthews and Matthews).

lindane, $C_6H_6Cl_6$, a synthetic insecticide; a chlorinated hydrocarbon containing 99% or more of the gamma isomer of BHC; somewhat more toxic to mammals than DDT, acute oral LD_{50} for rats 88 to 125 mg/kg (Pfadt).

line, a narrow streak or stripe (T-B); as a term of measurement, one-twelfth of an inch (T-B).

line of anastomosis, in adult Trichoptera, cord, q.v. (Betten).

line precedence, occurrence of a name on an earlier line of the same page than another name for the same taxon (Mayr).

linea (Latin), line, q.v. (T-B).

linea calva, in many adult Aphelinidae, Encyrtidae, and Eupelmidae (Hymenoptera), an oblique hairless strip of wing membrane running from the stigmal vein to the hind margin (Gauld and Bolton).

linea ventralis, in Protura, the ventral groove that originates at the base of the labium and extends backward a short distance behind the plicae orales, not reaching the cervix (Tuxen); in Collembola, the ventral groove originates at the labial base and extends backward to the apex of the ventral tube (Snider, pers. comm.).

linear, straight; in the form of a straight line (T-B).

linear mine, a mine that is narrow and only a little winding (T-B); see mine.

lineate, lineated, lineatus (Latin), longitudinally marked with raised or depressed parallel lines; with linear marks (T-B; Harris, after Munz).

lineola (pl., **lineolae**), a delicate fine line (T-B).

lineolate, finely lineate, longitudinally marked with very fine raised or deep lines (Harris, after Marchant and Charles).

lineolet, lineola, q.v. (T-B).

lingua, tongue, q.v., or hypopharynx, q.v. (T-B); in Collembola, Diplura, and Archaeognatha, a median lobe of the hypopharynx between superlinguae (T-B; Mackerras, in CSIRO); in adult Lepidoptera and Diptera, proboscis, q.v. (T-B; Leftwich); in larval Chironomidae (Diptera), ligula, q.v. (Saether); in adult Hymenoptera, glossa, q.v. (T-B).

lingua spiralis, in adult Lepidoptera, proboscis, q.v. (T-B).

lingual, connected with the tongue; of or pertaining to the tongue (T-B).

lingual glands, in Psocoptera and Phthiraptera (Amblycera and Ischnocera), lingual sclerites, q.v., on the ventral aspect of the hypopharynx, connected to the cibarial sclerite by filamentous ducts and involved in the uptake of atmospheric water (T-B, after Imms; Rudolph; Lyal).

lingual sclerites, paired sclerites of the hypopharynx hinged with suspensory sclerites and receiving muscles from the tentorium and the labium (Chapman).

Linguatulida, Pentastomida, q.v. (Borror et al.).

linguiform, tongue-shaped; linear, with the extremities obtusely rounded (T-B).

lingula (pl., **lingulae**), lingual sclerite, q.v. (T-B, after MacGillivray); in Aleyrodidae (Hemiptera: Sternorrhyncha), the fingerlike or elongate structure situated under the operculum and within the vasiform orifice (Stoetzel, in Stehr); in Auchenorrhyncha (Hemiptera), anal style, q.v. (Tuxen); in ♂ *Melitaea* (Lepidoptera: Nymphalidae), tonguelike structure overhanging and sometimes completely closing the "penis groove", formed from lateral margin of anellus, posterior to base of condyle, being rolled mesad and caudad (Tuxen, after Higgins); in ♂ Syrphidae (Diptera), unpaired median distal process of hypandrium (Tuxen, after Fluke); in bees (Hymenoptera: Apoidea), glossa, q.v. (T-B, after Leuckart, J. B. Smith).

lining membrane of theca, in ♂ Heteroptera (Hemiptera), basiconjunctiva, q.v. (Tuxen, after Christophers and Cragg).

link plates, in adult Siphonaptera, small lateral sclerites linking the head to the prothorax, the prothorax to the mesothorax, the mesothorax to the metathorax, and the metathorax to the first abdominal segment in some species (Lewis, pers. comm.).

linkage, the association of genes that results from their being on the same chromosome (T-B; Allaby); see sex linkage.

Linnaean hierarchy, a structure of categorical ranks for taxa where each category except the lowest includes one or more subordinate categories (Mayr); see hierarchy.

Linnaean tautonymy, the identical spelling of a new generic or subgeneric name and a pre-1758 name, cited as a synonym of only one of the species or subspecies originally included in that genus (ICZN).

linthal bees, white head, q.v. (Steinhaus and Martignoni).

liocyte, chromophile, q.v. (Tulloch, after Jones).

liocytoid, chromophile, q.v. (Tulloch, after Jones).

lip, in ♂ Heteroptera (Hemiptera), hypandrium, q.v. (Tuxen, after Sharp).

lipase, enzyme capable of breaking down fats by splitting the ester linkages to form free fatty acids and glycerol (T-B; Gilmour, in CSIRO; Chapman).

lipid, fat, q.v. (Gilmour, in CSIRO).

lipid epicuticle, the outer portion of the epicuticle of larvae of the higher Diptera (Tulloch, after Richards).

lipochromous, without color (T-B).

Lipognatha, hypothesized monophyletic group within the Phthiraptera, including the Rhynchophthirina and the Anoplura (Boudreaux).

lipoid, a fat or fatlike substance, insoluble in nonpolar solvents, utilized by living organisms (T-B).

lipolytic, of or pertaining to the enzyme lipase; having the action of lipase (T-B).

lipomicrons, minute fat particles found in the blood of insects (T-B).

lipoproteins, diglycerides associated with proteins found in the hemolymph (Chapman).

Lipoptera, Mallophaga, q.v. (T-B).

liquefaction, conversion into liquid (T-B).

listel, in Collembola, the central partition of the postantennal organ, dividing the structure into 2 halves (Christiansen and Bellinger).

Lithobiomorpha, order within the Anamorpha (Chilopoda), including the stone centipedes, characterized by spiracles paired and located laterally, each leg-bearing segment with a separate tergite, antennae and legs relatively short, and eyes not compound, but consisting of single ocelli or groups of ocelli, or absent (Borror et al.).

littoral, in freshwater ecosystems, in shallow water where light penetration extends to the bottom sediments which are colonized by rooted plants (Allaby); in marine ecosystems, intertidal, q.v. (Allaby); inhabiting the shore; see riparian.

litura (Latin), (pl., **liturae**), a blot (R. W. Brown); an indistinct spot with pale margins, appearing blotted (T-B).

liturate, lituratus, marked with litura (T-B).

livid, lividus (Latin), lead-colored, i.e., bluish-black (T-B, after Kirby and Spence; R. W. Brown).

loaiasis, disease of man in Africa caused by the roundworm *Loa loa* (Nematoda) and transmitted by *Chrysops* spp. (Diptera: Tabanidae) (Colless and McAlpine, in CSIRO; Borror et al.); see filariasis.

lobate, lobatus, with lobes; divided by deep, undulating and successive incisions (T-B).

lobe(s), lobus (Latin), a rounded projection or protuberance (T-B; R. W. Brown); in ♀ Neuropteroidea, stylus, q.v. (Tuxen, after Ferris and Pennebaker); in ♂ Lepidoptera, valvae, q.v. (Tuxen, after Scudder and Burgess); see lobus.

lobe of pygidium, in Diaspididae (Hemiptera: Sternorrhyncha), one of the projections of the pygidium (Kosztarab, pers. comm.).

lobes of aedeagus, in ♂ Siphonaptera, modifications and sclerotizations of the hollow end chamber of the aedeagus (Rothschild and Traub).

lobes of ovipositor, in ♀ Lepidoptera, papillae anales, q.v. (Tuxen, after Pierce).

lobes of phallus, in ♂ Grylloblattodea, phallomeres, q.v. (Tuxen, after Walker).

lobes of posterior edge of sternite VIII, in ♀ Chironomidae, gonoapophysis VIII, q.v. (Saether).

lobes of pronotum, in Orthoptera, the spaces or areas formed by 3 transverse impressions on the pronotum (T-B).

lobi, pleural of lobus, q.v.

lobi antici (sing., **lobus anticus**), in ♀ Zoraptera, paired lobes beneath and anterior to vulva (Tuxen, after Silvestri).

lobi apicales penis (sing., **lobus apicalis penis**), in ♂ *Buthalis, Argynnis* (Lepidoptera: Nymphalidae), apical lobate dilations and processes of aedoeagus (Tuxen, after Petersen).

lobi convergentes (sing., **lobus convergens**), in ♀ Zoraptera, paired lobes beneath and lateroposterior to vulva (Tuxen, after Silvestri).

lobi fulcri laterales (sing., **lobus fulcri lateralis**), in ♂ Siphonaptera, paired ventrolateral lobes of fulcrum (Tuxen, after Smit).

lobi hypopygiales, in ♂ Auchenorrhyncha (Hemiptera), lateral lobes of pygofer, q.v. (Tuxen).

lobi inferi (sing., **lobus inferus**), in ♀ Zoraptera, paired lobes behind vulva (Tuxen, after Silvestri).

lobi laterales (sing., **lobus lateralis**), in ♀ Zoraptera, paired lobes beneath and lateral to vulva (Tuxen, after Silvestri); in ♂ Auchenorrhyncha (Hemiptera), lateral lobes, q.v. (Tuxen); in ♀ Auchenorrhyncha (Hemiptera), lateral lobes of pygofer, q.v. (Tuxen); in ♂ Siphonaptera, lobi fulcri laterales, q.v. (Tuxen, after Peus).

lobi postici (sing., **lobus posticus**), in ♀ Zoraptera, paired lobes behind vulva (Tuxen, after Silvestri).

lobi sublaterales (sing., **lobus sulateralis**), in ♀ Zoraptera, paired lobes beneath and lateral to vulva, posterior to lobi laterales (Tuxen, after Silvestri).

lobiform, shaped like a lobe (T-B).

loboids, in ♂ Siphonaptera, lobes of aeadeagus, q.v. (Tuxen).

Lobopodia, hypothesized monophyletic group including the Onychophora and Arthropoda (Boudreaux, after Snodgrass).

lobopodia (sing., **lobopodium**), in Onychophora, ventral, paired, non-articulated, lobelike, locomotory appendages having both extrinsic and intrinsic muscles (Boudreaux).

lobulate, divided into, or with many small lobes or lobules (T-B).

lobuli vaginales (sing., **lobulus vaginalis**), in ♀ Pieridae (Lepidoptera), more or less sclerotized folds, processes, etc. of abdominal sternum VIII and the intersegmental membrane of segments VII–VIII especially on either side of ostium bursae (Tuxen, after Kusnezov).

lobulus, in adult Diptera, alula, q.v., of wing (T-B; Saether); in some adult Hymenoptera, claval lobe, q.v., of jugal lobe, q.v., of hind wing (T-B).

lobulus basalis (pl., **lobuli basales**), in ♂ Lycaenidae (Lepidoptera), the more or less united and moveable sacculi (Tuxen, after Toxopeus).

lobus (Latin) (pl., **lobi**), lobe, q.v. (T-B; R. W. Brown); in ♂ Siphonaptera, the dorsal (or anterior) projection (lobus 1) or the ventral (or posterior) projection (lobus 2) of a sinuate processus basimeris ventralis (Tuxen, after Smit).

lobus externus (pl., **lobi externi**), in Protura, 2 long, pointed or hook-shaped lobes on the maxilla usually interpreted as laciniae, located on the stipes, the lobus internus appearing between them (Tuxen).

lobus fulcri medialis (pl., **lobi fulcri mediales**), in ♂ Siphonaptera, central sclerite, q.v. (Tuxen, after Smit).

lobus inferior, lacinia, q.v., of maxilla (T-B).

lobus internus, in Protura, a lobe on the maxilla usually interpreted as a galea, distally located on the stipes, weakly sclerotized, long and pointed in *Acerentomon* spp., broad and digitate in *Eosentomon* spp. (Tuxen).

lobus maxillae, galea, q.v. (T-B).

lobus medianus, in ♀ Zoraptera, unpaired lobe behind vulva (Tuxen, after Silvestri).

lobus papillatus, in ♂ Caelifera (Orthoptera), the inner process of a divided lophus (Tuxen).

lobus portae, in ♀ Ischnocera (Phthiraptera), subgenital lobe, q.v. (Tuxen, after von Kéler; Lyal).

lobus superior, galea, q.v. (T-B).

local population, the individuals of a given locality which potentially form a single interbreeding community (Mayr); see deme.

loco citato (Latin), from the same source cited previously; abbrev., l.c. (T-B).

locomotion, coordinated movement of the body (Chapman).

locomotor, locomotory, q.v. (T-B).

locomotory, of or pertaining to locomotion or movement from place to place; serving for locomotion (T-B).

locomotory ridge, in Diptera larvae, creeping welt, q.v. (Teskey, in McAlpine).

locomotory spinules, in Diptera larvae, spinules on the prolegs (Teskey, in McAlpine).

locus, the position of a gene along a chromosome (Mayr).

locusts, members of the family Acrididae (Orthoptera: Acridoidea) that at times form dense, strongly migrating swarms (Key, in CSIRO).

lodge, to throw or beat down, as growing grain (Pfadt).

lodix (pl., **lodices**), in ♀ Noctuidae (Lepidoptera), median, caudad structure of abdominal sternum VII more or less covering sterigma and sinus vaginalis (Tuxen, after Pierce).

logistic curve, sigmoid curve of normal population growth with population size on the y axis and time on the x axis (Borrror et al.).

logotype, type species, q.v.; species subsequently selected as the type of a genus (O'Brien, pers. comm.; Metcalf and VanDuzee); see haplotype and orthotype.

Lonchopteroidea, superfamily within the series Aschiza within the infraorder Muscomorpha (Diptera: Brachycera), including only the family Lonchopteridae, possessing adults with rather lanceolate, pointed wings with R_{4+5} terminating at apex and crossveins confined to base; larvae retaining maxillae and a vestigial head capsule which is not withdrawn into an atrium; pupa coarctate (Colless and McAlpine, in CSIRO; McAlpine).

long-horned grasshopper, a member of the superfamily Tettigonioidea (Orthoptera) (Key, in CSIRO); see katydid.

long-tongued bees, bees (Hymenoptera: Apoidea), including the Megachilidae, Apidae, and Anthophoridae, in which the glossa of adults is elongated and pointed, usually being longer than the prementum (Riek, in CSIRO); see short-tongued bees.

longicorn, having the antennae as long as or longer than the body (T-B); specifically a member of the Cerambycidae (Coleoptera) (T-B).

Longicornia, family Cerambycidae (Coleoptera), i.e., long-horned beetles (T-B).

longipennate, long winged (T-B).

longitudinal, in the direction of the long axis (T-B).

longitudinal furrow, in adult Chironomidae (Diptera), furrow on median line of postnotum (Saether).

longitudinal moulting suture, in Aleyrodidae (Hemiptera: Sternorrhyncha), the longitudinal suture on the median thoracic dorsum, extending posteriorly at the transverse moulting suture (Gill); see dorsal ecdysial line.

longitudinal ridge, in adult Lepidoptera, prominent elevated structures usually composed of overlapping scutes extending from the base to the apex on the obverse side of a scale (Downey and Allyn).

longitudinal sensillum, in adult Chalcidoidea (Hymenoptera), multiporous plate sensillum, q.v. (Gauld and Bolton).

longitudinal veins, wing veins that normally extend lengthwise either directly from the base or as branches of one that originates there (T-B).

longus (Latin), long (T-B).

loop, in ♂ frenate moths (Lepidoptera), retinaculum, q.v. (T-B).

looped, having a closed or nearly closed curve at the end, like a loop (T-B).

looper, larval Geometridae or other Lepidoptera in which some or all of the middle abdominal prolegs are wanting, and which moves by bringing tail to thorax, forming a loop of the intervening segments (T-B); see semilooper.

looplure, synthetic sex pheromone of the ♀ cabbage looper, *Trichoplusia ni* (Lepidoptera: Noctuidae); (Z)-7-dodecenyl acetate, q.v. (Pfadt).

Lophocornonia, an infraorder of Lepidoptera, including only the superfamily Lophocoronoidea (Common).

Lophocoronoidea, only superfamily of infraorder Lophocoronina (Lepidoptera) containing one family Lophocoronidae; adults small, without ocelli, mandibles rudimentary without muscles, proboscis short without muscles, homoneurous wing venation, scales of primitive type, and ♀ with piercing ovipositor (Common).

lophus (pl., **lophi**), in ♂ Caelifera (Orthoptera), an undivided or divided posterior process of epiphallus (Tuxen).

lorium enation disease, disease of grass (*Lorium*) caused by a reovirus (*Fijivirus*) transmitted propagatively by *Javesella* (Hemiptera: Auchenorrhyncha: Delphacidae) (Nault and Ammar).

Lorsban (trade name), chloropyrifos, q.v. (Pfadt).

Lorsch disease, a disease of larval may beetles (*Melolontha* spp., *Amphimallon* spp, and other Scarabaeidae [Coleoptera]), caused by *Rickettsiella melolonthae* (Rickettsiaceae) (Steinhaus and Martignoni).

lorum (pl., **lora**), the chitinous bands connecting the submentum with the cardo of the maxilla (T-B, after Comstock); the submentum; small cords upon which the base of the proboscis is seated (T-B, after Say); the anterior part of the genae at the edge of the mouth (T-B); in Hemiptera, maxillary plate, q.v. (T-B; Woodward et al., in CSIRO); in adult Diptera, maxillary tendon, q.v. (T-B); in certain Diptera, the corneous processes to which the muscles for flexing the mouth are attached, in that sense, the palpifer of the maxilla (T-B); in adult Apoidea (Hymenoptera), V-shaped submentum supporting the elongate proboscis (T-B, after Imms; Borror et al.; Leftwich).

lotic, pertaining to or living in moving water (streams and rivers) (T-B, after Needham; Adkins, pers. comm.).

louse, sing. lice, q.v. (Borror et al.).

lower appendage of IXth abdominal segment, in ♂ Mecoptera, hypovalva, q.v. (Tuxen, after Hobby and Killington).

lower appendages, in ♂ Mecoptera, hypovalvae, q.v. (Tuxen, after Esben-Petersen).

lower arm of clasper, in ♂ Heteroptera (Hemiptera), paramere, q.v. Tuxen, after McDonald).

Lower Austral Zone, warm temperate North America (T-B).

lower calypter, in adult Diptera, the proximal calypter of the wing, typically situated below the upper calypter, being especially large in Tabanidae, Acroceridae, and Calyptratae (Harbach and Knight; McAlpine).

lower endomere, in ♂ Phthiraptera, unpaired endodermal sclerite lying ventral to and between base of parameres (Tuxen, after Cummings).

lower face, in adult Hymenoptera, area of face between the mouth margin and margin of toruli (Gauld and Bolton).

lower facial margin, in adult Diptera, the lower margin of the face (McAlpine).

lower field, in Orthoptera, costal field, q.v., of tegmen (T-B).

lower fronto-orbital bristles, in Diptera, those on the lower part of frons, above the antennae and along the orbit (T-B).

lower margin, costal margin, q.v., of tegmen (T-B, after Thomas).

lower mesepimeral scale, in adult Culicidae (Diptera), one of the scales occurring in a group on the ventroanterior quarter of the mesanepimeron (Harbach and Knight).

lower mesepimeral seta, in adult Culicidae (Diptera), one of the setae occurring in groups on the anterior, middle and/or posterior area of the mesanepimeron below the level of the metathoracic spiracle (Harbach and Knight, after Edwards).

lower meskatepisternal scale, in adult Culicidae (Diptera), one of the scales occurring in a group located immediately in front of the lower meskatepisternal setae (Harbach and Knight).

lower meskatepisternal seta, in adult Culicidae (Diptera), one of the setae occurring in more or less ventral line along the posterior margin of the meskatepisternum at about the level of the mesotrochantin (Harbach and Knight).

lower ocular seta, in adult Culicidae (Diptera), one of the setae occurring along the lateral margin of the compound eye (Harbach and Knight, after Knight).

lower penis cover, in ♂ Hydroptilidae (Trichoptera), an unpaired basal part of inferior appendage (Tuxen).

lower penis lobe, in ♂ Odonata, terminal curled or T-shaped portion of flagella (Tuxen, after Kimmins).

lower plate, in ♀ Psyllidae (Hemiptera: Sternorrhyncha), ventral plate, q.v. (Tuxen).

lower pleurotergite, in adult Culicidae (Diptera), the lower division of the pleurotergite located immediately above the metathoracic spiracle (Harbach and Knight).

lower pleurotergite apodeme, in adult Culicidae (Diptera), the apodeme borne along the upper margin of the lower pleurotergite (Harbach and Knight).

lower postpronotal scale, in adult Culicidae (Diptera), one of the scales occurring in a group on the ventral part of the postpronotum (Harbach and Knight).

lower prealar scale, in adult Culicidae (Diptera), one of the scales occurring in a group on the posterior mesanepisternum below the prealar setae (Harbach and Knight).

lower proepisternal scale, in adult Culicidae (Diptera), one of the proepisternal scales occurring in a group mesad of the forecoxa and below the upper proepisternal scales (Harbach and Knight).

lower proepisternal seta, in adult Culicidae (Diptera), one of the proepisternal setae occurring in a group mesad of the forecoxa and below the upper proepisternal setae (Harbach and Knight).

lower radial vein, in adult Lepidoptera, second medial vein (M_2) (T-B, after Holland).

lower rhabdopoda, in ♂ Ephemeroptera, genostyles, q.v. (Tuxen, after Packard).

lower sector of triangle, in adult Odonata, second branch of cubitus (Cu_2) (T-B).

Lower Sonoran Faunal Area, faunal area comprising the most arid deserts of North America, beginning west of lat. 98° in Texas, with narrow arms going into southern New Mexico; interrupted by the Continental Divide; it covers a large part of western and southern Arizona, southwestern Nevada, southwestern California, a part of central California, and most of Lower California (T-B).

lower vaginal lip, in ♀ Culicidae (Diptera), the sclerotized and pigmented rim of the floor of the vagina, articulated with the upper vaginal lip by a hinge (Harbach and Knight, after Laffoon and Knight).

lower vaginal sclerite, in some ♀ Culicidae, e.g. *Aedes* subgenera *Neomacleaya* and *Verrallina* (Diptera), a pigmented sclerite on the vaginal floor other than the vaginal lip (Harbach and Knight, after Reinert).

lower valve, in ♀ Psyllidae (Hemiptera: Sternorrhyncha), ventral plate, q.v. (Tuxen).

LT$_{50}$, amedian lethal time, q.v. (Steinhaus and Martignoni).

lubricate, lubricatus, lubricous, slippery (T-B).

lucid, lucidate, lucidatus, lucidus (Latin), bright; shining (T-B; R. W. Brown).

luciferase, enzyme catalysing oxidation of luciferin (T-B; Tulloch; Chapman); see bioluminescence.

luciferin, chemical whose oxidation produces light (T-B; Tulloch; Chapman); see bioluminescence.

luciferous, light-giving (T-B).

lucifugous, lucifulgus (Latin), light-shunning (T-B; R. W. Brown); see nocturnal.

lumen (pl., **lumina**), the enclosed space or cavity of any hollow or vesicular organ or structure (T-B).

luminescence, bioluminescence, q.v. (T-B).

luminescent, light-producing (Chapman).

lumper, one who, in decribing species or genera, recognizes only prominent or obvious characters to the exclusion of minor color or variable characters of maculation or structure (T-B); a taxonomist who emphasizes the demostration of relationship in the delimitation of taxa and who tends to recognize large taxa (Mayr); see splitter.

lunar sclerite, in ♂ Siphonaptera, tectum, q.v. (Tuxen, after Peus).

lunare, lunaris, lunate (T-B).

lunate, lunatus (Latin), crescent-shaped (T-B; R. W. Brown).

lung books, in Arachnida, book lungs, q.v. (T-B, after Snodgrass).

lunula (pl., **lunulae**), lunule, q.v. (T-B).

lunular sclerite, in ♂ Siphonaptera, tectum, q.v. (Tuxen, after Hopkins and M. Rothschild).

lunulate, lunulatus, crescentic; made up of a series of small lunules, as a line (T-B).

lunule, a small lunate mark or crescent, sometimes colored (T-B); any moon-shaped structure (Leftwich); in adult Diptera, frontal lunule, q.v. (Borror et al., McAlpine); in adult Hymenoptera, one of the crescent-shaped marks near the orbits (T-B, after J. B. Smith).

lunulet, lunule, q.v. (T-B).

lura (pl., **lurae**), in ♀ Siphonaptera, when differentiated, portion of bursa copulatrix immediately following its opening into vagina (Rothschild and Traub).

lurid, luridus (Latin), pale-yellow (T-B; R. W. Brown).

lutein, yellow xanthophyll pigment, e.g., in the larva of *Sphinx* (Lepidoptera: Sphingidae) (Chapman).

luteotestaceous, dark clay yellow (T-B).

luteous, luteus (Latin), yellow in color (T-B, after Kirby and Spence; R. W. Brown).

lutescens, lutescent, becoming or approaching luteous (T-B).

lutose, lutosus, apparently or actually covered with dirt (T-B).

lycopene, red pigment found in *Coccinella* (Coleoptera: Coccinellidae) and in *Pyrrhocoris* (Heteroptera: Pyrrhocoridae) (Chapman).

Lygaeoidea, superfamily within the infraorder Pentatomomorpha of the Heteroptera, including the Lygaeidae and other families with 6 or fewer longitudinal veins in the forewing membrane (Woodward et al., in CSIRO).

Lyme disease, a spirocheatosis of humans transmitted by the deer tick, *Ixodes dammini* and other related ticks (Acari: Ixodidae) (Falco and Fish).

Lymexyloidea, superfamily within the Polyphaga (Coleoptera), including only the family Lymexylidae, possessing elongate, soft body, 5-5-5 tarsal formula, anterior coxal cavities confluent and open behind, and midcoxal cavities contiguous (Britton, in CSIRO).

Lymexylonidea, Lymexyloidea, q.v. (Hennig).

Lymexylonoidea, Lymexyloidea, q.v. (Borror et al.).

lymph gland, in larval *Drosophila* (Diptera: Drosophilidae), hemopoietic organ, q.v. (Tulloch, after Stark and Marshall).

lymphatic, producing, carrying or relating to the hemolymph (T-B).

lymphocyte, plasmatocyte, q.v. (Tulloch).

lymphocyte of Hollande, prohemocyte, q.v. (Tulloch).

Lyonnet's gland, in larval Lepidoptera, a small gland joining the duct of the labial gland, which possibly lubricates the tube through which the silk passes (Chapman).

lyra (pl., **lyrae**), in ♂ Geometridae (Lepidoptera), a lyre-shaped sternum VIII (Tuxen, after Philpott).

lyrate, lyriform, lyre-shaped, q.v. (T-B).

lyre, in larval Lepidoptera, the upper wall or border of the spinning tube (T-B).

lyre-shaped, resembling the musical instrument, with bowed sides and 2 free outward projecting arms (Peterson).

lysine, $C_6H_{14}N_2O_2$, an essential amino acid in the diet insects (Gilour, in CSIRO).

lysolecithin, one of the substances in the venom of bees and wasps (Hymenoptera: Aculeata), being a very toxic substance which breaks down the cells of its victim and sets free histamine (Leftwich).

M

M, media, q.v., of wing (McAlpine).

m, medial crossvein, q.v. (McAlpine).

M appendage, in larval Chironomidae (Diptera), medioventral appendage of prementum (Saether).

m-scales, in larval Chironomidae (Diptera), median lamellae, q.v. (Saether).

MA, media anterior, q.v., of wing (Mackerras, in CSIRO).

Machiloidea, Archaeognatha, q.v. (Boudreaux, after Hardlirsch).

macraner, an unusually large ♂ ant (Hymenoptera: Formicidae) (T-B; Leftwich).

macrergate, an unusally large worker ant (Hymenoptera: Formicidae) (T-B; Leftwich).

macrocephalic female, in the social Halictidae (Hymenoptera: Apoidea), a larger ♀ possessing a disproportionately large head, usually being the egg layers of a colony (Wilson).

macrocephalic phase, in Muscomorpha (Diptera), the phanerocephalic pupa when head of normal size and before the adult structures appear (Peterson, after Dean).

macrochaeta(e), macroseta, q.v. (T-B; Christiansen and Bellinger).

macrocyte, plasmatocyte, q.v. (Tulloch).

macrogamete, the mature ♀ gametocyte of the malarial protozoan, *Plasmodium*; the ♀ gamete of the malarial organism produced by the macrogametocyte (T-B); see malaria.

macrogametocyte, the ♀ sex cell developed from the merozoite of the malarial protozoan; the gametocyte which produces the ♀ gamete or egg cell in the malarial organism; see gametocyte (T-B); see malaria.

macrogyne, an unusually large queen ant (Hymenoptera: Formicidae) (T-B; Leftwich).

macrolabia, in Dermaptera, especially long cerci (T-B).

Macrolepidoptera, in Lepidoptera with relatively large adults, including the superfamilies Hesperioidea, Papilionoidea, Hedyloidea, Geometroidea, Mimallonoidea, Bombycoidea, Sphingoidea, and Noctuoidea (Borror et al.); see Microlepidoptera.

macronucleocyte, prohemocyte or plasmatocyte, q.v. (Tulloch).

macrophagous, feeding on large particles of food (T-B).

macrophthalmic, having large compound eyes, or having compound eyes larger than near relatives (T-B); see microphthalmic.

macroplasmatocyte, a large variety of plasmatocyte (Tulloch, after Jones); see mesoplasmatocyte and microplasmatocyte.

macroplastron, a layer of hairs longer than those of the plastron that store air and serves as a physical gill, e.g., in adult *Hydrophilus* (Coleoptera: Hydrophilidae) and *Elmis* (Coleoptera: Elmidae) (Chapman); see plastron.

macropore, in Coccoidea (Hemiptera: Sternorrhyncha), oraceratubae, q.v. (T-B, after MacGillivray).

macropterous, fully-winged; wings showing no abbreviation (T-B); see apterous, brachypterous, and micropterous.

macropterous forms, in termites (Isoptera), alates, q.v. (T-B).

macropterous reproductive, in Isoptera, alate, q.v. (Krishna, pers. comm.).

macroseta (pl., **macrosetae**), a seta conspicuously larger than adjacent setae (Christiansen and Bellinger).

macrosomites, the primitive regions of the primitive band of the insect embryo (T-B).

macrotrichia (sing., **macrotrichium**), in adult Diptera and Trichoptera, trichoid sensilla, q.v., on the wing membrane (T-B; Chapman; McAlpine); see microtrichia.

macula, a spot or mark (T-B; R. W. Brown).

macular fascia, a fascia made up of distinct spots (T-B).

maculate, maculated, maculatus (Latin), spotted; with many superficial marks or spots (T-B; Harris, after Funk); see adsperse, atomarious, irrorate, and immaculate.

maculation, the pattern of marks or spots on a surface (T-B; Harris, after Marchant and Charles, and R. W. Brown); see sculpture.

maculose, maculosus (Latin), maculate, q.v. (T-B; Harris).

madreporiform bodies, in Coccoidea (Hemiptera: Sternorrhyncha), cribriform plates, q.v. (T-B, after MacGillivray).

maerianum, in some adult Coleoptera, meriaeum, q.v. (T-B, after Say).

magenta, purplish-red in color (T-B).

maggot, in most Muscomorpha (Diptera), legless larva lacking a distinct head, with cephalic end pointed and caudal end blunt (T-B; Peterson); see acephalous larva.

magis, more (T-B).

main body, in ♂ Lepidoptera, tegumen, q.v. (Tuxen, after Scudder and Burgess).

maintenance activities, activities, such as general locomotion, grooming, and feeding that keep an individual in good shape but usually have little influence on others of its kind (Matthews and Matthews).

maize chlorotic dwarf, disease of corn, sorghum, and Johnson grass caused by the isometric virus transmitted through the foregut by *Graminella* and other genera (Hemiptera: Auchenorrhyncha: Cicadellidae) (Borror et al.; Nault and Ammar).

maize mosaic, disease of corn and sorghum caused by a rhabdovirus and transmitted propagatively by *Peregrinus* (Hemiptera: Auchenorrhyncha: Delphacidae) (Borror et al.; Nault and Ammar).

maize rayado fino, disease of maize caused by a marafivirus transmitted propagatively by *Dalbulus* (Hemiptera: Auchenorrhyncha: Cicadellidae) (Nault and Ammar).

maize rough dwarf, disease of maize caused by a reovirus (*Fijivirus*) transmitted propagatively by *Laodelphax, Delphacodes, Javesella,* and *Sogatella* (Hemiptera: Auchenorrhyncha: Delphacidae) (Nault and Ammar).

maize sterile stunt, disease of maize caused by a rhabdovirus transmitted propagatively by *Sogatella* and *Peregrinus* (Hemiptera: Auchenorrhyncha: Delphacidae) (Nault and Ammar).

maize streak, disease of maize caused by a geminivirus transmitted circulatively by *Cicadulina* (Hemiptera: Auchenorrhyncha: Cicadellidae) (Nault and Ammar).

maize stripe, disease of maize caused by a tenuivirus transmitted propagatively by *Peregrinus* (Hemiptera: Auchenorrhyncha: Delphacidae) (Nault and Ammar).

major, in termites (Isoptera) and ants (Hymenoptera: Formicidae), major worker, q.v. (T-B; Tulloch).

major soldier, in Isoptera, species with dimorphic castes, the larger of the 2 soldier forms (Krishna, pers. comm.).

major worker, in termites (Isoptera) and ants (Hymenoptera: Formicidae), a member of the largest worker subcaste which is usually specialized for defense (Wilson); see soldier, media worker, and minor worker.

mala, a lobe of a jaw (T-B); mola, q.v. (T-B).

mala mandibularis, mola, q.v. (T-B).

mala maxillae, either of the lobes of the maxilla, i.e., the galea and the lacinia (T-B); a single lobe of the maxilla, where only one is present (Peterson).

Malacodermata, group of Coleoptera (Polyphaga), recognized by older authors consisting of superfamily Cantharoidea and the families Lymexylidae, Melyridae, Dascillidae, and Cleridae (Britton, in CSIRO).

Malacopsylloidea, in Siphonaptera, superfamily containing the families Malacopsyllidae and Rhopalopsyllidae, the members of which lack true ctenidia, a trabecula centralis, a squamulum, or spiniform setae on the inner surface of the hind coxa, possess conspicuous anterior branches of the tentorium, a bifid mesopleural rod, only one antepygidial seta per side, ♂ genitalia lacking spiniform setae, females with anal stylet and only one spermatheca (Smit).

Malacostraca, class within the Crustacea, including the orders Amphipoda, Isopoda, Stomatopoda, and Decapoda, characterized by all body segments except the last (the telson) bearing appendages, 7–8 pairs on the thorax and 6 (rarely more) on the abdomen (Borror et al.).

Malaise trap, tentlike structure with fine netting into which flying insects wander and move upwards into a collection apparatus (Borror et al.).

malar space, in adult Hymenoptera, the shortest distance between the base of the mandible and the ventral margin of the compound eye (T-B, after MacGillivray; Gauld and Bolton).

malar sulcus, in some adult Hymenoptera, subocular sulcus, q.v. (Gauld and Bolton).

malaria, an acute or chronic disease of man caused by the presence of the sporozoan parasite, *Plasmodium* spp. (Plasmodiidae), in red blood cells, transmitted by mosquitoes of the genus *Anopheles* (Diptera: Culicidae) (Borror et al.; Allaby); see benign tertian malaria, malignant tertian malaria, and quartan malaria.

malathion, $C_{10}H_{19}O_6PS_2$, a synthetic insecticide; an organophosphate, diethyl mercaptosuccinate, *S*-ester with *O,O*-dimethyl phosphorodithioate; slightly toxic to mammals, acute oral LD_{50} for rats 1500 mg/kg (Pfadt).

malaxation, softening by chewing with the mandibles, e.g., chewing and squeezing by fossorial wasps (Hymenoptera) of prey captured as food for their larvae (T-B; Leftwich).

Malaya disease, a lethal disease of larvae of the rhinocerous beetle, *Orytes rhinocerus* (Coleoptera: Scarabaeidae), caused by a virus, in which the larvae cease to feed and appear shiny and turgid (Steinhaus and Martignoni).

male, that sex having organs for the production of spermatozoa; designated by ♂, the astronomical sign for Mars (T-B).

male accessory glands, in ♂ insects, ectodermal pouches or blind ducts branching from the upper end of the ejaculatory duct (T-B, after Snodgrass); see accessory genital glands, ectadenia, and mesadenia.

male genital chamber, genital chamber, q.v. (T-B, after Snodgrass).

male haploidy, the production of males from unfertilized eggs (White, in CSIRO); see haplo-diploidy.

male hooks, in ♂ Heteroptera (Hemiptera), parameres, q.v. (Tuxen, after Hickman).

male plates, in ♂ Auchenorrhyncha (Hemiptera), genital plates, q.v. (Tuxen).

male squama genitalis, in Protura, the external ♂ genitalia consisting of 2 parts, the periphallus and distal phallus (Tuxen, after Berlese).

male ventral organ, in some ♂ Onychiuridae (Collembola), one or more groups of sctae, slightly to highly modified, on the venter of abdominal segments II, III, and IV (Christiansen and Bellinger).

malic acid, $C_4H_6O_5$, an organic acid found in fruit such as apples, also being an intermediate in glucose oxidation and commonly found in high concentrations in the hemolyph (Gilmour, in CSIRO).

malignant tertian malaria, tropical and most dangerous type of malaria caused by *Plasmodium falciparum* (Welch) (Borror et al.).

malipedes, the third and fourth pair of footjaws in centipedes (T-B, after Packard).

malleoli, in adult Diptera, halteres, q.v. (T-B); in Solifugae, racquet organs, q.v. (Borror et al.).

Mallophaga, former suborder within the Phthiraptera, including Amblycera Ischnocera, and Rhyncophthirina, including lice with chewing mouthparts (Calaby, in CSIRO; Lyal, pers. comm.); Amblycera, q.v. (Boudreaux).

malonyl-CoA, immediate donor of 2 carbon units, formed from ester of maonic acid with coenzyme A, in the synthesis of long-chain fatty acids (Gilmour, in CSIRO).

Malpighian glands, glands lining the Malpighian tubules of insects, functioning in the larvae of some Coleoptera and Neuropteroidea to spin silk (Leftwich); see Malpighian tubules.

Malpighian tubes, Malpighian tubules, q.v. (T-B).

Malpighian tubules, long, thin, blind tubes arising from the gut near the junction of midgut and hind gut, involved in amino acid synthesis, light production, nitrogenous excretion, salt regulation, silk production, spittle production, water regulation, and sometimes housing microorganisms (Chapman).

maltase, a digestive enzyme, by which maltose is hydrolyzed and converted into glucose (T-B).

maltose, a disaccharide consisting of 2 glucose molecules united by an alpha-linkage, with the glucose molecules differing in their orientation from those in the disaccharide trehalose (Chapman).

mammiform, having the form of a breast or nipple (Peterson).

mammillate, mammillated, mammillatus (Latin), papillate, q.v. (T-B; Harris).

mammulae, in Araneae (Arachnida), spinnerets, q.v. (T-B).

mandibles, the first pair of jaws in insects, being stout and jawlike in chewing insects, or needle- or sword-shaped (stylets) in piercing-sucking insects (T-B, after Wardle); in larval Muscomorpha (Diptera), mouth hooks, q.v. (Peterson).

mandibular, of or pertaining to the mandibles (T-B).

mandibular brush, in larval Chironomidae (Diptera), seta interna, q.v. (Saether).

mandibular brushes, in larval Tabanoidea (Diptera), a group of dorsolateral spines on mandible (Teskey, in McAlpine).

mandibular comb, in some larval Nematocera (Diptera), a linear group of spicules on the ventroanterior margin of the mandible (Harbach and Knight); pecten mandibularis, q.v. (Saether).

mandibular flange, in larval Chironomidae (Diptera), lower, inner sclerotized flange of mandible, particularly pronounced in Tanypodinae (Saether).

mandibular fossa, in larval Coleoptera, acetabulum of head receiving dorsal condyle of mandible (Peterson, after Böving and Craighead).

mandibular ganglia, the nerve masses which control the mandibles, being part of the larger suboesophageal ganglion (T-B).

mandibular glands, in Archaeognatha, Zygentoma, Blatteropteroidea, Coleoptera, and Hymenoptera, paired saclike structures in the head opening near the base of the mandibles (T-B, after Snodgrass); in larval Lepidoptera, tubular salivary glands in the thorax on each side of the alimentary canal, communicating with the mouth by a pore at the base of the mandible (T-B); in *Apis* (Apidae) and some ants (Formicidae) (Hymenoptera), a saclike gland opening at the inner angle of each mandible, being larger in the queen and poorly developed in the drone, producing pheromones concerned with colony control, such as an alarm pheromone in workers (T-B, after Imms; Chapman).

mandibular lever, in Hemiptera, the chitinous structure at the base of the mandible, which through the action of retractor and protractor muscles facilitates movement of the stylet (Cobben).

mandibular nerves, paired nerves arising from the suboesophageal ganglion which innervate the mandibles.

mandibular palp, in Ephemeroptera, lacinia mobilis, q.v. (T-B).

mandibular plate, in Hemiptera, plate lateral to the clypeus and above the maxillary plate (T-B; Woodward et al., in CSIRO).

mandibular pouch (sheath), in Thysanoptera, an invagination in the head containing the single functional left mandible (T-B, after Snodgrass).

mandibular scar, in certain Coleoptera, a round or oval area on the mandible which served as a support for the deciduous provisional mandibles of the pupa (T-B, after Imms).

mandibular sclerite(s), in larval Muscomorpha (Diptera), mouth hooks, q.v. (Ferrar); in Hemiptera, mandibular plate, q.v. (T-B, after Comstock).

mandibular scrobe, in some adult Coleoptera, a broad deep groove on outer side of mandible (T-B).

mandibular segment, a gnathal segment of the head, bearing the mandibles (T-B); see head.

mandibular suspensorium, in adult Culicidae (Diptera), a small sclerite articulated with the proximal end of the mandible ventrally and the subgenal ridge dorsally (Harbach and Knight, after Robinson).

mandibular tooth, in adult Culicidae (Diptera), one of a series of small toothlike processes occurring distally along the outer margin of the mandible (Harbach and Knight, after Lee).

mandibularia, in larval Symphyta (Hymenoptera), a small sclerite between the base of the mandible and gena (Gauld and Bolton); see pleurostoma.

mandibularis, in adult Siphonaptera, piercing-sucking mouthparts composed primarily of the laciniae of maxillae, mistakenly judged to be mandibles (T-B, after MacGillivray; Dunnet, in CSIRO).

Mandibulata, insects with chewing mouthparts (T-B); hypothesized monophyletic group including the Crustacea, Myriapoda, and Hexapoda, possessing antennae, mandibles, and first maxillae (Boudreaux, after Snodgrass).

mandibulate, mandibulated, mandibulatus (Latin), having opposable jaws (T-B); in Isoptera, mandibulate soldier, q.v. (Tulloch).

mandibulate larva, in some Hymenoptera parasitoids, early instar larva with large, heavily sclerotized, more or less prognathous head, posteriorly constricted body, and a pair of sickle-shaped mandibles (Gauld and Bolton).

mandibulate mouthparts, chewing mouthparts, q.v.

mandibulate soldier, in eusocial insects, e.g., termites (Isoptera), a soldier which has large mandibles used in colony defense (Wilson; Krishna, pers. comm.).

mandibuliform, mandibuliformis, mandible or jaw-shaped (T-B).

manditory change, a change in the spelling of a suffix of a family-group name required by the Code (ICZN); a change in the termination of a specific or subspecific name required by the Code (ICZN).

mandogenal suture, subgenal sulcus, q.v. (T-B, after MacGillivray).

mandoris, mouth, q.v. (T-B, after MacGillivray).

manducate, pertaining to the mandibles; capable of chewing (T-B).

mane, in some ♂ Siphonaptera, a group of manelike bristles on the thoracic nota, especially bat fleas (Ischnopsyllidae) (Lewis, pers. comm.).

mange, a group of contagious skin diseases in livestock caused by certain parasitic mites (Acari) (Pfadt).

manica (Latin), (pl., **manicae**), sleeve; glove (R. W. Brown); in ♂ Lepidoptera, innermost layer of the invaginated anellus, immediately surrounding aedoeagus and fastened to it at the zone (T-B; Tuxen, after Pierce).

manicate, manicatus, furlike; clothed with irregular depressed hair (T-B).

maniform, maniformis, hand-shaped (T-B).

manitrunk, manitruncus (Latin), prothorax, q.v. (T-B, after Kirby and Spence).

manna, sweet sugarlike material, being the solidified honeydew produced by the tamarisk manna scale, *Trabutina mannipara* (Hemiptera: Sternorrhyncha: Pseudococcidae) (Tulloch; Borror et al.).

Manometabola, insects with a slight or gradual metamorphosis and without a resting stage, e.g., the Orthoptera (T-B); see Paurometabola.

mantid, praying mantid, q.v.

mantis, praying mantid. q.v.

Mantispoidea, superfamily within the Planipennia, including the Mantispidae, Berothidae, and Sisyridae, possessing adults with fewer than 5 crossveins between R_1 and R_s, anterior branch of cubitus (CuA) of forewing not forming a large convex triangular area, nygmata not present between posterior 2 branches of radial sector (R_s), and pterostigma present (Riek, in CSIRO); sometimes included within the Hemerobioidea (Borror et al.).

mantle cell, corneagen cell, q.v., of ommatidium retina (T-B, after Snodgrass).

mantle of phallosome, in ♂ Siphonaptera, palliolum, q.v. (Tuxen, after Jordan).

Mantodea, mandibulate, predaceous, exopterygote order within the Neoptera (Insecta), having raptorial forelegs with large mobile coxae, pronotum without large descending lobes, wing rudiments of nymph not reversing their orientation in later instars, and eggs enclosed in an ootheca (Key, in CSIRO).

Mantoidea, Mantodea, q.v. (Borror et al.).

manubrium (Latin), (pl., **manubria**), handle (R. W. Brown); in Collembola, the large median base of the furcula bearing the dentes (T-B; Christiansen and Bellinger); in ♂ Dermaptera, membranous extension, with a sclerotized margin, of proximal edge of abdominal sternum IX, forming a support for genital armature (Tuxen, after Burr); also applied in ♂ Dermaptera to parameral lever, q.v. (Tuxen, after Burr and Jordan); in ♂ Zoraptera, horseshoe-shaped basal plate, q.v. (Tuxen, after Denis); in ♂ Coleoptera, unpaired process (apophysis, apodeme) of tegmen (or of penis) (Tuxen); in adult Elateridae (Coleoptera), that part of the mesosternum fitting into the cavity of the prothorax (T-B); in ♂ Siphonaptera, the ventral, handlelike extension of the clasper body (Tuxen, after Wagner; Lewis, pers. comm.) (see apodeme of tergum IX); in adult Chironomidae, brachiolum, q.v., at base of wing (Saether); in Diptera larvae, metacephalic rod, q.v. (Teskey, in McAlpine); in ♂ Hymenoptera, gonocoxite, q.v. (Tuxen, after Hartig) or parapenial lobe, q.v. (Tuxen, after Rohwer).

manubrium dorsale, in ♂ Siphonaptera, apodeme of tergum IX, q.v. (Tuxen).

manus, foretarsus, q.v. (T-B).

manuscript name, in taxonomy, an unpublished scientific name (T-B; Mayr); see nomen nudum.

mappa (pl., **mappae**), in ♂ Sterrhinae (Lepidoptera: Geometridae), flat, sclerotized process of posterior edge of abdominal sternum VIII, flanked by the paired cerata and partially covering them (Tuxen, after Prout).

Marafivirus, an RNA plant virus with spherical inclusion bodies transmitted propagatively by leafhoppers (Hemiptera: Auchenorrhyncha: Cicadellidae) (Naut and Ammar).

marble galls, dark brown spherical galls formed on oak trees by the larvae of *Andricus kollari* or *Cynips kollari* (Hymenoptera: Cynipidae) (T-B; Leftwich); see oak apple.

marbled, variegated, gray and white, like marble (T-B).

marcescent, shrivelling; in the act of shrivelling (T-B).

margaritaceous, margaritaceus, nacreous, q.v. (T-B).

Margarodoidea, Archaeococcoidea, q.v. (Hennig).

margin, margo (Latin), a more or less narrow part of a surface within the edge, bounded on the inner side by the submargin (T-B); in ♂ Noctuidae (Lepidoptera), distal margin of cucullus (Tuxen, after Pierce).

marginal, of, belonging to, or near the margin (T-B).

marginal accessory veins, intercalary veins, q.v. (T-B, after Comstock).

marginal area, in Acridoidea (Orthoptera), the area of the hind femur between the upper carina and the upper carinula, or between the lower carina and lower carinula (Otte, pers. comm.); in Orthoptera, mediastinal area, q.v., of wing (T-B).

marginal bristle, in adult Diptera, median marginal seta, q.v. (T-B, after Comstock).

marginal cell (MC), a wing cell beyond the pterostigma (T-B, after J. B. Smith); in adult Hymenoptera, one or 2 closed radial cells of wing immediately posterior or distal to pterostigma and bordering costal margin (T-B; Borror et al.; Gauld and Bolton); in adult Diptera, first radial cell (r_1) (T-B, after Williston).

marginal cellule, marginal cell, q.v., of wing (T-B).

marginal field, in adult Orthoptera, costal field, q.v., of tegmina (T-B).

marginal gland openings, in Coccoidea (Hemiptera: Sternorrhyncha), dorsal pores, q.v. (T-B, after MacGillivray).

marginal lunar pores, in Coccoidea (Hemiptera: Sternorrhyncha), dorsal pores, q.v. (T-B, after MacGillivray).

marginal nervure, in Orthoptera, costa, q.v., of wing (T-B, after Comstock); in adult Hymenoptera, radial sector (R_s), q.v., delimiting marginal cell(s) posteriorly (T-B, after Norton); see marginal vein.

marginal pores, in Coccoidea (Hemiptera: Sternorrhyncha), dorsal pores, q.v. (T-B, after MacGillivray).

marginal scales, in Lepidoptera, scales occurring along the margins of the wings, often being long and piliform with longitudinal ridges on all surfaces (Downey and Allyn).

marginal scutellar bristles, marginal scutellars, in Diptera, usually a distinct row of large bristles on the margin of the scutellum (T-B, after Comstock).

marginal seta, in adult Culicidae (Diptera), any one of the setae occurring along the inner and outer margins of the fourth and fifth palpomeres of the maxillary palpi (Harbach and Knight).

marginal setae, in adult Chironomidae (Diptera), posterior transverse row of setae on tergites when an anterior transverse row (basal setae) is also recognizable (Saether); see lateral setae.

marginal spines, in ♂ Lepidoptera, large spines on ventrocaudal margin of valvula (Tuxen, after Pierce).

marginal vein, in adult Chalcidoidea and Scelionidae (Hymenoptera), portion of single composite vein along wing margin, between submarginal vein and postmarginal vein (Gauld and Bolton); see stigmal vein and marginal nervure.

marginate, marginatus (Latin), margined, q.v. (T-B).

margined, bounded by an elevated or attenuated margin (T-B); with the margin edged by a flat border (T-B); with a sharp or keellike lateral edge (Borror et al.).

margo externus (pl., **margines externi**), in ♂ Lepidoptera, the peripheral margin of valva (Tuxen, after Petersen).

margo labralis, in larval Chironomidae (Diptera), labral margin, q.v. (Saether).

margo subgnathalis, in larval Chironomidae (Diptera), subgenal margin, q.v. (Saether).

marine, of or pertaining to the sea (Norris, in CSIRO); see estuarine, intertidal, and littoral.

mark, in pupal Chironomidae (Diptera), scar, q.v. (Saether).

marmoraceous, marmorate, marmoratus (Latin), marbled, q.v. (T-B).

marsupium, the pouch in which certain Coccoidea (Hemiptera: Sternorrhyncha) carry eggs and young, made up of the anal plates (T-B).

mask, in Odonata, the modified extensible labium of the nymph, which at rest conceals the other mouthparts (T-B).

masked pupa, a pupa without free appendages, e.g., coarctate pupa and obtect pupa (T-B).

mass communication, the transfer of information among groups of individuals of a kind that cannot be transmitted from a single individual to another, e.g., spatial organization of army ant raids, regulation of numbers of worker ants on odor trails (Hymenoptera: Formicidae), and certain aspects of the thermoregulation of nests (Wilson).

mass provisioning, in solitary bees and wasps (Hymenoptera: Aculeata), provisioning cells with sufficient food for the developing larva and closing them before the eggs hatch (T-B, after Imms); the act of storing all of the food required for the development of a larva at the time the egg is laid (Wilson); see progressive provisioning.

masticate, to chew (T-B).

mastication, the act of chewing (T-B).

masticatory, formed for chewing or grinding (T-B).

masticomorphic, masticatory, q.v. (Peterson).

mastigium (pl., **mastigia**), a teloscopic anal filament in certain caterpillars, serving to repel attacks of parasites, e.g., puss moth, *Cerura vinula* (Lepidoptera: Notodontidae) (T-B; Leftwich).

material, in taxonomy, the sample for taxonomic study (Mayr); see hypodigm and series.

matinal, of or in the morning, as in reference to activity patterns of insects.

mating, sequence of events surrounding the insemination of the ♀ by the ♂ (Chapman); see copulation and courtship.

mating flight, nuptial flight, q.v. (T-B; Leftwich).

mating gland, in ♂ Ephemeroptera, one of the large unicellular globular glands embedded in the hypodermal layer of the forceps, derived from the hypodermal cells (T-B, after Needham).

mating plug, in Lepidoptera, sphragis, q.v.

mating spines, in ♀ Ephemeroptera, compound conical spines covering lower surface of egg valve and supposed by Needham to hold ♂ genitalia in place at time of mating (Tuxen, after Needham).

mating swarm, a conspicuous cloud of insects, usually males, dancing or hovering over a marker or in the lee of an obstruction, serving to attract solitary members of the other sex, e.g., many Nematocera (Diptera) and Enicocephalidae (Hemiptera: Heteroptera) (Leftwich; Schuh, pers. comm.).

matrifilial, eusocial Hymenoptera with colonies consisting of mother(s) and daughters (Michener).

matrix, the substance between the cells of animal and plant tissue (T-B); see character matrix.

matrone, in *Aedes* (Diptera: Culicidae), a substance, consisting of 2 proteins, contained in the secretions of the ♂ accessory glands, which after being transferred to the ♀ makes her unreceptive to subsequent mating (Chapman).

maturation, the nuclear changes in the egg before fertilization (T-B, after Wardle); developmental events culminating in formation of gametes (Tulloch).

maturation period, that part of the life cycle of an insect between adult eclosion and sexual maturity, including the formation of gametes.

maturation phase, in invertebrate pathology, a phase or period in virus infections, following the eclipse period, during which infective particles are completed (Steinhaus and Martignoni); see vegetative phase.

maturation zone, that part of the sperm tube beyond the zone of growth, in which the maturation divisions of the sperm take place (T-B, after Snodgrass).

maturus junior, fourth, preadult stage of Protura, with 12 segments but incomplete chaetotaxy and no genital armature (Wallace and Mackerras, in CSIRO).

maxilla (pl., **maxillae**), second pair of jaws in insects with chewing mouthparts, represented by some structure in all insects with functional mouthparts (T-B); see cardo, galea, lacinia, maxillary palp, and stipes.

maxillaria, (pl., **maxillariae**), hypostoma, q.v. (T-B, after MacGillivray).

maxillary, attached or belonging to the maxilla (T-B).

maxillary articulating area, the area between stipes and cardo, exteriorly, and mentum and submentum interiorly (Peterson, after Böving and Craighead).

maxillary blade, in adult Diptera, lacinia in the form of a stylet (McAlpine).

maxillary bridge, in certain Tubulifera (Thysanoptera) a median extension of the maxillary guide (Stannard).

maxillary chaetae, in larval Chironomidae (Diptera), lacinial chaetae, q.v. (Saether).

maxillary gills, in nymphs of some Ephemeroptera, paired membranous outgrowths that occur at inner base of the stipes (T-B, after Needham and Murphy).

maxillary glands, in Protura, Collembola, Heteroptera (Hemiptera), and some larval Neuroptera and Hymenoptera, usually small paired glands opening near the bases of the maxillae (T-B; Chapman).

maxillary guide, in certain Tubulifera (Thysanoptera), sclerotized inner margin of maxillary (lacinial) sheath (Stannard).

maxillary lever, in Tubulifera (Thysanoptera) and Hemiptera, the chitinous structure at the base of the maxilla, which through the action of retractor and protractor muscles facilitates movement of the stylet (Cobben).

maxillary lobe, galea, q.v. (T-B).

maxillary palp or **palpus** (pl., **palps** or **palpi**), one to 7 segmented appendage of the insect maxilla, carried by the stipes on its outer end, being sensory in function (T-B, after Imms; Leftwich).

maxillary pillar, in Tubulifera (Thysanoptera), maxillary (lacinial) lever (Stannard).

maxillary plate, in Hemiptera, plate lateral to the clypeus and below or posterior to mandibular plate (T-B; Woodward et al., in CSIRO); in larval Diptera, hypostoma, q.v. (Teskey, in McAlpine).

maxillary pleurites, the lateral pieces, epimera and episterna of the maxillary segment (T-B, after J. B. Smith).

maxillary sclerite(s), in larval Empididae and Dolichopodidae (Diptera), sclerites representing remnants of maxilla (Teskey, in McAlpine); in Hemiptera, maxillary plate, q.v.

maxillary segment, a gnathal segment of the head, bearing the maxillae (T-B; McAlpine); see head.

maxillary stylets, in Hemiptera, the inner pair of stylets, containing the food canal and the salivary canal (T-B).

maxillary tendon(s), in adult Muscomorpha (Diptera), paired slender rods in the basal third of the proboscis, the remnants of the palpifers, to which the muscles for flexing the proboscis are attached (T-B).

maxillary tentacle, in ♀ yucca moths (Lepidoptera: Prodoxidae), an elongate, coiled appendage from the base of the maxillary palpus used for collecting pollen (T-B, after Comstock; Davis).

maxillary tooth, in adult Culicidae (Diptera), one in a series of proximally directed toothlike processes borne on the outer margin of the distal end of the lacinia (transl. "Maxillarzahn" Martini, in Harbach and Knight).

maxillipeds, in Crustacea, one of the 3 pairs of appendages posterior to the second maxillae, the first pair sometimes (Amphipoda) united to form a labiumlike structure attached to the head (T-B, after Snodgrass).

maxillolabial, of or pertaining to both the maxilla and the labium (T-B).

maxillulae (sing., **maxillula**), in Zygentoma, superlinguae, q.v. (T-B, after J. B. Smith); see hypopharynx.

maximal nonlethal dose, the dose which will just fail to kill all or most of the subjects of a given species or strain (Steinhaus and Martignoni).

maxime, maximus, very much or very large (T-B).

maxipalp, maxipalpus, maxillary palpus, q.v. (T-B).

May disease, a group of maladies of adult honey bees (Hymenoptera: Formicidae), having similar syndromes but different etiologies, e.g., constipation in bees infected with *Saccharomyces applicatus* (Steinhaus and Martignoni); see Bettlach May disease.

Maya's disease, a lethal disease of larvae, pupae, and adults of rhinoceros beetles, *Oryctes* spp., and other Scarabaeidae (Coleoptera), involving the appearance of spheroid vacuolated inclusions in the fat body of diseased insects (Steinhaus and Martignoni).

mayfly, a member of the order Ephemeroptera (Riek, in CSIRO).

Mayrian furrow, in certain ♂ ants (Hymenoptera: Formicidae), Y-shaped groove on the mesonotum, consisting of the notauli (T-B; Brown, pers. comm.).

meadowsweet galls, small swellings often seen in large numbers on the leaves of meadowsweet (*Filipendula ulmaria*; Rosaceae), caused by the small orange-colored larvae of *Perrisia ulmariae* (Diptera: Cecidomyiidae) (Leftwich).

mealworm, larva of *Tenebrio* (Coleoptera: Tenebrionidae) (Borror et al.).

mealy, farinose, q.v. (T-B; Harris).

mean square, variance, q.v. (Allaby).

measuring worm, looper, q.v. (Borror et al.).

meatus (Latin), passage; course (R. W. Brown); a channel or duct (T-B).

mecaglossa, in Mecoptera, prementum, q.v. (T-B, after MacGillivray).

Mecaptera, Mecoptera, q.v. (T-B, after Packard).

mechanical control, control of pests by mechanical means, e.g., window screens and earth barriers (Pfadt); see physical control.

mechanical vector, transport host, q.v. (Steinhaus and Martignoni).

mechanistic theory, the theory that all animal action depends only on stimuli received through or from a nerve from purely external or objective sources (T-B).

mechanoreception, the perception of any mechanical distortion of the body (Matthews and Matthews).

mechanoreceptor, sensillum or group of sensilla functioning in mechanoreception (Tulloch; Chapman); see campaniform sensillum, chordotonal organ, trichoid sensillum, and tympanal organ.

meconium, the substance excreted by certain holometabolous insects soon after their emergence from the chrysalis or pupa (T-B); the first fecal matter voided by most newly emerged insects which have a quiescent pupal stage (Tulloch).

Mecoptera, mandibulate, holometabolous order of Neoptera (Insecta), possessing adults with a head produced into a rostrum but with mandibulate mouthparts; abdominal tergum 1 fused to thorax; normally 2 pairs of subequal wings, with simple venation; larvae with compound eyes and mandibulate mouthparts; and decticous pupa (T-B; Riek, in CSIRO).

Mecopterida, Panorpoidea, q.v. (Boudreaux).

Mecopterodea, Mecoptera, q.v. (Boudreaux).

Mecopteroidea, hypothesized monophyletic group including the Trichoptera, Lepidoptera, Mecoptera, and Diptera (Hennig); see Panorpoidea.

medalaria, anterior notal wing process, q.v. (T-B, after MacGillivray).

medalifera, posterior basalare, q.v. (T-B, after MacGillivray).

Medamoptera, Siphonaptera, q.v. (Lewis, pers. comm., after Leach).

medi-, Latin prefix; middle (T-B).

media (M), the fifth longitudinal vein system (M), originating on the median plate (when present), usually divided into a generally convex anterior branch (MA) and concave posterior branch (MP), themselves often subdivided (MA to M_1 and M_2, MP to M_3 and M_4) (T-B, Comstock; Ross et al., after Hamilton) (see media anterior and media posterior); in ants (Hymenoptera: Formicidae), media worker, q.v. (T-B, after W. M. Wheeler).

media anterior (MA), anterior branch of media, being absent in the Holometobola (Harbach and Knight); see media posterior.

media posterior (MP), posterior branch of media (Harbach and Knight); see media anterior.

media worker, in polymorphic ant (Hymenoptera: Formicidae), series involving 3 of more worker subcastes, an individual belonging to the medium-sized subcaste(s) (Wilson); see minor worker and major worker.

mediad, toward the median plane or middle (T-B).

medial, referring to, or at the middle (T-B).

medial area, in Acridoidea (Orthoptera), the outer face of the hind femur bounded by the upper and lower carinula (Otte, pers. comm.).

medial cell, a wing cell bounded anteriorly by the media or one of its branches (T-B).

medial commissure, in adult Chironomidae (Diptera), fusing line of the 2 sclerites forming the antepronotum (Saether).

medial crossvein, a crossvein connecting 2 branches of the media (T-B, after Comstock; Borror et al.).

medial field, in ♂ Chironomidae (Diptera), inferior volsella, q.v. (Saether).

medial fracture, in the forewing of adult Heteroptera, longitudinal furrow delimiting exocorium (or embolium) from endocorium (Štys, pers. comm.); see embolar groove and median furrow.

medial plate(s), in some ♂ Enicocephalidae (Hemiptera: Heteroptera), internal part of ♂ genitalia of unknown homology (Štys); in adult Diptera, median plates, q.v., of wing (Saether).

medial scar, in adult Chironomidae (Diptera), weakly sclerotized medial longitudinal line or narrow area on scutum (Saether).

mediale, second axillary sclerite, q.v. (T-B, after Crampton).

median, in or at the middle; of or pertaining to the middle (T-B); along the midline of the body (Borror et al.).

median accessory gland, in ♀ *Dysdercus* (Heteroptera: Pyrrhocoridae), diverticulum ductus, q.v. (Tuxen, after Gupta).

median anepisternum II, in adult Chironomidae (Diptera), median portion of anepisternum (Saether).

median antenodal, in pupal Chironomidae (Diptera), median seta (or group of setae) on each side of antepronotum (Saether).

median anterior promontory scale, in adult Anophelinae (Diptera: Culicidae), one of the scales usually forming a tuft at the middle of the anterior margin of the anterior promontory (Harbach and Knight).

median anterior promontory seta, in adult Culicidae (Diptera), any seta occurring in a small cluster anteriorly on the midline of the anterior promontory (Harbach and Knight, after Knight and Laffoon).

median apodeme, in ♂ Plecoptera, basal anchor, q.v. (Tuxen, after Walker).

median area, in wings of Orthoptera, area between the radius and media (T-B, after Comstock); in adult Apocrita (Hymenoptera), middle of propodeum, divided longitudinally by carinae into basal area, areola, and petiolar area (T-B).

median arm of sternum IX, in ♂ Siphonaptera, distal arm (of sternum IX), q.v. (Tuxen).

median carina, any ridge set medially on a part of an insect (T-B); in Orthoptera, a median dorsal ridge on head (T-B), or frontal ridge, that extends down the middle of frons from the fastigium (T-B); of the prothorax, that ridge along the middle of pronotum (T-B).

median caudal filament, in Ephemeroptera, filum terminale, q.v. (Tuxen, after Imms).

median caudal seta, in Ephemeroptera, filum terminale, q.v. (Tuxen, after Eaton).

median cell, in adult Hymenoptera, radial cell at the base of the wing (T-B; Riek, after Ross, in CSIRO).

median cercus, filum terminale, q.v. (T-B, after Wardle).

median claw, any single unpaired claw; not to be confused with those cases in which one of a pair disappears at the last moult of the nymph in some Hemiptera (T-B).

median cord, in the insect embryo, a chain of cells separated from the ectoderm lining the neural groove (T-B, after Imms).

median crossveins, in adult Odonata, those which cross the median space (T-B, after J. B. Smith).

median dorsal lobe, in ♀ Plecoptera, supraanal lobe, q.v. (Tuxen, after Kimmins); in ♂ Siphonaptera, the apicodistal extension of the apodeme of the aedeagus that extends over the end chamber and is paired in some species (Rothschild and Traub).

median dorsal process, in ♀ Psyllidae (Hemiptera: Sternorrhyncha), inferior intervalvula, q.v. (Tuxen).

median ecdysial line, coronal ecdysial line, q.v. (Gauld and Bolton).

median effective dose (ED$_{50}$), the dose which will produce a response in half the test subjects, being an indirect measure of the mean tolerance of a batch of insect subjects (Steinhaus and Martignoni); see median lethal dose.

median effective time (ET$_{50}$), the time at which a response occurs in half the test subjects after exposure to a pathogenic (including toxicological) stimulus (Steinhaus and Martignoni); see median survival time.

median endomere, in ♂ Chironomidae (Diptera), median volsella, q.v. (Saether).

median fingerlike process, in ♂ Zoraptera, uncus, q.v. (Tuxen, after Gurney).

median flap, in ♂ Embiidina, mesally directed flap along inner margin of right hemitergite of abdominal tergum X (Ross, in Tuxen).

median foramen, in ♂ Coleoptera, basal orifice, q.v. (Tuxen).

median forks, in Orthoptera, the forks of the media (T-B).

median fovea, in some adult Hymenoptera, a rounded or angular pit located near the ventral margin of the frontal crest (T-B); see antennal fovea.

median foveola, in Orthoptera, the foveate depression of the vertex between the eyes (T-B).

median frontal nerve, nerve of the stomatogastric nervous system extending from frontal ganglion to the wall of the pharynx (Chapman).

median furrow, the longitudinal furrow between radius and media (T-B); see medial fracture and median flexion line.

median gonapophyses, in ♀ Odonata, a pair of processes springing from inner side of base of lateral gonapophyses and forming part of ovipositor (Fraser and Asahina, in Tuxen).

median gonopods, in ♀ Psocoptera, valvae dorsales, q.v. (Tuxen, after Pearman).

median gonopore, in ♀ Coleoptera, the opening of the oviductus communis into vagina (Tuxen, after Bissell).

median groove, in ♀ Isoptera, groove in floor of inner vestibulum extending from gonopore along intersternal fold (Tuxen, after Weesner); in ♂ Heteroptera (Hemiptera), a medially depressed groove on the floor of the genital chamber, acting as guide for distal part of phallus, its edges passing dorsoanterior to suspensory apodemes and posterior to inferior process (Tuxen, after Leston).

median knob of sternum VIII, in ♂ Plecoptera, median lobe of abdominal sternum VIII, q.v. (Tuxen, after Needham and Claassen).

median lamellae, in larvae of most Orthocladiinae and Chironominae (Diptera), median lamellae of M appendage (Saether).

median lamina, in ♂ Siphonaptera, the median aedeagal apodeme or penis plate, accompanied by delicate lateral laminae (Rothschild and Traub).

median lethal concentration (LC$_{50}$), the concentration which produces death in half of the test subjects, usually being applied to fumigants and measured in parts per million (ppm) (Pfadt).

median lethal dose (LD$_{50}$), the dose which will produce death in half the test subjects (Steinhaus and Martignoni); see median effective dose.

median lethal time (LT$_{50}$), in a time-dependent biological assay procedure, the period of exposure to a pathogenic (including toxicological) stimulus which will produce death in half the test subjects, being a direct measure of dosage (Steinhaus and Martignoni); see median survival time.

median line, meson, q.v. (McAlpine).

median lines, on the forewings of many moths (Lepidoptera), the transverse anterior line and the transverse posterior, q.v. (T-B).

median lobe, in ♂ Embiidina, hypandrium process, q.v. (Tuxen, after Snodgrass); in ♂ Coleoptera, penis, q.v. (Tuxen); in ♀ Plecoptera, median sclerotization at opening of genital duct (transl. "lobe médian" Aubert, after Tuxen); in ♀ Limnephilidae (Trichoptera), median part of vulvar scale (Tuxen).

median lobe of labium, in Odonata, mentum, q.v. (T-B, after Garman).

median lobe of sternum VIII, in ♂ Isoperlinae (Plecoptera), median lobe on posterior margin of abdominal sternum VIII (Tuxen, after Frison).

median longitudinal carinae, in adult Aculeata (Hymenoptera), longitudinal carinae on propodeum delimiting median area, q.v. (T-B).

median marginal seta, in adult Diptera, seta inserted medially on the posterior margin of an abdominal tergum (McAlpine).

median mesoscutal lobe, in many adult Symphyta (Hymenoptera), a median triangular area of mesoscutum formed by posterior meeting of notauli (Gibson; Gauld and Bolton); see parapsides.

median metascutal sulcus, in some adult Symphyta (Hymenoptera), median longitudinal groove of mesoscutum (Gibson; Gauld and Bolton).

median nerve cord, the median strand of nerve tissue produced from the ventral neuroblasts (T-B, after Snodgrass).

median nerves, unpaired nerves arising from the ganglia of the ventral nerve cord between the roots of the connectives (T-B, after Snodgrass).

median nervules, in adult Lepidoptera, third median vein (M$_3$) and 2 branches of cubitus anterior (CuA$_1$ and CuA$_2$) (T-B, after Holland); see median veins.

median nexus, in the wings of Myrmeleontidae (Planipennia), a conjunction of adjacent veins which joins the tip of vein M$_{1+2}$ with the vein on each side of it (T-B, after Needham).

median notch, in Coccoidea (Hemiptera: Sternorrhyncha), a notch in the edge of the pygidium, at the posterior extremity of the body (T-B, after MacGillivray); see mesal notch.

median orifice, in ♂ Coleoptera, ostium, q.v. (Tuxen).

median oviduct, in ♀ insects, oviductus communis, q.v. (Tuxen).

median plane, a vertical plane which divides animals into right and left parts (T-B).

median plate(s), one or 2 plates at the base of the wing from which the media (M) and cubitus (Cu) arise (T-B; Chapman) (see first median plate and second median plate); in Odonata and Neoptera, the basal wing sclerite from which the radius, sector, and media originate (Ross et al., after Hamilton); in ♂ Embiidina, epiproct, q.v., of genitalia (Tuxen, after Imms).

median prescutellar scale, in adult Culicidae (Diptera), one of the prescutellar scales occurring in a transverse line on the anterior margin and/or in a median longitudinal line on the prescutellar area of the scutum (Harbach and Knight).

median process, in ♂ Heteroptera (Hemiptera), hypandrium, q.v. (Tuxen, after Leston).

median processus of tegmen, in ♂ Coleoptera, unpaired apophysis of tegmen (Tuxen).

median processus of terebra, in ♀ Odonata, median gonapophyses, q.v. (Tuxen, after Tillyard).

median projection (of transtilla), in ♂ *Zarcorisa* (Lepidoptera: Tortricidae), slender, paired processes of transtilla knob, directed mediad (Tuxen, after Diakonoff).

median ramus, in ♀ Heteroptera (Hemiptera), anterior connecting leaf of gonapophysis VIII, q.v. (Tuxen, after Davis).

median ridge, in ♂ Siphonaptera, lamina media, q.v. (Tuxen, after Sharif).

median rod, in ♂ *Zorotypus zimmermani* Gurn. (Zoraptera), rod extending from dorsal part of central body to lateral and basal plates (Tuxen).

median sclerite, in ♂ Phasmida, sclerotization of copulatory organ (Tuxen, after Snodgrass); in ♂ Embiidina, sclerite arising on mediobasal margin of abdominal tergum X (Ross, in Tuxen); in ♂ Dermaptera, median strengthening of basal region or penis (Tuxen); in some ♀ Helotrephidae (Hemiptera: Heteroptera), proximal part of transformed ovipositor pertaining to abdominal segment IX (Papáček, Tonner, and Štys); in ♂ Simuliidae (Diptera), a dorsal extension arising from the ventral plate (Peterson, in McAlpine); in higher Diptera, distinct median sclerite of occiput (Colless and McAlpine, in CSIRO).

median sclerotized style, in ♂ Hymenoptera, detached rhachies, q.v. (Tuxen, after Ries).

median sector, in adult Odonata, third branch of media (M_3) (T-B).

median segment, in adult Apocrita (Hymenoptera), propodeum, q.v. (T-B).

median scutal fossal scale, in adult Culicidae (Diptera), one of the scales occurring in a group on the central area of the scutual fossa (Harbach and Knight).

median scutal fossal seta, in adult Culicidae (Diptera), one of the setae occurring in a group near the center of the scutual fossa (Harbach and Knight).

median scutellar scale, in adult Culicidae (Diptera), one of the scales occurring in a group on the middle lobe of the scutellum (Harbach and Knight).

median scutellar seta, in adult Culicidae (Diptera), one of the setae occurring in a group on the middle lobe of the scutellum (Harbach and Knight).

median seta, in Ephemeroptera, filum terminale, q.v. (Tuxen, after Phillips).

median setae, in adult Chironomidae (Diptera), median rows of setae on tergites, when anterior transverse rows of setae (basal setae) are lacking (Saether).

median shade, median line, q.v. (T-B).

median space, in Lepidoptera, the area between the median lines (T-B); in Odonata, the cubital cell (T-B, after Comstock); the basilar space of the wing, q.v. (T-B, after Garman); the space at the base of the wing between radius and first anal (T-B); medial cell of Comstock (T-B, after Selys).

median spermatheca, in ♀ Heteroptera (Hemiptera), receptaculum seminis, q.v. (Tuxen, after Scudder).

median spermathecal gland, in ♀ Heteroptera (Hemiptera), vermiform gland, q.v. (Tuxen, after Scudder).

median sternal groove, in adult Hymenoptera, discrimen, q.v. (Gauld and Bolton).

median strut of tegmen, in ♂ Coleoptera, unpaired apophysis of tegmen (Tuxen).

median superior anal appendage, in ♂ Anisoptera (Odonata), appendix dorsalis, q.v. (T-B, after Imms).

median survival time (ST_{50}), time at which death occurs in half the test subjects after exposure to a pathogenic (including toxicological) stimulus (Steinhaus and Martignoni); see median lethal time.

median suspensory ligament, the ligaments of the 2 ovaries when combined into one (T-B, after Snodgrass).

median suture, a longitudinal suture on the midline line of the tergites and sternites (T-B, after Comstock); in some larval Chironomidae (Diptera), secondary suture running from apex (or base) of mentum posteriorly to postoccipital margin along ventral midline of head capsule (Saether).

median terminal lobe, in larval Symphyta (Hymenoptera), terminal lobe arising from prementum formed from fusion of glossae, paraglossae, and part of the hypopharynx (Gauld and Bolton); see ligule.

median unpaired sclerite, in adult Chironomidae (Diptera), sternapodeme (Saether).

median valves, in ♀ Auchenorrhyncha (Hemiptera), second gonapophyses, q.v. (Tuxen).

median vein, media, q.v. (Chapman).

median ventral tuft, in ♀ *Aedes aegypti* (L.) (Diptera: Culicidae), a small tuft of spicules occurring on the midline of the vaginal floor just inside the lower vaginal lip (Harbach and Knight, after Jones and Wheeler).

median volsella, in ♂ Chironomidae (Diptera), apparent basal, median appendage of gonocoxite IX (Saether).

mediary segment, in adult Hymenoptera, propodeum, q.v. (T-B).

mediastinal, relating to the longitudinal median line or area (T-B).

mediastinal area, in Orthoptera, area between subcosta and costal margin (T-B); see costal cell.

mediastinal cell, in adult Diptera, subcostal cell, q.v. (Colless and McAlpine, in CSIRO, after Schiner).

mediastinal vein, in wing of adult Orthoptera and Diptera, subcosta, q.v. (T-B, after Schiner, Curran; Colless and McAlpine, in CSIRO).

medico-legal entomology, branch of forensic entomology devoted to the use of insects to determine postmortem interval in criminal cases (Adkins, pers. comm.).

medifurca, furca, q.v., of mesosternum (T-B, after Packard).

medigynium (pl., **medigynia**), in ♀ Mecoptera, internal apparatus above subgenitale (Tuxen).

mediocubital, of or pertaining to the media and cubitus of the wing (T-B).

mediocubital crossvein (m-cu), crossvein connecting media and cubitus (T-B; Chapman; Saether).

mediotergite, in Heteroptera (Hemiptera), major unpaired plate of an abdominal tergum with delimited paired laterotergites (Štys); in adult Diptera, median portion of longitudinally divided postnotum (T-B, after Crampton; Colless and McAlpine, in CSIRO).

medioventral line, in larval Lepidoptera, line along middle of the under side (T-B).

medipectus, mesosternum, q.v. (T-B).

mediproboscis, haustellum, q.v. (T-B, after MacGillivray).

medisternite, in ♀ Isoptera, small median sclerotized area in intersegmental membrane between abdominal sterna VIII and IX (Tuxen, after Browman).

medithorax, mesothorax., q.v. (T-B).

meditruncus, mesothorax, q.v. (T-B).

medituberculum, in ♂ Mecoptera, median tooth on inner margin of stylus (Tuxen).

mediuncus (pl., **mediunci**), in ♂ Neuropteroidea, median backward directed process from upper part of gonarcus (Tuxen, after Tjeder); in some ♂ Chrysopidae (Planipennia), arcessus, q.v. (Tuxen, after Adams); in ♂ Berothidae (Planipennia), penisfilum, q.v. (Tuxen, after Adams and MacLeod).

medius, middle (T-B); media, q.v., of wing (T-B).

medlure, a synthetic attractant for baiting the Mediterranean fruit fly, *Ceratitis capitata* (Diptera: Tephritidae); *sec*-butyl 4(or 5)-chloro-2-methylcyclohexanecarboxylate (Pfadt).

medulla, in brachiopod Crustacea, the proximal of the 2 ganglionic bodies (T-B, after Snodgrass); in insects, the central area of a ganglion (T-B, after Wardle).

medulla externa, neuropile mass of optic lobe located between lamina ganglionaris and medulla interna (Chapman).

medulla interna, proximal neuropile mass of optic lobe (Chapman); see lamina ganglionaris and medulla externa.

medullary substance, neuropile, q.v. (T-B, after Snodgrass).

medullary tissue, neuropile, q.v. (T-B).

mega-, megalo-, Greek prefix; large (T-B).

megachromosomes, giant chromosomes, q.v. (Leftwich).

megacyte, extremely large cell with colorless vacuoles found in *Forficula* (Dermaptera: Forficulidae) hemolymph (Tulloch, after Arvy and Lhoste, Jones).

Megalodontoidea, superfamily within the suborder Symphyta (Hymenoptera), including only the Megalodontidae and Pamphilidae, possessing adults with a highly modified head capsule with separate mandibular foramina (Gauld and Bolton).

megalohemocyte, an abnormal, hypertrophoid plasmatocytelike cell (Tulloch, after Jones).

Megaloptera, order within the Holometabola, possessing adults with 2 pairs of slightly dissimilar functional wings; larvae aquatic with well-developed mandibulate mouthparts, three-segmented labial palpi, well-developed prothorax, functional legs, and lateral abdominal gills; pupae decticious, exarate (Riek, in CSIRO); sometimes treated as a suborder of Neuroptera (Borror et al.) (see Neuropteroidea).

Megalyroidea, superfamily within the Apocrita (Hymenoptera), including the family Megalyridae, possessing adults with subantennal groove for reception of basal articles of antenna, with spurs on hind tibia not modified for preening, subsessile gaster, and antennae with 14 articles (Riek, in CSIRO; Gauld and Bolton).

Meganisoptera, extinct order of Paleoptera (Insecta), from the Carboniferous Period to the Triassic Period, possessing adults with long, narrow bodies, prominent eyes and mandibles, oblique thoracic segments, spiny legs, and all main veins, except for radial sector (R_s) originating separately from base (Riek, in CSIRO).

Megasecoptera, extinct order of Paleoptera (Insecta), from the Carboniferous Period to the Permian Period, possessing adults with rather slender bodies and very long cerci (Riek, in CSIRO); see Eumegasecoptera and Paramegasecoptera.

megetic, applied to the size variations in insects exhibiting polymorphism (Tulloch); see epimegetic, eumegetic, and hypomegetic.

meiapterous morph, in Gerromorpha (Hemiptera: Heteroptera), short-winged morphs (Andersen).

meiosis, a process requiring 2 cell divisions in which the diploid number of chromosomes is reduced to the haploid number (Tulloch).

meiotic parthenogenesis, automictic parthenogenesis, q.v. (Chapman).

melanic, with a blackish infusion (T-B).

melanin, insoluble brown or black cuticular pigment consisting of polymerized indole rings, formed by oxidation of the amino acid tyrosine in the presence of specific melanogenic enzymes (T-B; Leftwich; Chapman).

melanism, an unusual darkening of color owing to increased amounts of dark pigment (T-B; Mayr); see albinism and industrial melanism.

melanistic, dark or blackish (T-B).

melanochroic, dark colored or tending to blackness.

melanosis, a disease of queen honey bees (Hymenoptera: Apoidea), characterized by discoloration of the egg cells and trophocytes, which turn from yellow-brown to black, and producing sterility in affected queens (Steinhaus and Martignoni); see B-melanosis and H-melanosis.

melezitose, an isomer of sucrose, being common in honeydew excreted by aphids (Hemiptera: Sternorrhyncha: Aphidoidea) (Chapman).

meliphagous, meliphagus, honey-eating (T-B).

melissaeus, balm-scented (T-B).

melissic, of, pertaining to, or obtained from honey or beeswax.

melittin, a poisonous proteinlike substance present in the venom of bees (Hymenoptera: Apoidea) (Leftwich).

melittology, the study of bees (Hymenoptera: Apoidea) (Wilson).

melittophile, any guest, parasite or predator in the society of bees (Hymenoptera: Apoidea) (Tulloch, after Gaul).

melittophily, insect-flower pollination syndrome involving bees (Hymenoptera: Apoidea) (Matthews and Matthews, after Baker and Hurd).

mellifera, honey-makers; applied to bees (Hymenoptera: Apoidea) as a whole (T-B).

melliferous, honey-producing (T-B); pollen and nectar gathering, e.g., bees (Apoidea) and some Vespidae (Hymenoptera) (Riek, in CSIRO).

mellisugous, honey-sucking; feeding on honey (T-B).

melocephalic, having a pseudohypognathous type of head (T-B, after MacGillivray).

melolonthoid, *Melolontha*-like; resembling a June beetle or chafer (Coleoptera: Scarabaeidae) (T-B).

Meloidea, superfamily within the Polyphaga (Coleoptera), including the Meloidae, Mordellidae, Rhipiphoridae, Anthicidae, Pedilidae, and Euglenidae, more recently included within the Tenebrionoidea (Borror et al.; Lawrence, in Parker).

melting brood, European foulbrood, q.v. (Steinhaus and Martignoni).

member, appendage, q.v. (T-B).

membrana, membrane, q.v. (T-B).

membrana fenestrata, in insects, basement membrane, q.v., of compound eye, q.v. (T-B, after Snodgrass).

membrana retinens, in Lepidoptera, Osborne membrane, q.v. (T-B).

membranaceous, membranaceus (Latin), membranous, q.v. (T-B).

membranal lobi, in ♂ Calyptratae (Diptera), sclerotizations of distiphallus (Tuxen, after Zumpt and Heinz).

membrane, a thin, flexible, usually transparent, film of tissue, e.g., tissue between wing veins (T-B; Borror et al.); in adult Heteroptera (Hemiptera), membranous apical portion of hemelytron (T-B; Woodward et al., in CSIRO); in ♀ Chironomidae (Diptera), membrane or sclerotized hinge, dorsad of and between dorsal lobes, connecting gonapophyses VIII (Saether).

membrane potential, charge differential across the plasma membrane of an axon produced by Donnan equilibrium, q.v., being commonly about -70 mV for nerve axons (Chapman).

membranization, change into a membrane (T-B).

membranous, like a membrane; thin and more or less transparent (wings); thin and pliable (cuticle) (T-B; Borror et al.).

membranous appendage, in ♂ Siphonaptera, a membranous extension of the apex of ♂ abdominal sternum IX (Rothschild and Traub).

membranous flap, in ♂ Siphonaptera, membranous appendage, q.v. (Tuxen, after Rothschild).

membranous veil, in ♀ Coleophoridae (Lepidoptera), colorless sheath around proximal (caudal) part of ductus bursae, clothed internally with numerous spines (Tuxen, after Toll).

membranula intercoronaria, in ♂ *Zygaena* (Lepidoptera: Zygaenidae), finely spined area in lamina dorsalis of aedoeagus (Tuxen, after Loritz).

membranule, in adult Anisoptera (Odonata), small opaque expansion behind first anal vein (1A) at extreme base of hind wing (T-B; O'Farrell, in CSIRO).

membrum virile, in ♂ Auchenorrhyncha (Hemiptera), aedeagus, q.v. (Tuxen, after Then).

Mendelian population, a population with unrestricted interbreeding of individuals and free reassortment of genes (Mayr).

meniscoidal, crescent-shaped; concavoconvex; one side convex and the other concave (T-B).

menognatha, insects in which both immatures and adults feed by mandibles, e.g., the Orthoptera (T-B); see menorhyncha and metagnatha.

menorhyncha, forms in which both immatures and adults take food by suction, e.g., Hemiptera (T-B); see menognatha and metagnatha.

menotaxis, partial or indefinite orientation (T-B); movement in a direction that makes a constant angle with a source of light, as for instance in the case of some ants (Hymenoptera: Formicidae), so as to keep a constant visual pattern (Leftwich); see light-compass reaction.

mensis, in ♂ Tortricidae (Lepidoptera), the differentiated sclerotized margin of abdominal segment VIII, usually shaped as a narrow rod (Tuxen, after Diakonoff).

mensis dorsalis, in ♂ Tortricidae (Lepidoptera), dorsocaudal margin of mensis (Tuxen, after Diakonoff).

mensis ventralis, in ♂ Tortricidae (Lepidoptera), ventrocaudal margin of mensis (Tuxen, after Diakonoff).

mental, of or pertaining to the mentum (T-B).

mental plate, labial plate, q.v. (Peterson).

mental setae, in nymphs of Odonata, setae on the inner surface of the prementum (T-B, after Garman; Borror et al.; Chapman).

mental suture, the line between the submentum and the gula (T-B).

mentasuture, mental suture, q.v. (T-B, after MacGillivray).

mentigerous, bearing or having a mentum (T-B).

mentum (pl., **menta**), distal subdivision of postmentum (Chapman); in nymphs of Odonata, prementum, q.v. (T-B, after Garman); in ♂ Plebeiinae (Lepidoptera: Lycaenidae), the jutting distal part of processus superior of costa of valva (Tuxen, after Nabokov); in adult Diptera, postmentum, q.v. (McAlpine, after Crampton); in larval Chironomidae (Diptera), usually toothed, sclerotized, double-walled medioventral plate of head capsule consisting of dorsomentum and ventromentum with the latter often expanded laterally into ventromental plates (Saether); see prementum and submentum.

meracanthus, in some Psyllidae (Hemiptera: Sternorrhyncha), distinct, conical, posterior projection from hind coxa (Woodward et al., in CSIRO).

meral plate, in adult Diptera, meron, q.v. (T-B).

merdivorous, feeding upon dung or excrement (T-B); see scatophagous.

meriaeum, the plate or plates of the anterior surface of the sockets of the posterior legs, behind the acetabulum and parapleuron (T-B, after Knoch); in Coleoptera, the posterior inflected part of the metasternum (T-B, after Smith).

meridic, pertaining to a medium (used for growing organisms) in which the chemical identity of certain, but not all, of absolutely essential molecules has been established (Steinhaus and Martignoni); see holidic and oligidic.

Meridogastra, Ricinulei, q.v. (Borror et al.).

meristic variation, variation in characters that can be counted (Mayr).

meriston, the most proximal annulus of the antennal flagellum (Chapman).

mermithaner, a ♂ ant (Hymenoptera: Formicidae), parasitized by the nematode *Mermis* (T-B); see mermithophore.

mermithergate, a worker ant (Hymenoptera: Formicidae), parasitized by the nematode *Mermis* (T-B); see mermithophore.

mermithized, the condition of being parasitized by members of the genus *Mermis* (Nematoda) (Tulloch, after Gaul).

mermithodinergate, a soldier mermithophore (Tulloch).

mermithogyne, a queen ant (Hymenoptera: Formicidae), parasitized by the nematode *Mermis* (T-B); see mermithophore.

mermithophore, any anomolous form or any form resulting from parsitism by *Mermis* nematodes, e.g., mermithaner, mermithergate, and mermithogyne (Tulloch).

mermithostratiotes, mermithodinergate, q.v. (Tulloch).

meroblastic cleavage, the type cleavage found in lecithal eggs, in which only the nucleus and the nuclear cytoplasm are divided (T-B, after Snodgrass; Tulloch).

merocrine, of or pertaining to merocriny (T-B).

merocrine secretion, merocriny, q.v. (Borror et al.).

merocriny, the passage of a digestive enzyme into the lumen of the gut or salivary duct through the free borders of the secretory cells (T-B, after Wardle); see holocriny.

meroistic egg tube, meroistic ovariole, q.v. (T-B, after Snodgrass).

meroistic ovariole, ovariole in which nurse cells or trophocytes are present (T-B, after Imms; Chapman); see panoistic ovariole, polytrophic ovariole, and telotrophic ovariole.

meron, posterior part of basicoxite, being very large in adult Neuropteroidea, and Panorpoidea, while in the higher Diptera being separated from the coxa altogether and forming part of meropleurite (T-B, after Imms; Colless and McAlpine, in CSIRO; Chapman; McAlpine).

Meronida, hypothesized menophyletic group including the Neuropteroidea and Panorpoidea (Boudreaux).

meropleurite, in higher Diptera, fused meron and katepisternum (T-B, after Crampton; McAlpine).

meropleuron, (pl., **meropleura**), in higher Diptera, meropleurite, q.v. (Borror et al.; Colless and McAlpine, in CSIRO) or meron, q.v. (McAlpine).

meropodite, in the generalized leg of Arthropoda, the fourth segment, corresponding to the femur in insects (T-B).

merosome, metamere, q.v. (Boudreaux).

Merostomata, class within the subphylum Chelicerata (Arthropoda), including the Eurypterida and Xiphosura (Borror et al.).

merozoite, stage in the asexual development of the protozoan *Plasmodium* (Plasmodiidae), which causes malaria, derived from the schizont, which infects another red blood cell and forms a trophozoite (T-B, after Comstock; Tulloch).

mesad, toward or in the direction of the meson of the insect body (T-B).

mesadene gland, in some ♂ Heteroptera, e.g., *Mesovelia furcata* (Mesoveliidae), a pair of glands which enter the ejaculatory duct dorsally (Andersen); see mesadenia and ectadenia.

mesadenia, in some ♂ insects, e.g., Orthoptera and *Tenebrio* (Coleoptera: Tenebrionidae), accessory genital glands of mesodermal origin, associated with the vasa deferentia (T-B; Chapman); see ectadenia.

mesal, pertaining to, situated on, or in the meson (T-B).

mesal penellipse, in larval Lepidoptera, e.g., Pyralidae, an almost complete circle (at least two-thirds) of crochets open or incomplete on the lateral margin (Peterson).

mesal plates, in certain Coccoidea (Hemiptera: Sternorrhyncha), the plates of wax located on the meson between the dorsal plates, limited to the mesothorax, metathorax and first abdominal segments (T-B, after MacGillivray).

mesanapleural suture, in adult Culicidae (Diptera), anapleural suture of mesothorax (Harbach and Knight).

mesanepimeral ridge, in adult Culicidae (Diptera), an internal ridge along the ventral margin of the mesanepimeron serving for the attachment of wing muscles (Harbach and Knight).

mesanepimeron, the anepimeron of the mesothorax (Harbach and Knight).

mesanepisternum, the upper area of the mespisternum separated from the meskatepisternum by the mesanapleural suture (Harbach and Knight).

mesarima, the fissure separating the glossae (T-B, after MacGillivray).

mesaxon, spiral arrangement of a glial cell around an axon (Chapman).

mesenchyma, mesenchyme, mesoblastic tissue formed of loosely connected or scattered cells (T-B, after Snodgrass).

mesenchymatous cell, hemocyte, q.v. (Tulloch).

mesenteron, midgut, q.v. (T-B; Borror et al.).

mesenteron rudiments, groups of endodermal cells that generate the midgut, including an anterior, a posterior, and sometimes an intermediate rudiment (T-B, after Snodgrass; Hinton and Mackerras, in CSIRO).

Mesephemeroidea, extinct superfamily of Ephemeroptera from the Upper Permian and Upper Jurassic, including Mesephemeridae (Landa and Soldán).

mesepimeral microtrichia, in Lepidoptera, a dense patch of minute spines located ventral to the basalare sclerite on the mesepimeron which intermesh with the subhumeral microtrichia of the forewing when the wings are folded at rest (Davis).

mesepimeral scale, in adult Culicidae (Diptera), any scale borne on the mesepimeron (Harbach and Knight).

mesepimeral seta, in adult Culicidae (Diptera), any seta borne on the mesepimeron (Harbach and Knight).

mesepimeron (pl., **mesepimera**), the epimeron of the mesothorax (T-B; Borror et al.).

mesepisternal groove, in adult Diptera, katepisternal sulcus, q.v. (McAlpine).

mesepisternal sulcus, in adult Simuliidae (Diptera), katepisternal sulcus, q.v. (Peterson, in McAlpine).

mesepisternal suture, in adult Culicidae (Diptera), the line of demarcation extending along the anterodorsal margin of the combined meskatepisternum and posterior mesanepisternum (Harbach and Knight, after Patton and Evans); see katepisternal sulcus.

mesepisternum (pl., **mesepisterna**), the episternum of the mesothorax (T-B, after J. B. Smith; Borror et al.).

mesially, at or toward the middle (T-B).

mesinfraepisternum, katepisternum, q.v., of mesothorax (T-B; Borror et al.).

meskatepisternal bridge, in adult Diptera, the narrow ridge uniting the ventral extremities of the meskatepisterna between the pro- and mesosterna (Harbach and Knight).

meskatepisternal scale, in adult Culicidae (Diptera), any scale borne on the meskatepisternum (Harbach and Knight).

meskatepisternal seta, in adult Culicidae (Diptera), any seta borne on the meskatepisternum (Harbach and Knight).

meskatespisternum, in adult Diptera, katepisternum of the mesothorax (Harbach and Knight).

mes(o)-, Greek prefix; the middle; being used to indicate the middle part or structure, e.g., mesothorax, mesoderm (T-B).

mesobasal lobe, in ♂ *Nemoura,* sbg. *Malenka* (Plecoptera: Nemouridae), large, inward directed process of cercus (Tuxen, after Ricker).

mesobasisternum, in adult Diptera, basisternum of the mesothorax (Harbach and Knight).

mesobiliverdin, blue bilin pigment commonly combined with protein in asssocation with a yellow carotenoid to produce the green color of many insects (Chapman).

mesoblast, mesoderm, q.v. (T-B).

mesoblastic, of or pertaining to the mesoblast (T-B).

mesoblastic somites, segmental divisions of the embryonic insect mesoderm (T-B).

mesocephalic pillars, in the honey bee (Hymenoptera: Apoidea), 2 large, oblique, strongly chitinous bars which form a brace between the anterior and posterior walls of the head (T-B, after Snodgrass).

mesocerebrum, deutocerebrum, q.v. (Leftwich).

mesocoxa, midcoxa, q.v. (T-B).

mesocoxal cavity, a coxal cavity of the mesothorax (Harbach and Knight).

mesocuticle, an elastic derivative of procuticle found between exocuticle and endocuticle and in numerous elastic structures (Tulloch, after Rockstein); layer of cuticle between the exocuticle and endocuticle that is sclerotized but not fully darkened (Chapman).

mesoderm, in the insect embryo, the meroblastic tissue which takes the form of the definite middle cell layer, giving rise later to visceral muscles, somatic muscles, fat body, and gonads (T-B, after Snodgrass; Chapman).

mesodermal tube, dorsal vessel, q.v. (Tulloch).

Mesodermaptera, infraorder within the suborder Catadermaptera (Dermaptera), including the families Carcinophoridae and Labiduridae (Steinmann).

mesodiscaloca, in Coccoidea (Hemiptera: Sternorrhyncha), discaloca, q.v. (T-B, after MacGillivray).

mesodont, in ♂ Lucanidae (Coleoptera), mandibles intermediate in size between the teleodont or large, and the priodont or small, mandibles.

mesoepimerum, mesepimeron, q.v. (Harbach and Knight, after Snodgrass).

mesoepisternum, mesepisternum, q.v. (T-B).

mesofacial plate, in adult Diptera, face, q.v. (T-B).

mesofemur, midfemur, q.v.

mesofrons, in adult Diptera, frontal vitta, q.v. (McAlpine).

mesofurca, furca of the mesothorax (Harbach and Knight).

mesofurcasternum, area of mesosternum bearing the mesofurca (Harbach and Knight); see furcasternum.

mesolobes, in ♂ Schizophora Calyptratae (Diptera: Muscomorpha), cerci, q.v. (McAlpine).

mesolobus, in ♂ Calyptratae (Diptera), cerci, q.v. (Tuxen).

mesomeral arch, in ♂ Phthiraptera, apically-fused mesomeres (Lyal).

mesomere(s), in ♂ insects, median phallomeres when primary phallic lobes are secondarily divided, the lateral ones being parameres, uniting into phallus (Tuxen, after Snodgrass); in ♂ Phthiraptera, paired sclerites articulated to or fused with posterodorsal angle of basal apodeme, sometimes being fused apically (Lyal); see mesomeral arch.

mesomeron, meron of the mesothorax (Harback and Knight, after Knight and Laffoon).

mesomeros, in adult Lepidoptera, abdominal segments II–V (T-B); see metameros.

meson, midline of the body (T-B; Borror et al.).

mesonotal disc, in adult Culicidae (Diptera), the area of the scutum comprising the acrostichal and the dorsocentral areas (Harbach and Knight, after Schick).

mesonotal process, in some adult Chironomidae (Diptera), scutal process, q.v. (Saether).

mesonotal lamella, in adult Chironomidae (Diptera), scutal lamella, q.v. (Saether).

mesonotal setae, in pupal Chironomidae (Diptera), dorsocentrals, q.v. (Saether).

mesonotal tubercle, in adult Chironomidae (Diptera), scutal tubercle, q.v. (Saether).

mesonotum, notum of mesothorax (T-B; Peteron; Harbach and Knight); see scutum.

mesopedes, midlegs, q.v. (T-B).

mesophragma, an internal prolongation of the metaprescutum, affording attachment to some of the wing muscles (T-B).

mesophyll, in plants, the leaf tissue lying between the upper and lower epidermis (T-B); see parenchyma.

mesoplasmatocyte, plasmatocyte of intermediate size (Tulloch); see megaplasmatocyte and microplasmatocyte.

mesopleural, of or pertaining to the mesopleuron (T-B).

mesopleural bristles, in adult Diptera, general term for any large setae on the pleuron of the (meso)thorax in Diptera, (Borror et al.).

mesopleural ridge, pleural ridge of mesothorax (Harbach and Knight, after Knight and Laffoon).

mesopleural suture, pleural sulcus of mesopleuron (T-B, after Comstock; Harbach and Knight).

mesopleuron (pl., **mesopleura**), pleuron of mesothorax (T-B; Harbach and Knight); in adult Diptera, mesanepisternum, q.v. (T-B, after Comstock; McAlpine).

mesopleurosternal ridge, in adult Culicidae (Diptera),, invagination of the mesopleurosternal suture (Harbach and Knight).

mesopleurosternal suture, in adult Culicidae (Diptera), the external groove between the meskatepisternum and the mesobasisternum, or the mesosternum when the mesobasisternum is not discernible (Harbach and Knight).

mesopostnotal scale, in adult Culicidae (Diptera), one of the scales occurring in a small cluster on the posteromesial area of the mediotergite (Harbach and Knight, after Belkin).

mesopostnotal seta, in adult Culicidae (Diptera), one of the setae occurring in a small group on the median posterior area of the mediotergite (Harbach and Knight).

mesopostnotum, postnotum of mesothorax (Chapman).

mesoscutellum, scutellum of the mesothorax (T-B).

mesoscutum, scutum of the mesothorax (Borror et al.).

mesoseries, in larval Lepidoptera, a band of crochets or hooks extending longitudinally on the mesal side of a proleg (Peterson).

mesosoma (pl., **mesosomata**), the middle of the 3 major divisions of the insect body, in most insects being strictly equivalent to the thorax, but in some Apocrita (Hymenoptera) including the propodeum (Wilson) (see alitrunk); in ♂ Lithosiinae (Lepidoptera: Arctiidae), sclerotized plate connecting the 2, usually more or less modified, valvellae ventrad of aedoeagus, which it supports (Tuxen, after Birket-Smith); see alitrunk.

mesosome, in ♂ Phthiraptera, collective name for sclerites of endophallus (Tuxen); in ♂ Heteroptera (Hemiptera), endosoma, q.v. (Tuxen, after Christophers and Cragg); in ♂ Diptera, aedeagus, q.v. (Tuxen, after Edwards; Colless and McAlpine, in CSIRO; McAlpine).

mesospermalege (pl. **mesospermalegia**), in some Cimicoidea (Hemiptera: Heteroptera), subintegumental mesodermal part of the spermalege into which the spermatozoa are injected (Carayon, in Usinger); see ectospermalege.

mesosternal cavity, in Elateridae (Coleoptera), the opening into which the prosternal spine or mucro is fitted (T-B).

mesosternal epimera, in Coleoptera, the narrow pieces separating the mesosternal from the metasternal episterna (T-B).

mesosternal episterna, in Coleoptera, those on each side of mesosternum between the anterior border and the epimera, generally separated by a distinct suture (T-B).

mesosternal interspace, in Caelifera (Orthoptera), a deep median notch diving the mesosternal lobes (Key, pers. comm., after Uvarov).

mesosternal lobes, in Orthoptera, mesosternellum, q.v. (T-B).

mesosternal ridge, in adult Culicidae (Diptera), the median longitudinal invagination marked externally by the mesosternal suture (Harbach and Knight).

mesosternal suture, in adult Culicidae (Diptera), the external groove marking the mesosternal ridge, extending from the mesopleurosternal sutures to the intersegmental suture between the meso- and metathorax (Harbach and Knight); see discrimen.

mesosternals, in adult Chironomidae (Diptera), preepisternals, q.v. (Saether).

mesosternellum, in Orthoptera, 2 median lobes of the mesosternum, one on each side of the mesosternal interspace (T-B); in general, the sternellum of the mesothorax (T-B).

mesosternepisternum, in adult Chironomidae (Diptera), preepisternum, q.v., of mesothorax (Saether).

mesosternum, sternum of mesothorax (T-B).

mesostethidium, mesothorax, q.v. (T-B).

mesostigmal plates, in adult Odonata, small sclerites surrounding the mesothoracic spiracles (T-B, after Garman).

mesosulcus, in adult Hymenoptera, discrimen, q.v. (T-B).

mesotarsus, midtarsus, q.v. (T-B).

mesotergum, mesonotum, q.v. (T-B).

mesothoracic, of or pertaining to the mesothorax.

mesothoracic leg, midleg, q.v. (McAlpine).

mesothoracic spiracles, spiracles of the mesothorax (Harbach and Knight); in adult and larval Diptera, anterior spiracles, q.v. (McAlpine; Teskey, in McAlpine).

mesothoracotheca, the pupal covering of the mesothorax (T-B).

mesothorax, the second or middle thoracic segment bearing the midlegs and the forewings (T-B).

mesotibia, midtibia, q.v.

mesotrochanter, midtrochanter, q.v.

mesotrochantin, the precoxal sclerite of the mesopleuron (Harbach and Knight).

Mesozoic Era, time period in the geological history of the earth, including the Triassic, Jurassic, and Cretaceous periods, extending between about 225 to 70 million years before the present (Riek, in CSIRO).

Mesoveloidea, superfamily of Heteroptera within the infraorder Gerromorpha including the predatory water-surface dwelling family Mesoveliidae (Andersen).

messorial, in many larval Nematocera (Diptera), premandible, q.v. (Teskey, in McAlpine).

Mesurol (trade name), methiocarb, q.v. (Pfadt).

meta-, Greek prefix; designating the posterior (generally the third) part of a structure (T-B).

metaanepisternum, in adult Odonata, the anepisternum of the metathorax (T-B, after Garman).

metabasisternum, the basisternum of the metathorax (Harbach and Knight).

metablastic, relating to the ecto- or metablast or ectoderm (T-B).

metabolic water, see tissue water (T-B).

metabolism, the total of all the chemical processes of living organisms (Tulloch); see anabolism, basal metabolism, and katabolism.

metabolites, metabolized substances; in general any of the products of metabolism; substances which take part in a process of metabolism (T-B).

metabolous, undergoing metamorphosis or transformation, i.e., paurometabolous, hemimetabolous, or holometabolous (T-B); see ametabolous.

metacephalic rods, in hemicephalic larvae of some orthorrhaphous Brachycera (Diptera), elongate pair of dorsal sclerites within the thorax, representing posterior portion of the head (Colless and McAlpine, in CSIRO).

metacephalon, in adult Diptera, genal dilation, q.v. (T-B, after Curran).

metacerebrum, tritocerebrum, q.v. (Leftwich).

metachemogenesis, post-emergence biochemical maturation in holometabolous insects, exclusive of sexual maturation (Tulloch, after Rockstein).

metacoxa, hind coxa, q.v.

metacoxal cavity, in adult Culicidae (Diptera), the coxal cavity of the metathorax (Harbach and Knight).

metacoxal plate, in adult Coccinellidae (Coleoptera), that portion of the first visible abdominal sternite anterior to the ventral line (T-B).

metaepisternum, metepisternum, q.v. (T-B).

metafemur, hind femur, q.v.

metafurca, furca of the metasternum (Harbach and Knight).

metafurcasternum, the area of the metasternum bearing the metafurca (Harbach and Knight).

metagenesis, alternation of generations, q.v. (T-B).

metagnatha, insects which feed with jaws as immatures and with a tubular proboscis as adults, e.g., the Lepidoptera; see menognatha and menorhyncha.

metagonia, anal angle, q.v., of wing (T-B).

metakatepisternum, katepisternum of metapleuron, e.g., *Dolichopeza* (Diptera: Tipulidae), but usually indistinct in other Diptera (McAlpine).

metala, hind wing, q.v. (T-B).

metaldehyde, $(CH_3CHO)_4$, a chemical with slug-killing properties; moderatley toxic to mammals, acute oral LD_{50} for rats 630 mg/kg (Pfadt).

metalkamate, $C_{13}H_{19}NO_2$, a synthetic insecticide; a carbamate, *m*-(1-ethylpropyl)phenyl methylcarbamate mixture (1-4) with *m*-(1-butylethyl)phenyl methylcarbamate; moderately toxic to mammals; acute oral LD_{50} for rats 87 to 170 mg/kg (Pfadt).

metallic, having the appearance of metal; applied to a surface or color (T-B).

metaloma, anal margin, q.v., of wing (T-B).

metameral scale, in adult Culicidae (Diptera), one of the scales occurring in a small cluster on the metameron (Harbach and Knight).

metamere, a body segment arising through primary segmentation (T-B); see somite.

metameric, divided into primary body segments or metameres (T-B); of or pertaining to metamerism (T-B).

metameric sac, osmeterium, q.v. (T-B).

metameric segmentation, primary segmentation, q.v. (Leftwich).

metamerism, primary segmentation, q.v. (T-B).

metameron, the meron of the metathorax (Harbach and Knight).

metameros, in adult Lepidoptera, the sixth to eighth abdominal segments (T-B); see mesomeros.

metamorphosis, the series of changes through which an insect passes in its growth from the egg to the adult stage (T-B); a drastic change in form during development (Mayr); see complete metamorphosis and incomplete metamorphosis.

metamorphotype method, in Trichoptera, technique for associating larva, pupa, and adult of a given species, whereby the pharate adult is identifiable within its pupal exuviae and sclerites of its last larval instar are retained (except by Leptoceridae and Molannidae) in the posterior end of its pupal case (Wiggins).

metanepisternum, in adult Diptera, anepisternum of metapleuron (McAlpine).

metanotal gland, in ♂ *Oecanthus* (Orthoptera: Tettigoniidae) and some Blattaria, a large gland indicated externally by a deep depression in the metanotum producing secretions that are fed upon by the ♀ (T-B, after Imms; Chapman).

metanotal groove, in some adult Hymenoptera, transverse groove representing fusion of mesonotum and metanotum (Gauld and Bolton).

metanotal slope, in adult Diptera, laterotergite, q.v. (T-B, after Curran).

metanotals, in pupal Chironomidae (Diptera), setae on postnotum behind covering case of halteres (Saether).

metanotum, tergum of the metathorax (Peterson); in adult Diptera, mediotergite, q.v. (T-B).

metaparameres, in ♂ Dermaptera, parameres, q.v. (Tuxen, after Burr).

metaparapteron, in ants (Hymenoptera: Formicidae), postnotum, q.v. (T-B, after W. M. Wheeler).

metapedes, hind legs, q.v. (T-B).

metaphragma, the hindmost internal thoracic septum (T-B).

metaplanta, second tarsomere, q.v. (T-B).

metapleural bristles, in some adult Diptera, a fanlike row of bristles on the laterotergite (T-B, after Comstock).

metapleural gland, in most Formicidae (Hymenoptera), a large gland with an external bulla and a small orifice, opening on each side of the metathorax at its lower posterior corners (Brown and Taylor, in CSIRO).

metapleural ridge, the pleural ridge of the metathorax (Harbach and Knight).

metapleural suture, pleural suture of metapleuron (T-B, after Garman; McAlpine).

metapleuron (pl., **metapleura**), pleuron of the metathorax (T-B; Borror et al.); in adult Diptera, sometimes used for laterotergite, q.v. (McAlpine).

metapneustic respiratory system, in larvae, chiefly Diptera (e.g., Culicidae), an oligopneustic type in which only the last abdominal pair of spiracles is open (T-B; Chapman, after Keilin).

metapnystega, the circular area of the metanotum behind the postscutellum (T-B).

metapodeon, in Hymenoptera, gaster, q.v. (T-B).

metapostnotum, the postnotum of the metathorax (Chapman).

metapostscutellum, in adult Hymenoptera, metapostnotum, q.v. (T-B).

Metapterygota, name proposed for a group including the Odonata and Neoptera, excluding the Ephemeroptera (Hennig, after Börner).

metapygidium (pl., **metapygidia**), in Dermaptera, second plate of opisthomeres (Tuxen).

metarhodopsin, isomer of rhodopsin that serves as a photopigment within the rhabdom (Chapman).

metascutal microtrichia, in Lepidoptera, usually paired patches of minute spines near the sides of the adult metascutum that intermesh with the subanal microtrichia to hold the forewing at rest (Davis, after Common).

metascutellum, the scutellum of the metathorax (T-B).

metascutum, the scutum of the metathorax (T-B).

metasoma (pl., **metasomata**), the posterior principle division of the insect body, in most insect groups being strictly equivalent to the abdomen, in adult Apocrita (Hymenoptera), gaster, q.v. (T-B, after Michener; Wilson).

metaspiracle, a spiracle of the metathorax (T-B, after MacGillivray).

metastasis (pl., **metastases**), in invertebrate pathology, the transfer of pathogenic microorganisms to parts of the body remote from the original foci of infection (Steinahus and Martignoni); the transfer of malignant tumor cells from one organ or part to another, where they grow and form secondary tumors (Steinhaus and Martignoni); a secondary tumor (Steinhaus and Martignoni).

metastasize, to form metastases (Steinhaus and Martignoni).

metasternal, of or relating to the metasternum (T-B).

metasternal epimera, small sclerites separating the metasternal episterna from the ventral segments (T-B).

metasternal episterna, sclerites situated on each side of the metasternum, immediately behind the mesosternal epimera (T-B).

metasternal gland, in adult ants (Hymenoptera: Formicidae), metapleural gland, q.v. (Tulloch).

metasternal ridge, in adult Culicidae (Diptera), the median longitudinal invagination of the metasternum (metabasisternum) marked externally by the metasternal suture (Harbach and Knight).

metasternal suture, in adult Culicidae (Diptera), the groove produced incidental to the median longitudinal invagination, metasternal ridge, of the metasternum (metabasisternum), extending from the intersegmental suture between the meso- and metathorax to the sternocostal suture (Harbach and Knight).

metasternal wing, in certain aquatic Coleoptera, e.g., Dytiscidae, a leaf-like expansion of the antecoxal piece (T-B).

metasternellum, sternellum of the metathorax (T-B).

metasternum, sternum of the metathorax (T-B).

metastethidium, metathorax, q.v. (T-B).

metastethium, metasternum, q.v. (T-B).

metastoma, in Orthoptera, hypopharynx, q.v. (T-B).

metatarsus (pl., **metatarsi**), basitarsus, q.v., especially where it differs greatly in length or otherwise from the other tarsomeres (T-B; Mackerras, in CSIRO); hind tarsus, q.v. (Eickwort, pers. comm.).

metatentoria (sing., **metatentorium**), posterior tentorial arms, q.v. (T-B, after MacGillivray).

metatentorina, posterior tentorial pit, q.v. (T-B, after MacGillivray).

metatergum, metanotum, q.v. (T-B).

metathetely, neoteny, q.v. (T-B, after Folsom and Wardle; Tulloch).

metathoracic, of or pertaining to the metathorax.

metathoracic gland, in Heteroptera (Hemiptera), metathoracic scent gland, q.v.

metathoracic leg, hind leg, q.v. (McAlpine),

metathoracic scent gland, in Heteroptera (Hemiptera), major and universally occurring adult system of scent glands with single or paired opening on first abdominal sternum, thoracic metasternum or (usually) near metacetabular cavities with external outflow pathways usually situated at metepisterna, and with paired or unpaired internal components (Štys, pers. comm.).

metathoracic spiracle, spiracle of the metathorax (Harbach and Knight); in adult Diptera, posterior thoracic spiracle, q.v. (McAlpine).

metathoracotheca, the pupal covering of the metathorax (T-B).

metathorax, the third thoracic ring or segment, which bears the hind legs and hind wings (T-B), sometimes closely united with the mesothorax and sometimes appearing as part of the abdomen (T-B).

metatibia, hind tibia, q.v.

metatrochanter, hind trochanter, q.v.

metatype, a specimen compared by the author of a species with the type and determined by him as conspecific with it (T-B, after Banks and Caudell); by certain authors also required to be topotypic with type (T-B); see homeotype.

metazona, in Orthoptera, the dorsal surface of the prothorax behind the principal sulcus (T-B).

metazonite, in millipedes (Diplopoda), the posterior portion of a tergum when the tergum is dividided by a transverse groove (Borror et al.).

metecdysis, teneral period, q.v. (Leftwich).

metepimeron (pl., **metepimera**), epimeron of the metathorax (Borror et al.).

metepisternal scale, in adult Culicidae (Diptera), one of the scales occurring in a small group on the mesepisternum just below the metathoracic spiracle (Harbach and Knight).

metepisternum (pl., **metepisterna**), episternum of the metathorax (Borror et al.).

meter, the standard of length in the metric system; 39.37 inches (T-B); see centimeter and millimeter.

methamidophos, a synthetic insecticide; an organophosphate, O,S-dimethyl phosphoramidothioate; highly toxic to mammals, acute oral LD_{50} of 75% technical 21 mg/kg (Pfadt).

methanol, methyl alcohol, q.v.

methidathion, $C_6H_{11}N_2O_4PS_3$, a synthetic insecticide and acaricide; an organophosphate, S-((2-methoxy-5-oxo-Δ_2,1,3,4-thiadiazolin-4-yl) methyl) O,O-dimethyl phosphorodithioate; highly toxic to mammals, acute oral LD_{50} for rats 25 to 48 mg/kg (Pfadt).

methiocarb, $C_{11}H_{15}NO_2S$, a synthetic, broad spectrum insecticide and acaricide; a carbamate, 4-(methylthio)3,5-xylyl methylcarbamate; moderately toxic to mammals, acute oral LD_{50} for rats 87–130 mg/kg (Pfadt).

methionine, $C_5H_{11}NO_2S$, an essential amino acid in the diet of insects (Gilmour, in CSIRO).

methomyl, $C_5H_{10}N_2O_2S$, a synthetic insecticide and acaricide; a carbamate, methyl N-[(methylcarbamoyl)oxyl] thioacetimidate; highly toxic to mammals; acute oral LD_{50} for rats 17 to 24 mg/kg (Pfadt).

methoprene, a synthetic insect growth regulator; an acylclic sesquiterpenoid similar to juvenile hormone of the cecropia moth, *Hyalophora cecropia* (Lepidoptera: Saturniidae); isopropyl (E,E)-11-methyoxy-3,7,11-trimethyl-2,4-dodecadienoate; relatively nontoxic, acute oral LD_{50} for rats greater than 34,600 mg/kg (Pfadt).

methoxychlor, $C_{16}H_{15}Cl_3O_2$, a synthetic insecticide; a chlorinated hydrocarbon related to DDT, 1,1,1-trichloro-2,2-bis(p-methoxyphenyl) ethane; acute oral LD_{50} for rats about 6000 mg/kg (Pfadt).

methyl alcohol, CH_3OH; wood alcohol; wood spirits; produced by the destructive distillation of wood; a colorless, more or less ill-smelling liquid when impure, used as a substitute for ethyl alcohol in a limited way (T-B); see alcohol.

methyl bromide, CH_3Br, insecticidal fumigant for treatment of mills, warehouses, vaults, ships, freight cars; also a soil fumigant; exposure to 2000 ppm for 1 hr causes serious injury to mammals (Pfadt).

methyl parathion, $C_8H_{10}NO_5PS$, a synthetic insecticide and acaricide; an organophosphate, O,O-dimethyl-O-p-nitrophenyl phosphorothioate, extremely toxic to mammals acute oral LD_{50} for rats 9 to 25 mg/kg (Pfadt).

metinfraepisternum, in adult Odonata, katepisternum, q.v., of metathorax (T-B; Borror et al.).

metochy, inquilinism, q.v. (T-B).

metol, methyl alcohol, q.v. (T-B).

metopic suture, coronal suture, q.v. (T-B, after Berlese).

metopidium, in Membracidae (Hemiptera: Auchenorrhyncha), the anterior declivous surface of the prothorax (T-B).

metric system, a decimal system of measures (with the meter as its base) and weights (with the gram as its base) (Mayr).

mevinphos, $C_7H_{13}O_6P$, a synthetic insecticide and acaricide, aplant systemic; an organophosphate, methyl 3-hydroxy-α-crotonate, dimethyl phosphate; extremely toxic to mammals, acute oral LD$_{50}$ for ♂ rats alpha isomer 3 mg/kg (Pfadt).

MGK 264 (trade name), a synergist for pyrethrum; chemically, *N*-(2-ethyl-hexyl)-5-norborene-2,3-dicarboximide; relatively nontoxic to mammals, acute oral LD$_{50}$ for rats 2800 mg/kg (Pfadt).

micans, shining or twinkling, in part or all together (T-B; Harris, after R. W. Brown); see glabrous, nitid, and politus.

micellae, the elongate submicroscopic crystalline parts of the chitin fibers lying parallel with their axes (T-B, after Snodgrass).

micralifera, a rarely present minute sclerite located posterior to the subalare (T-B, after MacGillivray).

micraner, an abnormally small ♂ ant (Hymenoptera: Formicidae) (T-B; Leftwich).

micrergate, a dwarf worker ant (T-B; Leftwich).

microbial control, that part of biological control concerned with controlling insects (or other organisms) by the use of microorganisms (including viruses) (Steinhaus and Martignoni).

microbial insecticide, a pathogenic microorganism or its products (toxins, etc.) used to suppress an insect population (Steinhaus and Martignoni).

microbial persistence, a phenomenon characterized by the continued presence of a pathogenic microorganism within the host in the absence of overt disease but following an episode of overt disease (Steinhaus and Martignoni).

microbiota, the combined microflora and microfauna of an organism, or, the microflora or microfauna considered separately (Steinhaus and Martignoni).

microcephalic phase, in Muscomorpha (Diptera), the earliest phase of the phanerocephalic substage in which the head is very small (Peterson, after Dean).

microchaeta, setula, q.v. (T-B).

microclimate, climate of the microhabitat in which the individual lives (Tulloch).

Microcoryphia, Archaeognatha, q.v. (Watson, in CSIRO; Borror et al.).

microcyte, a very small prohemocyte (Tulloch, after Jones).

microergate, micrergate, q.v. (T-B).

microgamete, the ♂ gamete, derived from the microgametocyte of the malarial protozoan *Plasmodium* (Plasmodiidae) (T-B); see malaria.

microgametocyte, the ♂ gametocyte developed from the merozoite in the malarial protozoan *Plasmodium* (Plasmodiidae), which by exflagellation produces several ♂ gametes (microgametes) (T-B; Tulloch); see malaria.

microgeographic race, a local race, restricted to a very small area (Mayr).

microgyne, a dwarf queen ant (Hymenoptera: Formicidae) (T-B).

microhabitat, the immediate habitat in which an organism lives, comprising its environment.

microinjector, a devise for injecting measured, minute amounts of fluids, composed usually of a fine metal or glass needle adapted to a syringe and of a mechanism for the advancement of the piston (micrometer or rachet) (Steinhaus and Martignoni).

microlecithal eggs, alecithal eggs, q.v. (Riek, in CSIRO).

Microlepidoptera, a general term for the most primitive families of moths whose members usually have the smallest body size among Lepidoptera, including Micropterigoidea, Eriocranioidea, Hepialoidea, Incurvarioidea, Nepticuloidea, Tineoidea, Yponomeutoidea, Gelechioidea, Cossoidea, Sesioidea, Tortricoidea, and sometimes Pyraloidea and Zygaenoidea; characterized either by forewing with jugal lobe or vestigial jugal fold, including all families of pyraloid grade and below (Sharplin), or by larva with 3 prespiracular setae on prothorax, including all families of tortricoid grade and below (Forbes).

microleucocyte, a small hemocyte (T-B); see prohemocyte.

micron, the unit of microscopic measurement; .001 mm; represented by the symbol μ; the symbol $\mu\mu$ represents .001 of a micron.

micronucleocyte, plasmatocyte, spherule cell, or granular hemocyte, q.v. (Tulloch).

micropapillae, in *Entomobrya* (Collembola: Entomobryidae), minute projections of the labral papillae (Christiansen and Bellinger).

Micropezoidea, superfamily within the series Schizophora of the division Cyclorrhapha (Diptera: Brachycera), including the Cypselosomatidae, Micropezidae, Pseudopomyzidae, Neriidae, and Megamerinidae, adults with a prosternum with a strongly sclerotized posterior part, being broadly continuous with mesosternal region, precoxal bridges absent, preapical tibial bristles absent, epandrium channelled ventrally to receive an elongate, rigid basiphallus, and the ♀ abdomen elongate, forming an ovipositor sheath, the more distal segments telescopic, not forming a piercing organ but with small, separate cerci (Colless and McAlpine, in CSIRO; Bickel, in Parker).

microphagy, the act of feeding on microorganisms (T-B).

microphthalmic, having compound eyes that are smaller than usual or smaller than those of near relatives; see maerophthalmic.

micropinocytosis, retrieval of axon membrane to form small neurosecretory vesicles (Chapman).

microplasmatocyte, a small variety of plasmatocyte which typically has a small amount of vacuolar cytoplasm (Tulloch).

Micropterigoidea, the only superfamily of the suborder Zeugloptera (Lepidoptera), including the family Micropterigidae, including small, usually diurnal, moths with moniliform antennae bearing multibranched sensilla (ascoids), functional mandibles, an infrabuccal pouch or triturating basket, and wings sluglike, with specialized setae, reduced in number, and leglike ventral processes lacking muscles on first 8 abdominal segments; pupae decticous (Kristensen; Common).

micropterism, microptery, q.v. (T-B).

micropterogyne, a ♀ form with small wings, which may be a normal form for some species (Tulloch); an anomolous ♀ ant (Hymenoptera: Formicidae), having very small or vestigial wings which may exist with normal females or as the only type of queen in a colony (Tulloch).

micropterous, having small or vestigial wings, being more reduced than brachypterous (T-B; Leftwich); see apterous, brachypterous, and macropterous.

microptery, the state of having small wings; the tendency to produce small wings (T-B); see micropterous.

Micropterygoidea, Micropterigoidea, q.v. (Borror et al.).

micropylar, of or pertaining to the micropyle (T-B).

micropylar plate, in Phasmida, longitudinal, scarlike area associated with micropyle of eggs (Key, in CSIRO).

micropyle, one of the minute openings in the chorion of an insect egg, through which sperm enter in fertilization (T-B; Borror et al.).

microscopic setae, in larval Lepidoptera, minute primary setae of the head, thorax and abdomen, thought to be proprioceptors (Stehr, after Hinton).

microseta (pl., **microsetae**), a seta notably smaller than adjacent setae (Christiansen and Bellinger); see macroseta.

microsomites, small secondary rings or somites of the macrosomites in the embryo, which afterward become the body segments (T-B).

microspines, minute microscopic spines on the exterior of the body wall only visible under a high power microscope (Peterson).

microsporidian (pl., **microsporidia**), a member of the Microsporidea.

Microsporidea, class of protozoans which live parasitically inside the cells of a wide range of invertebrates and some lower vertebrates, including the genus *Nosema,* the species of which cause diseases of economic importance in silkworms, *Bombyx mori* (Lepidoptera: Bombycidae) and in honey bees, *Apis mellifera* (Hymenoptera: Apidae) (Allaby).

microsporidiosis, in invertebrate pathology, infection with microsporidia (Steinhaus and Martignoni).

microsymbiote, the smaller organism, or microorganism, of a symbiotic association (Steinhaus and Martignoni); see symbiote.

Microthelyphonida, Palpigradi, q.v. (Borror et al.).

microtholi (sing., **microtholus**), in some ♂ Chrysopidae (Planipennia), domelike, hollow organs on abdominal segments (Tuxen, after Tjeder).

microthorax, a thin necklike prothorax of some insects, e.g., dragonflies (Odonata) (T-B, after Garman; Leftwich); a term for the neck or cervix of insects, so employed in the view that the cervix is a reduced body segment (T-B, after Snodgrass).

microtrichia (sing., **microtrichium**), spicules or cuticular hairs on the surface of the wing membrane, e.g., in adult Mecoptera and Diptera (T-B; Chapman); see macrotrichia.

microtubercules, in adult heterocerous Lepidoptera, minute tubercules often scattered over the wing membrane (Davis).

microtubular duct, in Putoidae (Hemiptera: Sternorrhyncha: Coccoidea) circular structure with more than 5 divisions (Miller, in Stehr).

microtymbal, in Arctiidae (Lepidoptera), a grooved metepisternum, flexed by muscular action to produce ultrasound (Fenton and Roeder); see tymbal.

microtype eggs, in Tachinidae (Diptera), tiny eggs layed on host's food plant which are ingested and later hatch, with the larvae penetrating the host's gut wall (Colless and McAlpine, in CSIRO); see alecithal egg.

middle apical area, in adult Hymenoptera, internal area, q.v. (T-B).

middle clasper, in ♂ Hymenoptera, digitus, q.v. (Tuxen).

middle field, in Orthoptera, discoidal field, q.v. (T-B).

middle plate, in ♂ Siphonaptera, lamina media, q.v. (Tuxen).

middle pleural area, in adult Hymenoptera, the median of the 3 areas between the lateral and pleural carinae of propodeum (T-B).

middle segment of penis, in ♂ Odonata, body of penis, q.v. (Tuxen, after Kennedy).

middle tail, in Ephemeroptera, filum terminale, q.v. (Tuxen, after Needham, Travers and Hsu).

midcoxa, coxa of midleg (Harbach and Knight).

midcoxal prong, in most adult Muscomorpha (Diptera), specialized process of midcoxa (McAlpine).

middorsal ecdysial line, in larval Trichoptera, dorsal ecdysial line, q.v. (Wiggins).

middorsal glands, in larval Lymantriidae (Lepidoptera), colored, dorsal glands on abdominal segments VI and VII (Common).

middorsal spot, in some Isoptera, a small, unpigmented or lightly colored area surrounding the fontanelle (Krishna, pers. comm.).

middorsal thoracic carina, a ridge or elevated line at the meeting of the mesepisterna in Odonata (T-B).

midfemur, femur of the midleg (Harbach and Knight).

midgular suture, the single mesal suture when the gula is infolded and concealed, formed through the fusion of the 2 gular sutures (T-B, after MacGillivray).

midgut, central region of alimentary canal, derived from endoderm and lacking a cuticular lining, in which most of the digestion and absorbtion of food normally take place (T-B; Leftwich; Chapman).

midintestine, midgut, q.v. (T-B).

midleg, leg of the mesothorax (Harbach and Knight; McAlpine).

midrib, the central longitudinal rib of a plant leaf (T-B).

midtarsus, the tarsus of the midleg (Harbach and Knight).

midtibia, tibia of the midleg (Harbach and Knight).

midtrochanter, trochanter of the midleg (Harbach and Knight).

midunguis, claw, q.v., of midleg (Harbach and Knight).

midventral extension of basal plate, in ♂ Heteroptera (Hemiptera), ligamentary processes, q.v. (Tuxen, after Drake and Davis).

migrant, any organism either in the process of migration or having recently arrived through migration.

migrantes, in Aphididae (Hemiptera:Sternorrhyncha), winged parthenogenetic viviparous females, developed from the second or later generations of fundatrigeniae, developing on the primary host, then flying to the secondary host (T-B, after Imms).

migration, adaptive mass movement (Matthews and Matthews); flight activity in which vegetative activities (feeding and mating) are supressed and flight behavior dominates, frequently carrying an insect beyond the limits of its habitat, e.g., migration of the milkweed butterfly, *Danaus plexippus* (Lepidoptera: Danaidae), from its summer breeding grounds in the northern United States to areas where it overwinters in California and Mexico (Leftwich; Chapman).

migratory, subject to migration (T-B).

migratory flight, in adult insects, flight which dominates over all other forms of behavior (Matthews and Matthews); see appetitive flight.

migratory ookinete, the *Plasmodium* stage produced by the union of the ♂ and ♀ gametes in the alimentary canal of *Anopheles* (Diptera: Culicidae) (T-B, after Comstock); see malaria.

mihi (Latin), of me; belonging to me; abbrev., m. (T-B).

Milichioidea, superfamily within the Schizophora-Acalyptratae (Diptera: Brachycera), including the families Milichiidae, Sphaeroceridae, Braulidae, Tethinidae, and Canacidae (Colless and McAlpine, after Hennig, in CSIRO; Borror et al.); see Chloropoidea.

milk glands, in certain viviparous ♀ Hippoboscidae (e.g. *Melophagus*) and *Glossina* (Glossinidae) (Diptera), specialized accessory glands in the uterus producing secretions fed upon by larvae (T-B, after Comstock; Chapman).

milky disease, any of a group of maladies of larval Scarabaeidae (Coleoptera), caused by species of *Bacillus,* including type A caused by *Bacillus popilliae* and type B caused by *Bacillus lentimorbus,* in which bacteria multiply and sporulate in the hemolymph causing marked turbidity or milkiness (Steinhaus and Martignoni).

millimeter (mm), 1/1,000 meter, or 0.03937 inch (T-B; Mayr); see metric system.

millipede, a member of the Diplopoda (Borror et al.).

Mimallonoidea, superfamily of infraorder Ditrysia (Lepidoptera) containing one family Mimallonidae; adult with stout body, proboscis vestigial or absent, maxillary palpi absent, antennae pectinate, wings broad, forewing often falcate; larvae stout, with brightly marked prothoracic shield, crochets in circle (Munroe, in Parker).

mimesis, mimicry, q.v. (T-B).

mimetic, imitative (T-B).

mimetic polymorphism, in Lepidoptera, polymorphism in which the various morphs resemble other species distateful or poisonous to a predator, often being restricted to females (Mayr; Matthews and Matthews).

mimetic synoekete, an inquiline which mimics its host in color, form or pilosity (Tulloch, after Gaul).

mimic, in the theory of mimicry, a species which closely resembles another species of a different group (T-B, after Folson and Wardle; Chapman).

mimicry, resemblance of one species (model) by another (mimic), living together in the same area, with protection from predators conferred upon the mimic (T-B; Chapman); see Batesian mimicry and Müllerian mimicry.

mine, gallery or borrow visible beneath the epidermis of plant tissue, made by a larva (T-B); see leaf mine.

mineral, an inorganic homogenous substance; an inorganic foodstuff (Pfadt).

miniate, miniatus (Latin), bright red (T-B; R. W. Brown).

minima, in ants (Hymenoptera: Formicidae), minor worker, q.v. (Wilson).

minimal lethal dose, the dose just sufficient to kill most subjects of a given species or strain (Steinhaus and Martignoni); see maximal non-lethal dose.

minor, in termites (Isoptera) and ants (Hymenoptera: Formicidae), minor worker, q.v. (T-B; Tulloch).

minor soldier, in Isoptera species with dimorphic castes, a soldier of the smaller of the 2 forms (Krishna, pers. comm.).

minor worker, in termites (Isoptera) and ants (Hyemnoptera: Formicidae), a member of the smallest worker subcaste (Wilson); see media worker and major worker.

minute, minutus (Latin), very small (Borror et al.).

Miocene Epoch, epoch within the Tertiary Period, between the Oligocene Epoch and the Pliocene Epoch, extending between about 25 and 11 million years before present (Riek, in CSIRO).

Miomoptera, extinct order among the Acercaria from the Permian, including small insects with short bodies, long wings, and rather simplified venation (Riek, after Martynov, in CSIRO); sometimes included within the Paraplecoptera (Boudreaux).

Miroidea, group proposed to include the Miridae and Tingidae (Hemiptera: Heteroptera: Cimicomorpha) (Woodward et al., after Drake and Drake, in CSIRO); see Tingoidea.

mirror, in ♂ Tettigonoidea and Grylloidea (Orhoptera), membranous area whose proximal border is formed by the posterior cubitus (CuP) on right forewing, serving as a sounding board during stridulation (Key, in CSIRO) (see chordal area and harp); in Cicadidae (Hemiptera: Auchenorrhyncha), tympanum, q.v., on postero-ventral portion of first abdominal segment (T-B, after Imms; Woodward et al., in CSIRO); in Psocoptera, membranous area forming part of Pearman's organ (Badonnel).

mite, a member of the order Acari (Arachnida), excluding the suborder Ixodida comprising the ticks (Borror et al.).

miticide, any poisonous substance used to kill and control mites (Acari) (Pfadt).

mitochondrion, (pl., **mitochondria**), oval, or occasionally round or thread-shaped, organelle occurring in large numbers in the cytoplasm of eucaryotic cells, concerned in the release of energy of organic compounds (T-B; Allaby).

mitosis, cell division, involving the exact duplication of chromosomes and the distribution of one member of each chromosome pair along with approximately one half of the cytoplasmic mass to each of 2 daughter cells (Tulloch); see meiosis.

mitosoma, the middle piece of a developing spermatozoon (T-B).

Mitox (trade name), chlorbenside, q.v. (Pfadt).

mitrate, having the shape of a bishops miter or hat (Fennah).

mixed infection, concurrent infection by 2 or more pathogenic micro-organisms (Steinhaus and Martignoni); see secondary infection.

mixed nest, a nest containing colonies of 2 or more species of social insects, in which mixing of both adults and brood occurs (Tulloch; Wilson); see compound nest.

mixed segment, in some Termitidae (Isoptera), the section of the intestine where a portion of the midgut extends over the hind gut (Noirot et al., in Krishna and Weesner).

mixocoel, in insect embryo, hemocoel, q.v., formed from the union of coelomic cavities and epineural sinus (Chapman).

mixoploidy, mosaic of large and small cells with different numbers of chromosomes within the same tissue (White, in CSIRO).

Mnesarchaeoidea, superfamily of infraorder Exoporia (Lepidoptera) containing one family Mnesarchaeidae; adults very small, diurnal, with well-developed proboscis, 3-segmented maxillary palpi, rudimentary mandibles, homoneurous wing venation, scales of 2 types (primitive and normal), ♀ genitalia exoporian, ovipositor nonpiercing; larvae elongate, slender, with normal thoracic legs and prolegs; pupae adecticous (Dugdale; Gibbs; Kristensen).

mobbing, a type of group defense in which a predator is harrassed by a number of maneuverable prey individuals, e.g., social Hymenoptera (Matthews and Matthews).

mobile, moveable; having the power of motion (T-B).

Mocap (trade name), ethoprop, q.v. (Pfadt).

mode, in an acoustical signal, a third-order grouping, consisting of a series of closely spaced pulse-train groups, e.g., most buzzes, rattles, ticks, etc., heard by the unaided human ear (Matthews and Matthews).

model, in the theory of mimicry, a distasteful species serving as a model for a mimic (T-B; Matthews and Matthews); see mimic.

moderate, in proportion, neither large nor small (T-B).

modioliform, shaped like the nave or hub of a wheel; more or less globular with truncated ends (T-B).

mola, the ridged or roughened grinding surface of the mandible, corresponding to the subgalea of the maxilla when the mandible is compound (T-B); in larval Chironomidae (Diptera), weakly sclerotized area of inner margin of mandible between seta subdentalis and seta interna (Saether).

molar, mola, q.v. (T-B).

molar area, mola, q.v. (Peterson).

molar lobe, mola, q.v. (T-B).

molar plate, in Collembola, the projecting basal lobe of a typical mandible, directed toward the midline of the head and usually equipped with many rows of teeth (Christiansen and Bellinger).

mollicute, a member of the class Mollicutes (Borror et al.).

Mollicutes, class of prokaryotic organisms, including mycoplasmas and spiroplasmas, in which the cells have no walls, being saprotrophic, parasitic, or pathogenetic (Allaby).

molt, moult, q.v. (Wilson).

molting fluid, moulting fluid, q.v. (Borror et al.).

molting hormone, moulting hormone, q.v. (Borror et al.).

molula, femorotibial joint, q.v. (T-B).

Monandria, Eudermaptera, q.v.

monarsenous, polygamous, q.v. (T-B).

monecious, monoecious, q.v. (Borror et al.).

moniliform, beaded like a necklace, e.g., moniliform antennae (T-B; McAlpine); possessing distinct necklike constrictions between successive segments (Peterson); see filiform.

moniliform antenna, antenna with beadlike antennomeres, e.g., adult Rhysodidae (Coleoptera) (T-B); see filiform antenna.

Monitor (trade name), methamidophos, q.v. (Pfadt).

monitor, to observe or check, especially for a special purpose, as to keep track of crop development and insect infestation (Pfadt).

mono-, Greek prefix; alone or only one (T-B).

monobasic, applied to genera originally based on one species only (T-B).

monochromatic, of one color throughout (T-B).

Monocondylia, Archaeognatha, q.v. (Boudreaux, after Hennig).

monocondylic, having one condyle (T-B).

monocondylic joint, a joint with a single point of articulation between segments (T-B, after Snodgrass).

monocornu, in some ♂ Mecoptera, unpaired tergal process on abdominal segment V or VI (Tuxen).

monocrotophos, a synthetic insecticide and acaricide, plant systemic; an organophosphate, 3-hydroxy-N-methyl-*cis*-crotonamide dimethyl phosphate; highly toxic to mammals; acute oral LD_{50} for rats 21 mg/kg (Pfadt).

monodactyle, monodactylus, with a single moveable claw which closes on the tip of the other leg structures, as in *Pediculus* (Phthiraptera: Anoplura: Pediculidae) (T-B).

monodomous, in ants (Hymenoptera: Formicidae) , having one nest only for each colony (T-B).

monoecious, hermaphroditic, q.v. (Borror et al.).

monoembryonic, characterized by or pertaining to monoembryony (T-B).

monoembryony, the production of one embryo from an egg (T-B); see polyembryony.

monogamous, pertaining to a union where a ♀ is fertilized by one ♂ only (T-B).

monogamy, the condition of being monogamous or of having one mate only (T-B).

monogenic, determined by a single gene (Mayr); see polygenic.

Monognatha, Onychophora, q.v. (Hennig, after Tiegs, Manton).

monograph, in taxonomy, an exhaustive treatment of a taxon, including all information pertinent to taxonomic interpretation, comparative anatomy, biology, ecology, and distribution (T-B; Mayr); see revision and synopsis.

monographic, of or pertaining to a monograph; in the manner or style of a monograph (T-B).

monogynous, condition in colonies of eusocial Hymenoptera in which there is only one fecund female or queen (T-B; Eickwort, pers. comm.); see polygynous.

monogyny, in eusocial insects, the existence of only one functional queen in the nest (Wilson); see polygyny.

monolectic, describing bees (Hymenoptera: Apoidea) that use pollen of only a single plant species (Gauld and Bolton); see oligolectic and polylectic.

Monomalata, name for Myriapoda, excluding the Symphyla (Mackerras, in CSIRO).

monomeri, insects with tarsi with one tarsomere (T-B).

monomerous, having only one segment or article (T-B).

monometrosis, monogyny, q.v. (Tulloch).

monomorphic, having only one form (T-B); see dimorphic and polymorphic.

monomorphism, the existence of one form, within a species, sex, or caste (T-B); see dimorphism or polymorphism.

mononomial, mononominal, q.v. (T-B).

mononominal, of or pertaining to a name consisting of a single word; see binominal.

mononominal name, a name consisting of a single word applied to supraspecific taxa; see binominal name.

monophagous, monophagus (Latin), feeding upon only one kind of food, e.g., one species of plant (T-B; Norris, in CSIRO); see oligophagous and polyphagous.

monophagy, restriction to one species of food plant or food animal (T-B; Norris, in CSIRO).

monophasic allometry, polymorphism in which the allometric regression line has a single slope; in ants (Hymenoptera: Formicidae), the use of the term also implies that the relation of some of the body parts measured is nonisometric (Wilson).

monophthalamous gall, gall with a single cavity containing a single insect larva, e.g., marble gall (T-B, after Comstock; Leftwich).

monophyletic, derived from a single ancestral form (T-B); describing a group including an ancestor and all of its descendants (Hennig); also used to describe a taxonomic group including all species derived from a common ancestor; a grouping recognized on the basis of synapomorphy; see paraphyletic and polyphyletic.

monophyly, the condition of being monophyletic.

monosynaptic pathway, neural pathway in which a sensory nerve cell synapses with an effector nerve cell without any intervening internerone (Chapman).

monothelious, polyandrous, q.v. (T-B, after Say).

monothely, polyandry, q.v. (T-B, after Say).

Monotrocha, adult Hymenoptera that lack a trochantellus (T-B); see ditrocha.

monotrochous, in adult Hymenoptera, lacking a trochantellus (T-B).

Monotrysia, suborder within the order Lepidoptera, including the superfamiles Nepticuloidea, Palaephatoidea, Tischerioidea, and Incurvarioidea, including moths with heteroneurous venation and a monotrysian type of ♀ genitalia (Munroe, in Parker; Davis); see Ditrysia and Exoporia.

monotrysian type of genitalia, in ♀ Lepidoptera, type in which there is a single opening for copulation and oviposition, found in the suborders Zeugloptera (in which even a cloaca occurs, a common opening of vagina and tuba analis), Dacnonypha, Exoporia, and Monotrysia (Tuxen; Common, in CSIRO); see exoporian type of genitalia and ditrysian type of genitalia.

monotype, a holotype of a species based on a single specimen (T-B, after Banks and Caudell).

monotypic, containing but one immediately subordinate taxon, as a genus containing but one species, or a species containing but one (the nominate) subspecies (Mayr).

monotypical, monotypic, q.v. (T-B).

monotypy, the situation when an author establishes a nominal genus or subgenus for a single species denoted by an available name (which is then the type-species by monotypy (ICZN); when an author bases a nominal species-group taxon on a single specimen (ICZN); see subsequent monotypy.

Monura, an extinct order of primitively wingless Insecta, from the Carboniferous Period-Permian Periods, the adult members with tergal rudiments of the mandibular and labial segments, tarsi with a single article, and no cerci (Mackerras, Riek, in CSIRO, after Sharov).

morbid drone-laying, a disease of queen honey bees (Hymenoptera: Apidae), in which mated queens become drone layers, laying unfertilized eggs into cells reserved for worker bees (Steinhaus and Martignoni).

morbidity, in invertebrate pathology, incidence, q.v. (Steinhaus and Martignoni).

Morestan (trade name), oxythioquinox, q.v. (Pfadt).

moribund, dying; near death (Steinhaus and Martignoni).

Morison's cell inclusions, strongly basophilic cytoplasmic inclusions appearing in the hind gut epithelium of honey bees (Hymenoptera: Apoidea), showing chronic paralysis, the inclusions being largest in the cells immediately posterior to the openings of the Malpighian tubules (Steinhaus and Martignoni).

Morocide (trade name), binapacryl, q.v. (Pfadt).

morph, any of the genetic forms (individual variants) that account for polymorphism (Mayr).

morphological, relating to form and structure (T-B).

morphology, study of form and structure (T-B, after Tillyard; Borror et al.); see anatomy.

morphopathology, that branch of pathology dealing with the morbid changes occurring in the structure of cells, tissues, and organs, as distinguished from physiopathology (Steinhaus and Martignoni).

morphospecies, a species recognized on the basis of morphological differences (Mayr); see phenon and species.

morphotype, the type of the dimorphic form of a species (T-B, after Banks and Caudell).

mortality rate, death rate, being the number of deaths per unit of population during a given period of time (Steinhaus and Martignoni).

morula (pl., **morulae**), in ♂ *Melitaea* (Lepidoptera: Nymphalidae), small, densely spiny structure above ostium fold of aedoeagus and part of vesica (Tuxen, after Higgins).

mosaic, a form of individual in which the characteristics of more than one sex or polymorphic form may be evident, either symmetrically or asymmetrically, e.g., a gynandromorph or an ergatoid (Tulloch, after Gaul).

mosaic evolution, evolution involving unequal rates for different structures, organs, or other components of the phenotype (Mayr); see heterobathmy.

mosaic theory of vision, the explanation of the functioning of the insect compound eye, where each ommatidium conveys a single point of light to each retinula, which combine to produce the single erect optical image (T-B).

muscalure, synthetic sex pheromone of the ♀ house fly, *Musca domestica* (Diptera: Muscidae); (Z)-9-tricosene (Pfadt).

moschate, moschatus (Latin), with a musky odor (T-B).

mosquito (pl., **mosquitoes** or **mosquitos**), a member of the family Culicidae (Diptera), the ♀ being a blood-feeder and major vector of vertebrate diseases, as e.g., malaria.

moss gall, bedeguar gall, q.v. (Leftwich).

mossy rose gall, bedeguar gall, q.v. (Borror et al.).

mother cell, prohemocyte, q.v. (Tulloch).

moth, a member of the order Lepidoptera, adults with antennae that are not clubbed (Borror et al.); see Heterocera.

motile, moving or being able to move (T-B).

motor nerve, one that controls motions (T-B).

motor nervous system, that part of the nervous system which transmits external stimuli, received through sensory nerve cells, to the muscles.

motor neurocyte, perikaryon of a motor nerve cell (T-B).

motor neuron or **neurone,** a nerve cell with an axon that terminates in an effector (T-B, after Snodgrass).

moula, in insects, the bulbous proximal end of the tibia (T-B).

moult (**molt**), to undergo moulting; the period during moulting (T-B).

moulting, the periodic formation of new cuticule, often accompanied by structural changes in the body wall and other organs, followed by ecdysis (T-B, after Snodgrass; Chapman); see imaginal moulting.

moulting fluid, a liquid secreted by glands of the epidermis of an insect, having the function of dissolving away the endocuticle by enzyme action (Leftwich; Chapman).

moulting glands, epidermal glands that secrete moulting fluid (T-B, after Snodgrass; Leftwich).

moulting hormone, ecdysone, q.v. (Chapman).

moulting liquid, moulting fluid, q.v. (T-B).

mound nest, in Isoptera, a nest at least part of which is constructed of a mound of soil or carton material that projects above the ground surface, the architecture often being elaborate, specific in plan to the species, and contributing to microclimatic control within the nest (Wilson).

mouth, the anterior opening to the alimentary canal (T-B).

mouth beard, in adult Asilidae (Diptera), mystax, q.v. (T-B).

mouth brushes, in some larval Nematocera (Diptera), ventral, moveable, brushlike organs of the labrum, which strain food particles from the water (Colless and McAlpine, in CSIRO).

mouth cavity, preoral cavity, q.v. (T-B).

mouth cone, in Collembola, buccal cone, q.v. (Christiansen and Bellinger); in *Pediculus* (Phthiraptera: Anoplura: Pediculidae), a small protractile snoutlike tube terminating the elongate head; in Thysanoptera, the partially united labrum, labium, and maxillary stipites, which contain the stylets (Heming); see rostrum, proboscis, and prostomium.

mouth dilators, a pair of muscles arising on the clypeus and inserted on the stomodaeum just within the mouth (T-B, after Snodgrass).

mouth fork, in Psocoptera, paired laciniae of maxillae (T-B).

mouth hooks, in larval Muscomorpha (Diptera), clawlike structures, operating vertically, one on each side of the atrial opening (T-B, after Snodgrass; Colless and McAlpine, in CSIRO), thought to be homologous with the mandibles by some authors (Teskey, in McAlpine).

mouthparts, a collective name for the labrum, mandibles, maxillae, labium and hypopharynx (T-B; Chapman); see buccal appendages and jaws.

moveable finger, in ♂ Siphonaptera, telomere, q.v. (Tuxen).

moveable hook, in nymphal Anisoptera (Odonata), labial hook, q.v. (T-B, after Imms).

moveable process, in ♂ Siphonaptera, a membranous extension of the apex of ♂ abdominal sternum IX (Rothschild and Traub).

MP, media posterior, q.v. (Mackerras, in CSIRO).

mucilaginous, viscid, like mucilage (T-B).

mucoprotein, a mucopolysaccharide in which large numbers of disaccharide units are bound to a protein chain (Allaby).

mucoreous, mucoreus (Latin), appearing as if moldy (T-B).

mucro (pl., **mucrones**), a short, sharp, pointed process (T-B, after

Kirby and Spence); the median posterior part of epigastrium when differentiated by elevation (T-B); the terminal spine or process of an obtect pupa (T-B); in Collembola, the third (terminal) segment of the furcula, arising from the apex of the dens (T-B; Christiansen and Bellinger); in adult Elateridae (Coleoptera), prosternal process (T-B); in ♀ Symphyta (Hymenoptera), pointed apices of the 2 gonapophyses IX used as a driving wedge when ovipositing into plant tissues (Tuxen, after E. L. Smith).

mucrodens, in Collembola, one of the 2 distal branches of the furcula in species in which this organ is reduced and the mucro is not separate from the dens (Christiansen and Bellinger).

mucron, in Collembola, mucro, q.v. (Chapman).

mucronate, mucronatus, having pointed processes (T-B); terminating in a sharp point or mucro (T-B).

mucus, a viscid secretion (T-B).

mucus gland, in aculate Hymenoptera, poison gland, q.v. (Gauld and Bolton).

mud cells, in Eumeninae, Vespidae, and some Sphecidae (Hymenoptera), cells made of mud into which are placed caterpillar (Lepidoptera) prey (Riek, in CSIRO).

mulberry corpuscle, spherule cell, q.v. (Tulloch, after Glaser).

Müllerian association, a group of species belonging to different genera, often different families, or even orders, having similar colors, possessing more or less distasteful qualities and living in the same locality (T-B).

Müllerian mimicry, similarity (usually consisting of a similar warning coloration) of several species which are distasteful, poisonous, or otherwise harmful (T-B, after Folsom and Wardle; Mayr).

Müller's organ, a group of numerous scolophores forming a swelling applied to the inner surface of the tympanum (Imms).

Müller's thread, ovarial ligament, q.v. (T-B; Tulloch).

multangulate, with many angles (T-B).

multi-, Latin prefix; many (T-B).

multiarticulate, multiarticulatus (Latin), many-jointed (T-B).

multicellular, consisting or made up of 2 or more cells (T-B).

multicellular processes, in the bodywall, cuticular structures which are hollow outgrowths of the entire body wall, usually large and spinelike in form (T-B, after Snodgrass).

multicolonial, pertaining to a population of social insects which is divided into colonies that recognize nest boundaries (Wilson); see unicolonial.

multifid, multifidous, multifidus (Latin), with many clefts (T-B; R. W. Brown).

multiforous spiracle, a spiracle with 3 or more accessory openings within or adjacent to peritreme (Peterson).

multilaral, one or more on a side, e.g., in Entomobryidae (Collembola), multilaterally ciliate setae (Christiansen and Bellinger).

multilobate sensillum of maxilla, in larval Chironomidae (Diptera), raised socle near dorsal margin of galea of maxilla carrying one to several tiny hyaline lobes or sensilla (Saether).

multilocular, with many large cells, spaces or cavities (T-B).

multilocular pores, in nymphal and ♀ Coccoidea (Hemiptera: Sternorrhyncha), pores with more than 3 openings, located on the surface of the body (Woodward et al., in CSIRO; Kosztarab, pers. comm.); see bilocular pores and trilocular pores.

multinucleate, having many nuclei; applied to cells (T-B).

multiordinal crochets, in larval Lepidoptera, crochets which are arranged in a single row but of many alternating lengths (Peterson).

multiparasitism, the coincident parasitism of an insect by 2 or more species of parasites (T-B).

multipartite, divided into many parts (T-B).

multiple original spellings, 2 or more different original spellings for the same name (ICZC).

multiplicate, plicate, q.v. (Harris).

multipolar cell, a nerve cell with more than 2 nerves (T-B).

multiporous plate sensillum, in adult Chalcidoidea (Hymenoptera), elongate plate organ on the flagellomeres of the antenna (Gauld and Bolton, after Barlin and Vinson).

multiramous plasmatocyte, plasmatocyte with 3 instead of 2 spindle ends (Tulloch, after Yeager, Jones).

multiramous vermiform cell, a rare variety of vermiform cell with 3 instead of 2 spindle ends (Tulloch, after Yeager, Jones).

multiserial bands, in some larval Lepidoptera, 2 transverse bands of crochets associated with the same proleg (T-B, after Imms).

multiserial circle, in larval Lepidoptera, multiserial crochets, q.v. (T-B).

multiserial crochets, in some larval Lepidoptera, e.g., Hepialidae and Acrolophinae (Tineidae), crochets arranged in several concentic rows or series (Peterson).

multisetiferous, bearing many setae (Peterson).

multispinose, with many spines (T-B).

multivariate analysis, one or more techniques allowing for the simultaneous analysis of several variables (Mayr).

multivoltine, having more than one generation or brood in a year (T-B); see bivoltine and univoltine.

mumia, pupa, q.v. (T-B).

mumia pseudonympha, Lamarck's name for a pupa capable of some degree of locomotion (T-B); see exarate pupa.

mummylike, with all appendages in a fixed position and adjacent to the body; see obtect pupa.

munite, munitus (Latin), a surface armed with spines or excrescences (T-B; Harris, after Marchant and Charles); see inermis.

muricate, muricatus (Latin), scabrous, q.v. (T-B; Harris).

muriculate, with a covering of fine, short, sharp, thick excrescences; irregularly scabriculous (Harris, after Munz).

murine, murinus (Latin), mouse-grey (R. W. Brown); grey with a yellowish cast (T-B).

murine typhus, endemic typhus, q.v. (Borror et al.).

muscardine, mycoses of insects in which the fruiting bodies of the pathogenic fungi (muscardine fungi) arise on the exterior of the insect, producing a thick covering about the animal (Steinhaus and Martignoni); see green muscardine and white muscardine.

muscaridine of the silkworm, mycosis of silkworm larvae, *Bombyx mori* (Lepidoptera), caused by the hypomycetous fungus *Beauveria bassiana,* in which infection occurs by mycelial penetration through the larval integument (Steinhaus and Martignoni); see white muscardine.

muscidian, of or pertaining to the Muscidae (Diptera).

muscidiform larva, coniform larva, q.v. (Peterson).

muscle, applied to a tissue made up of specialized cells which by contraction produce movement of appendages or organs; a sheet, bundle or mass of such tissue; see skeletal muscle and visceral muscle.

muscle marks, in adults and pupal Chironomidae (Diptera), oval or oblong, usually pale lateral spots or areas void of microtrichia anterior and sublaterally and caudomesally on tergites and between tergites and paratergites (Saether).

muscle scars, in larval Trichoptera, attachment points for muscles of the head visible as round spots from the exterior (Wiggins).

muscoid, flylike (T-B).

muscoid fly, a member of the Schizophora (Diptera: Brachycera) (T-B; Borror et al.).

Muscoidea, superfamily within the Schizophora (Diptera: Brachycera), including the Muscidae, Anthomyiidae, Gasterophilidae, Hippoboscidae, Streblidae, and Nycteribiidae, but excluding the Oestroidea, q.v. (Borror et al.); superfamily within the Schizophora-Calyptratae within the infraorder Muscomorpha (Diptera: Brachycera), including the Muscidae, Anthomyiidae, and Scatophagidae, but excluding the Oestroidea and Hippoboscoidea (McAlpine); see Pupipara.

Muscomorpha, infraorder within the Brachycera (Diptera), including the Aschiza and Schizophora, being equivalent to the Cyclorrhapha (McAlpine).

muscular bag, in ♀ Saldidae (Hemiptera: Heteroptera), vaginal pouch, q.v. (Tuxen, Ekblom).

muscularis, a muscular sheath investing all parts of the insect alimentary canal (T-B, after Snodgrass).

musculated, furnished or supplied with muscles (T-B).

musculature, a system of muscles (T-B); the entire muscular structure of an organism (T-B).

mushroom bodies, in the brain, corpora pedunculata, q.v. (T-B; Leftwich).

mushroom-shaped gland, of Huxley, the large compact mass formed by the ♂ accessory glands (T-B, after Imms); a cluster of glandular seminal vesicles at the junction of the 2 vasa deferentia with the ejaculatory duct of a ♂ insect (Leftwich); see accessory genital gland, ectodenia, and mesadenia.

mustard oils, secondary plant chemicals in the plant family Cruciferae (Chapman).

mutant, an individual with an aberrant phenotype arising from mutation; see aberration.

mutation, in genetics, a discontinous change in a genetic factor, usually the replacement or loss of one or several base pairs in the DNA (T-B; Mayr); a change in a gene which is inherited by the offspring (Tulloch).

mutation theory, a theory of the origin of new forms in organisms, which arise from the parent form (which itself remains unchanged), abruptly, regardless of environment and without transitional forms.

mute, silent; without power to produce audible sound (T-B).

mutic, muticus (Latin), unarmed; lacking processes where such usually occur (T-B; Harris); see inermis.

mutilate, mutilatus, cut off; mutilated; abbreviated; not complete (T-B).

mutualism, symbiosis, q.v. (T-B); symbiosis that benefits the members of both participating species, usually being obligatory (Steinhaus and Martignoni; Wilson).

mycangium (pl., **mycangia**), any one of a variety of special pocket-shaped receptacles used to carry symbiotic fungi, e.g., in bark beetles (Coleoptera: Scolytidae) (Wilson).

mycelium, in fungi, the threadlike vegetative part (T-B); see hypha.

mycethemia, the presence of a fungus or some of its stages in the hemolymph (Steinhouse and Martignoni).

mycetocyte, one of the cells that make up a mycetome, housing intracellular symbiotic (mutualistic and commensalistic) microorganisms (T-B; Tulloch; Steinhaus and Martignoni; Chapman); see mycetome.

mycetome, a structure housing intracellular symbiotes, e.g., bacteria, rickettsia, yeasts, and fungi, and consisting of mycetocytes (Tulloch; Steinhaus and Martignoni; Chapman).

mycetophagous, feeding upon fungi (T-B).

Mycetophiliformia, Sciaroidea, q.v. (Hennig).

Mycetophiloidea, superfamily within the Nematocera, including the Mycetophilidae, Sciaridae, Hyperoscelididae, Scatopsidae, and Cecidomyiidae (Borror et al.); see Sciaroidea.

mycoplasma(s), prokaryotic organism similar to a bacterium, belonging to the class Mollicutes, but having no cell wall, being saprophagous, parasitic, or pathogenic (Allaby).

mycosis, in invertebrate pathology, a disease caused by the presence of fungi (Steinhaus and Martignoni).

mycotoxicosis, in invertebrate pathology, a disease caused by the action of a mycotoxin (Steinhaus and Martignoni); see toxemia and toxinosis.

mycotoxin, in invertebrate pathology, a toxin produced by fungi (Steinhaus and Martignoni).

myelin, white fatty substance forming a sheath around certain nerve fibers.

myelinated, of nerve fibers, ensheathed by myelin (T-B).

myelophagy, feeding on the pith of small stems (Wood).

Mygalomorphae, suborder of spiders (Araneae), characterized by having large and powerful chelicerae that move in a plane more or less parallel to the median sagital plane of the body (Borror et al.).

myiasis, disease or injury caused by the attack of larval Diptera (T-B); condition arising from infestation by parasitic flies (Diptera) (Steinhaus and Martignoni); diseases of man and other animals due to infestation by the larvae of Diptera which are not necessarily parasitic (Leftwich); see apimyiasis and pseudomyiasis.

mymariform larva, endophagous larva found in many Mymaridae and Trichogrammatidae (Hymenoptera), lacking an obvious constriction between the cephalothorax and abdomen and bearing a conical process anteriorly on the head (Gauld and Bolton, after Jackson).

myoblast, a cell which produces muscular tissue (T-B; Chapman).

myofibrillae (sing., **myofibrilla**), myofibrils, q.v. (T-B).

myofibrils, in muscle cells, fine strands, composed of molecular filaments consisting mainly of myosin and actin, embedded in the sarcoplasm and extending continuously from one end of the muscle fiber to another (Chapman).

myogenic activity, subsequent contractions initiated by muscles themselves following a nerve impulse (Chapman).

myoglobin, oxygen-carrying molecule in mammalian muscle (Gilmour, in CSIRO).

Myoglossata, an informal group embracing all Lepidoptera in which the proboscis is provided with intrinsic muscles (Kristensen and Nielsen).

myoglyphides, in Coleoptera, the muscle notches in the posterior margin of the collum (T-B).

myhaematin, an iron-containing pigment of insect muscle (T-B, after Folsom and Wardle).

myiology, study of insects in the order Diptera (Adkins, pers. comm.).

myology, the study of muscles (T-B).

myophily, insect-flower pollination syndrome involving members of the families Syrphidae and Bombyliidae (Diptera) (Matthews and Matthews, after Baker and Hurd).

myosin, protein constituent of myofibrils (Chapman).

myotome, a division of the body muscles corresponding to a metamere (T-B, after Snodgrass).

myriapod, a member of the Myriapoda (Borror et al.).

Myriapoda, group within the phylum Arthropoda, including the classes Pauropoda, Chilopoda, Diplopoda, and Symphyla, possessing 9 or more pairs of legs, being present on most of the body segments behind the head, head distinct from rest of body, and body elongate and wormlike (T-B; Mackerras, in CSIRO; Borror et al.).

Myriapodomorpha, hypothesized monophyletic group including the Arthropleurida and the Atelocerata (Boudreaux).

Myrientomata, Protura, q.v. (Borror et al.).

myrmecoclepty, the form of symbiosis exhibited by the ant-guest *Atelura* (Zygentoma: Lepismatidae), in which the symbiont steals regurgitated honey in its passage from the mouth of one ant (Hymenoptera: Formicidae) to the other (T-B).

myrmecodomatia, structures in higher plants that appear to have evolved, in the course of mutualistic evolution, to serve as dwelling places for ants (Hymenoptera: Formicidae) (Wilson).

myrmecology, the study of ants (Hymenoptera: Formicidae) (T-B; Wilson).

myrmecomorph, insects other than Formicidae (Hymenoptera) which resemble ants.

myrmecophage, an insect which preys on ants but does not live with them, e.g., spiders (Araneae), ant-lions (Planipennia: Myrmeleontidae), etc. (T-B, after W. M. Wheeler).

myrmecophile, an insect nest mate or parasite of ants (Hymenoptera: Formicidae), harbored in their nests, either cared for by the ants or preying upon the ants or their brood (T-B, after W. M. Wheeler); an organism that must spend at least part of its life cycle with ant colonies (Wilson); see inquiline.

myrmecophilous, ant-loving, being applied to insects that live in ant (Hymenoptera: Formicidae) nests (T-B).

myrmecophily, the relation between ants and guest insects (T-B).

myrmecoxene, symphile, q.v., in the nest of ants (T-B).

Myrmeleontidea, Myrmeleontoidea, q.v.

Myrmeleontoidea, superfamily within the Planipennia, including the Myrmeleontidae, Nymphidae, Ascalaphidae, and Nemopteridae, possessing adults with subcosta (Sc) and R_1 fused at apex for a considerable distance, nygmata not present between posterior 2 branches of radial sector (R_s), and a more or less defined pterostigma; and larvae with antennae and palpi with more than 2 segments and gular plate of head covered by ventral extensions of genae meeting in midventral line (Riek, in CSIRO).

myrmeophile, myrmecophile, q.v. (Tulloch).

mystacine, mystacinous, with a hairy fringe above mouth (T-B).

mystax (Greek), hair on upper lip (R. W. Brown); in certain adult Diptera (e.g., Asilidae), a patch of stiff setae above the mouth, on the lower part of the median facial plate, above the vibrissae (T-B; Leftwich; McAlpine).

mytiliform, shaped like a mussel shell (T-B).

Myxophaga, suborder of Coleoptera, including the single superfamily Sphaerioidea, possessing small adults (length less than 1 mm) with notopleural sutures, clubbed antennae, basal abdominal sternite not divided by hind coxae, aedeagus with a basal piece, and hind wings spirally rolled at apex at rest and fringed with long hairs; larvae aquatic with mola on mandible, left mandible with an articulated tooth, maxilla with a lacinia, and labrum visible (Britton, in CSIRO).

N

nacreous, having an iridescent luster like mother of pearl (T-B).

NAD, nicotinamide adenine dinucleotide, q.v. (Chapman).

nagana, disease of wild and domestic animals of Equatorial Africa caused by *Trypanosoma brucei* (Protozoa) transmitted by tsetse flies, *Glossina* spp. (Diptera: Glossinidae) (Borror et al.).

naiad, the aquatic nymph of hemimetabolous insects, i.e., Odonata, Ephemeroptera, and Plecoptera (T-B, after Imms; Peterson).

nail, claw, q.v. (T-B).

Nairobi eye, conjunctivitis caused when juices of crushed beetles, *Pachypaederus puncticollis* and *Paederus sabaeus* (Coleoptera: Staphylinidae) are rubbed into the eye (Adkins, pers. comm.); see Paederus vesicular dermatitis.

naked, nude, q.v. (T-B); of a pupa, not enclosed in a cocoon or other covering (T-B).

naked eyes, in adult Chironomidae (Diptera), compound eyes in which the microtrichia between the corneal lenses are shorter than the height of lens (Saether); see hairy eyes.

naled, $C_4H_7Br_2Cl_2O_4P$, a synthetic insecticide and acaricide; an organophosphate, 1,2-dibromo-2,2-dichloroethyl dimethyl phosphate; moderatley toxic to mammals, acute orla LD_{50} for rats 430 mg/kg (Pfadt).

name-bearing type, the type genus, type species, holotype, lectotype, series of syntypes (which, together, form the name-bearing type), neotype, type slide, or hapantotype, that provides the objective standard of reference whereby the application of the name of a taxon can be determined (ICZN); see Principle of Name-bearing Types.

nanitic workers, in ants (Hymenoptera) or termites (Isoptera), dwarf workers produced from either the first brood or later broods that have been subjected to starvation (Gay, in CSIRO; Wilson).

Nannolepidoptera, Nepticuloidea, q.v.

Nanopsocetae, group within the suborder Troctomorpha (Psocoptera), including the Liposcelidae and Pachytroctidae, and Sphaeropsocidae, differing from the Amphientometae by possessing only a single anal vein (1A) (Smithers, in CSIRO).

naphthalene, $C_{10}H_8$, a white crystalline, aromatic hydrocarbon used as a fumigant in insect collections and in homes.

narcotize, to place under the influence of a narcotic or sleep-producing agent (T-B).

nasal carina, in Ephemeroptera, the longitudinal ridge of the head in front of the middle ocellus, often noselike when viewed from the side (T-B, after Needham).

nasal suture, frontoclypeal suture, q.v. (T-B).

nasale, in larval Coleoptera, an anterior median projection from the frons, formed by either the fusion of the frons, clypeus and labrum, or sometimes by the frons and clypeus alone, in the latter case the labrum being small and hidden below the nasale projection (Peterson, after Böving and Craighead).

nascent, beginning to exist or to grow (T-B).

Nassanov's gland, in worker honey bees (Hymenoptera: Apidae), a pheromone-producing gland beneath the intersegmental membrane between abdominal terga VI and VII (Chapman).

nasus, the nose, i.e., that part of the insect head with which the labrum articulates, frequently noselike (T-B); postclypeus, q.v. (T-B, after J. B. Smith); in Odonata, the clypeus or a modification of it (T-B); in some Nasutitermitinae (Isoptera: Termitidae), snoutlike organ possessed by soldiers, being used to eject poisonous or sticky fluid at intruders (Wilson); in adult Tipulinae (Diptera: Tipulidae), small projection of rostrum (Alexander and Byers, in McAlpine); in certain Hymenoptera, the anterior termination of the face (T-B).

nasute, nasutus, (pl., **nasutes** or **nasuti**), nasute soldier, q.v. (T-B; Leftwich).

nasute soldier, in Nasutitermitinae (Isoptera: Termitidae), a soldier with a snoutlike prolongation of the head capsule, or nasus, q.v., used to eject a poisonous or sticky secretion in defense (T-B).

nasutiform termite, nasute soldier, q.v. (Borror et al.).

nasutoid soldier, in some Rhinotermitidae (Isoptera), a soldier with a highly elongated, grooved labrum, along which defensive secretions flow; not to be confused with true nasute soldiers (Weesner, in Krishna and Weesner).

natatorial, natatorious, natatory, fitted for swimming, being generally applied to swimming legs in aquatic bugs (Heteroptera: Nepomorpha) and water beetles (Coleoptera) (T-B; Leftwich).

natatory lamellae, in the Tridactylidae (Orthoptera), long slender plates of the hind tibia (T-B, after Comstock).

natural classification, a system of classifying or sorting out living beings so as to show their relationship or connection each with others, generally along the lines of organic evolution (T-B); a highly predictive classification; see cladistic classification and evolutionary classification.

natural control, the reduction of pest populations by the forces of nature such as climatic factors, parasites, predators, and disease (Pfadt); see biological control.

natural host, in invertebrate pathology, a host in which the pathogenic microorganism (or parasite) is commonly found and in which the pathogen can complete its development (Steinhaus and Martignoni, after Hopps and Price).

natural requeening, in *Bombus* (Hymenoptera: Apoidea), the continuance of a colony upon the death or loss of the foundress ♀, by the entrance of another ♀ of the same species (Tulloch, after Plath).

natural selection, the unequal contribution of genotypes to the gene pool of the next generation, through differential mortality and differences in reproductive success, caused by components of the environment (T-B; Mayr); see artificial selection and sexual selection.

Naucoroidea, superfamily of Heteroptera within the infraorder Nepomorpha including the predaceous aquatic Aephelocheiridae and Naucoridae, the former family possessing a true physical gill in the form of a plastron (Schuh).

naupliiform larva, early larva of the form or shape of the nauplius larva in Crustacea (T-B, after Comstock), e.g., first-instar larva of Platygasteridae (Hymenoptera) (Peterson); see cyclopoid larva.

nauplius larva, the first, free-swimming, planktonic larva of most marine and some freshwater Crustacea, lacking obvious segmentation of the body and with 3 pairs of appendages (Allaby).

navicula (pl., **naviculae**), third axillary sclerite, q.v. (T-B, after MacGillivray); in ♂ Tubulifera (Thysanoptera), distal sclerotized part of phallotheca (Heming) or endophallus (Lyal); in ♂ *Ariadne* (Lepidoptera: Nymphalidae), sclerotized, hairy plate formed from abdominal sternum VIII (Tuxen, after Roepke).

navicular, navicularis (Latin), cymbiform, q.v. (T-B).

neala, jugum, q.v., of wing (T-B, after Martynov); jugal lobe, q.v. (T-B, after Snodgrass).

neallotype, an allotype described after the publication of the original description (T-B).

neanic, referring to the pupal stage (T-B).

neanide, nymph, q.v. (Štys).

nearctic, distributed within the Nearctic Region.

Nearctic Region, the North American part of the Holarctic Region, including Alaska, Canada, Greenland, the continental United States, and the Central Mexican Plateau; see Neotropical Region and Palearctic Region.

nebenkern, fused mitochondria of spermatid (Chapman).

nebula, a cloud; a vague, undefined, dusky shading (T-B).

nebulose, nebulosus (Latin), **nebulous,** cloudy; without definite form or outline (T-B).

neck, cervix, q.v. (T-B; Chapman; McAlpine); collar, q.v. (T-B); in Heteroptera (Hemiptera), cephalic neck, q.v.; in ♂ Siphonaptera, a constriction of the median lamina of the aedeagal apodeme immediately anterior to the fulcrum (Lewis, pers. comm.).

neck of apodemal strut, in ♂ Siphonaptera, neck, q.v. (Tuxen, after Jordan).

neck of spermatheca, in ♀ Siphonaptera, hilla, q.v. (Tuxen).

necrophoric behavior, necrophoresis, q.v. (Wilson).

necrophagous, necrophagus, feeding on dead or decaying animals (T-B); see saprophagous.

necrophoresis, in social insects, transport of dead members of the colony away from the nest, a highly developed and stereotyped behavior in ants (Hymenoptera: Formicidae) (Wilson).

Necroscioidea, in Phasmida, superfamily containing the families Heteronemiidae, Lonchodidae, Necrosciidae, Pachymorphidae, and Palophidae (Kevan).

necrosis, decay (T-B).

necrotic, in a dead or decayed condition (T-B); of or pertaining to necrosis (T-B).

necrotize, in invertebrate pathology, to kill cells and tissues in a living organism (Steinhaus and Martignoni).

nectar, the sugary secretion of the plant, produced by flowers or other structures, frequently scented; the main or only food of many insects, particularly Apoidea (Hymenoptera), adult Lepidoptera and some adult Diptera (T-B).

nectar guides, patches at the bases of flower petals that fail to reflect ultraviolet light (Matthews and Matthews).

nectary, in plants, spur or sac of a flower which secrete the sweetened liquid termed nectar (T-B); see extrafloral nectary.

nectopod, a swimming limb (T-B).

Neelipleona, suborder within the Collembola, including only the family Neelidae, possessing a globose body, the thorax relatively enlarged and the abdomen fused to it without visible segmentation (Bellinger, pers. comm.).

negative phototaxis, movement away from a light source (Chapman); see positive phototaxis.

negative phototropism, reaction away from light (T-B).

negative tropism, one in which the stimulus repels (T-B, after Wardle).

Neguvon (trade name), trichlorfon, q.v. (Pfadt).

nekton, free-swimming organisms in aquatic ecosystems, including fish, amphibians and large swimming insects (T-B; Allaby); see benthos and plankton.

nektonic, free-swimming in an aquatic habitat (T-B).

Nemathelminthes, Nematoda, q.v. (Borror et al.).

nematid, threadlike (T-B).

Nematocera, suborder within the Diptera, including the infraorders Tipulomorpha, Blephariceromorpha, Axymyiomorpha, Bibionomorpha, Psychodomorpha, Ptychopteromorpha, and Culicomorpha, possessing adults with antennae often filiform with usually 6–14 articles and maxillary palpus usually with 3–5 segments; larvae generally with a well-formed head capsule with mandibles usually of the chewing type, toothed, opposable, and moving in a horizontal or oblique plane (T-B; Colless and McAlpine, in CSIRO).

nematocerous, with long, threadlike antennae; pertaining to the Nematocera (Diptera) (T-B).

nematocyte, a very elongate variety of vermiform cell, q.v. (Tulloch, after Yeager, Jones).

nematocytoid, a variety of vermiform cell, q.v. (Tulloch, after Yeager, Jones).

Nematoda, class within the phylum Aschelminthes, including eelworms, roundworms, and threadworms, ranging in length from about 1 mm to 5 cm, being parasites in plants or animals, or free-living (Allaby).

nematode, a member of the class Nematoda.

Nematomorpha, class within the phylum Aschelminthes, including hairworms, possessing narrow hairlike bodies with thick cuticle, the young being parasitic and the mature adults free-living in freshwater forms (Allaby).

Nematophora, Chordeumida, q.v. (Borror et al.).

Nemocera, Nematocera, q.v. (T-B; Borror et al.).

nemoglossata, bees (Hymenoptera: Apoidea), with a threadlike tongue (T-B).

nemoricolous, living in open, sunny woods (T-B).

Nemouroidea, superfamily within the infraorder Euholognatha (Plecoptera: Arctoperlaria), including the families Taeniopterygidae, Notonemouridae, Nemouridae, Capriidae, and Leuctridae (Zwick, in Hennig).

Neoblattodea, group proposed to include the extinct families Mylacrididae, Poroblattinidae, and Mesoblattinidae, and extant Blattaria (Hennig, after Laurentiaux); see Eoblattodea.

Neococcoidea, group within the Coccoidea (Hemiptera: Sternorrhyncha), characterized by adult females with a distinct apical seta on the labium and adult males lacking faceted compound eyes (Kosztarab, in Parker).

neogallicolae-gallicolae, dimorphs of the phylloxeran fundatrigeniae (Hemiptera: Sternorrhyncha: Phylloxeridae), which will become gallicolae (T-B, after Imms).

neogallicolae-radicolae, dimorphs of the phylloxeran fundatrigeniae (Hemiptera: Sternorrhyncha: Phylloxeroidea), which pass to the root and become radicolae (T-B, after Imms).

neogeic, belonging to the Western Hemisphere or New World (T-B); see gerontogeic.

Neoheteroptera, subdivision of the Heteroptera including Gerromorpha and Panheteroptera (Schuh, after Štys); see Euheteroptera.

Neolepidoptera, hypothesized monophyletic group including all haustellate Lepidoptera, including the Exoporia, Monotrysia, and Ditrysia, with adecticous pupae (T-B, after Packard; Kristensen).

Neomecoptera, order proposed for the single family Boreidae of the Mecoptera (Riek, after Hinton, in CSIRO).

neontology, the science dealing with recent organisms (Mayr); see paleontology.

neoplasm, in invertebrate pathology, an abnormal mass of tissue not required for repair of organs, the growth of which exceeds and is uncoordinated with that of the normal tissues and persists in the same excessive manner after cessation of the stimulus which evoked the changes in growth pattern (Steinhaus and Martignoni).

Neopseustina, infraorder of suborder Glossata containing the superfamily Neopseustoidea (Common).

Neopseustoidea, only superfamily of infraorder Neopseustina (Lepidoptera) with one family Neopseustidae; adults relatively small moths, without ocelli, but with mandibles having muscles, with short, double-tube proboscis, homoneurous wing venation, scales of normal type, ♀ ovipositor nonpiercing (Davis).

Neoptera, infraclass within the class Insecta, including the Polyneoptera, Paraneoptera, and Holometabola, possessing wings that are articulated by discrete axillaries that permit the them to be folded back along the body (except in secondarily specialized forms), venation with few or no triadic veins and usually a less dense reticulation of crossveins than in the Paleoptera, and the abdomen usually with cerci but lacking appendix dorsalis (Mackerras, in CSIRO).

neoptery, the ability to flex the wings back over the abdomen (Hennig).

Neopterygota, Neoptera, q.v. (Hennig, after Crampton).

neosminthurid seta, in Sminthuridae (Collembola), an elongate seta, usually covered with small scalelike spicules, sometimes plumose, closely appressed to the body surface, and lack sclerotized ring around point of insertion, located laterally on the greater abdomen, dorsal of fureal insertion (Richards).

neoteinia, neoteny, q.v. (T-B, after Comstock).

neoteinic, neotenic, q.v. (T-B, after Tillyard).

neoteinin, juvenile hormone, q.v. (Leftwich).

neoteiny, neoteny, q.v. (T-B).

neotenic, retaining characters of the immature stages in the adult (Kostarab and Kozár).

neotenic reproductive, in Isoptera, a term applied to royalties newly developed in a termite society on the occasion of the loss or death of the original royal pair which retain some juvenile characters (T-B, after Tillyard); see ergatoid reproductive and nymphoid reproductive.

neoteny, retention of juvenile characters in the adult (Tulloch; Chapman).

neotheca, in ♂ Colobathristidae (Hemiptera: Heteroptera), a sclerotized phallic segment distal to ejaculatory reservoir, i.e., not pertaining to phallosoma (phallotheca) (Tuxen, after Štys).

neotropical, distributed within the Neotropical Region.

Neotropical Region, biogeographic region including South America, the West Indies, and Middle America south of the Central Mexican Plateau; see Nearctic Region (Folsom and Wardle).

neotype, the single specimen designated as the name-bearing type of a nominal species or subspecies for which no holotype, or lectotype, or syntype(s), or prior neotype, is believed to exist (ICZN).

nephridium (pl., **nephridia**), tubular structure functioning in excretion in Annelida and Onychophora (T-B); in insects, Malpighian tubule, q.v. (T-B, after J. B. Smith).

nephridial, of or pertaining to nephridia (T-B).

nephrocyte, cell that takes up foreign chemicals of relatively high molecular weight from the hemolymph, which the Malpighian tubules may be incapable of dealing with (T-B, after Snodgrass; Chapman); see pericardial cells.

nepionic, referring to a stage of development immediately succeeding the embryonic (T-B).

Nepoidea, superfamily of Heteroptera within the infraorder Nepomorpha including the predaceous aquatic Nepidae (including Ranatrinae) and Belostomatidae (Schuh, after Rieger).

Nepomorpha, infraorder of Heteroptera, including the littoral families Gelastocoridae and Ochteridae, and true aquatic families Corixidae, Notonectidae, Helotrephidae, Naucorididae, Betostomatidae, and Nepidae, characterized by their small, inconspicuous antennae usually received in a groove below the eye (Schuh).

Nepticuloidea, superfamily of the infraorder Heteroneura (Lepidoptera) containing the Nepticulidae and Opostegidae, including very small moths with antennal scape expanded into a broad eye cap, antennal flagellum with specialized sensilla, five-segmented maxillary palpi, greatly reduced heteroneurous wing venation, ♀ with nonpiercing ovipositor and monotrysian genitalia; larvae apodous, mining in leaves, petioles or bark; pupae with 3 pairs of coxae visible, abdomen dorsally spined, protruded at ecdysis (Common).

Nerioidea, Micropezoidea, q.v. (McAlpine).

nerve, a bundle of nerve fibers that transmits nerve impulses (T-B); vein, q.v. of wing (T-B).

nerve cell, basic element in the nervous system consisting of a cell body containing the nucleus and long cytoplasmic projections which extend to make contact with other nerve cells (Chapman); see perikaryon.

nerve cord, ventral nerve cord, q.v. (McAlpine).

nerve fiber, axon or other branch of a nerve cell (T-B, after Snodgrass).

nerve sheath, a nonnervous sheath clothing the entire central nervous system, extending over the larger peripheral branches and consisting of a noncellular neural lamella and a cellular perineurium (Chapman).

nerve tract, a strand of nerve fibers; usually applied to tracts within a nerve center (T-B, after Snodgrass).

nerve trunk, a bundle of nerve fibers, motor, sensory or both, in the peripheral system (T-B, after Snodgrass).

nervous system, a conducting system ensuring the rapid functioning and coordination of effectors, modifying their responses according to the imput of peripheral sense organs, in insects consisting of (1) a central nervous system with a brain situated dorsally in the head and a ventral chain of segmental ganglia from which nerves run to the peripheral sense organs and muscle systems, and (2) a stomatogastric system, consisting of a number of small ganglia connected to the brain and their associated nerves, controlling movements of the alimentary canal (Chapman).

nervulation, venation, q.v., of wings (T-B).

nervule, vein, q.v., of wing (T-B).

nervura costalis, costa, q.v., of wing (T-B).

nervuration, venation, q.v., of wings (T-B).

nervure, vein, q.v., of wing (T-B; Leftwich).

nervus antennalis, antennal nerve, q.v. (T-B).

nervus ganglii occipitalis, a short, slender nerve extending from brain to the corpus cardiacum (T-B, after Snodgrass).

nervus labrofrontalis, labrofrontal nerve, q.v. (T-B).

nervus subpharyngealis, subpharyngeal nerve, q.v. (T-B).

nervus tegumentalis, tegumentary nerve, q.v. (T-B).

Nesbitt's solution, clearing solution consisting of 25–50 ml of distilled water, 40 grams of chloral hydrate, and 2.5 ml of concentrated hydrocloric acid (Borror et al.).

nesium (pl., **nesia**), in most larval Scarabaeoidea (Coleoptera), one or 2 (right and left nesia) sclerotized, more or less projecting, marks in the space between the inner ends of the tormae, anterior to the crepis (T-B, after Böving).

nest aura, in ants (Hymenoptera: Formicidae), nest odor, q.v. (T-B).

nest odor, in ants (Hymenoptera: Formicidae), the distinctive odor of a nest, by which its inhabitants are able to distinguish the nest from those belonging to other colonies or at least from the surrounding environment (Wilson); see hive odor.

nest parasitism, the relation, found in some termites (Isoptera), in which colonies of one species live in the walls of the nest of a second (host species) and feed directly on the carton material of which it is constructed (Wilson).

nest robbing, cleptobiosis, q.v. (Wilson).

nettling hairs, urticating hairs, q.v. (Leftwich).

netwinged, having membranous wings with numerous crossveins, e.g., Odonata, Ephemeroptera, and Neuroptera (Leftwich).

netrion, in adult Hymenoptera, posterolateral region of the pronotum that is delineated externally by a row of foveae or a linear or foveolate sulcus, and internally by a ridge or apodeme (Gibson).

neuraforamen, the opening in the foramen through which passes the nervous system (T-B, after MacGillivray).

neural, connected with the nervous system; of or pertaining to the nerves or to the nervous system of an animal (T-B).

neural canal, an incomplete tunnel on the floor of the meso- and metathorax, formed by fusion of apodemes, serving for the reception and protection of the ventral nerve cord and for the attachment of muscles (T-B).

neural groove, the furrow in the primitive layer of the embryo in which the nerve cord is formed (T-B).

neural inhibition, the capacity of a nerve cell to exert a blocking action on cells connected to it (Matthews and Matthews).

neural lamella, noncellular, amorphous layer of neutral mucopolysaccharide and mucoprotein, providing mechanical support for the central nervous system, holding the cells and axons together while permitting such flexibility as is necessitated by the movements of the insect (Chapman); see nerve sheath.

neural ridges, the 2 longitudinal ventral ridges of the ectoderm of the germ band of the embryo in which are formed the lateral cords of neuroblasts (T-B, after Snodgrass).

neuration, venation, q.v., of wing (T-B).

neurilemma, the external sheath of a nerve fiber; the nucleated sheath of nerve tissue covering the ganglia, nerve trunks and terminal branches (T-B, after Snodgrass).

neurite, in a monopolar nerve cell, the single projection bearing the axon and the dendrite (Chapman).

neuroblast, in the insect embryo, a cell giving rise to nerve cells (T-B, after Imms; Chapman).

neurocyte, perikaryon, q.v. (T-B, after Snodgrass).

neuroglia, the supporting structure of nervous tissue, consisting of glial cells (Tulloch); see neuropile.

neurogloea, neuroglia, q.v. (T-B).

neurohemal organs, specialized organs for the release of hormones into the hemolymph, e.g., corpora cardiaca, q.v. (Chapman).

neuromere, in the insect embryo, the pairs of definite swellings of the neural ridges at the bases of the formative embryonic appendages, being the embryonic rudiments of a segmental ganglion (T-B, after Imms, J. B. Smith).

neurone, nerve cell, q.v. (T-B; Chapman).

neuropile, a complex of afferent, internucial and efferent nerve fibers and their supporting glial elements (T-B, after Snodgrass; Chapman).

neuropore, trichopore, q.v. (T-B).

Neuroptera, Neuropteroidea, q.v. (Borror et al.); Planipennia, q.v. (Boudreaux).

Neuropterida, Neuropteroidea, q.v. (Boudreaux).

neuropteroid orders, Neuropteroidea + Coleopteroidea (Borror et al.).

Neuropteroidea, hypothesized monophyletic group within the Holometabola, including the Megaloptera, Raphidioptera, Planipennia (Hennig), and as used elsewhere in this volume; Neuropteroidea + Coleopteroidea (Mackerras, in CSIRO).

neuropterous, of or pertaining to the Neuropteroidea (T-B).

neurosecretion, secretion of neurosecretory cells, containing neurosecretory hormones (Chapman).

neurosecretory cells, secretory cells normally occurring in the ganglia of the central nervous system and source of neurosecretions (Chapman); brain neurosecretory cells, q.v. (Tulloch).

neurosecretory hormone, hormone consisting of small proteins or peptides produced in the central nervous system (Chapman); see adipokinetic hormone, bursicon, diapause hormone, eclosion hormone, hypoglycaemic hormone, and prothoracotrophic hormone.

neurospongium, neuropile, q.v. (T-B, after Imms).

neurotoxin, toxin that affect the funtioning of the nervous system (Allaby).

neuter, the term applied to workers or nonreproductive females in Isoptera and Hymenoptera, being indicated by ♀ or ♀ , imperfect forms of the zodiacal sign Venus (T-B).

neutral synoekete, inquiline, q.v. (Tulloch, after Gaul).

neutral term, a taxonomic term of convenience, such as form or group, which may be employed without reference to the formal taxonomic hierarchy of categories, and which has no nomenclatural standing (Mayr).

new combination (n. comb.), the first combination of a generic name and a previously published species-group name (ICZN).

new name, new replacement name, q.v. (Mayr).

new replacement name, a name established expressly to replace an already established name (ICZN).

new scientific name, a scientific name, avaiable or unavailable, when first proposed for a taxon (ICZN).

new species (**n. sp.**), a newly described species heretofore unknown to science (T-B) see nova species.

New York bee disease, European foulbrood, q.v. (Steinhaus and Martignoni).

Newcastle disease, an acute, rapidly spreading repiratory and nervous disease of domestic poultry and other birds caused by a virus (Pfadt).

niche, the functional position of an organism in a community (Allaby); see environment.

nicotinamide adenine dinucleotide (**NAD**), hydrogen receptor in dehydrogenation reactions (Chapman).

nicotine, $C_{10}H_{14}N_2$, a botanical insecticide derived from leaves and stems of the tobacco plant; an alkaloid, l-1-mehtyl-2-(3'-pyridyl)-pyrrolidine; highly toxic to mammals, acute oral LD_{50} for rats 50 to 60 mg/kg (Pfadt).

nicotinic acid, $C_6H_5O_2N$, an essential vitamin in insects, belonging to the vitamin B complex (Gilmour, in CSIRO).

nictitant ocellus, an ocellate spot having a lunar spot of another color (T-B).

nidamentum, a name applied to the gelatinous mass within which *Chironomous* (Diptera: Chironomidae) lays all its eggs at one time (T-B, after Henneguy).

nidi (sing., **nidus,** groups of regenerative cells within the epithelium of the midgut (T-B, after Comstock; Chapman); in general, a definite cell-group (T-B).

nidificate, to nest, i.e, to prepare a receptaculum for eggs (T-B).

nidification, nest building (Matthews and Matthews).

niger (Latin), black; dark; dusky (T-B; R. W. Brown).

night eyes, dark-adapted eyes, q.v. (T-B, after Comstock).

night vision, vision sensitive to small amounts of light but at the expense of clarity of perception (Leftwich).

nigrescent, nigricans, nigricante, verging on black; blackish (T-B).

ninth coxopodite, in some ♂ Neuropteroidea, gonarcus, q.v. (Tuxen, after Acker, Aspöck); in ♂ Coniopterygidae (Planipennia), hypandrium, q.v. (Tuxen, after Acker).

ninth gonapophyses laterales, in ♀ Heteroptera (Hemiptera), gonoplacs, q.v. (Tuxen, after Ekblom).

ninth gonocoxites, in ♂ Neuropteroidea, parameres, q.v. (Tuxen, after Adams); in Berothidae (Planipennia), gonapophyses laterales, q.v. (Tuxen, after Adams and MacLeod).

ninth hemitergites, in ♀ Apoidea (Hymenoptera), lateral remnants of abdominal tergum IX (Tuxen, after Michener).

ninth parasternites, in ♀ Heteroptera (Hemiptera), gonocoxites of abdominal segment IX, q.v. (Tuxen, after Ekblom).

ninth sternal lobe, in ♂ Orthoptera, abdominal sternum IX (Key, pers. comm., after Snodgrass).

ninth sternite(s), in ♀ Neuropteroidea, gonapophyses laterales, q.v. (Tuxen, after Killington); in ♀ Heteroptera (Hemiptera), gonocoxites of abdominal segment IX (Tuxen, after Christophers and

Cragg); in adult ♀ Chironomidae (Diptera), coxosternapodeme, q.v. (Saether).

ninth tergite, in adult Chrysopidae (Planipennia), ninth tergum + ectoproct, q.v. (Tuxen, after Morse).

ninth tergosternum, in ♂ Diptera, hypandrium, q.v. (Tuxen, after Patton and Cushing).

nit, the egg of a sucking louse (Phthiraptera: Anoplura), when attached to a hair (T-B; Leftwich).

nitid, nitidus (Latin), shiny or glossy; reflecting light (T-B; Harris); see politus.

nitrogen excretion, nitrogenous excretion, q.v. (Gilmour, in CSIRO).

nitrogenous, containing nitrogen (T-B).

nitrogenous excretion, elimination of nitrogenous end products from the body, e.g., uric acid, urea, ammonia, allantoin, amino acids, or protein, in excreta or through storage excretion (Chapman).

niveous, niveus, snow-white; a pure white with an azure under-tint (T-B).

nobis (Latin), belonging to me, as a species; abbrev., nob (T-B).

Noctuoidea, superfamily within the division Ditrysia (Lepidoptera), including the Noctuidae, Arctiidae, Notodontidae (and related families), Lymantriidae, and other families, possessing adults with a metathoracic tympanum, which is rarely reduced or lost (Common, in CSIRO).

nocturnal, active at night (T-B; Borror); see crepuscular, diurnal, and matinal.

nodal furrow, in adult Odonata, a transverse suture, beginning at a point in costal margin corresponding to the nodus, and extending toward inner margin (T-B); in some Heteroptera, costal fracture, q.v. (Hungerford).

nodal line, in forewing of some Fulgoroidea and Cicadidae (Hemiptera: Auchenorrhyncha), a transverse line separating basal half of wing from apical membrane running from apex of costal cell to apex of clavus (Woodward et al., in CSIRO; O'Brien, pers. comm.).

nodal sector, in adult Odonata, media (M), arises from the upper sector of the arculus near the nodus and extending to the outer margin (T-B).

node, nodus, q.v. (T-B); in Heteroptera (Hemiptera), costal fracture, q.v. (Štys).

nodicorn, with antennae that have the apex of each article swollen (T-B).

nodiform, in the form of a knot or knob (T-B).

nodose, nodosus (Latin), full of knots; knotty (T-B; R. W. Brown); of slender articles, having swellings (T-B); of a surface, with isolated knots or protuberances (T-B); see nodulate.

nodular, nodulate, q.v. (T-B; Harris).

nodular hook, in Psocoptera, the in-flight wing coupler located ventrally on the nodulus (transl. "crochet du nodulus" Badonnel).

nodular sclerite, in adult Lepidoptera, epaulette, q.v., being a detached prong of the metepimeron (T-B, after Richards).

nodulate, a surface sculpturing of small knots or swellings (T-B; Harris); see acinose, colliculate, torulose, tuberculate, and verrucose.

nodule, nodulus (Latin), a small knot or swelling (T-B).

nodulose, nodulous, nodulosus (Latin), nodulate, q.v. (T-B; Harris).

nodulus (Latin), nodule, q.v. (T-B); in some adult Psocoptera, point where posterior cubitus (CuP) and anal vein (1A) meet near margin of wing (Smithers, in CSIRO).

nodus (pl., **nodi,** a knot or knob (T-B); in adult Odonata, the stout crossvein near the middle of the costal margin of the wing, joining the costa, subcosta and radius (T-B, after Needham); in adult Odonata, a notch marking the position of a prominent crossvein near the middle of the front edge of the wing (Leftwich); in adult Apocrita (especially ants) (Hymenoptera), petiole, q.v., or postpetiole, q.v. (T-B; Leftwich).

nomadic phase, in army ants (Hymenoptera: Formicidae), the period in which the colony forages more actively for food and moves frequently from one bivouac site to another, the queen does not lay eggs, and the bulk of the brood is in the larval stage (Tulloch, after Gaul; Wilson); see statary phase.

nomadism, the relatively frequent movement by an entire colony from one nest site to another, e.g., in army ants (Hymenoptera: Formicidae) (Wilson).

nomen conservandum (Latin), conserved name, q.v. (T-B; ICZN).

nomen dubium (pl., **nomina dubia**) (Latin), a descriptive term meaning name of unknown or doubtful application (ICZN).

nomen inquirendum (Latin), a name to be inquired into or whose status is subject to investigation (T-B); see incertae sedis and nomen dubium.

nomen novum (pl., **nomina nova**) (Latin), new replacement name, q.v. (ICZN).

nomen nudum (pl., **nomina nuda**) (Latin), a name that is not available according to the Code (ICZN).

nomen oblitum (pl., **nomina oblita**) (Latin), a descriptive term meaning forgotten name (ICZN).

nomenclator, a book containing a list of scientific names assembled for nomenclatural, rather than taxonomic purposes (Mayr); see catalog.

nomenclatorial, relating to nomenclators such as the *Index Animalium* by C. D. Sherborn; formerly used in the sense of nomenclatural (ICZN).

nomenclatural, relating to nomenclature (ICZN).

nomenclatural act, a published action that affects the status of a work or scientific name, or the fixation of a name-bearing type (ICZN).

nomenclature, a system of names, and provisions for their formation and use (T-B; ICZN); see binominal nomenclature and zoological nomenclature.

nominal taxon, a nomenclatural taxon, denoted by an available name, and based, actually or potentially, upon its name-bearing type but having no defined taxonomic boundaries, e.g., a nominal family, a nominal genus, a nominal species (ICZN); see taxonomic taxon.

nominalism, a school of philosophy, denying the existence of universals, and emphasizing the importance of man-given names for the grouping of individuals (Mayr).

nominate, nominotypical, q.v. (Mayr; ICZN).

nominotypical, of or pertaining to a nominotypical taxon.

nominotypical taxon, the taxon at a lower rank within the family group, the genus group, or the species group that contains the name-bearing type of a divided taxonomic taxon of that group and has exactly the same name in the case of genus-group and species-group names, but whose suffix is amended in family-group names according to rank (ICZN), e.g., Apinae is the nominotypical subfamily of the family Apidae (Hymenoptera); *Apis mellifera mellifera* is the nominotypical subspecies of the species *Apis mellifera*.

non-, prefix; not (T-B); see nec.

non viso (Latin), not seen (T-B).

noninclusion, nonoccluded, q.v. (Steinhaus and Martignoni).

noninclusion viruses, insect viruses that occur free in tissues as viruses do in higher animals and plants; the viruses are not included in crystals, granules, or other inclusion bodies; as yet only a small number of these viruses have been found in insects; found in larval Diptera, Lepidoptera, Coleoptera, and in larval and adult Hymenoptera (Pfadt).

noninvaginated tubular ducts, in Pseudococcidae (Hemiptera: Sternorrhyncha: Coccoidea), cylindrical dermal structure without cup-shaped apex, usually with single sclerotized band (Miller, in Stehr).

nonnucleate, without a nucleus (T-B).

nonoccluded, in invertebrate pathology, said of viruses in which the virions are not occluded in a dense protein crystal (Steinhaus and Martignoni).

nonpersistent transmission, plant virus transmission in which the insect vector remains capable of inoculating plants for only a relatively short period of time (Nault and Ammar, after Watson and Roberts); see persistent transmission and semipersistent transmission.

norma (pl., **normae**), in ♂ Lycaenidae (Lepidoptera), rod-shaped, geniculate structure at base of orbiculus (juxta) (Tuxen, after van Eecke).

normal host, natural host, q.v., or typical host, q.v. (Steinhaus and Martignoni).

northern cereal mosaic, disease of cereal grains caused by a rhabdovirus transmitted propagatively by *Laodelphax, Muellerianella, Ribautodelphax,* and *Unknodes* (Hemiptera: Auchenorrhyncha: Delphacidae) (Nault and Ammar).

nose, in a few pupal Chironomidae (Diptera), distolateral projection of wing sheath (Saether).

nosema disease, a disease of adult honey bees (Hymenoptera: Apoidea), caused by the microsporidian *Nosema apis* Zander, the protozoan developing within the cells of the midgut epithelium (Steinhaus and Martignoni).

nosemosis, in invertebrate pathology, infection with microsporidia of the genus *Nosema* (Steinhaus and Martignoni).

nosography, a branch of pathology that deals with the description of diseases (Steinhaus and Martignoni).

nosology, a branch of pathology that deals with the classification of diseases; a treatise comprising such a classification (Steinhaus and Marignoni).

nostril, rhinarium, q.v. (T-B).

notal comb, in adult Siphonaptera, a row of conspicuous spines on the posterior margin of the prothorax (T-B).

notal organ, in ♂ Panorpidae (Mecoptera), median posterior process of abdominal tergum III (Crampton).

notal ridge, in adult Siphonaptera, the post-median vertical ridge of the metathorax, the ventral end of which fuses with the posterior end of the transverse ridge of the metanotal area to form the roof of the pleural arch (Rothschild and Traub).

notal wing processes, lateral processes of the scutum which articulate with the axillary sclerites in the wing base (Chapman), see anterior notal wing process, median notal wing process, and posterior notal wing process.

notate, notatatus (Latin), marked by spots; with a series of depressed marks as a sculpture (T-B; Harris); see impressed, innotate, maculate, and ordinate.

notaulice, in adult Diptera, lateral parapsidal suture, q.v. (McAlpine).

notaulix (pl., **notaulices**), in adult Hymenoptera, notaulus, q.v. (T-B, after Snodgrass; Riek, in CSIRO).

notaulus (pl., **notauli**), in many adult Hymenoptera, one of a pair of posteriorly converging lines on mesoscutum (Gauld and Bolton); see median mesoscutal lobe and parapsidal line.

notched, indented, cut or nicked; usually of a margin (T-B).

notepisternum, anepisternum, q.v. (T-B, after MacGillivray; Saether).

Nothyboidea, Tanypezoidea, q.v. (Colless and McAlpine, in CSIRO; Borror et al.).

notocephalon, in Notonectidae (Hemiptera: Heteroptera), vertex, q.v., of head (T-B).

notodont, with toothed back (T-B); used to describe larvae of the Notodontidae (Lepidoptera), that are more or less conspicuously humped on the dorsal surface (T-B).

Notodontoidea, superfamily within the Ditrysia (Lepidoptera), frequently treated as a monophyletic subgroup of the Noctuoidea, including the families Notodontidae, Thaumetopoeidae, Dioptidae, and sometimes Thyretidae, the last now usually assigned to the Arctiidae, possessing adults with a ventrally-directed metathoracic tympanum, forewing with second branch of media (M_2) not arising nearer to M_3 than to M_1, larvae with 2 MD setae on first abdominal segment (Common).

Notogaea, a proposed biogeographical region, including the Australia, Polynesia, and Hawaiian Islands (T-B).

Notonectoidea, superfamily within the infraorder Nepomorpha of the

Heteroptera (Hemiptera), including the Notonectidae, Pleidae, and Helotrephidae (Woodward et al., in CSIRO).

notopleural, of or relating to the notopleuron (T-B).

notopleural bristles, in adult Diptera, usually 2 bristles inserted on notopleuron (T-B, after Comstock; Borror et al.).

notopleural suture, in Adephaga, Archostemata, and Myxophaga (Coleoptera), the suture separating the pronotum from the proepisternum (Britton, in CSIRO).

notopleuron (pl., **notopleura,** in higher Diptera, clearly delimited sunken area in the anterior region of the scutum, between the postpronotal lobe and the wing base (T-B, after Curran; Borror et al.; McAlpine).

Notoptera, Grylloblattodea, q.v. (Borror et al.).

notoptera, in adult Coleoptera, the parallel ridges or thickenings of the posterior part of the metascutum (T-B, after MacGillivray).

notopterale, first axillary sclerite, q.v. (T-B, after Crampton).

notopteraria, in adult Coleoptera, the median groove of metascutum (T-B, after MacGillivray).

notorganum (pl., **notorgana**), in ♂ Mecoptera, median unpaired structure on abdominal tergum III (Tuxen).

Notostigmophora, Scutigeromorpha, q.v. (Hennig).

Notostraca, order within the class Branchiopoda (Crustacea), including the tadpole shrimps, characterized by having an oval convex carapace covering the anterior part of the body; 35–71 pairs of thoracic appendages; and 2 long, filamentous caudal appendages (Borror et al.).

nototheca, that part of the pupa covering upper surface of the abdomen (T-B).

notum (pl., **nota,** tergum of a thoracic segment, i.e., pronotum, mesonotum, or metanotum (T-B; Peterson; Leftwich); in ♂ Hymenoptera and other orders, fused dorsal rami of gonapophyses IX (Tuxen, after E. L. Smith); in ♀ Hymenoptera and other orders, fused dorsal rami of gonapophyses IX, usually produced into a ridge or swelling (Tuxen, after E. L. Smith; Saether); see eunotum, tergum, and tergite.

nova species, new species; abbrev., n. s., n. sp., nov. sp. (T-B).

novaectoapophysis, in ♂ Chironomidae (Diptera), sternapodeme, q.v. (Saether).

novasternal coria, in Isoptera, flexible membrane between abdominal sterna VIII and IX (Tuxen, after Geyer).

novavalvae, in ♀ insects, third valvulae, q.v. (T-B, after MacGillivray); in ♀ Chironomidae (Diptera), labia, q.v., of genitalia (Saether).

novum (Latin), new; abbrev., nov. (T-B).

novum genus, new genus; abbrev., n. g., nov. gen. (T-B).

nozzle, in adult Formicinae (Hymenoptera: Formicidae), modified hypopygium bearing acidopore (Gauld and Bolton).

nucha (Latin), nape of the neck (R. W. Brown); the upper surface of the cervix connecting head and thorax (T-B).

nuclear cytoplasm, in insect eggs, the small mass of cytoplasm containing the nucleus (T-B, after Snodgrass).

nuclear polyhedrosis, nucleopolyhedrosis, q.v. (Steinhaus and Martignoni).

nuclear polyhedrosis viruses, nucleopolyhedrosis virus, q.v. (Pfadt).

nucleate, nucleated, nucleiform, having a nucleus; of the shape of a nucleus (T-B).

nucleocapsid, in invertebrate pathology, the sructure composed of the capsid with enclosed viral nucleic acid, some being naked but others enclosed in an envelope (limiting membrane) (Steinhaus and Martignoni).

nucleolus, a clearly defined, often spherical area of the eukaryotic nucleus, composed of densely packed fibrils and granules, rich in RNA and protein, and the site of origin of ribosomes (T-B; Allaby).

nucleopolyhedrosis, a usually fatal, viral disease of insects, mainly the larvae of certain Lepidoptera and Hymenoptera, characterized by the formation of polyhedral inclusion bodies (polyhedra) in the nuclei of infected cells, with the virus multiplying in the epidermis, tracheal matrix, fatbody, and hemocyctes of Lepidoptera and in the midgut epithelium of Hymenoptera (Steinhaus and Martignoni); see grasserie, jaundice, polyhedrosis, wilt disease, and Wipfelkrankheit.

nucleoprotein, a conjugated protein, composed of a histone or protamine bound to a nucleic acid as the nonprotein portion (T-B; Allaby).

nucleus, a well-defined, differentiated, round or oval body imbedded in the cell contents.

nude, nudus (Latin), naked; devoid of hair, scales, or other surface vestiture (T-B; Harris); see denudate, glabrous, immaculate, and investitus.

nuditas, nudity, nakedness; the condition of being without covering or vestiture (T-B).

Nudrin (trade name), methomyl, q.v. (Pfadt).

nulliparous, no egg development having occurred (Adkins, pers. comm.); see parous.

numerical phenetics, the determination of relationships of taxa determined by the calculation of values of overall similarity (Mayr); see cladistics.

numerical taxomomy, classification based upon overall phenetic resemblance (Borror et al., after Sokal).

nuptial feeding, courtship feeding, q.v. (Matthews and Matthews).

nuptial flight, in ants (Hymenoptera: Formicidae), the mating flight of winged queens, males, or both (Wilson; Brown, pers. comm.).

nurse, young worker bee (Apidae) or small worker ant (Formicidae) (Hymenoptera) whose chief occupation is feeding larvae and caring for eggs and pupae (T-B; Eickwort, pers. comm.).

nurse cell, trophocyte in a meroistic ovariole (T-B, after Comstock; Chapman); trophocyte of the ovary or testis (T-B, after Snodgrass).

nutans, nutant, nodding; with the tip bent horizontally (T-B).

nutricial castration, in eusocial bees (Hymenoptera: Apidae), the loss of fertility through selective feeding during the larval period by the brood nurses; the basis of the theory of the trophogenic determination of caste (Tulloch).

nutritive chamber, in telotrophic ovarioles, germarium, q.v. (T-B).

nutritive cord, in a telotrophic ovariole, a cytoplasmic extension connecting each oocyte with the trophic core of the germarium (Chapman).

nutritive layer, in galls of Cynipidae (Hymenoptera), the innermost tissue of the gall, lining the larval cell (T-B, after Kinsey).

nygmata (sing., **nygma**), in some adult Neuropteroidea, Mecoptera, Trichoptera, and Symphyta (Hymenoptera), presumed sensory spots on the wings (Riek, in CSIRO).

nymph, an immature stage of hemimetabolous insects, e.g., Heteroptera (Hemiptera) (T-B, after Imms); in Acari, immature stage that has 8 legs (Borror et al.); see larva and naiad.

nympha inclusa, coarctate pupa, q.v. (T-B).

nymphal, of or pertaining to a nymph; in an immature stage called a nymph; see larval.

nymphiparous, bearing living young (nymphs) (T-B); see larviparous and pupiparous.

nymphoid reproductive, in Isoptera, a supplementary or replacement reproductive bearing wing buds (Miller).

O

O-setae, in larval and pupal Chironomidae (Diptera), minute setae on extreme anterior margins of abdominal terga and sterna (Saether).

oak apple, a relative large spongy, spherical gall on leaves or stems of oaks (*Quercus* spp.) produced by larvae of various Cynipidae (Hymenoptera) (T-B; Borror et al.); see marble gall.

oak button-gall, small, flat, circular gall produced on the surface of oak (*Quercus* spp.) leaves by the larva of *Neuroterus* spp. (Hymenoptera: Cynipidae) (Leftwich).

oak hedgehog gall, hedgehog oak-gall, q.v. (Leftwich).

oak marble gall, marble gall, q.v. (Leftwich).

oak root-gall, gall on roots of oak trees (*Quercus* spp.), produced by larval Cynipidae (Hymenoptera) (Leftwich).

oat blue dwarf, disease of oats caused by a marafivirus transmitted propagatively by *Nesoclutha* and *Cicadulina* (Hemiptera: Auchenorrhyncha: Cicadellidae) (Nault and Ammar).

oat sterile dwarf, disease of oats caused by a reovirus (*Fijivirus*) transmitted propagatively *Javesella, Diranotropis,* and *Ribautodelphax* (Hemiptera: Auchenorrhyncha: Delphacidae) (Nault and Ammar).

oat striate mosaic, disease of oats caused by a rhabdovirus transmitted propagatively by *Graminella* (Hemiptera: Auchenorrhyncha: Cicadellidae) (Nault and Ammar).

ob-, Latin prefix; toward; reversal; in the way of (T-B).

obconic, obconical, in the form of a reversed cone, i.e., with the cone base at the apex and the cone apex at the base (T-B).

obcordate, obcordatus, inversely heart-shaped; with the point applied to the base of another object or part (T-B).

obese, obesus (Latin), fat (T-B; R. W. Brown); unnaturally large and distended; usually applied to the abdomen (T-B); see physogastric.

objective synonym, each of 2 or more synonyms that is based on the same name-bearing type (ICZN).

object orientation, spatial orientation associated with searching for and approaching resources and avoiding stresses in a patchy environment (Matthews and Matthews, after Jander).

oblate, oblatus (Latin), flattened at the poles (of a spheroid) (T-B; R. W. Brown).

obligatory diapause, in univoltine insects, quiescence occurring invariably during an unfavorable season of the year (Common).

obligatory parasite, a parasite living on one host exclusively (T-B).

obligatory parthenogenesis, parthenogenesis in which a species reproduces entirely without males.

oblique, obliquus (Latin), slanting; any direction between perpendicular and horizontal (T-B).

oblique sternals, very short muscles connecting the adjacent edges of the abdominal sterna (T-B).

oblique tergals, the short muscles connecting the edges of the abdominal terga (T-B).

oblique vein, in adult Odonata, a slanting crossvein, being the most proximal crossvein posterior to third radial vein (T-B; O'Farrell, in CSIRO).

obliterate, obliterated, obliteratus (Latin), erased; indistinct (T-B; R. W. Brown).

oblong, oblongus (Latin), longer than broad (T-B; R. W. Brown).

oblong plates, in ♀ Aculeata (Hymenoptera), second gonocoxae, q.v. (T-B, after Imms; Tuxen, after Snodgrass).

oblongulum, in Archostemata and Adephaga (Coleoptera), a special closed cell in the hind wing formed by crossveins connecting the media (M) and the anterior cubitus (CuA). (T-B, after Tillyard; Britton, in CSIRO).

obovate, obovatus (Latin), inversely ovate, i.e., with narrower end downward (T-B).

obpyriform, inversely pyriform, i.e., with the narrower end downward (T-B).

obscure, obscurus (Latin), dark; not readily seen; not well defined (T-B; Harris); see confused and intricate.

obscure-aeneous, obscure-aeneus, an indistinct copper color (T-B).

observation nests, artifically constructed nests used for observing the behavior of social insects (Gauld and Bolton).

obsite, obsitus (Latin), covered, e.g., with scales (T-B; R. W. Brown).

obsolescent, in the process of disappearing or of becoming nonfunctional (T-B).

obsolete, obsoletus (Latin), almost or entirely absent; indistinct; not fully developed (T-B); see rudimentary and vestigial.

obtect, obtected, obtectus (Latin), covered; concealed (T-B; R. W. Brown).

obtect pupa, pupa or chrysalis found in most butterflies and moths (Lepidoptera) in which the wings and appendages are appressed to the body and most of the abdominal segments are immovable (T-B; Leftwich; Chapman).

obtuse, obtusus (Latin), blunt; dull (R. W. Brown); at an angle greater than a right angle, opposed to acute (T-B).

obtuse-angulate, forming an obtuse angle; as markings or angles (T-B).

obtusilingues, those bees (Hymenoptera: Apoidea) with short tongues having an obtuse or bifid tip (T-B); see acutilingues.

obumbrant, obumbrans, overhanging (T-B).

obverse, head on; viewed head on (T-B).

obverse surface, in scales of adult Lepidoptera, the top or principal scale surface which usually lies away from the wing surface (Downey and Allyn); see reverse surface.

occipital, of or pertaining to the occiput or the back part of the head (T-B).

occipital arch, the area of the cranium between the occipital and postoccipital sutures, its dorsal part being the occiput and its lateral parts being the postgenae (T-B, after Snodgrass).

occipital carina, in adult Hymenoptera, carina delimiting the occiput peripherally (Gauld and Bolton).

occipital cilia, in adult Diptera, postocular setae, q.v. (T-B, after Curran).

occipital condyles, processes on the margin of the postocciput to which the cervical sclerites are articulated (T-B, after Snodgrass; Chapman).

occipital dilation, in adult Muscomorpha (Diptera), genal dilation, q.v. (McAlpine).

occipital foramen, opening at the back of the head through which the alimentary canal, nerve cord, and some muscles pass (T-B; Chapman).

occipital fringe, in adult Diptera, postocular setae, q.v. (T-B, after Curran).

occipital ganglion, hypocerebral ganglion, q.v., or corpus cardiacum, q.v. (T-B, after Snodgrass).

occipital horns, in adult Odonata, chitinous horns just below the occipital ridge on each side of the head (T-B, after Garman).

occipital margin, in larval Chironomidae (Diptera), postoccipital margin, q.v. (Saether).

occipital orbit, genal orbit, q.v. (T-B, after MacGillivray).

occipital region, occiput, q.v. (Leftwich).

occipital ridge, in adult Odonata, a ridge extending between the compound eyes on the caudodorsal angle of the head (T-B, after Garman).

occipital setae, in adult Diptera, setae scattered over lateral portions of occiput (McAlpine); see postocular setae and supracervical setulae.

occipital sinus, in larval Lepidoptera, epicranial notch, q.v. (Peterson, after Whelan).

occipital spine, in adult Odonata, a spine on the caudodorsal surface of the head, between the compound eyes (T-B, after Garman).

occipital sulcus, a transverse groove sometimes present on the back of the head ending ventrally anterior to the posterior articulations of the mandibles, separating the vertex from the occiput dorsally and the genae from the postgenae laterally (Chapman, after Snodgrass).

occipital suture, occipital sulcus, q.v. (T-B, after Snodgrass).

occipito-orbital bristles, in adult Diptera, postocular setae, q.v. (T-B).

occiput, the posterior part of the epicranium between the vertex and the neck, being rarely present as a distinct sclerite (T-B, after Imms); dorsal part of the head between the occipital sulcus and the postoccipital sulcus (Chapman, after Snodgrass); in adult Diptera, postcranium, q.v. (T-B, after J. B. Smith; McAlpine); in Siphonaptera, that portion of the head behind the interantennal suture (Lewis, pers. comm.); see median sclerite.

occluded, in invertebrate pathology, said of those virions which are occluded in a dende crystal, large enough to be visible with a light microscope (e.g., polyhedrosis viruses and granulosis viruses) (Steinhaus and Martignoni).

occlusor, occlusor muscle, any closing muscle of an elastic opening; a muscle of the spiracles which, by contracting, closes the communication between the spiracular atrium and the trachea proper (T-B, after Imms).

occlusor muscle apodeme, apodeme that is the site of origin of the spiracular occlusor muscle (Gibson).

occult, occultus (Latin), hidden; concealed (T-B; R. W. Brown).

occult virus, in invertebrate pathology, a special phase of some viruses, characteristic of latent infections, in which the pathogenic agent is presumed to differ from the infective phase, and in which virions cannot be detected (Steinhaus and Martignoni).

oceanic, of or pertaining to the ocean; appled to animals which inhabit the open sea; pelagic (T-B).

ocellae, ocelli, q.v., and stemmata, q.v. (T-B, after MacGillivray).

ocellalae, the grouped simple eyes in nymphs and adults of Collembola (T-B, after MacGillivray).

ocellanae, in nymphal and adult exopterygote insects, ocelli, q.v. (T-B, after MacGillivray).

ocellar basin, in adult Hymenoptera, a concave area occupying the median portion of the frontal area, varying greatly in form and size in the different families and subfamilies (T-B).

ocellar bristles, in adult Diptera, ocellar setae, q.v. (T-B).

ocellar center, brain center of an ocellus, located in the outer end of an ocellar pedicel (T-B, after Snodgrass).

ocellar furrow, in adult Hymenoptera, a transverse furrow extending between the ends of the vertical furrows near the dorsal margin of the lateral ocelli, frequently being confluent with the space around the lateral ocelli (T-B).

ocellar group, in certain larval Lepidoptera, the 6 stemmata on lateral aspect of head (Peterson).

ocellar nerve, ocellar pedicel, q.v. (T-B, after Snodgrass).

ocellar pair, in adult Diptera, see ocellar setae, q.v. (T-B, after Comstock).

ocellar pedicel, the long slender nerve stalk which connects the ocellus with the protocerebrum (T-B, after Snodgrass).

ocellar plate, in adult Diptera, ocellar triangle, q.v. (T-B, after Comstock).

ocellar ribbon, a crescent-shaped, smooth, thin belt across the eye region in butterfly (Lepidoptera) chrysalides (T-B).

ocellar ridge, in adult Odonata, a ridge just behind the ocelli (T-B, after Garman).

ocellar setae, in adult Diptera, bristles on vertical triangle, usually near the anterior ocellus (McAlpine).

ocellar spots, in Conchaspididae (Hemiptera: Sternorrhyncha: Coccoidea), weakly pigmented, oval area on submedial region of head (Miller, in Stehr).

ocellar stripe, in adult Odonata, a pale stripe on the dorsum of the head behind the ocelli (T-B, after Garman).

ocellar triangle, in adult Diptera, triangular area bearing the 3 ocelli (T-B, after Comstock; McAlpine).

ocellar tubercle, in adult Diptera, raised vertical triangle, defined by grooves, e.g., Asilidae (T-B, after Curran; Colless and McAlpine, in CSIRO; McAlpine).

ocellara (pl., **ocellarae**), in larval endopterygote insects, stemma, q.v. (T-B, after MacGillivray).

ocellarium, in adult Diptera, ocellar triangle, q.v. (Colless and McAlpine, in CSIRO).

ocellasae (sing., **ocellasa**), in adult endopterygote insects, ocelli, q.v. (T-B, after MacGillvray).

ocellate, ocellated, ocellatus (Latin), provided with ocelli or simple eyes (T-B); marked with spots (T-B; R. W. Brown).

ocelli, pl. ocellus, q.v. (T-B).

ocelliform spots, in Blattaria, ocelli, q.v. (Mackerras, in CSIRO).

ocelligerous, ocelligerus, furnished with, or bearing, ocelli (T-B).

ocelloid, ocelliform, i.e., resembling an ocellus (T-B); in wingless Liposcelidae (Psocoptera), a visual element of a reduced compound eye (Pearman).

ocellus (pl., **ocelli**), in adult insects, simple eye consisting of a single beadlike lens, occurring singly or in small groups (T-B); in holometabolous larvae, stemma, q.v. (T-B); a colored spot surrounded by a ring of different color, e.g., eye spot or eyelike pattern on the wing of a butterfly or moth (Lepidoptera) (T-B; Leftwich); in Collembola, a rudimentary visual organ lying between the antennal bases, usually recognizable only by the presence of a pigment spot, being frontal or median (Christiansen and Bellinger).

ocellus coecus, blind ocellus, q.v. (T-B).

ocellus simplex, simple ocellus, q.v. (T-B).

ocherous, pale yellow, q.v. (R. W. Brown).

ochraceous, ochraceus, ochraeus, ochreous, ochreus, pale yellow, q.v. (T-B).

ochroleucus, whitish yellow (T-B); see ocherous.

Ochteroidea, superfamily within the infraorder Nepomorpha of the Heteroptera, including the families Ochteridae and Gelastocoridae (Schuh).

octacerores, in Asterolecaniidae (Hemiptera: Sternorrhyncha: Coccoidea), 8-shaped pores, q.v. (T-B, after MacGillivray).

octapophyses, first gonapophyses, q.v. (T-B, after MacGillivray).

octasternal coria, in Isoptera, flexible membrane between abdominal sterna VII and VIII (Tuxen, after Geyer).

octaval, in ♂ Lepidoptera, paired, hairy or scobinate, caudal process of caudal margin of abdominal sternum VIII (Tuxen, after Pierce).

octavalvae, in ♀ insects, first gonapophyses, q.v. (Tuxen, after MacGillivray).

octavalvifer(s), in ♀ insects, gonangulum, q.v. (Tuxen, after MacGillivray); in ♀ Chironomidae (Diptera), gonocoxapodeme, q.v. (Saether).

octoon, abdomen segment VIII (T-B).

ocular, of or pertaining to the compound eyes (T-B).

ocular emargination, in Amblycera and Ischnocera (Phthiraptera), a lateral emargination of the head in which the eye is received posteriorly (T-B).

ocular field, in pupal Chironomidae (Diptera), covering case of eye (Saether); see ophthalmotheca.

ocular fleck, in Amblycera and Ischnocera (Phthiraptera), a small, intensely black spot of pigment in the eyes (T-B).

ocular fringe, in Amblycera and Ischnocera (Phthiraptera), closely set small hairs on posterior half of ocular emargination, sometimes extending on the temporal margin (T-B).

ocular line, in adult Culicidae (Diptera), the area along the anterior border of the vertex between the margin of the compound eye and the row of ocular setae (Harbach and Knight, after Knight).

ocular lobes, protocerebrum, q.v. (T-B); in larval Chironomidae (Diptera), genae, q.v. (Saether).

ocular neuromere, in the insect embryo, the primitive cephalic ganglion from which the optic lobe of the brain arises (T-B).

ocular region, protocerebrum, q.v., of brain (T-B).

ocular ridge, apodeme marked externally by the ocular suture (Harbach and Knight).

ocular scale, in adult Culicidae (Diptera), one of the scales occurring on the ocular line of the head (Harbach and Knight).

ocular sclerite, narrow sclerite surrounding compound eye (T-B; Harbach and Knight).

ocular segment, acron, q.v., of head (T-B, after J. B. Smith).

ocular seta(e), in many groups of Heteroptera, usually a pair of setae located in the dorsal posterior portion of the compound eye of early instars, often lost later in development (Cobben; Andersen); in adult

Culicidae (Diptera), one of the setae occurring in a line on the head near the posterior margin of each compound eye (Harbach and Knight).

ocular suture, the line of inflexion in the cranial wall encircling the compound eye (T-B, after Snodgrass).

ocular tubercles, in Aphididae (Hemiptera: Sternorrhyncha), a group of prominent facets on the posterior portion of the compound eye (T-B).

ocularium (pl., **ocularia**), in larval Holometabola, the more or less elevated or pigmented area bearing stemmata (Peterson, after MacGillivray).

oculata, ocular sclerite, q.v., or ocular ridge, q.v. (T-B, after MacGillivray).

oculocephalic, of or pertaining to the eyes and the head; applied to the imaginal buds destined to produce the cephalic region in Hymenoptera (T-B).

oculomalar space, the area separating the inferior angle of the eye from the insertion of the mandible (T-B, after Needham).

oculus (Latin), (pl., **oculi**), eye (R. W. Brown); in insects, compound eye, q.v. (T-B).

odona, toothed; applied to Odonata by Fabricius because of the long teeth on the maxilla and labium (T-B, after J. B. Smith).

Odonata, predaceous order of Paleoptera (Insecta), including the dragonflies and damselflies, possessing adults with 2 equal or subequal wings and complex accessory genitalia developed from abdominal sternum II or III of ♂; nymphs aquatic with an elongate prehensile labium modified for seizing prey, and respiration by tracheal gills (T-B; O'Farrell, in CSIRO).

odonate, member of the Odonata (T-B); bearing toothed mouthparts, like those of adult Odonata (T-B); of or pertaining to the Odonata (T-B).

Odonatoptera, hypothesized monophyletic group including the Odonata and the extinct order Meganisoptera (Boudreaux, after Martynov).

Odonatopterata, Odonatoptera, q.v. (Boudreaux).

odor trail, a chemical trace laid down by one insect and followed by another, the odorous material being referred to either as the trail pheromone or the trail substance (Wilson).

odorate, odoratus, odoriferous, q.v. (T-B).

odoriferous, giving off a scent (T-B).

odoriferous gland, in Heteroptera (Hemiptera), metathoracic scent gland, q.v., or dorsal abdominal scent gland, q.v. (T-B).

oedaeagus, in ♂ Lepidoptera, aedoeagus, q.v. (Tuxen).

oedagus, aedeagus, q.v. (T-B).

oedeagus, aedeagus, q.v. (Tuxen).

oedeagus guards, in ♂ Hesperiidae (Lepidoptera), processes of anellus or fultura superior (Tuxen, after Elwes and Edwards).

oedoeagus, aedeagus, q.v. (T-B); in ♂ Lepidoptera, aedoeagus, q.v. (Tuxen).

oedymeroid, in ♂ Tubulifera (Thysanoptera), the enlarged apterous major forms of gregarious polymorphic species (Stannard).

oenocyte, a large, commonly yellow, cell of ectodermal origin, generally more than 100 μ in diameter, in a group on either side of each abdominal segment, associated with the midgut, fat body, or epidermis, or forming clusters in the body cavity, and probably concerned with the production of lipids in the cuticle (T-B; Tulloch, after Richards; Chapman).

oenocytelike cell, oenocytoid, q.v. (Tulloch, after Yeager).

oenocytoid, in insect blood, large, nonphagocytic rounded or spherical cell with strongly acidophile cytoplasm (so-called for their resemblance to oenocytes) (T-B); in Coleoptera, Lepidoptera, and some Diptera and Heteroptera, hemocytes which are usually large, thick, basophilic cells containing canaliculi, strands of granules or crystals (T-B; Tulloch, after Jones; Chapman).

oeruginous, oeruginus, aeruginous, q.v. (T-B).

oesophageal bone, in Psocoptera, a plate below the anterior part of the oesophagus (T-B).

oesophageal bulb, cibarial pump, q.v. (T-B).

oesophageal commissures, circumoesophageal connectives, q.v. (T-B, after Folsom and Wardle).

oesophageal diverticulum, crop, q.v. (T-B).

oesophageal ganglion, hypocerebral ganglion, q.v., or corpus cardiacum, q.v. (T-B; Leftwich).

oesophageal invagination, stomodael valve, q.v. (Gilmour, in CSIRO).

oesophageal lobes, paired lobes of tritocerebrum (T-B).

oesophageal sclerite, in Amblycera and Ischnocera (Phthiraptera), a greatly developed thickening of the chitinous lining of the anterior part of the oesophagus (T-B).

oesophageal sympathetic nervous system, stomatogastric nervous system, q.v. (T-B, after Imms).

oesophageal valve, stomodaeal valve, q.v. (T-B).

oesophagus, that part of the alimentary canal between the mouth and the crop (T-B).

Oestroidea, superfamily within the series Schizophora of the infraorder Muscomorpha (Diptera: Brachycera), including the families Oestridae, Rhinophoridae, Calliphoridae, Sarcophagidae, and Tachinidae (McAlpine).

Official Index, a list of names or works suppressed or declared invalid by the Commission (Mayr; ICZN).

Official List, a list of names or works which have been conserved or declared to be valid by the Commission (Mayr; ICZN).

olecranon (pl., **olecrana**), in ♂ Lepidoptera, rounded process capping coecum penis (Tuxen, after Higgins).

oleic aid, $C_{17}H_{33}COOH$, a monounsaturated fatty acid, being a common constituent of storage fats (Gilmour, in CSIRO).

olfaction, perception of chemicals in a gaseous state in relatively low concentrations (T-B; Chapman); see chemoreception and contact chemoreception.

olfactory, pertaining to olfaction (T-B).

olfactory cone, basiconic peg, q.v. (T-B).

olfactory lobes, antennal lobes, q.v., of deutocerebrum (T-B).

olfactory pit, sensory pit, q.v. (Leftwich).

Oligentomata, Collembola, q.v. (Borror et al.).

oligidic, pertaining to a medium (used for growing organisms) consisting wholly or largely of crude materials, in which no molecule (other than water) has been established as an absolute nutritional requirement (Steinhaus and Martignoni); see holidic and meridic.

Oligocene Epoch, epoch within the Tertiary Period, between the Eocene Epoch and the Miocene Epoch, extending between about 40 and 25 million years before the present (Riek, in CSIRO).

Oligoentomata, Collembola, q.v. (Boudreaux, after Berlese).

oligogenic character, determined by only a few genes (Mayr); see monogenic and polygenic.

oligogyny, polygyny in which there are from 2 to several functional queens in the colony (Wilson).

oligolectic, used to describe bees (Hymenoptera: Apoidea) that gather pollen from only a few species of related flowers (Riek, after Linsley, in CSIRO); see monolectic and polylectic.

Oligoneoptera, Holometabola, q.v. (Mackerras, after Martynov, in CSIRO).

oligonephrous, with few Malpighian tubules (T-B).

Oligoneura, group of Diptera, including the Brachycera and most Nematocera, characterized by a deep axillary incision in the hind margin of the wing (Hennig); see Polyneura.

Oligoneurioidea, superfamily proposed for the family Oligoneuridae (Ephemeroptera), more generally included within the Heptagenioidea (Hennig, after Demoulin).

oligoneurous, having few wing veins, being specifically applied in Diptera to some Cecidomyiidae (Diptera) (T-B).

oligophagous, having a restricted range of food plants of related plant orders, of a single order, or even of a single genus (T-B, after Folsom and Wardle; Chapman); having a very restricted range of food or, in the case of parasites, infesting a limited number of host species (Leftwich); see monophagous and polyphagous.

oligophagy, accepting a limited range of foods and usually prefering one or 2 (Matthews and Matthews).

oligopneustic respiratory system, respiratory system with 1 or 2 functional spiracles on each side, including amphipneustic, metapneustic, and propneustic respiratory systems (Chapman, after Keilin); see apneustic respiratory system and polypneustic respiratory system.

oligopod larva, an active larva with well-developed, functional thoracic legs, but no abdominal prolegs, and a well-developed head capsule with mouthparts similar to the adult, e.g., campodeiform larva, elateriform larva, and scarabaeiform larva (T-B; Leftwich; Chapman); see apodous larva and polypod larva.

oligopod phase, in the insect embryo, a phase which has reached an advanced condition of development (T-B, after Imms).

oligotrophic, oligophagous, q.v. (Tulloch, after Gaul).

olim, formerly (T-B).

olistheter(s), in adult Hymenoptera and other orders, sliding interlock between gonapophyses VIII and IX, consisting of a tongue, rachis along ventral ramus of gonapophysis IX, fitting into a groove, aulax, on dorsal ramus of corresponding gonapophysis VIII (Tuxen, after E. L. Smith).

olistheter scales, in adult Hymneoptera and other orders, ovate projections covering surfaces of rhachis and aulax, sometimes modified into spines on disengaged gonapophyses IX (Tuxen, after E. L. Smith).

olivaceous, olivaceus, olive green, i.e., yellowish-green (T-B).

Olognatha, Helminthomorpha, q.v. (Borror et al.).

omaulus, in adult Hymenoptera, epicnemial carina, q.v. (Bohart and Menke, after Pate).

Omaloptera, Pupipara (Diptera), q.v. (T-B).

Omite (trade name), propargite, q.v. (Pfadt).

ommateum, compound eye, q.v. (T-B).

ommatidial, of or pertaining to an ommatidium (T-B).

ommatidium (pl., **ommatidia**), one of the visual elements of the compound eye (T-B).

ommatin, blue-violet pigment serving as background for Tyndall blue coloration, e.g., dragonflies (Odonata) (Chapman).

ommochrome, a pigment derived from the amino acid tryptophan via kynurenine and 3-hydroxykynurenine, serving as a masking pigment in the accessory cells of the eyes and producing yellow, red, and brown colors in the epidermis (Chapman); see insectorubin.

ommochrome pigment, ommochrome, q.v. (Leftwich).

omnivorous, feeding generally on animal or vegetable food, or on both (T-B).

omphalian type, in adult Heteroptera, metathoracic scent gland apparatus usually with a single (rarely double) opening on the metasternum (rarely on abdominal sternum I), with paired on unpaired internal structures (transl. from "type omphalien" Carayon; Štys, pers. comm.); see diastomian type.

omphalium, in adult Heteroptera, prominent metasternal opening of omphalian type of metathoracic scent gland (T-B; Štys, pers. comm.).

onchocerciasis, cutaneous disease of man caused by the filariae of *Onchocerca volvulus* (Nematoda) and transmitted by black flies, *Simulium* spp. (Diptera: Simuliidae) (Borror et al.; Allaby); see river blindness.

Oncopoda, group proposed for the Onychophora, Tardigrada, and Pentastomida (Boudreaux, after Weber); Onychophora, q.v. (Tulloch).

oncus (pl., **onci**), a welt (T-B); in larval Lepidoptera, a weltlike ridge (T-B).

onisciform larva, larva shaped like a sowbug, *Oniscus* sp. (Crustacea:

Isopoda), i.e., depressed and broadly spindle-shaped, e.g., larval Lycaenidae (Lepidoptera) (T-B; Peterson); see platyform larva.

onomatophore, in taxonomy, type, q.v. (Mayr, after Simpson).

ontogenetic, relating to the development of an individual (T-B).

ontogeny, the developmental history of an individual organism from egg to adult (T-B; Mayr); see phylogeny.

onyches, pretarsal claws, q.v. (T-B).

onychii, pulvilli, q.v. (T-B, after Comstock).

onychium (pl., **onychia**), a nail or claw (T-B); any of a variety of hooklike or padlike structures associated with the pretarsus of insects (T-B; Leftwich); see arolium, pretarsal claw, empodium, and pulvillus.

Onychophora, phylum closely related to the Arthropoda, its members being elongate and wormlike; possessing short, segmented antennae and a varying number of short, unsegmented legs, mouth with a pair of mandibles and surrounded by a series of tonguelike lips, a pair of short oral papillae on either side of the mouth, and possessing some characteristics of both the phyla Annelida and Arthropoda (T-B, after Snodgrass; Mackerras, in CSIRO; Borror et al.).

onychophoran, member of the Onychophora (T-B).

ooblast, germ cell, q.v., of ♀ (T-B).

oocyst, one of the resting nodular bodies in the life cycle of *Plasmodium* (Plasmodiidae), being a stage found in the body cavity of the mosquito (Diptera: Culicidae) which by asexual reproduction (sporogony) gives rise to sporozoites (T-B; Tulloch); see malaria.

oocyte, the immature egg cell within the ovariole differentiated from the oogonium (T-B, after Snodgrass); see egg.

oogenesis, egg maturation (T-B); the formation of polar bodies in the egg (T-B).

oogenesis flight syndrome, a distinct behavioral and physiological syndrome closely intertwined with reproductive timing and strategy in which migration takes place prior to egg development (Matthews and Matthews, after Johnson).

oogonium (pl., **oogonia**), the first stage of differentiation of an egg cell from a ♀ germ cell, within the germarium (T-B, after Snodgrass; Chapman); see oocyte.

ookinete, a motile zygote of the malarial organism (*Plasmodium*), which penetrates into the body cavity of the mosquito (Diptera: Culicidae) and forms an oocyst (Tulloch); see malaria.

oolemma, vitelline membrane, q.v. (T-B).

oophagy, egg cannibalism; in social insects, the eating by a colony member of its own eggs or those laid by a nestmate (Wilson).

ooporus, in ♀ Lepidoptera with ditrysian type of genitalia, the opening for discharge of eggs (Tuxen, after Weber).

ootaxonomy, taxonomy based on eggs (Carlberg, pers. comm.).

ootheca (pl., **oothecae**), a collection of eggs enclosed in secretions usually formed by the ♀ accessory glands; in Mantodea, Acrididae (Orthoptera), Tortricidae (Lepidoptera), and *Coptosoma* (Hemiptera: Heteroptera: Plataspidae), a foamlike covered egg mass; in Blattaria, a parallel row of eggs enclosed in a tanned, proteinaceous capsule; in certain Chironomidae (Diptera) and Trichoptera, an egg mass enclosed in a gelatinous matrix (T-B; Chapman); see egg case and egg pod.

oothecal membrane, ootheca, q.v. (T-B).

oothecalike mass, in *Mastotermes* (Isoptera: Mastotermitidae), a batch of eggs cemented together in 2 rows, resembling the ootheca of cockroaches, though without an envelope (Krishna, pers. comm.); see egg pod.

Oothecaria, Blattaria + Mantodea (Boudreaux, after Verhoeff); see Dictyoptera.

ooze, the soft mud or slime at the bottom of bodies of water (T-B).

opacus (Latin), **opaque,** without any surface lustre (T-B); not transparent (T-B).

opalescent, iridescent, q.v. (T-B).

opaline, opalinus, resembling an opal in color (T-B); see iridescent.

open cell, a cell which extends to the margin of the wing (T-B, after Comstock); see closed cell.

open clavus, in adult Fulgoroidea (Hemiptera: Auchenorrhyncha), claval suture that turns and parallels the wing margin, eventually fading out or reaching margin well beyond normal clavus (O'Brien, pers. comm.).

open coxal cavity, in adult Coleoptera, coxal cavity bounded posteriorly by a sclerite on the next segment (front coxal cavities), or one touched by one or more pleural sclerites (midcoxal cavities) (Borror et al.); see closed coxal cavity.

operaria, in eusocial Hymenoptera, workers, q.v. (T-B).

opercula (sing., **operculum**), in ♂ Aphididae (Hemiptera: Sternorrhyncha), claspers, q.v. (Tuxen, after Theobald).

opercula ani, in ♀ Sphingidae (Lepidoptera), papillae anales, q.v. (Tuxen, after Baltzer).

opercular spine, in some ♂ Collembola, one of the characterisitc modified setae of the dorsal abdominal organ (Christiansen and Bellinger).

operculiform, of the shape or form of a lid or cover, or operculum (T-B).

operculum (pl., **opercula**), a lid or cover (T-B); a valvelike opening (Peterson); in eggs of Phasmida, Embiidina, Phthiraptera, and many Heteroptera (Hemiptera), egg cap, q.v. (Chapman); in ♂ Phasmida, poculum (Tuxen; Key, pers., comm.); in ♀ Phasmida ventral covering of genital chamber, originating from sternum V (Tuxen); in Aleyrodidae (Hemiptera; Sternorrhyncha), the structure or lid of variable size and shape, situated over the lingula and within the faciform orifice (T-B; Stoetzel, in Stehr); in ♀ Coccoidea (Hemiptera: Sternorrhyncha), the anal plates taken together or singly (T-B, after MacGillivray); in tube-making Machaerotidae (Hemiptera: Auchenorrhyncha: Cercopoidea), modified abdominal terga V and VI (Woodward et al., in CSIRO); in Cicadidae (Hemiptera: Auchenorrhyncha), a projection from the thorax on the ventral surface, enclosing a cavity containing the tympanum (Chapman); in Cicadidae (Hemiptera: Auchenorrhyncha), a forward extension from the metathoracic epimere covering the tymbal (T-B; Woodward et al., in CSIRO); in larval Psephenidae (Coleoptera), abdominal sternum IX covering cloacal chamber containing retracted anal gills (Britton, in CSIRO); in ♂ Lepidoptera, a specialized abdominal tergum VIII, extended caudad to cover tegumen and uncus, usually with paired, caudally extending processes (Tuxen, after Roepke); in ♀ *Macaria clathrata* (Lepidoptera: Geometridae), flaplike, sometimes asymmetrical process of lamella postvaginalis covering ostium bursae (Tuxen, after Pierce); in Syrphidae (Diptera), the convex cap or anterior end of the puparium which splits off in 2 pieces when the fly emerges (Peterson, after Heiss).

operculum genitalis, in ♂ Hymenoptera, abdominal sterna VIII and IX (Tuxen, after Radoszkowski).

opere citato (Latin), work cited; abbrev., op. cit., op. c. (T-B).

ophionome, a linear or serpentine larval mine created when the larva moves (feeds) in one direction (Hering).

ophiphysonome, a linear-blotch larval mine, consisting of a combination of track and inflated blotch mine (Hering).

ophistigmatonome, a linear-blotch larval mine, consisting of a combination of track and blotch (Hering).

ophthalmic, relating to the compound eye (T-B); see macrophthalmic and microphthalmic.

ophthalmotheca, part of pupal cuticle that covers the compound eye (T-B).

Opilones, order within the Arachnida (Chelicerata), including the harvestmen, possessing a distinctly segmented opisthosoma without a taillike projection and not constricted at base, pedipalps not chelate, and lacking a broad flap at anterior end of prosoma covering chelicerae (Borror et al.).

Opisthandria, Pentazonia, q.v. (Borror et al.).

opisthognathous, with a posterior ventral position of the mouthparts resulting from a deflexion of the facial region, as in Auchenorrhyncha and Sternorrhyncha (Hemiptera) (T-B, after Snodgrass).

Opisthogoneata, group including the Symphyla, Chilopoda, and Hexapoda (Boudreaux, after Pocock); Chilopoda, q.v. (Hennig, after Verhoeff).

opisthogoneate, in the Myriapoda, one of a group in which the genital opening is at the posterior end of the body (T-B).

opisthogonia, anal angle, q.v., in hind wing (T-B).

opisthomeres, in Dermaptera, 3 plates, pygidium, metapygidium and telson at end of abdomen between base of forceps; however, telson may be lost or fused with metapygidium (Tuxen, after Burr).

opisthophallic sclerite, in ♂ Dixidae and some Culicidae, a supporting sclerite on each side of the opsithophallus (Harbach and Knight, after Belkin).

opisthophallus, in ♂ Dixidae and some Culicidae (Diptera), a transverse lobiform element of the phallosome located between the phallus and the proctiger, supported on either side by an opisthophallic sclerite (Harbach and Knight, after Belkin).

Opisthoptera, group including the Ephemeroptera and Neoptera (Insecta) (Boudreaux, after Lemche).

Opisthopterata, Opisthoptera, q.v. (Boudreaux).

opisthosoma, in Arachnida, the posterior portion of the body behind the prosoma (Allaby).

Opisthospermophora, group within the superorder Helminthomorpha (Diplopoda), including the Spirobolida, Spirostrepida, and Cambalida, possessing stipes of gnathochilarium widely separated by mentum and laminae linguales; terminal segment of body lacking setae-bearing papillae, and body usually with 26 or more segments (Borror et al.).

Opomyzoidea, superfamily within the series Schizophora of the division Cyclorrhapha (Diptera: Brachycera), including the Opomyzidae and other families, characterized by adults with wing cells M and CuP complete, postvertical bristles divergent or almost parallel, ♂ postabdomen with abdominal sternite VI asymmetrical, sternite VII laterally displaced, or with these sternites lost and symmetry restored, and ♀ postabdominal segments elongate (Colless and McAlpine, in CSIRO).

opponentes, in ♂ Blattopteroidea, apophysis, q.v. (Tuxen, after Crampton).

opposable mandibles, mandibles which move from side to side and meet on the meson; typical of most chewing insects (Peterson).

optic, relating to vision (T-B).

optic centers, the brain centers of the compound eye, situated in the optic lobes (T-B, after Snodgrass).

optic disc, in larval Muscidae (Diptera), a disclike thickening near the brain in each of the brain appendages, a histoblast which develops into the compound eye of the adult (T-B, after Comstock).

optic ganglia, optic lobes, q.v. (T-B).

optic lobes, the lateral lobes of the protocerebrum in which are centered the nerves supplying the compound eyes (T-B; Chapman).

optic segment, protocerebral segment, q.v., of head (T-B).

optic tract, optic lobes, q.v. (T-B).

opticon, medulla interna, q.v. (T-B; Leftwich).

ora, edge; border margin (T-B; R. W. Brown); also pl. of os, q.v. (T-B).

orad, toward the mouth (T-B).

oral, pertaining to the mouth (T-B).

oral cavity, buccal cavity, q.v. (T-B); in adult Diptera, subcranial cavity, q.v. (McAlpine).

oral fossa, in Ischnocera (Phthiraptera), a furrow lying in front of the mandibles (T-B); in adult Hymenoptera, preoral cavity, q.v. (Gauld and Bolton).

oral hooks, in larval Diptera, mouth hooks, q.v. (T-B).

oral pocket, in larval Muscomorpha (Diptera), atrium, q.v. (Teskey, in McAlpine).

oral ridges, in larval Muscomorpha (Diptera), series of ridges situated

on antennomaxillary lobes on either side of the preoral cavity, usually each bearing a row or comb of lamellae (Teskey, in McAlpine).

oral rim duct, in Pseudococcidae (Hemiptera: Sternorrhyncha: Coccoidea), dermal mushroom-shaped duct with a terminal filament
(Kosztarab and Kozár).

oral sclerite, in larval *Calliphora* (Diptera: Calliphoridae), slender, rodlike sclerite, which is slightly expanded at its posterior end, and lying
in the membranous ridge between the 2 atria in which the mandibles
retract (Teskey, after Roberts, in McAlpine); see accessory oral sclerites.

oral segment, the ring or segment which bears the mouth (T-B).

oral setae, in adult Diptera, subvibrissal setae, q.v. (McAlpine).

oral setulae, in adult Diptera, subvibrissal setulae, q.v. (McAlpine).

oral sucker, in adult Diptera, a broad disc formed by the large soft pads
of the labella when spread outward from the end of the stipital stalk
(T-B, after Snodgrass).

oral vibrissae, in adult Diptera, vibrissae, q.v. (Borror et al.;
McAlpine).

orale processus, in ♀ Lepidoptera, apophyses posteriores, q.v. (Tuxen,
after van Eecke).

orb, orbis (Latin), a globe; a circle (T-B; R. W. Brown).

orbicula, in adult Hymenoptera, a small dorsal sclerite at the base of
the arolium and distad of the unguifer, being the sclerotized chitinized area on the dorsal aspect of the pretarsus (T-B, after
MacGillivray).

orbicular, orbicularis, round and flat (T-B).

orbiculate, orbiculatus (Latin), orb-shaped (T-B).

orbit, an imaginary border around the compound eye (T-B) (see ocular
sclerite); in adult Diptera, fronto-orbital plate, q.v. (McAlpine).

orbital, of or relating to the orbit of the compound eye (T-B).

orbital bristles, in adult Diptera, fronto-orbital setae, q.v. (T-B, after
Curran).

orbital plate, in adult Diptera, fronto-orbital area, q.v. (Borror et al.);
in some adult Diptera, esp. Calyptratae (Muscomorpha), upper division of fronto-orbital plate continuous with vertex (McAlpine).

orbital sclerite, ocular sclerite, q.v. (T-B).

orbital setae, in some adult Diptera, (Muscomorpha), fronto-orbital
setae on orbital plate (McAlpine); in adult Chironomidae (Diptera),
setae located around the margin of the eye in frontal aspect, ventral
of dorsal end of compound eye (Saether).

orbital setulae, in some adult Diptera, fronto-orbital setulae on orbital
plate (McAlpine).

order, a subdivision of a class or subclass, containing a related group of
superfamilies or families (T-B; Borror et al.).

ordinal, of or pertaining to an order (T-B); used to describe the length
or arrangment of the ends of crochets, e.g., biordinal, triordinal
(Peterson).

ordinary crossvein, in adult Diptera, radial-medial crossvein (r-m), q.v.
(T-B, after Curran).

ordinate, ordinatus (Latin), spots or sculpturing arranged in rows or other regular pattern (T-B; Harris, after R. W. Brown); see perlate.

Ordovician Period, period within the Paleozoic Era, between the Cambrian Period and the Silurian Period, extending between about 500 and 440 million years before the present (Riek, in CSIRO).

oreillets, in ♂ Odonata, processes shaped like the human ear and situated on abdominal tergum II on each side of fenestra, being the commonest form of dirigones (Tuxen).

organ culture, the maintenance or growth of organ primordia or the whole or parts of an organ in vitro so as to allow differentiation and preservation of the architecture and/or function (Steinhaus and Martignoni); see cell culture and tissue culture.

organ of Berlese, in some ♀ Cimicoidea (Hemiptera: Heteroptera), Berlese's organ, q.v. (T-B; Tuxen).

organ of Herold, in ♂ Lepidoptera, the developmental anlage of penis with surrounding structures of diaphragma, forming an invagination of the central area of the developing diaphragma (transl. "Heroldsche Taschen Zander," after Tuxen).

organ of Hicks, campaniform sensillum, q.v. (T-B).

organ of Johnston, Johnston's organ, q.v. (T-B).

organ of Jullien, in ♂ *Satyrus* (Lepidoptera: Satyridae), modification of abdominal tergum VIII, caudally and laterally sclerotized and bearing a pair of lateral, projecting lobes, sometimes crowned posterad with modified, rod-shaped scales, the rods of Jullien (transl. "Jullienisches Organ" Fruhstorfer, in Tuxen).

organ of Reverdin, in ♂ *Eunica* (Lepidoptera: Nymphalidae), abdominal sternum VIII when consisting of paired processes, directed dorsad, usually dentate or spinulate along posterior margin (transl. "Reverdinisches Organ" Fruhstorfer, after Tuxen).

organ of Ribaga, in Cimicoidea, Ribaga's organ, q.v. (Tulloch; Chapman).

organ of Tömösvary, postantennal organ, q.v. (Wallace and Mackerras, in CSIRO).

organ of vom Rath, vom Rath's organ, q.v.

organ X, in ♂ Siphonaptera, Wagner's organ, q.v. (Tuxen, after Wagner).

organism, an organic entity, either animal or plant (T-B).

organismal biology, branch of biology dealing with whole organisms or groups of organisms, including ecology, evolutionary biology, population biology, and taxonomy.

organogeny, in insect embryo, the development of organ systems (Chapman).

organophosphate, organic compound containing phosphorous (Pfadt).

orichalceous, orichalceus, aurichalceous, q.v. (T-B).

orient, to determine or establish position or direction (T-B).

Oriental Realm, Oriental Region, q.v. (T-B).

Oriental Region, biogeographical region including Asia east of the Indus River, south of the Himalayas and the Yangtse-kiang watershed, Ceylon, Sumatra, Java and the Philippines, being approximately equivalent to Wallace's Oriental Realm but with the south-eastern limit lying within a transition zone between Wallace's line and Weber's line, called Wallacea (T-B; Mackerras, in CSIRO).

oriental sore, dermal leishmaniasis of man in the Old World, caused by *Leishmania tropica* (Protozoa) and transmitted by sand flies, *Phlebotomus* and *Lutzomyia* spp. (Diptera: Psychodidae) (Borror et al.; Adkins, pers. comm.); see espundia.

orientation, the sense of direction (T-B).

orientation flight, in bees and wasps (Hymenoptera: Aculeata), the flight by which they learn the location of their nest through landmark's recognized and remembered (Matthews and Matthews).

orifice, in ♂ Geometridae (Lepidoptera), opening of aedoeagus at its junction with vesica (Tuxen, after Pierce); in adult Chironomidae (Diptera), opening of salivary duct on labial lonchus (Saether); see orificium.

orificial canal, in Heteroptera (Hemiptera), ostiolar canal, q.v.

orificium (pl., **orificia**), the anal or genital opening (T-B); in ♂ Lepidoptera, distal opening of aedoeagus (Tuxen, after Hering); see orifice.

orificium genitale, in ♂ *Eusthenes* (Hemiptera: Heteroptera: Tessaratomidae), secondary gonopore, q.v. (Tuxen, after Handlirsch).

orificium receptaculi, in ♀ Heteroptera (Hemiptera), orificium spermathecea, q.v. (Tuxen, after Dohrn).

orificium spermathecae, in ♀ Heteroptera (Hemiptera), aperture of spermatheca into vagina, being a small pore, a bulb, or even a large mouth according to the diameter of ductus spermathecae (Stys, pers. comm.).

orificium vaginae, in ♀ Siphonaptera, gonotreme, q.v. (Tuxen).

origin, of a muscle, its attachment to a stationary base (T-B).

original description, the description of a nominal taxon when it is established (ICZN).

original designation, the designation of the name-bearing type of a nominal taxon when it is established (ICZN).

original publication, the work in which a name or nomenclatural act was first published (ICZN); of a name or nomenclatural act, publication for the first time (ICZN).

original spelling, the spelling or one of the spellings of a name employed when it is established (ICZN).

oroyo fever, visceral, highly fatal form of Carrion's disease (Adkins, pers. comm.); see verruga peruana.

orphan colony, a colony of eusocial insects which has lost its reproductives (Michener).

orphan nest, in social insects, a nest containing live brood but no adults (T-B, after Rau); see orphan colony.

Orthandria, a group including the Symphyta, excluding the Tenthredinoidea, and the Apocrita within the Hymenoptera (Hennig, after Crampton, Ross); a group proposed for those members of the Symphyta (Hymenoptera) with the larval stemmata posteroventral to the antennae and by a tendency for the larvae to exist in confined situations (Gauld and Bolton, after Rasnitzyn); see Strophandria.

orthandrous copulation, in ♂ nontenthredinoid Symphyta, some Xyelidae, and all Apocrita (Hymenoptera), copulation in which the genitalia are not rotated, but ♂ must mount back of ♀ and curve abdomen beneath hers (Tuxen, after Crampton); see strophandrous copulation.

Orthene (trade name), acephate, q.v. (Pfadt).

Orthezoidea, Archeococcoidea, q.v. (Kosztarab and Kozár).

Ortho 9006 (trade name), methamidophos, q.v. (Pfadt).

orthogenesis, evolution of phyletic lines following a predetermined pathway, the direction not being determined by natural selection (T-B; Mayr).

orthogenetic selection, orthogenesis, q.v. (T-B).

orthognathous, hypognathous, q.v. (Gauld and Bolton).

orthokinesis, a reaction to a stimulus in which there is a positive correlation between the rate of response and the intensity of stimulation (Tulloch).

Orthomyaria, Plagioptera, q.v. (Hennig, after Shvanvich).

Orthoptera, mandibulate, exopterygote order within the Neoptera (Insecta), including the suborders Caelifera and Ensifera, with the hind legs usually saltatorial, hind coxae nearly always small and well separated, pronotum with large descending lateral lobes, and wing rudiments reversing their orientation in the later instars (T-B; Key, in CSIRO); Orthoptera + Mantodea + Phasmida + Blattaria + Gryllobattodea (Borror et al.).

Orthopterida, hypothesized monophyletic group including the Phasmida and Orthoptera (Boudreaux); see Orthopteroidea.

Orthopterodida, hypothesized monophyletic group including the Grylliformida and Blattiformida (Boudreaux).

orthopteroid, Orthoptera-like in form or characters (T-B).

orthopteroid orders, series of orders within the blattoid-orthopteroid orders, including the extant orders Orthoptera, Grylloblattodea, Dermaptera, Plecoptera, Phasmida and Embiidina, and the extinct orders Protelytroptera, Protoblattodea, Paraplecoptera, and Protorthoptera (Mackerras, Riek, in CSIRO); Polyneoptera, q.v. (Borror et al.); see Orthopterida and Orthopterodida.

Orthopteroidea, Orthopterida, q.v. (Hennig, after Sharov); Orthopterodida, q.v. (Boudreaux, after Handlirsch).

Orthopteromorpha, Polyneoptera, q.v. (Hennig).

Orthorrhapha, division within the suborder Brachycera (Diptera), including the superfamilies Tabanoidea, Asiloidea, and Empidoidea, possessing adults with the radial sector (R_s) three-branched in wing, hemicephalous larva, and obtect pupa (enclosed in unmodified larval skin in Stratiomyidae) (Colless and McAlpine, in CSIRO); orthorrhaphous Brachycera, originally from Braver, 1863, q.v. (T-B).

orthorrhaphous, straight-seamed, referring to the T-shaped opening left in last larval skin by pupa or adult (T-B; McAlpine); belonging to the Orthorrhapha (T-B).

orthorrhaphous Brachycera, members of the suborder Brachycera (Diptera) in which the pupa or adult escapes from the last larval skin through a T-shaped opening in the back (McAlpine).

orthosomatic larva, larva with the ventral and dorsal surfaces of body straight, flat and usually subparallel, and with the lateral aspects also usually subparallel (Peterson).

orthotype, type species, q.v., of a genus which is fixed by original designation (O'Brien, pers. comm., after Metcalf and Van Duzee); see haplotype and logotype.

Orussoidea, superfamily within the Symphyta (Hymenoptera), including the family Orussidae, closely related to, and perhaps justifiably combined with, the Siricoidea (Gauld and Bolton).

Orussomorpha, infraorder porposed for the symphytan family Orrusidae (Hymenoptera), placing it within the Apocrita (Gauld and Bolton, after Rasnitsyn).

ortus tergi X, in ♂ Lepidoptera, uncus, q.v. (Tuxen, after Schroeder).

os (pl., **ora**), mouth, q.v. (T-B).

Osborne membrane, in the shed larval skin of Lepidoptera at pupation, the stretched part of the membrane around the rectum and the anal prolegs, intimately associated with the rectal ligament (T-B, after Packard).

oscillogram, a visual record of modulations in the volume of a sound over time (Matthews and Matthews).

osmeterium (pl., **osmeteria**), in some larval Papilionidae (Lepidoptera), fleshy, tubular, eversible processes producing a penetrating odor, capable of being projected by hemolymph pressure through a slit in the prothoracic segment (T-B; Chapman), but sometimes used in reference to nonhomologous structures of similar function, e.g., in larvae of the puss moth, *Cerura vinula* (Notodontidae) (Leftwich); in adult Sepsidae (Diptera), specialized scent producing area on the hind tibia (McAlpine).

osmoregulation, maintenace of water balance (Gilmour, in CSIRO).

osmosis, the equilibrium-seeking movements of the molecules of a liquid, which at different concentrations are separated by a semipermeable membrane such as the plasma membrane of a cell (Tulloch).

osmotic, pertaining to osmosis (T-B; Tulloch).

osmotic pressure, the relative tendency for fluid to diffuse into another fluid, e.g., the hemolymph, controlled by the concentration of ions and dissolved organic constituents (Gilmour, in CSIRO).

Osmyloidea, superfamily within the Planipennia, including the families Osmylidae, Ithonidae, Dilaridae, Polystoechotidae, and Neurorthidae, possessing adults with nygmata present between the posterior branches of the radial sector (R_s) and possessing a pterostigma on wings (Riek, in CSIRO); see Ithonoidea.

osseous, bony; resembling bone (T-B).

ossicle, a small nodule of chitin resembling a bone (T-B).

ossicula, axillary plates, q.v. (T-B).

ostia, pl. ostium, q.v. (T-B).

ostial, of or pertaining to an ostium (T-B).

ostial lamellae, in ♂ Coleoptera, dorsal parts of penis framing ostium on each side (transl. "Ostiallamellen" Brundin, in Tuxen).

ostial valves, valvelike pouches of the heart wall containing the ostia at their inner ends (T-B, after Snodgrass).

ostiola (pl., **ostiolae**), in Heteroptera (Hemiptera), ostiole, q.v., of metathoracic scent gland (T-B).

ostiolar canal, in Heteroptera (Hemiptera), external outflow pathway of metathoracic scent gland (Stys).

ostiolar groove, in Heteroptera (Hemiptera), ostiolar canal, q.v. (Stys).

ostiolar peritreme, in Heteroptera (Hemiptera), evaporatorium, q.v. (Stys, pers. comm.).

ostiole(s), a small opening (Borror); in Heteroptera (Hemiptera), external opening of metathoracic scent gland (Stys); in Pseudococcidae and Putoidae (Hemiptera: Sternorrhyncha: Coccoidea), small dermal invaginations on dorsosubmarginal areas of prothorax and abdominal segment VII (Miller, in Stehr).

ostium (pl., **ostia**), a slitlike opening in the heart by which hemolymph flows into the heart from the pericardial sinus (T-B; Leftwich); in ♂ Coleoptera, opening or area through which internal sac is everted during copulation, usually situated dorsally and distally on penis (Tuxen); in ♀ Lepidoptera, ostium bursae, q.v. (Tuxen, after John).

ostium bursae, in ♀ ditrysian Lepidoptera, the copulatory entrance to the bursa copulatrix, more or less surrounded by sclerotizations of sterigma which often form one or more strong protrusions (Tuxen, after Petersen), equivalent to the vulva of ♀ insects having the genital opening on the eighth segment (T-B, after Snodgrass); in ♀ Siphonaptera, opening of ductus bursae into vagina (cephalad of opening of vestibulum vaginae) (Tuxen).

ostium cover, in ♀ Lepidoptera, lamella postvaginalis, q.v. (Tuxen, after F. M. Brown).

ostium ductus ejaculatorii, in ♂ Lepidoptera, ostium penis, q.v. (Tuxen, after Kusnezov).

ostium fold, in ♂ Lepidoptera, dorsal fold of membrane at ostium penis, being part of vesica (Tuxen, after Suschkin).

ostium genitale, in ♀ Tortricidae (Lepidoptera), ostium bursae, q.v. (Tuxen, after Diakonoff).

ostium keel, in ♂ Lepidoptera, dorsal keel of ostium penis (Tuxen, after Suschkin).

ostium oviductus, in ♀ Lepidoptera, the primary ♀ genital opening through which the eggs are laid, situated in the region of abdominal segment IX, presumably between sterna IX and X, between papillae anales (Tuxen, after Petersen).

ostium penis, in ♂ Lepidoptera, posterior aperture of vesica (Tuxen, after Suschkin).

ostium pouch, in ♀ Pyralidae (Lepidoptera), invaginated, often sclerotized pouch of sinus vaginalis near ostium (Tuxen, after Bleszynski).

ostium vaginae, in ♀ Lepidoptera, ostium oviductus, q.v. (Tuxen, after de Graaf).

ostium vestibulare (pl., **ostia vestibularia**), in ♀ Isoptera, external opening of vestibulum (Tuxen, after Roonwal).

Ostracoda, group within the Crustacea, including marine and fresh-water forms, possessing appendages on all body segments except the last few, thoracic appendages slender and cylindrical, body short, unsegmented, and covered by a bivalved carapace, 4 pairs of head appendages, and 3 pairs of thoracic legs (Borror et al.).

-osus, suffix, signifying saturation, or the possession of the quality expressed in the stem word (T-B).

Otitoidea, Tephritoidea, q.v. (Colles and McAlpine, in CSIRO).

Oudeman's fluid, preservation fluid for mites consisting of 87 parts of 70% ethyl alcohol, 5 parts of glycerine, and 8 parts of glacial acetic acid (Borror et al.).

out group comparison, in cladistic analysis, examination of related taxa in order to determine character polarity, employing parsimony to choose which of 2 alternative states is plesiomorphic and which is apomorphic.

outer appendages of anal tergum, in ♂ Diptera, surstyli, q.v. (Tuxen, after Graham-Smith).

outer caudal setae, in Ephemeroptera, cerci, q.v. (Tuxen, after Phillips).

outer clasper, in ♂ Hymenoptera, gonocoxite + gonostylus (Tuxen, after Michener).

outer claspers, in ♂ Auchenorrhyncha (Hemiptera), genital plates, q.v. (Tuxen, after McAtee).

outer division, in ♂ *Culex* (Diptera: Culicidae), the dorsal and lateral part of the lateral plate of the phallosome (Harbach and Knight, after Belkin).

outer dorsocentral scale, in adult Culicidae (Diptera), one of the scales occurring in a rather indistinct row located laterad of the dorsocentral setae on the dorsocentral area of the scutum (Harbach and Knight).

outer genital chamber, in ♀ Isoptera, outer vestibulum, q.v. (Tuxen, after Weesner); in ♂ Delphacidae (Hemiptera: Auchenorrhyncha), space behind genital phragm (Tuxen).

outer hood, in ♂ Siphonaptera, end chamber, q.v. (Lewis, pers. comm.).

outer internal rod, in adult Siphonaptera, a vertical thickening of the inner wall of the outer surface of the coxa (Lewis, pers. comm.).

outer lamellae, in ♂ Lepidoptera, sclerotized structures of outer folds of anellus (transl. "äussere Lamellen" Zander, in Tuxen).

outer lobe, of the maxilla, galea, q.v. (T-B).

outer margin, apical margin, q.v. of wing (T-B);

outer pairs of valves, in ♀ Aleyrodidaea (Hemiptera: Sternorrhyncha), lateral valves, q.v. (Tuxen, after Quaintance and Baker).

outer plates, in ♀ Nepidae (Hemiptera: Heteroptera), gonocoxites of abdominal segment VIII, q.v. (Tuxen, after Hamilton); in aculeate Hymenoptera, ninth hemitergites, q.v. (T-B; Tuxen).

outer ramus of stipes, in ♂ Hymenoptera, gonostylus, q.v. (Tuxen).

outer rhabdites, in ♂ Ephemeroptera, genostyles, q.v. (Tuxen, after Packard).

outer rods, in ♀ Lepidoptera, apophyses anteriores, q.v. (Tuxen).

outer sheaths, in ♀ Psyllidae (Hemiptera: Sternorrhyncha), dorsal valvulae, q.v. (Tuxen).

outer squama, in adult Diptera, the squama arising from the wing base behind the third axillary vein, evidentally representing the jugal lobe of other insects (T-B, after Snodgrass).

outer surface of the leg, the dorsal surface when the insect leg is extended at a right angle to the body (T-B, after Snodgrass).

outer surstyli, in ♂ Tephritoidea (Diptera), an outer pair of surstyli articulating with the epandrium (McAlpine).

outer vertical bristles, in adult Diptera, outer vertical setae, q.v. (Colless and McAlpine, in CSIRO; Borror et al.).

outer vertical setae, in adult Diptera, large lateral setae on the vertex between the ocelli and the compound eyes and lateral to the inner vertical setae (Saether; McAlpine); see ocellar setae.

outer verticals, outer vertical setae, q.v. (Saether).

outer vestibulum, in ♀ Isoptera, outer (distal or posterior), portion of vestibulum (genital chamber) where the latter is divided (Tuxen, after Roonwal).

ova, (sing., **ovum**), q.v. (T-B).

oval, ovate or elliptical (T-B).

oval organs, in Collembola, external proprioceptors that closely resemble campaniform sensilla found on pterygote insects (Snider and Loring).

oval pores, in Coccoidea (Hemiptera: Sternorrhyncha), dorsal pores, q.v. (T-B, after MacGillivray).

oval sclerites, in ♂ Caelifera (Orthoptera), lateral sclerites of epiphallus, q.v. (Tuxen, after Dirsh).

ovaliform, oval, q.v. (T-B).

ovarial, of or pertaining to the ovary (T-B).

ovarial ligament, a ligamentous strand attaching the terminal filaments of an ovary to the dorsal diaphragm or to the body wall, sometimes united with that from the opposite side in a median ligament attached to the ventral wall of the dorsal blood vessel (T-B, after Snodgrass).

ovarial sack, in ♀ Orthoptera, corpus bursae, q.v. (Tuxen, after Bethune-Baker).

ovarial strand, in ♀ Strepsiptera, one of several groups of ovarioles lacking oviducts, on either side of the midgut (Chapman); see ovarial ligament.

ovarian tube, ovariole, q.v. (T-B).

ovarian tubule, ovariole, q.v. (T-B).

ovariole, in ♀ insects, one of the separate tubes which together to form the ovary, consisting of a distal germarium in which oocytes are produced from oogonia, and more proximal vitellarium in which the oocytes grow as yolk is deposited in them (T-B; Chapman); see panoistic ovariole, meroistic ovariole, polytrophic ovariole, and telotrophic ovariole.

ovary (pl., **ovaries**), in ♀ insects, paired structures, each consisting of a number of ovarioles (T-B; Chapman); the ♀ gonad in which the ova are produced (T-B, after Tillyard).

ovate, ovatus (Latin), egg-shaped, with the broader end at the base (T-B); see obovate.

overall similarity, a (usually numerical) value of similarity calculated by the summation of similarities in numerous individual characters (Mayr); see numerical taxonomy.

ovicauda, in ♀ Diptera, oviscapt, q.v. (Tuxen, after Crampton).

oviduct, oviductus, q.v. (T-B); in ♀ Siphonaptera, the duct from ovaries to end of vagina (Tuxen); ovipositor, q.v. (T-B).

oviductal, of or pertaining to the oviduct (T-B).

oviductus (pl., **oviductus**), in ♀ insects, the tubes leading from ovaries to beginning of vagina, including oviductus laterales and oviductus communis (Tuxen).

oviductus communis (pl., **oviductus communes**), in ♀ insects, the unpaired, median, mesodermal part of oviduct, from fusion of paired oviductus laterales to gonopore (T-B; Tuxen); in ♀ Heteroptera (Hemiptera), proximal portion of pars communis of genital ducts, between oviductus laterales (whether ectodermal or endodermal) and vagina (Tuxen).

oviductus duplex, in ♀ Lepidoptera, oviductus or oviductus laterales, q.v. (Tuxen).

oviductus laterales (sing., **oviductus lateralis**), in ♀ insects, the paired canals leading from ovaries to oviductus communis, most frequently mesodermal, but in certain Heteroptera proximally mesodermal and distally ectodermal (Tuxen).

oviductus simplex, in ♀ Lepidoptera, oviductus communis, q.v. (Tuxen).

oviform, ovate, q.v. (T-B).

ovigerous, carrying eggs; applied to the fertilized ♀ (T-B).

oviparity, laying of eggs by the ♀ (Chapman); see ovoviviparity and viviparity.

oviparous, reproducing by eggs laid by the ♀ (T-B); see ovoviviparous and viviparous.

ovipilum (pl., **ovipila**), in some ♀ Berothidae (Planipennia), dilated and projecting, tubelike apical part of spermathecal duct (Tuxen, after Tjeder); supposed to be core of spermatophore (Tuxen, after MacLeod and Adams).

ovipore, in ♀ insects, gonopore, oviporus, or ostium oviductus, q.v. (Tuxen).

oviporus, in ♀ insects, secondary gonopore (Tuxen); in ♀ Lepidoptera, ostium oviductus, q.v. (T-B, after Snodgrass; Tuxen).

oviposit, to deposit or lay eggs or ova (T-B).

oviposition, the act of depositing eggs (T-B); see larviposition.

oviposition tube, in adult Diptera, ovipositor, q.v. (McAlpine).

ovipositor (pl., **ovipositores**), in ♀ insects, the organ by which the eggs are deposited, formed either by a prolongation or modification of the posterior abdominal segments (oviscapt), or by appendicular parts of abdominal segments VIII and IX (appendiculate ovipositor) (T-B; Tuxen); in ♀ Japygidae (Diplura), papilla genitalis, q.v. (Tuxen, after Gyger); in ♀ Archaeognatha and Zygentoma, gonapophyses VIII + IX (Sturm, pers. comm., after Davis); in ♀ Ephemeroptera, subgenital plate, q.v. (Tuxen); in ♀ Heteroptera (Hemiptera), gonapophyses, q.v. (Tuxen, after Verhoeff); in ♀ *Sialis* (Megaloptera: Sialidae), gonapophyses laterales, q.v. (Tuxen, after Ross); in ♀ Mecoptera, medigynium, q.v. (Tuxen, after Grell); in ♀ Trichoptera and Diptera, oviscapt, q.v. (Tuxen).

ovipositor lobe, in ♀ Hymenoptera, gonoplac, q.v. (Tuxen).

ovipositor lobes, in ♀ Lepidoptera, papillae anales, q.v. (Tuxen); in ♀ Diptera, hypogynial valves, q.v. (McAlpine).

ovipositor plate, in ♀ Incurvariidae (Lepidoptera), the modified, sclerotized abdominal segments IX and X, forming part of a piercing and cutting ovipositor (Tuxen, after Wood).

ovipositor sheath, in ♀ Psyllidae (Hemiptera: Sternorrhyncha), the fused apices of second gonapophyses (Tuxen); in ♀ Nabidae, Miridae, and other Heteroptera (Hemiptera), the sheath in which the ovipositor lies, formed by parts of body wall and genitalia (gonocoxites IX + styloids) (Tuxen, after Ekblom); in some higher ♀ Diptera, transformed abdominal segment VII (Tuxen); in ♀ Hymenoptera, gonoplacs, q.v. (Tuxen).

ovipositores anteriores, in ♀ Heteroptera (Hemiptera), gonapophyses of abdominal segment VIII, q.v. (Tuxen, after Verhoeff).

ovipositores posteriores, in ♀ Heteroptera (Hemiptera), gonapophyses of abdominal segment IV, q.v. (Tuxen, after Verhoeff).

oviprovector, in ♀ Tephritoidea and Drosophilidae (Diptera), membrane connecting oviscapt with penultimate sternite, being modified, with dense scales (Grimaldi, after Steyskal).

ovisac, in some ♀ Coccoidea (Hemiptera: Sternorrhyncha), e.g., Eriococcidae, Pseudococcidae, and Ortheziidae, a waxen sac into which eggs are laid and which sometimes encloses all or part of the ♀ (T-B; Woodward et al., in CSIRO); in adult Diptera, uterus, q.v. (McAlpine).

oviscape, in some ♀ Muscomorpha (Diptera), e.g., Nerioidea, Tephritoidea, and Agromyzidae, modification of abdominal segment VII into a bulbous structure (McAlpine); see oviscapt.

oviscapt, in some ♀ insects, e.b., Trichoptera (Annulipalpia) and Diptera, ovipositor, nonhomologous with the orthopterous ovipositor, consisting of a prolongation or modification of the posterior abdominal segments rather than appendicular parts of abdominal segments VIII and IX (Tuxen, after Crampton); in ♀ Blephariceridae (Diptera), hypogynial plate, q.v. (McAlpine); see appendicular ovipositor.

ovivalvula (pl., **ovivalvulae**), in ♀ Ephemeroptera and Plecoptera, subgenital plate, q.v. (Tuxen, after Palmén); in ♀ Heteroptera (Hemiptera), subgenital plate, q.v. (Tuxen, after Heberdey).

ovoid, ovoidal, ovate, q.v. (T-B).

ovolarviparity, ovoviviparity, q.v. (Hinton and Mackerras, in CSIRO).

ovotestis, gonad in hermaphroditic insects with an ovarian part and a testicular part (White, in CSIRO).

ovoviviparity, viviparity in which hatching occurs just before the immature insect leaves the mother, so that all the nourishment of the embryo came from the egg and no special nutritional structures are present in the mother (Chapman); see oviparity and viviparity.

ovoviviparous, producing living young by the hatching of the ovum while still within the mother (T-B).

ovulation, the passage of the oocyte into the oviduct (Chapman).

ovum (pl., **ova**), egg, q.v. (T-B).

oxidase, an enzyme which facilitates the addition of molecular oxygen to a substance (Tulloch).

oxidation, a reaction in which an electron is lost by one molecule (and is transferred to another molecule, which in turn is reduced) (Tulloch, after Rockstein).

oxydemetonemethyl, $C_6H_{15}O_4PS_2$, a synthetic insecticide and acaricide, a plant systemic; an organophosphate, S-[2-(ethylsulfinyl)ethyl] O,O-dimethyl phosphorothioate; moderately toxic to mammals; acute oral LD_{50} for rats 65 to 75 mg/kg (Pfadt).

oxythioquinox, a synthetic acaricide and fungicide, 6-methyl-2,3-quinoxalinedithiol cyclic S,S-dithiocarbonate; slightly toxic to mammals; acute oral LD_{50} for rats 3000 mg/kg (Pfadt).

P

p seta (**Podonominae seta**), in ♂ Podonominae (Diptera: Chironomidae), stout, vertically directed seta situated dorsally near base of subapical lobe of gonostylus (Saether).

pabulum (Latin), food (T-B; R. W. Brown).

Pachyneuroidea, superfamily within the infraorder Bibionomorpha (Diptera: Nematocera), including the single family Pachyneuridae (McAlpine).

Pacific coast humid area, the faunal area comprising the western parts of Washington and Oregon between the Coast Mountains and Cascade range, and parts of northern California south to the Santa Barabara Mountains (T-B).

paddle, in aquatic Heteroptera (Hemiptera), the flattened articles of the posterior tarsi (T-B).

Paederus vesicular dermatitis, vesicular dermatitis caused by juices of crushed beetles, *Pachypaederus puncticollis* and *Paederus sabaeus* (Coleoptera: Staphylinidae) (Adkins, pers. comm.); see Nairobi eye and whiplash dermatitis.

paedogenesis, reproduction by immature insects (T-B; Chapman).

paedogenetic, reproducing in the immature or larval stage, e.g., *Miastor* (Diptera: Cecidomyiidae) and *Micromalthus* (Coleoptera: Micromalthidae) (T-B; Peterson; Leftwich).

paedomorphous, neotenic, q.v.

paedoparthenogenetic, reproducing by paedogenesis and parthenogenesis, e.g., form of *Micromalthus* (Coleoptera: Micromalthidae)
(Chapman) and some Cecidomyiidae (Diptera) (T-B; Chapman).

page precedence, the order in which 2 species or genera precede one
another on the same page or on different pages of a publication
(T-B); however, it alone does not specify priority under the Code
(ICZN); see first reviser.

pagina, the surface of a wing (T-B); in Orthoptera, the external flattened surface of the hind femora (T-B).

pagina inferior, the lower side of a wing (T-B).

pagina superior, the upper side of a wing (T-B).

Pagiopoda, that unnatural assemblage of Heteroptera in which the
posterior coxae are not globose and the articulation is a hinge joint
(T-B); see Trochalopoda.

pagiopodous, in Heteroptera (Hemiptera), having the coxae of the
hind legs hinged (T-B).

pairing, in Isoptera, the association of a ♂ and a ♀ imago involving
wing-shedding and the ♂ following the ♀ in tandem, just after the
dispersal flight and prior to the selection of a nesting site (Krishna,
pers. comm.).

pala (pl., **palae**), in Corixoidea (Hemiptera: Heteroptera), tarsus of
foreleg modified into a hair-fringed scoop for particle feeding (T-B;
Woodward et al., in CSIRO), and in the ♂ for attachment to the ♀
during mating or sexual display.

Palaeolepidoptera, a name applied to the family Eriocraniidae (Lepidoptera), in which the adult has mandibles, and a functional proboscis, and the pupa is decticious (T-B, after Packard; Common, pers.
comm.).

Palaeoptilota, Paleoptera, q.v. (Hennig, after Lameere).

Palaephatoidea, superfamily of infraorder Heteroneura (Lepidoptera)
containing one family Palaephatidae; adults small with filiform antennae, scape usually with pecten, maxillary palpi four- or five-segmented, ♀ genitalia monotrysian, papillae anales fused, with prominent median ridge carrying sensory setae (Common).

palatal bar, in larval Nematocera (Diptera), epipharyngeal bar, q.v.
(Teskey, in McAlpine).

palatal seta, in adult Culicidae (Diptera), one of 4 small peglike cibarial
setae borne on the anterior hard palate (Harbach and Knight).

palate, hypopharynx, q.v. (T-B).

palatum, in adult Culicidae (Diptera), the oral surfaces of the labrum
and clypeus, bounded posteriorly by the mouth, limited laterally by
the margins of the clypeus and the dorsal sclerites of the labrum
(Harbach and Knight); in larval Diptera, epipharynx, q.v. (Teskey, in
McAlpine); in larval Chironomidae (Diptera), epipharynx or
epipharynx plus premandibles and labral margin (Saether); see labropalatum and clypeopalatum.

paleace, paleaceous, paleaceus, like chaff; having chafflike scales (T-
B, after Say).

Palearctic Region, that part of the Holarctic Region including Europe,

Africa north of the Sahara, and Asia as far south as the southern edge of the Yangtse-kiang watershed and the Himalayas (T-B, after Wallace); see Oriental Region.

paleobotany, the study of fossil plants (T-B).

Paleocene Epoch, earliest epoch within the Tertiary Period, extending between about 70 and 60 million years before the present (Riek, in CSIRO).

paleoclimatology, the study of prehistoric climates (Mackerras, in CSIRO).

Paleodictyoptera, extinct order of Paleoptera (Insecta), from the Carboniferous Period and Permian Period, possessing bristlelike antennae, prothoracic paranota, subequal and discrete thoracic segments, slender legs, cerci rather short, and no caudal style (T-B, after Scudder, Handlirsch; Riek, in CSIRO).

Paleodictyopterata, Paleodictyoptera, q.v. (Boudreaux).

paleoentomology, the branch of paleontology devoted to fossil insects (T-B).

paleontological method, phylogenetic analysis in which taxa are grouped together based upon identified ancestors in the fossil record.

paleontology, the science that deals with life of past geological periods (Mayr); see neontology.

Paleoptera, infraclass within the class Insecta, including the extant orders Ephemeroptera and Odonata, and extinct orders Meganisoptera, Megasecoptera, Paleodictyoptera, and Archodonata, possessing adults with fore- and hind wings with humeral and axillary plates fused with the veins and wings not capable of being folded against the body at rest, abdomen with at least rudiments of cerci, and immatures aquatic in extant orders (Mackerras, Riek, in CSIRO); see Neoptera.

Paleozoic Era, era with the geological history of the earth, including the Cambrian, Ordovician, Silurian, Carboniferous, and Permian periods, extending between about 600 and 225 million years before the present (Riek, in CSIRO); see Caenozoic Era and Mesozoic Era.

palidium (pl., **palidia**), in larval Scarabaeoidea (Coleoptera), a group of pali on raster arranged in a single row, or 2 or more rows, either medially placed across the venter in front of the lower anal lip, or paired and extending forward and inward from one of the ends of the anal slit, or paired and straight (T-B, after Böving).

palingenesis, that phase in the development of an individual plant or animal which repeats the evolutionary history of the group to which it belongs; see cenogenesis.

palingenetic, of or relating to palingenesis.

Palingenioidea, superfamily within the Ephemeroptera, proposed for the Palingeriidae and Behningiidae, both of which are more generally placed within the Ephemeroidea (Hennig, after Demoulin).

palisade, in dark-adapted eucone apposition ommatidium, the clear region formed around the rhabdom (Chapman).

palisade layer, in Aleyrodidae (Hemiptera: Sternorrhyncha), a layer of thick, upright columnar wax supporting the submargin of the pupa (Gill).

pallescent, becoming pale or light in color or tint (T-B).

pallial plates, in ♂ Tetrigidae (Orthoptera), 2 large, oblong, longitudinal sclerites replacing pallium (Tuxen).

pallid, pallidus (Latin), pale, q.v. (T-B; R. W. Brown).

palliolum (pl., **palliola**), in ♂ Siphonaptera, end chamber, q.v. (Tuxen, after Smit).

pallium (pl., **pallia**), in ♂ Caelifera (Orthoptera), a membrane from the free margin of subgenital plate covering the retracted phallus (Tuxen).

Pallopteroidea, Opomyzoidea, q.v. (Colles and McAlpine, in CSIRO).

palm, palma (Latin), inside of the hand (R. W. Brown); in Corixidae (Hemiptera: Heteroptera), that portion of the pala, usually pilose, lying between the upper and lower row of palmar hairs, sometimes furnished with striduatory pegs (T-B; Hungerford).

palmar hairs, in Corixidae (Hemiptera: Heteroptera), usually a row of long hairs on the lower margin of the pala, and a row of short hairs along the upper margin of the palm (Hungerford).

palmate, palmated, palmatus (Latin), like the palm of a hand, with fingerlike processes (T-B).

Palmén body, Palmén's organ, q.v. (T-B).

Palmén organ, Palmén's organ, q.v. (Tulloch).

Palmén's organ, in the head of larval and adult Ephemeroptera, a cuticular nodule at the junction of the 4 tracheae middorsally behind the eyes, resulting from the accumulation of cuticle with successive moults (Tulloch; Chapman); see induvia.

palmitic acid, $CH_3(CH_2)_{14}CO_2H$, a common fatty acid found as constituents of storage fats (Gilmour, in CSIRO).

palmula, pulvillus, q.v. (T-B).

palp, palpus, q.v. (Chapman).

palp formula, in adult Hymenoptera, 2 numbers, the former indicating the number of segments in the maxillary palpus, the latter the number of segments in the labial palpus (Gould and Bolton).

palpal, belonging, relating or attached to a palpus (T-B).

palparium, in some Coleoptera and other insects, the membranous support to which the labial palpi are attached, and which permits an amount of extension not otherwise possible (T-B).

palpi genitalium, in ♂ Diptera, pregonites, q.v. (Tuxen, after Wesché).

palpicorn, with long, slender, antennalike palpi (T-B).

Palpicornia, Hydrophiloidea, q.v. (Britton, in CSIRO).

palpifer, any palp-bearing part (T-B); a small sclerite bearing the maxillary palpus and itself articulated to the stipes (T-B); see palpiger.

palpiferous, bearing a palpus (T-B).

palpiform, shaped like a palpus (T-B).

palpiger, a sclerite bearing a palpus (T-B); the palpus-bearing structure of the mentum (T-B); see palpifer.

palpigerous, palpiferous, q.v (T-B).

palpigerous stipes, in larval Coleoptera, palpifer, q.v., of maxilla (T-B).

Palpigrada, Palpigradi, q.v. (Borror et al.).

Palpigradi, order of Arachnida (Chelicerata), including the micro-whipscorpions, possessing a distinctly segmented opisthosoma with a whiplike prolongation, second ventral segment of opisthosoma without comblike organs, pedipalps slender and similar to legs, and small size (5 mm or less in length) (Borror et al.).

Palpigradida, Palpigradi, q.v. (Borror et al.).

palplike appendages, in ♀ Aculeata (Hymenoptera), gonostyli, q.v. (T-B, after Imms).

palplike process, in ♀ Nepidae (Hemiptera: Heteroptera), gonoplac, q.v. (Tuxen, after Hamilton).

palpognath, in Chilopoda, the second maxilla (T-B, after Comstock).

palpomere, palp segment (Saether).

palpuli, the maxillary palpi in adult Lepidoptera, when visibly developed (T-B).

palpus (pl., **palpi**), tactile, usually segmented (fingerlike) structures borne by the maxillae (maxillary palpi) and labium (labial palpi) (T-B; Peterson); in ♀ Hymenoptera, gonoplac, q.v. (Tuxen, after Snodgrass); see maxillary palpus and labial palpus.

palpus maxillaris, in larval Chironomidae (Diptera), maxillary palpus, q.v. (Saether).

paludicolous, living in or frequenting marshes (T-B).

palus (pl., **pali**), a straight pointed spine (T-B); in larval Scarabaeoidea (Coleoptera), a component of the palidium, usually recumbent with the apices directed toward the septula (T-B, after Böving).

Pangea, ancient landmass from which Laurasia and Gondwanaland were derived (Mackerras, after Wegener, in CSIRO).

panduriform, violin-shaped; oblong, with rounded ends, medially constricted (T-B).

Pangola stunt, a disease of grass (*Pangola*), caused by a reovirus (*Fijivirus*), transmitted propagatively by *Sogatella* (Hemiptera: Auchenorrhyncha: Delphacidae) (Nault and Ammar).

Panheteroptera, subdivision of the Heteroptera including the infraorders Leptopodomorpha, Nepomorpha, Cimicomorpha, and Pentatomomorpha (Schuh, after Štys); see Euheteroptera and Neoheteroptera.

Panisoptera, Zoraptera, q.v. (Tulloch).

Panmecoptera, Panorpoidea, q.v. (Hennig, after Wille).

Panneuroptera, group proposed to include the Neuropteroidea, Coleoptera, Strepsiptera, and Hymenoptera (Hennig, after Crampton, Wille).

pannicular, in ♀ Geometridae (Lepidoptera), adjective, descriptive of a corpus bursae only partially clothed internally with spines (Tuxen, after Pierce).

panoistic egg tube, panoistic ovariole, q.v. (T-B, after Snodgrass).

panoistic ovariole, in Diplura, Archaeognatha, Zygentoma, Odonata,

Plecoptera, Orthoptera, Phasmida, Isoptera, and Siphonaptera, an ovariole with no specialized nurse cells (T-B; Chapman; von Kéler).

Panorpatae, Mecoptera, q.v. (T-B).

panorpoid complex, group proposed to include the Planipennia, Megaloptera, and Raphidioptera with the Panorpoidea (Mackerras, after Tillyard, in CSIRO).

panorpoid orders, Panorpoidea, q.v. (Riek, in CSIRO; Borror et al.).

Panorpoidea, hypothesized monophyletic group of endopterygote orders, including the Mecoptera, Siphonaptera, Diptera, Trichoptera, and Lepidoptera (Mackerras, after Hinton, in CSIRO; Boudreaux, after Handlirsch).

Panorthoptera, Orthopterodida, q.v. (Boudreaux, after Crampton).

Panota, suborder of Ephemeroptera, including the superfamilies Ephemerelloidea and Caenoidea (Landa and Soldán).

Panprotura, Ellipura, q.v. (Hennig, after Crampton).

Pantaphaga, group proposed for the suborders Adephaga, Polyphaga, and Myxophaga (Coleoptera) (Bachr, in Hennig, after Klausnitzer).

pantherine, spotted like a leopard (T-B).

pantonome, a larval mine of variable outline that is usually determined by the shape of the plant part attacked; applicable particularly to mines in narrow stems or leaves (e.g., grass mines) (Hering).

pantophagous, omnivorous, q.v. (T-B).

pantothenic acid, $C_9H_{17}O_5N$; an essential water-soluble vitamin in insects, belonging to the vitamin B complex (Gilmour, in CSIRO).

pantropical, inhabiting both the Old and New World tropics (Mackerras, in CSIRO).

panzootic, denoting a disease affecting all, or a large proportion of the animals of a region; extensively epizootic (Steinhaus and Martignoni).

P.A.O., postantennal organ, q.v. (Christiansen and Bellinger).

papatasi fever, viral disease of man in the Mediterranean region, India, and Ceylon, transmitted by the sand fly *Phlebotomus papatasii* (Diptera: Psychodidae) (Borror et al., Allaby); see sand-fly fever.

papilioform, formed like a butterfly wing (T-B).

papilionaceous, butterflylike in shape or aspect (T-B).

Papilionoidea, superfamily within the division Ditrysia (Lepidoptera), including the Papilionidae and related families (Common, in CSIRO).

papilla (pl., **papillae**), a minute, soft projection (T-B); primitively paired outgrowths around coelomoducts between coxosternites and gonocoxites VIII and IX, each originally bearing a gonopore, but openings coalescing into a single median aperture in Hymenoptera, with papillary rudiments to either side (♀ labia) or united into a median penis or aedeagus (♂) (Tuxen, after E. L. Smith); in ♀ Protura, papilliform distal continuation of perigynium above styli (Tuxen); in larval Lepidoptera, modified ligula, i.e., spinneret, q.v. (T-B); in ♀ Siphonaptera, small sclerotized knob at apex of hilla (Tuxen, after Smit); see papillae.

papilla genitalis, in Diplura and ♂ Collembola, papilla carrying genital opening (Tuxen).

papillae (sing., **papilla**), in ♀ Phoenicoccidae (Hemiptera: Sternorrhyncha: Coccoidea), ierregular, dermal projections on the anterior and posterior ends of the body (Kosztarab); in ♂ Coleoptera, parameres, q.v. (Tuxen, after Hopkins).

papillae anales (sing., **papilla analis**), in ♀ Lepidoptera, a pair of soft, oval or reniform, hairy lobes, situated caudally on abdominal segments IX and X on either side of anus and ostium oviductus (Tuxen, after Kusnezov).

papillae genitales (sing., **papilla genitalis**), in ♀ Lepidoptera, membranous, paired lobes, perhaps derived from abdominal segment X, lying on either side of ostium oviductus (Tuxen, after Kusnezov).

papillary, having nipplelike processes with the tips rounded (T-B).

papillate, papillatus (Latin), covered with small, nipplelike surface elevations, often porous at the tip (T-B; Harris, after R. W. Brown, and Harrington and Durrell); see acinose, colliculate, papillulate, and pustulate.

papillate seta, a seta arising from a socket on an elevated papilla (Christiansen and Bellinger).

papilliform, of the shape of a papilla (T-B).

papilliform process of sternum IX, in ♀ Neuroptera, stylus, q.v. (Tuxen, after Killington).

papillose, papillous, papillosus (Latin), papillate, q.v. (T-B; Harris).

papillulate, beset with depressions or elevations with a small elevation in the center (a papillule) (T-B; Harris); see papillate.

papillule, an elevation with another small elevation in the center (T-B).

pappataci fever, papatasi fever, q.v. (Borror et al.).

pappose, downy; made up or clothed with pappus (T-B).

pappus, a fine down (T-B).

papyraceous, paper- or papyruslike; papery (T-B).

para-, Greek prefix; next to; near by; at the side of (T-B).

paraanal plates, in ♂ Plecoptera, paragenital plates, q.v. (Tuxen, after Hagen).

parabasal lobe, in ♂ Anophelinae (Diptera: Culicidae), a variably-developed lobe located dorsobasally on the gonocoxite, bearing one or more parabasal setae (Harbach and Knight, after Christophers).

parabasal seta, in ♂ Anophelinae (Diptera: Culicidae), any distinct seta, usually borne on parabasal lobe, located dorsobasally (prerotation sense) on the gonocoxite (Harbach and Knight).

parabasal spine, in ♂ Culicidae (Diptera), parabasal seta, q.v. (Tuxen).

parabiosis, in Formicidae (Hymenoptera), the utilization of the same nest and sometimes even the same odor trails by colonies of different species, which nevertheless keep their brood separate (Wilson).

parabursa, in ♀ Lepidoptera, appendix bursae, q.v. (Tuxen, after Wehrli).

paracardo, subcardo, q.v. (T-B, after MacGillivray).

paracephalic suture, epicranial arm, q.v. (T-B, after MacGillivray).

paracercus, in Ephemeroptera, filum terminale, q.v. (Tuxen).

parachuting, in spiders (Araneae), ballooning, q.v. (Borror et al.).

paraclypeal fold, in larval Culicidae (Diptera), tentorial phragmata, q.v. (Teskey, after Cook, in McAlpine).

paraclypeal lobe, in Heteroptera (Hemiptera), mandibular plate, q.v. (T-B).

paraclypeal phragma (pl., **phragmata**), in larval Culicidae (Diptera), tentorial phragmata, q.v. (Teskey, after Cook, in McAlpine); in larval Muscomorpha (Diptera), tentoropharyngeal sclerite, q.v. (Ferrar).

paraclypeus, in larval Lepidoptera, a narrow sclerite bordering the clypeus at the sides (T-B); in Hemiptera, mandibular plate, q.v. (Woodward et al., in CSIRO); see clypealia.

Paracoleoptera, Archicoleoptera, q.v. (Hennig, after Laurentiaux).

paracoxal ridge, in adult Culicidae (Diptera), the apodeme marked externally by the paracoxal suture, extending from the pleural apophysis to the mesopleurosternal ridge (Harbach and Knight).

paracoxal suture, in adult Culicidae (Diptera), the line of inflection that separates the mesotrochantin from the mesokatepisternum (Harbach and Knight).

parademe, phragma, q.v. (T-B, after MacGillivray).

Paradermaptera, an infraorder within the suborder Catadermaptera (Dermaptera), the members of which possess an excessively flattened, gaily colored body, and which contains only the family Apachyidae (Steinmann); see Protodermaptera and Mesodermaptera.

paradichlorobenzene, $C_6H_4Cl_2$, an insecticidal fumigant; doses over 300 mg/kg for humans begin to be harmful, acute oral LD_{50} for rats 500 mg/kg (Pfadt).

paradorsal muscle, in insects, a longitudinal muscle or group of longitudinal fibers situated on the lateral part of the dorsum above the line of the spiracles (T-B).

paraecie, in Isoptera, the empty space separating a subterranean nest from the surrounding soil (Noirot, in Krishna and Weesner).

parafacial, in adult Schizophora (Diptera: Muscomorpha), area between ptilinal fissure and eye, abutting fronto-orbital plate dorsally and the gena ventrally (T-B, after Curran; McAlpine).

paraffin, a white, waxy, solid, substance consisting of a mixture of hydrocarbons, used for embedding tissues for sectioning in histology; any member of a group of hydrocarbons having the general formula C_nH_{2n+2}.

paraffin epicuticle, wax layer, q.v. (Tulloch, after Richards).

parafrontal plates, in adult Diptera, fronto-orbital plates, q.v. (McAlpine).

parafrontalia, parafrontals, q.v. (T-B).

parafrontals, in adult Diptera, the parts of the face between the facial ridges and the eyes (T-B, after Curran; Colless and McAlpine, in CSIRO); see fronto-orbital areas.

paragenital plate, in ♀ Isoptera, abdominal sternum VIII (Tuxen, after Fuller).

paragenital plates, in ♂ Plecoptera, laterobasal plates of supraanal lobe, i.e., sclerotizations of cowl (Tuxen, after Frison); also applied to stylets, q.v. (Tuxen, after Frison).

paragenital sinus, in Cimicoidea (Hemiptera: Heteroptera), external pocket or channel leading to external aperture of ectospermalege (Štys, pers. comm.)

paragenital system, in many Cimicoidea (Hemiptera: Heteroptera), various structural differentiations in females correlated with the traumatic insemination absent among insects exhibiting normal insemination (Carayon, in Usinger); see spermalege.

paragenitals, in ♂ Plecoptera, paragenital plates, q.v. (Tuxen, after Smith).

paraglossa (pl., **paraglossae**), paired labial structure at the apex of the prementum, lying at each side of the glossae, being connected to the later, free, or two-jointed, and corresponding to the galea of the maxilla (T-B; Chapman); in larval Chironomidae (Diptera), paraligula, q.v. (Saether); see glossa.

paragnatha (sing., **paragnath** or **paragnathus**), superlinguae, q.v. (T-B, after Comstock, Tillyard).

paragula, the part of the postgena along the lateral side of the gular suture (T-B, after MacGillivray); a paired, usually elongate, sclerome on either side of the gula, e.g., *Tenebroides mauritanicus* (Coleoptera: Trogossitidae) (Peterson).

paralabial combs, in larval Chironomidae (Diptera), dorsomentum, q.v., or mentum, q.v. (Saether).

paralabial plates, in larval Chironomidae (Diptera), ventromental plates, q.v. (Teskey, in McAlpine; Saether).

paralabials, in larval aquatic Diptera, ventromental plates, q.v. (Peterson).

paralabral surface, in larval Diptera, surface of mandible facing the labrum (Teskey, in McAlpine).

paralectotype, each specimen of a former syntype series remaining after the designation of a lectotype (ICZN).

paraligula, in larval Chironomidae (Diptera), curved scales, small sclerotized rods, deeply serrated plates, single pointed or serrated scales at each side of ligula at ventral apex of prementum (Saether).

parallel mandibles, mouth hooks, q.v. (Peterson).

parallelism, the independent acquisition of similar characters in related evolutionary lines (Mayr); see convergence.

paralobi, in ♂ Muscomorpha (Diptera), surstyli, q.v. (Tuxen).

Paramecoptera, extinct suborder of Mecoptera from the Permian Period, possessing wings with few costal crossveins and anterior cubitus (CuA) forked in forewing but not in the hind wing (Riek, in CSIRO).

paramedial, paramedian, lateral and parallel to the midline (Christiansen and Bellinger).

paramedian lamellae, in some larval Chironomidae (Diptera), e.g., Orthocladiinae and Chironominae, apicolateral lamellae of M appendage (Saether).

paramedian scales, in larval Chironomidae (Diptera), paramedian lamellae, q.v. (Saether).

Paramegasecoptera, suborder of the extinct order Megasecoptera, including the families Elmoidae, Diaphanopteridae, Martynoviidae, Asthenohymenidae, and Biarmohymenidae, possessing wings that could be flexed backward over the abdomen (Brues et al.); see Eumegasecoptera.

paramentum, in larval Coleoptera, a paired, usually elongate sclerome on either side of the mentum (Peterson, after Böving).

paramera, parameres, q.v. (Tuxen).

parameral apodeme, in ♂ Diptera, rodlike apodeme projecting from paramere into interior of genital segment, serving for muscle attachment (Tuxen; McAlpine).

parameral bridge, bridge connecting inferior appendages in ♂ Trichoptera and valvae in ♂ Lepidoptera (Tuxen, after Snodgrass).

parameral lever, in ♂ Dermaptera, strongly sclerotized lateral rod supporting penis (Tuxen).

parameral plate, in ♀ Hymenoptera, gonocoxite, q.v. (Tuxen, after Snodgrass).

parameral spine, in ♂ Hymenoptera, gonostylus, q.v. (Tuxen, after Richards).

paramere(s), in ♂ insects, lateral phallomeres when primary phallic lobes are secondarily divided (in most orders of Neoptera), the median ones being mesomeres (Tuxen, after Snodgrass); in ♂ Protura, penis valves, q.v. (Tuxen, after Crampton); in ♂ Archaeognatha and Zygentoma, pairs of annulated gonapophyses of gonopods of abdominal segments VIII and IX (Tuxen, after Denis); in ♂ Ephemeroptera, penial spines, q.v., or penial bar, q.v. (Tuxen, after Walker); in ♂ Blatteropteroidea, epiphallus, q.v. (Tuxen, after Walker); in ♂ Orthoptera, dorsal phallic lobes, q.v. (Tuxen, after Walker); in ♂ Dermaptera, distolateral clasping organs (Tuxen); in ♂ Psocoptera, external parameres, q.v. (Tuxen, after Badonnel) or external + internal parameres (Tuxen); in ♂ Phthiraptera, paired sclerites articulated to or fused with posterolateral angles of basal apodeme (Clay, in Tuxen), sometimes being fused to each other or to mesomeral arch (Lyal); in ♂ Cicadoidea and Fulgoroidea (Hemiptera: Auchenorrhyncha), styles, q.v. (Tuxen, after Singh-Pruthi); in ♂ Psyllidae (Hemiptera: Sternorrhyncha), forceps, q.v. (Tuxen); in ♂ Aleyrodidae (Hemiptera: Sternorrhyncha), claspers, q.v. (Tuxen); in ♂ Heteroptera (Hemiptera), copulatory hooks lying in the adult genital chamber lateral to and independent of phallus but arising post embryologically from the exterolateral parts of 2 buds (primary phallic lobes), the internomedian parts of which give rise to phallus (Tuxen, after Singh-Pruthi) or (in Lygaeidae, unorthodox usage), processus phallothecae, q.v. (Tuxen, after Bonhag and Wick); in ♂ *Eusthenes* (Hemiptera: Heteroptera: Tessaratomidae), lateral parts of external wall of various phallic segments, i.e., phallosomal plates and inner parameres, q.v. (transl. "Parameren" Handlirsh, after Tuxen); in ♂ Thysanoptera, one or 2 paired appendages of periandrium or phallobase (Heming), dorsal parameres and ventral parameres (Tuxen, after Verhoeff); in ♂ Coleoptera, a pair of appendages (sometimes coalescent or even completely joined) forming distal (apical) part of tegmen and usually protruding on either side of penis (Tuxen), or applied in a wider sense to tegmen, q.v. (Tuxen, after Heberdey); in ♂ Neuroptera, a pair of lateral processes arising close to base of penis (Tuxen); in ♂ *Chrysopa* (Planipennia: Chrysopidae), entoprocessus, q.v. (Tuxen, after Killington); in Mecoptera, a pair of lateral processes arising close to base of penis (Tuxen); in ♂ Mecoptera, paired processes arising from ventral or dorsal base of aedeagus (Byers); in some ♂ Trichoptera, rodlike or complicated structures arising from the endotheca, generally paired, but unpaired in Glossosomatidae (Tuxen); in ♂ *Hydroptila occulata* Eaton (Trichoptera: Hydroptilidae), branches of inferior appendages, q.v. (Tuxen, after Nielsen); in ♂ Lepidoptera, a costa largely isolated from remainder of valva (Tuxen, after Bastelberger), separated paired arms of gnathos (Tuxen, after Chapman), or valvae, q.v. (Tuxen, after Hofmann); in ♂ Diptera, a pair of unsegmented paraphallic processes situated between the posterolateral base of the aedeagus and the dorsomedial base of the gonocoxite (Tuxen; McAlpine) or gonopods, q.v. (Tuxen, after Crampton); gonocoxites (= basimeres) + gonostyli (= telomeres) (Griffiths); in ♂ Siphonaptera, a pair of clasping organs joined to abdominal tergum IX and consisting of a basimere with an anterior apodeme (manubrium) and one or 2 telomeres (Tuxen, after Snodgrass), hamuli, q.v. (Tuxen, after Jordan), palliolum, q.v. (Tuxen, after Jordan, Hopkins and M. Rothschild), or (in *Ctenophthalmus*) subapical sclerites, q.v. (Tuxen, after Wagner); in ♂ Hymenoptera, paired appendages forming a conical capsule containing more delicate parts of the genitalia (Tuxen, after Beck; Gauld and Bolton), gonostyli, q.v. (Tuxen, after Snodgrass), gonocoxites + gonostyli (Tuxen, after LaPorte), gonocoxites + gonostyli + volsellae (Tuxen, after Verhoeff), or in Formicidae, the genitalia (Tuxen, after Wheeler).

paramere bases, in ♂ Orthoptera, laminae phalli, q.v. (Tuxen, after Walker).

paramere sac, in ♂ Tettigoniidae (Orthoptera), titillator cavity, q.v. (Tuxen, after Walker).

paramerite, in ♂ Staphylinidae (Coleoptera), the main, distal part of paramere if divided (Tuxen, after Brundin); in ♂ Coleoptera, applied to parameres, q.v. (Tuxen).

paramerophore, in ♂ Chironomidae (Diptera), inferior volsella, q.v. (Saether).

paramerum, in ♂ Heteroptera (Hemiptera), paramere, q.v. (Tuxen, after Piotrowski).

paramyosin, protein filament within the core of a myofibril (Chapman); see myosin.

paranal, at the side of or next to the anus or anal structures (T-B).

paranal forks, in some larval Lepidoptera, 2 lateral, bristlelike structures, used to throw frass pellets to a distance (T-B).

paranal lobe, paraproct, q.v. (Tuxen).

paranal plates, in Coccoidea (Hemiptera: Sternorrhyncha), the tenth pair of dorsal plates on abdominal segment VI (T-B, after MacGillivray).

parandrium (pl., **parandria**), in ♂ Heteroptera (Hemiptera), one of a pair of expansions of external wall of pygophore in lateroventral position, provided with setae but not muscles (Tuxen, after Crampton); in ♂ *Bittacus* (Mecoptera: Bittacidae), lateral expansion of abdominal sternum IX (Byers, pers. comm., after Crampton).

parandrite, paramere, q.v. (Mackerras, after Crampton).

Paraneoptera, hypothesized monophyletic group including the Acercaria and the order Zoraptera (Hennig, after Martynov).

Paraneuroptera, Odonata, q.v. (T-B, after Imms).

paranota (sing., **paranotum**), lateral expansions of the thoracic tergal region (T-B, after Wardle); in Peloridiidae (Hemiptera: Coleorrhyncha), lateral expansions of pronotum (Woodward et al, in CSIRO); in certain Heteroptera (Hemiptera), specifically the Tingidae, the flattened or lamellate sides of the pronotum (T-B); parapsides, q.v. (T-B, after MacGillivray); see paranotal lobes.

paranotal expansions, paranotal lobes, q.v. (T-B, after Tillyard).

paranotal hypothesis, paranotal theory, q.v. (T-B).

paranotal lobes, lateral lobes of the pronotum in certain fossil insects, e.g., certain Paleodictyoptera and Paraplecoptera, and theoretical lobes of the mesonotum and metanotum supposed to be the precursors of wings (T-B; Riek, in CSIRO); in the insect embryo, the wing rudiments of the thorax in winged insects (T-B, after Snodgrass); see paranota.

paranotal suture, in adult Culicidae (Diptera), lateral parapsidal suture, q.v. (Harbach and Knight).

paranotal theory, theory on the origin of insect wings, which holds that they rose from lateral expansions, or paranotal lobes, situated along the sides of the thoracic terga (T-B, after Crampton; Mackerras in CSIRO).

paraoesophageal commissure, circumoesophageal connective, q.v. (Gilmour, in CSIRO).

parapatry, of populations or species, in nonoverlapping geographical contact without interbreeding (Mayr).

parapenial lobe, in ♂ Hymenoptera, dorsal, inner, marginal lobe of gonocoxite, often projecting distad over aedeagus (Tuxen, after Crampton).

parapenis, in ♂ Hymenoptera, parapenial lobe, q.v. (Tuxen, after Crampton).

paraphallic lobes, in ♂ Diptera, parameres, q.v. (McAlpine, after Snodgrass).

paraphallus (pl., **paraphalli**), in ♂ Diptera, sclerotizations of distiphallus (Tuxen); in ♂ Blatteropteroidea, hypophallus, q.v. (Tuxen, after Wesché).

parapharynx, salivarium, q.v. (T-B, after MacGillivray).

paraphyletic, used to describe a taxonomic group that does not include all the descendants of a common ancestor (Hennig); see monophyletic and polyphyletic.

paraphyses (sing., **paraphysis**), in ♂ insects, parameres, q.v. (Tuxen, after Snodgrass); in Diaspididae (Hemiptera: Sternorrhyncha: Coccoidea), usually slender scleroses in the spaces between the pygidial lobes on the dorsal margin (T-B; Kosztarab and Kazár).

Paraplecoptera, extinct order among the orthopteroid orders (Insecta: Neoptera), possessing an anojugal fan in the hind wing, stems of main wing veins free at base, and both anterior media (MA) and posterior media MP) developed (Riek, in CSIRO).

parapleuron (pl., **parapleura**), in some adult Coleoptera, the undivided pleuron of the thorax, situated on each side of the sternum (T-B, after Tillyard).

parapodia (sing., **parapodium**), in larval Diptera, prolegs, q.v. (Teskey, in McAlpine); see parapods.

parapodium (pl., **parapodia**), in Polychaeta (Annelida), usually biramous, muscular, lateral projection of the body, paired and extending from the body segments, more or less compressed laterally, and bearing setae (T-B; Allaby); in larval Diptera, pseudopodium, proleg, or parapod, q.v. (T-B, after Packard); in Symphyla, a slender cylindrical process of the proximal leg segment (T-B, after Comstock).

parapod(s), in larval Chironomidae (Diptera), fleshy, unjointed, ventral protuberances or false feet on prothorax (anterior parapods) and last abdominal segment (posterior parapods) carrying apical claws (Saether); see parapodia.

parapodial plates, in Isoptera and adult Diptera, paraprocts, q.v. (Tuxen).

paraproct(s), in lower insects (e.g., Archaeognatha, Zygentoma, Odonata, and Embiidina), a pair of plates on the sides of and below anus, belonging to abdominal segment XI (in Isoptera and Embiidina said to belong to abdominal segment X) as its subdivided sternum (Tuxen); in Archaeognatha and Zygentoma, plates at bases of cerci (Tuxen); in Ephemeroptera, ventral, paired portion of abdominal segment XI (Tuxen); in Embiidina, the 2 parts of abdominal sternum X on either side of anus (Ross, in Tuxen); in Plecoptera, subanal plates, q.v. (Tuxen, after Crampton); in ♀ Phthiraptera, pair of posterior lobes at the end of the last abdominal segment (Lyal); in adult Psocoptera, a pair of sclerites on the sides of anus, probably part of tergum X (Tuxen); in adult Ascalaphidae and Mantispidae (Neuroptera), ectoproct, q.v. (Tuxen, after Crampton); in adult *Corydalus* (Megaloptera: Corydalidae), *Ithone* (Planipennia: Ithonidae), and Myrmeleontidae (Planipennia), abdominal tergum IX, q.v. (Tuxen, after Crampton); in ♂ Neuroptera, ectoproct, q.v. (Tuxen, after Michener); in ♀ Coleoptera, the halves of tergum IX (Tuxen, after Tanner); in ♀ *Protohermes* (Megaloptera: Corydalidae), catoprocessus, q.v. (Tuxen, after Tjeder); in ♀ Coniopterygidae (Planipennia), gonapophyses laterales, q.v. (Tuxen, after Withycombe); in adult Diptera, sclerotizations in proctiger supposedly homologous with paraprocts of lower insects (Tuxen).

paraproct crown, in ♂ *Culex* (Diptera: Culicidae), a collection of spicules borne at or near the apex of the paraproct (Harbach and Knight).

paraproctal lobes, in ♂ Tridactylidae (Orthoptera), delimited lobes on paraprocts (Tuxen); in Phasmida, paraprocts, q.v. (Tuxen, after Snodgrass).

paraproctal plates, in ♂ Plecoptera, subanal plates, q.v. (Tuxen, after Crampton).

paraproctal processes, in ♂ Ensifera (Orthoptera), one or more processes of paraprocts (Tuxen).

parapsidal, of or pertaining to the parapsides (T-B).

parapsidal furrow, in adult Proctotrupidae (Hymenoptera: Proctotrupoidea), notaulus, q.v. (T-B); see parapsidal line.

parapsidal line, in numerous Apocrita (Hymenoptera), a marking, lateral of notaulus, typically extending anteriorly from posterior region of mesoscutum (Gauld and Bolton).

parapsidal suture, in many adult Nematocera (Diptera), esp. certain Psychodidae and Chironomidae, paired, more or less longitudinally aligned sutures on mesoscutum, continuing caudally in a sublateral (dorsocentral) position (Saether; McAlpine); in ants (Hymenoptera: Formicidae), notaulus, q.v. (T-B, after W. M. Wheeler).

parapsides (sing., **parapsis**), in adult Mecoptera and many Symphyta (Hymenoptera), lateral pieces of mesoscutum, separated from mesal part by grooves (notauli) (T-B; Riek, in CSIRO); see median mesoscutal lobe.

parapteron (pl., **paraptera**), basalare, q.v., or subalare, q.v. (T-B; Leftwich); in Aleyrodidae (Hemiptera: Sternorrhyncha), 6 small sclerites located laterally on proscutum, mesoscutum, and metascutum of adults (Gill); in adult Hymenoptera and Lepidoptera, tegula, q.v. (T-B).

parapulvillus, pulvillus, q.v. (T-B).

parascolus, in larval Coccinellidae (Coleoptera), a modification of scolus in which projection is not more than 3 times as long as wide and usually not more than twice (Peterson, after Gage).

parascrobal area, in many adult Chalcididae (Hymenoptera), raised lateral area next to antennal scrobes (Gault and Bolton).

parascutal area, alar area, q.v. (Peterson).

parascutal carina, in adult Hymenoptera, lateral carina of mesoscutum that divides the dorsal, more or less horizontal, mesoscutal surface from the lateral, more or less vertical, mesoscutal surface (Gibson).

parascutal lobe, in adult Syricidae (Hymenoptera: Symphyta), region of the mesoscutum delineated by an oblique furrow anteroventral to the scutellum (Gibson).

parascutellar inflection, in adult Culicidae (Diptera), an internal bladelike process projecting ventrad from the parascutellum (Harbach and Knight, after Owen).

parascutellar process, in adult Culicidae (Diptera), the small angular area located near the center of the parascutellum, represented internally by an apodeme which bears the insertion of the direct wing muscles (Harbach and Knight, after Owen).

parascutellar seta, in adult Culicidae (Diptera), any seta borne on the parascutellum (Harbach and Knight).

parascutellars, in adult Chironomidae (Diptera), supraalars, q.v. (Saether).

parascutellum, area on each side of the scutellum (T-B, after Crampton); in adult Culicidae (Diptera), the small caudolateral lobe or area of the mesonotum caudad of the posterior notal wing process and caudolaterad of the scutellum, usually with one or more setae (Harbach and Knight, after Crampton).

Parasita, Anoplura, q.v. (T-B).

parasite, an organism that lives in or on another (the host), from which it obtains food, shelter, or other requirements (T-B; Allaby); see ectoparasite, endoparasite, and parasitoid.

parasitic, living as a parasite (T-B; Borror et al.).

Parasitica, Anoplura, q.v. (T-B); poorly defined division of the Apocrita (Hymenoptera) in which the ovipositor is not modified into a sting, including the superfamilies Megalyroidea, Stephanoidea, Trigonalyoidea, Evanioidea, Ichneumonoidea, Chalcidoidea, Cynipoidea, Ceraphronoidea, and Proctotrupoidea, whose larvae are parasites (Gauld and Bolton); see Aculeata.

parasitism, symbiosis in which members of one species (the parasite) exist at the expense of members of another species (the host), usually without going as far as to cause their deaths (T-B; Steinhaus and Martignoni; Wilson).

parasitize, to attack as a parasite (T-B).

parasitoid, an internal or external parasite, e.g., many Hymenoptera and Tachinidae (Diptera), that slowly kills the host, this event occurring near the end of the parasite's larval development; also used as an adjective (T-B, after Comstock; Wilson); see idiobiont and koinobiont.

parasitology, the science and study of parasites living in or on animals and man (T-B).

parasocial, presocial condition in which individuals display one or 2 of the following 3 traits: cooperation in care of young, reproductive division of labor, or overlap of generations of life stages that contribute to colony labor (Wilson).

parasporal body, in invertebrate pathology, a particle which lies alongside the spore or is included in the sporangium along with the spore, formed during sporulation of a number of *Bacillus* species (Steinhaus and Martignoni).

parasternites, in Heteroptera (Hemiptera), laterosternites, q.v. (Štys, pers. comm.).

parasternites (7th and **8th),** in ♂ Cryptostemmatidae (Hemiptera: Heteroptera), appendagelike structures, provided with a spiracle and articulating on abdominal terga VII and VIII (Tuxen, after Wygodzinsky).

parasternites (8th), in ♀ Heteroptera (Hemiptera), ventral laterotergites VIII, q.v. (Tuxen, after Larsén) (incorrect usage).

parasternites (**8th** and **9th**), in ♀ Heteroptera (Hemiptera), gonocoxites (VIII and IX), q.v. (Tuxen, after Ekblom) (incorrect usage).

parasternites (**8th** and **9th**), in ♀ Heteroptera (Hemiptera), ventral laterotergites, q.v. (Tuxen, after Ekblom) (incorrect usage).

parastigma, pterostigma, q.v. (T-B); in some adult Chalcididae (Hymenoptera), a dilation at junction of submarginal and marginal veins (Gauld and Bolton); see prestigma.

parastigmatic pores, in some Coccoidea (Hemiptera: Sternorrhyncha), small, circular pores around the spiracles which secrete a waxy powder (T-B); see spiracular pore band.

parastipes, the sclerite bordering the stipes mesally (T-B, after Crampton).

parastomal bars, in some larval Muscomorpha (Diptera: Brachycera), a pair of slender sclerotized rods projecting from each side of the anterior margin of the tentoropharyngeal sclerite above the hypopharyngeal sclerite (Teskey, in McAlpine).

parastomal sclerites, parastomal bars, q.v. (Farrar).

parastylos, in ♀ Psocoptera, valvae ventrales, q.v. (Tuxen, after Kolbe).

parategula, in adult Eumeninae (Hymenoptera: Vespidae), posterolateral process of mesocutum (Carpenter, after Carpenter and Cumming).

paratergal plates, in some Anoplura (Phthiraptera), lateral plates of abdominal terga (Calaby, in CSIRO).

paratergal scale, in adult Culicidae (Diptera), one of the scales occurring in a group on the paratergite (Harbach and Knight, after Belkin).

paratergite(s), the lateral marginal region of the notum (T-B, after Crampton); in some Poduromorpha (Collembola), a sclerite or region defined by furrows, lateral to and intercalated between the thoracic terga (Christiansen and Bellinger); in Heteroptera (Hemiptera), lateral flanges on pregenital segments of abdomen (Woodward et al., in CSIRO); in some Lygaeidae (Hemiptera: Heteroptera), lateral subdivisions of mediotergites, mesal to dorsal laterotergites (Štys); in adult Nematocera and many orthorrhaphous Brachycera (Diptera), a narrow lateral sclerite in front of the wing, representing a vestige of the prescutum of the mesothorax (Colless and McAlpine, in CSIRO); in adult Chironomidae (Diptera), lateral sclerite of abdominal segments (Saether); see laterotergite.

paratergites (**8th** and **9th**), in ♀ Heteroptera (Hemiptera), ventral laterotergites, q.v. (Tuxen, after Bonhag and Wick).

parathion, $C_{10}H_{14}NO_5PS$, insecticide and acaricide; an organophosphate, O,O-dethyl O-p-nitrophenyl phophorothioate; highly toxic to mammals, oral LD_{50} to rats 4 to 13 mg/kg (Pfadt).

paratopotype, a paratype from the same locality as the holotype (Tulloch).

paratorma, in some adult Diptera, the strongly chitinized plate connecting the lateral margins of the pharynx with the tormae (T-B, after MacGillivray).

Paratrichoptera, extinct suborder of Mecoptera from the Mesozoic

Era, possessing wings with a rather distinctive alignment of the veins and a tendency to looping of the anal veins (Riek, in CSIRO).

paratype, each specimen of a type series other than the holotype (ICZN).

paravertical bristles, in adult Diptera, pair of bristles located just posterior to vertical bristles (McAlpine).

paraxial seta (of galea), in larval Chironomidae (Diptera), one seta, or sensillum chaeticum, on dorsal side of galea of maxilla and basal and anterior to lacinia (Saether).

parcidentate, with few teeth (T-B).

parecium, the air space surrounding the fungus garden in the nest of a macrotermitine (Isoptera: Termitidae) (Wilson).

parempodia (sing., **parempodium**), in Heteroptera (Hemiptera), paired setiform or lamellate processes arising distally from the unguitractor plate, between the claw bases (Cobben; Goel and Schaefer; Schuh); see arolium and empodium.

parental investment, behaviors (investments of time and/or energy) that increase the probability of some offspring surviving to reproduce at the cost of the parents ability to generate additional offspring (Matthews and Matthews).

parental manipulation theory, hypothesis for the evolution of eusociality in Hymenoptera in which the mother manipulates her offspring (either genetically, behaviorly, or physiologically), so that she dominates and controls her daughters in such a way that her own fitness is enhanced (Gauld and Bolton, after Alexander, and Brothers and Michener); see kin selection theory.

paria (pl., **pariae**), in larval Scarabaeoidea (Coleoptera), a lateral paired region of the epipharynx extending from the clythrum, epizygum and haptomerum (or in their place, the tylus) back to the parietal elements, the dexiotorma and laeotorma, and marked off internolaterally from the pedium by bristles or asperites of the subregion chaetoparia and the phobae (T-B, after Böving).

parietal, of or pertaining to the wall of a cavity of the body or of an organ (T-B).

parietal lobe, in larval Chironomidae (Diptera), gena, q.v. (Saether).

parietal processes, in ♂ Heteroptera (Hemiptera), phragmal processes, q.v. (Tuxen, after Dupuis) or pygophoral processes, q.v. (Tuxen after Dupuis, later usage).

parietal seta(e), in adult Chironomidae (Diptera), inner and outer verticals, q.v. (Saether); in larval Chironomidae (Diptera), dorsal seta (cephalic seta 8) of head on gena about halfway between eye and posterior margin and just lateral of frontal (frontoclypeal) apotome (Saether).

parietalia, the dorsal sclerites of the head between the frontal and occipital regions (T-B, after Crampton).

parietals, the lateral areas of the cranium between the frontal and occipital areas, separated above by the coronal suture, each area bearing an antenna, one of the lateral ocelli and a compound eye (T-B, after Snodgrass).

parietes, wall (T-B); the perpendicular sides of the honey comb (T-B); the inner walls of any body cavity (T-B).

Paris green, an arsenic-based insecticide, copper acetoarsenite; highly toxic to mammals (Pfadt).

paronychium (pl., **paronychia**), in Heteroptera (Hemiptera), parempodium, q.v. (T-B).

parossiculus, in ♂ Hymenoptera, volsella except for digitus (Tuxen, after Crampton).

parous, egg development having occurred (Adkins, pers. comm.); see nulliparous.

parovaria (sing., **parovarium**), in ♀ Diptera, accessory glands, q.v. (McAlpine).

paroxyism, in invertebrate pathology, a sudden onset of symptoms, especially in diseases with recurrent manifestations (Steinhaus and Martignoni).

pars anterior (of distal arm of abdominal sternum IX), in ♂ Siphonaptera, anterior part of a secondarily divided distal arm of abdominal sternum IX (Tuxen).

pars articularis, in ♀ Hymenoptera, gonagulum, q.v. (Tuxen, after Oeser).

pars basalis, cardo, q.v. (T-B); in ♂ *Crambus* (Lepidoptera: Pyralidae), dorsoproximal process of valva, being part of costa (Tuxen, after Petersen); in ♂ Coleoptera, basal piece, q.v. Tuxen); in ♂ Chironomidae (Diptera), phallapodeme, q.v. (Saether).

pars communis, in ♀ Heteroptera (Hemiptera), the part of the complex of ectodermal ♀ genital ducts which constitutes the actual course that the eggs follow, including the ectodermal lateral oviducts (if present), oviductus communis and vagina (Tuxen, after Dupuis).

pars communis of spermathecal duct, in ♀ Siphonaptera, ductus communis, q.v. (Tuxen, after Dampf).

pars dilatata, in ♀ Siphonaptera, enlarged part of ductus spermathecae (Tuxen, Oudemans).

pars distalis, in ♂ Chironomidae (Diptera), aedeagal lobe, q.v. (Saether).

pars dorsalis, in ♀ Lepidoptera, the parts of the genitalia situated at the dorsal half (Tuxen, after Niculescu).

pars finalis, in ♂ Coleoptera, parameres, q.v. (Tuxen, after Escherich).

pars inflabilis ductus ejaculatorii, in ♂ Lepidoptera, vesica, q.v. (Tuxen, after Kusnezov).

pars intercerebralis, mass of cells of protocerebrum located anterodorsally, on each side of the midline containing one group of neurosecretory cells, i.e., median neurosecretory cells (T-B; Chapman).

pars intermedialis, in ♀ Heteroptera (Hemiptera), part of spermatheca (or its homologous vermiform gland) between ductus receptaculi and capsula seminis, frequently differentiated—in the true spermatheca—into a muscular pump with flanges (Tuxen, after Dupuis).

pars posterior, in ♂ Siphonaptera, posterior part of a secondarily divided distal arm of abdominal sternum IX (Tuxen).

pars stipitalis labii, prementum, q.v. (T-B).

pars subvaginalis, in ♀ *Cyrestis* (Lepidoptera: Nymphalidae), lamella postvaginalis, q.v. (Tuxen, after de Graaf).

pars ventralis (pl., **partes ventrales**), in ♀ Lepidoptera, the parts of the genitalia situated at the ventral half (Tuxen, after Niculescu); in ♂ Chironomidae (Diptera), single or double lobe ventrally between very bases of gonocoxites (Saether).

parsimony, in cladistics, a criterion used to select phylogenetic hypotheses most in accord with available observation, requiring minimizing the postulated number of homoplasies in the phylogenetic reconstruction, i.e., the minimum number of *ad hoc* hypotheses.

partes oris, mouthparts, q.v. (T-B).

parthenogenesis, egg development without fertilization (T-B; Tulloch; Chapman); see amphitoky, apomictic parthenogenesis, arrhenotoky, automictic parthenogenesis, haplo-diploidy, and telyotky.

parthenogenetic, reproducing by parthenogenesis (T-B).

partial claustral colony founding, in social insects, the procedure during which the queen founds the colony by isolating herself in a chamber but stll occasionally leaves to forage for part of her food supply (Wilson).

partim, (Latin), part (T-B).

partite, partitus (Latin), divided, e.g., the eyes of Gyrinidae (Coleoptera) (T-B).

parturition, the period during which the ♀ is producing eggs or larvae, following gestation (T-B; Chapman).

paryptera, in Psyllidae (Hemiptera: Sternorrhyncha), usually tubular, oval, or circular sclerites, sometimes as flat quadrate plates (Hodkinson and White).

Paspalum striate mosaic, disease of grass (*Paspalum*) caused by a geminivirus transmitted circulatively by *Nesoclutha* (Hemiptera: Auchenorrhyncha: Cicadellidae) Nault and Ammar).

patagium (pl., **patagia**), paranotum, q.v. (T-B, after Imms); paranotal lobe, q.v. (Leftwich); in adult Lepidoptera, paired articulated dorsal plates of prothorax (Common, in CSIRO), sometimes confused with tegula, q.v. (T-B, after Imms); in some ♂ Psychodinae (Diptera: Psychodidae), a saclike organ on cervical membrane above each cervical sclerite (Quate and Vockeroth, in McAlpine).

patella (pl., **patellae**), small pan; dish (T-B; R. W. Brown); in ♂ Dytiscidae (Coleoptera), the enlarged 3 basal articles of the foretarsus (T-B); in Chelicerata, a leg segment between the femur (meropodite) and the tibia (carpopodite) (T-B).

patellar, pertaining to the patella (T-B).

patellariae, in ♂ Dytiscidae (Coleoptera), suckers, q.v., on the underside of the patella (T-B).

patelliform, panlike or dishlike (T-B).

patellotibial, of or pertaining to both the patella and tibia (T-B).

patens, patentes, open; diverging; spreading apart (T-B).

pathogen, any mircoorganism or product thereof which causes disease (Tulloch; Steinhaus and Martignoni).

pathogenic, disease-causing or disease-producing, being applied to organisms which cause or carry disease (T-B).

pathogenesis, the origination and development of a disease or morbid process (Steinhaus and Martignoni).

pathogenicity, the quality or state of being pathogenic; the potential ability to produce disease; the genetically determined ability to produce disease (Steinhaus and Martignoni); see virulence.

pathognomonic, describing a symptom that points with certainty to a particular disease or malfunction (Steinhaus and Martignoni).

pathological, diseased or abnormal; unhealthy or arising from unhealthy conditions (T-B).

pathology, the science that deals with all aspects of disease; the study of the cause, nature, processes, and effects of disease (Steinhaus and Martignoni).

patria (Latin), home or country of origin (T-B).

patrolling, the act of investigating the nest interior (Wilson).

patronymic, in nomenclature, a dedicatory name based upon the name of a person or persons (Mayr).

patterned aggressive signal, rivalry sound, q.v. (Matthews and Matthews).

patterned song, song showing repetition of some basic element (Matthews and Matthews).

patulose, patulosus, patulous, patulus (Latin), open; spreadout; broad (T-B; R. W. Brown).

paunch, any pounchlike appendage of the alimentary canal (T-B); in Isoptera, the voluminous, dilated, second or third segment of the hind gut, containing symbiotic protozoa (Noirot, in Krishna and Weesner); in some Phthiraptera, a croplike accessory pouch (T-B).

Paurometabola, a grouping of exopterygote insects in which the nymphs are terrestrial and resemble the adults in general form and mode of life except for the absence of functional wings and reproductive organs, including, for example, Orthoptera, Blattaria, Dermaptera, and Hemiptera, but excluding Odonata, Ephemeroptera, and Plecoptera, in which the nymph is aquatic and differs in form and habits from the adult (T-B; Leftwich); see Hemimetabola.

paurometabolous, having an incomplete metamorphosis in which the changes of form are gradual or inconspicuous, e.g., Hemiptera (T-B, after Comstock); see ametabolous, hemimetabolous, heterometabolous, and holometabolous.

Pauropoda, class of Myriapoda, included individuals of small size (1.0–1.5 mm in length) with branched antennae, 9 pairs of legs, one pair per body segment; small head, and genital ducts opening near the anterior end of the body (T-B; Borror et al.).

Pavan's gland, in ants (Hymenoptera: Formicidae), gland opening on the ventral surface of the abdomen above abdominal sternite VI, producing trail pheromone in Dolichoderinae (Chapman).

pavillions, the sheds or cells sometimes built by ants (Hymenoptera: Formicidae), as shelter for groups of Aphidae (Hemiptera: Sternorrhyncha) (T-B).

pavimentosa, (adj.), in ♂ *Zygeana* (Lepidoptera: Zygaenidae), basal zone of lamina ventralis of aedeagus having a cellular lattice (Tuxen, after Loritz).

Pawlowsky's glands, in *Pediculus* (Phthiraptera: Anoplura: Peduculidae), the pair of glands opening into the stylet sac (T-B).

paxillus, a small stake or peg; a bundle of spicular processes (T-B); in some ♂ Siphonaptera, a strong, peglike, outwardly directed sclerite on the crochet which functions as a strong coupling device with abdominal sternum IX (Rothschild and Traub).

PDB, paradichlorobenzene, q.v. (Pfadt).

pe-la, a commercial Chinese wax, secreted by *Ericerus pela* (Hemiptera: Sternorrhyncha: Coccidae) (T-B).

pea enation mosaic, disease of peas, beans, alfalfa, and clover, caused by an isometric virus and transmitted circulatively by aphids (Hemiptera: Sternorrhyncha: Aphididae) (Borror et al.).

pea gall, spherical green gall about the size of peas but having a number of small spikelike projections, occurring on rose leaves and caused by gall wasp *Diplolepis nervosa* and related species (Hymenoptera: Cynipidae) (Leftwich); see spiked pea gall.

peach X-disease, disease of peach trees caused by a mycoplasma and transmitted propagatively by leafhoppers (Hemiptera: Auchenorrhyncha: Cicadellidae) (Borror et al.); see phony peach disease.

pearl row, in pupal Chironomidae (Diptera), row or rows of small, blunt tubercles, sometimes with apical pore, along margin of wing sheath (Saether).

pearlaceous, having the appearance of pearl (T-B).

Pearman's organ, in many families of Psocoptera, a supposed stridulatory organ on the inner surface of the hind coxae consisting of a small rugose dome and an adjacent membranous area of integument (mirror) (Badonnel; Smithers, in CSIRO).

pebrine, a disease of the silkworm, *Bombyx mori* (Lepidoptera: Bombycidae), caused by the microsporidian *Nosema bombycis,* producing dark pepperlike spots on the integument of diseased larvae (Steinhaus and Martignoni).

pecten, any comblike structure or organ (T-B; Leftwich); a comblike stridulating organ on some insects (Leftwich); in certain Lepidoptera, cubital pecten, q.v. (T-B) or an anterior comb of stiff, hairlike scales on antennal scape (Common, in CSIRO); in larval Culicidae (Diptera), the comblike teeth on the ventrolateral portion of the respiratory siphon (Peterson); in adult Hymenoptera, rigid, incurved setae on the basal parts of maxilla and labium (T-B); in pollen-gathering bees (Hymenoptera: Apoidea), the rows of spines on the tarsi (T-B); in many burrowing Hymenoptera, e.g., Sphecoidea, Pompiloidea, and Scolioidea, row of special, long, flattened bristles on the lateral margin of foretarsus (Riek, in Hymenoptera); see pectinate.

pecten epipharyngis, in some larval Chironomidae (Diptera), 3 median scales, lamellae, spines, or rods directly behind labral margin (tormal bar), being smooth or apically pectinate or serrate (Saether).

pecten galearis, in some Orthocladiinae (Diptera: Chironomidae), row of small, sclerotized rods or teeth on dorsal surface of galea just lateral of 2 basiconic pegs and multilobate sensillum (Saether).

pecten hypopharyngis, in larval Chironomidae (Diptera), several transverse rows (or one row to each side in Tanypodinae) of scales, teeth, rods, or spines mesiobasal on hypopharynx (Saether).

pecten labralis, in larval Chironomidae (Diptera), labral lamellae, q.v., when these are formed as long transverse plates with apical teeth (Saether).

pecten mandibularis, in many larval Chironominae and *Odontomesa* (Diptera: Chironomidae), comb of mostly stiff, straight setae on distal mesal side of mandible (Saether).

pectina (pl., **pectinae**), in Coccoidea (Hemiptera: Sternorrhyncha), one of the broad fringed plates of the pygidium (T-B, after Comstock).

pectinase, enzyme in saliva of many phytophagous Hemiptera, causing the disruption of the middle lamellae of the plant cell walls (by hydrolyzing pectin) and aiding penetration of the tissues of the host plant (Chapman).

pectinate, pectinated, pectinatus (Latin), comblike (T-B; R. W. Brown); applied especially to antennae or claws, with even processes like the teeth of a comb (T-B; Borror et al.); see bipectinate and serrate.

pectinate setae, in ♂ Chironomidae (Diptera), lamellate setae of median volsella of foliate type, but with several apical points (Saether).

pectinately, in a pectinate manner (T-B).

pectinatofimbriate, having pectinations that are fringed with hair (T-B).

pectines, 2 moveable processes below the hind legs fixed to the metasternum (T-B); in ♂ and ♀ genitalia, distally pointing rows of comblike teeth lining mesal corium of gonapophyses (Tuxen, after E. L. Smith); in Protura, serrate edges of the abdominal laterotergites, especially of the segments VI and VII (Bellinger, pers. comm.).

pectinifer, in ♂ Lepidoptera, a comb of setae or sensilla on the valva of some Nepticuloidea and Incurvarioidea (Common).

pectiniform, pectinate, q.v. (T-B).

pedal, pertaining to the leg, proleg, or other locomotory structure of an insect (T-B).

pedal line, in larval Lepidoptera, a line extending along the base of the prolegs (T-B).

pedal lobe, in larval Coleoptera, a fleshy, bumplike, nonsegmented rudiment of a leg (Peterson, after Böving and Craighead).

pedal nerve, a nerve controlling a leg (T-B).

pedal tubercle, in larval Lepidoptera, a tubercle on the thoracic and abdominal segments, on the anterior side of the base of the leg or proleg and in a corresponding position on apodal segments (T-B, after Dyar).

pederin, in Coleoptera (Staphylinidae), a complex nonproteinaceous toxic chemical produced by species of *Paederus*, being an amide with

2 tetrahydropyran rings, pederamide and pedaldehyde, causing dermatitis in humans (Frank and Kanamitsu).

pedes, legs or prolegs, q.v. (T-B); see pes (T-B).

pedes raptorii, raptorial legs (T-B).

pedes spurii, prolegs, q.v. (T-B).

pedes spurii A, in pupal Chironomidae (Diptera), whorl of spinules in caudolateral corners of abdominal sterna IV–VIII, usually distinct on IV and absent on VII and VIII (Saether).

pedes spurii B, in pupal Chironomidae (Diptera), caudolateral hump or extension of abdominal segment II and occasionally on abdominal segment III (Saether).

pedicel, pedicellus (Latin) (pl., **pedicelli**), a stalk or stem supporting an organ or other structure (T-B); the second segment of the insect antenna, supporting the flagellum (Chapman); fine duct connecting an ovariole with the oviduct (Chapman); the waist of an ant (Formicidae) or of other Hymenoptera, made up of either one segment (the petiole) or 2 segments (the petiole plus the postpetiole) (T-B, after W. M. Wheeler; Wilson).

pedicel (of halter), in adult Diptera, stalk, q.v., of halter (Harbach and Knight; McAlpine).

pedicellate, supported by a pedicel (T-B); see petiolate and pedunculate.

pedicle, in ♂ Reduviidae (Hemiptera: Heteroptera), the true phallosoma, supported by the basal plates prolongation (ligamentary processes) (transl. "pédicule" Galliard; Tuxen, after Davis).

pediculosis, in man, lousiness, or the abnormal condition caused by the multiplication of lice, *Pediculus humanus* (Phthiraptera: Anoplura); see phthiriasis.

pediculous, lousy; infested with lice, *Pediculus humanus* (Phthiraptera: Anoplura) (T-B).

pedigerous, feet-bearing.

pediment, in adult Culicidae (Diptera), the basal part of a cone, bearing the filament anteriorly (Harbach and Knight).

pedipalpi (sing., **pedipalpus**), pedipalps, q.v. (T-B).

pedipalps, in Arachnida, second pair of appendages of the cephalothorax, corresponding to the mandibles of insects (T-B; Borror et al.).

pedisulcus, in many adult Simuliidae (Diptera: Nematocera), a variably deep notch on the posterior margin of the second tarsomere of the hind leg (Peterson, in McAlpine).

pedium (pl., **pedia**), in larval Scarabaeoidea (Coleoptera), the bare central region of the epipharynx, extending between the haptomerum and haptolachus and limited laterally by the internolateral features of the right and left paria, sometimes marked on the left by the epitorma (T-B, after Böving).

pedogenesis, paedogenesis, q.v. (T-B).

pedotheca (pl., **pedothecae**), in obtect pupal Nematocera and most orthorrhaphous Brachycera (Diptera), pupal cuticle covering the leg (Colless and McAlpine, in CSIRO).

peduncle, pedunculus (Latin) (pl., **pedunculi**), a stalk or petiole (T-B);

a stalklike structure supporting an organ or another structure (T-B); in Auchenorrhyncha (Hemiptera), scape, q.v., of antenna (T-B); the large stalk of the corpora pedunculata of the brain (T-B); in Formicidae (Hymenoptera), a basal or apically narrowed stalk of the petiole (Brown, pers. comm.); see pedunculi.

peduncular, of or pertaining to a peduncle (T-B).

pedunculate, pedunculated, pedunculatus (Latin), set on a stalk or peduncle (T-B); see petiolate.

pedunculated body, corpora pedunculata, q.v. (T-B).

pedunculus (pl., **pedunculi**), in ♂ Tortricidae (Lepidoptera), lateral parts of tegumen, often shaped like rods, extending ventrad from cephaloventral angles of tegumen and articulating with dorsal parts of vinculum (Tuxen, after Diakonoff); see penduncle.

peering movements, movements concerned with judging distance, involving side to side swaying movements of the body with the feet still and the head vertical, but moving through an arc extending 10° or more on either side of the body axis, e.g., grasshoppers and other insects that jump (Chapman).

peg, a short blunt projection (Christiansen and Bellinger).

peg plates, in Gerromorpha (Hemiptera: Heteroptera), minute circular depressions bordered by a shallow rim and filled with a number of subconical pegs, generally found on the head and body, and in some species also on certain leg segments (Andersen).

peg sensillum (of Lauterborn organ), in larval Chironomidae (Diptera), stiff, thick-walled peg at apex of second antennal segment (Saether).

peglike, elongate, cone-shaped, pointed at one end and truncate at the other (T-B).

peglike larva, coniform larva, q.v. (Peterson).

pelagic, inhabiting the open sea; ocean-dwelling (T-B; Borror et al.).

pellicle, in Diaspididae (Hemiptera: Sternorrhyncha: Coccoidea), larval exuviae attached to the puparium (T-B).

pellit, pellitus, covered with long, drooping hairs, irregularly placed (T-B).

pellucid, pellucidate, pellucidus, transparent (T-B).

Peloridioidea, single superfamily within the Coleorrhyncha (Hemiptera), including only the family Peloridiidae, possessing adults with tarsi with fewer than 3 tarsomeres, forewings with many closed cells formed by raised veins, and well developed lateral pronotal expansions (paranota) (Woodward et al., in CSIRO).

pelotons, the balls of fine tracheae in larvae, developed to supply the adult organism (T-B).

pelottae, arolia, q.v. (T-B).

pelta (Latin) (pl., **peltae**), a small shield (T-B; R. W. Brown); in Tubulifera (Thysanoptera), the reduced shield-shaped tergum of abdominal segment I (Stannard); in some ♂ Ascalaphidae and Myrmeleontidae (Planipennia: Myrmeleontoidea), shieldlike, obovate or elongate structure with sensory hairs, situated between apices of parameres (Tuxen, after Tjeder).

peltate, shield-shaped (T-B).

penal, penial, q.v. (Tuxen).

penal claspers, in ♂ Proctotrupidae (Hymenoptera), lateral fringed processes of the genitalia (T-B; Tuxen).

pencil, a little, elongated brush of hair (T-B); in adult Diptera, a group of sensory hairs on the flagellum of the antenna (T-B); see hair pencil, plumose antenna, and verticillate antenna.

pendent, pendulous, pendulus (Latin), hanging (T-B).

penellipse, in the caterpillar proleg, the figure formed when a part less than half of a uniserial circle of crochets is absent (T-B); lateral or mesal penellipse, q.v. (Peterson).

penes, pl. penis, q.v. (T-B).

penial bar(s), in ♂ Ephemeroptera, a simple plate or a pair of arms, supporting the 2 penes (Tuxen, after Brinck); in ♂ *Chloroperla* (Plecoptera), supporting sclerotizations for penis (Tuxen).

penial basal arm, penial bar, q.v. (Tuxen, after Snodgrass).

penial basal plate, in ♂ Ephemeroptera, penial bar, q.v. (Tuxen, after Snodgrass).

penial bulb, in ♂ Psocoptera, endophallus, q.v. (Badonnel).

penial frame, in ♂ Psocoptera, frame of penis formed by the coalesced external parameres (transl. "cadre pénien", Badonnel, in Tuxen).

penial sac, in ♂ Plecoptera, penis, q.v. (Tuxen, after Balinsky).

penial setae, in ♂ Ensifera (Orthoptera), setae on phallic lobes (Ander, in Tuxen).

penial shaft, in ♂ Plecoptera, proximal part of the protruded genital cavity (Tuxen).

penial sheath, in ♂ Corixidae (Hemiptera: Heteroptera), ligamentary processes, q.v. (Tuxen, after Hungerford).

penial spines, in ♂ Ephemeroptera, sclerotized processes of penes (Tuxen, after Kimmins).

penial theca, in ♂ Heteroptera (Hemiptera), phallotheca, q.v. (Tuxen, after Baker).

Penicillata, subclass within the Diplopoda, including the order Polyxenida (Hoffman, in Parker).

penicillate, penicillatus, with a long flexible brush or pencil of hairs, often at the end of a thin stalk (T-B).

penicilli, in ♂ Planipennia, pleuritosquamae, q.v. (Tuxen, after Navás); in ♂ Noctuidae (Lepidoptera), peniculi, q.v. (Tuxen, after Forbes); in bees (Hymenoptera: Apoide), setae forming a brush at the hind tibial apex of adult females, used in spreading components of cell linings (Eickwort, pers. comm., after Michener); in various ♂ Hymenoptera, one-segmented cerci, q.v. (T-B, after J. B. Smith; Brown, pers. comm.); see penicillus.

penicilliform, penicilliformis, shaped like or similar to a small painter's brush or pencil (T-B).

penicillium (pl., **penicillia**), in ♂ *Vindula* (Lepidoptera: Nymphalidae), hairy, conica process at base of valva (Tuxen, after Roepke).

penicillus (pl., **penicilli**), a pencil or brush of hair (T-B); a small setiferous process or bunch of fine hairs at the base of the mandible on the inner margin (Peterson); in some ♂ moths (Lepidoptera), hair pencil, q.v. (T-B); in adult Meliponinae (Hymenoptera: Apidae), a brush, on pollen press of hind tibia (Carpenter, pers. comm., after Kimsey); see penicilli.

peniculi (sing., **peniculus**), in ♂ Noctuidae (Lepidoptera), paired, hairy, lobate processes of lateral margin of tegumen near the articulation of dorsoproximal angle of valva (Tuxen, after Pierce).

penis (pl., **penes**), ♂ intromittent organ which is nonhomologous throughout the Pterygota (Tuxen; Sturm); in Protura, phallus, q.v. (Tuxen, after Prell) or styli, q.v. (Tuxen, after Denis); in Diplura, three- or four-lobed structure around gonopore, divided into phallobase and aedeagus (Tuxen, after Silvestri; von Kéler); in ♂ Archaeognatha and Zygentoma, unpaired organ for sperm transfer (Tuxen); in Ephemeroptera, bilobed, sometimes fused, copulatory organ between genostyles (Tuxen); in Odonata, prophallus, q.v. (Tuxen); in Blatteropteroidea, left epiphallus and phallus (Tuxen, after Peytoureau), apophysis, q.v. (Tuxen, after Chopard), hypophallus, q.v. (Tuxen, after Walker), or phallus, q.v. (Tuxen, after Wesché); in some Isoptera, pointed, but nonsclerotized, membranous, median papilla on intersegmental membrane between abdominal sterna IX and X, on which ductus ejaculatorius opens (Tuxen); in Zoraptera, the hook-shaped unpaired lobe protruding from the posterior end and bearing postuncus at its apex and genital opening at its base (Tuxen, after Paulian); in Plecoptera, the protrusible part of genital cavity modified for mating (Tuxen), supraanal lobe, q.v. Tuxen, after Hagen), or (in *Nemoura*) the apex of subgenital plate (Tuxen, after Wu); in Orthoptera, phallus, q.v. (Tuxen) or (in Caelifera) aedeagus, q.v. (Tuxen, after Chopard); in Embiidina, hypandrium process, q.v. (Tuxen, after Krauss); in ♂ Dermaptera, intromittent organ, single or paired, proximally fused (Tuxen) or distal lobe, q.v. (Tuxen, after Zacher); in ♂ Psocoptera, sclerotized outer end of ductus ejaculatorius, supported by parameres, and bearing radula (Tuxen); in ♂ Psocoptera, endophallus, q.v. (Tuxen, after Chapman); in ♂ Phthiraptera, sclerotized tubular process formed from wall of the endophallus surrounding gonopore (Tuxen, after Ferris; Lyal); in Thysanoptera, aedoeagus + parameres (Tuxen); in Auchenorrhyncha (Hemiptera), phallus, q.v. (Tuxen, after Snodgrass) or aedeagus, q.v. (Tuxen); in Heteroptera (Hemiptera), phallus, q.v. (Tuxen, after Peytoureau) or phallosoma, q.v. (Tuxen, after Ekblom); in Coleoptera, apical (distal), unpaired part of copulatory apparatus, containing terminal portion and orifice of ductus ejaculatorius (Tuxen) or (in Coccinellidae) basal lobe, q.v. (Tuxen, after Verhoeff); in Strepsiptera, exsertile stylet in aedeagus issuing through the hook (Tuxen); in Neuropteroidea, intromittent organ of aedeagus, most often membranous (Tuxen); in *Sialis* (Megaloptera: Sialidae) mediuncus, q.v. (Tuxen, after Berland and Grassé); in ♂ Mantispidae (Planipennia), penisfilum, q.v. (Tuxen, after Ferris); in ♂ Mecoptera (e.g., Bittacidae), intromittent organ of aedeagus (Tuxen); in ♂ Trichoptera, phallus, q.v. (Tuxen);

in Lepidoptera, the whole complex, intromittent organ, derived embryonically from phallus and consisting chiefly of aedeagus and vesica (Tuxen) or referring to aedeagus, q.v., or vesica, q.v., alone (Tuxen); in Diptera, aedeagus, q.v. (Tuxen; McAlpine), membranous parts at its tip (Tuxen), or sclerotizations of the tip often divided up into 2 or 3 tubercles (penis filaments) (Tuxen); in Chironomidae, endophallus, q.v., or pars ventralis, q.v. (Saether); in Siphonaptera, tube enclosed by endophallus and traversed by ejaculatory duct (Tuxen, after Snodgrass), phallosome, q.v. (Tuxen, after Beier), tubus interior, q.v. (Tuxen, after Jordan), aedeagus, q.v. (Tuxen, after Jordan and Rothschild), or endophallus, q.v. (Tuxen, after Landois); in Hymenoptera, the median unpaired part of genitalia, terminating in phallotreme (Tuxen, after Audouin), aedeagus, q.v. (Tuxen, after Hartig; Gauld and Bolton), in *Apis,* endophallus, q.v. (Tuxen, after Snodgrass), or, in Apoidea median remnant of aedeagus (Tuxen, after Snodgrass).

penis accessorius, in ♂ Phasmida, vomer subanalis, q.v. (Tuxen, after Günther).

penis bipartitus, in ♂ Ephemeroptera, penis, q.v. (Tuxen, after Hagen).

penis bulb, a peculiar oval body carried within the upper part of the penis by the drone honey bees (Hymenoptera: Apidae) in the marriage flight (T-B, after Packard).

penis cavity, in ♂ Chironomidae (Diptera), cavity into which the endophallus is folded up when in resting position (Saether).

penis cover, in ♂ Trichoptera, dorsal plate, q.v. (Tuxen).

penis filaments, in ♂ Diptera, sclerotizations of the tip of the intromittent organ often coiled up into 2–3 tubercles (Tuxen).

penis funnel, in ♂ Lepidoptera, anellus, q.v., or manica, q.v. (Tuxen, after Rothschild and Jordan).

penis guard, in ♂ Diptera, aedeagal guide, q.v. (McAlpine).

penis lobe, in ♂ Chironomidae (Diptera), lobe covering endophallus (Saether).

penis lobes, in ♂ Odonata, flagella, q.v. (Tuxen, after Kimmins); in ♂ Ephemeroptera, penis, q.v. (Tuxen, after Eaton); in ♂ Dermaptera, distal lobes, q.v. (Tuxen); in juvenile ♂ Heteroptera, buds in the larval genital chamber, the exterolateral parts of which give rise to parameres, and the internomedian ones to phallus (Tuxen, after Rawat); in adult Heteroptera, lateral and median penis lobes, q.v. (Tuxen, after Baker).

penis opening, in ♂ Heteroptera (Hemiptera), secondary gonopore, q.v. (Tuxen, after Ekblom).

penis plate, in ♂ Siphonaptera, aedeagal apodeme, q.v. (Tuxen, after Jordan and Rothschild) or lamina media, q.v. (Tuxen, after Hopkins and M. Rothschild).

penis pouch, penis sheath, q.v. (T-B).

penis rods, in ♂ Siphonaptera, virga penis, q.v. (Tuxen, after Snodgrass); in ♂ Hymenoptera, parameres, q.v. (Tuxen, after Crampton).

penis sclerite(s), in ♂ Neuropteroidea, parameres, q.v. (Tuxen, after

Withycombe); in ♂ Chironomidae (Diptera), phallapodeme, q.v. (Saether).

penis sheath(s), the layer of membrane which surrounds the aedeagus (T-B); in ♂ Coccoidea (Hemiptera: Sternorrhyncha), a sheathlike, apical prolongation of abdominal segment IX enclosing penis while at rest (Tuxen); in ♂ Auchenorrhyncha (Hemiptera), theca, q.v. (Tuxen, after China); in ♂ Tipulidae (Diptera), aedeagal guide, q.v. (Tuxen, after Wesché); in ♂ Chironomidae (Diptera), phallapodeme, q.v. (Saether); in ♂ Tabanoidea (Diptera), aedeagal sheath, q.v. (McAlpine); in ♂ Syrphidae (Diptera), hypandrium, q.v. (Tuxen, after Fluke); in ♂ Lepidoptera, aedeagus, q.v. (Tuxen, after Rothschild and Jordan), manica + anellus (Tuxen, after Chapman); in ♂ Trichoptera, parameres, q.v. (Tuxen, after McLachlan).

penis tube, in ♂ Siphonaptera, tubus interior, q.v. (Tuxen); in ♂ Chironomidae (Diptera), penis cavity, q.v. (Saether).

penis valve(s), in ♂ Protura, side plates, q.v. (Tuxen); in ♂ Ephemeroptera, penis, q.v. (Tuxen, after Crampton); in ♂ *Agulla* (Raphidioptera: Raphidiidae), hypovalvae, q.v. (Tuxen, after Michener); in ♂ Mecoptera, ventral parameres, q.v. (Tuxen, after Michener); in ♂ Chironomidae (Diptera), phallapodeme, q.v. (Saether); in ♂ Diptera, parts of parameral lobes which may coalesce with intromittent organ in ontogeny (Tuxen) or parameres, q.v. (McAlpine); in ♂ Hymenoptera, parameres, q.v.

penis vesicle, in ♂ Odonata, vesicula spermalis, q.v. (Tuxen, after Imms).

penisfilum (pl., **penisfila**), a threadlike extension of the insect penis (T-B, after Tillyard); in ♂ Zoraptera, long filament with spinelike projections, enclosed by clasping organs (Tuxen, after Denis); in ♂ Heteroptera (Hemiptera), vesica, q.v. (Tuxen, after Baker) or (in Saldidae) processus gonopori (?), q.v. (Tuxen, after Cobben); in ♂ Mecoptera and Planipennia, threadlike extension of penis (Tuxen); in ♂ Lepidoptera, filiform distal part of aedoeagus (Tuxen, after Tillyard).

penisflagellum, in ♂ Heteroptera (Hemiptera), processus gonopori (?), q.v. (Tuxen, after Larsén).

penislobus, in ♂ Blatteropteroidea, hypophallus, q.v. (Tuxen, after Crampton).

penisvalvae, in ♂ Zoraptera, clasping organs, q.v. (Tuxen, after Crampton); in ♂ Neuroptera, parameres, q.v. (Tuxen, after Crampton); in ♂ Hymenoptera, parameres, q.v. (Tuxen, after Crampton).

pennaceous, pennaceus, pennate, pennatus, feathered (T-B).

penniform, featherlike in form (T-B).

Pentac (trade name), a specific miticide; a chlorinated hydrocarbon, decachlorobis-2,4-cyclopentadien-1-yl; slightly toxic to mammals, ♂ rat acute oral LD_{50} greater than 3160 mg/kg (Pfadt).

pentachlorophenol, C_6HCl_5O, a wood preservative, used to control termites (Isoptera) and to protect cut timber from wood-boring insects and from fungal rots; moderately toxic to mammals, acute oral LD_{50} for rats 50 to 140 mg/kg (Pfadt).

pentagon, pentagonum, a five-sided figure with 5 equal or unequal angles (T-B); in ♂ Lepidoptera, fold in the dried diaphragma mistaken for a distinct structure (Tuxen, after Gosse).

pentagonal, five-angled, that is five-sided (T-B).

Pentamera, Coleoptera with all tarsi pentamerous (T-B).

pentamerous, having tarsi each with 5 tarsomeres (T-B).

Pentastomida, class of Arthropoda, including parasitic tongueworms, which are elongate and wormlike, cylindrical or flattened, and ringed, without differentiation of body regions (Borror et al.).

Pentatomoidea, superfamily within the infraorder Pentatomomorpha (Hemiptera: Heteroptera), including including Urostylidae, Cydnidae, Acanthosomatidae, Pentatomidae, Phloeidae, Plataspidae, Scutelleridae, Tessaratomidae and several other (not universally recognized) families, possessing lateral abdominal trichobothria and the scutellum often reaching or surpassing the apex of the clavus, and many families with five-segmented antennae; terrestrial, mostly phytophagous, a few mycetophagous or secondarily predaceous (Schuh; Štys, pers. comm.).

Pentatomomorpha, infraorder within the Heteroptera, including the Pentatomoidea, Coreoidea, Idiostoloidea, Lygaeoidea, Pyrrhocoroidea, Piesmatidae and Aradoidea, characterized by the possession of ventral abdominal trichobothria, except in the Aradoidea (Woodward et al., after Southwood, in CSIRO; Schuh).

Pentazonia, superorder within the subclass Chilognatha (Diplopoda), including the orders Glomerida, Glomeridesmida, and Sphaerotheriida (Hoffman, in Parker).

penultimate, next to the last (T-B).

penultimate sternite, in Dermaptera, last visible abdominal sternum, sternum X in ♂, sternum VIII in ♀ (Tuxen, after Burr).

penultimate ventral sclerite, in Dermaptera, penultimate sternite, q.v. (Tuxen, after Burr).

penunci (sing., **penuncus**), in ♂ Mecoptera, dorsal valves, q.v. (Tjeder, in Tuxen); in ♂ *Nymphes* (Neuroptera: Nymphidae), hypostylus, q.v. (Tuxen, after Crampton); in ♂ *Raphidia* (Raphidioptera: Raphidiidae), parameres, q.v. (Tuxen, after Crampton).

peptide, linear molecule comprising 2 or more amino acids linked by peptide bonds (Allaby).

peptidase, digestive enzyme which splits linkages between amino acids in peptides (Gilmour, in CSIRO).

per-, Latin prefix; through; by; very; entirely (T-B).

per os, peroral, q.v. (Steinhaus and Martignoni).

percipient, perceiving; perceptive (T-B).

percolate, to pass through a porous substance; to filter (T-B).

percurrent, running through the entire length; continuous (T-B).

percussion knob, in certain ♂ *Anacroneuria* (Plecoptera: Perlidae), hammer, q.v. (Tuxen, after Kimmins).

pereion, prothorax, q.v. (T-B).

perennial, continuing for several years (T-B).

perennial colony, in social Hymenoptera, a colony that lasts more than one season (T-B; Eickwort, pers. comm.).

perfect insect, a specimen with all its parts (T-B); adult, q.v. (T-B).

perfoliate, perfoliatus, divided into leaflike plates; applied to antennae with disclike expansions connected by a stalk passing nearly through their centers; also to any part possessing a well-developed leaflike or platelike expansion (T-B).

perforate, perforatus, with holes, especially in a row.

perforate mandible, a mandible possessing a blood channel (Peterson).

pergameneous, pergamentaceous, thin, partly transparent, resembling parchment; parchmentlike (T-B).

peri-, Greek prefix; around; near; enclosing; surrounding (T-B).

periadenian type, in Heteroptera (Hemiptera), omphalian or diastomian type of metathoracic scent glands, with gland cells uniformly distributed in paired or unpaired components of the system without differentiation of the scent reservoir (transl. from "type periadenien" Carayon).

perianal pad, in Diptera larvae, distinctive padlike structure surrounding cleft of anus (Teskey, in McAlpine).

periandrial fold, in Muscomorpha (Diptera), the strong infolding of the integument between the sides of the periandrium and the base of the aedeagus (Griffiths).

periandrial theory, in ♂ Muscomorpha (Diptera), theory that the andrium is the product of the fusion of the gonocoxites, and that the true epandrium is completely lost (McAlpine, after Griffiths).

periandrium (pl., **periandria**), in ♂ Aeolothripidae (Thysanoptera), basal, ring- or double-ring-formed sclerotization (phallobase) of genital apparatus (Tuxen, after de Gryse and Treherne; Heming); in ♂ Auchenorrhyncha (Hemiptera), the bulblike growth of the segmental membrane around base of the aedeagus (Tuxen, after Singh-Pruthi) or theca, q.v. (Tuxen, after authors); in ♂ Muscomorpha (Diptera), genital sclerite formed by the dorsal growth and fusion of the basimeres (gonocoxites) (Griffiths).

periatrial sclerites, in ♀ Culicidae (Diptera), pre- and postatrial plates (Tuxen, after Christophers).

pericardial, around the heart (T-B).

pericardial cavity, pericardial sinus, q.v. (T-B).

pericardial cells, nephrocytes present on the surface of the heart (T-B; Chapman).

pericardial chamber, pericardial sinus, q.v. (T-B).

pericardial cord, in Protura, a longitudinal troughlike filament in the position of the dorsal pulsatory vessel (T-B, after Berlese).

pericardial diaphragm, dorsal diaphragm, q.v. (T-B).

pericarial sinus, dorsal portion of the hemocoel, cut off by the dorsal diaphragm from the perivisceral sinus (T-B; Chapman).

perigynium (pl., **perigynia**), in ♀ Protura, basal part of genital armature carrying basal apodemes (Tuxen).

periintestinal, perivisceral, q.v. (T-B).

perikaryon (pl., **perikarya**), cell body of a nerve cell (Chapman).

perilemma, mesodermal sheath enveloping the brain and ventral nerve cord, consisting of perineurium and neural lamella (Hinton and Mackerras, in CSIRO).

perinaeum (pl., **perinaea**), in ♀ Lepidoptera, portion of tubus analis forming a wall between anal opening and ostium oviductus (Tuxen, after Herold).

perinephric membrane, relatively impermeable membrane enclosing cryptonephridial Malpighian tubules (Chapman).

perineural, situated around a nerve (T-B).

perineural sinus, ventral portion of hemocoel, containing the nerve cord, cut off from the perivisceral sinus by the ventral diaphragm (T-B; Chapman).

perineurium, cellular portion of nerve sheath beneath the neural lamella that passes nutrients from the hemolymph to the nervous tissue (Chapman).

perinuclear, round about or surrounding the cell nucleus (T-B).

period, in the geological time scale, a subdivision of an era.

period of lethal infection, in cases of progessive infection, the time interval between invasion by a microorganism and death of the host (Steinhaus and Martignoni).

periodical, recurring at regular intervals (T-B).

periopods, legs or limbs or appendages for walking in arthropods (T-B, after Snodgrass).

periopticon, lamina ganglionaris, q.v. (T-B).

periphallic organs, in ♂ insects, structures peripheral to median intromittent apparatus (phallic organs) and belonging to abdominal segment IX or other segments, being moveable or immoveable and having a grasping or clasping function (Tuxen, after Snodgrass).

periphallic processes, in ♂ Trichoptera, external apophyses outside the plane of the phallic shield and its adjoining genital chamber membranes (Morse); see strips.

periphallus (pl., **periphalli**), in ♂ Protura, the basal part of the squama genitalis which is subdivided into 2 wings, the basiperiphallus and acroperiphallus (Tuxen); in some ♂ Thysanoptera, complex structures surrounding phallus (epiphallus and parameres) (Tuxen, after de Gryse and Treherne); in ♂ Noctuidae, sclerotization in anellus dorsad of aedoeagus (Tuxen, after Berio).

peripheral, relating to the outer margin (T-B).

peripheral nervous system, an exceedingly delicate network or plexus of nerve fibers and multipolar nerve cells situated in the integument below the epidermis, connected with the sensilla (T-B, after Imms).

peripheral pad, the persistent part of the peripodial membrane (Bugnion).

periphery, the outer margin (T-B).

periplasm, in the insect egg, the bounding layer of protoplasm lying just beneath the vitelline membrane and surrounding the yolk (T-B, after Imms; Chapman).

peripneustic respiratory system, polypneustic respiratory system with

9 functional pairs of spiracles: one mesothoracic and 8 abdominal, e.g., many insect larvae (T-B; Petersen; Chapman, after Keilin).

peripodial cavity, pouch in the embryo in which the rudiment of a future leg or wing developes (T-B); in holometabolous insects, cavity in the larva in which the rudiment of a appendage develops from an imaginal disc before being everted at pupation (Chapman).

peripodial membrane, epidermis lining peripodial cavities (T-B; Chapman).

peripodal sac, peripodial membrane, q.v. (T-B, after Packard).

periproct, telson, q.v. (T-B, after Snodgrass).

perirectal cavity, cavity between perinephric membrane and rectal epithelium containing cryptonephridial Malpighian tubules (Chapman).

perispiracular gland, in larval Diptera, gland associated with spiracle, producing an oily secretion with hydrofuge properties (Chapman).

peristaethium, peristethium, mesosternum, q.v. (T-B, after Smith).

peristalsis, the wave motion of the intestines which moves the gut contents toward the anal extremity (T-B).

peristigmatic gland, perispiracular gland, q.v. (Chapman).

peristoma, peristome, peristomium, the border of the mouth or oral margin (T-B).

peristomal hairs, in adult Diptera, subvibrissal setae, q.v. (McAlpine).

peristomial, of or pertaining to the peristomium (T-B).

peritoneal, of or pertaining to the peritoneum (T-B).

peritoneal envelope, peritoneum, q.v. (T-B, after Comstock).

peritoneal membrane, peritoneum, q.v. (T-B).

peritoneal sheath, the covering of the entire insect ovary in young stages, and sometimes in the adult, consisting of an envelope of adventitious connective tissue; the outer investment of the testicle, containing all the sperm tubes (T-B, after Snodgrass).

peritoneum, a layer of connective tissue lining the hemocoel and enveloping the viscera (T-B); see peritoneal sheath.

peritracheal, surrounding the trachea.

peritreme, the sclerotic plate about any body opening, especially about any spiracle (T-B); in Diptera larvae, margin of spiracular plate (Teskey, in McAlpine); see evaporatorium.

peritrophic, of or pertaining to the peritrophic membrane (T-B).

peritrophic membrane, in some insects, delicate, noncuticular lining of midgut, containing protein and chitin, secreted as a viscous fluid at the anterior end of the midgut or formed by a delamination of the whole surface of the midgut (T-B, after Matheson; Chapman).

perivisceral, around, or about, the alimentary canal and its appendages (T-B).

perivisceral sinus, the central region of the hemocoel, between the dorsal diaphragm and the ventral diaphragm if the latter is present (T-B, after Snodgrass; Chapman).

perivulvar pores, in Diaspididae (Hemiptera: Sternorrhyncha), normally 4 or 5 groups of pores surrounding vulva (Kosztarab and Kozár).

Perlaria, Plecoptera, q.v. (Leftwich).

perlate, beaded; bearing relieved, rounded points in series (T-B; Harris); see ordinate.

Perlodida, hypothesized monophyletic group including the recent order Plecoptera and the extinct order Paraplecoptera (Boudreaux).

Perloidea, superfamily with the infraorder Systellognatha (Plecoptera: Arctoperlaria), including the families Perlodidae, Perlidae, and Chloroperlidae (Zwick, in Hennig); Perlodida, q.v. (Boudreaux, after Handlirsch).

permanent social parasitism, social parasitism, q.v. (Wilson).

Permian Period, last period within the Paleozoic Era, extending between about 270 and 225 million years before the present (Riek, in CSIRO).

Permoplectoptera, Ephemeroptera, q.v. (Boudreaux, after Tillyard).

Permopsocida, extinct suborder of Psocoptera from the Lower Permian, possessing subequal wings with generalized venation, the radial sector (R_s) two-branched, media (M) four-branched, anterior cubitus (CuA) two-branched and with no fusion between the middle sections of the veins, and foretarsi with 4 tarsomeres (Riek, in CSIRO); extinct order of Neoptera from the Permian Period, being the possible stem group of the Psocodea (Hennig).

Permotrichoptera, extinct order of Neoptera (Insecta), including *Platychonista*, regarded as the stem group of the Amphiesmenoptera (Trichoptera + Lepidoptera) (Willmann, in Hennig).

peronea, in insects, clasper, q.v. (T-B, after MacGillivray; Tuxen).

peroral, by way of or through the mouth (Steinhaus and Martignoni).

Perrisoptera, four-winged fossils from the Permian, proposed as a suborder of the Diptera (Riek).

persistent, remaining constantly; always present (T-B).

persistent transmission, plant virus transmission in which the insect vector remains capable of inoculating plants for its entire life, once it has acquired the virus (Nault and Ammar, after Watson and Roberts); see nonpersistent transmission and semipersistent transmission.

personal fitness, an individual's total lifetime effect on the gene pool of succeeding generations through production of one's own offspring (Matthews and Matthews).

personate, personatus (Latin), masked; disguised (T-B; R. W. Brown).

Perthane (trade name), $C_{18}H_{20}Cl_2$, a synthetic insecticide; a chlorinated hydrocarbon; 1,1-dichloro-2,2-bis(p-ethylphenyl)ethane; low mammalian toxicity, oral LD_{50} for rats 8170 mg/kg (Pfadt).

perula (pl., **perulae**), in ♀ Siphonaptera, an enlargement or dilation of the dorsal or terminal end of the bursa copulatrix into which, in some species, one of the penis rods fits during copulation (Rothschild and Traub).

pes (Latin) (pl., **pedes**), tarsus, q.v., or leg, q.v. (T-B).

pessella, 2 small acute processes one in each socket of the hind legs of ♂ Cicadidae (T-B, after Kirby and Spence).

pest management, the control of pest populations by a program that selects and utilizes available control methods so that economic damage is avoided and adverse effects on the agroecosystem are minimized; or the reduction of pest problems by actions selected after the ecology or life systems of the pests are understood and the ecological as well as the economic consequences of these actions have been predicted to be in the best interest of man (Pfadt); see integrated pest management.

pesticide, a chemical that is used to poison and control pests, either animal or plant (Pfadt).

Petanoptera, Mecopteroidea, q.v. (Hennig, after Grassé).

petiolar, of or pertaining to a petiole (T-B).

petiolar area, in adult Apocrita (Hymenoptera), posterior-most of the 3 median areas on propodeum (T-B); see area.

petiolar segments, in adult Formicidae (Hymenoptera), pedicel, q.v. (Gauld and Bolton).

petiolarea, in adult Apocrita (Hymenoptera), petiolar area, q.v. (T-B).

Petiolata, Apocrita, q.v. (T-B; Leftwich).

petiolate, petiolatus (Latin), stalked; placed upon a stalk (T-B).

petiole, petiolus (Latin), a stem or stalk (T-B); in certain Diptera, the slender segment between the thorax and abdomen (T-B); in Apocrita (Hymenoptera), the narrow second abdominal segment behind the propodeum, or the first segment of a 2 segmented pedicel in some Formicidae (T-B; Wilson; Chapman).

petioliform, of the form or shape of the petiole in Hymenoptera (T-B).

petiolus (Latin) (pl., **petioli**), petiole, q.v. (T-B).

petiolule, a small petiole (T-B).

pH, symbol denoting the relative concentration of hydrogen and hydroxly ions in solution, ranging on a scale from 0 to 14, with a pH of 7 being neutral, a higher value being more acidic, and a lower value being more basic (T-B; Tulloch).

phaeism, in butterflies (Lepidoptera), a duskiness in coloration restricted to a limited region (T-B).

phagocyte, phagocytic hemocyte (T-B; Tulloch, after Jones; Chapman); see granular hemocyte and plasmatocyte.

phagocyte of Ogel, granular hemocyte, q.v. (Tulloch).

phagocytic, functioning in phagocytosis (T-B; Chapman).

phagocytic index, in a population of phagocytic cells, the percentage of cells that have taken up particles by phagocytosis (Steinhaus and Martignoni, after Newsome); see avidity index.

phagocytic organs, in *Forficula* (Dermaptera: Forficulidae) and some Orthoptera (e.g., Tettigonioidea and Grylloidea), well-defined aggregates of phagocytes arranged bilaterally either just below the pericardial cells on either side, or on the concave side of the dorsal diaphragm (T-B, after Wardle; Chapman).

phagocytosis, cytoplasmic engulfing of a microorganism or a foreign particle by a cell, especially by phagocytic hemocytes (T-B; Steinhaus and Martignoni; Chapman).

phagostimulant, chemical promoting feeding activity (Chapman).

Phalaenae, a Linnaean term embracing most of the heterocerous Lepidoptera; more specifically applied to the Geometridae (T-B).

phalaenophily, insect-flower pollination syndrome involving small moths (Lepidoptera) (Matthews and Matthews, after Baker and Hurd).

Phalangida, Opilones, q.v. (Borror et al.).

phalanx (pl., **phalanges**), tarsomere, q.v. (T-B); a taxonomic category of uncertain value, similar to tribe (T-B).

phalerated, phaleratus (Latin), perlate, q.v. (T-B; Harris).

phallandrium, in ♂ *Phallopirates* (Heteroptera: Enicocephalidae), a conspicuous bulbous copulatory organ built largely of novel components including the genital plates (Štys).

phallapodeme, in ♂ Diptera, rod-shaped appendage at base of intromittent organ (Tuxen, after van Emden and Hennig); in ♂ Chironomidae (Diptera), strong apodeme articulating with sternapodeme and carrying aedeagal lobes (Saether); paramere, q.v.

phallic, of or pertaining to the phallus (T-B).

phallic apodeme, in ♂ Trichoptera, coalesced anterior parts of phallocrypt and phallobase (Tuxen); in ♂ Diptera, phallapodeme, q.v. (Tuxen, after Crampton).

phallic complex, in ♂ Orthoptera, phallic organs and epiphallus (Tuxen).

phallic lobes, in ♂ Ensifera (Orthoptera), the lobes which compose phallus (Tuxen); in ♂ Phasmida, membranous lobes of copulatory organ (Tuxen, after Snodgrass); in ♂ Grylloblattodea, phallomeres, q.v. (Tuxen, after Snodgrass); see primary phallic lobes.

phallic organ, median intromittent apparatus immediately concerned with the function of coition, arising as median genital outgrowths of abdominal segment IX in contrast to periphallic organs, consisting of phallus or phallomeres and lobes from phallobase (Tuxen, after Snodgrass).

phallic pivot, in ♂ Heteroptera (Hemiptera), the 2 suspensorial apodemes (Tuxen, after Bonhag and Wick).

phallic sclerites, in ♂ Psocoptera, parameres and radula, q.v. (Pearman).

phallic shaft, in ♂ Corixidae (Hemiptera: Heteroptera), ligamentary processes, q.v. (Tuxen, after Griffith).

phallic shield, in ♂ Trichoptera, a sclerotized rim in the phallocrypt membranes at their junction with the phallobase (Morse).

phallic structure, in ♂ Caelifera (Orthoptera), phallic complex, q.v. (Tuxen, after Roberts).

phallicata, in ♂ insects, the distal sclerotized portion of a divided phallus, q.v. (Ross); see aedeagus and distiphallus.

phallite, in ♂ Siphonaptera, hamuli, q.v. (Tuxen, after Jurik).

phallites, in ♂ Siphonaptera, lobes of aedeagus, q.v. (Tuxen).

phallobase, in ♂ insects, proximal part of phallus, in contrast to aedeagus, sometimes a large basal structure supporting aedeagus, sometimes a thecal fold or sheath about aedeagus, sometimes represented only by basal phallic sclerites in wall of genital chamber (Tuxen, after

Snodgrass); also applied to basal part of parameres (sensu Snodgrass) and aedeagus (Tuxen, after Snodgrass); in ♂ Zygentoma, basal part of penis (Tuxen, after Snodgrass); in ♂ Plecoptera, penial shaft, q.v. (Tuxen, after Despax); in some ♂ Phthiraptera, basal apodeme, q.v. (Tuxen, after Schmutz; Lyal); in ♂ Auchenorrhyncha (Hemiptera), basal part of phallus, including connective (Tuxen, after Fennah); in some ♂ Heteroptera (Hemiptera), phallotheca, q.v. (Tuxen, after Bonhag and Wick), phallosoma, q.v. (Tuxen, after Poisson), or complex including articulatory apparatus and phallosoma (Tuxen, after Snodgrass); in ♂ Coleoptera, basal piece, q.v. (Tuxen, after Snodgrass); in ♂ Trichoptera, proximal part of phallus if divided, as distinct from aedeagus (Tuxen, after Nielsen); in ♂ Diptera, basiphallus, q.v. (McAlpine); in ♂ Hymenoptera, gonobase + gonocoxites + volsellae (Tuxen, after Snodgrass).

phallobasis, in ♂ Heteroptera (Hemiptera), phallosoma, q.v. (Tuxen, after Larsén); see phallobase.

phallocrypt, in ♂ insects, pocket of phallobase or wall of genital chamber containing base of aedeagus (Tuxen, after Snodgrass); in ♂ Trichoptera, tubelike depression from which the phallic apparatus arises (Tuxen, after Nielsen); in ♂ Siphonaptera, aedeagal pouch, q.v. (Tuxen).

phallomeres, in ♂ Blatteropteroidea and Grylloblattodea, genital lobes at sides of gonopore when not united to phallus (Tuxen, after Snodgrass) or secondary divisions of primary phallic lobes, laterally parameres, medially mesomeres (Tuxen, after Snodgrass); in ♂ Blatteropteroidea, epiphallus and hypophallus (Tuxen, after Snodgrass); in ♂ Zoraptera, clasping organs, q.v. (Tuxen, after Snodgrass); in ♂ Grylloblattodea, a pair of outgrowths from region of genital aperture (Tuxen).

Phalloneopterata, hypothesized monophyletic group including the Acercaria and Holometabola (Boudreaux).

phallophore, in ♂ Diptera, basiphallus, q.v. (Tuxen; McAlpine).

phallos internus, in ♂ Lithosiinae (Lepidoptera: Arctiidae), well-sclerotized internal part of aedoaegus cephalad of zone (Tuxen, after Birket-Smith).

phallosoma (pl., **phallosomata**), in ♂ Heteroptera (Hemiptera), proximal segment of phallus supported by or incorporating ligamentary process and surrounding ductus seminis proximalis down to ejaculatory reservoir (excluded) or homologous level, if entirely or partly sclerotized known as phallotheca (Tuxen, after Singh-Pruthi); in ♂ Reduviidae (Hemiptera: Heteroptera), improper usage, the true endosoma, the phallosoma being the pedicle supported by basal plate prolongation (Tuxen, after Singh-Pruthi); in ♂ Pentatomomorpha (Hemiptera: Heteroptera), phallotheca, q.v. (Tuxen, after Singh-Pruthi); in ♂ Auchenorrhyncha (Hemiptera), theca, q.v. (Tuxen, after Singh-Pruthi); see phallosome.

phallosoma appendages, in ♂ Heteroptera (Hemiptera), processus phallothecae, q.v. (Tuxen, after Singh-Pruthi).

phallosoma foramen, in ♂ Tingidae (Heteroptera (Hemiptera), basal foramen (Tuxen, after Livingstone).

phallosoma plates, in ♂ Heteroptera (Hemiptera), the sclerotizations of the wall of phallosoma (transl. "Phallosomaplatten" Larsén) (Tuxen).

phallosome, in ♂ Psocoptera, penis, q.v. (Tuxen, after Smithers); in ♂ Heteroptera (Hemiptera), phallus, q.v. (Tuxen, after Christophers and Cragg), phallosoma, q.v. (Tuxen, after Dupuis), or (in Reduviidae), incorrectly, endosoma, q.v. (Tuxen, after Galliard); in ♂ Siphonaptera, the whole intromittent organ, consisting of aedeagus, aedeagal apodeme, and endophallus (Tuxen, after Snodgrass); in ♂ Coleoptera, penis, q.v. (Tuxen); in ♂ Mecoptera, aedeagus, q.v. (Tuxen, after Crampton); in ♂ Diptera, aedeagal guide, q.v. (McAlpine); in ♂ Tipulidae (Diptera), basiphallus, q.v. (Tuxen); in ♂ Culicidae (Diptera), aedeagus, q.v. (Tuxen) or complex consisting of basal pieces, parameres, prosophallus, phallus, and opisthophallus (Harbach and Knight); in ♂ Muscomorpha (Diptera), aedeagus, often including phallapodeme (Tuxen); see phallosome.

phallotheca (pl., **phallothecae**), in ♂ insects, fold or tubular extension of phallobase partly or totally enclosing aedeagus (Tuxen, after Snodgrass); in some ♂ Phthiraptera, fold of phallobase enclosing aedeagus (Tuxen, after Schmutz); in ♂ Heteroptera (Hemiptera), the major and most frequently sclerotized proximal part of phallosoma (q.v.), especially in Pentatomomorpha (Tuxen, after Dupuis); in ♂ Saldoidea and Reduviidae (Hemiptera: Heteroptera), improper usage, sclerotized endosoma (Tuxen, after Cobben, Davis); in ♂ Trichoptera, external side of phallobase (Tuxen).

phallotrema (pl., **phallotremata**), in ♂ insects, distal opening of endophallus, usually at end of aedeagus (Tuxen, after Snodgrass); in ♂ Blatteropteroidea, opening of gonoduct on hypophallus (Tuxen, after Snodgrass); in ♂ Orthoptera, opening of endophallic cavity (spermatophore sac; Tuxen); in ♂ Diptera, gonopore, q.v. (McAlpine).

phallotremal sclerite, in ♂ Integripalpia (Trichoptera), a typically U-shaped sclerite at the gonopore opening of the endophallus (Nielsen).

phallotreme, phallotrema, q.v. (T-B; Chapman); in ♂ Coleoptera, ostium, q.v. (Tuxen, after Snodgrass); in ♂ Reduviidae (Hemiptera: Heteroptera), primary gonopore, q.v. (Tuxen, after Davey).

phallotreme duct, in ♂ Caelifera (Orthoptera), the short wide duct between spermatophore sac and phallotrema (Tuxen).

phallus (pl., **phalli**), in ♂ insects, the unpaired median intromittent organ, including phallobase, aedeagus, endophallus and various processes of phallobase and aedeagus if present (Tuxen, after Snodgrass); in ♂ Protura, distal part of genital armature, retractable into periphallus and consisting of stipes and styli (Tuxen); in ♂ Ephemeroptera, penis, q.v. (Tuxen, after Crampton); in ♂ Plecoptera, penis, q.v. (Tuxen, after Crampton); in ♂ Blatteropteroidea, the unpaired intromittent organ (Tuxen) or pseudophallus, q.v.

(Tuxen, after Beier); in ♂ Orthoptera, the intromittent organ (Tuxen); in ♂ Thysanoptera, the whole genital organ (Tuxen, after de Gryse and Treherne); in ♂ Auchenorrhyncha (Hemiptera), copulatory organ consisting of phallobase (theca + connective) and aedeagus (Tuxen); in ♂ Heteroptera (Hemiptera), the median intromittent organ as a whole, arising post embryologically from internomedian parts (mesomeres) of larval primary phallic lobes following their division, the externolateral parts of which give rise to parameres (Tuxen, after Handlirsch); in ♂ Coleoptera, aedeagus, q.v. (Tuxen, after Snodgrass); in ♂ Mecoptera, aedeagus, q.v. (Tuxen, after Ferris and Rees); in ♂ Trichoptera, the whole copulatory organ, whether divided or not (Tuxen, after Nielsen); in ♂ Diptera, distiphallus, q.v. (Tuxen, after Crampton) or (in Calliphoridae) aedeagus, q.v. (Tuxen, after Séguy); in ♂ Dixidae and some Culicidae (Diptera), the median lobe of phallosome located between the prosophallus and opisthophallus (Harbach and Knight, after Belkin); in ♂ Hymenoptera, penis, q.v. (Tuxen); in ♂ Phthiraptera, penis, q.v. (Tuxen, after Schmutz).

phallus body, in ♂ Caelifera (Orthoptera), proximal parts of phallus (Tuxen).

phanerocephalic substage, in Muscomorpha (Diptera), any phase of the pupa after the eversion of the head (Peterson, after Snodgrass, Wahl).

pharate, cloaked; within the cuticle of a preceding stage (Chapman).

pharate instar, a stage in the development of an insect during which the cuticle has become separated from the hypodermis but has not yet been ruptured or cast off, e.g., a pharate pupa within but separated from the last larval cuticle or a pharate adult within but free from the pupal integument (Leftwich); see coarctate pupa.

pharmacophagous, drug-eating (T-B).

pharyngaris, in adult Diptera, cibarial pump, q.v. (T-B, after Mac Gillivray).

pharyngeal duct, in Hemiptera, cibarium, q.v. (T-B).

pharyngeal filter, in some nonpredaceous larval Nematocera (Diptera), a complex filtering apparatus within the pharynx for straining suspended food particles from the water and then ejecting the excess water from the mouth (Teskey, in McAlpine).

pharyngeal ganglion, corpus cardiacum, q.v. (T-B).

pharyngeal gland, hypopharyngeal gland, q.v. (Chapman).

pharyngeal grinding mill, in larval Stratiomyidae (Diptera), mechanism within the head capsule functioning on the principle of a mortar and pestle, involving sclerotization of pharynx together with its fusion with the tentorial arms (Teskey, after Roberts).

pharyngeal pump, pharynx and associated dilator muscles arising ventrally on the tentorium and dorsally on the frons, these muscles being best developed in sucking insects, e.g., adult Lepidoptera and Hemiptera (T-B; Chapman); in adult Culicidae (Diptera), the bulblike posterior expansion of the pharynx behind the brain and the subesophageal ganglion (Harbach and Knight); see cibarial pump.

pharyngeal sclerite, in larval Muscomorpha (Diptera), tentoropharyngeal sclerite, q.v. (T-B; Teskey, in McAlpine).

pharyngeal skeleton, in larval Muscomorpha (Diptera), the conspicuous sclerotic structure lying in the anterior end of the maggot, and formed of the strongly sclerotized lateral walls of the pump and the walls of the clypeal wings leading back to the antennoocular pouches (T-B; Chapman); see cephalopharyngeal skeleton.

pharyngeal tube, in Phthiraptera, a pair of structures each in the form of a half tube, arising from the floor of the first chamber of the pharynx and fitting closely together to form a tube (T-B, after Imms).

pharyngeal valve, in adult Lepidoptera, a valve within the pharynx (Common, in CSIRO).

pharyngosinusal theca, in larval Muscomorpha (Diptera), tentoropharyngeal sclerite, q.v. (Teskey, in McAlpine).

pharynx, the part of the foregut between the buccal cavity and the oesophagus (T-B; Harbach and Knight; Chapman).

pharynx supports, in larval Diptera, tentorial phragmata, q.v. (Teskey, in McAlpine).

phase, one of the kentromorphic forms of locusts (Orthoptera) and some other insects, e.g., solitary (low-density) phase and gregarious (high-density) phase (Key, pers. comm.); see kentromorphism.

phase gregaria, gregarious phase, q.v. (Key, pers. comm.).

phase solitaria, solitary phase, q.v. (Key, pers. comm.).

Phasmatidea, infraorder of Phasmida, containing the superfamilies Necroscioidea and Phasmatoidea (Kevan).

Phasmatodea, suborder of the Phasmida, including the infraorders Bacillidea and Phasmatidea (Kevan); sometimes misused for the order Phasmida.

Phasmatoidea, in Phasmida, superfamily with the infraorder Phasmatidea, containing the families Bacteriidae and Phasmatidae (Kevan).

Phasmatoptera, Phasmida, q.v. (Borror et al.; Vickery).

Phasmida, mandibulate, phytophagous, exopterygote order within the Neoptera (Insecta), including the walking sticks and leaf insects, having all legs gressorial, with small, well separated coxae, pronotum without large descending lateral lobes, wing rudiments of nymph not reversing their orientation in later instars, and eggs free, thick-shelled, provided with a conspicuous operculum (Key, in CSIRO; Vickery).

Phasmodea, Phasmida, q.v. (Borror et al.).

Phasmoidea, Phasmida, q.v. (Borror et al.).

Phauloptera, Coccoidea, q.v. (T-B, after Laporte).

phenetic, pertaining to phenetic analysis.

phenetic analysis, classificatory analysis in which taxa are grouped on the basis of overall similarity; see numerical phenetics.

pheneticist, an individual who believes that relationships among taxa can be determined on the basis of overall similarity (Mayr).

phenetics, the principles of phenetic analysis.

phenogram, a diagram of relationships among taxa based on overall similarity (Mayr); see cladogram, dendrogram, and phylogenetic tree.

phenol, carbolic acid, q.v. (T-B).

phenolase, an enzyme that oxidizes a phenol to produce a quinone (Gilmour, in CSIRO).

phenology, the study of the impact of climate on the seasonal occurrance of plants and animals (T-B; Allaby).

phenon, a sample of phenotypically similar specimens (Mayr).

phenotype, the totality of characteristics of an individual (its appearance) as a result of the interaction between genotype and environment (Mayr).

phenylalanine, essential amino acid in the diet of insects (Gilmour, in CSIRO).

pheromonal parsimony, multifunctional use of a single chemical as pheromone (Matthews and Matthews).

pheremone, pheromone, q.v. (Tulloch).

pheromone, a chemical substance, usually a glandular secretion, which is used in communication within a species, such that one individual releases the material as a signal and another responds after sensing it (Wilson).

phial, phiala (Latin), a broad, flat vessel; bowl; saucer (R. W. Brown); a small sac which receives fluid for the purpose of increasing the weight of the wing (T-B, after Kirby and Spence).

Philopotamoidea, a superfamily within the Curvipalpia (Trichoptera: Annulipalpia), including the families Philopotamidae and Stenopsychidae (Weaver).

Phleboptera, Hymenoptera, q.v. (T-B).

phlebotomus fever, sand-fly fever, q.v. (Allaby).

phloem, plant tissue, comprising various types of cells, which transports dissolved organic and inorganic materials over long distances within vascular plants, distinguished from xylem by the general absence of thickened cells and by the presence of cells containing areas resembling a sieve (Allaby); see cambium and xylem.

phloem necrosis, disease of elm trees transmitted by *Scaphoideus luteolus* (Hemiptera: Auchenorrhyncha: Cicadellidae) (Borror et al.).

phloeophagy, feeding on phloem tissues of the inner bark (Wood).

phoba (Latin) (pl., **phobae**), curl; tuft (R. W. Brown); among larval Scarabaeoidea (Coleoptera), hairlike, often forked, projections forming a dense fringe at the inner edge or paria of the epipharynx (Peterson, after Böving).

phobotaxis, a reflex action by which an insect turns to avoid an adverse stimulus and by repeated trial and error moves away from it (Leftwich).

phonatome, an individual behavioral song component (Matthews and Matthews).

phonoreceptor, a sense organ responsive to sound (T-B, after Snodgrass).

phonoresponse, upon hearing a noise replying by making one (Matthews and Matthews).

phonotaxis, direct locomotory response to a sound (Matthews and Matthews).

phony peach disease, disease of peach trees caused by a rickettsia and transmitted circulatively by leafhoppers (Hemiptera: Auchenorrhyncha: Cicadellidae) (Borror et al.); see peach X-disease.

phorate, $C_7H_{17}O_2PS_3$, a synthetic insecticide and acaricide, a plant systemic with high contact activity; an organophosphate, O,O-diethyl S-ethylthiomethyl phosphorodithioate; extremely toxic to mammals, oral LD_{50} for rats 2 to 4 mg/kg (Pfadt).

phoresis, phoresy, q.v. (Norris, in CSIRO).

phoresy, a type of relationship in which one organism is carried on the body of a larger organism but does not feed on the latter, e.g., small flies traveling on the backs of dung beetles, small species of Chalcididae carried on the legs of ants (Hymenoptera: Formicidae), and triungulin larval Meloidae (Coleoptera) carried on the bodies of bees and wasps (Hymenoptera: Aculeata) (T-B; Chapman); symbiotic relationship in which one organism associates with another species in order to obtain transportation (Steinhaus and Martignoni); see parasitism.

phoretic copulation, in several groups of wasps (Hymenoptera), copulation in which winged males carry highly modified parasitic females for considerable periods of time (Matthews and Matthews).

Phoroidea, superfamily within the series Aschiza of the division Cyclorrhapha (Diptera: Brachycera), including the Phoridae, Platypezidae, and Sciadoceridae, possessing adults with an arista, wing cell CuP more or less shortened, and preabdomen of ♂ consisting of 6 segments (Colless and McAlpine, in CSIRO; Borror et al.); see Platypezoidea.

phosalone, $C_{12}H_{15}ClNO_4PS_2$, a synthetic insecticide and acaricide, a plant systemic; an organophosphate, S-[(6-chloro-2-oxo-3-benzoxazolinyl)methyl] O,O-diethyl phosphorodithioate; moderately toxic to mammals; acute oral LD_{50} for rats 125 to 180 mg/kg (Pfadt).

Phosdrin (trade name), mevinphos, q.v. (Pfadt).

phosmet, $C_{11}H_{12}NO_4PS_2$, a synthetic insecticide and a acaricide and an animal systemic; an organophosphate, O,O-dimethyl S-phthalimidomethyl phosphorodithioate, moderately toxic to mammals; acute oral LD_{50} for rats 147 to 299 mg/kg (Pfadt).

phosphamidon, a plant systemic insecticide and acaricide; an organophosphate, 2-chloro-N,N-diethyl-3-hydroxycrotonamide, dimethyl phosphate; highly toxic to mammals, acute oral LD_{50} for rats 15 to 33 mg/kg (Pfadt).

phosphatidic acid, intermediate metabolite in the synthesis of triglycerides and phospholipids (Gilmour, in CSIRO).

phospholipids, storgae fats found in cell membranes and yolk of eggs (Chapman).

phosphorescence, in insects, bioluminescence, q.v. (Leftwich).

phosphorescent, luminescent, q.v. (T-B).

phosphorylase, enzyme that breaks down glycogen within the fat body (Gilmour, in CSIRO).

Phostex (trade name), a synthetic insecticide and acaricide; a phosphorous-containing compound, bis(dialkoxyphosphinothioyl) disulfides (alkyl ration 25% isopropyl, 75% ethyl); low toxicity to mammals, acute oral LD_{50} for rats 2500 mg/kg (Pfadt).

photochemical, a chemical compound or substance which by its composition is acted upon by light, e.g., nitrate of silver ($AgNO_3$) (T-B); relating to or produced by the chemical action of light (T-B).

photocyte, cell of a light-producing organ (Chapman).

photofobotaxis, negative phototaxis, q.v. (Tulloch).

photogenic organ, light-producing organ, q.v. (Leftwich).

photogenetic, light-producing, i.e., producing a luminescent glow (T-B).

photogeny, light production (T-B).

photokinesis, the greater activity of an organism in the sunlight than in shade (Tulloch).

photopathy, negative phototaxis, q.v. (T-B).

photoperiod, day length, i.e., the number of hours of daylight during a 24-hour period (Chapman).

photoperiodism, the response of an organism to periodic, often rhythmic, changes either in the intensity of light or, more usually, to the relative length of day (Allaby).

photophilous, light-loving (T-B).

photophobic, averse to light; light-avoiding (T-B).

photoreceptor, a sense organ responsive to light (T-B, after Snodgrass).

phototactic, of the nature of, or relating to, phototaxis (T-B).

phototaxis, orientation to light (T-B); a directional movement in relation to a source of light (Leftwich); see negative phototaxis and positive phototaxis.

phototelotaxis, the spontaneous direct movement of an animal toward shade near at hand (Tulloch); orientation with form vision so that some degree of orientation to light is still possible after unilateral blinding (Matthews and Matthews); see telotaxis.

phototonus, an action whereby the tonus of certain muscles is affected by the presence or absence of light so that an insect will take up a different attitude in the dark from that which it takes up in the light (Leftwich).

phototropic, of or pertaining to phototropism (T-B).

phototropism, reaction to light; response to light (T-B).

phototropotaxis, orientation in which movement is mediated by both eyes so that unilateral blinding causes an organism to move in circles in the light (Matthews and Matthews).

phragma (pl., **phragmata**), partition; wall (R. W. Brown); a partition or dividing membrane or structure (T-B); a projecting structure or internal ridge from the endocuticula to which a muscle is attached, occurring at the junction of tergites, pleurites and sternites, especially in the thorax (T-B, after Wardle); extensive internal plate developed from an antecostal ridge, providing attachment for the large longitudinal flight muscles of the mesothorax and the metathorax

(Chapman); in adult Diptera, media anterior, q.v. (McAlpine); in larval Chironomidae, pleurostoma, q.v. (Saether).

phragma genitale, in ♂ Delphacidae (Hemiptera: Auchenorrhyncha, genital phragm, q.v. (Tuxen).

phragmal processes, in ♂ Heteroptera (Hemiptera), processes of internal wall (diaphragm) of pygophore such as inferior processes, q.v., superior processes, q.v., suspensorial apodemes, q.v. (Tuxen, after Dupuis) which mark the sites of muscle insertions for the parameres.

phragmanotum, postnotum, q.v. (T-B).

phragmatal, of or pertaining to a phragma (T-B).

phragmina, antecostal suture, q.v. (T-B, after MacGillivray).

phragmocyttares, social wasps (Hymenoptera: Vespidae), in which the combs of the nest are wholly or partly supported by the covering envelope (T-B); see stelocyttares and poecilocyttares.

phragmocyttarous, pertaining to nests, and especially wasp nests (Hymenoptera: Vespidae), in which combs are attached laterally to the inner surface of a baglike envelope (Wilson).

phragmosis, the habit exhibited by insects and other animals of closing the entrances to nests and burrows with portions of the body (Tulloch), e.g., ants (Hymenoptera: Formicidae) and termites (Isoptera), usually in the soldier caste (Wilson).

phragmotic head(s), in soldier termites (Isoptera), e.g., *Cryptotermes* (Kalotermitidae), truncated stopperlike heads used for plugging nest entrances (Gay, in CSIRO; Krishna, pers. comm.).

Phryganaeoidea, superfamily within the infraorder Plenitentoria (Trichoptera: Integripalpia), including the family Phryganeidae and Phryganopsychidae (Weaver).

Phryneida, Amblypygi, q.v. (Borror et al.).

Phrynichida, Amblypygi, q.v. (Borror et al.).

Phrynides, Amblypygi, q.v. (Borror et al.).

Phthiraptera, apterous, dorsoventrally flattened, exopterygote order within the Neoptera, including the suborders Amblycera, Ischnocera, Rhynchophthirina, and Anoplura, being ectoparasites of birds and mammals that spend their entire life on the host (Tulloch; Calaby, in CSIRO).

Phthiriapterida, Phthiraptera, q.v. (Boudreaux).

phthiriasis, a diseased condition of the skin caused by sucking lice (Phthiraptera: Anoplura) (T-B); see pediculosis.

phthisaner, in ants (Hymenoptera: Formicidae), a pupal ♂ in which the wings are suppressed and the legs, head, thorax and antennae remain abortive owing to the extraction of the juices of the larval or semipupal stage by the ectoparasite *Orasema* (Hymenoptera: Chalcidoidea: Eucharitidae) larva (T-B, after W. M. Wheeler).

phthisergate, in ants (Hymenoptera: Formicidae), a pupal worker parasitized by *Orasema* (Hymenoptera: Chalcidoidea: Eucharitidae), which is unable to pass to the imaginal stage; an infraergatoid form (T-B, after W. M. Wheeler).

phthisodinergate, a pupated soldier ant (Hymenoptera: Formicidae), that never develops into an adult because of parasitism (Tulloch).

phthisogyne, in ants (Hymenoptera: Formicidae), a form arising from a ♀ larva under the same conditions as a phthisaner, q.v. (T-B, after W. M. Wheeler).

phyla, pl. of phylum, q.v. (Borror et al.).

phylacobiosis, a form of symbosis exhibited by *Camponotus mitarius* (Hymenoptera: Formicidae), which nests in the hills of termites and seems to be on friendly terms with them (T-B, after Wasmann).

phyletic, pertaining to a line of descent (Mayr); see phylogeny.

phyletic evolution, anagenesis, q.v.

phyletic weighting, character weighting, q.v. (Mayr).

phylliform, leaf-shaped (T-B).

phyllobombycin, a metabolite of chlorophyll found in the feces of certain larval Lepidoptera (Tulloch).

Phyllioidea, in Phasmida, superfamily within the Bacillidea, containing the family Phylliidae, known as leaf insects or walking leaves (Kevan).

phyllonome, a larval leaf or petiole mine (Hering); see mines.

phyllophagous, leaf-feeding (T-B); see herbivorous and phytophagous.

Phylloptera, Phasmida, q.v. (Leftwich); see Phyloptera.

Phylloxeroidea, superfamily proposed for the Phylloxeridae and Adelgidae (Hemiptera: Stornorrhyncha), both generally placed in the Aphidoidea (Ilharco and Van Harten, after Heie).

phylogenetic, relating to phylogeny (T-B).

phylogenetic analysis, establishing the relationships among living organisms along the lines of organic evolution; see cladistic analysis, paleontological method, and phenetic analysis.

phylogenetic classification, cladistic classification, q.v. (T-B).

phylogenetic systematics, cladistics, q.v. (Hennig).

phylogenetic tree, a diagrammatic presentation of inferred lines of descent, based on paleontological, morphological, and other evidence (Mayr); see cladogram, dendrogram, and phenogram.

phylogenetics, the principles of phylogenetic analysis.

phylogeny, the evolutionary history of a group of organisms (Mayr).

phylogram, phylogenetic tree, q.v. (Mayr); see dendrogram, cladogram, phenogram, and phylogenetic tree.

Phyloptera, a supraordinal term proposed to include all the net-veined orders, e.g., Orthoptera, Dermaptera, etc. (T-B; Leftwich); see Phylloptera.

phylum (pl., **phyla**), one of the major divisions of the animal kingdom, e.g., phylum Arthropoda (T-B; Borror et al.).

physergate, large worker ants (Hymenoptera: Formicidae), capable of egg production, but used mainly for honey storage (Tulloch, after Gaul).

physical control, control of pests by physical means such as heat, cold, electricity, sound waves, and so on (Pfadt); see mechanical control.

physical gill, in aquatic insects, a bubble or film of air acting as a gill (Chapman); see plastron.

physiographic barriers, dividing lines between distinct groups of organisms arising from the formation of the land, e.g., the Rocky Mountains (T-B).

physiography, physical geography; the surface structure of the earth, as mountains, oceans, etc. (T-B).

physiologic species, physiological species, a group of a given species differentiated from other groups apparently structurally identical by its life history and physiologic activities (habitat, food plants, etc.) (T-B); see cryptic species and host race.

physiopathology, the study of abnormal function, involving pathological alteration of bodily function (Steinhaus and Martignoni).

physogastric, having a swollen abdomen (T-B).

physogastry, the swelling of the abdomen to an unusual degree due to the hypertrophy of fat bodies, ovaries, or both (Wilson).

physonome, a larval blister mine; a blotch mine with the epidermis wrinkled or inflated and arched over the mine (Hering).

Physopoda, Thysanoptera, q.v. (T-B).

phytogeography, plant geography, i.e., the study of the distribution of plants over the earth's surface (T-B); see biogeography and zoogeography.

Phytophaga, Chrysomeloidea, q.v. (T-B; Britton, in CSIRO).

phytophagous, phytophagus (Latin), feeding in or on plants (T-B; Gauld and Bolton).

phytophagy, feeding on plants (Matthews and Matthews).

phytophilous, phytophilus, plant loving; applied to species that live on plants (T-B).

phytophily, the love of plants, e.g., in ants (Hymenoptera: Formicidae), visiting, or in part living in, certain plants (T-B, after W. M. Wheeler).

Phytophthira, Aphidoidea, q.v. (T-B).

phytoplankton, plankton consisting of microscopic plants, especially diatoms (Allaby); see zooplankton.

phytosaprophagous, feeding on dead or decaying plant material, e.g., many species of Collembola and Zygentoma, the many larval Diptera, and numerous species of Coleoptera (Leftwich).

phytosuccivorous, sap-sucking; sap-eating (T-B).

phytotoxic, poisonous to plants (Gauld and Bolton).

pi group, in larval Lepidoptera, subventral group, q.v., of setae (Peterson, after Fracker).

pian, yaws, q.v. (Adkins, pers. comm.).

piceous, piceus, black (T-B, after Kirby and Spence; R. W. Brown).

picine, picinus, black, with a bluish oily luster (T-B).

pick, in Psocoptera, lacinia, q.v. (T-B).

Pierce's disease, disease of grapes caused by a rickettsia transmitted circulatively by leafhoppers (Hemiptera: Auchenorrhyncha: Cicadellidae) (Borror et al.).

piercing-sucking mouthparts, mouthparts with mandibles or maxillae or both (modified into stylets) fitted for piercing plant or animal tissue, e.g., Hemiptera, Anoplura (Phthiraptera), adult Siphonaptera, and some adult Diptera.

Piesmatoidea, superfamily of Heteroptera within the infraorder Pentatomomorpha recognized by some authors to contain the single family Piesmatidae (Schuh).

pieza, mandibulate-sucking mouthparts of Hymenoptera (T-B, after Fabricius).

Piezata, Hymenoptera, q.v. (T-B, after Fabricius).

pigment, any coloring matter or material that gives a color appearance by reflecting certain wave lengths of light and absorbing others, e.g., melanin, biliverdin, ommochrome, anthraquinone, carotinoid, and pterine (T-B; Leftwich); pigmentary colors.

pigment bodies, in scales of Pieridae (Lepidoptera), cluster of pigment, or pigments, in elliptical or rod shaped structures in the intertrabecular sinuses (Downey and Allyn).

pigment cell, primary pigment cell, q.v., secondary pigment cell, q.v., or retinula cell, q.v. (T-B; Chapman).

pigment layer, in the insect compound eye, primary pigment cells, forming the iris (T-B, after Needham).

pigmental borders, in ♂ Plecoptera, dorsal processes, q.v. (T-B, after Mosely).

pigmentary, of or pertaining to pigment (T-B).

pigmentary colors, colors derived from the presence of substances of a definite chemical composition (pigments, q.v.), which absorb some light waves and reflect others as colors, these substances being the products of metabolism and excretory in nature (T-B, after Imms); see T-B); see iridescence.

pigmented, colored; more heavily colored (T-B).

pilaceroris (pl., **pilacerores**), in Diaspididae (Hemiptera: Sternorrhyncha: Coccoidea), gland spine, q.v. (T-B, after MacGillivray).

pilae cornulae basis (sing., **pila cornulae basis**), in ♂ Zygaena (Lepidoptera: Zygaenidae), basal spines in coronula of aedoeagus (Tuxen, after Loritz).

pile, a hairy or furlike covering; thick, fine, short, erect hair, giving a surface appearance like velvet (T-B).

pileolus (pl., **pileoli**), in ♀ Blatteropteroidea, sclerite at base of valvulae superiores, a vestige of abdominal sternum VIII (Tuxen); in ♀ Phasmida, gonangulum, q.v. (Tuxen, after Cappe de Baillon); in ♀ Ensifera (Orthoptera), gonangulum, q.v. (Tuxen, after Cappe de Baillon); in ♀ Caelifera (Orthoptera), basivalvula, q.v. (Tuxen, after Chopard); in ♂ Zygaena (Lepidoptera: Zygaenidae), hood-shaped part of vinculum (Tuxen, after Loritz).

pileus, in Heteroptera (Hemiptera), anal tube, q.v. (Tuxen, after Kullenberg).

pilifer(s), in some adult Philorheithridae and Stenopsychidae (Trichoptera), fingerlike processess bearing sensory hairs arising above the base of the maxillary palp (Riek, in CSIRO; Mey, pers. comm., after Neboiss); in pupal and adult Lepidoptera, lateral projection on each side of labrum (T-B; Common, in CSIRO).

piliferous, piligerous, bearing hair; covered with fine hair or pile (T-B).

piliferous tubercle, verruca, q.v. (T-B, after Comstock).

piliform, hairlike in shape or form (T-B).

piliger, in Lepidoptera, pilifer, q.v. (T-B).

pill millipedes, members of the order Glomerida (Diplopoda) (Borror et al.).

pillared eye, in adult Ephemeroptera, turbanate eye, q.v. (T-B).

pillbugs, terrestrial Isopoda (Crustacea) that are capable of rolling up into a ball (Borror et al.).

pilose, pilous, pilosus (Latin), covered with fine, long setae or hairs (T-B, after Kirby and Spence).

pilosity, a covering of fine, long hair (T-B).

pin seta, in Isotomidae (Collembola), found on the fourth antennal segment, a slightly subapical seta modified with a wide base and sharp, needlelike point, often with a secondary seta (Christiansen and Bellinger).

pin-cushion gall, bedeguar gall, q.v. (T-B).

pinaculum (pl., **pinacula**), in larval Lepidoptera, a small, flat or slightly elevated chitinized area bearing from one to 4 setae (T-B, after Tillyard; Peterson).

pincers, claspers or gonopods of ♂ insects for grasping ♀ when mating (T-B; Leftwich); in Dermaptera, cerci, q.v., used in defense (Leftwich); (pincerlike) jaws, q.v. (Leftwich).

pineapple gall, spruce cone-gall, q.v. (Leftwich).

pinene, $C_{10}H_{16,}$ a volatile, insect-repelling terpene found in trees and a component of the defense secretion of certain termites (Isoptera) (Chapman).

pinguis (Latin), fat (T-B; R. W. Brown); see physogastric.

pink eye, in cattle, an infectious disease of the eyes in which the eye and its protective membranes become inflammed (Pfadt).

pinna (Latin) (pl., **pinnae**), feather; wing; leaflet (T-B; R. W. Brown); in Orthoptera, one of oblique ridges running to the median line in the posterior femora (T-B).

pinnate, pinnatus (Latin), feathered; plumed; winged (T-B; R. W. Brown); cleft, like the wings of *Alucita* (Lepidoptera: Alucitidae); with markings resembling a feather (T-B); bipectinate, q.v. (T-B).

pinnatifid, divided into feathers, as when wings are cleft nearly to the base (T-B).

pinning block, a small, step-shaped block of wood, metal, plastic, or other material, each step with a fine hole of a standard depth; used to place insects or labels on pins at a standard height.

piperonyl butoxcide, a synergist for pyrethrum and rotenone; a[2-(2-butoxyethoxy)ethoxyl]-4,5-methylenedioxy-2-propyltoluene; relatively nontoxic to mammals, acute oral LD_{50} for rats 7500 to 12,800 mg/kg (Pfadt).

piping, the sound emitted by young honeybee queens (Hymenoptera:

Apoidea) after their emergence that induces return calls ("quacking") from other virgin queens still in the royal cells and stimulates swarming behavior by the workers (Wilson).

pirimicarb, a systemic insecticide; a carbamate, 5,6-dimethyl-2-dimethylamino-4-pyridinyl dimethylcarbamate; moderately toxic to mammals, acute oral LD_{50} for rats 147 mg/kg (Pfadt).

Pirimor (trade name), pirimicarb, q.v. (Pfadt).

Piroplasmea, class of protozoans which are parasitic in a range of vertebrates where they infect red and white blood cells, and cells of the liver (Allaby); see babesioses.

piroplasmosis, any disease produced by Piroplasmea (T-B; Tulloch).

pistazinus, yellowish green, with a slight brownish tinge (T-B).

pitchy, piceous, q.v. (T-B).

pitfall trap, trap for ground-dwelling arthropods, consisting of a steep-sided container that is sunk into the ground so that the opening is level with the surface of the ground, being either baited or not (Borror et al.).

placoid, platelike, q.v. (T-B).

placoid receptor, plate organ, q.v. (Leftwich).

placoid sensillum, plate organ, q.v. (T-B).

plaga (Latin) (pl., **plagae**), zone; region (R. W. Brown); a spot, stripe or streak of color (T-B).

plagate, marked with plagae (T-B).

Plagioptera, group of pterygote insects including the extant order Odonata and the extinct order Paleodictyoptera, Megasecoptera, and Meganisoptera, characterized by a reduced filum terminale and wing veins tending to curve posteriorly at tips (Hennig, after Lemche; Boudreaux).

Plagiopterata, Plagioptera, q.v. (Boudreaux).

plague, bubonic plague, q.v., or sylvatic plague, q.v. (Dunnet, in CSIRO).

plaited, plicate, q.v. (T-B; Harris).

planate, planatus (Latin), with flattened surface (T-B).

plane, planus (Latin), even; level; flat; plain; clear; smooth (T-B; R. W. Brown).

plane of symmetry, the median plane (T-B).

planidial larval, planidium, q.v. (Gauld and Bolton).

planidiform larva, planidium, q.v. (Peterson).

planidium, in parasitic Diptera (e.g., Acroceridae, Nemestrinidae, and Tachinidae) and parasitic Hymenoptera (e.g., Perilampidae) with hypermetamorphosis, free-living, flattened, first-instar larvae (T-B, after Imms, Borror et al.).

planipennate, flat-winged (T-B).

Planipennia, endopterygote order within the Neoptera, including the superfamilies Myrmeleontoidea, Mantispoidea, Hemerobiioidea, Coniopterygoidea, and Osmyloidea, possessing mouthparts of the simple biting type, antennae with many articles, compound eyes always present, generally 2 pairs of large, equal or subequal, many-veined wings, often divided into many small cells by numerous crossveins; larvae with distinctive sucking jaws and modified alimentary canal; pupae decticous, within a silken cocoon (T-B; Riek, in CSIRO; Hennig).

plankton, minute aquatic organisms that drift with water movements, generally having no locomotive organs, including phytoplankton and zooplankton (T-B; Allaby); see benthos and nekton.

Planoneoptera, hypothesized monophyletic group including Plecoptera, Zoraptera, Acercaria and Holometabola (Boudreaux, after Hamilton).

plant louse, member of the Aphidoidea or Psylloidea (Hemiptera: Sternorrhyncha); see aphid and jumping plant louse.

planta (Latin) (pl., **plantae**), sole of the foot (T-B; R. W. Brown); in larval Lepidoptera, the retractible lobe at the end of the abdominal proleg on which the crochets are borne (T-B; Peterson; Chapman); in pollen-gathering Hymenoptera, sarothrum, q.v. (T-B); see euplantulae, plantar surface, and unguitrator plate.

plantar, of or pertaining to the planta (T-B).

plantar lobes, in some adult Hymenoptera, euplantulae, q.v. (Gauld and Bolton).

plantar region, in some adult Diptera, ventral surface of arolium merged with the distal end of the unguitractor plate (McAlpine).

plantar surface, of the tarsi of insects, that surface which is applied to the ground in walking (T-B); in general, the lower surface of the tarsus (T-B).

planthopper, a member of the superfamily Fulgoroidea (Hemiptera: Auchenorrhyncha) (Metcalf).

plantigrade, walking on the plantar surface of the tarsus, not on the claws alone (T-B).

plantula (pl., **plantulae**), euplantula, q.v. (T-B; Lefwich) or pulvillus, q.v. (T-B); see arolium.

planum terminale (pl., **plana terminalia**), in ♂ *Zygeana* (Lepidoptera: Zygaenidae), sharply cut-off end of uncus and socii (Tuxen, after Loritz).

plaque(s), in Collembola, relatively large discrete area of integument apparently formed by fusion of usual tubercles (Christiansen and Bellinger); in some Naucoridae, e.g., *Criphocricos* (Hemiptera: Heteroptera), the small leathery hemelytron (T-B).

plasma, the liquid part of the hemolymph (T-B; Chapman).

plasmatic, of, pertaining to or composed of the plasma of the hemolymph (T-B).

plasmatocyte, phagocytic hemocyte with a basophilic cytoplasm containing large numbers of ribosomes, mitochondria and vacuoles of various sizes (Tulloch, after Yeager, Jones; Chapman); see elongated plasmatocyte, eoplasmatocyte, eoplasmatocytoid, macroplasmatocyte, macroproleucocytoid, mesoplasmatocyte, microplasmatocyte, and multiramous plasmatocyte.

Plasmodiidae, family of parasitic protozoans, including the single genus *Plasmodium,* which undergo schizogony in the red blood cells, as well as in the cells of other tissues, in a vertebrate host, being transmitted by a mosquito vector (Diptera: Cullicidae) (Allaby); see malaria.

Plasmodium, the genus of the malarial protozoan (Plasmodiidae), including blood-cell parasites (T-B); see malaria.

plasmolysis, contraction of the living cell through loss of water (T-B).

plastic, formative; in an easily molded condition; of animals, capable of change in characteristics, or in a changeable state (T-B).

plasticisation, disruption of the weak bonding between the protein and chitin microfibrils so that they can slide with respect to each other, allowing the cuticle to be stretched (Chapman).

plasticity, the capacity for being formed, molded or developed (T-B).

plastron, in aquatic insects, a film of air on the outside of the body, providing an extensive air-water interface for gaseous exchange (Chapman); in Aphelocheiridae (Hemiptera: Heteroptera: Naucoroidea), a physical gill formed by a dense mat of microtrichia on the ventral body surface (Schuh, pers. comm.); see physical gill.

plastron plate, in pupal Chironomidae (Diptera), e.g., Aphroteniinae, Podonominae, and Tanypodinae, apical, porous plate on thoracic horn (Saether).

plate, any broad flattened piece (T-B); in Diaspididae (Hemiptera; Sternorrhyncha: Coccoidea), one of the thin projections of the pygidium (T-B, after Comstock); in ♂ Cicadelloidea (Hemiptera: Auchenorrhyncha), genital plate, q.v. (T-B, after J. B. Smith).

plate (of ostium), in ♀ Geometridae (Lepidoptera), sterigma, q.v. (Tuxen, after Pierce).

plate of sternum X, in Embiidina, sinistral or dextral paraproct in ♀, sinistral paraproct in ♂ (Tuxen, after Imms).

plate of tergum X, in ♂ Embiidina, hemitergite, q.v. (Tuxen, after Imms).

plate organ, olfactory sensillum in the form of a flat plate commonly found on antennae (T-B; Chapman).

plate-shaped ovipositor, in some ♀ Heteroptera, e.g. most Pentatomoidea, ovipositor with fused, reduced, and often dorsoventrally compressed gonapophyses (Štys, pers. comm.); see laciniate ovipositor.

platelet, a little plate or sclerite of chitin in a membrane (T-B).

platform, in ♂ Pentatomoidea (Hemiptera: Heteroptera), hypandrium, q.v. (Tuxen, after McDonald).

Platydesmida, order within the Helminthomorpha (Diplopoda), including the families Platydesmidae and Andrognathidae, possessing tergites with a median groove and usually pink in color (Borror et al.; Hoffman, in Parker).

platyform larva, plate-shaped larva, e.g., water penny (Coleoptera: Psephenidae) (Peterson; Borror et al.); see onisciform larva.

Platyoptera, an obsolete ordinal name, meaning flat and broad-winged, included Isoptera, Psocoptera, and Embiidina (T-B; Leftwich).

Platypezoidea, superfamily within the series Aschiza of the infraorder

Muscomorpha (Diptera: Brachycera), including the Platypezidae and Phoridae (McAlpine); see Phoroidea.

Plecoptera, mandibulate, exopterygote order within the Neoptera (Insecta), with membranous wings and aquatic nymphs (T-B; Riek, in CSIRO).

Plecopterida, hypothesized monophyletic group including the recent orders Embiidina and Plecoptera, and the extinct order Paraplecoptera (Boudreaux); see Plecopteroidea.

Plecopteroidea, group proposed to include the extant orders Embiidina and Plecoptera (Hennig); see Plecopterida.

Plectoptera, Ephemeroptera, q.v. (T-B, after Packard; Borror et al.); Plecoptera, q.v. (T-B); genus within the family Blattellidae (Blattaria) (Borror et al.).

plectrum, in sound production, scraper, q.v. (Chapman).

plegma (pl., **plegmata**), in larval Scarabaeoidea (Coleoptera), a single fold pertaining to the plegmatium and proplegmatium (T-B, after Böving).

plegmatium (pl., **plegmatia**), in larval Scarabaeoidea (Coleoptera), a lateral paired space with a plicate, somewhat sclerotized surface, bordered by marginal spines with acanthoparia, with one plegma inside of each spine (T-B, after Böving).

pleiotropy, the capacity of a gene to affect several characters, i.e., several aspects of the phenotype (Mayr).

Pleistocene Epoch, epoch within the Quaternary Period, extending between about 1 million and 15,000 years before the present (Riek, in CSIRO).

plenary powers, special powers granted to the International Commission of Zoological Nomenclature (ICZN) (Mayr).

Plenitentoria, infraorder within the Integripalpia (Trichoptera), including the superfamilies Phryganaeoidea and Limnephiloidea, possessing larvae with a prosternal horn (Weaver); see Brevitentoria.

pleometrosis, in Formicidae (Hymenoptera), primary polygyny, q.v. (Tulloch; (Wilson).

pleon, abdomen, q.v. (T-B).

plerergate, in Formicidae (Hymenoptera), replete, q.v. (T-B; Tulloch).

plesiobiosis, in animals, a primitive form of association approaching symbiosis (T-B); in Formicidae (Hymenoptera), the close proximity of 2 or more nests, accompanied by little or no direct contact between the colonies inhabiting them (Wilson).

plesiomorphic, relatively primitive in comparing 2 or more homologous character states.

plesiomorphy, an ancestral character state (Hennig); see apomorphy.

plesiotype, hypotype, q.v. (T-B, after Banks and Caudell); any specimen identified with a described or named species by a person other than the describer (T-B, after J. B. Smith).

plethosphragis, in Lepidoptera, a second sphragis formed on a ♀ already bearing a sphragis from a previous copulation (Tuxen).

pleura, pl. of pleuron, q.v. (T-B).

pleuradema (pl., **pleurademae**), pleural apophysis, q.v. (T-B, after MacGillivray).

pleurademina, a pleural apophyseal pit, q.v. (T-B, after MacGillivray).

pleural, pertaining to the pleura, or lateral sclerites of the body (T-B; Borror et al.).

pleural arch, in adult Siphonaptera, a caplike structure, situated on top of the pleural wing process, largely composed of resilin, being the site of energy storage preceding the jump (Lewis, pers. comm.).

pleural apophyseal pit, the external depression marking the point of origin of the peural apophysis, usually located at the lower end of the pleural suture (Harbach and Knight).

pleural apophysis, the internal arm of the pleural ridge (T-B, after Snodgrass; Chapman).

pleural areas, in some Apocrita (Hymenoptera), the 3 spaces on the propodeum between the lateral and pleural carinae (T-B); the metameric divisions of the pleural region, q.v. (T-B).

pleural arm, pleural apophysis, q.v. (T-B).

pleural carina, in Apocrita (Hymenoptera), the ridge along the exterior margin of the propodeum (T-B).

pleural coxal process, coxifer, q.v. (T-B, after Snodgrass; Harbach and Knight).

pleural furrow, pleural suture, q.v. (T-B, after MacGillivray).

pleural membrane, membranous portion of pleuron, between the tergum and sternum, especially on abdominal segments (Harbach and Knight; McAlpine); in adult Simuliidae (Diptera), anepisternal membrane, q.v. (McAlpine).

pleural muscles, paradorsal muscles, q.v. (T-B).

pleural plate, in Helotrephidae (Hemiptera: Heteroptera), proepimeral lobe occupying most of the propleural area (Papáček, Tonner, and Štys, after Esaki and China).

pleural process, pleural wing process, q.v. (Chapman); coxifer, q.v. (McAlpine).

pleural region, the podial region, or ventrolateral parts of the body on which the limbs are implanted, metamerically divided into segmental pleural areas (T-B, after Snodgrass).

pleural ridge, the internal ridge formed by the pleural suture, bracing the pleuron above the leg, or between the coxal articulation and the wing support (T-B, after Snodgrass; Chapman); see pleural apophysis.

pleural ridge fold, in Siphonaptera, a longitudinal ridge running down the center of the pleural ridge, bending anteriorly, which forms the point of origin for various muscles (Rothschild and Traub).

pleural rod, in Siphonaptera, a vertical or oblique rod usually separating the mesepisternum from the mesepimeron, at least partly detached from the pleural wall (Rothschild and Traub).

pleural sulcus, pleural suture, q.v. (Chapman).

pleural suture, the external groove of the pleural ridge, separating the episternum from the epimeron (T-B, after Snodgrass).

pleural thread, in adult Culicidae (Diptera), a strand of cuticle extending from the pleural apophysis to a small projection at the upper end of the mesopleural ridge (Harbach and Knight).

pleural wing process, the produced dorsal margin of the pleuron, at the upper end of the pleural ridge, which serves as a fulcrum for the movement of the wing (T-B; Chapman).

pleural wing recess, in adult Ephemeroptera, a deep, cup-shaped thick-walled cavity in the wing base, opening downward (T-B, after Needham).

pleurergate, replete, q.v. (T-B).

pleurifera, pleural wing process, q.v. (T-B, after MacGillivray).

pleurite(s), a lateral or pleural sclerite (Borror et al.); in ♂ Noctuidae (Lepidoptera), paired sclerites in abdominal segment IX ring, between tegumen and dorsal ends of vinculum (Tuxen, after Forbes).

pleurites (8th and **9th),** in ♀ Heteroptera (Hemiptera), ventral laterotergites, q.v. (Tuxen, after Christophers and Cragg).

pleuritocava (sing., **pleuritocavum**), in some ♂ Mantispidae, Myrmeleontidae, and Nemopteridae (Planipennia), eversible pockets or sacs between preapical segments (Tuxen, after Tjeder).

pleuritosquamae (sing., **pleuritosquama**), in some ♂ Myrmeleontidae (Planipennia), paired external structures in pleurites of abdominal segments VII or VI and VII (Tuxen, after Tjeder).

pleurocoxal, of or pertaining to the pleuron and coxa together (T-B).

pleuron (pl., **pleura**), in the thorax of pterygote insects, the subcoxal sclerotizations above, before and behind the coxa (T-B, after Snodgrass); the lateral region of any segment of the body, commonly of the thoracic segments (T-B).

pleuropod, pleuropodium, q.v. (Hinton and Mackerras, in CSIRO).

pleuropodia (sing., **pleuropodium**), in the insect embryo, temporary appendages of the first abdominal segment, functioning as glandular organs secreting an enzyme that helps dissolve the shell of the egg and to facilitate hatching of the insect (T-B; Leftwich; Chapman).

pleuropodite, pleuron, q.v. (T-B).

pleuroprocessi, in ♂ Heteroptera (Hemiptera), superior lateral process, q.v. (Tuxen, after Crampton).

pleurosquamae, in ♂ Planipennia, pleuritosquamae, q.v. (Tuxen, after Tjeder).

pleurosternal, of or pertaining to the pleurosternum (T-B).

pleurosternal suture, in adult Coleoptera (excl. Curculionoidea), suture separating prosternum from proepisternum (Britton, in CSIRO).

pleurosternite, laterosternite, q.v. (T-B).

pleurosternum, coxosternum, q.v. (T-B).

pleurostict, in some Scarabaeidae (Coleoptera), e.g., subfamilies, Melolonthinae, Rutelinae, and Dynastinae, having at least some of the abdominal spiracles situated on the abdominal sterna so that at least the last pair are not covered by the elytra (T-B; Britton, in CSIRO); see laparostict.

pleurostoma, the region of the subgena above the mandible (T-B, after Snodgrass; Chapman).

pleurostomal, of or pertaining to the pleurostoma (T-B).

pleurostomal margin, in larval Coleoptera, lateral marginal thickening of each epicranial half between the dorsal and ventral mandibular articulations (Peterson, after Böving and Craighead); see pleurostoma.

pleurostomal sulcus, the part of the subgenal suture above the mandible (Chapman).

pleurostomal suture, pleurostomal sulcus, q.v. (T-B, after Snodgrass).

pleurotergite, in adult Diptera, laterotergite, q.v., of postnotum (T-B, after Curran, Crampton; Colless and McAlpine, in CSIRO; Harbach and Knight); a sclerite containing both pleural and tergal elements (Borror et al.).

pleurotrochantin, in adult *Tipula* (Tipulidae), *Plecia* (Bibionidae), and Culicimorpha (Diptera: Nematocera), a small pleurite of katepimeral origin (T-B, after Crampton; McAlpine).

pleuroventral line, the line of separation between the pleural region and the venter, lying mesad of the limb bases, but obscured when the latter are fused with the sterna (T-B, after Snodgrass).

pleurum, pleuron, q.v. (T-B); in ♂ Diptera, basiphallus, q.v. (Tuxen, after Snodgrass).

pleustonic, of or pertaining to the air-water interface, e.g., the Gerridae (Hemiptera: Heteroptera) are pleustonic (Andersen).

plexus (Latin), braided; plaited; interwoven (R. W. Brown); applied to a knotlike mass of nerves or tracheae (T-B).

plica (pl., **plicae**), a fold or wrinkle (T-B).

plica analis, claval furrow, q.v., of wing (T-B).

plica anojugalis, jugal fold, q.v., of wing (T-B).

plica basalis, basal fold, q.v., of wing (T-B).

plica centripetalis (pl., **plicae centripetales**), in ♂ Lithosiinae (Lepidoptera: Arctiidae), a usually well-sclerotized fold from dorsal part of basis valvae extending mesad into diaphragma (Tuxen, after Burket-Smith).

plica jugalis, jugal fold, q.v. (T-B, after Snodgrass).

plical lobe, in adult Hymenoptera, claval lobe, q.v. (Gauld and Bolton).

plica oralis (pl., **plicae orales**), in Protura, Collembola, and Diplura (Entotrophi), a fold connecting the labrum and labium and covering the mandible and maxilla (Tuxen).

plica vannalis, claval furrow, q.v. (T-B, after Snodgrass).

plical vein, in winged insects, the concave unbranched seventh longitudinal vein system (P), originating on the cubital plate (when present), lying in a plical furrow not to be confused with the claval furrow of Neoptera (Ross et al., after Hamilton); variously second cubitus (Cu_2) or first anal vein (1A) of Comstock and Needham; postcubitus or first postcubitus (PCu) of Snodgrass; see cubitus posterior.

plicate, plicatus (Latin), folded; with folds; impressed with striae to produce the appearance of having been folded or pleated (T-B; Harris); see explicate and striate.

plications, folds, e.g., folds on the hind wings of Orthoptera (T-B).

plicatura, (pl. **plicaturae**), in adult Aleuropteryginae (Planipennia: Coniopterygidae), a small, exserted and articulated organ found on some abdominal sternites (Tjeder).

Plicipennia, Trichoptera, q.v. (T-B, after Latreille).

Pliconeoptera, Orthopterodida, q.v. (Boudreaux, after Hamilton).

Plictran (trade name), cyhexatin, q.v. (Pfadt).

Pliocene Epoch, last epoch within the Tertiary Period, extending between about 11 and 1 million years before the present (Riek, in CSIRO).

plumate, plumatus, plumose, q.v. (T-B).

plumbeous, plumbeus (Latin), lead-colored, i.e., bluish-grey; (T-B, after Kirby and Spence).

plume, in ♂ Siphonaptera, vexillum, q.v. (Tuxen, after Hubbard).

plume scale, in adult Culicidae (Diptera), one of a set of erect and usually long linear scales which together with the wing vein to which they are attached somewhat resemble a plume feather (Harbach and Knight, after Patton and Evans).

plumiliform, plumose, q.v. (T-B).

plumose, plumosus (Latin), featherlike (T-B; Borror et al.).

plumose antennae, antennae in which flagellomeres (antennomeres) bear whorls of setae, e.g., ♂ Culicidae (Diptera) (T-B; Borror et al.); see pencil.

plumose hairs, feathery hairs; hairs furnished with threadlike branches, as featherlike unicellular processes of the body wall (T-B, after Snodgrass).

plump, with full, rounded outlines, but not obese (T-B).

plumule, in adult Syrphidae (Diptera), produced posteroventral margin of subalare (McAlpine).

plumules, in ♂ Lepidoptera, specialized androconia (T-B).

plumulose, plumose, q.v. (T-B).

pluri-, Latin prefix; many (T-B).

plurichaetosis, in some Collembola, the presence of supplementary setae in addition to those forming the basic pattern (Christiansen and Bellinger).

pluridentate, with many teeth (T-B).

plurilobed, with many lobes (T-B).

plurisegmental, with many segments (T-B).

plurisetose, bearing many setae (T-B).

pluteus (Latin) (pl., **plutei**), in ♂ *Zygaena* (Lepidoptera: Zygaenidae), raised ridge on which uncus and socii insert (Tuxen, after Loritz).

pm scales, in larval Chironomidae (Diptera), paramedian scales, q.v. (Saether).

pneumatisation, replacement of liquid by gas in the tracheal system immediately following ecdysis and in the embryonic insect (Chapman).

pneumophysis (pl., **pneumophyses**), in ♂ *Apis* (Hymenoptera: Apidae), cornua, q.v. (Tuxen, after Snodgrass).

pneustocera, breathing horns; erroneously applied to the prolongations of the ostiolar peritreme in Berytidae (Hemiptera: Heteroptera) (T-B).

pnystega, in Odonata, applied by Charpentier to a part of mesonotum (T-B, after J. B. Smith); a scale or plate covering the spiracles of the mesopleura (T-B, after Kirby and Spence).

pocket makers, in Hymenoptera, pouch makers, q.v. (Eickwort, pers. comm.).

pockets, in Aleyrodidae (Hemiptera: Sternorrhyncha), a pair of invaginations extending cephalad from the submedian part of the seventh abdominal suture (Russell).

poculiform, goblet-shaped, i.e., hollow, cylindrical, with a hemispherical base, the sides at top straight (T-B).

poculum (Latin), cup; goblet (R. W. Brown); in ♂ Phasmida, subgenital plate, q.v., consisting of abdominal sternum IX (Key, in CSIRO).

podeon, in adult Hymenoptera, petiole, q.v. (T-B).

podeum, podeon, q.v. (Leftwich).

podex (Latin), fundiment; anus (R. W. Brown); the pygidium or hind part of the abdomen of an insect, consisting of the last 2 or 3 segments sometimes fused together or modified for specific functions (Leftwich); in ♂ Strepsiptera, proctiger, q.v. (Tuxen, after Kirby).

podial region, pleural region, q.v. (T-B).

podical plates, paraprocts, q.v. (T-B; Tuxen); in ♀ Plecoptera, subanal plates, q.v. (Tuxen, after Crampton).

podilegous, in bees (Hymenoptera: Apoidea), having pollen baskets on the legs (Tulloch).

podite, a limb segment of an insect or other arthropod which has independent musculature (T-B, after Snodgrass; Leftwich).

podocyte, medium to large, very thin, flattened hemocyte having from 3–10, pointed, nonpseudopodial cytoplasmic extensions found in certain Lepidoptera and in some Diptera (Tulloch, after Yeager, Jones); see stellate cell.

Podogonata, Ricinulei, q.v. (Borror et al.).

podomere, podite, q.v. (T-B; Leftwich).

podshaped body, in ♂ Heteroptera (Hemiptera), phallosoma, q.v. (Tuxen, after Ekblom).

podotheca, that part of the pupa that covers the legs of the future adult (T-B).

Poduroidea, superfamily within the suborder Arthropleona (Collembola), including the families Poduridae and Onychiuridae, possessing several small setae on prothorax (Wallace and Mackerras, in CSIRO).

poecilandry, having more than one form of ♂ (Tulloch).

poecilocyttares, social wasps (Hymenoptera: Vespidae) that build their combs around the branch or other support covered by the envelope (T-B); see stelocyttares and phragmocyttares.

poecilogeny, a form of larval polymorphism in certain Diptera, in which there is more than one form, certain of the forms being paedogenetic and others developing normally into winged sexual adults (T-B).

poecilogony, as used by entomologists, the coexistence of 2 or more larval forms of the same sex (Tulloch); see poecilogeny.

poecilogyny, having more than one form of ♀ (Tulloch).

poikilothermal, of poikilothermic animals (T-B).

poikilothermic, cold-blooded, i.e., the body temperature rising or falling with ambient temperatures (T-B; Borror et al.).

poikilothermous, poikilothermic, q.v. (T-B).

point, a small triangle of stiff paper, used in mounting small insects (Borror et al.).

poisers, in adult Diptera, halteres, q.v. (T-B).

poison, venom, q.v. (Leftwich; Chapman).

poison duct, in ♀ aculeate Hymenoptera, tube connecting venom reservoir with bulb of sting (Chapman); in larval Atharicidae, Pelecorhynchidae, and Tabanidae (Diptera), duct of venom glands opening subapically on the anterior edge of the blade of the mandible (Teskey, in McAlpine).

poison glands, in certain Diptera (Asilidae and Empididae) and Heteroptera (e.g., *Platymerus*), salivary glands, q.v. (T-B; Chapman); in ♀ aculeate Hymenoptera, abdominal glands producing venom that is discharged through the sting (T-B; Chapman); in larval Athericidae, Pelecorhynchidae, and Tabanidae (Diptera), glands within the head capsule whose duct opens subapically on the anterior edge of the blade of the mandible (Teskey, in McAlpine).

poison sac, in ♀ aculeate Hymenoptera, the saclike reservoir for venom produced by the poison glands (T-B; Chapman).

poison seta, a hollow seta through which certain insects discharge an irritating venom from poison gland cells (T-B, after Snodgrass).

poisoned honey, honey poisonous to man, produced in New Zealand by bees (Hymenoptera: Apidae) feeding on honeydew from *Scolypopa australis* (Hemiptera: Auchenorrhyncha: Fulgoroidea: Ricaniidae) when it feeds on tutu (*Coriaria arborea* Lindsay). (O'Brien and Wilson, in Nault).

polar body, in the insect egg, one of the daughter nuclei of the primary oocyte, with very little cytoplasm, resulting from meiotic divisions of the nuclear material in maturation (T-B; Tulloch; Chapman).

polar chemical, a chemical compound composed of molecules with a dipole (a pair of equal an opposite charges separated by a small distance), such as water, ethyl alcohol, and salt solutions (Pfadt).

polar granules, granules, rich in RNA, within the pole plasm that differentiate during oogenesis (Chapman).

polar nucleus, nucleus resulting from the fusion of 2 polar bodies that degenerates except in the case of polyembryony (Chapman).

polarity, the condition of having poles (T-B); see character polarity.

polarized light, light in which the waves are distributed in a particular plane (Chapman).

pole, either end of an axis (T-B).

pole cells, at the start of embryonic development in Diptera and some Coleoptera and Hymenoptera, certain cells of the posterior end of the egg from which the primitive germ cells are derived (T-B; Chapman).

pole plasm, at the start of embryonic development in Diptera and some Coleoptera and Hymenoptera, an area of cytoplasm at the posterior end of the egg differentiated from the rest and containing polar granules (Chapman).

polex, pygidium, q.v. (T-B).

politus, polished; smooth shiny (T-B; Harris, after R. W. Brown, and Marchant and Charles); see glabrous, micans, and nitid.

pollen basket, in bees (Hymenoptera: Apoidea), a concave, smooth space on posterior tibia, fringed with hairs and functioning to hold collected pollen, q.v. (T-B; Chapman).

pollen brush, scopa, q.v. (T-B; Leftwich).

pollen comb, in adult bees (Hymenoptera: Apoidae), scopa, q.v. (Leftwich); antenna cleaner, q.v. (Leftwich), or pecten on hind tarsus, q.v. (Eickwort, pers. comm., after Snodgrass).

pollen compressor, pollen press, q.v. (Leftwich).

pollen plate, corbicula, q.v. (T-B).

pollen press, in bees (Hymenoptera: Apoidae), process proximal on basitarsus of hind legs used to press pollen into pollen basket on outer surface of tibia (Chapman).

pollen storers, bumble bee species (Hymenoptera: Apidae) that store pollen in abandoned cocoons and feed it to larvae by regurgitation (Wilson); see pouch makers.

pollenophagous, pollen-eating (T-B).

pollex (pl., **pollices**), a thumb (T-B); the stout fixed spur at the inside of the tip of the tibia (T-B); in ♂ Lepidoptera, digitate process at anal angle of cucullus (Tuxen, after Pierce).

pollex hamuli, in ♂ Siphonaptera, small lateral outgrowth on outer side of basal half of hamulus, fitting into recess of distal arm of abdominal sternum IX (Tuxen, after Smit).

pollicate, pollicatus, produced inwardly into a short, bent spine or thumb, as a tibia (T-B).

pollination, transfer of pollen (the ♂ germ cells) from the stamens to stigma of a flower (Borror et al.); see cross-pollination and self-pollenation.

pollinia, pollen masses of flowers (T-B); specialized packets in Orchidaceae (and Asclepiadaceae), containing pollen grains, which adhere to pollinating insects in a variety of locations characteristic of each given orchid species (Matthews and Matthews).

polliniferous, pollinigerous, formed for collecting pollen; pollen bearing (T-B).

pollinose, pollinosus (Latin), covered with a loose, mealy, often yellow dust like the pollen of flowers; fine meal (T-B; Harris, after R. W. Brown, and Jaeger); see farinaeous, farinose, pruinose, pulverulent, and rorulent.

pollinosity, a pollinose covering (McAlpine); see pruinescence.

polster, in ♀ Auchenorrhyncha (Hemiptera), ventral surface of py-gofer (Tuxen).

polus bursae (pl., **poli bursae**), in ♀ Lepidoptera, cephalic pole of fundus bursae (Tuxen, after Petersen).

poly-, Greek prefix; many (T-B).

polyandry, the condition of one ♀ having numerous ♂ mates (T-B).

polybasic, with many bases; applied to genera originally founded on a number of species (T-B).

polycalic, describing a subterranean termite (Isoptera) nest with mul-tiple calies (Noirot, in Krishna and Weesner).

Polychaeta, class of annelid worms possessing distinct metameric seg-mentation and bristly parapodia (Allaby).

polychaete, a member of the Polychaeta.

polychromatic, many colored (T-B).

Polydesmida, order within the superorder Helminthomorpha (Diplopoda), the members of which possess a more or less flattened body with 18–22 segments with lateral carinae, and lack eyes (Borror et al.).

polydomous, having many abodes or nests; applied to ants when one colony has several nests (T-B).

polyembryonic, pertaining to polyembryony (T-B).

polyembryony, the production of several to many embryos from a single egg, especially in parasitic insects, e.g., *Halictoxenos* (Strep-siptera: Stylopidae), *Aphelopus* (Hymenoptera: Dryinidae), and *Platy-gaster* (Hymenoptera: Platygasteridae) (T-B; Chapman).

polyethism, division of labor among members of a colony (Wilson).

polygamous, mating with many females (T-B).

polygamy, the condition of a single ♂ having many ♀ mates (T-B); the state in which an individual has 2 or more mates, none of which mates with other individuals, including polygyny and polyandry (Matthews and Matthews).

polygenic, of a character, controlled by several or numerous genes (Mayr).

polygonal, polygonous, many angled (T-B).

polygoneutic, in insects, several brooded (T-B).

polygynous, in social insects, having more than one egg-laying ♀ in a colony (T-B); see monogynous.

polygyny, the coexistence in the same colony of 2 or more egg-laying queens (Wilson); see primary polygyny and secondary polygyny.

polyhedral, many sided or many angled (T-B).

polyhedron (pl., **polyhedra**), crystallike inclusion body (enclosing a number of polyhedrosis virus particles) produced in the cells of tis-sues affected by certain insect viruses, usually formed in the nuclei of the host cells (Steinhaus and Martignoni).

polyhedrosis, a virus disease of certain insects characterized by the formation of polyhedral inclusions (polyhedra) in the tissues of the infected insect (Steinhaus and Martignoni); see nucleopolyhedrosis.

polylectic, among bees (Hymenoptera: Apoidea), gathering pollen from many kinds of flowers (Riek, after Linsley, in CSIRO); see monolectic and oligolectic.

polymorphic, polymorphous, exhibiting polymorphism (T-B).

polymorphism, the condition of having several forms in the adult (T-B); the simultaneous occurrence of several discontinuous phenotypes or genes in a population, with the frequency even of the rarest type higher than can be maintained by recurrent mutation (Mayr); in social insects, the coexistence of 2 or more functionally different castes within the same sex (Wilson); in ants (Hymenoptera: Formicidae), the occurrence of nonisometric growth occurring over a sufficient range of size variation within a normal mature colony to produce individuals of distinctly different proportions at the extremes of the size range (Wilson).

Polyneoptera, hypothesized monophyletic group of exopterygote Neoptera, including the extant orders Plecoptera, Embiidina, Blattaria, Isoptera, Dermaptera, Orthoptera, Zoraptera, and Phasmida, and the extinct orders Paraplecoptera, Protorthoptera, Caloneurodea, Glosselytrodea, Protelytroptera, and Protoblattodea (Hennig, after Martynov; Boudreaux); see Paraneoptera.

Polyneopterata, Polyneoptera, q.v. (Boudreaux).

Polyneura, group of Diptera, including the Tipulidae, Trichoceridae, Cylindrotomidae, and Limnobiidae, hypothesized to be the sister-group of the Oligoneura (Hennig); see Tipulomorpha.

polynominal nomenclature, a system of nomenclature consisting of a scientific designation of a species through more than 2 words, being the antecedent of the Linnaean system of "binomial" nomenclature (Mayr).

Polyphaga, suborder of Coleoptera, including the superfamilies Staphylinoidea, Hydrophiloidea, Eucinetoidea, Dascilloidea, Scarabaeoidea, Byrrhoidea, Buprestoidea, Dryopoidea, Elateroidea, Cantharoidea, Dermestoidea, Bostrichoidea, Lymexyloidea, Cleroidea, Cucujoidea, Tenebrionoidea, and Chrysomeloidea, possessing adults with prothorax lacking notopleural sutures, hind wings lacking an oblongum cell, hind coxae moveable, not fused to metasternum and not dividing the basal abdominal sternite into 2 lateral pieces, testis not tubular and coiled, ovarioles acrotrophic; and larval mandibles always with a mola (Britton, in CSIRO; Lawrence, in Parker).

polyphagia, polyphagy, q.v. (T-B).

Polyphagoidea, superfamily within the Blattaria, including the family Polyphagidae, usually included within the Blaberoidea (Hennig, after Princis).

polyphagous, eating many kinds of food (T-B); feeding on a variety of different foods or parasitizing a number of different hosts, but not completely omnivorous (Leftwich).

polyphagy, eating everything, i.e., the condition of being unspecialized as to food (T-B); condition of accepting a wide variety of foods, but showing decided preferences (Matthews and Matthews).

polyphyletic, a term applied to a composite taxon whose members are derived from 2 or more ancestral sources, i.e., not being of a single immediate line of descent (T-B; Hennig; Mayr); see monophyletic and paraphyletic.

polyphyly, the unnatural grouping together of taxa derived from 2 or more phylogenetically separate lines; see monophyly and paraphyly.

polyploid, having a nuclear complement of homologous chromosomes in an integral multiple (greater than 2) of the haploid number (Mayr); see diploid and haploid.

polypneustic lobes, in certain larval Diptera (e.g., third-instar *Glossina,* Glossinidae), 2 heavily sclerotized lobes on the terminal segment of the abdomen, each of which is crossed by 3 longitudinal bands of perforations leading into the tracheal system (T-B; Chapman).

polypneustic respiratory system, respiratory system with at least 8 functional spiracles on each side, including hemipneustic, holopneustic, and peripneustic respiratory systems, q.v. (T-B; Chapman, after Keilin); see apneustic repiratory system and oligopneustic system respiratory.

polypod larva, caterpillar, q.v. (T-B); larvae of Lepidoptera, some Mecoptera, and Tenthredinidae (Hymenoptera), with abdominal prolegs in addition to thoracic legs (T-B; Peterson; Chapman); see apodous larva and oligopod larva.

polypod phase, in the insect embryo, a phase in which the embryo has acquired its complete segmentation and full number of appendages, and in which the other organs are further advanced (T-B, after Imms).

polypodeiform larva, cylindrical, segmented, endophagous larva of many Proctotrupoidea and Cynipoidea (Hymenoptera), possessing paired, fleshy, ventral processes of approximately equal length on many of the thoracic and abdominal segments (Gauld and Bolton); see polypod larva.

polypodous, having many feet like Myriapoda (T-B); see polypod larva.

polysaccharide, any of a group of carbohydrates that decompose by hydrolysis into more than 3 molecules of monosaccharides (T-B).

polyspermy, entrance of more than one spermatozoon into one ovum (Tulloch).

polytene chromosome, giant, cablelike chromosome, containing many identical chromosomes closely associated along their lengths, formed by the repeated duplication without division (White, in CSIRO).

polythalamous gall, a gall containing several developing larvae in separate compartments, e.g., hedgehog oak gall, q.v. (T-B, after Comstock; Leftwich); see monothalamous gall.

polythetic, of taxa, possessing a majority of a set of characters (Mayr).

polytopic, occurring in different places as, for instance, a subspecies composed of widely separated populations (Mayr).

polytrophic, having many trophi (trophocytes) (T-B); polyphagous, q.v. (Leftwich);

polytrophic egg tube, polytrophic ovariole, q.v. (T-B, after Snodgrass).

polytrophic ovariole, in Dermaptera, Phthiraptera, and throughout the holometabolous orders (excl. Siphonaptera), an ovariole with trophocytes enclosed in the follicles with each oocyte (T-B, after Imms; Chapman).

polytypic, containing 2 or more taxa in the immediately subordinate category, as a genus with several species or a species with several subspecies (Mayr); see monotypic.

Polyxenida, order of Diplopoda, the members of which possess 13 pairs of legs, soft integument, body hairs forming long lateral tufts, and are 2–4 mm in length (Borror et al.).

Polyzoniida, order within the Helminthomorpha (Diplopoda), including the families Polyzoniidae, Hirudisomatidae, Siphonocryptidae, and Siphonotidae (Hoffman, in Parker).

poma (pl., **pomata**), in ♂ Noctuidae (Lepidoptera), transverse midventral sclerite between cephalocaudal ends of valvae (Tuxen, after Berio).

Pompiloidea, superfamily within the suborder Apocrita (Hymenoptera), including the Pompilidae and Rhopalosomatidae, possessing adults with spiracle cover lobe of pronotum margined with close fine hairs, hind wing without closed basal cells, and lateral pronotum and mesopleuron (or prepectus) overlapping and with considerable free movement, the lower portion of the pronotal lobe being rounded (Riek, in CSIRO); included within the Vespoidea (sensu Gauld and Bolton, after Brothers).

pone, behind (the middle) (T-B).

pons (pl., **pontes**), in ♂ Pyralidae (Lepidoptera), band of secondary sclerotization across fultura superior (Tuxen, after Bleszynski).

pons cerebralis, protocerebral bridge, q.v. (T-B).

pons coxalis, in ♂ *Ptilostomis semifasciata* (Trichoptera: Phryganeidae), parameral bridge, q.v. (Tuxen, after Snodgrass).

pons glomerulus, protocerebral bridge, q.v. (T-B).

pons parameralis, in ♂ Siphonaptera, transverse sclerite linking the parameres (Tuxen, after Günther).

pons valvularum, in ♀ Orthoptera, the sclerotized part of the fused dorsobasal part of inner valvulae (Tuxen).

ponticulus (pl., **ponticuli**), in ♂ Caelifera (Orthoptera), the bridge connecting dorsal aedeagal valves (Tuxen); frenulum, q.v. (T-B).

ponticulus basilaris, in ♂ Heteroptera (Hemiptera), ductifer, q.v. (Tuxen, after Singh-Prithi) or ponticulus transversalis, q.v. (Tuxen, after Ashlock).

ponticulus medianalis (pl., **ponticuli medianales**), in ♂ Heteroptera (Hemiptera), dorsal extension of ductifer joining it to ponticulus transversalis (Tuxen, after Davis).

ponticulus transversalis, in ♂ Heteroptera (Hemiptera), large dorsal and rodlike transverse superior connection between the 2 basal plates (Tuxen).

pooter (British), aspirator, q.v.

population, a group of individuals of the same species set in a frame that is limited and defined with regard to both time and space (Steinhaus and Martignoni); local population, q.v. (Mayr).

population density, the number of individuals of one population per unit area or volume (Steinhaus and Martignoni).

porcate, porcatus (Latin), with several parallel, longitudinal ridges with deep, broad sulcations (T-B; Harris); see canaliculate, carinate, costate, cristate, striate, and sulcate.

pore, porus (Latin), any small round opening on the surface of the cuticle (T-B, after Kirby and Spence); see puncture.

pore-bearing plate, in Hyocephalidae (Hemiptera: Heteroptera), an ovoid structure bearing pores on each side of the abdominal sternum III (Woodward et al., in CSIRO).

pore canals, channels of the cuticula beneath the seta of other external part of many sense organs (T-B, after Snodgrass); fine channels running through the cuticle at right angles to the surface (Chapman); the erroneous name given formerly to the protoplasmic upgrowth from an underlying epithelial cell (T-B, after Wardle).

pore plate, plate organ, q.v. (T-B, after Folsom and Wardle).

porettes, in Aleyrodidae (Hemiptera: Sternorrhyncha), minute structures resembling, and associated with, disk pores (Russell).

poriferous, punctate, q.v. (T-B; Harris).

poriform, resembling a pore in shape (T-B).

porose, porosus (Latin), **porous,** having pores (T-B; Harris).

porous areas, in ♀ ticks (Acari: Ixodida), a pair of depressions on the dorsal surface of the basis capituli, made up of minute open pores (T-B, after Matheson).

porous plate, in pupal Chironomidae (Diptera), plastron plate, q.v. (Saether).

porphyrin, a tetrapyrole in which the pyroles form a ring, being the basis of cytochromes and hemoglobins (Chapman).

porrect, extending foward horizontally, e.g., porrect antennae (T-B; Borror et al.); of the head, projecting (T-B) or prognathous, q.v. (Peterson).

portal of entry, in invertebrate pathology, point at which the invading microbe enters the body of an animal (Steinhaus and Martignoni).

porus, in adult Chironomidae (Diptera), orifice, q.v. (Saether).

position precedence, all other things being equal, the nonmandatory use of position in a work (page or line) by a first reviser in giving precedence to a name, nomenclatural act, or spelling, or by an author in designating a type species (ICZN).

positional orientation, remaining in one position, maintaining it by compensating for disturbances (Matthews and Matthews, after Jander).

positive phototaxis, movement toward a light source (Chapman); see negative phototaxis.

positive tropism, tropism in which the stimulus attracts (T-B, after Wardle).

post-, Latin prefix; after; behind (T-B).

post mortem, after death (Steinhaus and Martignoni).

postabdomen (pl., **postabdomina**), the modified, slender, posterior segments of the abdomen, including the genital segments (T-B); in ♂

Diptera, the modified posterior abdominal segments (in Muscomorpha usually abdominal segment VI and following) (Tuxen); see terminalia.

postacrostichal, in adult Diptera, postsutural acrostichal seta, q.v. (T-B, after Comstock).

postal vein, in adult Hymenoptera, costa, q.v., of wing (T-B).

postalar arm, postalar bridge, q.v. (Chapman).

postalar bridge, a lateral extension of the postnotum of a wing-bearing segment behind the wing base, generally united with the epimeron (T-B, after Snodgrass).

postalar callosity, in adult Diptera, postalar callus, q.v. (T-B).

postalar callus, in adult Brachycera (Diptera), swelling at posterolateral angle of scutum, between the base of the wing and the scutellum, marked off anteriorly by the posterolateral scutal suture and posteriorly by the scutoscutellar suture (T-B; Colless and McAlpine, in CSIRO; Borror et al.; McAlpine).

postalar declivity, in adult Diptera, postalar wall, q.v. (McAlpine).

postalar ridge, in adult Diptera, a ridge running from the anterolateral angle of scutellum to the wing base (McAlpine).

postalar wall, in adult Diptera, ventrolateral surface below the postalar ridge (McAlpine).

postalare, postalar bridge, q.v. (T-B).

postalaralia (pl., **postalaraliae**), postalar bridge, q.v. (T-B, after MacGillivray).

postalars, in adult Chironomidae (Diptera), supraalars, q.v. (Saether).

postalifera, subalare, q.v. (T-B, after MacGillivray).

postanal field, in *Mastotermes* (Isoptera: Mastotermitidae), the posterior lobe of the forewing (T-B, after Holmgren).

postanal ridges, in many larval Brachycera (Diptera), transverse ventral ridges posterior to anus on terminal abdominal segment, sometimes bearing spinules, and functioning in the same way as creeping welts (Teskey, in McAlpine).

postannellus, in adult Hymenoptera, the fourth article of the antenna and second of the flagellum (T-B).

postantennal appendages, the second antennae in insects, reduced in the embryo and absent in the adult (T-B, after Snodgrass).

postantennal organ (P.A.O.), in Symphyla and many Arthorpleona (Collembola), a ringlike structure or multituberculate sensory area located just posterior to the base of the antenna (T-B; Wallace and Mackerras, in CSIRO).

postapophysis, in ♀ Lepidoptera, apophyses posteriores, q.v. (Tuxen, after Diakonoff).

postarticular, placed or set after a joint (T-B).

postarcular field, in adult Diptera, the portion of the wing distal to the axillary incision (Hennig).

postartis, ventral condyle, q.v., of mandible (T-B, after MacGillivray).

postatrial sclerite, in ♀ Culicidae (Diptera), posterior portion of abdominal sternum IX bordering atrium posteriorly (Tuxen, after Christophers).

postaxial surface of the leg, the posterior surface of the insect leg when it is extended at a right angle to the body (T-B, after Snodgrass).

postcalcar, in ♀ Hymenoptera, proximal (trailing) edge of sawtooth (Symphyta) or sting barb (Apocrita) (Tuxen, after E. L. Smith).

postcerebral, behind the cerebrum (brain) (T-B).

postclypeus, posterior or upper part of the clypeus when any line of demarcation exists (T-B); in adult Odonata, the upper of 2 parts into which the clypeus is divided (T-B; O'Farrell, in CSIRO); see anteclypeus.

postcornu (pl., **postcornua**), in ♂ Orthoptera, lophus, q.v. (Tuxen, after Walker); in wood-, stem- or grass-boring sawfly larvae (Hymenoptera: Symphyta), a single, suranal, sclerotized caudal projection (Peterson).

postcosta, subcosta, q.v., of wing (T-B).

postcostal, following after the costa (T-B).

postcostal space, in Odonata, the cell or cells lying posterior to the postcosta; the anal cell of Comstock (T-B).

postcoxal, after or behind the coxa (T-B).

postcoxal apodeme, in adult Culicidae (Diptera), an internal ridge having its origin at the base of the apophysis and extending along the posterior margin of the mesocoxal cavity, receiving the attachment of the indirect wing muscles (Harbach and Knight, after Owen).

postcoxal bridge, the postcoxal part of the pleuron, often united with sternum behind coxa (T-B, after Snodgrass); the sclerite extending behind the coxa and connecting the epimeron with the furcasternum (T-B, after Crampton).

postcoxale, postcoxal bridge, q.v. (T-B; Harbach and Knight).

postcranium, in adult Diptera, the entire posterior surface of the cranium (McAlpine).

postcubital crossveins, in adult Odonata, postnodal crossveins, q.v. (T-B).

postcubitals, the postnodal spaces, q.v. (T-B, after J. B. Smith).

postcubitus, the usual sixth vein of the wing, represented by an independent trachea in most nymphal wings, associated basally with the cubitus in the adult; first anal (1A) of Comstock and Needham in most cases (T-B, after Snodgrass); see cubitus posterior.

postdorsulum, the intermediate piece between the mesophragma and the postscutellum (T-B).

postembryonic, after or following the embryonic period, i.e., after the insect hatches from the egg (T-B).

postepipleurite, an area on sawfly larvae caudoventrad of spiracles and dorsad of prolegs (Peterson).

postepistoma, in adult Hymenoptera, that part of the head behind the clypeus (T-B); see frons and postclypeus.

posteriad, toward the posterior end.

posterior, hinder or hindmost, opposed to anterior (T-B); hind or rear (Borror et al.).

posterior anepisternum II, in adult Chironomidae (Diptera), posterior portion of anepisternum (Saether).

posterior angle, in ♂ Lepidoptera, ventrocaudal angle of valva (transl. "Hinterwinkel" Petersen, in Tuxen).

posterior apophysis, in ♀ Orthoptera, intervalvular apodeme, q.v. (Tuxen, after Walker).

posterior apophyses, in ♀ Lepidoptera, apophyses posteriores, q.v. (Tuxen).

posterior appendages, in ♂ Aleyrodidae (Hemiptera: Sternorrhyncha), claspers, q.v. (Tuxen).

posterior arculus, in the wings of certain insects, that part of the arculus which is formed by a crossvein (T-B, after Comstock).

posterior arms, in ♀ Mecoptera, lamnae, q.v. (Tuxen, after Carpenter).

posterior basalare, posterior part of basalare, usually attached to the anterodorsal margin of the epimeron in Diptera (McAlpine).

posterior branch, in generalized wing, posterior, concave ($-$) branch of major longitudinal vein, e.g., cubitus posterior (CuP) (McAlpine).

posterior calosity, postalar callus, q.v. (T-B, after Curran).

posterior callus, postalar callus, q.v. (T-B, after Curran).

posterior cells, in adult Diptera, open cells along posterior margin of the wing between last branch of radius and combined anterior cubitus (CuA) + first anal vein (1A), numbered beginning with the most distal cell (Borror et al.; Colless and McAlpine, in CSIRO).

posterior cephalic foramen, in Odonata, occipital foramen, q.v. (T-B).

posterior clypeus, postclypeus, q.v. (T-B).

posterior connecting leaf of gonapophysis VIII (connective VIII P), in ♀ Heteroptera (Hemiptera), posterior leaf of 8th gonapophysis connecting it to the articulatory sclerotizations of the body wall between abdominal segments VIII and IX (gonangulum) (transl. "feuillet connectif postérior de la gonapophyse VIII" Dupuis, after Tuxen).

posterior connecting leaf of gonapophysis IX (connective IX P), in ♀ Heteroptera (Hemiptera), posterior leaf of 9th gonapophysis connecting it to the membrane (intergonocoxal membrane) uniting the 9th gonocoxites posteriorly (transl. "feuillet postérior de la gonapophyse XI" Dupuis, after Tuxen).

posterior crossvein, in adult Diptera, medial crossvein, q.v., closing discal cell apically (T-B, after Curran; Colless and McAlpine, in CSIRO; Borror et al.); see discal medial-cubital crossvein.

posterior cubital cell, in most orthorrhaphous Brachycera and Muscomorpha (Diptera), a closed cell formed by apical union of second branch of cubitus anterior (CuA$_2$) and first anal vein (1A) (McAlpine).

posterior cubitus, cubitus posterior, q.v.

posterior dorsocentral area, in adult Culicidae (Diptera), the part of the dorsocentral area caudad of a point near the median corner of the scutal fossa at about the level of the antealar area (Harbach and Knight, after Belkin).

posterior dorsocentral bristle, in adult Diptera, postsutural dorsocentral seta, q.v. (T-B, after Comstock).

posterior dorsocentral scale, in adult Culicidae (Diptera), one of the scales occurring laterad of the posterior dorsocentral setae on the posterior dorsocental area of scutum (Harbach and Knight).

posterior dorsocentral seta, in adult Culicidae (Diptera), a dorsocentral seta occurring on the posterior dorsocentral area, occurring in one or more rows merging posteriorly with the prescutellar setae (Harbach and Knight); see postsutural dorsocentral seta.

posterior edge, anal margin, q.v., of wing (T-B, after Say).

posterior fibula(e), in ♀ Heteroptera (Hemiptera), anterior connecting leaf of gonapophysis IX, q.v. (Tuxen).

posterior field, in Orthoptera, anal field q.v., of tegmina (T-B).

posterior foramen, occipital foramen, q.v. (T-B); in ♂ Heteroptera (Hemiptera), pygophoral opening, q.v. (Tuxen, after Stehlik).

posterior gonapophyses, in ♀ Orthoptera, second gonapophyses, q.v. (Tuxen, after Walker); in ♀ Heteroptera (Hemiptera), gonapophyses of abdominal segment IX (Tuxen, after Wygodzinsky); in ♂ Diptera, postgonites, q.v. (Tuxen).

posterior gonopods, in ♀ Psocoptera, valvae dorsales, q.v. (Tuxen, after Pearman).

posterior hard palate, in adult Culicidae (Diptera), the large platelike posterior area of the clypeopalatum, bearing ventral setae near the base of each ventral flange (Harbach and Knight, after Thompson).

posterior intervalvula, in ♀ Orthoptera, superior intervalvula, q.v. (Tuxen, after Snodgrass).

posterior intestine, rectum, q.v. (T-B, after Snodgrass).

posterior labral muscle, one of the 2 pairs of long muscles which move the labrum, inserted posteriorly, usually on the epipharyngeal processes of the tormae (T-B, after Snodgrass).

posterior lamina, in ♂ Odonata, lamina posterior, q.v. (Tuxen).

posterior lateral sclerites, in ♂ Dermaptera, posterior side wall of basal region or penis carrying parameres (Tuxen).

posterior lobe, in ♂ Anisoptera (Odonata), preputial fold, q.v. (Tuxen, after Kennedy); in adult Diptera, alula, q.v. (T-B; Saether).

posterior margin, anal margin, q.v., of wing (T-B).

posterior media, media posterior, q.v.

posterior medial scutal seta, in adult Culicidae (Diptera), one of the setae occurring in a V-shaped group on the midline of the scutum at the posterior end of the row of acrostichal setae and anterior to the prescutellar area (Harbach and Knight, after Knight and Laffoon).

posterior median, media of Comstock (T-B, after Tillyard).

posterior mesanepisternum, in adult Culicidae (Diptera), the vertically narrow posterior part of the mesanpisternum, separated from the anterior mesanepisternum by the anepisternal cleft (Harbach and Knight).

posterior mesenteron rudiment, in the insect embryo, the posterior group of cells of the ventral endoderm remnant that regenerates the mesenteron (T-B, after Snodgrass).

posterior mesepimeral scale, in adult Culicidae (Diptera), one of the scales occurring in a group on the ventroposterior quarter of the mesanepimeron (Harbach and Knight).

posterior mesopleuron, in adult Chironomidae (Diptera), epimeron II, q.v. (Saether).

posterior notal wing process, a posterior lobe of the lateral margin of the alinotum supporting the third axillary sclerite of the wing base (T-B, after Snodgrass).

posterior oblique suture, in adult Pompilidae (Hymenoptera), a groove extending from the episternal scrobe to the lower end of the epicranial carina (Gauld and Bolton).

posterior orbit, in adult Diptera, the part of the head immediately behind the eye (T-B, after Curran).

posterior parameres, in ♂ Diptera, postgonites, q.v. (Tuxen).

posterior parapods, in larval Chironomidae (Diptera), parapods, q.v., on last abdominal segment (Saether).

posterior pereion, metanotum, q.v. (T-B).

posterior pharynx, a pharyngeal chamber of the modified stomodaeum behind the brain, present in Orthoptera, Coleoptera, and some other insects (T-B, after Snodgrass).

posterior plates, in ♀ Hymenoptera, second gonocoxae, q.v. (Tuxen).

posterior point, in ♂ Auchenorrhyncha (Hemiptera), posterior lateral angle of foot of style (Tuxen, after Young).

posterior process, in ♂ Emesinae (Hemiptera: Heteroptera: Reduviidae), hypandrium, q.v. (Tuxen, after Wygodzinsky); in ♂ Siphonaptera, telomeres ventralis, q.v. (Tuxen, after Hubbard).

posterior process of tergum III, in adult Panorpidae (Mecoptera), notorganum, q.v. (Byers, pers. comm.).

posterior pronotal lobe, in Heteroptera (Hemiptera), posterior expansion of the pronotum overlaying the anterior parts of the mesonotum (Štys, pers. comm.).

posterior pronotal setae, in pupal Chironomidae (Diptera), lateral antepronotals, q.v. (Saether).

posterior pronotum, in adult Diptera, postpronotum, q.v. (McAlpine).

posterior pygophore foramen, in ♂ Heteroptera (Hemiptera), pygophoral opening, q.v. (Tuxen, after Štys).

posterior ramus, in ♀ Heteroptera (Hemiptera), anterior connecting leaf of gonapophsis IX, q.v. (Tuxen, after Slater).

posterior respiratory process, among larval Syrphidae (Diptera), entire caudal respiratory organ composed of 2 more or less completely fused tubes (Peterson, after Heiss).

posterior sclerotic tube, in ♂ Siphonaptera, tubus interior, q.v. (Tuxen, after Sharif).

posterior scutal fossal scale, in adult Culicidae (Diptera), one of the scales occurring in a more or less distinct line extending diagonally from the scutal angle to the dorsocentral scales along the posterior margin of the scutal fossa (Harbach and Knight).

posterior scutal fossal seta, in adult Culicidae (Diptera), one of the setae usually occurring in a short row on the posterior margin of the scutal fossa between the scutal angle and the dorsocentral area (Harbach and Knight).

posterior scutellar ridge, in adult Culicidae (Diptera), the external ridge which extends from the lateroposterior angle of the scutellum and unites with the axillary cord of the wing (Harbach and Knight, after Owen).

posterior spiracles, most caudal pair of spiracles (Peterson); in larval Diptera, terminal, eighth pair of abdominal spiracles (Teskey, in McAlpine); in larval Syrphidae (Diptera), apertures or breathing openings on each posterior spiracular plate (Peterson, after Heiss).

posterior spiracular disc, in some larval Muscomorpha (Diptera), the flattened posterior surface of the last abdominal segment (Ferrar).

posterior spiracular plate, among larval Syrphidae (Diptera), the flattened or slightly rounded tip of each tube which bears the posterior spiracles (Peterson, after Heiss).

posterior stigmatal tubercle, in larval Lepidoptera, lateral tubercle, q.v. (T-B).

posterior surstylar lobes, in ♂ Lonchaeidae (Diptera), posterior lobe articulated with epandrium (McAlpine).

posterior tentorial arms, the cuticular invaginations arising from the posterior tentorial pits in the lower ends of the postoccipital sutures (T-B, after Snodgrass).

posterior tentorial pits, external pits marking the posterior arms of the tentorium, located at the ends of the postoccipital suture (T-B; Chapman); see anterior tentorial pits.

posterior thoracic spiracle, in adult and larval Diptera, metathoracic spiracles, q.v. (McAlpine; Teskey, in McAlpine).

posterior trapezoidal tubercle, in larval Lepidoptera, a subdorsal, posterior tubercle on the thoracic and abdominal segments (T-B).

posterior valves, in ♀ Isoptera, inner valves, q.v. (Tuxen).

posterior valvulae, in ♀ Orthoptera, outgrowths of coxopodites of abdominal segment IX, situated laterally and dorsally to the other 2 pairs of valvulae (Tuxen); in ♀ Heteroptera (Hemiptera), gonapophyses of abdominal segment IX (Tuxen, after Rawat).

posterior wall, in ♀ Heteroptera (Hemiptera), the part of bursa copulatrix lying between posterior fibulae and below roof (transl. "hintere Wand" Kullenberg) (Tuxen, after Slater).

posterior wing root, in adult Culicidae (Diptera), line of thickening at the wing base associated with the bases of the media, cubitus and anal veins (Harbach and Knight, after Christophers).

posterior wings, hind wings, q.v. (T-B).

posterodorsal pouch, in ♀ Cydnidae, Scutelleridae, and Pyrrhocoridae (Hemiptera: Heteroptera), vaginal pouch, q.v. (Tuxen, after Scudder).

posterodorsals, in Diptera, the leg bristles at the meeting of the dorsal and posterior faces (T-B).

posterolateral, toward the rear and side (T-B).

posterolateral bare space, in adult Culicidae (Diptera), the area of scutum posterior to the scutal fossa between the dorsocentral setae and the antealar and supraalar setae (Harbach and Knight).

posterolateral pronotal inflection, in adult Hymenoptera, internal ridge along the posterolateral edge of the pronotum, hypothesized to be the degenerate prepectus fused to the pronotum (Gibson).

posterolateral scutal suture, in some adult Diptera, more or less transverse suture on scutum posterior to tergal fissure (McAlpine).

posteroventrals, in adult Diptera, leg bristles at the meeting of the ventral and posterior faces (T-B).

postfeeding larva, in Diptera, mature larva that no longer feeds, which undergoes physiological and behavioral changes, but is not a separate instar (Ferrar); see prepupa.

postfrenum, postfroenum, in Coleoptera, the part of the metathorax in which the postscutellum lies (T-B, after Kirby and Spence); postscutellum, q.v. (T-B, after Snodgrass).

postfrons, in adult Diptera, frons, q.v. (McAlpine).

postfrontal pharyngeal dilators, one or more pairs of muscles arising on the postfrontal region of the cranium, inserted on the pharynx before the brain (T-B, after Snodgrass).

postfrontal ridge, apodemes marked externally by the postfrontal sutures (Harbach and Knight).

postfrontal sutures, facial suture in some insects diverging from the coronal suture laterad of the antennal bases (T-B, after Snodgrass); see frontal sutures.

postfurca, metafurca, q.v. (T-B).

postgena (pl., **postgenae**), the lateral part of the occipital arch, behind the occipital suture (T-B, after Snodgrass; Chapman); in adult Diptera, the part of the gena behind the genal suture (T-B, after Comstock); subgena, q.v. (T-B, after Imms); hypostoma, q.v. (T-B, after MacGillivray).

postgenal, of or pertaining to the postgena; situated behind the gena (T-B).

postgenal bridge, in some adult Hymenoptera, ventral bridge of head formed by median fusion of postegenae (Gauld and Bolton); see genal bridge and hypostomal bridge.

postgenal seta, in adult Culicidae (Diptera), one of the setae occurring in a group on the postgena at the posteroventral area of the cranium (Harbach and Knight).

postgenital lobe, in ♀ Culicidae (Diptera), the weakly to moderately sclerotized median caudal lobe below the anus and above the upper vaginal lip (Harbach and Knight, after Laffoon and Knight).

postgenital plate, in ♂ Odonata, secondary sclerotization in intersegmental area behind gonopore (Tuxen, after Snodgrass); in ♀ Ephemeroptera, the produced abdominal sternum IX (Tuxen, after Brinck); in ♀ Taeniopterygidae (Plecoptera), the produced abdominal sternum IX (Tuxen; Zwick, pers. comm.); in ♀ Culicidae (Diptera), plate behind genital opening, being abdominal sternum X and XI (Tuxen, after Gerry); in ♀ Chironomidae (Diptera), usually weakly developed posteroventral plate on ♀ genitalia between bases of cerci, possibly representing segment XI (Saether).

postgenital segments, any abdominal segments posterior to the genitalia (T-B, after Snodgrass); in adult Diptera, abdominal segments posterior to the main genital opening (McAlpine).

postgenitale, in ♀ Neuropteroidea, plate- or bladderlike structure below abdominal segment IX (Tuxen, after Tjeder).

postgonites, in ♂ Muscomorpha (Diptera), appendages of genital segment at side of intromittent organ (aedeagus) (Tuxen, after Crampton; Griffiths); see parameres.

postgradular area, in adult Hymenoptera, area behind gradulus of a tergum or sternum (Tuxen, after Michener); see pregradular area.

postgula, in Dermaptera, a sclerite at the extreme base of the underside of the head (T-B).

posthumeral bristles, in adult Diptera, bristles on anterolateral surface of scutum, just posterior to postpronotal lobe (T-B; Colless and McAlpine, in CSIRO; Borror et al.).

postical vein, in adult Diptera, combined third and fourth medial veins, M_{3+4} (T-B, after J. B. Smith).

posticus (Latin), hinder (T-B).

postlabial area, postmentum, q.v. (T-B).

postlabium, postmentum, q.v. (T-B).

postmandibular, posterior to or behind the mandible (T-B).

postmarginal vein, in adult Chalcidoidea (Hymenoptera), vein along the costal margin of the forewing, beyond the point where the stigmal vein arises (T-B; Riek, in CSIRO; Borror et al.).

postmedial line, in adult Lepidoptera, transverse posterior line, q.v. (T-B).

postmedian notal wing process, in adult Culicidae (Diptera), a flange of the scutum located caudad and slightly ventral to the anterior notal wing process, articulating with the posterior part of the first axillary sclerite (Harbach and Knight, after Owen).

postmental, of or pertaining to the postmentum (T-B); back or behind the mentum in position (T-B).

postmental elements, in larval Bibionidae (Diptera), reduced remnants of postmentum (Teskey, in McAlpine).

postmentum, basal part of the labium proximal to the prementum, consisting of a single plate or divided into a proximal submentum and distal mentum (T-B, after Snodgrass).

postmesosternal scale, in adult Culicidae (Diptera), one of the scales occurring in a small group on the intersegmental membrane immediately behind the metasternum (Harbach and Knight).

postmetamorphic, following or succeeding metamorphosis (T-B).

postmetaspiracular scale, in Tabanidae and Athericidae (Diptera), a small scalelike elevation in the strong membrane immediately posterior to the metathoracic spiracle (Stuckenberg).

postnodal costal spaces, in adult Odonata, the cells below costal margin from nodus to stigma (T-B).

postnodal crossveins, in adult Odonata, crossveins between costa and subcosta and between nodus and pterostigma (T-B, after Garman).

postnotal plate, postnotum, q.v. (T-B, after Snodgrass).

postnodal pruina, in Corixidae (Hemiptera: Heteroptera), a white, frosted area along the lateral border of the corium posterior to the nodal furrow (Lauck, in Menke).

postnodal radial spaces, in adult Odonata, the cells between radius and media from nodus to the outer margin (T-B).

postnodal sector, in adult Odonata, a longitudinal vein lying between first branch of media (M_1) and second branch of media (M_2) (T-B).

postnotals, in adult Chironomidae, setae of postnotum (Saether).

postnotum, an intersegmental plate of the thoracic dorsum associated with the tergum of the preceding segment, bearing the antecosta and usually a pair of phragmatal lobes serving as attachment sites for the dorsal longitudinal muscles (T-B, after Snodgrass); in adult Diptera, the dorsal sclerite below and behind the scutellum of the mesothorax (Colless and McAlpine, in CSIRO); see subscutellum.

postnupial moulting, imaginal moulting, q.v. (Boudreaux).

postoccipital carina, in larval Nematocera (Diptera), thickened border of occipital foramen (Teskey, in McAlpine); see postoccipital margin.

postoccipital groove, postoccipital suture, q.v. (Mackerras, in CSIRO).

postoccipital margin, in larval Chironomidae (Diptera), extreme posterior sclerotized rim of head capsule (Saether); see postoccipital carina.

postoccipital ridge, the internal aspect of the postoccipital suture, often produced into apodemal plates on which are attached the dorsal prothoracic and neck muscles of the head (T-B, after Snodgrass).

postoccipital sulcus, in larval Nematocera, slight groove delimiting postoccipital carina anteriorly (Teskey, in McAlpine); see postoccipital suture.

postoccipital suture, posterior submarginal groove having the posterior tentorial pits in its lower end, separating the postocciput from the rest of the cranium (T-B, after Snodgrass); see postoccipital sulcus.

postocciput, the extreme posterior rim of the cranium behind the postoccipital suture, probably a sclerotic remnant of the labral somite (T-B, after Snodgrass).

postocellar area, in adult Hymenoptera, the region on the dorsal aspect of the head bounded by the ocellar furrow, the vertical furrows and the caudal margin of the head (T-B).

postocellar bristle, in adult Diptera, postocellar seta, q.v. (T-B, after Curran).

postocellar glands, in the honey bee (Hymenoptera: Apidae), a mass of glands situated just above the ocelli in the drones and queen (T-B, after Bordas).

postocellar seta, in adult Diptera, one of a pair (or more) of setae arising just behind the ocelli on the vertex (McAlpine).

postocular, back of or behind the compound eyes (T-B); in adult Chironomidae (Diptera), postocular seta, q.v. (Saether).

postocular seta, in adult Diptera, one of the setae occurring in a row along the posterior margin of the compound eye (McAlpine).

postocular spots, in adult Odonata, pale spots on the dorsum of the head, in Zygoptera, behind and usually laterad of the ocelli (T-B, after Garman).

postoesophageal commissure, the commissure joining the tritocerebral lobes and passing immediately behind the oesophagus (T-B; Chapman).

postoral segment, gnathal segment, q.v. (T-B; McAlpine); see preoral segment.

postorbital bristle, in adult Diptera, postocular seta, q.v. (T-B, after Comstock; Saether); in pupal Chironomidae (Diptera), mostly 2 setae on caudal and caudolateral margin of ocular field, divided into lower and upper postorbitals (Saether).

postorbital ridge, in Psyllidae (Hemiptera: Sternorrhyncha), ridge extending behind the eye from the outer posterior margin of the vertex (Hodkinson and White).

postorganum (pl., **postorgana**), in ♂ Mecoptera, median unpaired structure on tergum IV (Tuxen).

postparadensa, in certain Coccoidea (Hemiptera: Sternorrhyncha), the posterior group of paradensae when they are in 2 groups (T-B, after MacGillivray).

postparapteron (pl., **postparaptera**), subalare, q.v. (T-B, after Comstock).

postparapterum, supraepimeron, q.v. (T-B, after MacGillivray).

postpectoral carina, in adult Ichneumonidae (Hymenoptera), carina at posterior rim of mesosternum (van Achterberg, pers. comm., after Townes).

postpectus, the under surface of the metathorax; in Hymenoptera, the fused sternum and pleuron (T-B).

postpedes, metathoracic legs (T-B); anal prolegs, q.v. (T-B).

postpedicel, in adult Diptera, first flagellomere (McAlpine).

postpetiole, in ants (Hymenoptera: Formicidae), the second segment of the pedicel when it has 2 segments, being abdominal segment III (T-B, after Comstock; Wilson).

postpharyngeal dilator, muscle arising on the vertex, inserted on the stomodaeum behind the brain, serving to dilate the pharynx (T-B, after Snodgrass).

postpharynx, pharynx, q.v. (T-B, after MacGillivray).

postphragma, the posterior phragma or partition of any segment (T-B, after Comstock); an internal, posterior phragma of the postnotum, esp. in adult Diptera (T-B, after Imms, MacGillivray; Colless and McAlpine, in CSIRO).

postpleuron, epimeron, q.v. (T-B, after MacGillivray).

postprocoxal membrane, in adult Culicidae (Diptera), a membrane between the forecoxa and the mesokatepisternum (Harbach and Knight, after Laffoon and Knight).

postprocoxal scale, in adult Culicidae (Diptera), one of the scales occurring in a small group on the postprocoxal membrane (Harbach and Knight).

postpronotal lobe, in higher Diptera, posterolateral lobe of postnotum, being intimately associated with mesonotum (McAlpine).

postpronotal scale, in adult Culicidae (Diptera), any scale borne on the postpronotum (Harbach and Knight).

postpronotal seta, in Diptera, one of the setae in an arcuate line on the upper posterior margin of the postpronotum (Harbach and Knight; McAlpine).

postpronotum, the posterior region of the pronotum (T-B, after Crampton); in adult Diptera, especially Nematocera, e.g., Tipulidae and Chironomidae, lateral region of pronotum posterior to antepronotum fused with scutum dorsally and with mesopleural area ventrally (Saether; McAlpine); in higher Diptera, postpronotal lobe, q.v. (McAlpine).

postretinal, behind the retina of the eye (T-B).

postretinal fiber, nerve fiber arising from an ommatidium which passes into the ganglionic plate of the insect brain (T-B, after Packard).

postscutellar furrow, in adult Chironomidae (Diptera), longitudinal furrow, q.v. (Saether).

postscutellum, in adult Diptera, postnotum, q.v. (T-B, after Mac Gillivray, Curran; Saether), or subscutellum, q.v. (McAlpine); in adult Hymenoptera, dorsellum, q.v. (Gauld and Bolton).

postscutum, in adult Trichoptera, the small plate behind the scutellum of mesothorax; the postscutellum (T-B); see postnotum.

postspiracular area, area caudad of spiracles (Peterson); in adult Culicidae (Diptera), sclerotized area of the anterior anepisternum lying posterior to the mesothoracic spiracle (Harbach and Knight).

postspiracular scale, in adult Culicidae (Diptera), one of the scales occurring in a group on the postspiracular area of the anterior mesanepisternum (Harbach and Knight).

postspiracular sclerite, in most Symphyta (Hymenoptera), sclerite positioned between the pronotum and mesepisternum and between the mesothoracic spiracle and basalare (Gibson).

postspiracular seta, in adult Culicidae (Diptera), one of the setae occurring in a group on the postspiracular area on the anterior mesanepisternum (Harbach and Knight).

poststernellum, spinasternum, q.v. (T-B, after Imms; Mackerras, in CSIRO).

poststernite, the postcostal lip of a definitive sternal plate that includes the adjacent posterior intersegmental sclerotization (T-B, after Snodgrass).

poststigmatal cell, that part of the marginal cell beyond the stigma in bees (Hymenoptera: Apoidea); the second radial$_1$ of Comstock (T-B, after Smith).

poststigmatal primary tubercle, in larval Lepidoptera, a tubercle on a thoracic segment posterior to the spiracle (T-B).

postsubterminal, in adult Lepidoptera, following the subterminal transverse line (T-B).

postsutural acrostichal seta, in adult Diptera, acrostichal seta posterior to the transverse suture (McAlpine).

postsutural area, in adult Diptera, area of the mesoscutum posterior to the transverse suture (McAlpine).

postsutural dorsocentral, in adult Diptera, posterior dorsocentral seta, q.v. (T-B).

postsutural dorsocentral seta, in adult Diptera, a dorsocentral seta posterior to the transverse suture (McAlpine).

postsutural seta, in Diptera, seta on the postsutural area (T-B; McAlpine).

posttarsus, pretarsus, q.v. (Harbach and Knight, after MacGillivray; McAlpine).

posttegula, in Stratiomyidae (Diptera), a possible remanant of the calpyter or tegula of the hind wing, appearing as a small lobe just posterior and medial to the halter (Daniels).

posttentoria, posterior tentorial arms, q.v. (T-B, after Crampton).

postterga, in larval Coleoptera, the posterior dorsal scutes of the segments (T-B).

posttergite, the narrow postcostal lip of a postnotal thoracic plate (T-B, after Snodgrass); the posterior sclerite of the eunotum (Crampton).

posttriangular cell, in adult Odonata, discoidal areolet, q.v. (T-B).

postuncus (pl., **postunci**), in ♂ Zoraptera, hook carried by penis (Tuxen, after Crampton).

postural hairs, hair plate, q.v. (Leftwich).

postvaginal plate, in ♀ Lepidoptera, lamella postvaginalis, q.v. (Tuxen, after Rothschild and Jordan).

postvaginal sclerites, in ♀ Acridoidea (Orthoptera), sclerotized areas of the floor of the ♀ chamber (Key, pers. comm., after Randell).

postvertex, the posterior area of the vertex when divided into 2 parts by the fusion of the compound eyes (T-B, after MacGillivray).

postvertical bristle, in adult Diptera, postocellar seta, q.v. (T-B, after Comstock; Borror et al.).

postvertical cephalic bristle, in adult Diptera, postocellar seta, q.v. (T-B).

postvertical, in adult Diptera, postocellar seta, q.v. (T-B).

potassium ammonium selenosulfide, an inorganic acaricide; highly toxic to mammals (Pfadt).

potassium hyrdroxide (KOH), commonly called caustic potash, used in an approximately 10% concentration to remove muscle tissue from structures to be cleared or slide mounted.

potato scab, disease of potato plants transmitted by *Pnyxia scabei* (Diptera: Sciaridae) (Borror et al.).

potato yellow dwarf, disease of potato plants caused by a rhabdovirus and transmitted propagatively by *Aceratagallia, Agallia,* and *Agalliopsis* (Hemiptera: Auchenorrhyncha: Cicadellidae) (Nault and Ammar).

potruncus, metathorax, q.v. (T-B, after Kirby and Spence).

pouch, a large sac (T-B);

pouch makers, bumble bee (Hymenoptera: Apidae) species that build special wax pouches on the sides of larval cells and fill them with pollen on which the larvae feed directly (Wilson); see pollen stores.

pouch of Herold, in ♂ Lepidoptera, organ of Herold, q.v. (Tuxen).

ppm, parts per million (Pfadt).

prae-, pre-, q.v. (T-B).

prasinous, prasinus, grass-green; light green tending to yellow (T-B).

pratinicolous, frequenting or living in grassy meadows or bogs (T-B).

praying mantid, a member of the order Mantodea (Key, in CSIRO; Hennig).

pre-, Latin prefix; before, in space, time, or degree (T-B).

pre-Linnaean name, a name published prior to Jan. 1, 1758, the starting date of zoological nomenclature (T-B; Mayr).

preabdomen (pl., **preabdomina**), the unmodified anterior abdominal segments (T-B, after Snodgrass); in ♂ Muscomorpha (Diptera), the large abdominal segments I–IV (Tuxen); in ♀ Muscomorpha (Diptera), broader basal portion of abdomen, consisting of abdominal segments I–V or I–VI (Colless and McAlpine, in CSIRO; McAlpine); see postabdomen.

preacrostichal, in adult Diptera, presutural acrostichal seta, q.v. (T-B, after Comstock).

preadaptation, a previously existing behavior pattern, physiological process, or morphological structure, already functional in some other context, that becomes available as a stepping stone to a new adaptation (Matthews and Matthews).

prealar, anterior to the ala or wing (T-B).

prealar apophysis, in adult Culicidae (Diptera), an apodeme arising internally from the area of the prealar bridge (Harbach and Knight, after Owen).

prealar arm, prealar bridge, q.v. (Chapman).

prealar bridge, extension from the lateral part of the prescutum in front of the wing connecting the notum and the episternum (T-B, after Needham, Crampton); in adult Tipulidae (Diptera), narrow strip extending from scutum just behind the lateral extremity of the transverse suture, joining the dorsal part of the anterior basalare (McAlpine); in adult Culicidae (Diptera), a small sclerite extending dorsad from the upper anterior edge of the posterior mesanepisternum to the supraalar groove (Harbach and Knight, after Owen).

prealar bristle, in adult Diptera, prealar seta (T-B, after Comstock).

prealar callus, in adult Diptera, swollen area lying just behind the lateral extremities of the transverse suture anteromedial to the anterior notal wing process (T-B, after Comstock; McAlpine).

prealar knob, in adult Culicidae (Diptera), the convex protuberance borne on the upper part of the posterior mesanepisternum anterior to the wing (Harbach and Knight).

prealar mesopleurite, in adult Chironomidae (Diptera), median or posterior anepisternum, q.v. (Saether).

prealar scale, in adult Culicidae (Diptera), any scale borne anterior to the wing on the posterior mesanepisternum (Harbach and Knight).

prealar seta, in adult Diptera, most anterior supraalar seta (T-B, after Curran); in adult Nematocera (Diptera), one of the setae occurring in a group on the prealar knob of the posterior mesanepisternum (Harbach and Knight); in adult Chironomidae (Diptera), setae dorsal and anterior to wing, confined to posterior region of prealar callus (Saether); in pupal Chironomidae (Diptera), setae in front of wing sheath (Saether).

prealaralia (pl., **prealaraliae**), prealar bridge, q.v. (T-B, after MacGillivray).

prealare, prealar bridge, q.v. (T-B).

prealifera, basilare, q.v. (T-B, after MacGillivray).

preanal, above or before the anal opening (T-B).

preanal area, jugum, q.v., of wing (T-B, after Comstock).

preanal bristle bearer, in larval Chironomidae (Diptera), procercus, q.v. (Saether).

preanal lamina, supraanal plate, q.v. (T-B).

preanal lobe, in adult Hymenoptera, claval lobe, q.v., of hind wing (T-B, after Comstock).

preanal papilla, in larval Chironomidae (Diptera), procercus, q.v. (Saether).

preanal plate, supraanal plate, q.v. (T-B).

preanal region, remigium, q.v., of wing (T-B).

preanal ridges, in many larval Brachycera (Diptera), ridges, sometimes bearing spinules, anterior to anus on ventral surface of terminal abdominal segment, functioning in the same way as creeping welts (Teskey, in McAlpine); see postanal ridges.

preanal setae, in larval Chironomidae (Diptera), anal setae, q.v. (Saether).

preanal setal tubercle, in larval Chironomidae (Diptera), procercus, q.v. (Saether).

preantennae, theoretically a pair of primitive procephalic appendages anterior to the antennae; possibly represented in *Scolopendra* and *Dixippus* (Chilopoda) by a pair of embryonic preantennal lobes; absent in all adult arthropods (T-B, after Snodgrass); see second antennae.

preantennal, anterior to or before antenna (T-B).

preantennal appendages, structures in front of the antennae (T-B).

preantennal suture, in adult Culicidae (Diptera), a line delimiting the ventral area of the frons from the antennal socket laterally (Harbach and Knight, after Christophers).

preapical, just before the apex (T-B; Borror et al.).

preapical bristle, in adult Diptera, a short bristle situated dorsally before the end of the tibia (T-B, after Curran).

preapical claw, in Gerroidea (Hemiptera: Heteroptera), a condition in which the pretarsus is inserted proximal to the apex of the last tarsal segment (Andersen).

preapical comb, in larval Chironomidae (Diptera), pecten mandibularis, q.v. (Saether).

preapical diverticulum, in Acrididae (Orthoptera), the main vesicle of the spermatheca (Key, pers. comm., after Slifer).

prearculus, in adult Diptera, a more or less distinct crossvein or transverse furrow between the radius and the subcosta in line with the arculus (Harbach and Knight, after Belkin).

prearticular, placed or set anterior to an articulation (T-B).

prearticular field, in adult Diptera, the portion of the wing proximal to the axillary incision (Hennig).

preartis, dorsal condyle, q.v. (T-B, after MacGillivray).

preatrial sclerites, in ♀ Culicidae (Diptera), part of abdominal sternum VIII bordering atrium anteriorly and consisting of sigma and insula (Tuxen, after Christophers); see postatrial sclerites.

preatrium (pl., **preatria**), in ♂ Auchenorrhyncha (Hemiptera), ventral part of socle (Tuxen, after Young).

preaxial, anterior to or placed before the axis (T-B).

preaxial surface of the leg, the anterior surface when the limb is extended at a right angle to the body (T-B, after Snodgrass).

preaxillary excision, in the hind wings of Hymenoptera, a second excision of the apex of claval furrow (T-B, after Comstock).

prebalancer, prehalter, q.v. (T-B).

prebasilar, before the base (T-B).

prebasilare, in some millipedes (Diplopoda), a narrow transverse sclerite just basal to mentum of gnathochilarium (Borror et al.).

prebursa (pl., **prebursae**), in ♀ Zygaenidae (Lepidoptera), the transformed ductus bursae which receives the spermatophore, the corpus bursae being reduced to a simple appendage (Tuxen, after Alberti).

precalcar, in ♀ Hymenoptera, distal (leading) edge of sawtooth (Symphyta) or sting barb (Apocrita) (Tuxen, after E. L. Smith).

precardo, distal part of bipartite cardo (Peterson).

precedence, the order of seniority of available names or nomenclatural acts determined by the commission or by a first reviser choosing between 2 or more available names or nomenclatural acts published simultaneously, whether in the same or different works (ICZN); see position precedence.

precephalic, anterior to the front of the head (T-B).

precerebral, anterior to the brain (T-B).

precinctive, endemic, q.v. (Mackerras, in CSIRO).

precinctorium, in adult Lepidoptera, median expansion of the intersegmental thoracoabdominal membrane, being especially well developed in Crambidae (Maes, after Minet).

precipitin, antibodies produced in the hemolymph with the introduction of an antigen (T-B, after Imms).

precipitin reaction, the formation of a visible precipitate at the interface when an antigen and the corresponding antiserum are brought together (Mayr).

preclavus, remigium, q.v., of wing (T-B).

preclypeus, anteclypeus, q.v. (T-B, after MacGillivray); in larval Chironomidae (Diptera), labral sclerites, q.v. (Saether).

precocious adult eye, in larval Chaoboridae and Culicidae (Diptera), eye with numerous ommatidia anterior to larval eye (Teskey, in McAlpine).

precocious stages, all the stages of development from the fertilized egg to the pupa (T-B).

precorneals, in pupal Chironomidae (Diptera), setae (usually 3) in front of thoracic horn (or corresponding site when horn is lacking) numbered from anterior to posterior (Saether).

precostal area, in adult Fulgoroidea (Hemiptera: Auchenorrhyncha), the space between costa and the costal margin (T-B, after Tillyard).

precostal field, in Orthopteroidea (Insecta: Neoptera), expanded area of the wing anterior to the costa (Hennig).

precostal spur, in some insects, a false vein in the costal angle at the base of the hind wings (T-B).

precoxa, in Collembola, subcoxa, q.v. (T-B; Christiansen and Bellinger).

precoxa process, in Sminthuridae (Collembola), integumentary lobe on anteroventral surface of meso- and metathoracic precoxae (Richards).

precoxal, of or pertaining to the precoxa (T-B); anterior to the coxa (T-B).

precoxal bridge, the precoxal part of pleuron anterior to the trochantin, usually continuous with the episternum, frequently united with basisternum, sometimes a distinct sclerite (T-B).

precoxal suture, in some adult Hymenoptera, groove near base of midcoxa extending sinuously forward (Gauld and Bolton); see stenopleural suture.

precoxale (pl., **precoxalia**), precoxal bridge, q.v. (T-B).

precubital furrow, in adult Culicidae (Diptera); a dorsal furrow in cell M_4 lying near and parallel to the cubitus anterior, ending just short of the cubitomarginal ridge distally (Harbach and Knight, after Colless).

predaceous, predacious, living by preying upon other organisms, e.g., Odonata, Mantodea, Heteroptera (e.g., Reduviidae), larvae and many adults of Megaloptera, Raphidioptera, Planipennia, Mecoptera (Bittacidae), Diptera (many families, especially as larvae), Coleoptera (e.g., Adephaga; larval Lampyridae and Coccinellidae), and Hymenoptera (T-B; Borror et al.).

predator, an organism that obtains energy (as food) by consuming, usually killing, 2 or more prey organisms during its lifetime (T-B; Allaby; Common, pers. comm.).

predatory, predaceous, q.v. (T-B).

predictive value, the capacity of a classification to make predictions on newly employed characters or newly discovered taxa (Mayr).

predisposing factors, in invertebrate pathology, factors which, by their actions, render an organism specially susceptible to a certain disease (Steinhaus and Martignoni); see secondary etiologic factors.

preepipleurite, an area immediately ventrad of spiracles (Peterson).

preepiproct, in ♂ Mecoptera, epiandrium, q.v. (Tuxen, after Snodgrass).

preepisternal groove, in adult Culicidae (Diptera), the depression between the forecoxae where the proepisterna are separated by the confluent propleurosternal sutures (Harbach and Knight, after Owen).

preepisternals, in adult Chironomidae (Diptera), setae of preepisternum (Saether).

preepisternum, the anterior part of the episternum marked as a separate plate (T-B, after Imms); a sclerite in front of the episternum in some more generalized insects (T-B, after Comstock); in adult *Dendroctonus* (Coleoptera: Scolytidae), anterior part of the episternum (McAlpine, after Hopkins); in adult Diptera, katepisternum, q.v. (McAlpine); in adult Chironomidae (Diptera), large sclerite below anapleural suture, joined along ventral midline (Saether).

prefemur, ischiopodite, q.v. (T-B).

prefollicular tissue, cells in germarium of ovariole that give rise to follicular epithelium (Chapman).

preformation, hypothesis that the development of an organism occurs by the unfolding and growth of characters already present in the egg at the beginning of development (T-B; Allaby); see epigenesis.

prefrons, in Psocoptera, postclypeus, q.v., often presenting an inflated appearance (T-B); in adult Diptera, face, q.v. (McAlpine).

pregenicular, proximal to the knee (T-B); in Orthoptera, the part of the femur proximad to the knee (T-B).

pregenicular annulus, in Orthoptera, a more or less conspicuous color ring on the hind femora proximad to the knee (T-B).

pregenital, preceding or anterior to genital segments (T-B).

pregenital plate, in ♀ Plecoptera, abdominal sternum VII when not produced posteriorly to a subgenital plate (covering genital opening) (Tuxen, after Brinck).

pregenital segments, abdominal segments anterior to the genital segments (T-B, after Snodgrass).

pregenitale (pl., **pregenitalia**), in ♀ Neuroptera, paired or unpaired, plate- or toothlike structure between apex of abdominal sternum VII and subgenitale (Tuxen, after Tjeder).

pregonites, in some ♂ Muscomorpha (Diptera), a pair of lobes near the base of the aedeagus (gonites of McAlpine) (Griffiths, after Crampton); see gonopods.

pregradular area, in adult Hymenoptera, the slightly raised area in front of gradulus which slides on the duplication of the preceeding tergum or sternum (Tuxen, after Michener).

pregula, an anterior part of the gular plate found in front of a median gular suture, e.g., in many larval Hydrophilidae and Staphylinidae (Coleoptera) (Peterson, after Böving and Craighead); see submentum.

prehalter, a membranous scale in front of the true halter of a fly (T-B);

in adult Ptychopteridae (Diptera), a peculiar appendage arising anteriorly from the base of the halter (McAlpine).

prehensile, fitted or adapted for grasping, holding or seizing (T-B).

prehension, the act of grasping or holding (T-B).

prehensor, in ♀ Scirtidae (Coleoptera), a processus emanating from ventral part of vagina and functioning as a copulatory apparatus (Tuxen, after Nyholm).

prehensores, in ♂ Lepidoptera, valvae, q.v. (Tuxen, after Kirby and Spence).

prehypopygial sclerite, in ♀ Diptera, syntergosternite, q.v. (McAlpine).

preimaginal, preceding the imago (T-B).

preimago, the last phase of a pupal stage when the structures of the apparently completed adult can be seen within the pupal covering (Peterson); in Protura, the fifth, last preadult, instar in males (Bellinger, pers. comm.); see pharate instar and subimago.

prelabial sclerite, in many larval Ichneumonoidea (Hymenoptera), a more or less Y-shaped sclerited supporting the opening of the silk press (Gauld and Bolton, after Short).

prelabium, the distal part of the labium, comprising the prementum, the ligula, and the palp (T-B, after Snodgrass).

prelabrum, in adult Diptera, clypeus, q.v., or anteclypeus, q.v. (Colless and McAlpine, in CSIRO).

prelarva, in Protura, the first instar (Bellinger, pers. comm.).

premandible(s), in some larval Nematocera (Diptera), a pair of ventral appendagelike structures on labrum, taking the form of toothed plates or processes (e.g., in Trichoceridae, Chironomidae) (Colless and McAlpine, in CSIRO); in some larval Nematocera, labral sclerite articulating posteriorly with each torma, often bearing one or more teeth sometimes resembling a comb (Teskey, in McAlpine).

premandibular, situated in front of the mandible (T-B).

premandibular appendages, postantennal appendages, q.v. (T-B).

premandibular brush, in larval Chironomidae (Diptera), brush of small microtrichia sometimes present on mesal margin of premandible (Saether).

premandibular segment, intercalary segment, q.v., of head (T-B).

prematuration period, that part of the lifecycle of an insect between emergence from the egg and commencement of sexual maturity (T-B, after Folsom and Wardle).

premental, of or pertaining to the prementum (T-B).

premental elements, in larval Bibionidae (Diptera), reduced remnants of prementum (Teskey, in McAlpine).

premental gutter, in adult Culicidae (Diptera), the median dorsal longitudinal groove of the prementum which houses the fascicle (Harbach and Knight, after Knight).

premento-hypopharyngeal complex, in larval Chironomidae (Diptera), soft double-lobed structure dorsad of and to a large extent covered by mentum in ventral view and posteriorly, and opposed to labrum, consisting of prementum and hypopharynx (Saether).

prementum, the stipital region of the labium, containing the muscles of palpi and the ligular lobes, and giving insertion to the cranial muscles of the labium (T-B, after Snodgrass); an appendage of the insect labium, borne on the notum (palpiger of some authors) (T-B, after Imms); the region of the labium distal to the mentum and formed by the palpigers and labial stipites (T-B, after Crampton); in larval Coleoptera, the area lying in front of the mentum, consisting of the fused labial stipites and the labial palpigers, and excluding the ligula and the labial palpi (T-B, after Böving and Craighead); in larval Chironomidae (Diptera), soft ventral lobe of premento-hypopharyngeal complex separated from hypopharynx by salivary outlet, and bearing ligula, paraligula, labial palpus, and M sclerite (Saether).

premorse, premorsus, terminating in an irregular truncate apex as if bitten off (T-B, after Kirby and Spence).

premoulting, preceding or before moulting (T-B).

prenota, prescutum, q.v. (T-B, after MacGillivray).

prensisetae, in ♂ Diptera, e.g. Tephritidae and Drosophilidae, heavily sclerotized, blunt setae on surstylus (McAlpine; Grimaldi).

prensors, in ♂ Lepidoptera, valvae, q.v. (T-B; Tuxen, after Meyrick).

prenymph, in Protura, immature, hatching from the egg, with 9 abdominal segments and incomplete appendages (Wallace and Mackerras, in CSIRO); see maturus junior.

preoccupied, already in use in another category; in zoology, referring to names (T-B).

preocellar band, in adult Odonata, a dark pigment stripe immediately in front of the ocelli (T-B, after Garman).

preocellar bristles, in adult Diptera, a pair of small bristles sometimes found anterior to the median ocellus (T-B, after Comstock).

preocular, before the eyes (T-B).

preocular antenna, one inserted close to the front of the eyes (T-B).

preocular ridge, in Acridoidea (Orthoptera), a vertical ridge running from below the antennae to the base of the mandible (Otte, pers. comm.); see lateral carina.

preoculars, in adult Chironomidae (Diptera), orbitals or frontals, q.v. (Saether).

preopercular organ, in ♀ Phasmida, external pouch of posterior part of abdominal sternum VII covered anteriorly by a sclerotic process (Tuxen).

preoral, before the mouth in position (T-B).

preoral cavity, the space enclosed by the labrum and the mouth appendages (T-B; Chapman); see cibarium and salivarium.

preoral lobe, prostomium, q.v. (T-B).

preoral segment, head segment anterior to the mouth, including the acron, antennal segment, and intercalary segment (McAlpine).

preoral tuber, in Siphonaptera, an incrassation immediately in front of the oral angle, particularly conspicuous in some bat fleas (Ischnopsyllidae) (Lewis, pers. comm.).

preparapteron (pl., **preparaptera**), basalare, q.v. (T-B, after Comstock).

prepectus, an anterior marginal sclerite of the sternopleural areas of a segment, set off by a transverse suture continuous through the sternum and episternum (T-B, after Snodgrass); in adult Hymenoptera, sclerite between the pronotum and mesepisternum, site of origin of the spiracular occlusor muscle (T-B, after Comstock; Gibson); in some Tubulifera (Thysanoptera), paired prothoracic sternites (Stannard).

prepenalis, in ♂ Blatteropteroidea, hypophallus, q.v. (Tuxen, after Berlese).

prepharynx, preoral cavity, q.v. (T-B, after MacGillivray).

prepupa, in Thysanoptera and ♂ Coccoidea (Hemiptera: Sternorrhyncha), propupa, q.v. (T-B, after Imms; Chapman); in Holometabola, the active but nonfeeding, last instar larva of the pharate pupa (T-B, after Wardle; Hinton and Mackerras, in CSIRO); see pharate instar.

prepupal, preceeding the change to pupa (T-B).

preputial, of or pertaining to the preputium (T-B).

preputial fold, in many ♂ Odonata, process projecting from body of prophallus beneath glands (Tuxen, after Fraser).

preputial glands, in ♂ insects, glands associated with external opening of ductus ejaculatorius (Tuxen, after Snodgrass).

preputial sac, in ♂ Dermaptera, hollow sac in penis lobe carrying sclerotized plate on wall and virga at anterior end (Tuxen, after Zacher); in ♂ Phthiraptera, endophallus, q.v. (Clay, in Tuxen; Lyal); see endophallus; in ♂ Lepidoptera, vesica, q.v. (Tuxen, after Snodgrass).

preputium (pl., **preputia**), the external membranous covering of the penis (T-B); in ♂ Orthoptera, sheath of penis, q.v. (transl. "prépuce" Chopard; Tuxen); in ♂ Coleoptera, second connecting membrane, q.v. (transl. "prépuce" Tuxen); in ♂ Lepidoptera, vesica, q.v. (Tuxen, after Hofmann); in ♂ Diptera, juxta, q.v. (Tuxen, after Hall); in ♂ Hymenoptera, basal ring, q.v. (Tuxen, after Konow), basal ring + bases of gonocoxites + volsellae (Tuxen, after Hartig), or bases of parapenial lobes plus volsellae (Tuxen, after Rohwer).

prerectal, anterior to the rectum (T-B).

presacculus (pl., **presacculi**), in ♂ Thyatiridae (Lepidoptera), distal process of sacculus (Tuxen, after Werny).

presaepium, in larval Camponotini (Hymenoptera: Formicidae), shallow depression on the ventral surface of certain anterior abdominal somites (G.C. and J. Wheeler).

prescutal ridge, the internal ridge formed by the prescutal suture (T-B, after Snodgrass).

prescutal pits, in some adult Tipulidae, Ceratopogonidae, Culicidae, and Chironomidae (Diptera), pits coincident with prescutal suture (Harbach and Knight; McAlpine).

prescutal suture, a transverse groove of the mesonotum or metanotum behind the antecostal suture, setting off a prescutum from the scutum, being largely obsolescent in adult Diptera (T-B, after Snodgrass); in adult Hymenoptera, notaulus, q.v. (Gauld and Bolton).

prescutellar area, in adult Chironomidae (Diptera), a somewhat sunken and flat area of central region of posterior half of scutum

(Saether); in adult Culicidae (Diptera), the median posterior area of the scutum between the acrostichal area and the scutellum (Harbach and Knight, after LaCasse and Yamaguti).

prescutellar bristles, in adult Diptera, prescutellar setae, q.v. (T-B, after Comstock).

prescutellar callus, postalar callus, q.v. (T-B).

prescutellar row, in adult Diptera, prescutellar setae, q.v. (T-B).

prescutellar scale, in adult Culicidae (Diptera), any scale occurring on the prescutellar area of the scutum (Harbach and Knight).

prescutellar seta, in adult Diptera, a transverse row of setae in front of the scutellum consisting of the hindmost acrostichal and dorsocentral setae.

prescutellars, in adult Chironomidae (Diptera), prescutellar setae, q.v. (Saether).

prescutellum, in some adult Diptera, a small ridge preceeding the scutellum (T-B; Colless and McAlpine, in CSIRO).

prescutoscutal, pertaining to both the prescutum and the scutum (T-B).

prescutoscutal suture, in adult Diptera, prescutal suture, q.v. (McAlpine).

prescutum, the anterior area of the mesonotum or metanotum in front of the scutum, between the antecostal suture and the prescutal suture (T-B, after Snodgrass, Imms); in adult Diptera, presutural area, q.v. (McAlpine, after Curran); in adult Hymenoptera, median mesoscutal lobe, q.v. (Gauld and Bolton).

preseptular setae, in larval Scarabaeoidea (Coleoptera), a patch of either a few or numerous tegellar setae present between the anterior end of the septula and the very long and thin hairs at the anterior margin of the last abdominal segment (Peterson, after Böving).

presocial, applied to the condition or to the group possessing it, in which individuals display some degree of social behavior short of eusociality, being either subsocial or parasocial (Wilson).

presoldier, in Isoptera, an intermediate developmental stage between larva, pseudergate, or nymph and the definitive, mature soldier form, apparently not yet functional for defense (Miller, in Krishna and Weesner).

prespiracular area, in adult Culicidae (Diptera), the small area of the anterior mesanepisternum just anterior to the mesothoracic spiracle, set off from the postpronotum by a strong ridge (Harbach and Knight, after Knight and Laffoon).

prespiracular group, in larval Lepidoptera, lateral group of setae (L_1–L_3), q.v. (Peterson; Common, pers. comm.).

prespiracular pinaculum, in larval Lepidoptera, prespiracular wart, q.v. (Peterson).

prespiracular scale, in adult Culicidae (Diptera), one of the scales occuring in a small group on the prespiracular area of the anterior mesanepisternum (Harbach and Knight).

prespiracular seta(e), in larval Lepidoptera, lateral group of setae, q.v. (Common, pers. comm.); in adult Culicidae (Diptera), any seta occurring on the prespiracular area of the anterior mesanepisternum (Harbach and Knight).

prespiracular wart, in larval Lepidoptera, sclerotized area anterior to the prothoracic spiracle, bearing the kappa group (= lateral group) of setae (Peterson).

press, in larval Lepidoptera, silk press, q.v. (T-B).

pressure plate, auxilia, q.v., at base of pulvillus (T-B).

presternal, anterior to the sternum in position; of or pertaining to the presternum (T-B).

presternal suture, a suture associated with an internal submarginal ridge reinforcing the anterior part of the eusternum, setting off a narrow marginal area of the sternum, the presternum (T-B, after Snodgrass).

presternum, a narrow anterior area of the sternum sometimes set off from the basisternum by a submarginal suture of the eusternum (T-B, after Snodgrass); see acrosternite.

prestigma, in some adult Braconidae and Bethylidae (Hymenoptera), an accessory enlargement of pterostigma (Riek, in CSIRO); in adult Vespidae (Hymenoptera), extension of radial sector (R_s) toward pterostigma (Carpenter, pers. comm., after Carpenter and Cumming).

prestomal teeth, in some Muscomorpha (Diptera), e.g., *Haematobia* (Muscidae), teeth arising from the lateral margin of the discal sclerite of the labella, lying between the opening of 2 pseudotracheae (T-B, after Matheson; Colless and McAlpine, in CSIRO).

prestomum, in Diptera, the cleft between the labellar lobes anterior to the aperture of the food canal (T-B, after Snodgrass).

presubterminal, in adult Lepidoptera, preceding the subterminal transverse line (T-B).

presumptive organization, arrangement of cells in the embryo into groups which in normal development become a particular organ or tissue (Pfadt).

presutural acrostichal seta, in adult Diptera, acrostichal seta located anterior to the transverse suture (McAlpine).

presutural area, in adult Diptera, anterior portion of scutum separated from postsutural area by transverse suture (McAlpine).

presutural bristle, presutural supraalar seta, q.v. (T-B, after Comstock, Curran).

presutural depression, in Diptera, a depression, usually triangular, at the outer end of the transverse suture, near the notopleural suture (T-B, after Comstock).

presutural interalar bristle, in adult Diptera, presutural intraalar seta, q.v. (T-B).

presutural intraalar seta, in adult Diptera, an intraalar seta anterior to the transverse suture of the mesoscutum (McAlpine).

presutural supraalar seta, in adult Diptera, setae on mesoscutum immediately anterior to transverse suture and adjacent to notopleuron (T-B, after McAlpine).

presystolic notch, in a mechanical recording of heart activity, a slight dip immediately before systole indicating a slight expansion before the contraction (Chapman).

pretarsal bladder, in Thysanoptera, eversible sac at end of tarsus which is used for adhesion to varied surfaces (Heming); see arolium.

pretarsal claw(s), usually paired claws of the pretarsus, at the apex of the leg (Boudreaux).

pretarsal depressor muscle, muscle attached to the unquitractor tendon that depresses the pretarsal claws (Chapman).

pretarsus, last segment of the insect leg, being either a single-claw segment (Protura, some Collembola, and many holometabolous larvae) or a pair of claws, arolium, auxillae, and unguitractor plate (T-B; Chapman); in Collembola, the short apical segment attached to the tibiotarsus and bearing the unguis, the unguiculus (if present), and a pair of minute lateral setae (Christiansen and Bellinger); see dactylopodite.

pretentoria, anterior tentorial arms, q.v. (T-B, after MacGillivray, Crampton).

pretentorinae (sing., **pretentorina**), anterior tentorial pits, q.v. (T-B, after MacGillivray).

preterga, in larval Coleoptera, anterior thoracic scutes (T-B).

pretergite, acrotergite, q.v. (T-B, after Crampton).

pretornal, in Lepidoptera, preceding the tornus (T-B).

prevalence, in invertebrate pathology, the total number of cases of a particular disease at a given moment in time, in a given population (Steinhaus and Martignoni); see incidence.

prevertex, the cephalic area of the vertex when it is divided into 2 parts by the fusion of the compound eyes (T-B, after MacGillivray).

prickled body, in ♀ Coleophoridae (Lepidoptera), an additional small signum (Tuxen, after Toll).

prickly membrane, in ♀ Coleophoridae (Lepidoptera), caudal part of ductus bursae covered with tiny prickles (Tuxen, after Toll).

primapupa, in Thysanoptera, propupa, q.v. (Heming).

primary allometrosis, the alliance of females of different species of ants (Hymenoptera: Formicidae) to found a single colony (Tulloch, after Wasmann).

primary culture, a culture started from cells, tissues, or organs taken directly from organisms (Steinhaus and Martignoni); see cell culture, organ culture, and tissue culture.

primary cuticula, exocuticle, q.v. (T-B).

primary etiologic factors, in invertebrate pathology, direct causes, q.v. (Steinhaus and Martignoni).

primary eyes, in Coccoidea (Hemiptera: Sternorrhyncha), the simple eyes of the ♀ which persist throughout all the nymphal stages into the adult (T-B).

primary genitalia, in ♂ Odonata, the original, but highly reduced genitalia on abdominal segment IX, the copulating role being transferred to accessory genitalia (Tuxen).

primary gonopore, in ♂ Heteroptera (Hemiptera), distal end of ductus ejaculatorius before entering phallus at level of foramen ductus to emerge into ductus seminis (Tuxen, after Dupuis and Carvalho).

primary homonym, each of 2 or more identical species-group names established for different nominal taxa and originally combined with the same generic name (ICZN).

primary iris cells, primary pigment cells, q.v. (T-B, after Imms).

primary intergradation, a zone of intermediacy between 2 phenotypically distinct populations, having developed *in situ* as a result of selection (Mayr); see secondary intergradation.

primary ocelli, in adult insects, nymphs and naiads, ocelli, q.v. (T-B, after Comstock).

primary phallic lobes, in ♂ insects, a pair of small ectodermal outgrowths on nymph or larva, giving rise to external genitalia and containing terminal ampullae of vasa deferentia, developing in numerous insects as an invagination between abdominal sterna IX and X, remaining in Ephemeroptera as separate penes, fusing in Thysanura into a single penis, and dividing in higher orders into 2 phallomeres, viz. mesomeres and parameres (Tuxen, after Snodgrass).

primary pigment cells, pigmented corneagen cells lying outside of the Semper cells and the crystaline cone of an ommatidium (T-B, after Snodgrass; Chapman).

primary polygyny, polygyny when multiple queens found a colony together (Wilson).

primary reproductive, in termites (Isoptera), colony founding ♀ or ♂ derived from winged adult (Miller).

primary royal pair, in Isoptera, the king (♂) and the queen (reproductive ♀) of the colony (T-B, after Comstock).

primary segmentation, that type of segmentation which occurs in all soft-bodied arthropods and annelid worms; the embryonic form of segmentation (T-B, after Snodgrass).

primary sensorium (pl., **sensoria**), in Aphididae (Hemiptera: Sternorrhyncha), the circular opening apically on the penultimate antennal segment and basally on the ultimate antennal segment (Stoetzel, in Stehr); see secondary sensorium.

primary setae, in larval Lepidoptera, those setae with a definite arrangement and found in at least the first instar, and in all instars of generalized forms (T-B, after Comstock; Peterson); see secondary setae and subprimary setae.

primary somatic hermaphrodite, an insect which has the gonad or gonads of one sex only but parts of the secondary sexual apparatus, internal or external, of both sexes (T-B).

primary type, holotype, syntype, lectotype, or neotype (T-B); see name-bearing type.

primary zoological literature, literature presenting original research results, as opposed to catalogs, texts, and other compilations or summaries.

primer pheromone, pheromone that acts to physiologically alter the endocrine and reproductive systems of the receptor animal, reprogramming it for an altered response pattern (Matthews and Matthews).

primitive, nearest to a hypothetical ancestor (Leftwich); see plesiomorphic.

primitive streak, in the insect embryo, germ band, q.v. (T-B).

primitively eusocial, living as a eusocial colony in which castes are morphologically similar and food exchange among adults is absent or minimal (Michener).

principal armature, in ♂ *Isoperla* (Plecoptera: Perlodidae), principal part of the sclerotized armature of penis (transl. "armature principale" Despax, after Tuxen).

principal copulatory process, in ♂ Grylloblattodea, principal copulatory sclerite, q.v. (Tuxen, after Walker).

principal copulatory sclerite, in ♂ Grylloblattodea, large sclerite carried by right phallomere (Tuxen, after Scudder).

principal salivary gland, in Heteroptera (Hemiptera), the major salivary gland of the paired salivary system, with 2 or more lobes, always associated with an accessory salivary gland (Cobben; Miyamoto).

principal sulcus, in Orthoptera, a transverse impression of the prothorax, at or behind the middle (T-B).

principal vein, in Auchenorrhyncha (Hemiptera), the fused veins of the tegmen from subcosta (Sc) to first branch of cubitus (Cu_1) (T-B, after Tillyard).

Principle of Allocation, the concept that each animal must divide its time and energy among 3 major requirements, which are (in their usual order of descending importance) food, defense against predators, and reproduction (Matthews and Matthews, after Wilson).

Principle of Binominal Nomenclature, the principle that the scientific name of a species, and not of a taxon at any other rank, is a combination of 2 names (a binomen), the first being the generic name and the second the specific name (ICZN).

Principle of Coordination, the principle that within the family group, genus group, or species group, a name established for a taxon at any rank in the group is deemed to be simultaneously established with the same author and date for taxa based on the same name-bearing type at other ranks in the group (ICZN); see name-bearing type.

Principle of First Reviser, the principle that the relative precedence of 2 or more names or nomenclatural acts published on the same date, or of different original spellings of the same name, is determined by the first reviser (ICZN); see Principle of Priority.

Principle of Homonymy, the principle that an available name that is a junior homonym of another available name must not be used as a valid name (ICZN).

Principle of Name-bearing Types, the principle that each nominal taxon has, actually or potentially, its name-bearing type that provides the objective standard of reference by which the application of the name is determined (ICZN).

Principle of Priority, the principle that the valid name of a taxon is the oldest available name applied to it, provided that the name is not invalidated by any provision of the Code or by any ruling of the Commission (ICZN); see Principle of First Reviser.

printer's error, an incorrect spelling made in type setting; typographical error (ICZN); see *lapsus calami.*

priodont, a form of ♂ Lucanidae (Coleoptera) which has the smallest mandibles (T-B); see teleodont, mesodont, and amphiodont.

priority, seniority fixed by the date of publication (T-B; ICZN); see Principle of Priority.

prismatic, formed like a prism; with a play of colors similar to that produced through a prism (T-B); see iridescent.

pro-, Latin prefix; anterior, before, foward, fore or forth (T-B).

proacrosomal granule, in developing spermatid, a granule first appearing in the cup of the acroblast that later enlarges forming the acrosome (Chapman).

proala, forewing, q.v. (T-B).

proamnion, in the egg of *Machilis* (Archaeognatha: Machilidae), amnion, q.v. (Chapman; Sturm, pers. comm., after Larink).

proandropodites, in ♂ Diptera, primary phallic lobes, q.v. (Tuxen, after Christophers).

probasisternum, basisternum of prothorax (Harbach and Knight).

Proboscidea, Coccoidea, q.v. (T-B); all Diptera excluding the Pupipara (T-B, after Latreille).

proboscidial fossa, in adult Hymenoptera, preoral cavity, q.v. (Gauld and Bolton).

proboscipedia, in Diptera (e.g. *Drosophila*), developmental anomaly in which the labellum matures as a leg (Tulloch).

proboscis, any extended mouth structure (T-B); in Hemiptera, rostrum, q.v. (T-B); in adult Trichoptera, extended and elongate mouthparts, e.g., in Plectrotarsidae, Kokiriidae and Dipseudopsidae (Neboiss); in adult Lepidoptera, the coiled tube formed from the fused galeae of maxillae (T-B; Chapman); in adult Diptera, extensile mouthparts (T-B; Leftwich) or just labium (T-B, after McGillivray); in bees (Hymenoptera: Apoidea), elongate labium (Leftwich); see rostrum.

procaryotes, those microorganisms (viruses, bacteria, blue-green algae) that lack well-defined nuclei and meiosis (Mayr); see eucaryotes.

procephalic, relating or belonging to the procephalon (T-B).

procephalic antennae, in Arthropoda, antennules, q.v. (T-B).

procephalic lobes, in the embryo, part of the anterior overhanging portion of the head (T-B).

procephalon, in the embryo, that segment of the head which is formed by the coalescence of the first 3 primitive segments (T-B).

procerebral, protocerebral, q.v. (T-B).

procerebral lobes, protocerebral lobes, q.v. (T-B).

procerebrum, protocerebrum, q.v. (T-B; Leftwich).

procersus, in larval Chironomidae (Diptera), preanal tubercle carrying 1–20 apical setae and usually 2 lateral setae (Saether).

process, a prolongation of a surface, of a margin, or of an appendage (T-B).

process of left paraproct, in ♂ Embiidina, process on caudal margin of left paraproct (Ross, in Tuxen).

processes of aedeagus, in ♂ Siphonaptera, lobes of aedeagus, q.v. (Tuxen).

processes of posterior edge of sternite VIII, in adult Chironomidae, gonapophysis VIII, q.v. (Saether).

processionary behaviors, in Lepidoptera, movement in single file of gregarious larvae (Common).

processus (Latin), process, q.v. (Tuxen).

processus acetabuli, in ♂ Siphonaptera, acetabular projection, q.v. (Tuxen).

processus analis, in adult Chironomidae (Diptera), anal point, q.v. (Saether).

processus apicalis, in ♂ Lygaeidae (Hemiptera: Heteroptera), ? processus gonopori, q.v. (Tuxen, after Ashlock); in ♂ Pyrrhocoridae (Hemiptera: Heteroptera), process of paramere at base of processus hamatus (Tuxen, after Stehlik); in ♂ Coniopterygidae (Planipennia), apical process of each paramere (Tuxen, after Tjeder).

processus articularis, in ♂ Siphonaptera, telomere, q.v. (Tuxen, after Dampf); in ♀ Hymenoptera, dorsal ramus, q.v. (Tuxen, after Oeser).

processus basalis plicae, in ♂ Lithosiinae (Lepidoptera: Arctiidae), a more or less sclerotized process from plica centripetalis mesad of processus momenti (Tuxen, after Birket-Smith).

processus basalis valvae, in some ♂ Tortricidae (Lepidoptera), part of costa, attaching valva to fultura superior or diaphragma (Tuxen); in ♂ *Leucanitis* (Lepidoptera: Noctuidae), long, slender process from near base of valva, being part of harpe (Tuxen, after John).

processus basilaris, in ♂ Heteroptera (Hemiptera), basis parameri, q.v. (Tuxen, after Piotrowski).

processus basimeris, in ♂ Siphonaptera, dorsoapical projection of basimere (Tuxen, after Smit).

processus basimeris dorsalis, in ♂ Siphonaptera, dorsoanterior projection of processus basimeris (Tuxen, after Smit).

processus basimeris ventralis, in ♂ Siphonaptera, ventroposterior projection of processus basimeris (Tuxen, after Smit).

processus capitati, in ♂ Heteroptera (Hemiptera), capitate process, q.v. (Tuxen, after Dupuis).

processus conjunctivae, in ♂ Heteroptera (Hemiptera), paired or unpaired hooks and diverticula (not appendages) arising from conjunctiva (Tuxen, after Dupuis).

processus distalis plicae, in ♂ Lithosiinae (Lepidoptera: Arctiidae), a more or less sclerotized process from plica centripetalis distad of proximal momenti (Tuxen, after Birket-Smith).

processus dorsalis, in ♂ Siphonaptera, processus basimeris or processus basimeris dorsalis, q.v. (Tuxen, after Peus).

processus furculiformis, in ♂ Odonata, forked process at base of ligula (Tuxen).

processus gonopori, in ♂ Heteroptera (Hemiptera), secondary median process of phallic external wall, distal to endosoma or vesica and prolonging, not surrounding, ductus seminis (Tuxen, after Dupuis); in ♂ Heteroptera (Hemiptera), the true vesica when elongated (Pyrrhocoridae) or when the true conjunctiva (distal part of conjunctiva) is erroneously interpreted as a vesica (Lygaeidae) (Tuxen, after Ashlock, Stehlik); in ♂ Reduviidae (Hemiptera: Heteroptera), ductifer, q.v. (Tuxen, after Lent and Jurberg).

processus hamatus, in ♂ Heteroptera (Hemiptera), apical portion of the paramere (Tuxen, after Piotrowski).

processus inferior, in ♂ Pyrrhocoridae (Hemiptera: Heteroptera), inferior process, q.v. (Tuxen, after after Stehlik).

processus inferior (valvae), in ♂ *Argynnis, Brenthis* (Lepidoptera: Nymphalidae), elongate process of inner face of valva, being part of sacculus or harpe (Tuxen, after Petersen).

processus laterales (sing., **processus lateralis**), in ♂ Neuroptera, lateral processes of hypandrium (Tuxen, after Tjeder).

processus lateralis epiphalli, in ♂ Caelifera (Orthoptera), a lateral process of epiphallus (Tuxen).

processus liguloideus, in ♂ Anisoptera (Odonata), ligula, q.v. (Tuxen).

processus longus, in ♂ Muscomorpha (Diptera), sclerotizations of the upper wall of the periandrial fold consisting of a pair of lateral, rodlike sclerites (Griffiths); bacilliform sclerites, q.v. (Tuxen; McAlpine).

processus medianus, in ♀ Hymenoptera, notum (in part) and some of the rami (Tuxen, after Oeser).

processus medioventralis, in ♂ Lepidoptera, saccus, q.v. (Tuxen, after de Graaf).

processus momenti, in ♂ Lithosiinae (Lepidoptera: Arctiidae), an internal process or apodeme from dorsal edge of basis valvae, usually extending mesad or cephalad (Tuxen, after Birket-Smith).

processus phallothecae, in ♂ Heteroptera (Hemiptera), paired or unpaired diverticula (not appendages) arising from phallotheca (Tuxen, after Dupuis).

processus pleurae, in ♂ Lepidoptera, apophyses anteriores, q.v. (Tuxen, after van Eecke).

processus pontalis, in ♂ Siphonaptera, vertical strut on inner side of basimere supporting end of pons parameralis (Tuxen, after Günther).

processus spermathecae, in ♀ Trichoptera, complicated and extremely variable sclerite in the genital chamber, bearing the opening of the ductus spermathecae (Nielsen).

processus sternalis, in ♀ Protura, are flat stiffenings lying along the ventral side of the styli found distal to the perigynium (Tuxen, after Conde).

processus superior, in ♂ *Ariadne* (Lepidoptera: Nymphalidae), a strongly developed costa which stands out nearly separate from rest of valva (Tuxen, after Roepke).

processus superior valvae, in ♂ Lepidoptera, long, slender process, sometimes pointed, hooked, or finely spined, from near dorsal margin of valva, extending dorsocaudad (Tuxen, after Petersen).

processus terminalis (pl., **processus terminales**), in some Aphididae (Hemiptera: Sternorrhyncha), unguis, q.v. (Woodward et al., in CSIRO); in ♂ Neuropteroidea, apical process of hypandrium (Tuxen, after Tjeder).

processus valvulae, in ♀ *Cyrestis* (Lepidoptera: Nymphalidae), apophyses posteriores, q.v. (Tuxen, after de Graaf).

processus ventralis, in ♂ Siphonaptera, processus basimeris ventralis, q.v. (Tuxen, after Peus).

processus vesicae, in ♂ Nepidae (Hemiptera: Heteroptera), paired or unpaired hooks and diverticula arising laterally from vesica (not appendages) (Tuxen, after Dupuis).

procidentia (pl., **procidentiae**), in some ♂ Symphyta (Hymenoptera), a fluting on abdominal tergum VIII under which gonapophyses are everted (T-B; Tuxen, after Ross).

proclinate, inclined foward or downward, e.g., hairs and bristles of adult Diptera (T-B; Borror et al.; McAlpine).

procoxa, forecoxa, q.v.

procoxal cavity, coxal cavity of the prothorax (Harbach and Knight).

procrypsis, concealment from predators (Norris, in CSIRO); see anticrypsis.

procryptic coloration, coloration which is useful in protective resemblances, for concealment as protection against enemies (T-B).

proctifer, in ♀ Coleoptera, proctiger, q.v. (Tuxen, after Heberdey).

proctiger, reduced abdominal segment X, bearing the anus (T-B, after Tillyard; Tulloch); in ♂ Psyllidae (Hemiptera: Sternorrhyncha), abdominal segment X situated on anterior part of hypandrium (Tuxen); in Heteroptera (Hemiptera), anal tube, q.v. (Tuxen, after Crampton) or anal tube and anal segment together (Tuxen); in Neuroptera, papilla carrying anus (Tuxen); in *Agulla* (Raphidioptera: Raphidiidae), fused ectoprocts, q.v. (Tuxen, after Ferris and Pennebaker); in Trichoptera, abdominal segment X (Tuxen, after MacFarlane); in adult Diptera, the segments behind abdominal segment IX bearing the anus (Tuxen); in ♂ Strepsiptera, abdominal segment X (Tuxen); in ♀ Coleoptera, tergum X (Tuxen, after Tanner); see anal segment.

proctiger lobes, in ♂ Psyllidae (Hemiptera: Sternorrhyncha), posterior processes of lateral parts of proctiger (Tuxen).

proctodaeal, of or pertaining to the proctodaeum or hind gut (T-B).

proctodaeal feeding, in Kalotermitidae (Isoptera), social feeding on liquid excrement containing fragments of wood and intestinal flagellates of workers resulting in a transfer of symbionts (Chapman).

proctodeal food, in Isoptera, food passed from anus to mouth by adults (Tulloch).

proctodaeal valve, pyloric valve, q.v. (T-B, after Snodgrass).

proctodaeum, proctodeum, the anus and intestine as far foward as and including the Malpighian tubules formed by the ectodermal invagination of the epiblast (T-B; Chapman); see hind gut.

proctodone, in *Ostrinia* (Lepidoptera: Pyralidae), hormone secreted by the cells of the ileum (Chapman).

Proctotrupoidea, poorly defined superfamily within the Apocrita (Hymenoptera), including the Proctotrupidae and other families, possessing adults with a single foretibial spur, hind wing lacking closed cells, lateral pronotum vertically grooved for reception of forefemur, spiracle covering lobe of pronotum reaching back to tegula and not margined with close fine hairs, no subantennal groove, and hind tibia without spurs modified for preening (Riek, in CSIRO; Gauld and Bolton); see Ceraphronoidea.

procumbent, trailing; prostrate; lying flat (T-B).

procuticle, cuticle as it is first secreted, later being differentiated into exocuticle, mesocuticle, and endocuticle (Tulloch, after Richards; Chapman).

prodromal, in invertebrate pathology, relating to prodromes or the initial stage of a disease (Steinhaus and Martignoni).

prodrome, in inverebrate pathology, a premonitory sign, indicating the onset of disease (Steihaus and Martignoni).

produced, producted, productus (Latin), extended, prolonged, or projected (T-B; Borror et al.).

productile, protrusible, q.v. (T-B).

production, that part of any structure which has been produced or extended; the act of producing or extending (T-B).

proecdysis, the period of preparation for a moult in an insect or other arthropod (Leftwich).

proeminent, standing out; said of the head when it is horizontal and does not form an angle with the thorax (T-B).

proepimeral scale, in adult Culicidae (Diptera), one of the scales occurring in a group on the proepimeron (Harbach and Knight).

proepimeral seta, in adult Diptera, seta on proepimeron (McAlpine).

proepimeron (pl., **proepimera**), epimeron of the prothorax (T-B, after Garman; Borror et al.; McAlpine).

proepisternal scale, in adult Culicidae (Diptera), any scale borne on the proepisternum (Harbach and Knight).

proepisternal seta, in adult Culicidae (Diptera), a seta borne on the proepisternum (Harbach and Knight; McAlpine).

proepisternum (pl., **proepisterna**), episternum of the prothorax (T-B, after Garman; Borror et al.; McAlpine).

profemur, forefemur, q.v.

profile, outline as seen from the side or in lateral view (T-B; Borror et al.).

profound, profundus (Latin), deep (T-B; R. W. Brown).

profurca, the furca of the prosternum (T-B; Harbach and Knight).

profurcasternum, area of the prosternum posterior to the sternacostal suture and/or the apophyseal pits (Harbach and Knight).

progenital plate, in ♂ Diptera, part of hypandrium (Tuxen, after Graham-Smith).

prognathous, having the head horizontal with the jaws directed foward (T-B).

prognosis, in invertebrate pathology, forecast of the probable course of a disease (Steinhaus and Martignoni).

Progoneata, group within the Myriapoda, including the Chilopoda and Symphyla (Hennig; Boudreaux, after Pocock).

progoneate, with the genital opening on an anterior body segment (T-B).

progonia, humeral angle, q.v., of hind wing (T-B).

progrediens, in Aphididae (Hemiptera: Sternorrhyncha), nymphs of the third generation which develop into wingless agamic females (T-B, after Comstock); in Adelgidae (Hemiptera: Sternorrhyncha), wingless adults forming several generations on a secondary host (Carter).

progression rule, rule stating that the ancestral species, or the descendants of that ancestral species that retain the least apomorphic phenotype, are found in the center of origin of the group (Wiley, after Hennig).

progressive infection, in invertebrate pathology, an interaction between an infectious agent and its host, resulting in overt disease of the host (Steinhaus and Martignoni); see attenuated infection and infection.

progressive provisioning, the act of providing the larva with meals at intervals during its development, e.g., solitary bees and wasps Hymenoptera: Aculeata) (Wilson); see mass provisioning.

prohemocyte, small rounded cell with relatively large nuceli and intensely basophilic cytoplasm which contains a large number of ribosomes but little endoplasmic reticulum, dividing frequently and giving rise to other types of hemocytes (Tulloch; Chapman).

projecting blade(s), in ♂ *Phalera bucephala* (Lepidoptera: Notodontidae), apical process of costa of valva, being part of harpe (transl. "lame(s) saillante" de Geer, after Tuxen).

prolapsus vulvaris, in ♀ Lepidoptera, extensile, tortuous lengthening of ductus bursae, bearing ostium bursae and sterigma apically (Tuxen).

Prolate (trade name), phosmet, q.v. (Pfadt).

proleg, any process or appendage that serves the purpose of, but is not homologous with, a leg (T-B); in Lepidoptera and most Symphyta (Hymenoptera), hollow, paired, cylindrical outgrowths of the abdominal segments used in locomotion (T-B; Chapman); foreleg, q.v. (T-B, after MacGillivray); in Diptera larvae, round or fleshy tubercles usually located in pairs ventrally on the prothorax and terminal segment, on the terminal segment alone, or on one or more intermediate abdominal segments (Teskey, in McAlpine); in larval Chironomidae (Diptera), parapod, q.v. (Saether).

proleucocyte, prohemocyte, q.v. (T-B; Tulloch).

proleucocytoid, prohemocyte, q.v. (Tulloch, after Yeager).

proliferate, to increase in size by a repeated process of budding or cell division (T-B).

proliferation, growing by the rapid production of new cells (T-B).

proline, $C_5H_9O_2N$, an amino acid in insect hemolymph used as an energy source (Gilmour, in CSIRO).

proloma, costal margin, q.v., of hind wing (T-B).

prolonged, extended or lengthened beyond ordinary limits.

prolymphocyte, prohemocyte, q.v. (Tulloch, after Ermin).

promeros, the first abdominal segment in Lepidoptera (T-B).

premesonotal sclerite, in some adult Hymenoptera, united pronotum and mesonotum (Gauld and Bolton).

prometatarsus, proximal tarsal segment of a prothoracic leg (Peterson).

prominence, protuberance, q.v. (Borror et al.).

prominent, raised or produced above the surface or beyond the margin; standing out in relief; conspicuous by position (T-B; Harris).

promotor apodeme(s) (of phallobase), in ♂ Heteroptera (Hemiptera), capitate processes, q.v. (Tuxen, after Bonhag and Wick).

promuscidate, with a proboscis or extended mouth structure (T-B).

promuscis, proboscis, q.v. (T-B).

prone, lying on the venter (T-B).

prong, a slender sclerotized projection (Peterson).

prong of aedoeagus, in ♂ Coleophoridae (Lepidoptera), greatly elongate, sclerotized, slender and pointed distal part of the aedoeagus, single or double, sometimes armed with teeth (Tuxen, after Toll).

pronope, in adult Zelinae (Hymenoptera: Braconidae), a mediodorsal pit of the pronotum (van Achterberg).

pronotal carina, in Orthoptera and certain Heteroptera (Hemiptera), the main or median carina or keel on the pronotum (T-B).

pronotal comb, in adult Siphonaptera, a row of strong spines borne on the posterior margin of the pronotum (T-B; Borror et al.).

pronotal hypomenon, in adult Coleoptera, the inflexed portion of the pronotum, beneath the lateral margin (T-B).

pronotal lobe(s), in Orthoptera, large descending lateral lobes, which are usually subvertical and form the sides of the prothorax (Key, in CSIRO); in Heteroptera (Hemiptera), posterior pronotal lobe, q.v. (Andersen); in many adult Aculeata and Evanoidea (Hymenoptera), posterolateral region of the pronotum extending over the lateral edge of the mesepisternum so as to cover the mesothoracic spiracle (Gibson; Gauld and Bolton).

pronotum, the upper and dorsal part of the prothorax (T-B); see antepronotum and postpronotum.

pronucleus, the nucleus of ♂ and ♀ elements, spermatozoa and ova, the union of which forms the nucleus of a fertilized ovum (T-B).

pronymph, the newly hatched nymph of Odonata, Orthoptera, Blattaria, Mantodea, and Aphididae (Hemiptera: Sternorrhyncha), which shows a more or less embryonic appearance, being invested with a shining chitinous sheath, being a stage of extremely short duration (T-B, after Imms; Peterson; O'Farrell, Key, in CSIRO); in certain holometabolous insects, e.g., sawflies (Hymenoptera: Symphyta), pharate pupal stage in which the larval tissues are completely broken down and the imaginal tissues are just beginning to build up (T-B, after J. B. Smith; Hinton and Mackerras, in CSIRO).

pronymphal phase, in Symphyta (Hymenoptera), pronymph, q.v. (Gauld and Bolton).

proovigenic, completing ovigenesis after emergence from the pupa, e.g., most endoparasitic koinobionts (Gauld and Bolton); see synovigenic.

proparamere, in ♂ Dermaptera, proximal part of penis (Tuxen, after Burr).

pro parte (Latin), in part (T-B).

propagative transmission, circulative transmission of viruses in which the virus multiplies within the vector without cyclical change (Nault and Ammar; Adkins, pers. comm.); see cyclopropagative transmission and viral transmission.

propargite, $C_{19}H_{26}O_4S$, a synthetic acaricide, 2-(p-tert-butylphenoxy) cyclohexyl 2-propynyl sulfite; slightly toxic to mammals; acute oral LD_{50} for rats 2200 mg/kg (Pfadt).

propedes, prothoracic legs (T-B); in larvae, prolegs, q.v. (T-B).

Prophalangopsoidea, superfamily within the Ensifera (Orthoptera), including the hump-winged crickets of the family Prophalangopsidae, sometimes included within the Tettigonoidea (Hennig; Kevan, in Parker).

prophallus (pl., **prophalli**), the "penis" of the accessory genitalia, situated in floor of fenestra between hamuli and not visible during rest (Tuxen).

propharynx, cibarium, q.v. (T-B, after MacGillivray).

propleg, proleg, q.v. (T-B).

proplegmatium (pl., **proplegmatia**), in larval Scarabaeioidea (Coleoptera), a paired space with a plicate surface inside and usually somewhat in front of a plegmatium (T-B, after Böving).

propleural bristle, in adult Diptera, proepisternal seta, q.v. (T-B, after Curran; Borror et al.; McAlpine).

propleural ridge, pleural ridge of prothorax (Harbach and Knight).

propleural suture, pleural suture, q.v., on prothorax (McAlpine).

propleuron (pl., **propleura**), pleuron of the prothorax (T-B; Borror et al.).

propleurosternal ridge, pleurosternal ridge of prothorax (Harbach and Knight).

propleurosternal suture, pleurosternal suture of prothorax (Harbach and Knight).

propneustic respiratory system, oligopneustic respiratory system, q.v., with only mesothoracic pair of spiracles functional, being located on the prothorax, e.g., pupal Diptera (T-B; Leftwich; Chapman).

propodeon, propodeum, q.v. (T-B).

propodeal foramen, in adult Apocrita (Hymenoptera), socket of propodeum in which gaster articulates (Gauld and Bolton).

propodeal orifice, in adult Apocrita (Hymenoptera), propodeal foramen, q.v. (Carpenter, pers. comm., after Richards).

propodeal spiracles, in adult Apocrita (Hymenoptera), pair of spiracles on propodeum (Gauld and Bolton).

propodeal teeth, in adult Myrmecinae (Hymenoptera: Formicidae), spines on propodeum which protect the pedicel (Brown, pers. comm.).

propodeal triangle, in adult Apocrita (Hymenoptera), metapostnotum, q.v. (Gauld and Bolton).

propodeum, in adult Apocrita (Hymenoptera), the first abdominal segment when it forms a part of the alitrunk (T-B, after Comstock).

propodite, tarsus, q.v. (T-B, after Snodgrass).

propolis, a collective term for resins and waxes collected by bees (Hymenoptera: Apoidea) and brought to their nests for use in construction and sealing fissures in the nest wall (T-B; Wilson).

propoxur, $C_{11}H_{15}NO_3$, a synthetic insecticide; a carbamate, o-isopropoxyphenyl methylcarbamate; moderately toxic to mammals; acute oral LD_{50} for rats 95 to 104 mg/kg (Pfadt).

proprioreception, sensing pressure (Chapman); see mechanoreception.

proprioreceptor, a sense organ lying within the body cavity and responding to internal conditions of the organism (T-B, after Snodgrass); pressure sensitive sensillum that helps the insect maintain its position, both the relation of the various body parts to each other and the relation of its whole body with respect to gravity (Matthews and Matthews); see hair plate.

propulsatory, driving onward or forward; propelling (T-B).

propupa, in Thysanoptera and ♂ Coccoidea (Hemiptera: Sternorrhyncha), first of 2 or 3 quiescent instars (T-B, after C. V. Riley; Heming); see prepupa, pupa, and semipupa.

propygidium, in Coleoptera with short elytra, the penultimate abdominal tergum (VII), anterior to the pygidium (T-B, after Comstock; Britton, in CSIRO).

propygium, hypopygium, q.v. (T-B).

proscutum, scutum of pronotum (T-B).

proscutellum, scutellum of pronotum (T-B).

proserosa, in egg of *Machilis* (Archaeognatha: Machilidae), serosa, q.v. (Chapman; Sturm, pers. comm., after Larink).

prosoma, anterior part of the body, being the head or the cephalothorax (T-B; Borror et al.); in Coccoidea (Hemiptera: Sternorrhyncha), cephalothorax, q.v. (Kosztarab, pers. comm.); see mesosoma, metasoma, and opisthosoma.

prosomal, of or pertaining to the prosoma (T-B).

prosophallic sclerite, in ♂ Dixidae (Diptera), the transverse sclerite supporting the prosophallus (Harbach and Knight), in some ♂ Culicidae (Diptera), e.g., *Aedes* subg. *Verrallina*, one of a pair of sclerites which embody the prosophallus (Harbach and Knight).

prosophallus, in ♂ Dixidae and some Culicidae (Diptera), a ventral lobelike element of the phallosome located between the bases of the gonocoxites (Harbach and Knight, after Belkin).

Prosopistomatoidea, Baetiscoidea, q.v. (Riek, in CSIRO; Hennig; Edmunds, in Parker).

prostate glands, in ♂ Ensifera (Orthoptera), ejaculatory vesicles, q.v. (Key, in CSIRO; transl. "Prostatadrüse" Ander et al., in Tuxen).

prostemmatic, anteocular, q.v. (T-B).

prosternal, of or belonging to the prosternum (T-B).

prosternal epimeron, epimeron of prothorax (T-B).

prosternal episternum, episternum of prothorax (T-B).

prosternal furrow, in many Reduviidae (including Phymatinae) (Hemiptera: Heteroptera), a cross-striated longitudinal groove in the prosternum, by means of which stridulation is caused by rubbing the rugose apex of the rostrum in it by back-and-forth movements of the head (T-B; Štys).

prosternal grooves, in some Coleoptera, e.g., Elateridae, lateral grooves that receive the antennae (T-B).

prosternal horn, in many larval Integripalpia (Trichoptera), a membranous, fingerlike projection of the prosternum bearing the opening of Gilson's gland (Bicchierai and Moretti).

prosternal lobe, in adult Coleoptera, e.g., some Histeridae, an anterior prolongation of the prosternum (T-B).

prosternal process, a posterior prolongation of prosternum behind forecoxae, e.g., adult aquatic Coleoptera and Elateridae (T-B; Chapman).

prosternal spine, in adult Elateridae (Coleoptera), the acute prosternal process which extends backward into a mesosternal cavity (T-B); in some Orthoptera, sharp projection of the prosternum between forelegs (T-B).

prosternal suture, pleurosternal suture, q.v., of prothorax (T-B).

prosternal tubercle, in Acridoidea (Orthoptera), prosternal spine, q.v.

prosternellum, sternellum of prothorax (T-B).

prosternosome, in adult Siphonaptera, the fused pleurites and sternum of the prothorax (Lewis, pers. comm.).

prosternum, sternum of the prothorax (T-B; Harbach and Knight); fused eusternum of prothorax and first spinasternum (Chapman).

prostethium, prosternum, q.v. (T-B).

prostheca, a mandibular sclerite set with hair, articulated to the basalis, and equivalent to the lacinia of the maxilla (T-B); in larval Coleoptera, a fleshy or somewhat sclerotized flexible process, fringed, simple or lobelike, arising from the mesal surface of a mandible (Peterson); in larval Nematocera (Diptera), hair tuft nearest the molar surface on the upper paralabral surface (Teskey, in McAlpine); see lacinia mobilis.

prostigma, in adult Hymenoptera, pterostigma, q.v. (T-B, after Henneguy).

prostomial, of or pertaining to the prostomium, q.v. (T-B).

prostomial ganglion, in Annelida, archicerebrum, q.v. (T-B).

prostomial lobe, protocerebral lobe, q.v. (T-B).

prostomium, in Annelida, the anterior preoral unsegmented part of the trunk (T-B, after Snodgrass); see acron.

prostomum, in *Pediculus* (Phthiraptera: Anoplura: Pediculidae), mouth cone, q.v. (T-B).

protaesthesis, a primitive sensilla or sense bud (T-B, after Berlese).

Protamphibion, a name applied by P. Mayer to the hypothetical common ancestor of the Plecoptera, Ephemeroptera, and Odonata (T-B).

protandrium, in ♂ Muscomorpha (Diptera), syntergosternite, q.v. (Colless and McAlpine, in CSIRO; McAlpine); the portion of the postabdomen (in ♂ muscoid Diptera) between the preabdomen and the andrium, comprising abdominal somites 6 or 7 and 8 (Steyskal); see andrium.

protandry, the appearance of the males earlier in the season than the females (T-B).

Protanisoptera, extinct suborder of Odonata (Riek, in CSIRO).

Protaptera, hypothetical, few-segmented common ancestor of the Atclocerata (analogous with the nauplius larva of Crustacea) (Riek, after Tillyard, in CSIRO).

protarsus, foretarsus, q.v. (T-B).

protean, readily assuming many forms (T-B).

protean displays, unpredictable random flight of fleeing animals (Matthews and Matthews, after Humphries and Driver).

protease, a digestive enzyme which splits or breaks up proteins (T-B).

protective coloration, any pattern or arrangement of colors protecting an animal from predators, e.g., cryptic coloration, disruptive coloration, and mimicry (T-B; Leftwich).

protective layer, in galls of Cynipidae (Hymenoptera), a sclerified tissue best developed in galls of the European subgenus *Cynips*, the cell walls being thickened and the cells containing many crystalline materials (T-B, after Kinsey).

protective mimicry, mimicry, q.v. (T-B).

proteiform, having many forms or varieties (T-B); see protean.

protein, polymer with high relative molecular weight of amino acids (Allaby); see peptide.

protein epicuticle, inner epicuticle, q.v. (Tulloch, after Richards).

protelean parasite, parasitoid, q.v. (Gauld and Bolton).

protelum, abdominal segment XI (T-B).

Protelytroptera, extinct order of Polyneoptera from the Permian Period, related to the Dermaptera and Blattaria, including the Elytroneuridae, Megelytridae, Blattelytridae, Protelytridae, and Archelytridae, being small insects with short, thick antennae, robust legs and tarsi with 5 tarsomeres, forewings typically elytriform but showing traces of venation, hind wings larger and with longitudinal and transverse folds in the expanded anal area, broad abdomen, and short cerci (Brues et al.; Riek, in CSIRO).

Protentomobryomorpha, infraorder proposed for the extinct *Protentomobrya* and *Rhyniella* within the suborder Arthropleona (Collembola) (Hennig, after Laurentiaux); see Protocollembola.

protentomon, the hypothetical organism postulated as the archetype or ancestral form of the winged insects (T-B, after Imms).

proteolytic, protein-splitting, i.e., breaking up proteins into other compounds (T-B).

Protephemerida, Protoephemeroptera, q.v. (Boudreaux, after Handlirsch).

proterandric, having 2 kinds of males (T-B).

Protereismatoidea, extinct superfamily of Ephemeroptera from the Lower Permian and Triassic, including Misthodotidae, Protereismatidae, Jarmilidae, Oboriphlebiidae, and Mesoplectopteridae (Landa and Soldán).

protergite, prescutum, q.v. (T-B, after Berlese).

protergum, tergum of the prothorax (T-B).

proterotypes, primary types, including all the material upon which the original description is based (T-B); see primary type and type series.

proterophragma, the prephragma of the mesothorax (T-B).

proterosoma, in mites (Acari), the anterior part of the body when there is demarcation of the body between the second and third pair of legs (Pfadt); see prosoma.

Proterospermaphora, Polydesmida, q.v. (Borror et al.).

protest sound, high-intensity unpatterned sound of a broad frequency spectrum elicted primarily upon tactile stimulation (Matthews and Matthews).

prothetely, the possession of 2 pairs of true external wing pads by holometabolous insect larvae (T-B, after Folson and Wardle); abnormal metamorphosis, resulting from insufficient juvenile hormone, in which an immature insect possesses some adult characteristics and is sexually active even before the vagina is large enough to accommodate the passage of eggs, e.g., occasionally in *Locusta* (Orthoptera: Acrididae) (Tulloch; Leftwich; Chapman); see metathetely.

prothoracic, of or pertaining to the prothorax.

prothoracic bristle, in adult Diptera, proepisternal seta, q.v. (T-B, after J. B. Smith).

prothoracic epipleuron, pronotal hypomeron, q.v. (T-B, after J. B. Smith).

prothoracic glands, a pair of diffuse endocrine glands at the back of the head or in the thorax producing the moulting hormone, ecdysterone (Tulloch; Chapman); in Phasmida, defense glands, q.v. (T-B).

prothoracic hormone, ecdysone, q.v. (Borror et al.).

prothoracic leg, foreleg, q.v. (McAlpine).

prothoracic prolegs, in larval Diptera, paired prolegs on prothoracic segment (Teskey, in McAlpine).

prothoracic shield, in larval Lepidoptera, a sclerotized, dorsal plate on the prothorax, bearing the XD, SD, and D primary setae (Stehr).

prothoracic spiracles, in adult and larval Diptera, anterior spiracles, q.v. (McAlpine; Teskey, in McAlpine).

prothoracicotrophic hormone, hormone produced by the median neurosecretory cells of the protocerebrum that stimulates the prothoracic gland to produce the moulting hormone, ecdysone (Chapman).

prothoracotheca, the pupal covering of the prothorax (T-B).

prothorax, the first thoracic ring or segment, bearing the anterior legs but no wings (T-B); see mesothorax and metathorax.

protibia, foretibia, q.v.

protoarthropodan, the hypothetical primitive ancestral arthropod (T-B).

Protoblattaria, Protoblattoidea, q.v. (Boudreaux).

Protoblattarida, hypothesized monophyletic group including the recent order Grylloblattodea and the extinct order Protoblattoidea (Boudreaux).

Protoblattoidea, extinct order within the orthopteroid orders of Neoptera (Insecta) from the Carboniferous Period to the Permian Period, characterized by having a small head, projecting mandibles, often enlarged pronotum, strong legs, short cerci, forewings only slightly tegmenized, with a curving cross-fold extending from R_1 or Sc to the posterior margin, and wing venation differing significantly from that of the Blattaria (Riek, in CSIRO; Boudreaux, after Handlirsch).

protobranchiate, as in nymphs of Anisoptera (Odonata), having the respiratory apparatus contained in the rectum (T-B).

protocephalic, of or pertaining to the head of the insect embryo or protocephalon (T-B).

protocephalic region, primary head region of the insect embryo, including the brain (T-B; Hinton and Mackerras, in CSIRO); see protocormic region.

protocephalon, a general early stage in the evolution of the arthropod head, corresponding to the cephalic lobes of the embryo, comprising the prostomium and usually the first postoral somite, forming the procephalic region of the definite insect head, but persisting in Crustacea (T-B, after Snodgrass); protocephalic region, q.v. (Chapman).

protocerebral, of or pertaining to the protocerebrum (T-B).

protocerebral bridge, the mass of the protocerebrum lying in the dorsal and posterior part of the pars intercerebralis; the posterior dorsal commissure of Thompson (T-B, after Snodgrass).

protocerebral lobes, median paired lobes of protocerebrum, bearing the corpora pedunculata (T-B).

protocerebral region, that part of the primitive arthropodan brain which innervates the eyes; ocular region (T-B, after Snodgrass).

protocerebrum, the anterior part of the arthropod brain, containing the ocular and other association centers and lying anterior or dorsal to the deutocerebrum (T-B, after Snodgrass; Chapman).

Protocoleoptera, Protelytroptera, q.v. (Hennig, after Staesche; Boudreaux, after Tillyard).

Protocollembola, stem group of the Collembola, represented by the Devonian *Rhyniella* (Protentomobryidae) (Hennig).

protocorm, protocormic region, q.v. (Chapman).

protocormic, of or pertaining to the trunk of the insect embryo (T-B).

protocormic region, the primary trunk region of the insect embryo behind the protocephalic region (T-B; Hinton and Mackerras, in CSIRO).

protocosta, in wings of Lepidoptera, the thickened costal margin (T-B).

protocranium, the posterior part of the epicranium; sometimes the occiput (T-B).

Protodermaptera, infraorder with the suborder Catadermaptera (Dermaptera), including the superfamily Pygidicranoidea (Sakai, pers. comm.).

protodeutocerebral, of or pertaining to the proto- and deutocerebrum (T-B).

protodichthadiigyne, in Dorylinae (Hymenoptera: Formicidae), a highly fertile intermediate between ergatoid and dichthadiigyne (Tulloch).

Protodiptera, former name for an extinct suborder of Mecoptera, including forms with reduced cubitoanal venation and other dipterous features, but later found to be an unnatural assemblage (Riek, in CSIRO).

Protodonata, Meganisoptera, q.v. (Hennig).

Protoephemeroptera, extinct suborder of Ephemeroptera from the Upper Carboniferous in Europe, including the superfamily Triplosoboidea (Landa and Soldán).

protogonia, apical angle, q.v., of forewing (T-B).

protograph, an original description by a figure or picture made from the original type (T-B).

protogyny, the appearance of the females earlier in the season than the males (Tulloch).

Protohemiptera, extinct suborder of Paleodictyoptera, possessing mouthparts modified into a long, suctorial rostrum, which was not the forerunner of the hemipteran rostrum (Riek, in CSIRO; Boudreaux, after Handlirsch); see Eupaleodictyoptera.

Protohomoptera, hypothetical ancestral group to the Sternorrhyncha, Auchenorrhyncha, and Coleorrhyncha (Hemiptera) (Hennig, after Evans).

Protohymenoptera, Paramegasecoptera, q.v. (Hennig, after Carpenter).

Protolepidoptera, Zeugloptera, q.v. (T-B, after Packard).

protolog, the original description in words (T-B).

protoloma, costal margin, q.v., of forewing (T-B).

Protomecoptera, a suborder sometimes recognized within the Mecoptera, including the extinct family Kaltanidae and the extant family Meropeidae, possessing adults with 2 pretarsal claws, wings with many crossveins in costal space, and anterior cubitus (CuA) forked (Riek, in CSIRO; Penny).

protonymph, the second instar of a mite (Acari) (Borror, et al); a first stage nymph (Tulloch).

Protoperlaria, ordinal name proposed for the extinct family Lemmatophoridae (Paraplecoptera) (Riek, after Carpenter, in CSIRO; Boudreaux, after Tillyard).

protoplasm, a complex, translucent, colorless, colloidal substance within each cell, including the plasma membrance, but excluding the large vacuoles, masses of secretions, ingested material, etc. (T-B).

protoplasmic, of or pertaining to protoplasm (T-B).

protopod larva, a larva with undifferentiated internal and external organs, e.g., first instar larva of some endoparasitic Hymenoptera (T-B, after Folsom and Wardle; Chapman).

protopod phase, in the insect embryo, that phase in which metamerism is incomplete, the abdomen incomplete and appendages more or less rudimentary (T-B, after Imms).

protopodite, the first part of the maxilla; the basal piece of a segmented appendage in the Arthropoda (T-B).

Protopolyphaga, Haplogastra, q.v. (Hennig, after Schilder).

Protoptera, extinct order, including the family Paolidae of the Carboniferous Period, hypothesized as ancestor of both the Paleoptera and the Neoptera (Riek, after Sharov, in CSIRO).

Protorthoptera, extinct order within the orthopteroid orders (Insecta: Neoptera), possessing wings with the posterior media (MP) fused with the anterior cubitus (CuA) to form an oblique strut from MA to CuA and by the development of a precostal expansion at the base of the wing (Riek, in CSIRO).

Protorthopterida, hypothesized monophyletic group including the extinct orders Protorthoptera, Caloneurodea, and Glosselytrodea (Boudreaux).

Protosymphyla, hypothetical ancestor to the Symphyla and Hexapoda (Hennig, after Snodgrass).

prototergite, the anteriormost abdomen tergum (T-B).

protothorax, prothorax, q.v. (T-B).

prototype, a primitive form to which later forms can be traced (T-B); see ancestor and plesiomorphy.

Protozoa, phylum including single-celled animals (T-B; Borror et al.).

protozoan, of or pertaining to the Protozoa; a member of the Protozoa.

Protozygoptera, extinct suborder of Odonata (Riek, in CSIRO).

protracted, protractus (Latin), extended (T-B).

protracted head, a head not retracted into or withdrawn into the prothorax (Peterson).

protracted mouthparts, mouthparts arising from the cephalic portion of the head and having little or no association with the caudal margin; distance between the cardines and the caudal margin of the head as long or longer than the length of the frons, e.g. larval Cleridae and Cantharidae (Peterson).

protractile, capable of protraction or extension (T-B); see exsertile and protrusile.

protractor, protractor muscle, muscle that which extends or lengthens a structure (T-B).

protrochanter, foretrochanter, q.v.

protrusible, protrusile, q.v. (T-B).

protrusile, capable of being extended or protruded (Peterson).

protuberance, any excrescence above the surface (T-B; Harris); see prominence.

protuberant, rising or produced above the surface or general level (T-B).

Protura, class or order of tiny, elongate, mostly unpigmented Hexapoda with eyes and antennae absent, thorax slightly developed, five-segmented legs, 12-segmented abdomen in adult, with styles on segments I–III, gonopore between segments XI and XII, no cerci, and anamorphic larval development (T-B; Wallace and Mackerras, in CSIRO).

proturan, any one of the Protura; of or pertaining to the Protura (T-B).

proventricular, of or pertaining to the proventriculus (T-B).

proventricular valvule, in *Ptychoptera* (Diptera: Ptychopteridae), a circular fold of the intestinal wall (T-B, after Packard).

proventriculus, gizzard, q.v., i.e., the posterior part of the foregut behind the crop and before the midgut, being variously modified in different insects (T-B; Chapman).

proventriculus anterior, in *Blatta* (Blattaria), the densely sclerotized anterior half of the proventriculus, forming an armature of spiny plates (T-B).

proventriculus posterior, in *Blatta,* the more tapering posterior half of the proventriculus which has a circle of soft cushionlike lobes covered with caudally projecting spines (T-B).

provirus, in invertebrate pathology, a noninfectious intracellular form of a virus (Steinhaus and Martignoni); see infective phase and vegetative phase.

provisional mandibles, in certain Coleoptera, parts of the mandible found in the pupa, for cutting through the cocoon on the emergence of the imago (T-B, after Imms).

provisioning, act of adults providing foor for larvae (Wilson); see mass provisioning and progressive provisioning.

proxagalea, basigalea, q.v. (T-B, after MacGillivray).

proximad, toward the proximal end (T-B).

proximal, that part of an appendage nearest the body, as opposed to distal (T-B).

proximal arm (of sternum IX), in ♂ Siphonaptera, anterior arm of abdominal sternum IX (Tuxen, after Smit).

proximal brustia, in larval Chironomidae (Diptera), seta interna, q.v. (Saether).

proximal infrabrustia, in larval Chironomidae (Diptera), seta interna, q.v. (Saether).

proximal duct, in ♀ Heteroptera (Hemiptera), ductus receptaculi (in a vermiform gland), q.v. (Tuxen, after Davis).

proximal meatus, in ♂ Anisoptera (Odonata), proximal opening of seminal duct (Tuxen, after Borror).

proximal median plate, plate at base of wing distal to third axillary sclerite and proximal to distal median plate from which it is separated by the basal fold (McAlpine); in adult Chironomidae (Diptera), plate at wing base immediately posterior to brachiolum and between second axillary sclerite and distal median plate (Saether).

proximal plates, in some ♂ Enicocephalidae (Hemiptera: Heteroptera), basal segments of genital plates (Štys).

proximal rhachis, in ♂ Hymenoptera, portion of rhachis on either gonapophysis remaining attached to ventral ramus at bases of gonopods proximal to end of notum (Tuxen, after E. L. Smith).

proximal sensory area, in larval Scarabaeoidea (Coleoptera), haptolachus, q.v. (T-B, after Hayes).

proximal spur, in ♂ Siphonaptera, a sclerotized spur of the aedeagal pouch, arising on dorsal ridge of median lamina and extending caudad to connect with anal sternite (Rothschild and Traub).

proximal tarsal segment, basitarsus, q.v. (McAlpine).

proxistipes, the proximal portion of the maxillary stipes (Peterson).

prozona, the anterior part of the pronotum in certain insects, e.g., Orthoptera and Elateridae (Coleoptera); see metazona.

prozonite, in millipedes (Diplopoda), the anterior portion of tergum when it is divided by a transverse suture (Borror et al.).

pruinescence, a waxy bloom covering certain insects, e.g., some adult Odonata (T-B; O'Farrell, in CSIRO).

pruinose, pruinosus (Latin), **pruinous,** appearing covered with fine dust or coarse powder, but which cannot be rubbed off; the brightness of the surface somewhat obscured by the appearance of a bloom like that of a plum (T-B; Harris, after Munz); see farinaceous, farinose, pollinose, pulverulent, and rorulent.

prunosus, prunus, plum-colored, i.e., bluish-red (T-B).

prussic acid, hydrocyanic acid, q.v. (T-B).

Przibram's Factor, 1.26, or the cube root of 2 (T-B, after Wardle); see Przibram's Rule.

Przibram's Rule, an observational rule which states that the weight of an insect is doubled during each instar and at each moult all linear dimensions are increased by the ratio 1.26 or the cube root of 2 (Tulloch, after Wigglesworth; Chapman); see Dyar's Rule.

psammarotrum, in ♀ Ithonidae (Planipennia), gonapophyses laterales, q.v. (Tuxen, after Carpenter).

psammophilous, sand-loving; living in sandy places (T-B).

psammophore, in adult Formicidae and Vespidae (Hymenoptera), group of ammochaetae on underside of head (Brown, pers. comm., after Sartschi; G. C. and J. Wheeler; Carpenter, pers. comm., after Carpenter and Cumming).

Pselaphognatha, Penicillata, q.v. (Borror et al.).

pselaphotheca, that part of the pupa which covers the palpi.

pseud- or **pseudo-,** Greek prefix, false, spurious or merely resembling.

pseudalis, in certain Orthoptera, the small sclerite laterad of the tegula, near the prescutum (T-B, after MacGillivray).

pseudapophysis (pl., **pseudapophyses**), in ♀ Arrhenophanidae and other Tineoidea (Lepidoptera), paired, sclerotized apophyses of ventral surface of united abdominal segments IX and X (Tuxen, after Bradley).

pseudaposematic colors, in Batesian mimicry, false warning colors of mimic giving it a degree of protection from predators (Leftwich); see warning coloration.

pseudarolium (pl., **pseudarolia**), in Heteroptera (Hemiptera), parempodium, q.v. (Cobben).

pseudarthrosis, a false joint or articulation (T-B).

pseudempodial seta, in adult Lepidoptera, a middorsal pretarsal seta arising between the bases of the tarsal claws, or ungues (Kristensen).

pseudepiphallus (pl., **pseudoepiphalli**), in ♂ Grylloidea (Orthoptera), a sclerotization of the specialized dorsal phallic lobes (Tuxen).

pseudepisematic colors, colors in aggressive mimicry and alluring coloration (T-B); see anticryptic colors and pseudaposematic colors.

pseudergate, a caste found in the lower termites (Isoptera), comprised of individuals having regressed from nymphal stages by moults eliminating the wing buds, or being derived from larvae having undergone nondifferentiating moults, serving as the principal elements of the worker caste, but remaining capable of developing into other castes by further moulting (Wilson).

pseudidolum, nymph, q.v. (T-B).

pseudimago, subimago, q.v. (T-B).

pseudoaedoeagus (pl., **pseudoaedoeagi**), in ♂ Lithosiinae (Lepidoptera: Arctiidae), more or less irregular areas of sclerotization in wall of distal part of aedoeagus, usually invaginated with vesica, never forming a complete tube (Tuxen, after Birket-Smith).

pseudoanniliform, falsely or apparently annulate or segmented (Peterson).

pseudoaposematic colors, pseudaposematic colors, q.v. (T-B).

pseudobursa, in ♀ Lepidoptera, a strongly developed, mushroom-shaped bulla seminalis arising from near ostium bursae (Tuxen, after Petersen).

pseudocardia, dorsal vessel, q.v. (T-B, after Kirby and Spence).

pseudocelli, in certain Protura and Collembola, sense organs distributed over the body (T-B).

pseudocellula, accessory cell, q.v. (T-B).

pseudocellus (pl., **pseudocelli**), in Onychiuridae (Collembola), thin walled oval structures surrounded by cuticular rings, with patterns of ornamentation; believed to permit release of repellent body fluid as defense against predators (Christiansen and Bellinger); see postantennal organ.

pseudocephalic segment, in larval Muscomorpha (Diptera), cephalic segment, q.v. (Teskey, in McAlpine).

pseudocephalon, in larval Muscomorpha (Diptera), cephalic segment, q.v. (T-B).

pseudoceps, in ♂ Hymenoptera, distal rhachis + legula (Tuxen, after Ross).

pseudocerarii, in Coccoidea (Hemiptera: Sternorrhyncha), e.g., Tachardiidae, a pair of closely associated spines on the body margin near the anal opening (Miller, in Stehr).

pseudocercus (pl., **pseudocerci**), in Archaeognatha, Zygentoma, and Ephemeroptera, filum terminale, q.v. (T-B, Tuxen); in larval Coleoptera, urogomphus, q.v. (Borror et al.); in larval Symphyta (Hymenoptera), caudal protuberance, q.v. (Gauld and Bolton).

pseudochrysalis, semipupa, q.v. (T-B).

pseudocircle, an arrangement of crochets consisting of a well developed mesoseries and a row of small hooks (a lateroseries) on the lateral aspect of the proleg (Peterson, after Fracker).

pseudocoel, a false hollow; a hollow which does not form a tube (T-B).

pseudocone, a soft, gelatinous cone in the compound eye of some insects, replacing the crystalline cone of others (T-B); see pseudocone ommatidium.

pseudocone eyes, compound eyes with pseudocone ommatidia q.v. (T-B, after Snodgrass).

pseudocone ommatidia, ommatidia in which the Semper cells secrete an extracellular cone which is liquid-filled or gelatinous rather than crystalline, e.g., a few Coleoptera, some Odonata, and most Diptera (Chapman).

pseudocrochets, in ♂ Siphonaptera, differentiated ventrolateral part of palliolum (Tuxen, after Traub).

pseudocrop, in the Hemiptera, an enlargement of the anterior region of the midgut (T-B, after Wardle).

pseudocubitus, in adult Chrysopidae (Planipennia), a vein appearing as the cubitus, but actually formed by the fusion of the branches of the radial sector (R_s), media (M), and the anterior cubitus (CuA) (T-B, after Tillyard; Riek, in CSIRO; Borror et al.).

pseudoculi (sing., **pseudoculus**), in Protura, integumental structures found on the head consisting of a chitinized ring surrounding a membrane which, from front to back, is traversed by a chitin thickening, the whole structure somewhat elevated, having the appearance of a lid (Tuxen, after Berlese); in Collembola, paired organs on head, possibly representing antennal bases or postantennal organs (T-B, after Comstock; Mackerras, in CSIRO).

pseudoelytra, in adult Strepsiptera, pseudohalteres, q.v. (T-B).

pseudofrenulum, in some adult Lepidoptera, a series of bristles distal to the frenulum on the costa of the hind wing which press upon the anal area beneath the forewing (Common, in CSIRO).

pseudogamy, parthenogenetic development of the egg after the egg membrane has been penetrated by a ♂ gamete (Mayr).

pseudogerm, multicellular fragment of trophamnion liberated into host hemocoel on eclosion of braconid parasites (Hymenoptera), where they continue to feed as teratocytes, which later become vacuolated with their nuclei breaking down (Tulloch, after Hinton, Jones; Gauld and Bolton).

pseudognathos (pl., **pseudognathi**), in ♂ Eucosmini (Lepidoptera: Tortricidae), dilated bases of socii forming well-sclerotized connections with bases of gnathos and sometimes extended into transverse rodlike sclerites (Tuxen, after Diakonoff).

pseudogula, in adult Diptera, hypostomal bridge, q.v. (Colless and McAlpine, in CSIRO).

pseudogyna, a ♀ insect that reproduces without impregnation (T-B); in ants (Hymenoptera: Formicidae), pseudogyne, q.v. (T-B).

pseudogyna fundatrix, in Aphididae (Hemiptera: Sternorrhyncha), fundatrix, q.v. (T-B).

pseudogyna gemmans, in Aphididae (Hemiptera: Sternorrhyncha), fundatrigeniae, q.v. (T-B).

pseudogyna migrans, in Aphididae (Hemiptera: Sternorrhyncha), migrantes, q.v. (T-B).

pseudogyna pupifera, in Aphididae (Hemiptera: Sternorrhyncha), sexuparae, q.v. (T-B).

pseudogyne, in ants (Hymenoptera: Formicidae), an apterous ♀ which combines the size and gaster of the worker with the thoracic characters of the queen (T-B).

pseudohalter(es), in ♂ Coccoidea (Hemiptera: Sternorrhyncha), reduced hind wings (Woodward et al., in CSIRO); in ♂ Strepsiptera, specialized club-shaped forewings resembling the halters of Diptera (T-B; Leftwich; Kinzelbach).

pseudohypognathous, having the cephalic part of the head so bent that the insect appears prognathous although actually being hypognathous (T-B, after MacGillivray).

pseudomedia, in adult Chrysopidae (Planipennia), a vein appearing as the media, but actually formed by the fusion of some branches of radial sector (R_s) and media (M) (T-B, after Tillyard; Riek, in CSIRO; Borror et al.).

pseudomicropyle, in eggs of Cimicomorpha (Hemiptera: Heteroptera), hollow chorionic micropylelike processes used for gas exchange (Woodward et al., in CSIRO).

pseudomola, a false mola, i.e., a structure resembling a mola (Peterson).

pseudomyiasis, occurrence of living or dead larval Diptera in the intestinal tract of living humans and other vertebrates, unable to continue their development (Adkins, pers. comm.); see myiasis.

pseudonest, in *Bombus* (Hymenoptera: Apidae), a gathered mass of nest-building material frequently found around the entrance to nests; sometimes used to shelter workers (Tulloch, after Gaul).

pseudoneurium, spurious vein, q.v. (T-B).

Pseudoneuroptera, old taxon name for net-winged insects with incomplete metamorphosis, including the present Ephemeroptera, Odonata, Plecoptera, Isoptera and Psocoptera (T-B).

pseudonocytoid, oenocytoid, q.v. (Tulloch, after Yeager).

pseudonotum, postnotum, q.v. (T-B, after MacGillvray).

pseudonuclei, uratic spheres, q.v. (Tulloch).

pseudonychia (sing., **pseudonychium**), in some Isotomidae and Sminthuridae (Collembola), serration of the dorsal, laterobasal, ungual tooth (T-B; Christiansen and Bellinger).

pseudonymph, semipupa, q.v. (T-B).

pseudopenis (pl., **pseudopenes**), in ♂ Blatteropteroidea, pseudophallus, q.v. (Tuxen, after Crampton); in some ♂ Chrysopidae (Planipennia), tubelike unpaired organ situated externally on wall of gonosaccus (Tuxen, after Tjeder); in ♂ *Necyla* (Planipennia: Mantispidae), penisfilum, q.v. (Tuxen, after Tjeder); in ♂ Anoplura (Phthiraptera), mesomeral arch, q.v. (Clay, in Tuxen).

pseudoperculum, in some Heteroptera (Hemiptera) (and possibly other insects), an egg cap without a distinct sealing bar, and in which eclosion is not the result of fluid pressure (Cobben).

pseudophallic organs, in ♂ insects, embryologically homogenous entity different from euphallic organs and derived from buds of abdominal sternum IX (and VIII) representing the appendages of abdominal segment IX (and in rare cases also VIII) and situated anterior to the larval penis lobes (trans. "organes pseudophalliques" Dupuis, in Tuxen).

pseudophallus (pl., **pseudophalli**), in ♂ Blatteropteroidea, ventral process of left epiphallus (Tuxen, after Beier).

pseudoplacenta (pl., **pseudoplacentae**), in pseudoplacental viviparity, embryonic or maternal structure which is presumed to provide nourishment to the developing embryo (Chapman).

pseudoplacental viviparity, viviparity in which the eggs contain little or no yolk and the embryo presumably receives nourishment from a pseudoplacenta, e.g., *Hemimerus* (Dermaptera: Hemimeridae), *Archipsocus* (Psocoptera: Archipsocidae), and Polyctenidae (Hemiptera: Heteroptera) (Chapman).

pseudopod, pseudopodium, q.v. (T-B).

pseudopodium (pl., **pseudopodia**), in larval Diptera, proleg, q.v. (T-B; Teskey, in McAlpine); in larval Muscomorpha (Diptera), ventral locomotory welts (q.v.) produced into distinct protuberances covered with carved, clawlike spines (Farrar).

pseudopores, in Entomobryidae (Collembola), clear circular areas in the integument of manubrium and abdominal tergites (Christiansen and Bellinger).

pseudopositor, oviscapt, q.v. (T-B, after MacGillvray).

Pseudoptera, Coccoidea, q.v. (T-B, after Amyot).

pseudopteralia, in adult Ephemeroptera, several small sclerites in the axillary region of the wing (Hennig, after Snodgrass); see axillary sclerites.

pseudopulvillus (pl., **pseudopulvilli**), in Heteroptera (esp. Miridae) (Hemiptera), paired pretarsal structures arising laterally from the unguitractor plate, distinct from parempodia and often superficially resembling pulvilli (Schuh).

pseudopupa, in Coleoptera, a larva in a quiescent coarctate condition preceding one or more larval instars which are followed by the true pupa (T-B, after Imms); see coarctate larva.

pseudopupillae, in adult Odonata, the black spots seen on the compound eyes of the living insects (T-B).

pseudoradula, in larval Tanypodinae, excl. *Tanypus* (Diptera: Chironomidae), longitudinal band of minute spinules on dorsal side of M appendage (Saether).

pseudorhaphe, in larval Chironomidae (Diptera), median suture, q.v. (Saether).

pseudosaccus (pl., **pseudosacci**), in ♂ Lepidoptera, small sclerotized structure extending from cephaloventral ends of valvae (Tuxen).

pseudoscaphium (pl., **pseudoscaphia**), in ♂ Lycaenidae (Lepidoptera), a specialized, thorn-shaped uncus when no gnathos or scaphium is present (Tuxen, after Toxopeus).

Pseudoscorpiones, order within the Arachnida, including the pseudoscorpions, possessing a distinctly segmented opisthosoma without a taillike prolongation and chelate pedipalps (Borror et al.).

Pseudoscorpionida, Pseudoscorpiones, q.v. (Borror et al.).

pseudoscorpion, a member of the order Pseudoscorpiones (Borror et al.).

pseudosegment, in larval *Sylvicola* and *Mycetobia* (Diptera: Anisopodidae), narrow anterior subdivisions of prothorax and each abdominal segment (Teskey, in McAlpine).

pseudosematic colors, pseudaposematic colors, q.v. (T-B).

pseudoserosa, a membrane formed by the splitting of the blastoderm during the morula stage (T-B).

pseudosessile, having the abdomen so close to the thorax as to seem sessile, as in some Aculeata (Hymenoptera) (T-B).

pseudosetae, in adult Siphonaptera, slender, bristlelike spines lacking alveoli, and arising under the mesonotal collar in most families of the Ceratophylloidea and Malacopsylloidea, but absent in all Pulicoidea and a few Ceratophylloidea (Lewis, pers. comm.).

pseudosoldier, in Isoptera, presoldier, q.v. (Krishna, pers. comm.).

pseudospermathecae, in ♀ Cimicomorpha (Hemiptera: Heteroptera), one or 2 saclike or tubular diverticula from anteroventral or anterolateral parts of pars communis of genital ducts (vagina, common oviduct or lateral oviducts), superseding functionally the missing or obsolete spermatheca (Tuxen, after Davis).

pseudospiracle, a false spiracle (q.v.) found in Nepidae (Hemiptera: Heteroptera) and *Gryllotalpa* (Orthoptera: Gryllotalpidae) (T-B).

pseudospur, in adult Chironomidae (Diptera), spinelike seta often present at apex of tarsomeres 1–3 and sometimes also in ventral rows (Saether).

pseudosternite, in ♂ Rhaphidophoridae (Orthoptera: Ensifera), a sclerite between paraprocts and dorsal phallic lobes (Tuxen); in ♂ Caelifera (Orthoptera), epiphallus, q.v. (Tuxen, after Walker); in ♂ Grylloidea (Orthoptera), pseudepiphallus, q.v. (Tuxen, after Walker); in some ♂ Enicocephalidae (Hemiptera: Heteroptera), reduced remnants of external genitalia situated dorsad to the guide and representing remnants of the parameres and the supradistal plate (Stys, after Jeannel).

pseudostyle, in ♂ *Argynnis* (Lepidoptera: Nymphalidae), dorsal process of valva (Tuxen, after Viette).

pseudostylus (pl., **pseudostyli**), in ♀ Naucoridae, Notonectidae, and Nepidae (Hemiptera: Heteroptera), gonoplac, q.v. (Tuxen, after Verhoeff); in ♀ Ithonidae (Planipennia), strongly sclerotized process from lower margin of each gonapophysis lateralis (Tuxen, after Tjeder).

pseudosuture, in adult Diptera, prescutal suture, q.v. (McAlpine).

pseudosutural foveae, in some adult Nematocera, prescutal pits, q.v. (T-B, after Curran; McAlpine).

pseudosymphile, in social insects, a predator or parasite which nourishes itself at the expense of the trophallactic secretions of the host larvae (Tulloch, after Gaul).

pseudotergum (pl., **pseudoterga**), in ♂ Lepidoptera, distinct and more or less separate cephalic part of "tegumen," i.e., the dorsal part of vinculum that extending to middorsum cephalad of tergum IX portion of tegumen (Tuxen, after Bayard).

pseudotetramerous, having apparently 4 articles, although 5 are actually present (T-B).

pseudotrimerous, having apparently 3 articles, although 4 are actually present (T-B).

pseudotrachea (pl., **pseudotracheae**), on the labella of adult Diptera, one of the ridged grooves on the ventral surface (T-B; Chapman).

pseudouncus (pl., **pseudounci**), in ♂ Lepidoptera, uncus anticus, q.v. (Tuxen, after Spuler).

pseudovalves, in ♂ Lepidoptera, lateral edges of sternum IX (i.e. vinculum), enlarged and extended caudad, resembling valvae, supposedly replacing them functionally when the valvae reduced in size (Danaidae) or membranous (Hyponomeutidae).

pseudovary, the organ or mass of germ cells of a parthenogenetic insect (T-B).

pseudovalvifers, in ♀ Aradidae (Hemiptera: Heteroptera), the 2 parts of sternum VII when split longitudinally along midline (Tuxen, after Leston).

pseudovirga (pl., **pseudovirgae**), in ♂ Tubulifera and many Terebrantia (Thysanoptera), sclerotized part of epiphallus (endotheca [Heming] or endophallus [Lyal]), on tip of which is situated genital orifice (Tuxen, after Fábián); in ♂ Coleoptera, flagellum, q.v. (Tuxen).

pseudovitellus, mycetome, q.v. (T-B, after Imms; Tulloch).

pseudovum (pl., **pseudova**), the germ cell produced by parthenogenetic ♀ Aphididae (Hemiptera: Sternorrhyncha); see gametogenetic egg.

pseuduncus, superuncus, q.v. (J. S. Miller, pers. comm.).

pseudoworker, in Isoptera, pseudergate, q.v. (Krishna, pers. comm.).

psi, pounds per square inch, a unit of pressure (Pfadt).

Psocatropetae, group within the suborder Trogiomorpha (Psocoptera), including the Psyllipsocidae and Prionoglaridae, possessing long, vertical head; maxillary palp without sensillum on second segment; cubitus posterior (CuP) and first anal vein (1A) ending together at wing margin (nodulus) (Pearman; Badonnel).

Psocetae, group within the suborder Psocomorpha (Psocoptera), including the Psocidae, Psilopsocidae, Myopsocidae, and Thyrsophoridae (Smithers, after Badonnel, in CSIRO).

psocid, member of the order Psocoptera (Smithers, in CSIRO); member of the Psocidae (Psocoptera).

Psocida, Psocoptera, q.v. (Boudreaux).

Psocodea, exopterygote group including the orders Psocoptera and Phthiraptera, characterized by a collarlike fold of the epicuticle and exocuticle (but not of the endocuticle) at the base of the antennal flagellomeres and polytrophic ovarioles (Hennig, after Kristensen, Seeger).

Psocodida, Psocodea, q.v. (Boudreaux).

Psocoidea, Psocodea, q.v. (Boudreaux, after Weber).

Psocomorpha, suborder of Psocoptera, including the Epipsocetae, Homilopsocidea, Caecilietac, and Psocetae, possessing adults with tarsi with 2 or 3 tarsomeres; antennae usually with 13 articles; and a thickened pterostigma (Pearman; Badonnel; Mockford and Garcia Aldrete).

Psocoptera, order of small, free-living, exopterygote Neoptera (Insecta), with large mobile head, filiform antennae, bulbous postclypeus, asymmetrical mandibles, rod-shaped lacinia of maxilla, reduced labial palpi, membranous wings usually held roofwise over abdomen, with reduced venation, tarsi with 2 or 3 tarsomeres in adults, but 2 tarsomeres in nymphs, and no cerci (Smithers, in CSIRO).

psocopteran, any one of the Psocoptera (T-B); of or pertaining to the Psocoptera (T-B).

Psocopteroidea, Psocodea, q.v. (Boudreaux, after Jeannel).

Psychodoidea, superfamily within the infraorder Psychodomorpha (Diptera: Nematocera), including the single family Psychodidae (McAlpine).

Psychodomorpha, division within the suborder Nematocera (Diptera), including the Psychodidae and Tanyderidae, possessing adults with incomplete V-shaped suture on mesonotum and postphragma partly fused, but with distinguishable lobes (Colless and McAlpine, in CSIRO); infraorder within the suborder Nematocera (Diptera), including the superfamilies Psychodoidea, Trichoceroidea, Anisopodoidea, and Scatopsoidea (McAlpine).

psychogenesis, the origin and development of social and other instincts and habits (T-B).

psychophily, insect-flower pollination syndrome involving butterflies (Matthews and Matthews, after Baker and Hurd).

Psyllidea, fossil group judged to be the stem group of the Psylloidea (Hemiptera: Sternorrhyncha) (Hennig, after Bekker-Migdisoua).

Psyllina, Psylloidea, q.v. (Hennig).

Psylloidea, superfamily within the Sternorrhyncha (Hemiptera), including only the family Psyllidae, possessing enlarged hind coxae that are fused with the sternum (Hennig, after Schlee).

Psyllomorpha, infraorder within the suborder Sternorrhyncha (Hemiptera), including the superfamilies Psylloidea and Aleyrodoidea, possessing a sperm pump at the base of the ductus ejaculatorius, complete reduction of the ring muscles of the ductus ejaculatorius, stalklike abdomen with 2 basal segments reduced, and enlarged approximate coxae (Hennig, after Börner, Schlee).

pteralia, the small sclerites at the base of the wing which make up the articulation, including the humeral plate and the axillary sclerites (T-B, after Snodgrass).

pterergate, an exceptional form of worker ant (Hymenoptera: Formicidae) having the rudiments of wings (T-B; Leftwich).

pteridine, pterine, q.v. (Chapman).

pterigostium, pterygostium, q.v. (T-B).

pterine, nitrogen-containing compound found in animals and plants, producing white (leucopterine), yellow (xanthopterine), and red (erythropterine) colors (Tulloch; Chapman).

pterine pigment, pterine, q.v. (Tulloch).

pternotorma (pl., **pternotormae**), in larval Scarabaeoidea (Coleoptera), a stout curving process at the end of the laeotorma and sometimes of the dexotorma (T-B, after Böving).

pterodinergate, in ants (Hymenoptera: Formicidae), an individual of the soldier caste with vestigial wings (Tulloch, after Gaul).

pteroic acid, an essential substance for growth, being a constituent of the vitamin folic acid and important in the formation of pterine pigments (Leftwich).

pteropega, wing sockets or cavities into which the wings are inserted (T-B).

Pterophoroidea, superfamily within the Ditrysia (Lepidoptera), including Pterophoridae, small slender moths with cleft fore- and hind wings (Common, in CSIRO; Borror et al.).

pteropleural, in adult Chironomidae (Diptera), anepisternal seta, q.v. (Saether).

pteropleural bristle, in adult Diptera, anepisternal seta, q.v. (T-B; Borror et al.).

pteropleurites, in adult Diptera, anepimeron and katepimeron, q.v., of mesothorax (T-B, after Curran).

pteropleuron (pl., **pteropleura**), anepimeron, q.v., of the mesothorax, esp. adult Diptera (T-B, after Comstock; Mackerras, in CSIRO; Colless and McAlpine, in CSIRO).

pterostigma, on fore- and hind wings of Odonata and Mecoptera and on the forewings of many Hymenoptera and Psocoptera, a pigmented spot or cell on the anterior margin of the wing, usually near or just behind the apex of vein R_1, having a greater mass than an equivalent area of adjacent wing and by its inertia influencing the movement of the whole wing membrane during flight (T-B; Leftwich; Chapman).

pterotheca, that part of the pupal skin covering the developing wings (T-B; Leftwich).

pterothoracic, of or pertaining to the pterothorax (T-B).

pterothorax, the closely fused meso- and metathorax in certain winged insects (T-B, after Tillyard); the wing-bearing portion of the thorax of winged insects, i.e., the meso- and metathorax (T-B, after J. B. Smith; Leftwich; Wilson).

pterygium, small wing lobe at the base of the hind wing, e.g., adult Lepidoptera (T-B, after Kirby and Spence); a small basal wing lobe of certain insects (Leftwich); winglike lobe on any part of the body (Leftwich).

pterygodes, tegulae, q.v. (T-B).

pterygogenea, Pterygota, q.v. (T-B).

pterygoid, winglike (T-B).

pterygopolymorphism, the condition of having several forms of wings in a single species (T-B).

pterygostium (pl., **pterygostia**), vein, q.v., of wing (T-B).

Pterygota, subclass of Insecta including winged or secondarily apterous, terrestrial or aquatic insects (T-B, after Imms; Mackerras, in CSIRO).

pterygote, wing-bearing (T-B); a member of the Pterygota (Borror et al.).

ptilinal fissure, in adult Schizophora (Diptera: Muscomorpha), a transverse groove that crosses just above the antennae and extends down laterally, in the form of an inverted U, towards the clypeus (Colless and McAlpine, in CSIRO; McAlpine).

ptilinal suture, ptilinal fissure, q.v. (T-B, after Snodgrass; Chapman); see frontal suture.

ptilinum, in adult Schizophora (Diptera: Muscomorpha), an eversible sac capable of being thrust out of a fissure just above the bases of the antennae, thereby splitting off the cap of the puparium and permitting emergence of the adult (T-B; Colless and McAlpine, in CSIRO; Chapman); see ptilinal fissure.

ptychonome, in Gracillariidae (Lepidoptera), a tentiform mine; a modified blotch mine in which the epidemis on one side of the leaf contracts over the mine cavity forming folds in the epidermis (Hering).

Ptychopteroidea, superfamily within the infraorder Ptychopteromorpha (Diptera), including the single family Ptychopteridae, being moderate-sized adult flies lacking ocelli and possessing long antennae with many flagellomeres, long legs, long abdomen, and slender wings with 9 or ten longitudinal veins (McAlpine).

Ptychopteromorpha, infraorder within the suborder Nematocera (Diptera), including the superfamily Ptychopteroidea (McAlpine).

pubes (Latin), **pubescence,** short, fine, soft, erect hair or down (T-B).

pubescent, downy; clothed with soft, short, fine, loosely set hair (T-B).

pubescent eyes, in adult Diptera, compound eyes with microtrichia between corneal lenses (T-B); see hairy eyes.

Pulicoidea, superfamily within the Siphonaptera, including the Pulicidae and Tungidae, possessing adults with spiniform setae on lower part of inner side of hind coxa, outer internal ridge of midcoxa absent, mesonotum without pseudosetae under the collar, and abdominal terga 2–7 with not more than one row of setae (Dunnet, in CSIRO).

published work, a work published within the meaning of the Code and not excluded under provisions of the Code (ICZN).

pulmonarium (pl., **pulmonaria**), the membranous connection between the abdominal terga and sterna (T-B).

pulmonary space, pulmonarium, q.v. (T-B).

pulsatile, having the power of pulsating or moving in a rhythmic manner (T-B).

pulsatile organ, structures accessory to the dorsal vessel in the head, thorax, and appendages, consisting of small muscular membranes, that are connected with the hemocoel and which are concerned with maintaining a circulation of hemolymph though the appendages (T-B, after Snodgrass; Chapman).

pulsating membranes, pulsatile organs, q.v. (T-B, after Snodgrass).

pulsatory, of or pertaining to the pulse or beat of the heart or any other chamber of the insect body; pulsating; pulsatile (T-B).

pulse, heart beat (Allaby); the unit of sound production measured on an oscillogram in acoustic communication in insects (Matthews and Matthews); see pulse train.

pulse rate, rate of heart beat (Gilmour, in CSIRO).

pulse rate frequency (PRF), of the characteristics by which insects differentiate between calls of their species and other species (O'Brien, pers. comm.).

pulse train, in an acoustical signal, a first-order grouping of 2 or more pulses, preceded and followed by a period of silence substantially greater than any of the time intervals between pulses (Matthews and Matthews); see pulse train group.

pulse train group, in an acoustical signal, a second-order grouping of pulses (Matthews and Matthews); see pulse train.

pulverulent, pulverulentus (Latin), powdery or dusty; covered with very minute, powderlike scales (T-B; Harris, after Munz); see farinaceous, farinose, pollinose, pruinose, rorulent, and squarose.

pulvilli (sing., **pulvillus**), a bladderlike appendages arising ventrally on the pretarsal claws (T-B); in Heteroptera (Hemiptera), bladderlike pretarsal structures associated with the claws (Cobben; Goel and Schaefer) (see basipulvillus and distipulvillus); in Diptera, lateral lobes of the pretarsus arising beneath the bases of the claws (T-B, after MacGillivray; Chapman, after Snodgrass); in ♂ Ascalaphidae (Planipennia), a pair of usually fingerlike, sometimes strongly sclerotized, gonosetae-carrying projections from gonosaccus (Tuxen, after Tjeder); see arolium, empodium, euplantulae, parempodium, and pseudopulvillus.

pulvilliform, lobelike or padlike; shaped like a pulvillus, e.g., pulvilliform empodium of adult Tabanoidea (Diptera) (T-B; Colless and McAlpine, in CSIRO; Borror et al.).

pulvinate, pulvinatus, moderately convex (T-B).

pulvinus (Latin) (pl., **pulvini**), cushion; pad (R. W. Brown); in ♂ *Zonosoma* (Lepidoptera: Geometridae, Psychidae), elongate, rounded and hairy process of basal region of valva (Tuxen, after Bastelberger).

pumping bulb, in ♂ Siphonaptera, capsula, q.v. (Tuxen, after Sharif).

punch and suck mouthparts, in Thysanoptera, asymmetric mouthparts including 3 stylets: the left mandible (the right mandible degenerates during embryogenesis) and 2 maxillary lacinial stylets (Heming; Chisholm and Lewis).

punctate, punctatus (Latin), set with fine, impressed points or punctures appearing as pin-pricks (T-B; Harris, after R. W. Brown, and Marchant and Charles); see foveate, foveolate, impunctate, puncticulate, and punctulate.

punctate-striate, punctatostriatus, q.v. (T-B).

punctate substance, neuropile, q.v. (T-B).

punctation, pits or depressions of variable size in cuticle (T-B); see puncture.

puncticulate, sparsely punctate with very fine, widely spaced punctures (Harris, after Stearn, and Munz); see punctulate.

punctiform, punctiformis, shaped like a point or dot (T-B).

punctostriatus, punctured in longitudinal straight lines (T-B).

punctuation, punctation, q.v. (T-B).

punctulate, punctulatus (Latin), finely punctate; with numerous minute and closely set punctures (T-B; Harris, after Stearn, and Marchant and Charles); see puncticulate.

punctule, a minute puncture, dot, or pit.

punctum, a minute pit or spot, as on the elytra of Coleoptera (T-B).

puncturation, punctation, q.v.

puncture, a small impression on the cuticle, like that made by a needle (T-B); see pore.

punctured, punctate, q.v. (T-B; Harris).

puniceus, bright red with a violet tinge (T-B).

pupa, the inactive stage in all holometabolous insects, being the intermediate stage between the larva and the adult (T-B); in butterflies (Lepidoptera: Rhopalocera), chrysalis, q.v. (T-B); in some aberrant Exopterygota, e.g., Thysanoptera and some ♂ Sternorrhyncha (Hemiptera) (e.g., Aleyrodidae and Coccoidea), inactive last nymphal instars (T-B; Peterson; Woodward et al., in CSIRO); in Tubulifera (Thysanoptera), the second of 3 quiescent instars (pupa I) bearing wing pads in macropterae, and the third of 3 quiescent instars (pupa II) (Heming); see prepupa, propupa, pupiform larva, and semipupa.

pupa adectica, adecticous pupa, q.v. (Hennig).

pupa adheraena, an adherent pupa, i.e., one that hangs perpendicularly, head down (T-B).

pupa angularis (pl., **pupae angulares**), a pupa with a pyramidal process or nose on the back (T-B).

pupa coarctata, coarctate pupa, q.v. (Peterson).

pupa conica, a conical pupa, as opposed to pupa angularis (T-B).

pupa contigua, a pupa which remains upright against a vertical object and is supported by a girdle (T-B).

pupa custodiata, guarded pupa, q.v. (T-B).

pupa dectica, decticous pupa, q.v. (Hennig).

pupa dermata, a pupa which retains the larval skin and with no trace of the future limbs (T-B); see coarctate pupa.

pupa exarata, exarate pupa, q.v. (T-B).

pupa folliculata, encased pupa, q.v. (T-B).

pupa incompleta, in some Lepidoptera, a pupa in which the appendages are often partly free and more than 3 of the abdominal segments are moveable (T-B, after Imms).

pupa larvata, masked pupa, q.v. (T-B).

pupa libera, in some Lepidoptera, exarate pupa, q.v. (T-B, after Imms; Leftwich).

pupa nuda, naked pupa, q.v. (T-B); a pupa which lies free of any attachment (T-B).

pupa obtecta, obtect pupa, q.v. (T-B, after Imms, Wardle).

pupa subterranea, a pupa that is buried underground during the transformation (T-B).

pupal aster, in Tabanidae (Diptera), the terminal 3 pairs of large spines of the pupa (Tulloch, after Philip).

pupal cell, a cavity in the soil or made of plant material or debris in which the larva pupates (Hinton and Mackerras, in CSIRO); see cocoon.

pupal disc, imaginal disc, q.v. (Hinton and Mackerras, in CSIRO).

pupal respiratory horns, in numerous larval Muscomorpha (Diptera), hornlike processes, possessing numerous respiratory openings, which grow up from the pupa and pierce the upper portions of the operculum of saprophytic forms (Peterson, after Heiss; Farrar).

pupal sac, in some Culicidae (Diptera), the thin, semitransparent envelope of the head and thorax (Nuttall and Shipley).

pupariation, in Muscomorpha (Diptera), formation of the puparium (Chapman).

puparium (pl., **puparia**), in Muscomorpha (Diptera), the sclerotized, exuvium of the third larval instar, within which the pupa is formed (T-B); in Aleyrodidae (Hemiptera: Sternorrhyncha), last nymphal skin enveloping pharate adult (T-B; Hennig); in Strepsiptera, the skin of the seventh-instar larva in which the adult ♀ is enclosed (T-B, after Comstock); see prepupa and propupa.

puparium respiratory prongs, on puparia of Calliphoridae and Sarcophagidae (Diptera), inconspicuous sclerotized prongs located on the dorsolateral aspect of the first abdominal segment (Peterson).

pupate, to become a pupa (T-B).

pupation, the act of becoming a pupa (T-B).

pupation hormones, hormones controlling pupation, including juvenile hormone (Leftwich).

pupiferous, aphids (Hemiptera: Sternorrhyncha: Aphididae) which produce sexed individuals (T-B).

pupiform larva, in Phylloxeridae (Hemiptera: Sternorrhyncha), the sessile, nonfeeding, pupalike immatures of the sexuales (Stoetzel, in Stehr); see prepupa.

pupigenous, pupiparous, q.v. (T-B).

pupigerous, in Muscomorpha (Diptera), forming a larval puparium (T-B); see coarctate pupa.

pupil, pupilla (Latin), a small central spot of an ocellate spot (T-B).

pupillarial, in Diaspididae (Hemiptera: Sternorrhyncha: Coccoidea), an adult ♀ remaining within the cast exuvium of the second instar (Kosztarab and Kozár).

pupillate, pupillatus, with a spot resembling the pupil of an eye (T-B).

Pupipara, a series of Diptera within the superfamily Muscoidea, including the Glossinidae, Hippoboscidae, Nycteribiidae, and Streblidae, in which the females do not extrude the young until they have reached the stage ready to pupate (T-B; Leftwich).

pupiparid, any pupiparous insect (T-B); see Pupipara.

pupiparous, giving birth to larvae ready to pupate (T-B; Borror et al.); see larviparous and oviparous.

pupivorous, feeding upon pupae, especially applied to Hymenoptera (T-B).

purin, purine, q.v. (T-B).

purine, nitrogenous compound, e.g., uric acid, involved in nitrogen excretion (Chapman); compound resembling a six-membered pyrimidine ring fused to a five-membered imidazole ring, e.g., adenine and guanine of nucleic acids (Allaby).

purple brood, poisoning of unsealed brood of honey bees (Hymenoptera: Apidae) foraging on southern leatherwood, *Cyrilla racemiflora* (Cyrillaceae), in which the brood turn purple (Steinhaus and Martignoni).

purposive, having an intended or aimed at object, effect or result (T-B).

purpureal, purpureous, purpureus (Latin), purple (T-B).

purpurescent, becoming purple in shade (T-B).

pustula (Latin), **pustule,** blister; pimple; bubble (T-B; R. W. Brown); a colored point of moderate circumference (T-B).

pustulate, covered with small, blisterlike swellings larger than papillae and never with a terminal pore (T-B; Harris, after Stearn); see acinose, colliculate, and papillate.

pustulated hairs, in Phthiraptera, hairs arising from unchitinized spaces (T-B).

pustulose, pustulosus (Latin), **pustulous,** pustulate, q.v. (T-B; Harris).

pwaingyet, the commercial name for the cerumen of the East Indian stingless bee *Trigona laeviceps* (Hymenoptera: Apidae) (T-B).

Pycnogonida, class within the Chelicerata, the sea spiders, including spiderlike marine forms with usually 7 pairs of appendages, 5 pairs of legs, and a rudimentary abdomen (Borror et al.).

pycnosis, in larval histolysis, those cases in which the chromatin becomes distributed in the nodules of histolyzing tissue (T-B, after Henneguy).

pygal, belonging to the posterior end of the abdomen (T-B).

pygidial, of or pertaining to the pygidium (T-B).

pygidial area, pygidial plate, q.v. (T-B, after Comstock).

pygidial fringe, in Asterlecanidae (Hemiptera: Sternorrhyncha: Coccoidea), fringe, q.v., of the lateral margin of the pygidium (T-B, after MacGillivray).

pygidial glands, in adult Coleoptera, paired exocrine glands opening beneath the last visible abdominal tergum, secreting substances for defense and other purposes (T-B, after Imms; Chapman).

pygidial incision, in certain Coccoidea (Hemiptera: Sternorrhyncha), the deep mesal emargination of the caudal margin of the pygidium (T-B, after MacGillivray).

pygidial lobes, in Diaspididae (Hemiptera: Sternorrhyncha: Coccoidea), sclerotized dermal protrusions located on the posterior margin of the pygidium (Miller, in Stehr).

pygidial plate, in some Apoidea, Formicoidea, Sphecoidea, and Scolioidea (Hymenoptera: Aculeata), a usually flat area surrounded by a carina or line and sometimes produced as an apical projection present on the 6th gastral tergite in females and 7th gastral tergite of males (Riek, in CSIRO).

Pygidicranidea, Protodermaptera, q.v. (Popham).

Pygidicranoidea, single superfamily within the Protodermaptera, including the Pygidicranidae (Steinmann).

pygidium (pl., **pygidia**), the tergum of the last visible segment of the abdomen, whatever its numerical designation (T-B); in Ephemeroptera, epiproct, q.v. (Tuxen); in Plecoptera, supraanal lobe, q.v. (Tuxen, after Crampton); in Dermaptera, one of the 3 opisthomeres, q.v. (Tuxen); in ♂ *Nymphes* (Planipennia: Nymphidae), mediuncus, q.v. (Tuxen, after Crampton); in ♀ Diaspididae (Hemiptera: Sternorrhyncha: Coccoidea), a strongly sclerotized, unsegmented region terminating the abdomen, following the first 4 abdominal segments (T-B, after Comstock); in adult Coleoptera, the segment left exposed by the elytra (T-B); in ♂ Siphonaptera, sensilial plate, q.v. (Lewis, pers. comm.); in adult Hymenoptera, epipygium, q.v. (Gauld and Bolton); see epiproct, supraanal plate, supraanale, and suranal plate.

pygofer, in ♂ Cicadoidea, the fused tergal and pleural parts of abdominal segment IX, in ♂ Fulgoroidea (Hemiptera: Auchenorrhyncha), including also the sternal part (Tuxen); in ♀ Auchenorrhyncha (Hemiptera), tergum IX (Tuxen); in ♂ Heteroptera (Hemiptera), pygophore, q.v. (Tuxen); .

pygofer lobes, in ♂ Auchenorrhyncha (Hemiptera), lateral, backward projecting lobes or elongations of the pygofer (Tuxen).

pygophers, in ♂ Auchenorrhyncha (Hemiptera), side lobes of pygofer (Tuxen).

pygophor, in ♂ Auchenorrhyncha (Hemiptera), pygofer, q.v. (Tuxen); in ♂ Heteroptera (Hemiptera), pygophore, genital capsule, q.v. (Tuxen).

pygophoral appendages, in ♂ Podopinae (Hemiptera: Heteroptera: Pentatomidae), parandria, q.v. (Tuxen, after McDonald).

pygophoral opening, in ♂ Heteroptera (Hemiptera), mouth of the cup formed by pygophore, corresponding to inflexion of its external wall into diaphragm (Tuxen, after McDonald).

pygophore, in ♂ Heteroptera (Hemiptera), abdominal segment IX (Tuxen, after Myers and China); in ♂ Auchenorrhyncha (Hemiptera), pygofer (Tuxen).

pygopodia, a pair of eversible footlike organs at the hind end of the abdomen of certain larvae, used to assist in locomotion in cases where true legs are reduced or absent (Leftwich); pygopods.

pygopods, the appendages of the tenth abdominal segment collectively

(T-B, after Snodgrass); in ♂ Lepidoptera, the paired, segmental appendages of abdominal segment X (Tuxen); see socii.

pygostyles, in adult Hymenoptera, (one-segmented) cerci, q.v. (Riek, in CSIRO).

pygotheca, in ♂ Auchenorrhyncha (Hemiptera), genital capsule, q.v., or pygofer, q.v. (T-B).

pyloric, of or pertaining to the pylorus (T-B).

pyloric valve, sphincter at the junction between the midgut and hind gut (Gilmour, in CSIRO).

pylorus, first part of the hind gut, often giving rise to Malpigian tubules and sometimes forming a valve between the midgut and hind gut (Chapman).

Pyraloidea, superfamily within the division Ditrysia (Lepidoptera), including the families Pyralidae, Hyblaeidae, Thrididae, Tineodidae, and Oxychirotidae, being small to large moths possessing porrect labial palpi, epiphysis, and usually with entire wing margins; larvae concealed feeders (Common, in CSIRO).

pyramidal, pyramidate, pyramiform, resembling a pyramid in form; angular conical (T-B).

pyramidate fascia, an angulate fascia (T-B).

pyrethrin, a chemical constituent of pyrethrum, being one of 4 different esters: $C_{21}H_{28}O_3$, $C_{22}H_{28}O_5$, $C_{20}H_{28}O_3$, and $C_{21}H_{28}O_5$.

pyrethroid, synthetic chemical similar in structure to a pyrethrin, e.g., resmethrin.

pyrethrum, a botanical insecticide derived from the flowers of *Chrysanthemum* spp. (Asteraceae), primarily *C. cinerariaefolium*; slightly toxic to warm-blooded animals, acute oral LD_{50} for rats 1500 mg/kg (Pfadt); see pyrethrin and pyrethroid.

pyridoxine, essential vitamin in insects belonging to the vitamin B complex (Gilmour, in CSIRO).

pyriform, pear-shaped (T-B).

pyriform vesicle, Müller's organ, q.v. (T-B).

pyrophyllite, $H_2O \cdot Al_2O_3 4SiO_2$, a mineral used as a dust carrier for insecticides (Pfadt).

pyrrolizidine alkaloids, substances present in wilting and dead plants of the family Boraginaceae, sought by certain distasteful or toxic moths and butterflies (Lepidoptera), and used either for the production of pheromones or for defense (Common).

Pyrrhocoroidea, superfamily proposed for the families Pyrrhocoridae and Largidae in the infraorder Pentatomomorpha of the Heteroptera (Hemiptera) (Woodward et al., in CSIRO).

Q

Q fever, acute disease of a wide range of animals including domestic livestock, caused by *Coxiella burnetii* (Rickettsiaceae), being transmitted by ticks (Acari: Ixodida), with humans being infected from domestic animals, e.g., via contaminated milk on inhalation of contaminated dust (Allaby).

Q$_{10}$ Rule, van't Hoff's rule, q.v. (Tulloch).

Qikron (trade name), chlorofenethol, q.v. (Pfadt).

qua, Latin adjective; as being (T-B).

quacking, the calls emitted by virgin honey bee queens (Hymenptera: Apidae) in their cells in response to "piping" sounds of the first vigin queen to emerge in the same hive (Wilson).

quadra-, quadri-, quadro-, Latin prefix; four (T-B).

quadrangle, in adult Zygoptera (Odonata), quadrilateral, q.v. (T-B, after Garman).

quadrangular, four-angled; square (T-B).

quadrat, the usual unit for biotic study; on land, often 1 square meter, elected as representative of the larger area being studied (T-B, after Shelford).

quadrate, quadratus (Latin), four-sided (Borror et al.).

quadrate plates, in ♀ Hymenoptera, ninth hemitergites, q.v. (T-B, after Imms; Tuxen, after Snodgrass).

quadridentate, quadridentatus, four-toothed (T-B).

quadrifarius, four-fold or in fours, as rows (T-B).

Quadrifidae, quadrifine subfamilies, q.v. (Forbes).

quadrifids, quadrifine subfamilies, q.v. (Borror et al.).

quadrifine subfamilies, in Noctuidae (Lepidoptera), those subfamilies in which the adults are characterized by the second medial vein (M$_2$) of hind wing being well developed and closely associated with the third medial vein (M$_3$), so that CuA appears four-branched (Kitching), e.g., Euteliinae, Sarrothripinae, Plusiinae, Catocalinae, Ophiderinae, and Hypeninae (Common, in CSIRO); see trifine subfamilies.

quadrilateral, in adult Zygoptera (Odonata), four-sided discoidal cell between anterior media (MA) and posterior cubitus (CuP), immediately distal to posterior segment of arculus (Arc) (T-B; O'Farrell, in CSIRO); see subquadrilateral.

quadrilateral plate, in ♂ Diptera, part of hypandrium (Tuxen, after Graham-Smith).

quadrilocular pore, in Ortheziidae (Hemiptera: Sternorrhyncha: Coccoidea), flat, circular structure that is divided into 4 parts (Miller, in Stehr); see multilocular pore.

quadrimaculate, quadrimaculatus, with 4 maculae or spots (T-B).

quadripartite, quadripartitus, in 4 parts (T-B).

quadripinnate, quadripinnatus, with 4 featherlike branches or clefts (T-B).

quadrivalvate, quadrivalvular, four-valved (T-B).

quartan malaria, malaria caused by *Plasmodium malariae* (Borror et al.).

quasisocial, applied to the condition or to the group showing it in which members of the same generation use the same composite nest and cooperate in brood care (Wilson).

Quaternary Period, most recent period within the Caenozoic Era, beginning about 1 million years ago (Riek, in CSIRO).

queen, ♀ member of the reproductive caste in semisocial or eusocial species (Wilson); in Isoptera, usually, a dealated, fertilized ♀ imago, or primary reproductive, in an established colony; sometimes used as a term for any winged ♀ imago (Krishna, pers. comm.).

queen cell, in honey bees (Hymenoptera: Apidae), royal cell, q.v. (Norris, in CSIRO).

queen control, the inhibitory influence of the queen on the reproductive activities of the workers and other queens (Wilson).

queenright, referring to a colony, especially a honey bee colony (Hymenoptera: Apidae), that contains a functional queen (Wilson).

queen substance, originally, the set of pheromones by which the queen honey bee (Hymenoptera: Apidae) continuously attracts and controls the reproductive activities of the workers (Wilson); trans-9-keto-2-decenoic acid, the most potent component of the pheromone mixture, produced by the mandibular glands of queen bees (Wilson; Leftwich).

Queletox (trade name), fenthion, q.v. (Pfadt).

quiescence, a temporary slowing down of metabolism, e.g., aestivation or hibernation, being brought about by unfavorable conditions of temperature, humidity, or other climatic factors, by lack of some essential vitamins or other food substances, by failure to secrete particular hormones, or by a disturbance of the balance between opposing hormones (T-B, after Say; Leftwich); delay in development resulting as a direct consequence of prevailing conditions (Chapman); see diapause.

quiescent, not active (T-B).

quiescent stage, hibernating larvae, prepupae or pupae of insects with complete metamorphosis (Peterson).

quinones, a group of chemical substances (cyclic diketones) involved in the formation of some of the yellow and red pigments of insects and also in poisonous or repellent secretions such as those emitted by the cockroach genera *Diploptera* and *Deropeltis* (Blattaria), earwigs (Dermaptera), and some beetles (Coleoptera), e.g., *Brachinus* (Carabidae) and many Tenebrionidae (Leftwich); see anthraquinone, aphin, and hydroquinone.

quinquedentate, five-toothed (T-B).

quinquelocular pores, in nymphs and ♀ Coccoidea, e.g., Tachardiidae, Acleridae, and Dactylopiidae (Hemiptera: Sternorrhyncha), pores with 5 openings (Kosztarab and Kozár; Miller, in Stehr); see multilocular pores.

quod vide (Latin), which see; abbrev., q.v. (T-B).

R

R, radius, q.v. (Borror et al.).

r-selection, selection that acts to raise the maximum rate of population increase (Matthews and Matthews).

r-strategists, species that are r-selected, characteristically with high reproductive potential, good colonizing ability, and short adult life spans (Matthews and Matthews).

Rabon (trade name), stirofos, q.v. (Pfadt).

race, subspecies, q.v. (T-B; Mayr); see ecological race and host race.

racemose, racemosus (Latin), **racemous,** shaped like or resembling a raceme or bunch of grapes (T-B).

rachis, the shank of an antennal joint into which the lateral spines or other processes are inserted (T-B); in Collembola, the main body of the mucro, from which lamellae arise (Christiansen and Bellinger); in Aleyrodidae (Hemiptera: Sternorrhyncha), oblique, lobelike carinae in mediolateral area of abdominal segment of dorsal pupal disk (Gill); in larval Lepidoptera, a ridge or keel dividing the spinning canal at base (T-B); see rhachis.

racquet organs, in Solifugae, short, broad, T-shaped structures on coxa and trochanter of fourth legs (Borror et al.).

radial, arranged like rays starting from a common center (T-B); of or pertaining to the radius, or radial wing vein (T-B).

radial area, in Orthoptera, the space between the subcosta and radius (T-B).

radial blood sinus, in wings of ♂ Embiidina, a tapered sinus that becomes turgid with blood pressure during flight in position of radius vein (Ross).

radial cell, a wing cell bordered anteriorly by a branch of the radius (T-B, after Comstock; Borror et al.); in adult Hymenoptera, marginal cell, q.v. (Borror et al.).

radial cellule, marginal cell, q.v. (T-B).

radial crossvein (r), a crossvein connecting first radial vein (R1) and the branch of the radius immediately behind it (T-B, after Comstock; Borror et al.).

radial cuneate area, in certain Neuroptera, an expansion of the area of the wing lying between the distal part of vein R_5 and the media or between branches of vein R_5 (T-B, after Comstock).

radial fold, in adult Hymenoptera, a more or less distinct system of folds in the distal part of the forewing (Gauld and Bolton); see median flexion line.

radial-medial crossvein, in adult Diptera, radiomedial crossvein, q.v. (McAlpine).

radial planate vein, in the wings of Myrmeleontidae (Planipennia), that which traverses the interradial area, crossing the branches of the radial sector, in the direction of the wing apex (T-B, after Needham).

radial sector (R_s), in general, the posterior of 2 primary branches of radius (T-B, after Comstock; Borror et al.); in Odonata, an indirect branch from anterior segment of arculus (T-B; O'Farrell, in CSIRO).

radial vein, radius, q.v. (T-B; Chapman); a branch of the radius, e.g., R_1, R_2, etc. (T-B; Chapman); in Auchenorrhyncha (Hemiptera), the first important vein next to the costa between it and the ulnar (T-B); in adult Diptera, branch R_{2+3} of radius (T-B, after Schiner; Colless and McAlpine, in CSIRO); see radial sector.

radially, in the form or manner of radii or rays from a common center (T-B).

radiate, radiated, radiatus, seeming to emit or throw out rays, as a spot; marked with lines proceeding from a common center (T-B).

radiate veins, anal veins, q.v. (T-B).

radicicolus, living exclusively on roots (Tulloch, after Gaul).

radicle, scape, q.v. (T-B); narrowed base of antennal scape, e.g., in adult Hymenoptera with geniculate antennae (Riek, in CSIRO); see scape.

radicola (pl., **radicolae**), the root-gall forming Phylloxeridae (Hemiptera: Sternorrhyncha) (T-B).

radicula, radicle, q.v. (T-B).

radiomedial crossvein (**r-m**), crossvein between radius and media, typically extending from radial sector (R_s) and media (T-B, after Comstock).

radius (**R**), in the Comstock system of wing venation, the third longitudinal vein caudad to the subcosta (Sc), starting from the base of the wing and dividing into not more than 5 branches (R_1, R_2, R_3, R_4, and R_5) (T-B); in Pterophoridae (Lepidoptera), a single subdivision of a digitate wing (T-B, after Kirby and Spence); see radial sector and sector.

radix (pl., **radices**), wing base, q.v. (T-B); in adult Hymenoptera, basal segment of gonopod (Tuxen, after Ross).

radix forcipitis, in ♂ Hymenoptera, gonocoxite, q.v. (Tuxen, after Radoszkowski).

radula (pl., **radulae**), in larval Scarabaeoidea (Coleoptera), raster, q.v. (T-B, after Hayes); in ♂ *Neptis* (Lepidoptera: Nymphalidae), a series of strong dentations or teeth on distal part of aedoeagus (Tuxen, after Roepke); in ♂ Psocoptera, sclerotized papillae or other structures in regular patches on penis (Tuxen, after Ribaga).

radular spines, in Psyllidae (Hemiptera: Sternorrhyncha), minute cuticular protuberances occurring in distinct V-shaped clusters in the cells around the apical an anal margin of the wing (Hodkinson and White).

raft, in Culicidae (Diptera), egg raft, q.v. (T-B).

raised disc of sternum IX, in ♂ Plecoptera, hammer, q.v. (Tuxen, after Frison).

rake, in adult Apoidea (Hymenoptera), row of stout spines along the apical margin of the hind tibia used to remove pollen from the combs of the opposite hind leg (Chapman).

ramal, branching or branchlike (T-B).

ramellus, in the forewings of Ichneumonoidea (Hymenoptera), the distal stump of media when it is otherwise incomplete (T-B, after Tillyard).

rami of cingulum, in ♂ Caelifera (Orthoptera), a pair of ventrocaudad directed arms of cingulum (Tuxen).

rami of first valvulae, in ♀ Hymenoptera, slender basal parts of first gonapophyses (Tuxen, after Michener).

rami of inner valvulae, in ♀ Orthoptera, sclerotized ventral edges of inner valvulae (Tuxen).

rami of second valvulae, in ♀ Hymenoptera, slender basal parts of second gonapophyses (Tuxen, after Michener).

rami valvularum, in ♀ Heteroptera (Hemiptera), sclerotized parts of leaves connecting gonapophyses to gonocoxites and body wall (T-B, after Snodgrass; Tuxen); in ♀ Hymenoptera, rami of first and second gonapophyses (Tuxen, after Michener).

ramification, a branching out in every direction (T-B).

ramify, to branch out in every direction (T-B).

ramose, ramous, ramosus (Latin), with many branches (T-B; R. W. Brown).

ramose setae, in ♂ *Cladotanytarsus* (Diptera: Chironomidae), branched, apical setae of median volsella (Saether).

raphe, in larval Lepidoptera, the median sclerotic bar of the dorsal wall of the silk press of the silk-spinning appartus (T-B).

ramuli, in ♂ Lepidoptera, brachia, falces, gnathos (Tuxen, after Roepke).

ramus (pl., **rami**), a branchlike division of any structure or appendage (T-B); in adult Lepidoptera, elongate branch of a pectinate antenna (Common); in Collembola, one of the free ends of the tenaculum (T-B); in ♂ Lepidoptera, paired, lateral or ventrolateral process of abdominal sternum VIII, directed caudad, flattened, spinulose or hairy, sometimes hooked or recurved (Tuxen, after Stichel); in ♂ Hymenoptera, gonocoxite, q.v. (Tuxen, after Bradley); in ♀ Heteroptera (Hemiptera), posterior connecting leaf of gonocoxite VIII, q.v., and/or anterior connecting leaf of gonocoxite IX, q.v., or reinforced part of any of them (Tuxen, after Snodgrass); in ♀ Chironomidae (Diptera), apodeme in oviduct of genitalia (Saether), equally lateral arms of genital fork.

ramus of first valvula, in ♀ Heteroptera (Hemiptera), anterior connecting leaf of gonapophysis IX, q.v. (Tuxen, after Snodgrass).

rank, the level of a taxon in the zoological hierarchy (e.g., all families are at the same rank, lying between superfamily and subfamily) (ICZN).

rapacious, predaceous, q.v. (T-B).

Raphidida, Raphidioptera, q.v. (Boudreaux).

Raphidiodea, Raphidioptera, q.v. (Borror et al.).

Raphidioidea, Raphidioptera, q.v. (Borror et al.).

Raphidioptera, mandibulate, endopterygote order of Neoptera (Insecta), including the snakeflies of the families Rhaphidiidae and Inocellidae, possessing adults with a cylindrical, necklike prothorax, 2 pairs of subequal wings with simple venation and prominent pterostigmas and an elongate ovipositor in the ♀; larvae terrestrial, campodeiform and with well-developed mandibulate mouthparts; pupae exarate and decticous (Mackerras, in CSIRO; Borror et al.).

raptatory, raptorial, q.v. (T-B).

Raptoria, Mantodea, q.v. (T-B).

raptorial, adapted for seizing prey, e.g., forelegs of Mantodea, many predaceous Heteroptera (Hemiptera), and Mantispidae (Planipennia) (T-B; Borror et al.); see predaceous.

raptorious, raptorial, q.v. (T-B).

rasorial, formed for scratching, being applied to leg structures (T-B).

rasp, in insects, a roughened surface for the production of sound by scraping over it a moveable part, also roughened (T-B, after Folsom and Wardle); see file and scraper.

rasping mouthparts, punch and suck mouthparts, q.v. (Peterson; Borror et al.).

rasping-sucking mouthparts, punch and suck mouthparts, q.v.

Rassenkreis, polytypic species (Mayr, after Rensch); see subspecies.

raster (pl., **rastri**), in larval Scarabaeoidca (Coleoptera), a complex of definitely arranged bare areas, hairs and spines on the ventral surface of the last abdominal segment, in front of the anus, divided into septula, palidium, teges, tegillum, and campus (T-B, after Böving).

rastral organ, in Bourletiellidae (Collembola), consists of a longitudinal row of 5 or 6, spinelike, truncate, generally strongly serrate setae on inner surface of metatibiotarsus (Richards).

rastrate, rastratus (Latin), covered as if with longitudinal scratches (T-B; Harris, after Jaeger); see aciculate and scarified.

rat-tailed larva, in certain Syrphidae, e.g. *Eristalis,* (Diptera), larva in which the body terminates in a long, flexible, respiratory tube (T-B).

rational behavior, that form of behavior in which the actions are influenced by the memory of previous experiences (T-B).

ravenous, greedy; voracious; hungry (T-B).

ray, a conspicuous branch (Christiansen and Bellinger).

reaction, a response to a stimulus (T-B).

reactor glands, glands contructed in such a way that chemical precursors of the secretion are mixed only at the moment of discharge, e.g., millipedes (Diplopoda) and bombardier beetles (Carabidae: Brachininae) (Matthews and Matthews); see pygidial glands.

recapitulation, the theory that ontogeny recapitulates phylogeny, i.e., that changes observed in ontogeny parallel character transformations observed in adults (Mayr).

recent, of taxa which still exist (Mayr); taxa from the Recent Epoch; see fossil.

Recent Epoch, most recent epoch within the Quaternary Period, beginning about 15,000 years ago (Riek, in CSIRO).

receptacula ovorum, the receptacle holding eggs or ova in the ♀ insect (T-B).

receptaculum (pl., **receptacula**), in ♀ Nepticulidae and Gracillariidae (Lithocolletinae) (Lepidoptera), bursa copulatrix (Tuxen, after Petersen).

receptaculum seminalis, in ♀ Lepidoptera, receptaculum seminis, q.v. (Tuxen).

receptaculum seminis, in ♀ insects, spermatheca, q.v., but in some groups used in preference to that term (Tuxen); in ♀ Heteroptera (Hemiptera), spermatheca, q.v., median, dorsal, unpaired diverticulum from vagina, extremely variable, but frequently (including the homologous vermiform gland) consisting of ductus receptaculi + pars medialis + capsula seminalis (Tuxen, after von Siebold); in ♀ Miridae (Hemiptera: Heteroptera), (unpaired saclike) pseudospermatheca, q.v. (Tuxen, after Kullenberg); in ♀ Coleoptera, spermatheca, q.v., often including ductus spermathecae (Tuxen); in ♀ Lepidoptera, the final storage sac for spermatozoa, discharging into vestibulum of oviductus communis, comprising ductus receptaculi, glandula receptaculi, and lagena receptaculi (Tuxen), bulla seminalis, q.v. (Tuxen, after Alman), or (in Pterophoridae) bursa copulatrix, q.v. (Tuxen, after Hofmann).

receptive apparatus, the part of a sense organ primarily responsive to the stimulus transmitted by or through the peripheral parts, formed of the sense cell or cells (T-B, after Snodgrass).

receptor, sense organ, q.v., or sensillum, q.v. (T-B, after Snodgrass; Leftwich).

receptor potential, temporary change in the charge of a sensory cell membrane in response to an adequate stimulus (Matthews and Matthews).

recessive, of a gene, not effecting the phenotype of the heterozygote (Mayr).

recessus, in ♀ Siphonaptera, blind pocket of perula (Tuxen, after Landois).

reclinate, reclinatus (Latin), inclined backward and upward, e.g., reclinate bristles in adult Diptera (T-B; Borror et al.); see proclinate.

reclivate, reclivatus (Latin), forming a double curve (T-B).

reclivous vein, in adult Zelinae (Hymenoptera: Braconidae), a transverse vein of which the anterior end is further removed from the wing base than the posterior end (van Achterberg); see inclivous vein.

recondite, reconditus (Latin), concealed; hidden (T-B; R. W. Brown).

recruitment trail, in social insects, an odor trail laid by a single scout worker and used to recruit nestmates to a food find, a desirable new nest site, a breach in the nest wall, or some other place where the assistance of many workers is needed (opposed to exploratory trail) (Wilson).

rectal, of or pertaining to the rectum (T-B).

rectal caecum, rectal sac, q.v. (T-B).

rectal cauda, in Heteroptera (Hemiptera), anal tube, q.v. (T-B, after J. B. Smith; Tuxen, after Sharp).

rectal gills, in Anisoptera (Odonata), the gills within the rectum, in the branchial chamber of the nymph (T-B); in aquatic Syrphidae (Diptera), anal gills, q.v. (Ferrar).

rectal glands, rectal pads, q.v. (T-B; Leftwich).

rectal pads, subregions of wall of rectum, consisting of relatively thick columnar epithelium separated by narrow strips of small cuboidal epithelial cells, involved in reabsorbtion of water ions from the feces (Tulloch; Chapman).

rectal papillae, rectal pads, q.v. (Leftwich; Chapman); a modification of the rectal pad to form a blunt projection into the lumen of the hind gut, found in Diptera, adult fleas, etc. (Tulloch).

rectal pouch, in Isoptera, paunch, q.v. (Chapman); in larval Scarabaeidae, and adult Dytsicidae and Silphidae (Coleoptera), colon, q.v. (Gay, Britton, in CSIRO; Chapman).

rectal sac, the enlarged anterior part of the rectum, sometimes produced into a large rectal caecum (T-B, after Snodgrass).

rectal spinnerets, in Coccoidea (Hemiptera: Sternorrhyncha), rectal wax pores, q.v. (T-B).

rectal tracheal gills, in Anisoptera (Odonata), rectal gills, q.v. (T-B).

rectal valve, a circular or lobate fold of the proctodeal wall between the anterior intestine and the rectum (T-B, after Snodgrass).

rectal wax pores, in Coccoidea (Hemiptera: Sternorrhyncha), wax pores located in the rectum (T-B).

rectangular, rectangulate, rectangulatus, in the form of a right angle or rectangle (T-B).

rectate, straight (T-B).

rectigrade, applied to larval Lepidoptera, walking straight (usually with 3 pairs of thoracic legs and 5 pairs of prolegs) without pronounced looping (T-B).

rectilinear, in the form of a straight line (T-B).

rectum (pl., **recta**), posterior portion of hind gut important in the resorbtion of water, salts, and amino acids from urine, serving for storage of fecal matter, and functioning in gas exchange in certain aquatic insects (T-B; Tuxen; Chapman); in Lepidoptera, tuba analis, q.v. (Tuxen).

rectus (Latin), straight (T-B).

recumbent, lying down; reclining (T-B).

recurrent, running backward (T-B).

recurrent nerve, the median stomodeal nerve extending posteriorly from the frontal ganglion (T-B, after Snodgrass).

recurrent nervure, in adult Hymenoptera, recurrent vein, q.v., of wing (T-B, after Norton).

recurrent vein, in adult Hymenoptera, (second) mediocubital crossvein q.v. (T-B; Riek, after Ross, in CSIRO); in many adult Planipennia, humeral crossvein when recurved toward the base of wing, being frequently pectinately branched (T-B, after Comstock; Borror et al.).

recurvate, recurvatus (Latin), recurved, q.v. (T-B).

recurved, recurvus (Latin), curved upward or backward (T-B; Borror et al.).

recurved hooks, in ♂ Lycaenidae (Lepidoptera), falces (gnathos), q.v. (Tuxen, after Bethune-Baker).

recurved spine, in ♂ Lepidoptera, uncus, q.v. (Tuxen, after Packard).

recuspine, with points in a backward direction (T-B).

red muscaridine, various mycoses of insects caused by species of hyphomycetous fungi and characterized by the appearance of pink to brick-red colors on the body of dying or dead hosts, e.g., certain strains of *Beauveria bassiana* infecting silkworms (Lepidoptera: Bombycidae) and the fungus *Sorosporella uvella* infecting cutworm larvae (Lepidoptera: Noctuidae) and other insects (Steinhaus and Martignoni).

red-water fever, disease of cattle and many other animals caused by *Babesia* (Piroplasmea) and transmitted by ticks (Acari: Ixodida) (Allaby); see babesioses and Texas cattle fever.

redox potential, a measure of the oxidizing or reducing power of a substance expressed in terms of its tendency to lose or gain electrons (Chapman).

reduced, lessened or decreased in size (T-B).

reduction, meiosis, q.v. (T-B, after Folsom and Wardle); a lessening in size of parts of an insect, as compared with the norm (T-B).

reductionism, belief that complex phenomena can be entirely explained by reducing them to the smallest possible component parts and by explaining these (Mayr).

reductus (Latin), withdrawn; remote (R. W. Brown); a zigzag marking or corrugation (T-B).

reduplication, an abnormality in regeneration in which the missing organ is duplicated or triplicated (Tulloch); see homoosis.

Reduvioidea, superfamily within infraorder Cimicomorpha of the Heteroptera, including predaceous bugs of the family Reduviidae (assassin bugs) and Pachynomidae.

reel system, in ♂ Saldoidea (Hemiptera: Heteroptera), differentiation of ductus seminis at junction of ductus seminis proximalis and distalis into a coiled tube (Tuxen, after Cobben).

refaunation, reintroduction of mutualistic fauna in a host deprived of such fauna (Steinhaus and Martignoni).

reflected, reflex, reflexed, reflexus (Latin), bent or turned back (T-B; R. W. Brown).

reflective layer, tapetum, q.v., of eye (Gilmour, in CSIRO); layer of cells, containing urate granules, in light-producing organs serving to reflect light from light-producing cells back outward (Gilmour, in CSIRO).

reflector layer, reflective layer, q.v., of light-producing organ (T-B, after Imms).

reflex, in an animal, the simple reaction following an external stimulus or set of stimuli, acting on and through the nervous and motor mechanism (T-B).

reflex arc, simple pathway of a nerve impulse from a sensory nerve cell, through an association nerve cell, to a motor nerve cell, thereby initiating a muscle contraction (T-B; Gilmour, after Wigglesworth, in CSIRO).

reflex bleeding, the faculty by which some insects can eject blood through certain weak spots in the intersegmental membranes (T-B; Chapman); a defensive response, e.g., bleeding at the femorotibial arcticulation in adult Mexican bean beetles (*Epilachna varivestris,* Coccinellidae) (Matthews and Matthews).

refracted, refractus (Latin), bent back as if broken (T-B).

refractory period, period in the presence of an action potential during which further impulses cannot be initiated in a nerve (Chapman).

refringent, refractive; having the ability to refract or deflect rays of light (T-B).

regeneration, reproduction of a lost part at the molecular, cellular, tissue, or organ level, e.g., damaged or autotomized appendages of nymphs in Phasmida (T-B; Steinhaus and Martignoni; Key, in CSIRO).

regenerative cells, the cells that generate the replacement cells of the ventricular epithelium of the midgut (T-B, after Snodgrass; Chapman).

regenerative crypts, pouchlike diverticula or pockets of the midgut wall containing nidi, being visible as small papillae on the outside of the midgut in many Coleoptera (T-B; Chapman).

region, a space or area adjoining a specified point; a part of the body composed of a number of segments, as the head, the thorax, or the abdomen (T-B).

regression analysis, a form of multivariate analysis (Mayr).

regressive character, a character which is being reduced or lost in the course of phylogeny, sometimes independently in several related lines (T-B).

regurgitate, to voluntarily bring the crop or stomach contents up into the mouth (T-B).

regurgitation, the act of bringing up undigested, digested or partly digested food into the mouth voluntarily (T-B).

rein, in ♀ Plebeiinae (Lepidoptera: Lycaenidae), henia, q.v. (Tuxen, after Chapman).

reinfection, in invertebrate pathology, a second infection by the same microorganism or virus, after recovery from or during the course of a primary infection (Steinhaus and Martignoni); see secondary infection and superinfection.

reiterative behaviors, activities with a periodicity in the life of a single individual, e.g., feeding and locomotory cycles (Matthews and Matthews).

rejected name, any name, available, or unavailable, or vernacular, for a taxon other than its valid name (ICZN).

rejected work, any work that is rejected because it is not an available work, or because it has been rejected by the Commission and is included in the Official Index of Rejected and Invalid Works in Zoological Nomenclature (ICZN).

relapsing fever, disease of man and rodents caused by the spirochaete *Borrelia recurrentis* and *B. duttoni* and transmitted by ticks, *Ornithodorus* spp. (Acari: Ixodida) and the body louse, *Pediculus humanus humanus* (Phthiraptera: Anoplura) (Borror et al.).

relationship, affinity by descent (T-B).

relative, not absolute; depending on some other thing or concept as a norm, datum plane, or standard, agreed upon tacitly or by formal adoption (T-B).

relative growth, the relative increase of one body part with respect to another as total body size is varied; allometry (q.v.) is a special form of relative growth (Wilson).

releaser, specific stimulus (or stimuli) which serves as a signal that elicits a fixed motor pattern under normal conditions (Matthews and Matthews).

releaser pheromone, pheromone that stimulates an immediate behavioral response mediated wholly by the nervous system (Matthews and Matthews).

relicit eggs, eggs within the ♀ that are developed but have failed to be laid and may be partially or entirely resorbed (Adkins, pers. comm.).

Remetabola, Thysanoptera, q.v. (Takahashi).

remiform, oarlike in form (T-B).

remigial, of or pertaining to the remigium (T-B).

remigial region, remigium, q.v. (T-B, after Snodgrass).

remigial seta, in adult Diptera, any seta occurring on the remigium (Harbach and Knight).

remigium, the anterior rigid part of the wing chiefly productive of the movements of flight, and directly affected by the motor muscles of the wing (T-B, after Snodgrass); the region of the wing in front of the claval furrow containing the bulk of the veins (T-B, after Snodgrass; Chapman); in adult Diptera, stem vein, q.v. (McAlpine, after authors); in adult Chironomidae (Diptera), brachiolum, q.v. (Saether); in adult Culicidae (Diptera), part of radius basad of the arculus (Harbach and Knight, after Belkin).

remiped, having oar-shaped or oarlike feet used in rowing, as in aquatic insects (T-B).

remote, remotus (Latin), distant (T-B).

renal cell, nephrocyte, q.v. (T-B).

reniculus, a small, kidney-shaped, colored spot (T-B).

reniform, kidney-shaped (T-B).

reniform spot, in certain moths (Lepidoptera), a somewhat kidney-shaped spot at the end of the discal cell (T-B, after Comstock).

reniform vesicle, in ♂ Dermaptera, basal vesicle, q.v. (Tuxen, after Burr).

reovirus, plant virus with icosahedral, double-shelled inclusion bodies transmitted propagatively by leafhoppers and plant hoppers (Hemiptera: Auchenorrhyncha: Cicadellidoidea and Fulgoroidea) (Nault and Ammar).

repagula, the rodlike bodies which encircle the egg clusters of Ascalaphidae (Planipennia) below the point of deposition on grass stems, twigs, etc. (T-B, after Imms).

repand, repandus (Latin), bent backward; turned up; undulate (T-B; R. W. Brown).

repellant, substance that elicits an avoidance reaction (Pfadt).

replacement name, any available name used to replace an older available name (ICZN).

replacement reproductive, supplementary reproductive, q.v. (Wilson).

replete, an individual ant (Hymenoptera: Formicidae) whose crop is greatly distended with liquid food, to the extent that the abdominal segments are pulled apart and the intersegmental membranes are stretched tight, serving as living reservoirs, regurgitating food on demand to their nestmates (T-B; Tulloch; Wilson).

replicate, replicatus (Latin), refolded; doubled back or down (T-B).

replicatile, capable of being folded back (T-B).

reproductive capacity, reproductive potenital, q.v. (Leftwich).

reproductive effort, the caloric content of eggs and sperm and the energies expended in seeking mates, searching for oviposition sites, buiding nests, guarding eggs or young, feeding young, etc., and risks resulting from the performance of these behaviors (Matthews and Matthews).

reproductive isolation, a condition in which interbreeding between 2 or more populations is prevented by intrinsic factors (Mayr); see isolating mechanism.

reproductive opening, in adult Diptera, genital opening, q.v. (Mc Alpine).

reproductive potential, the capacity of an animal to increase its numbers through reproduction expressed by the equation, $N_n = N_1 \times b^{n-1}$, where N_n is the population in the nth generation, N_1 is the initial population, and b is the rate of increase (Borror et al.).

repugnatorial, repellent; so offensive as to drive away (T-B).

repugnatorial glands, defense glands, q.v. (T-B).

repugnatorial secretions, defensive secretions, q.v. (CSIRO).

reservoir, a case or cavity for the storage of any fluid or secretion (T-B).

reservoir of spermatheca, in ♀ Siphonaptera, bulga, q.v. (Tuxen).

resilient, elastic (T-B).

resilin, colorless, rubberlike protein found in elastic hinges (Chapman).

resistance, capacity or power to resist (Steinhaus and Martignoni); the ability of an organism to resist untoward circumstances such as toxic chemicals, microbial pathogens, etc., resulting from genetic selection (Steinhaus and Martignoni; Borror et al.); see immunity.

resistance factor, any condition in plants that protects them from insect attacks, such as structures, chemical substances in the plant or physiological attributes (T-B).

resistant host, a vertebrate that is not naturally affected by a pathogen (even in the absence of prior exposure, recovery, and development of an immune state) (Adkins, pers. comm.).

resmethrin, $C_{22}H_{26}O_3$, a synthetic pyrethroid insecticide; (5-benzyl-3-furyl) methyl-2,2-dimethyl-3-(2-methylpropenyl) cyclopropane-carboxylate; slightly toxic to mammals, acute oral LD_{50} for rats 4240 mg/kg (Pfadt).

resonator, a structure to intensify sound, in general, some sort of a thin vibrating plate or lamella (T-B, after Imms).

resonator ridge, in some adult Diptera, e.g., Agromyzidae and Chamaemyiidae, ridge on hind femur that rubs against stridulatory file on syntergite I + II of abdomen and on the pleural membrane (McAlpine).

resorb, to reabsorb (T-B).

respiration, oxidative reactions in cellular metabolism involving the sequential degradation of food substances and the use of molecular oxygen as a final hydrogen acceptor, with ATP, carbon dioxide, and water being the final products (Allaby); breathing through spiracles leading into tracheae and tracheoles or the exchange of gases across thin-walled portions of the external cuticle in aquatic insects, rarely (e.g., some larval Chironomidae) involving a respiratory pigment (hemoglobin) (T-B; Leftwich).

respiration tracheae, ventilation tracheae, q.v. (T-B).

respiratoria, in larvae of certain Diptera, polypneustic lobes, q.v. (T-B).

respiratory atrium, in pupal Chironomidae (Diptera), entire respiratory chamber in thoracic horn connecting trachea to plastron plate (Saether).

respiratory channels, in Notonectidae and nymphs of Nepidae (Hemiptera: Heteroptera), hair-lined grooves in which lie the spiracles dorsally on the abdomen of these aquatic taxa (Woodward et al., in CSIRO).

respiratory funnel, sclerotized tube formed by a reaction of the host tissue connecting endoparasitic larval Tachinidae (Diptera) with the external atmosphere (Colless and McAlpine, in CSIRO).

respiratory horn, on surface of eggs of some Hemiptera, Hymenoptera, and Diptera, protuberances with plastrons on their surface (Hinton and Mackerras, in CSIRO); in pupal Diptera, respiratory trumpet, q.v. (Colless and McAlpine, in CSIRO).

respiratory plastron, plastron, q.v. (Leftwich).

respiratory prong, puparium respiratory prong, q.v. (Peterson).

respiratory siphon, in some larval Nematocera, and some Syrphidae (Diptera), and Nepidae and Belostomatidae (Hemiptera: Heteroptera), the caudal breathing tube (Peterson; Woodward et al., in CSIRO; Colless and McAlpine, in CSIRO); in Nepidae (Hemiptera: Heteroptera), paired caudal structures derived from abdominal tergum VIII, forming a channel in nymphs and a long tube in adults, which connect with the eighth abdominal spiracles, and which serve to replenish the subhemelytral airstore in these aquatic insects (Menke, in Menke); in larval Scatopsidae (Diptera), one of a pair of short, tubular, sclerotized caudal breathing tubes, each bearing one of the posterior spiracles (Colless and McAlpine, in CSIRO).

respiratory spine, in some larval Tabanidae, *Chrysogaster* (Syrphidae), and *Notiphila* (Ephydridae) (Diptera), spinelike modification of posterior spiracles (Teskey, in McAlpine).

respiratory system, the anatomical adaptations of the animal that facilitate external respiration (T-B, after Snodgrass); see gills, plastron, spiracles, tracheae, and tracheoles.

respiratory trumpet, in pupae of many aquatic Diptera, e.g., Culicidae and Simuliidae, a respiratory protuberance, usually paired, on the prothorax (Peterson; Colless and McAlpine, in CSIRO).

restraining tendons, in Thysanoptera, paired elastic fibers in tibiae that antagonize action of pretarsal depressor muscle and cause withdrawal of pretarsal bladders (arolia) (Heming).

restricted, held back; confined to a limited area (T-B).

resupinate, resupinatus, upside down; horizontally reversed (T-B).

rete, fat body, q.v. (T-B); any structureless membrane or layer (T-B).

rete mucosum, endocuticle, q.v. (T-B; Tulloch).

retecious, reticious, q.v. (T-B; Harris).

retenative, tenacious; holding fast (Peterson).

reticious, reticulate, q.v. (T-B; Harris).

reticular, reticulate, q.v. (T-B).

reticulate, reticulated, reticulatus (Latin), superficially netlike or made up of a network of lines; meshed; netted (T-B; Harris, after Marchant and Charles, and Stearn); see alveolate, areolate, cancellate, clathrate, and goffered.

reticulate evolution, evolution dependent on repeated intercrossing between a number of lines, and thus both convergent and divergent at once (Mayr, after Huxley).

reticulose, reticulosus (Latin), **reticulous,** reticulate, q.v. (T-B; Harris).

reticulum, any netlike structure (T-B); the longitudinal and radiating filaments of the insect muscle (T-B, after Packard).

retina, that part of the eye upon which the image is formed, i.e., the retinula (T-B).

retina cells, retinula cells, q.v. (T-B).

retinacula (sing., **retinaculum**), in ♂ Diptera, blunt-tipped setae of cerci (Tuxen); in adult Psychodidae (Diptera), tenacula, q.v. (Quate and Vockeroth, in McAlpine).

retinacular comb, in ♂ *Anatoecus* (Phthiraptera: Ischnocera), comblike sclerotizations on wall of genital sac (Tuxen, after Cummings).

retinaculum (pl., **retinacula**), in Collembola, tenaculum, q.v. (Leftwich; Wallace and Mackerras, in CSIRO; Chapman); in ♂ *Pectinopygus* (Phthiraptera), retinacular comb, q.v. (Tuxen, after Cummings); in larval Coleoptera, the toothlike process in the middle of the mandible (T-B); in adult Lepidoptera, a hook, loop, or specialized scales attached to the under side of the forewings near the base, to receive the frenulum (T-B), and of 3 types: subcostal, subdorsal (Braun), and subanal (Davis); in Hymenoptera, horny, moveable scales serving to move the sting or to prevent its being darted out too far (T-B).

retinaculum magnum, in ♂ *Raphidia* (Raphidioptera: Raphidiidae), stylus, q.v. (Tuxen, after Berland and Grassé).

retinal, of or pertaining to the retina (T-B).

retinal pigment, the pigment layer of the compound eye just above the basilar or fenestrate membrane (T-B).

retinal pigment cells, retinula cells, q.v. (T-B, after Snodgrass).

retinal rod, rhabdom, q.v. (Leftwich).

retinene, a light-senitive pigment in the retinula cells of insects, similar to rhodopsin in the human eye and derived from vitamin A (Leftwich).

retineriae (sing., **retineria**), the microscopic setalike projections on the ventral side of the tarsi (T-B, after MacGillivray); in adult Diptera, hollow hairs sometimes present on empodium and pulvillus, through which a viscous fluid substance is secreted (McAlpine); see tenent hairs.

retinophora, retinula, q.v. (T-B).

retinue, a group of workers, not necessarily permanent or even long lasting in composition, which closely attends the queen (Wilson).

retinula, group of retinula cells of one ommatidium (T-B; Chapman).

retinula cells, sensory cells of the ommatidium, ocellus, or stemma, forming an internal rhabdom (composed of rhabdomeres), containing pigment granules within their cytoplasm, and each possessing a nerve axon which passes out the basement membrane at the back of the eye into the optic lobe (Chapman).

retinulae, retinula cells, q.v. (Leftwich).

retinular, of or pertaining to the retinula (T-B).

retort-shaped organs, in Hemiptera, oval areas of glandular tissue at the enlarged proximal ends of both pairs of the mouth stylets (T-B, after Imms).

retracted, retractus, drawn back or into another part; opposed to prominent (T-B).

retracted head, entire head and mouthparts retracted into prothorax (Peterson).

retracted mouthparts, in most larval Coleoptera, mouthparts with caudal portions of the maxillae and labium arising from caudal portion of head capsule, in contrast to protracted mouthparts arising from cephalic portion of head capsule, i.e., distance between cardines and caudal margin of the head much shorter than length of frons (Peterson).

retractile, capable of being produced and drawn back or retracted (T-B); see eversible.

retractile papilla, in Collembola (esp. in the apical antennal bulb), a papilla partly or completely invaginated below the surface, but presumably capable of protrusion (Christiansen and Bellinger).

retractor, any structure used in drawing in or back; specifically, a muscle (T-B).

retractor angulis oris, retractors of the mouth angles, q.v. (T-B, after Snodgrass).

retractor hypopharyngis, retractor of the hypopharynx; one of a pair of muscles arising in the tentorium and inserted laterally at the base of the hypopharynx (T-B, after Snodgrass).

retractor of claws, pretarsal depressor muscle, q.v. (T-B).

retractoral plate, in ♂ Capniidae (Plecoptera), an internal plate anteriorly connected with fusion plate (Tuxen, after Hanson).

retractores angulorum oris, retractors of the mouth angles, q.v. (T-B).

retractores ventriculi, the delicate muscles which assist in supporting the alimentary canal (T-B).

retractors of the mouth angles, a pair of large muscles arising dorsally on the frons, inserted on the oral branches of the suspensorial sclerites of the hypopharynx (T-B, after Snodgrass).

retro-, Latin prefix; backwards (T-B).

retroarcuate, curved backwards (T-B).

retrocerebral endocrine system, the corpora allata, corpora cardiaca and the ventral gland considered together (T-B).

retrocession, a going or moving backward (T-B).

retrogressive evolution, an evolutionary trend which results in simplification of an organism, usually through the complete or partial loss of one or more structures, e.g., loss of wings in many orders of insects (T-B, after Klots).

retromorphosis, an ontogenetic reversion from the derived condition of the larva to the primitive structure of the adult (Hennig, after Snodgrass).

retrorse, retrorsus (Latin), turned or bent backward (T-B; R. W. Brown).

retrorse tubercles, in some larval *Dermestes* (Coleoptera: Dermestidae), short urn-shaped structures with a single, short, spikelike seta arising from the center on the distal obtuse or flared end, projecting backwards on abdominal segments (Peterson).

returning vein, in the wings of certain polyphagous Coleoptera, the incompletely chitinized medial vein (M) (T-B, after Tillyard).

retuse, retusus (Latin), blunted; rounded; notched at the apex (T-B; R. W. Brown).

reversed, turned in an unusual or contrary direction, as upside down or inside out (T-B); said of wings when they are deflexed, with the margins of the hind wings projecting beyond those of the forewings (T-B).

revision, in taxonomy, the presentation of new material or new interpretations integrated with previous knowledge through summary and reevaluation (Mayr); see monograph and synopsis.

revolute, revolutus (Latin), turned over; rolled back (T-B; R. W. Brown).

rhabdites, a rod or bladelike process (T-B).

rhabdom, central zone of retinula, consisting of rhabdomeres of separate retinula cells and being the site of photoreception (T-B; Chapman).

rhabdomere, one of 7 or 8 subunits of rhabdom and inner portion of a single retinula cell, consisting of closely packed microvilli and containing pigment granules (Chapman).

rhabdopoda, in ♂ insects, claspers, q.v. (T-B).

rhabdovirus, plant virus, primarily of Gramineae, possessing bacilliform or bullet-shaped inclusion bodies, transmitted propagatively by leafhoppers and planthoppers (Hemiptera: Auchenorrhyncha: Cicadellidae and Delphacidae), aphids (Hemiptera: Sternorrhyncha: Aphididae), lace bugs (Hemiptera: Heteroptera: Tingidae) and mites (Acari) (Nault and Ammar).

Rhabdura, old term for the Campodeidae (Diplura) (Sturm, pers. comm., after Paclt).

rhachis (pl., **rhaches** or **rhachies**), ridge; stem (R. W. Brown); in adult Hymenoptera and other orders, tongue along ventral ramus of each gonapophysis IX fitting into aulax of dorsal ramus of corresponding gonapophysis VIII below (Tuxen, after E. L. Smith); see rachis.

rhegmatocyte, spherule cell, q.v. (Tulloch, after Yeager).

rhegmatocytoid, spherule cell, q.v. (Tulloch, after Yeager).

rheotactic receptors, sensory cells, hairs, or other structures that detect changes in the flow of water over the surface of the body such as that of an aquatic insect (Leftwich).

rheotaxis, a response whereby an aquatic insect moves in a definite direction in relation to the flow of water (T-B; Leftwich); see rheotropism.

rheotropism, orientation (as distinct from locomotion) in relation to the direction of flow of water, as for instance in the case of some insect larvae (T-B; Leftwich); see rheotaxis.

rhinarium (pl., **rhinaria**), in adult Odonata, anteclypeus, q.v. (T-B); in Aphididae (Hemiptera: Sternorrhyncha), primary sensorium, q.v. (Stoetzel, in Stehr); in adult Chalcidoidea (Hymenoptera), multiporous plate sensillum, q.v. (Gauld and Bolton).

Rhinogastra, Ricinulei, q.v. (Borror et al.).

Rhipiceroidea, superfamily within the Elateriformia (Coleoptera: Polyphaga), including the families Rhipiceridae and Callirhipidae, possessing adults with very strongly flabellate antennae in ♂, empodium large and bearing numerous setae, forecoxae elongate in the vertical direction, forecoxal cavities widely open behind, prosternal process not articulating with the mesosternum, hind coxae with a steep posterior face against which the femur can be retracted, 5-5-5 tarsal formula, and abdomen with 5 visible sternites (Britton, in CSIRO).

Rhipiptera, Strepsiptera, q.v. (T-B).

rhizome, the rootstock of plants (T-B).

rho group, in larval Lepidoptera, stemmal group, q.v., of setae (Peterson, after Fracker).

rhodopsin, a mammalian visual pigment (Gilmour, in CSIRO).

rhodopsins, a group of chromoproteins functioning as visual pigments and found within the membrane of the microtubules of the rhabdomeres (Chapman); see retinene.

Rhodoptera, old name for apterous insects with sucking mouth structures (T-B).

rhomb, rhombus (Latin), a diamond-shaped figure with opposite sides parallel and with 2 opposite angles acute and the other 2 obtuse (T-B).

rhomboid, rhomboidal, diamond-shaped (T-B).

Rhopalocera, Lepidoptera within the division Ditrysia in which the antennae are alike in both sexes and form a club at the tip, including the Hesperioidea, Papilionoidea, and sometimes also the Hedyloidea, most species of which are diurnal (T-B; Common, in CSIRO); see Heterocera.

Rhophoteira, Siphonaptera, q.v. (T-B, after Clairville).

Rhyacophiloidea, superfamily within the Spicipalpia (Trichoptera: Annulipalpia), containing the family Rhyacophilidae and Hydrobiosidae (Weaver).

Rhynchophora, Curculionoidea, q.v. (T-B; Britton, in CSIRO).

Rhynchophthirina, Rhyncophthirina, q.v. (Calaby, in CSIRO).

Rhynchota, Hemiptera, q.v. (archaic) (T-B; Leftwich).

rhynchus, proboscis, q.v. (T-B, after Fabricius); see rostrum.

Rhyncophthirina, suborder within the Phthiraptera, including the single family Haematomyzidae, possessing chewing mouthparts at the anterior end of a long proboscis; ectoparasites of elephants and wild pigs in Africa (K. C. Emerson; Lyal, pers. comm.); see Amblycera, Anoplura, and Ischnocera.

Rhyngota, Rhynchota, q.v. (T-B).

rhypophagus, filth-eating (T-B).

rhythm, regular periodic changes (T-B).

rhythmic, rhythmical, in a regularly, periodically fluctuating manner (T-B).

rhythmical movements, in Mantodea and Phasmida, swaying or rocking movements (Key, in CSIRO).

rhythms, circadian rhythms, q.v. (Borror et al.).

Ribaga's organ, in some Cimicoidea (Hemiptera: Heteroptera), ectospermalege or spermalege, q.v. (Carayon, in Usinger).

riboflavin, $C_{17}H_{20}O_6N_4$, an essential vitamin in insects belonging to the vitamin B complex (Gilmour, in CSIRO).

rice black-streaked dwarf, disease of rice caused by a reovirus (*Fijivirus*) transmitted propagatively by *Laodelphax* and *Unkanodes* (Hemiptera: Auchenorrhyncha: Delphacidae) (Nault and Ammar).

rice dwarf, disease of rice caused by a reovirus (*Phytoreovirus*) transmitted propagatively by *Nephotettix* and *Recelia* (Hemiptera: Auchenorrhyncha: Cicadellidae) (Nault and Ammar).

rice gall dwarf, disease of rice caused by a reovirus (*Phytoreovirus*) transmitted propagatively by *Nephotettix* and *Recelia* (Hemiptera: Auchenorrhyncha: Cicadellidae) (Nault and Ammar).

rice grassy stunt, disease of rice caused by a tenuivirus transmitted propagatively by *Nilaparvata* (Hemiptera: Auchenorrhyncha: Delphacidae) (Nault and Ammar).

rice hoja blanca, disease of rice caused by a tenuivirus transmitted propagatively by *Sogatodes* (Hemiptera: Auchenorrhyncha: Delphacidae) (Nault and Ammar).

rice ragged stunt, disease of rice caused by a reovirus (*Fijivirus*) transmitted propagatively by *Nilaparvata* (Hemiptera: Auchenorrhyncha: Delphacidae) (Nault and Ammar).

rice stripe, disease of rice caused by a tenuivirus transmitted propagatively by *Laodelphax, Terthron,* and *Unkanodes* (Hemiptera: Auchenorrhyncha: Delphacidae) (Nault and Ammar).

rice transitory yellowing, disease of rice caused by a rhabdovirus transmitted propagatively by *Nephotettix* (Hemiptera: Auchenorrhyncha: Cicadellidae) (Nault and Ammar).

rice tungro bacilliform, disease of rice caused by a virus transmitted through the foregut by *Nephotettix* (Hemiptera: Auchenorrhyncha: Cicadellidae) (Nault and Ammar).

rice tungro spherical, disease of rice caused by an isometric virus transmitted throught the foregut by *Nephotettix* and *Recelia* (Hemiptera: Auchenorrhyncha: Cicadellidae) (Nault and Ammar).

Ricinulei, order within the Arachnida, including only the ricinuleids, the members of which possess a distinctly segmented opisthosoma without a taillike prolongation and not constricted at base, first pair of legs similar to the others, and chelicerae concealed by a broad flap at anterior end of prosoma (Borror et al.).

Ricinuleida, Ricinulei, q.v. (Borror et al.).

rickettsia (pl., **rickettsae**), gram-negative microorganisms, belonging to the Rickettsiaceae (Norris, after Steinhaus, in CSIRO).

Rickettsiaceae, family of gram-negative bacteria within the Rickettsiales which are parasitic in vertebrate and arthropod hosts (Allaby); see blue disease, Lorsch disease, Rocky Mountain spotted fever, and typhus fever.

rickettsiosis, infection with rickettsiae (Steinhaus and Martignoni).

ridge, in ♂ Heteroptera (Hemiptera), median groove, q.v. (Tuxen, after Baker), or the convex dorsal margin of paramere (transl. "dos" Dupuis, after Tuxen).

ridges (of spermatheca), in ♀ Siphonaptera, strigillae, q.v. (Tuxen).

riffle, a rapid or ripple in a stream or current (T-B).

rigid, rigidus (Latin), stiff; inflexible (T-B).

rigor, rigidity; stiffness (Steinhaus and Martignoni).

rigor mortis, rigidity of the muscles after death (Steinhaus and Martignoni).

Riker mount, a thin, glass-topped exhibition case filled with cotton (Borror et al.).

rima (Latin) (pl., **rimae**), cleft; fissure (T-B; R. W. Brown); in Diptera larvae, a marginal supporting sclerotization on an elongate spiracular opening (Teskey, in McAlpine).

rimose, rimosus (Latin), **rimous,** with minute, narrow, and nearly parallel excavations (rimae) running into each other; chinky; resembling the cracked bark of a tree (T-B; Harris, after Marchant and Charles, R. W. Brown, and Jaeger); see corticinus, fatiscent, fissate, rimulose, rivose, and undose.

rimulose, minutely rimose; with minute cracks or fissurelike openings with sharp edges (Harris, after R. W. Brown).

ring, in ♀ *Aphelocheirus* (Hemiptera: Heteroptera: Naucoridae), ring sclerites, q.v. (Tuxen, after Larsén); in ♂ Coleoptera, tegmen, q.v. (Tuxen, after Hopkins).

ring gland, in larval Muscomorpha (Diptera), structure surrounding the aorta just above the brain formed from the fused corpora allata, corpora cardiaca, and prothoracic glands (Tulloch; Chapman); see ringed glands.

ring joints, in insect antennae, the much shorter proximal articles of the flagellum (T-B, after Comstock); see anellus.

ring organ, in larval Chironomidae (Diptera), campaniform sensillum present on basal antennal segment, at base of mandible, and on ventrobasal sclerite of maxillary palpus (Saether).

ring sclerite(s), in some ♂ Lygaeidae (Hemiptera: Heteroptera), cricoid sclerite, q.v. (Tuxen, after Ashlock); in some ♀ Heteroptera, paired or unpaired annular sclerotizations encircling ringed glands of vagina or of vaginal pouch (Tuxen, after Bonhag and Wick).

ring spot, disease of cabbage plants transmitted by *Myzus persicae* (Hemiptera: Sternorrhyncha: Aphididae) (Borror et al.).

ring vein, in Thysanoptera, ambient vein, q.v. (T-B, after Comstock).

ring wall, in ♂ Lepidoptera, anellus, q.v. (T-B; Tuxen).

ringed glands, in some ♀ Heteroptera, paired or unpaired glands, dorsally or ventrally on vagina or on vaginal pouch, sometimes ringed by annular sclerotizations known as ring sclerites (Tuxen, after Bonhag and Wick).

ringent, ringens (Latin), gaping (T-B; R. W. Brown).

riparian, riparious (T-B).

riparious, living on stream or river banks.

ripicolous, riparious, q.v. (T-B).

rivalry song, rivalry sound, q.v. (Chapman).

rivalry sound, patterned aggressive signal mediating competitive interactions between conspecific individuals, e.g., bark beetles (Coleoptera: Scolytidae) and crickets (Orthoptera: Ensifera) (Matthews and Matthews).

river blindness, extreme onchocerciasis in man caused by damage to capilleries resulting from the lodging of the small worms, and the blockage of the blood supply to the eye tissue (Allaby); see onchocerciasis.

rivose, rivosus (Latin), **rivous,** marked with sinuate furrows, like rivulets, not running in parallel direction (T-B; Harris, after Marchant and Charles, Stearn, and R. W. Brown); see rimose, rivulose, and venose.

rivulose, minutely rivose; with very small or fine sinuate furrows, like rivulets, which are not parallel (T-B, after R. W. Brown, and Marchant and Charles).

RMSF, Rocky Mountain spotted fever, q.v.

roach, cockroach, q.v. (Borror et al.).

robin's pin-cushion, bedegaur gall, q.v. (Leftwich).

Robles' disease, onchocerciasis, q.v. (Adkins, pers. comm.).

robust, stout or thickened (T-B).

rock crawler, a member of the Grylloblattodea (Borror et al.).

Rocky Mountain spotted fever (RMSF), disease of man in North America caused by *Rickettsia rickettsii* (Rickettsiaceae), and transmitted by various ticks, mainly *Dermacentor andersoni* and *D. variabilis* (Acari: Ixodidae) (Borror et al.; Allaby).

rod, in ♂ Coleoptera, spicules, q.v. (Tuxen, after Hopkins); in ♀ Coleoptera, spiculum ventrale, q.v. (Tuxen); in adult Culicidae (Diptera), one of the specialized spicules comprising the cibarial teeth (Harbach and Knight, after Arnett et al.).

rod of the eye, rhabdom, q.v. (T-B).

rods of Jullien, modified scales, shaped like sclerotized rods, crowning posterior lobes of organ of Jullien (transl. "Jullienische Stäbchen" Fruhstorfer, after Tuxen).

rolling, rotation about the longitudinal axis in flight (Chapman).

ronnel, $C_8H_8Cl_3O_3PS$, a synthetic insecticide, an animal systemic and contact insecticide; an organophosphate, O,O-dimethyl O-2,4,5-trichlorophenyl phosphorothioate; slightly toxic to mammals, acute oral LD_{50} for rats 1740 mg/kg (Pfadt).

roof, in ♀ Miridae (Hemiptera: Heteroptera), level dorsal part of vagina bearing the ringed glands (transl. "Dach" Kullenberg, in Tuxen).

root, in adult Culicidae (Diptera), a basal supporting ridge or a cone arising from the flat ventral surface of the cibarium (Harbach and Knight, after Christophers).

Rophoteira, Siphonaptera, q.v. (Lewis, pers. comm., after Schellenberg de Clairville).

ropy brood, American foulbrood, q.v. (Steinhaus and Martignoni).

rorulent, rorulentus (Latin), covered with a bloom of fine dust that can be rubbed off (T-B; Harris, after Marchant and Charles, and Stearn); see farinaceous, farinose, pollinose, pruinose, and pulverulent.

rosaceous, rosaceus, like a rose in scent (T-B); of or pertaining to the plant family Rosaceae.

roseate, roseous, roseus, rose-colored, i.e., reddish (T-B).

rose-shaped process, in ♂ *Leuctra* (Plecoptera), supraanal lobe, q.v. (Tuxen, after Morton).

rosette gall, a type of gall formed on the end of a growing shoot and causing terminal leaves to become shorter and clustered together in a rosette, e.g., those on willow shoots caused by the gall midge *Rhabdophaga* (Diptera: Cecidomyiidae) (Leftwich).

rostellum (pl., **rostella**), in ♂ Plebeiinae (Lepidoptera: Lycaenidae), the free, ventral curving, distal part of processus superior valvae (Tuxen, after Nabokov); in ♂ *Neptis* (Lepidoptera: Nymphalidae), elongate, pointed projection of ventral edge of orifice of aedoeagus (Tuxen, after Roepke).

rostral, pertaining or attached to a rostrum (T-B).

rostral filaments, in Coccoidea (Hemiptera: Sternorrhyncha), mandibular and maxillary stylets, q.v. (T-B).

rostral groove, in Heteroptera (Hemiptera), labial groove, q.v. (Andersen).

rostralis, in Hemiptera, mandibular and maxillary stylets, q.v. (T-B, after MacGillivray).

rostrate, rostratus (Latin), having a rostrum, a long protraction bearing the mouthparts (T-B).

rostriform, produced like a beak or snout (T-B).

rostrulum, the proboscis of the fleas (Siphonaptera) (T-B).

rostrum (Latin) (pl., **rostra**), a snoutlike projection or rigid extension of the head, bearing the mouthparts at the end, e.g., adult weevils (Coleoptera: Curculionoidea) (T-B; Leftwich); in Protura, an anterior dorsal prolongation of the head in the position of a labrum (Bellinger, pers. comm.); in Hemiptera, the jointed sheath formed from the labium, enclosing the mandibular and maxillary stylets (T-B); in adult Mecoptera, elongate clypeus and labrum (also maxillae and labium) (Riek, in CSIRO); in adult Diptera, proboscis, q.v. (Colless and McAlpine, in CSIRO); in adult Tipulomorpha (Diptera), elongate structure formed from fused clypeus, genae, subgenae, and related structures (McAlpine); in adult Trichoptera, proboscis, q.v.

(Riek, in CSIRO); in ♂ Lepidoptera, saccus, q.v. (Tuxen, after Cholodkowsky); in ♂ Lepidoptera, subapical, dorsocaudad extending process of dorsal edge of sacculus (Tuxen, after John); see proboscis.

rotate, wheel-shaped, with radiating parts (T-B).

rotation, a turning about an axis (T-B).

rotative, rotatory, q.v. (T-B).

rotator, any part or structure used in or for turning (T-B).

rotatory, turning entirely around or apparently so (T-B).

rotatory coxae, in Heteroptera (Hemiptera), nearly globose hind coxae with a ball and socket articulation in trochalopodous taxa (Drake and Davis, after Schiödte).

rotaxis, wing base, q.v. (T-B, after MacGillivray).

rotenoid, one of a group of toxic compounds (e.g., rotenone) found in certain plants of the family Leguminosae (Pfadt).

rotenone, $C_{23}H_{22}O_6$, a botanical insecticide; derived from the roots of *Derris elliptica, Lonchoncarpus utilis,* and *L. urucu* (Leguminosae); moderately toxic to mammals, acute oral LD_{50} for rats 132 mg/kg (Pfadt).

rotula, a small round segment sometimes present between the joints of the antennae and of the palpi (T-B).

rotule, trochantin, q.v. (T-B).

rotundate, rotundatus, rotundus (Latin), rounded; circular or in the form of a segment of a circle; with rounded angles passing gradually into each other (T-B).

round spot, orbicular spot, q.v. (T-B).

roundworm, a parasitic nematode.

royal cell, in honey bees (Hymenoptera: Apidae), the large, pitted, waxen cell constructed by workers to rear queen larvae (Wilson); in some species of termites (Isoptera), the special cell in which the queen is housed (Wilson).

royal chamber, the space reserved for the accommodation of king and queen termites (Isoptera), or the space reserved for the queen of an ant colony (Hymenoptera: Formicidae) (Tulloch).

royal jelly, in Apidae (Hymenoptera), a material supplied by workers to ♀ larvae in royal cells which is necessary for the transformation of larvae into queens, secreted primarily by the hypopharyngeal glands and consisting of a rich mixture of nutrient substances, many possessing a complex chemical structure (T-B; Wilson); see worker jelly.

royal pairs, royalties, the sexually active males and females of social insects (T-B); see primary reproductive.

R$_s$, radial sector, q.v. (Borror et al.).

ruber (Latin), red (T-B).

rubescent, reddish (T-B).

rubiginose, rubiginosus (Latin), **rubiginous,** reddish-brown or reddish yellow (T-B).

rubineous, rubineus, of a ruby red; vivid red (T-B).

rubricans, of a bay or grey-black color (T-B).

rudiment, the beginning of any structure or part before it has developed (T-B).

rudimentary, undeveloped (T-B); see embryonic.

Ruelene (trade name), crufomate, q.v. (Pfadt).

rufescent, rufescens, somewhat reddish (T-B).

rufous, rufus (Latin), red; reddish (T-B; R. W. Brown).

ruga (pl., **rugae**), a wrinkle (T-B; R. W. Brown) ; in ♂ Siphonaptera, wrinkle or fold surrounding anterior angle of dorsal wall of aedeagus when this is a very large arch (Tuxen, after Peus); see rugula.

rugae (of spermatheca), in ♂ Siphonaptera, strigillae, q.v. (Tuxen).

rugose, rugosus (Latin), **rugous,** wrinkled (T-B; Harris, after Marchant and Charles, and R. W. Brown); see rugulose, salebrose, and scabrous.

rugosite, small or minute elevation either in the form of a dot or small ridge (Peterson).

rugula (pl., **rulgulae**), a small wrinkle (T-B); see ruga.

rugulose, rugulosus (Latin), minutely rugose; minutely wrinkled (T-B; Harris, after Jaeger); see scabriculous.

rumula (Latin), **rumule,** teatlike fleshy protuberances on the bodies of larvae (T-B, after Kirby and Spence).

runcinate, runcinatus, notched; cut into several transverse acute segments which point backward (T-B).

ruptor ovi, egg burster, q.v. (T-B; Leftwich).

rursus (Latin), turned back; backward; reversed (T-B; R. W. Brown).

rutilous, rutilus (Latin), red (T-B; R. W. Brown).

ryania, a botanical insecticide consisting of the ground stemwood of *Ryania speciosa*; active ingredient is the alkaloid ryanodine; slightly toxic to mammals, acute oral LD_{50} for rats of the ground *Ryania* stems 1200 mg/kg (Pfadt).

S

sabadilla, $C_{32}H_{49}NO_9$ (cevadine) and $C_{36}H_{51}NO_{11}$ (veratridine), a botanical insecticide made from the ground seeds of *Scheonocaulon officinale* (Liliaceae); active ingredient is a crude mixture of alkaloids termed veratrine; relatively nontoxic to warm-blooded animals (Pfadt).

sabroid, in adult Culicidae (Diptera), a sclerotized saber-shaped bar connected to the base of the cubitus (Harbach and Knight, after Owen).

sabulose, sabulosus (Latin), sandy or gritty (T-B).

sac, a small bladder or bladderlike vessel or structure (T-B); in Coccoidea (Hemiptera: Sternorrhyncha), the separate cottony envelope secreted by certain species (T-B); in ♀ Lepidoptera, corpus bursae, q.v. (Tuxen).

sac tube, in Phthiraptera, a trough composed of a pair of half-tubes, the prolongation of the mouth of the stylet sac forward into the buccal funnel (T-B, after Imms).

sacbrood, a lethal disease of larval honey bees, (Hymenoptera: Apidae) caused by a virus infecting cells of the fat body, causing death in the prepupal stage after cocoon spinning (Steinhaus and Martignoni).

saccate, gibbous or inflated toward one end (T-B).

Saccharomycetes, organisms harbored in the mycetome of aphids (Hemiptera: Sternorrhyncha: Aphididae) (T-B).

saccharose, sucrose, q.v. (T-B).

sacci oviducti, in ♀ Lygaeidae (Hemiptera: Heteroptera), (unpaired saclike) pseudospermatheca, q.v. (Tuxen, after Carayon).

sacciform larva, in some Dryinidae, Mymaridae, and Trichogrammatidae (Hymenoptera), an ovoid featureless larva that lacks visible segmentation and setae (Gauld and Bolton).

saccoid gill, a swollen saclike gill (T-B).

saccular, sacculated, saclike or sac-formed (T-B).

saccular type, in ♀ Coleoptera, genitalia without separate bursa copulatrix (Tuxen).

saccule, a little sac or pouch (T-B); see sacculus.

sacculi laterales, in ♂ Lepidoptera, coremata, q.v. (Tuxen) or abdominal osmeteria (Tuxen, after Zerny and Beier).

sacculus (pl., **sacculi**), in ♂ Noctuidae and other Lepidoptera, ventroproximal region of valva, usually easily distinguishable, sometimes largely isolated from rest of valva, bearing various processes, from slight swellings to large, heavily sclerotized arms (Tuxen, after Pierce); in ♂ Lepidoptera, saccus, q.v. (Tuxen, after Roepke); in ♂ Coleophoridae (Lepidoptera), ventral, mesal and more or less caudad projecting part of valva, partly equivalent to sacculus of Pierce (Tuxen, after Toll).

sacculus vaginae, in ♀ Siphonaptera, diverticulum in dorsal wall of vagina alongside and in front of lura of ductus bursae, but caudad of duplicatura vaginalis (Tuxen, after Smit).

saccus (Latin) (pl., **sacci**), bag (R. W. Brown); in ♂ Lepidoptera, midventral, internal, cephalic evagination of vinculum, usually cylindrical, sometimes flat, sometimes very short or absent, sometimes very long (Tuxen, after Zander); vinculum, q.v. (Tuxen, after Bethune-Baker).

saccus glandulosus (pl., **sacci glandulosi**), in ♂ Lepidoptera, pouches containing coremata (Tuxen, after Kusnezov).

saccus gynatrialis, in ♀ Heteroptera (Hemiptera), vaginal pouch, q.v. (Tuxen, after Štys).

saccus sebaceus (pl., **sacci sebacei**), in ♀ Lepidoptera, dilation of basal portion of a glandula sebacea (Tuxen, after Stitz).

saccus seminalis, in ♀ Tingidae (Hemiptera: Heteroptera), (paired saclike) pseudospermathecae, q.v. (Tuxen, after Carayon).

sacellus, in ♂ Lepidoptera, coremata (Tuxen, after Roepke).

sack, in adult Lepidoptera, sphragis, q.v. (Tuxen, after Spuler); in ♀ Lepidoptera, corpus bursae, q.v. (Tuxen, after authors).

sack of Herold, in ♂ Lepidoptera, organ of Herold, q.v. (Tuxen).

sack of spermatheca, in ♀ Siphonaptera, bulga, q.v. (Tuxen).

sacklike outgrowth of spermathecal duct, in ♀ Heteroptera (Hemiptera), diverticulum ductus, q.v.(Tuxen, after Pendergrast).

saclike spermathecae, in ♀ Tingidae (Hemiptera: Heteroptera), (paired saclike) pseudospermathecae, q.v. (Tuxen, after Scudder).

saddle, in larval Culicidae (Diptera), sclerite covering the dorsal surface of abdominal segment IX bearing the anus (Teskey, in McAlpine).

saffroning, in some adult Odonata, yellow pigment at base of wing (O'Farrell, in CSIRO).

sage apple, an aromatic gall produced on the sage plant *Salvia pomifera* by members of the genus *Aulax* (Hymenoptera: Cynipidae), eaten as a delicacy in the Middle East (Leftwich).

sagitta (Latin) (pl., **sagittae**), in ♂ Hymenoptera, digitus, q.v. (Tuxen) or volsella, q.v. (Tuxen, after Rohwer), paramere, q.v. (Tuxen, after Thomson).

sagittal, longitudinal, q.v. (T-B).

sagittal plane, the longitudinal vertical plane which divides an animal into right and left halves (T-B; McAlpine).

sagittate, sagittatus, shaped like an arrow head; elongate triangular (T-B).

sagum (Latin) (pl., **saga**), cloak; mantle (R. W. Brown); in ♂ Plebeiinae (Lepidoptera: Lycaenidae), paired, somewhat membranous structure, with serrate or scobinate edges, more or less surrounding aedoeagus, dorsal to and between arms of furca (Tuxen, after Nabokov).

sail, in ♂ Siphonaptera, velum, q.v. (Tuxen).

Saldoidea, superfamily within the infraorder Leptopodomorpha of the Heteroptera, including the Saldidae and Aepophilidae, a predator group found in littoral and intertidal situations; in the older literature sometimes used in the sense of Leptopodomorpha (Schuh).

salebrose, salebrosus (Latin), **salebrous,** rough, rugged or uneven (T-B; Harris, after Marchant and Charles); see asperous, rugose, scabrous, and squarrose.

salicylaldehyde, $C_7H_6O_2$, an aromatic aldehyde secreted as a defensive secretion by some beetles (Coleoptera) (Gilmour, in CSIRO).

salient, projecting; jutting out (T-B).

saliva, secretion of the salivary glands that serves to lubricate the mouthparts and containing enzymes which start digestion of food (T-B; Chapman).

salivarium, part of preoral cavity behind the hypopharynx and between it and the labium, into which the salivary duct opens (T-B, after Snodgrass; Chapman).

salivary canal, in Hemiptera, the posterior of the 2 canals formed by the maxillary stylets, through which salivary secretions are ejected by the salivary pump (T-B); in adult Culicidae (Diptera), the canal extended the length of the hypopharynx through which saliva passes from the salivary pump (Harbach and Knight, after Crampton); see salivary duct.

salivary duct, duct of labial glands opening at base of the hypopharynx (Harbach and Knight; Teskey, in McAlpine); see salivary canal.

salivary gland, gland producing saliva, usually corresponding to the labial gland, q.v., but corresponding to the mandibular glands in larval Lepidoptera (T-B; Chapman).

salivary gland chromosome, polytene chromosome, q.v. (Leftwich).

salivary meatus, salivary canal, q.v., or salivary duct, q.v. (T-B).

salivary pump, in fluid-feeding insects, e.g., Diptera and Hemiptera, modification of salivarium to form a pump that has a rigid lower wall and a flexible upper one that can be drawn upwards by dilator muscles causing fluid to be sucked into the lumen and which is expelled as the muscles are relaxed (Chapman).

salivary receptacle, a small cavity above the opening of the salivary duct, between the labium and hypopharynx (T-B); see salivarium.

salivary reservoir, a differentiated part of the salivary gland (Chapman).

salivary sheath, in plant-sucking Sternorrhyncha, Auchenorrhyncha, and some Heteroptera (Hemiptera), lipoprotein sheath left in plant tissue, formed from hardened salivary secretions, encasing the stylets as they penetrate plant tissue (Chapman).

salivary syringe, salivary pump, q.v. (T-B, after Snodgrass).

salivia (pl., **saliviae**), lingual sclerite, q.v. (T-B, after MacGillivray).

salivos, the mouth of the salivary duct (T-B, after MacGillivray).

saltation, discontinuous variation produced in a single step by major mutation (Mayr).

Saltatoria, Orthoptera, q.v. (T-B; Boudreaux, after Latreille); Siphonaptera, q.v. (Lewis, pers. comm., after Retzius).

saltatorial, adapted for jumping, usually describing the hind legs (T-B; Leftwich).

saltatorial appendage, in Collembola, furcula, q.v. (T-B).

saltatory, saltatorial, q.v. (T-B).

sample, that portion of a population which is actually available to the taxonomist (Mayr).

sand basket, in adult Aculeata (Hymenoptera), psammophore, q.v. (Brown, pers. comm.; Carpenter, pers. comm.).

sand-fly fever, disease caused by a virus transmitted by sand flies, *Phlebotomus* (Diptera: Psychodidae) (Allaby).

Sandaliorrhyncha, Corixoidea, q.v.

sanguine, sanguineous, sanguineus (Latin), blood-red, i.e., dark red (T-B),

sanguinivorous, blood feeding (T-B).

sanguinolent, bloody in color or appearance (T-B).

sapphirine, sapphirinus, sapphire blue, i.e., dark blue (T-B).

saprobiotic, living in or among decaying organic matter (T-B).

sapromyophily, insect-flower syndrome involving carrion and dung flies (Diptera) (Matthews and Matthews, after Baker and Hurd).

saprophage, a heterotrophic animal that consumes other dead, organisms (Allaby); see detritovore.

saprophagous, feeding on dead or decaying animal or vegetable matter (T-B); see detritovorous, necrophagous, and phytosaprophagous.

sarcode, protoplasm, q.v. (T-B).

sarcolemma, sheath of striated muscle fiber consisting of the plasma membrane of the cell plus the basement membrane (T-B; Chapman).

sarcolysis, the breaking down of muscles (T-B); see histolysis.

sarcolyte, in the blood of the pupae of Diptera, a muscle fragment in the process of disintegration; a fragment of muscular fiber with a nucleus (T-B, after Imms).

sarcomere, the short subunit of a muscle fiber separated from other sarcomeres by Krause's membrane (T-B; Chapman).

sarcomeric, of or pertaining to a sarcomere (T-B); of the character of a sarcomere (T-B).

sarcophagous, feeding on flesh (T-B); see necrophagous.

sarcoplasm, cytoplasm of muscle fiber in which the myofibrils are imbedded (T-B; Chapman).

sarcoplasmic reticulum, endoplasmic reticulum of muscle cells which is not connected to the plasma membrane (Chapman).

sarcosome, mitochondrion of a muscle cell (T-B; Chapman).

sarcostyle, myofibril, q.v. (T-B).

sarothrum, in adult Apoidea (Hymenoptera), basitarsus (q.v.) of hind leg (T-B).

satellite sclerite, in ♂ Siphonaptera, the tanned portion of the circular roof of the narrow exit of the capsule of the aedeagus, connecting the sclerotized inner tube and the tectum (Rothschild and Traub).

saturated, saturatus, deep, full; applied to any color (T-B).

saw, in ♀ Auchenorrhyncha (Hemiptera), first and second valvulae (ventral and inner valves) (Tuxen); in ♀ Hymenoptera, terebra, q.v. (Tuxen).

saw guide, in ♀ Symphyta (Hymenoptera), the 2 external flattened plates of the ovipositor (T-B).

sawblade, in ♀ Hymenoptera, first gonapophyses, q.v. (Tuxen).

sawcase, in ♀ Auchenorrhyncha (Hemiptera), third (dorsal) valvulae, enclosing saw (Tuxen).

sawfly, member of the suborder Symphyta (Hymenoptera) (Riek, in CSIRO).

sawing-clipping feeding, the method of feeding in the Notonectidae and Naucoridae (Hemiptera: Heteroptera), in which the stylets are moved back and forth in a straight line (Cobben); see lacerate-flush feeding.

sawsheath, in ♀ Symphyta (Hymenoptera), gonoplacs, q.v. (Tuxen).

sawtooth, in ♀ Symphyta (Hymenoptera), cutting projections on ventral ramus of gonapophysis VIII (Tuxen, after E. L. Smith).

saxicolous, living on stones, rocks, walls, etc. (T-B; Allaby).

SBP 1382 (trade name), resmethrin, q.v. (Pfadt).

scab, a contagious skin disease of animals caused by certain parasitic mites (Acari) (Pfadt); see mange.

scabellum, in adult Diptera, base, q.v., of halter (T-B, after Tillyard; Harbach and Knight; McAlpine).

scaber (Latin), scabrous, q.v. (T-B; Harris).

scaberulus, scabriculous, q.v. (Harris).

scabriculous, finely scabrous; with fine and regular short, sharp, wrinkles and/or projections (T-B; Harris, after R. W. Brown); see muriculate and shagreened.

scabrid, sparsely scabrous (Harris, after Stearn, and Munz).

scabridulous, scabriculous, q.v. (Harris).

scabrose, scabrous, q.v. (T-B; Harris).

scabrosus (Latin), scabrous, q.v. (T-B; Harris).

scabrous, rough; irregularly and roughly rugose; possessing short, sharp projections or wrinkles (T-B; Harris, after R. W. Brown); see rugose, salebrose, scabriculous, and squarrose.

scalariform, ladderlike; applied to venation when the veinlets between 2 longitudinal veins are regularly arranged like the rungs of a ladder (T-B).

scale, a flat unicellular outgrowth of the body wall of many groups of insects, of various shapes and usually representing modified setae (T-B, after Snodgrass); on body and wings of adult Lepidoptera, frequently a hairlike structure or flattened plate, the latter usually consisting of 2 lamellae, often with a space between containing pigment and attached to the cuticle by a short pedicel (T-B, after Imms; Chapman); in termites (Isoptera), wing scale, q.v. (T-B); in most Coccoidea (Hemiptera: Sternorrhyncha), a covering made of waxy substances for the protection of the eggs, nymphs, and adults (T-B; Kosztarab and Korár); in Diaspididae (Hemiptera: Sternorrhyncha: Coccoidea), test, q.v. (T-B); in Psyllidae (Hemiptera: Sternorrhyncha: Psylloidea), lerp, q.v. (Woodward et al, in CSIRO).

scale insect, a member of the superfamily Coccoidea (Hemiptera: Sternorrhyncha) (Woodward et al., in CSIRO).

scale tuft, in adult Lepidoptera, a tuft of scales raised above the general level of the wing scales (Common).

scalloped, crenate, q.v. (T-B; Harris).

scalpella, scalpellum, q.v. (T-B, after Kirby and Spence).

scalpellum (pl., **scalpelli**), mouthpart formed into a stylet, q.v. (T-B; Leftwich).

scalpriform, chisel-shaped (T-B).

scanning electron microscope (SEM), a microscope that utilizes an electron beam to produce images of surface features, magnifications in biological materials commonly ranging from 20–15,000 times.

scansorial, formed for climbing, being most commonly applied to legs fitted for climbing on hair, e.g., Anoplura (Phthiraptera) (T-B; Peterson; Leftwich).

scansorial warts, ampullae, q.v. (Peterson).

scapal plate, in adult Diptera, a group of campaniform sensilla on the dorsal and ventral surface of the halter at the base of the stalk (Chapman).

scapal setae, in some adult Chironomidae (Diptera), setae of scape (Saether).

scape, scapus (Latin), stem; shaft (R. W. Brown); the first or basal segment of the antenna (T-B; Chapman).

scaphiform, boat-shaped (T-B).

scaphium (pl., **scaphia**), in ♂ Lepidoptera, sclerotization in dorsal part of tuba analis (Tuxen, after Pierce); in ♂ Lepidoptera, gnathos, q.v. (Tuxen, after Stichel); in ♂ Lepidoptera, part of appendices angulares (Tuxen, after Klinkhardt); in ♂ Papilionidae (Lepidoptera), tegumen + scaphium + subscaphium (Tuxen, after Gosse); in ♂ *Plusia* (Lepidoptera: Noctuidae), part of harpe (Tuxen, after John); in ♂ Hesperiidae (Lepidoptera), subscaphium + gnathos (Tuxen, after Reverdin); in ♂ *Colias* (Lepidoptera: Pieridae), uncus, q.v. (Tuxen, after Stitz).

scapula (pl., **scapulae**), shoulder (T-B); in adult Hymenoptera, parapsis, q.v. (T-B; Borror et al.); in adult Lepidoptera, tegula, q.v. (T-B); see humerus.

scapular, of or pertaining to the scapula (T-B).

scapular area, in a wing, that part nearest the shoulder (T-B); in Orthoptera, radial area, q.v. (T-B).

scapular piece, the episternum, q.v.; also applied to the scapula (T-B).

scapular shield, in Isoptera, wing scale, q.v. (Thorne, pers. comm.).

scapular vein, in Orthoptera, radius, q.v. (T-B).

scapularia, mesepisternum, q.v. (T-B).

scar, in pupal Tanypodinae (Diptera: Chironomidae), characteristic, delineated spot on abdominal tergum I (Saether).

scarabaeiform larva, oligopod larva, as a white grub of the Scarabaeidae (Coleoptera), i.e., having a curved, fleshy abdomen and possessing limited mobility (Peterson; Leftwich; Chapman).

Scarabaeiformia, group within the suborder Polyphaga (Coleoptera), including the superfamilies Scarabaeoidea and Dascilloidea (Britton, in CSIRO).

scarabaeoid, scarablike (T-B); a member of the superfamily Scarabaeoidea (Coleoptera).

Scarabaeoidea, superfamily within the Polyphaga (Coleoptera), including the Scarabaeidae and other families, possessing adults with an asymmetrical antennal club consisting of 3 to 8 distal articles, head not covered dorsally by prothorax, and tarsal formula clearly 5-5-5 (Britton, in CSIRO).

scarabidoid, in larval Meloidae (Coleoptera), scarabaeiform larva, q.v. (T-B).

scarified, appearing clawed or scratched; furnished with fine, irregular grooves, coarser than aciculate (T-B; Harris, after R. W. Brown); see aciculate and rastrate.

scariose, scariosus (Latin), **scarious,** scaly (T-B).

scatophagous, coprophagous, q.v. (T-B; Leftwich).

Scatopsoidea, superfamily within the infraorder Psychodomorpha (Diptera: Nematocera), including the Scatopsidae and Synneuridae (McAlpine).

scavenger, an animal that feeds on dead plants or animals, or decaying materials, or on animal wastes (T-B; Borror et al.).

scent brush, in adult Lepidoptera, hair pencil, q.v. (T-B, after Klots; Common, in CSIRO).

scent gland apparatus, in Heteroptera (Hemiptera), metathoracic scent glands + evaporatoria, q.v. (Štys).

scent glands, exocrine glands producing either pheromones or defensive secretions (T-B; Chapman); in some ♂ Blattaria, tergal glands, q.v. (Mackerras, in CSIRO; Chapman); in some Blattidae (Blattaria), a bilobed abdominal sternal gland opening between abdominal sterna VI and VII or paired glands between terga V and VI, producing defensive secretions (Mackerras, in CSIRO); in Heteroptera (Hemiptera), dorsal abdominal scent gland in nymphs (sometimes persisting to adulthood) and several types of scent glands in adults (see metathoracic scent glands, Brindley's glands; other kinds with a more limited distribution also known), producing pheromones, allomones, venoms, and other substances, with often notorious and unpleasant smell for humans (Štys, pers. comm.); in some adult Planipennia, any eversible or noneversible glands opening in the membranous parts of the abdomen or thorax (Riek, in CSIRO); in some adult Trichoptera, eversible glands present on the head (Riek, in CSIRO), androconia on ♂ wings (Bicchierai and Moretti), and paired glands on abdominal segment V (Nielsen); in adult Lepidoptera, specialized pheromone-secreting glands on the abdomen, legs, or wings (Common, in CSIRO) (see androconia and hair pencils); in ♂ Bittacidae (Mecoptera), eversible pheromonal glands between abdominal terga 6–7 and 7–8 (Mackerras, in CSIRO); in ♂ Panorpidae and Panorpodidae (Mecoptera), pheronmonal glands in genital bulb (Thornhill); see defense glands.

scent pores, in Heteroptera (Hemiptera), ostioles, q.v.

scent reservoir, in Heteroptera (Hemiptera), paired or unpaired reservoir of the metathoracic scent glands (Štys, pers. comm.); see diadenian type, diastomian type, and omphalian type.

scent scales, androconia, q.v. (T-B).

scent tuft, hair pencil, q.v. (T-B).

Schistonota, suborder of Ephemeroptera, including the superfamilies Baetoidea, Heptagenoidea, Leptophleboidea, and Ephemeroidea (Landa and Soldán).

Schizodactyloidea, superfamily within the suborder Ensifera (Orthoptera), including splay-footed grasshoppers of the family Schizodactylidae (Hennig; Kevin, in Parker).

schizogony, the phase in the life cycle of the malaria parasite, *Plasmodium* spp. (Plasmodiidae), passed in the human host, involving the asexual production of spores by the splitting of a parent cell into several units (T-B; Tulloch); see schizont and merozoite.

Schizomida, order within the Arachnida, including the short-tailed whipscorpions, possessing a distinctly segmented opisthosoma with at most a short taillike appendage, lacking eyes, transverse suture present on prosoma, and pedipalps arching upward, foward, and then downward and moving vertically (Borror et al.).

schizont, second stage in the asexual development of malaria parasite, *Plasmodium* spp. (Plasmodiidae), derived from nuclear division of a trophozoite within a red blood cell or a liver parenchymal cell (T-B; Borror et al.).

Schizopeltida, Schizomida, q.v. (Borror et al.).

Schizophora, series of superfamilies within the Muscomorpha (Diptera), possessing adults with ptilinal fissure above base of antennae and wings with R_{4+5} unbranched and anterior cubitus (CuA) usually short and joining first anal vein (1A) well back from its apex (i.e., the wing margin), usually towards its base (Colless and McAlpine, in CSIRO); see Aschiza.

Schmidt's layer, zone of deposition of new cuticle (Chapman).

Schmitt box, wooden box used for the strorage of pinned insects, about 230 by 330 by 60 mm, with a tight-fitting lid and an inner bottom of sheet cork, composition board, or plastic foam (Borror et al.).

schottenol, sterol found in the cactus *Lophocereus schotteni,* required for development in *Drosophila pachea* (Diptera: Drosophilidae) (Chapman).

schradan, a synthetic insecticide and acaricide, a plant systemic; an organophosphate, octamethylpyrophosphoramide; extremely toxic to mammals, acute oral LD_{50} for rats 9 mg/kg (Pfadt).

Schreckensteinioidea, a superfamily of the infraorder Ditrysia (Lepidoptera) containing one family Schreckensteiniidae, adults being small moths, ocelli and chaetosemata absent, proboscis naked, forewing with pterostigma, and ♀ frenulum a single bristle; pupae with paired dorsal teeth, protruded from perforated cocoon at ecdysis (Minet).

Schwann cell, cell enveloping perikaryon and axon of sensory cell of a scolopidium (Gilmour, in CSIRO; Chapman).

scientific name, a name of a taxon that conforms to the Code, as opposed to a vernacular name, consisting of one name, a binomen, or a trinomen (ICZN); see vernacular name.

Sciaroidea, superfamily within the infraorder Bibionomorpha (Diptera: Nematocera), including the Sciaridae, Mycetophilidae, and Cecidomyiidae (McAlpine).

Sciomyzoidea, superfamily within the series Schizophora of the Muscomorpha (Diptera: Brachycera), including the Sciomyzidae and other families, possessing adults with costa of wing unbroken; subcosta (Sc) complete and separate from R_1, cell CuP short, not angularly produced, ♂ with sternites VI and VII, when present, laterally displaced, abdominal tergite VI of ♂ abbreviated or absent, ♀ postabdomen not modified to form an ovipositor with the cerci usually separate (Colless and McAlpine, in CSIRO); superfamily within the Schizophora-Acalyptratae (Diptera: Muscomorpha), including the Sciomyzidae, Coelopidae, Dryomyzidae, Ropalomeridae, and Sepsidae (McAlpine).

scissorial area, in larval Scarabaeidae (Coleoptera), the mesal area between the dentes and the molar area (Peterson, after Hayes).

sclerite, any plate of the body wall bounded by membrane or sutures (T-B; Chapman).

sclerite ypsilon, in ♂ Siphonaptera, solum, q.v. (Tuxen, after Peus).

sclerites of labral region, in larval Chironomidae (Diptera), sclerites in front of clypeus or frontoclypeal apotome (Saether).

sclerites of phallotreme wall, in ♂ Orthoptera, aedeagal valves, q.v. (Tuxen, after Snodgrass).

scleritization, sclerotization, q.v. (T-B).

scleroma (pl., **scleromata**), the sclerotic ring of a body segment in insects, as distinguished from the membrane uniting it to others (T-B, after Snodgrass); sclerite, q.v. (Peterson).

sclerome, scleroma, q.v. (T-B).

sclerora, in adult Hymenoptera, ventral ramus, q.v. (Tuxen, after Ross).

sclerotic, sclerotized, q.v. (T-B).

sclerotic dome, in adult Siphonaptera, the heavily sclerotized portion of the pleural rod occupying approximately the same area in the mesothorax as the pleural arch in the metathorax, but not necessarily homologous with it (Rothschild and Traub).

sclerotic rods, in ♂ Notonectidae (Hemiptera: Heteroptera), ligamentary processes, q.v. (Tuxen, after Truxal).

sclerotin, a hard nitrogenous substance, impermeable to water, found together with chitin in the cuticle, being composed of tanned proteins (T-B; Tulloch, after Richards; Leftwich); see melanin.

sclerotization, hardening of the cuticle involving the development of crosslinks between protein chains (T-B; Chapman).

sclerotization of gynatrial glands, in ♀ Lygaeidae, Coreidae, Malcidae (Hemiptera: Heteroptera), ring sclerites, q.v. (Tuxen, after Štys).

sclerotized, hardened through sclerotization (T-B; Chapman).

sclerotized evagination of bursa copulatrix, in ♀ Hydrometridae (Hemiptera: Heteroptera), vaginal pouch, q.v. (Tuxen, after Sprague).

sclerotized inner tube, in ♀ Siphonaptera, tubus interior, q.v. (Lewis, pers. comm.).

sclerotized opening, in ♂ Heteroptera (Hemiptera), foramen ductus, q.v. (Tuxen, after Schaefer).

sclerotized plate, in ♂ Dermaptera, accessory structure present in distal lobe (Tuxen, after Burr).

sclerotized pouches, in ♀ Thaumastocoridae (Hemiptera: Heteroptera), pseudospermathecae, q.v. (Tuxen, after Scudder).

sclerotized rings, in ♀ Miridae, Tingidae (Hemiptera: Heteroptera), ring sclerites, q.v. (Tuxen, after Slater).

sclerotized rod(s), in ♂ Dermaptera, accessory structure present in distal lobe (Tuxen, after Burr); in ♂ Notonectidae (Hemiptera: Heteroptera), ligamentary processes, q.v. (Tuxen, after Truxal).

scobina (Latin) (pl., **scobinae**), rasp (R. W. Brown); in ♀ Symphyta (Hymenoptera), rasp on distal portion of dorsal ramus of gonapophysis VIII (Tuxen, after E. L. Smith).

scobinate, covered with small rasplike projections (T-B).

scobination, a raised point (T-B).

scoleciasis, the invasion of man and animals by Lepidoptera larvae (T-B).

scoli, pl. of scolus, q.v. (T-B).

Scolioidea, superfamily within the Aculeata (Hymenoptera), including the family Scoliidae, possessing often apterous adults (both males and females), with pronotal lobe reaching back to tegula, antennae not geniculate, forewing with closed marginal cell, and distal quarter or more of wing membranes longitudinally striolate with a densely corrugated appearance (Gauld and Bolton, after Brown); Scolioidea + Tiphioidea (Riek, in CSIRO); included with the Vespoidea (sensu Gauld and Bolton, after Brothers).

scolopale (pl., **scolopalia**), a sheath of cuticlelike material enclosing the dendrite of a sensory cell of a mechanoreceptor (T-B, after Snodgrass; Chapman).

scolopale cell, within a scolopidium, cell producing tubular scolopale (Chapman).

Scolopendromorpha, order within the subclass Epimorpha (Chilopoda), the members of which possess antennae with 17 or more segments, 21–23 pairs of legs, and usually 4 or more ocelli on each side of head (Borror et al.).

scolophore, chordotonal organ, q.v. (T-B); a bipolar nerve cell continuous with a fiber of the chordotonal nerve (T-B, after Imms).

scolopidium (pl., **scolopidia**), a subunit of chordotonal organ, consisting of 3 cells arranged in a linear manner: a sensory nerve cell, the enveloping scolopale cells, and an attachment cap cell (Tulloch; Chapman).

scolopophorous organ, chordotonal organ, q.v. (T-B; Chapman).

scolopophorous sensillum, scolopidium, q.v. (Gilmour, in CSIRO).

scolops (pl., **scolopes**), scolopale, q.v. (T-B; Leftwich).

scolus (pl., **scoli**), in some larval Bombycoidea and certain butterflies (Lepidoptera), tubercles in the form of spinose projections of the body wall (T-B, after Comstock); in larval Coccinellidae (Coleoptera), a branched projection of the body wall, usually more than 5 times as long as wide (T-B, after Gage).

scolytoid larva, a fleshy larva resembling that of a scolytid beetle (Coleoptera: Scolytidae) (Borror et al.); see apodous larva and grub.

scopa (pl., **scopae**), a brush (T-B); in ♂ Lepidoptera, fringe of long, dense and sometimes modified scales along caudal margin of abdominal segment VIII (Tuxen, after Diakonoff); in ♂ Symphyta (Hymenoptera), an inflated, often pilose, apicoventral flange running most of the length of a gonostylus (Tuxen, after Ross); in adult bees (Hymenoptera: Apoidea), thick hair covering the hind tibia (T-B; Riek in CSIRO, Gauld and Bolton) (see ventral scopa).

scopa dorsalis, in ♂ Lepidoptera, scopa on tergum (Tuxen, after Diakonoff).

scopa ventralis, in ♂ Lepidoptera, scopa on sternum (Tuxen, after Diakonoff).

scopate, covered or funished with scopae (T-B).

scopiferous antenna, an antenna which has a thick brush of hair somewhere on it (T-B).

scopiform, formed like a brush (T-B).

scopiped, a tarsus in which the pulvilli are thickly covered with hair and appear brushlike (T-B).

scopula (pl., **scopulae**), a small, dense tuft of hair (T-B); in bees (Hymenoptera: Apoidea), scopa, q.v., on hind tibia (T-B).

scopula alaris, in adult Chironomidae (Diptera), projection on third axillary sclerite of wing base covered with thickly set spinelike microtrichia, securing wing in resting position by insertion into scopula thoracalis (Saether).

scopula thoracalis, in adult Chironomidae (Diptera), brush on scutum near supraalar callus, contacting scopula alaris when wing is folded (Saether).

scopulipedes, bees (Hymenoptera: Apoidea), with pollen-gathering structures on the tarsi (T-B).

scoriaceous, silvery-gray (T-B).

Scorpiones, order within the Arachnida, including the scorpions, possessing a distinctly segmented opisthosoma with a taillike prolongation terminating in a sting, and second abdominal segment ventrally with a pair of comblike organs (Borror et al.).

Scorpionida, Scorpiones, q.v. (Borror et al.).

Scorpionides, Scorpiones, q.v. (Borror et al.).

scorpionfly, member of the order Mecoptera (Riek, in CSIRO), particularly of Panorpidae and Panorpodidae (Byers); see hangingfly.

scorpion, member of the order Scorpiones (Borror et al.).

scraper, a ridged surface that is rubbed over a file in a stridulating organ (T-B; Chapman); in Gryllidae and Tettigonioidea (Orthoptera), the sharpened anal angle of the tegmen, being part of the stridulating mechanism (Borror et al.).

screening pigment, pigment in pigment cells of an ommatidium that screens each rhabdom from light from neighboring ommatidia (Chapman).

scribble mines, zig-zag mines produced by the larval *Ogmograptis scribula* (Lepidoptera: Yponomeutidae) in bark of smooth-barked *Eucalyptus* (Common, in CSIRO).

scriptus, lettered or marked with characters resembling letters (T-B).

scrobal suture, in many adult Aculeata (Hymenoptera), a groove extending between the episternal scrobe and the anterior oblique suture (Gauld and Bolton).

scrobes, mandibular scrobe, q.v. (T-B); grooves formed for the reception or concealment of an appendage (T-B); in adult Curculionoidea (Coleoptera), a pair of grooves, one on each side of the rostrum, in which the antennae can rest (T-B; Britton, in CSIRO); in many Chalcididae (Hymenoptera), single concavity formed from united antennal scrobes (Gauld and Bolton); see episternal scrobe.

scrobiculate, uniformly covered with short, oblong or trenchlike hollows (T-B; Harris, after R. W. Brown, and Jaeger); see exsculptate and fossulate.

scrotal membrane, peritoneal sheath, q.v. (T-B).

scrotiform, purse-shaped (T-B).

scrotum, peritoneal sheath, q.v. (T-B).

scrub typhus, disease of man in eastern Asia and Australia caused by *Rickettsia tsutsugamushi* and transmitted by chiggers, *Trombicula* spp.

(Acari: Trombiculidae), characterized by headache, apathy, general malaise, and fever (Borror et al.).

sculpture, the markings or patterns of impressions or elevations on the surface (T-B; Harris); see maculation.

sculptured, superficially marked with elevations or depressions or both, arranged in some definable manner (T-B; Harris); see embossed.

sculpturing, sculpture, q.v. (Leftwich).

scutal angle, in adult Culicidae (Diptera), the more or less distinct angular projection of the scutal margin just anterior to the prescutal suture, or just in front of the prespiracular area when the prescutal suture is not discernible (Harbach and Knight, after Edwards).

scutal fossa, in adult Culicidae (Diptera), the somewhat depressed anterolateral area of the scutum (prescutum) extending caudad to the level of the scutal angle and mesad before the prescutal suture to the dorsocentral area (Harbach and Knight, after Knight and Laffoon).

scutal suture, in adult Diptera, transverse suture, q.v., or a transverse suture sometimes present between the (true) transverse suture, q.v., and the scutoscutellar suture (McAlpine).

scutal tubercle, in some adult Chironomidae (Diptera), central medial hump or tubercle of scutum situated on medial scar at caudomesal corners of median vittae when these are present (Saether).

scutarea, in Hemiptera, scutellum, q.v. (T-B, after MacGillivray).

scutate, scutatus (Latin), covered with large, flat, scales; having a scutum; shield-shaped (T-B; Harris); see cataphracted, imbricate, scutellate, and squamate.

scutcheon, scutellum, q.v.; also used by some authors (Walker) for the pronotum in Sternorrhyncha and Auchenorrhyncha (Hemiptera) (T-B).

scute(s), scuta (Latin) (sing., **scutum**), shield (R. W. Brown); the sclerotized shield or plate on the segments of larvae (T-B); in scales of Lepidoptera, linear, narrow sclerotized processes on the crest of the longitudinal ridge inclined at a slight angle to the main axis of the scale and projecting distally from under the apex of more proximal scutes (Downey and Allyn); in adult Lepidoptera, the scalelike spines of the unguitractor plate (Davis).

scutel, scutellum, q.v. (T-B, after Say).

scutellar, in adult Diptera, scutellar seta, q.v.

scutellar angle, in adult Coleoptera, the angle in the elytra next to the scutellum when a wing is expanded (T-B).

scutellar bridge, in adult Diptera, a small ridge on each side of the scutellum connecting with the scutum, crossing the intervening suture (T-B, after Comstock).

scutellar lever, in adult Diptera (e.g., *Sarcophaga*, Sarcophagidae), lateral process of mesoscutum and mesoscutellum bearing posterior notal process (Chapman).

scutellar seta, in adult Diptera, any setae occurring on the scutellum (Harbach and Knight).

scutellar space, in Mantodea, an area between antennae and clypeus (T-B).

scutellary, of or pertaining to the scutellum (T-B).

scutellate, scutellatus (Latin), divided into surfaces like small plates; minutely scutate (T-B; Harris); see cataphracted, imbricate, and squamate.

scutellum (pl., **scutella**), any small, shield-shaped plate (Leftwich); the posterior division of the notum of the meso- and metathorax (T-B); in Heteroptera (Hemiptera), the triangular part of the mesothorax, generally placed between the bases of the hemelytra, but in some groups partly or completely overlapping them (T-B); in adult Coleoptera, the triangular piece at the base and between the elytra (T-B); in adult Diptera, mesoscutellum, q.v. (T-B; Colless and McAlpine, in CSIRO); see scutumin some adult Symphyta (Hymenoptera), axilla, q.v. (T-B, after Snodgrass).

scutiform, scutate, q.v. (T-B; Harris).

Scutigeromorpha, order within the subclass Anamorpha, including the common house centipede, possessing 7 unpaired spiracles located on middorsal line near posterior margin of tergites, long many segmented antennae, and compound eyes (Borror et al.).

scutoprescutum, in adult Hymenoptera, median mesoscutal lobe, q.v. (T-B, after Imms).

scutoscutellar sulcus, sulcus delineating the scutellum from the mesoscutum (Gibson).

scutoscutellar suture, scutoscutellar sulcus, q.v. (T-B, after Snodgrass).

scutulum (pl., **scutula**), in *Zygaena* (Lepidoptera: Zygaenidae), scutelliform terminal part of lamina ventralis of aedoeagus (Tuxen, after Loritz).

scutum (pl., **scuta**), any shield-shaped plate (Leftwich); the second dorsal sclerite of the meso- and metathorax, being the middle division of the notum and occupying most of the thoracic dorsum in Diptera (T-B; McAlpine); in ♀ *Melitaea* (Lepidoptera: Nymphalidae), wide, smooth area formed from posterior part of sternum IX or IX + X (Tuxen, after Higgins); in adult Diptera, postsutural area, q.v. (McAlpine, after some authors); in certain Hymenoptera, the major part of the alinotum set off by a transscutal suture, but not identical to the scutum of generalized insects (T-B, after Snodgrass); in ticks (Acari), the shield (T-B).

sealing bar, in eggs of Cimicomorpha and *Rhodnius* (Reduviidae) (Hemiptera: Heteroptera), a bar joining the cap to the rest of the chorion, consisting of a very thin layer of resistant endochorion and a thick amber layer (Chapman).

search deterrent substances, chemical cues left by searching and ovipositing ♀ parasitoids that repel other ♀ parasitoids (Matthews and Matthews).

seasonal coloration, seasonal dimorphism, q.v., in coloration, e.g., the European butterfly *Araschnia levana* (Lepidoptera: Nymphalidae) (T-B).

seasonal dimorphism, in bivoltine insects, difference in size, shape or color between the spring broods and autumn broods or between those hatched in the dry season and those of the wet season (Leftwich).

sebaceous, fatty or oily (T-B).

sebaceous glands, glands secreting fatty or oily material (Borror et al.).

sebific, sebaceous, q.v. (T-B).

sebific duct, a tube which carries the secretions of the colletrial gland to the bursa copulatrix (T-B).

sebific gland, colleterial gland, q.v. (T-B).

second antennae, the appendages of the tritocerebral somite of Crustacea; see postantennal appendages (T-B, after Snodgrass).

second antennal segment, intercalary segment, q.v., of head (T-B).

second axillary, second axillary sclerite, q.v. (T-B, after Snodgrass, Imms).

second axillary plate, second axillary sclerite, q.v. (McAlpine).

second axillary sclerite, axillary sclerite articulating ventrally with pleural wing process, distally with base of the radius, and posteriorly with the third axillary sclerite (Chapman, after Snodgrass).

second basal cell, in adult Diptera, basal median cell, q.v. (T-B, after Curran; McAlpine).

second clypeus, anteclypeus, q.v. (T-B).

second connecting membrane, in ♂ Coleoptera, tubular membrane (nonsclerotized part of genital tube) connecting tegmen to apex of abdomen (Tuxen) or first connecting membrane, q.v. (Tuxen, after Sharp).

second costal cell, in adult Symphyta (Hymenoptera), subcostal cell, q.v. (T-B, after Packard).

second-form reproductive, in Isoptera, nymphoid reproductive, q.v. (Wilson).

second gonapophyses, in ♀ insects, gonapophyses of abdominal segment IX, q.v. (Tuxen); in ♂ Hymenoptera, parameres, q.v. (Tuxen, after Michener).

second gonocoxae, in ♀ insects, gonocoxae of abdominal segment IX (Tuxen, after Scudder); in ♀ Heteroptera (Hemiptera), gonocoxites of abdominal segment IX, q.v. (Tuxen, after Scudder).

second gonocoxopodites, in ♀ Heteroptera (Hemiptera), gonocoxites of abdominal segment IX, q.v. (Tuxen, after Davis).

second gonoporus, in ♂ Pyrrhocoridae (Hemiptera: Heteroptera), secondary gonopore, q.v. (Tuxen, after Stehlik).

second jugal vein, vena cardinalis, q.v. (T-B, after Snodgrass).

second longitudinal vein, in adult Diptera, branch R_{2+3} of radius (T-B, after Williston).

second maxillae, labium, q.v. (T-B).

second maxillary segment, labial segment, q.v. (T-B).

second median plate, a variable sclerotization at the base of the mediocubital field, folding convexly on the outer edge of the first median plate along the plica basalis; often absent, or represented by the united bases of the medial and cubital veins (T-B, after Snodgrass).

second pair of hamules, in ♂ Odonata, hamuli posteriores, q.v. (Tuxen, after Thompson).

second phragma, phragma, q.v., of mesopostnotum, serving as attachment site for longitudinal flight muscles (Harbach and Knight).

second process of tergum X, in ♂ Embiidina, epiproct or median flap, q.v. (Tuxen, after Davis) or median flap, q.v. (Ross, in Tuxen).

second ramus, in ♀ Heteroptera (Hemiptera), anterior connecting leaf of gonapophysis IX (Tuxen, after Davis) or (unorthodox usage) posterior connecting leaf of gonapophysis VIII (Tuxen, after Southwood).

second segment of penis, in ♂ Odonata, stem, q.v. (Tuxen, after Borror) or body of penis, q.v. (Tuxen, after Selys-Longchamps).

second spiracle, metathoracic spiracle, q.v. (T-B, after Snodgrass).

second trochanter, ischiopodite, q.v. (T-B, after Snodgrass).

second valves, in ♀ Isoptera, second gonapophyses, q.v. (Tuxen); in ♀ Thysanoptera, dorsal blades of ovipositor borne by abdominal segment IX, q.v. (Tuxen).

second valvifers, in ♀ insects, second gonapophyses, q.v. (Tuxen, after Snodgrass); in ♀ Phasmida, sclerites at base of inner and superior valvulae (Tuxen); in ♀ Grylloidea (Orthoptera), specialization of basal portion of posterior valvulae (Tuxen); in ♀ Embiidina, perhaps a sclerotized flap beyond caudal margin of sternum VIII (Tuxen); in ♀ Heteroptera (Hemiptera), gonocoxites of abdominal segment IX, q.v. (Tuxen, after Snodgrass); in Aradidae and Pentatomidae (Hemiptera: Heteroptera) (incorrect usage), laterotergites IX, q.v. (Tuxen, after Leston); in ♀ Hymenoptera, second gonocoxae, q.v. (Tuxen).

second valvulae, in ♀ insects, second gonapophyses, q.v. (Tuxen, after Snodgrass); in ♀ Odonata, median gonapophyses, q.v. (Tuxen, after Snodgrass); in ♀ Blattopteroidea, valvulae internae, q.v. (Tuxen); in ♀ Isoptera, inner valves, q.v. (Tuxen); in ♀ Orthoptera, inner valvulae, q.v. (Tuxen); in ♀ Psocoptera, valvae dorsales, q.v. (Tuxen, after Broadhead).

second vein, in adult Diptera, radial sector (R_s) and its anterior branch, R_{2+3} (T-B, after Curran).

second ventral proctigeral sclerite, in ♂ Empididae (Diptera), abdominal sternite X (McAlpine).

secondaries, hind wings, q.v. (T-B).

secondary anal vein, in the wings of Odonata, a longitudinal vein sometimes regarded as the true anal vein running from the distal end of the anal crossing towards the base of the wing (T-B, after Comstock).

secondary bursa, in ♀ Lepidoptera, appendix bursae, q.v. (Tuxen, after F. M. Brown).

secondary cuticula, endocuticle, q.v. (T-B).

secondary etiologic factors, in invertebrate pathology, predisposing factors, q.v. (Steinhaus and Martignoni).

secondary fringe scale, in adult Culicidae (Diptera), one of the short fusiform scales (shorter than fringe scales) occurring in a row along the posterior margin of the wing (Harbach and Knight, after Christophers).

secondary gonopore, in ♂ Auchenorrhyncha (Hemiptera), phallotreme, q.v. (Tuxen); in ♂ Heteroptera (Hemiptera), the opening of ductus seminis at apex of phallus (Tuxen, after Dupuis and Carvalho).

secondary homonym, each of 2 or more identical species-group names having different name-bearing types and established in combination with different generic names but subsequently combined with the same generic name (ICZN).

secondary hypocostal ridge, in adult Heteroptera (Hemiptera), a secondary modification of the hypocostal lamina (Polhemus).

secondary infection, in invertebrate pathology, an infection occurring in an animal already infected by a pathogenic microorganism or virus of a different kind (Steinhaus and Martignoni).

secondary intergradation, a zone of hybridization or strong steepening of character gradients where 2 separately differentiated populations have reestablished contact (Mayr); see primary intergradation.

secondary iris cells, secondary pigment cells, q.v. (T-B, after Imms).

secondary medisternite, in ♂ Isoptera, median sclerite in intersegmental membrane between abdominal sterna VIII and IX (Tuxen, after Geyer); in ♀ Isoptera, median sclerite in intersegmental membrane between sterna VIII and IX posterior to medisternite (Tuxen, after Browman).

secondary parasite, a parasite which establishes itself in or upon a host that is a primary parasite (Pfadt); see hyperparasite.

secondary pigment cells, pigment cells surrounding the retinula cells, isolating each ommatidium from its neighbors (Chapman); see primary pigment cells.

secondary pleometrosis, in social insects, the presence of a number of queens of one species in a nest, occurring by one of 3 processes: the alliance of colonies, the adoption of alien queens of the same species, and the breeding of females from the same colony (Tulloch, after Gaul).

secondary polygyny, polygyny when supplementary queens are added after colony foundation (Wilson).

secondary reproductive, in Isoptera, nymphoid reproductive, q.v. (Wilson).

secondary sclerite, in acalyptrate Muscomorpha (Diptera), a weakly sclerotized, poorly defined but more or less lunulate plate, lying free in the membrane just anteroventral to the front coxa (Speight).

secondary segment, any apparent segmentation produced by further subdivision of the primary sclerites (Leftwich).

secondary segmentation, any form of body segmentation that does not strictly conform with embryonic metamerism (T-B); the usual segmentation of arthropods with a well-developed exoskeleton in which the membranous intersegmental rings are the posterior parts of the primary segments (T-B, after Snodgrass).

secondary sensorium (pl., **sensoria**), in Aphididae (Hemiptera: Sternorrhyncha), placoid sensillum occurring on any except the first and second antennal segments of adults (Stoetzel, in Stehr); see primary sensorium.

secondary setae, in larval Lepidoptera, numerous setae scattered over the cuticle, not constant in number or position as opposed to primary setae, q.v., usually absent in the first instar, often defensive in function (T-B, after Comstock; Stehr); see subprimary setae.

secondary sexual characters, characters which distinguish the 2 sexes of the same species but which do not (like gonads or accessory sexual characters) function directly in reproduction (T-B; Mayr); see sexual dimorphism.

secondary somatic hermaphrodite, an insect which has the gonad or gonads of one sex and the secondary sexual apparatus of that sex, but bearing in the same individual some or all of the secondary sexual characters of both sexes (T-B, after Imms).

secondary type, any type that is not a primary type, e.g., hypotype, topotype, and homeotype (T-B); see primary type.

secretion, any substance secreted or produced by a gland (T-B); in Coccoidea (Hemiptera: Sternorrhyncha), the waxy, fibrous, cottony, or silky substances forming the scales (T-B).

secretory, concerned in the process of secretion (T-B).

sectaseta, in Psylloidea (Hemiptera: Sternorrhyncha), seta shaped like a spearhead, or dagger, sometimes turncate at the distal end, and with a ring around the base; often with long wax filaments produced by and remaining attached to it (White and Hodkinson).

section, a neutral term usually employed with reference to a subdivision of a taxon or a series of related elements in one portion of a higher taxon (Mayr); a rank that if treated as a division of a genus or subgenus is deemed to be of subgeneric rank for the purpose of nomenclature (ICZN); a taxon at the rank of section (ICZN).

sector(s), in adult insects, the concave, fourth longitudinal vein system (S), often dichotomously branched, the anterior branch (SA) sub-branched (S_1 and S_2) and the posterior branch (SP) sub-branched (S_3 and S_4), q.v. (Ross et al., after Hamilton); radial sector (R_s), q.v. (Morse, pers. comm.); longitudinal veins in Odonata, which strike the principal veins at an angle, and usually reach the apex or hind margin (see radial, subnodal, principal, nodal, median, short, and upper and lower sector of triangle) (T-B).

sectoral branch, posterior branch, q.v., of primary wing vein (McAlpine).

sectorial crossvein, a crossvein connecting 2 branches of the radial sector (R_s) (T-B; Borror et al.); see radial crossvein,

sectoris coconis, in Lepidoptera, the tearing or cutting structure used in working out of the cocoon, being variously placed (T-B).

secund, pointing one way; unilateral (T-B).

securifer, in ♂ Siphonaptera, the ventral portion of Ford's sclerite that is sometimes prolonged into narrow lobes or hooklike projections (Rothschild and Traub).

securiform, hatchetshaped, e.g., the terminal segment of palpi of some Coleoptera (T-B; Britton, in CSIRO).

sedentary, not active; settled or remaining in one place (T-B).

seed-crushers, the huge-headed soldier ants (Hymenoptera: Formicidae) (T-B, after W. M. Wheeler).

seed lac, the granules of lac from stick lac (T-B); see shellac.

segmacoria, intersegmental membrane, q.v. (T-B, after MacGillivray).

segment, subdivision of the body or an appendage between areas of flexibility associated with muscle attachments (T-B), but commonly used for subdivisions of the flagellum, tarsus, or labium (of Hemiptera); see antennomere, article, flagellomere, podite, subsegment, and tarsomere.

segmental appendages, the paired ventrolateral segmental outgrowths of the body wall serving for locomotion and ingestion of food (T-B, after Snodgrass).

segmental dorsum, the dorsum of an individual segment (T-B, after Snodgrass).

segmental membrane, in ♂ Heteroptera (Hemiptera), diaphragm, q.v. (Tuxen, after Singh-Pruthi).

segmental pleural area, the pleural area of an individual body segment in an insect (T-B, after Snodgrass).

segmental spines, among larval Syrphidae (Diptera), twelve major bristles on each segment, approximately in a transverse row in definite positions (Peterson, after Heiss).

segmental venter, the venter in an individual body segment of an insect (T-B, after Snodgrass).

segmental vessels, in most Blattopteroidea, paired excurrent vessels arising from the dorsal vessel: 2 thoracic and 4 abdominal in Blattaria; 4 abdominal in Mantodea (Chapman).

segmentation, longitudinal subdivision of the body into functional units (T-B, after Imms; Chapman) (see primary segmentation and secondary segmentation); in embryological development, cleavage, q.v. (T-B).

segmentation cavity, blastocoele, q.v. (T-B).

segmented, composed of segments.

segmenter, schizont, q.v. (Tulloch).

segmentum genitale, genital segment, q.v. (Tuxen).

segregate, (n.), that which is set apart and separate; (v.), to set apart and separate (T-B).

segregated, detached or scattered into groups (T-B).

segregation, a separation or placing apart (T-B).

sejunctus (Latin), disjoined; separated (T-B; R. W. Brown).

selection, natural selection, q.v. (Mayr); see sexual selection.

seleniform cell, plasmatocyte, q.v. (Tulloch).

selfgrooming, grooming in which individuals clean their own bodies both by licking and stroking with the legs (Wilson).

selfpollination, pollination occurring within the same flower (Borror et al.); see cross-pollination.

sella (pl., **sellae**), in ♂ *Catonephele* (Lepidoptera: Nymphalidae), groove or anellus, sclerotized only ventrally (Tuxen, after Stichel); in Diptera, cervical organ sclerite, q.v. (Speight, after Lowne).

sellate, saddle-shaped (T-B).

Selocide (trade name), an acaricide containing about 30% potassium ammonium selenosulfide (Pfadt).

SEM, scanning electron microscope, q.v.

semaphoront, an organism at a particular stage in its life history (Hennig).

sematophore, spermatophore, q.v. (T-B).

sembling, assembling, q.v. (T-B).

semelparous, a type of life history in which the animal reproduces only once during its lifetime (Borror et al.).

semen, seminal fluid, q.v. (T-B).

semi-, Latin prefix; half (T-B).

semiaquatic, living in wet places or partially in water (Borror et al.).

semicircle, half of a circle (T-B).

semiclasps, in ♂ Hesperiidae (Lepidoptera), 2 apophyses of abdominal sternum IX (primary and secondary semiclasps) from which valvae are said to develop (Tuxen, after Warren).

semicomplete metamorphosis, incomplete metamorphosis, q.v. (T-B).

semicordate, half or partly heart-shaped (T-B).

semicoronate, partly surrounded by a margin of spines, hooks or the like (T-B).

semicoronet, a margin of spines or hooks partly surrounding a structure or process (T-B).

semicylindrical, shaped like half of a cylinder (T-B).

semidetached rod, in ♂ Siphonaptera, dorsal arm, q.v. (Tuxen, after Hopkins and M. Rothschild).

semiglobate, semiglobose, semiglobosus (Latin), hemispherical, q.v. (T-B).

semihyaline, hyaline in part only; not altogether transparent (T-B).

semilooper, a caterpillar (Lepidoptera) in which one or 2 pairs only of abdominal legs are wanting and where in progression only small loops are formed (T-B); see looper.

semilunar, in the form of half a crescent (T-B).

semilunar process, in jumping Orthoptera, a heavily sclerotized dark area at apex of hind femur just above the articulation with the tibia (Chapman).

semilunar valve, the valve guarding the auriculoventricular opening of the heart (T-B).

seminal canal, in ♀ Coleoptera, closed duct or open canal (not regularly present) connecting spermatheca with innermost part of vagina, functioning to transport sperm from spermatheca, and with 2 connections with vagina (Tuxen).

seminal capsule, in ♀ Heteroptera (Hemiptera), capsula seminalis, q.v. (Tuxen, after Carayon); in ♀ Chironomidae (Diptera), spermathecal capsule, q.v. (Saether).

seminal chamber, in ♂ Heteroptera (Hemiptera), ejaculatory reservoir, q.v. (Tuxen, after Sweet).

seminal depository, in ♀ Miridae, Nabidae, Tingidae (Hemiptera: Heteroptera), (paired or unpaired saclike) spermatheca(e), q.v. (Tuxen, after Davis).

seminal duct(s), in ♂ Odonata, duplicate opening on anterior surface of third segment of penis, serving for reception and emission of semen (Tuxen, after Borror); in ♂ Heteroptera (Hemiptera), ductus seminis, q.v. (Woodward et al., in CSIRO); in ♂ Nepidae (Hemiptera: Heteroptera), ductus seminis distalis, q.v. (Tuxen, after Lansbury); in ♂ Pentatomoidea (Hemiptera: Heteroptera), ductus seminis proximalis, q.v. (Tuxen, after McDonald); in ♂ Coleoptera, vasa deferentia, q.v. (Tuxen); in ♀ Coleoptera, seminal canal, q.v. (Tuxen); in ♀ Lepidoptera, ductus seminalis, q.v.

seminal fluid, fluid produced by the ♂ accessory glands, containing the sperm (Chapman).

seminal papilla, in ♀ Gryllidae (Orthoptera), a partly sclerotized papilla surrounding spermathecal aperture (transl. "papille séminale" Cappe de Baillon, after Tuxen).

seminal receptacle, in ♀ Coreidae (Hemiptera: Heteroptera), spermatheca, q.v. (Tuxen, after Payne).

seminal reservoir, in ♂ Heteroptera (Hemiptera), ejaculatory reservoir, q.v. (Tuxen, after Baker).

seminal sacs, in ♀ Tingidae (Hemiptera: Heteroptera), (paired saclike) pseudospermathecae, q.v. (Tuxen, after Drake and Davis).

seminal vesicle, in ♂ insects, vesicula seminalis, q.v. (T-B; Chapman; Tuxen); in ♂ Odonata, vesicula spermalis, q.v. (Tuxen, after Thomson); in ♂ *Pyrrhocoris* (Heteroptera: Pyrrhocoridae), the 2 vesiculae seminales (broadened vasa deferentia) (transl. "Samenblase" Mayer, after Tuxen).

seminiforous, semensecreting (T-B).

semiochemicals, all chemicals produced by one organism that incite a response in another organism (Matthews and Matthews).

semiology, symptomatology, q.v. (Steinhaus and Martignoni).

semipersistent transmission, plant virus transmission in which the insect vector is capable of inoculating plants for a period intermediate between nonpersistent transmission and persistent transmission (Nault and Ammar, after Sylvester).

semipupa, in hypermetamorphosis, that stage of the larva just preceding pupation, interpolated between the active larva and the true pupa (T-B); see prepupa.

semiring sclerite, in ♂ Colobathristidae (Hemiptera: Heteroptera), cricoid sclerite, q.v. (Tuxen, after Štys).

semisagittate, like a longitudinal half of an arrow head (T-B).

semisocial, applied to the condition or to the group showing it in which members of the same generation cooperate in brood care and there is also a reproductive division of labor, i.e., some individuals are primarily egg layers and some are primarily workers (Wilson).

semispecies, the component species of superspecies (Mayr); populations that have acquired some, but not yet all, attributes of species rank, being borderline cases between species and subspecies (Mayr)

Semper cells, cells located beneath the cornea of an ommatidium that produce an intracellular crystaline cone or an extracellular pseudocone (Chapman).

Semper's rib, in Lepidoptera, a degenerate trachea present alongside the ordinary trachea within the wing (T-B, after Imms).

senescence, the process or state of growing old.

senior homonym, of 2 homonyms, the first established (ICZN).

senior synonym, of 2 synonyms, the first established (ICZN).

sense bristle, trichoid sensillum, q.v. (T-B).

sense cell, the neurocyte of a sensory nerve cell; the receptive cell of a sense organ, with a proximal nerve process going to a nerve center (T-B, after Snodgrass).

sense cone, basiconic peg, q.v., or coeloconic sensillum, q.v. (T-B); ; in larval Scarabaeoidea (Coleoptera), nesium, q.v. (T-B, after Hayes).

sense dome, campaniform sensillum, q.v. (T-B).

sense hair, trichoid sensillum, q.v. (T-B).

sense organ, any specialized innervated structure of the body wall receptive to external stimuli (T-B, after Snodgrass); see chemoreceptor and mechanoreceptor.

sense peg, basiconic peg, q.v. (Borror et al.).

sense pore, a minute pit in the cuticula which marks externally the position of a sense organ (T-B, after Snodgrass).

sense rod, scolopale, q.v. (T-B).

sensilial plate, in Siphonaptera, the sclerite bearing the sensilium (Lewis, pers. comm.).

sensilium, in adult Siphonaptera, an elaborate organ possessing a number of sensory pits, occupying the position of abdominal tergum X (Dunnet, in CSIRO).

sensilla (sing., **sensillum**), in ♂ Siphonaptera, small sensory setae at dorsal margin of telomere (Tuxen).

sensilla linearea, in adult Chalcidoidea (Hymenoptera), multiporous plate sensilla, q.v. (Gauld and Bolton).

sensillum (pl., **sensilla**), a simple sense organ, or one of the structural units of a compound sense organ (T-B, after Snodgrass); see chemoreceptor and mechanoreceptor.

sensillum ampulaceum, coeloconic sensillum, q.v. (T-B).

sensillum apicalium (pl., **sensilla apicalia**), in adult Chironomidae (Diptera), short, thick-walled seta functioning as a mechanoreceptor (Saether).

sensillum basiconicum (pl., **sensilla basiconica**), basiconic peg, q.v. (T-B; Saether).

sensillum campaniformium (pl., **sensilla campaniformia**), campaniform sensillum, q.v. (T-B, after Snodgrass, Imms).

sensillum capitatum (pl., **sensilla capitata**), in adult Chironomidae (Diptera), one of a cluster of club-shaped sensilla arising from a pit or from a cup-shaped alveolus, e.g., on palpal segment III in Tanypodinae, Podonominae, and Diamesinae (Saether).

sensillum chaeticum (pl., **sensilla chaetica**), trichoid sensillum, q.v., in which the external part is spinelike or bristlelike (T-B, after Snodgrass), e.g., in adult Chironomidae (Diptera), thick-walled, slightly curved, sharp-tipped (tip may be branched) hairlike sensillum, being smooth-walled and arising from a shallow cuticular depression, bulbous base or distinct cuplike alveolus, serving as a tactile receptor, and commonly found on the metatarsi (Saether).

sensillum clavatum (pl., **sensilla clavata**), in adult Chironomidae (Diptera), slender stalks swelling into weak terminal bulbs, arising from shallow cuticular depressions, e.g., at apex of third palpal segment in many Orthocladiinae and Chironominae (Saether); see sensillum capitatum.

sensillum coeloconicum (pl., **sensilla coeloconica**), coeloconic sensillum, q.v. (T-B).

sensillum minusculum, in larval Chironomidae (Diptera), tiny sensillum ventrolaterally on mandible just lateral to long external seta near angle of convex edge (Saether).

sensillum opticum, any photoreceptor, or one of the ommatidia of a compound eye (T-B, after Snodgrass).

sensillum placodeum, plate organ, q.v. (T-B).

sensillum scolophorum, chordotonal organ, q.v. (T-B, after Snodgrass).

sensillum squamiformium, a sense organ of which the extenal part is scalelike in shape (T-B, after Snodgrass).

sensillum styloconicum, styloconic sensillum, q.v. (T-B, after Folsom and Wardle).

sensillum trichodeum (pl., **sensilla trichodea**), trichoid sensillum, q.v. (T-B, after Imms).

sensim, gradually (T-B).

sensitivity, the labile property of protoplasm that makes it responsive to stimuli, highly developed in nerve tissue (T-B, after Snodgrass).

sensomacula (pl., **sensomaculae**), in ♂ Plecoptera, sensory area on last abdominal tergum (Tuxen, after Crampton).

sensoria, in Aphidoidea (Hemiptera: Sternorrhyncha), the circular openings covered by a membrane, on the antennae or legs (T-B); in Margarodidae (Hemiptera: Sternorrhyncha: Coccoidea), 2 small porelike structures usually arranged linearly on each surface of trochanter (Miller, in Stehr); in larval Muscomorpha (Diptera), fleshy peglike sensory organs on the head (Peterson); in ♂ Strepsiptera, relatively large sensillae covering antennae (Riek, in CSIRO).

sensory, pertaining to sensation or to the senses; having sensation (T-B).

sensory appendix, accessory process, q.v. (Peterson).

sensory area, in adult Diptera, characteristic sensory area on third segment of the maxillary palpus (McAlpine).

sensory cell, sensory nerve cell, q.v. (T-B).

sensory cell of type I, bipolar sensory nerve cell lying either within or just beneath the epidermis of the body wall, or the epithelium of the ectodermal sense organs (T-B, after Snodgrass).

sensory cell of type II, bipolar or multipolar sensory sense cell, lying on the inner surface of the body and on the wall of the alimentary canal (T-B, after Snodgrass); see proprioreceptor.

sensory chaeta, trichoid sensillum, q.v. (T-B, after Wardle).

sensory field, in Neelidae (Collembola), depression found on head, thorax, and abdomen, having modified setae at its edges (Christiansen and Bellinger).

sensory hair, trichoid sensillum, q.v. (Leftwich).

sensory neuron, sensory nerve cell, q.v. (T-B).

sensory nervous system, that part of the nervous system which connects with the exterior and transmits external stimuli to the motor system (T-B).

sensory palp, in ♀ Hymenoptera, gonoplac, q.v. (Tuxen).

sensory papilla, in larval Muscomorpha (Diptera: Brachycera), papilla at apex of antennomaxillary lobe (Teskey, in McAlpine).

sensory peg, in larval Chironomidae (Diptera), peg sensillum, q.v. (Saether).

sensory pit, pit containing large numbers of chemosensory pegs, e.g., on antennae of some adult Diptera and labial palps of adult Lepidoptera and Neuropteroidea, functioning in olfaction (Chapman; McAlpine); see basiconic peg, coeloconic sensillum, and vom Rath's organ.

sensory plate, in adult Siphonaptera, sensilium, q.v. (T-B, after Imms).

sensory seta, trichoid sensillum, q.v. (T-B).

sensory setula, trichoid sensillum, q.v. (McAlpine).

sensory vesicle, sensory pit, q.v. (McAlpine).

sensu lato (Latin), in the wide sense; broadly speaking; abbrev., s. l., s. lat., sens. lat. (T-B).

sensu stricto (Latin), in the strict sense; abbrev., s.s., s. str., sens. str. (T-B).

sentus (pl., **senti**), among larval Coccinellidae (Coleoptera), an elongated conelike projection of the body wall which is not branched like a scolus, but bears a few short stout setae upon its trunk (Peterson, after Gage).

sepiapterin, pterine pigment in insects (Gilmour, in CSIRO).

septasternum, coxosternum, q.v. (T-B, after MacGillivray).

septicemia, in invertebrate pathology, a morbid condition caused by the multiplication of microorganisms in the blood (Steinhaus and Martignoni).

septula (pl., **septulae**), a small septum (T-B); any one of the smaller more or less raised ridges of the phragma, for the attachment of muscles (T-B); in larval Scarabaeoidea (Coleoptera), a narrow bare region of the raster between a pair of oblique palidia diverging backward to the end of the anal slit, or between a pair of backward diverging, or parallel, or curved palidia to inside the ends of the anal slit (T-B, after Böving).

septum (pl., **septa**), a wall or partition in a hollow organ (T-B); in ♂ Heteroptera (Hemiptera), membrane closing basal foramen (Tuxen, after Ludwig).

sequel, in invertebrate pathology, an after effect of disease or injury; a morbid condition arising as a consequence of a previous disease (Steinhaus and Martignoni).

sequestration, storage of secondary plant chemicals by certain insects for defense (Chapman).

serial, in larval Lepidoptera, referring to the distribution of the bases or points of attachment of the crochets, e.g., biserial (Peterson).

serial homology, the correspondence of an organ of one segment with that of another of a different segment if the 2 are derived from corresponding parts (T-B, after Tillyard).

serial vein, a wing vein made up of parts of other veins (T-B).

seriatim (Latin), placed in longitudinal rows (T-B).

seriations, lines arranged in parallel series, either in sculpture or in color, as in Corixidae (Hemiptera: Heteroptera) (T-B; Harris).

sericate, sericatus, sericeous, sericeus (Latin), silken (T-B).

sericin, a water-soluble gelatinous protein, being the outer part of silk (Chapman); see fibroin.

sericos, in larval Hymenoptera, opening for the duct of the silk glands (Gauld and Bolton); see salivos.

sericose, sericos, q.v. (Peterson).

sericterium (pl., **sericteria**), in caterpillars (Lepidoptera), (silk-producing) labial gland, q.v. (T-B), or spinneret, q.v. (T-B).

serictery, in ants (Hymenoptera: Formicidae), sericos, q.v. (Brown, pers. comm.).

sericulture, commercial raising of silkworms, *Bombyx mori* (Lepidoptera: Bombycidae), for their silk (Borror et al.).

series, in taxonomy, the sample which the collector takes in the field (Mayr); see material and hypodigm.

serific glands, silk glands, q.v. (T-B).

serine, $C_3H_7NO_3$, an amino acid, being a major component of sericin (Gilmour, in CSIRO).

serology, the study of the nature and interactions of antigens and antibodies (Mayr).

serosa, in the egg, the outer membranous layer, derived from the blastoderm, surrounding the yolk (T-B; Chapman).

serosal cuticle, in the insect egg, a cuticle produced by the serosa inside the chorion (Tulloch; Chapman); see white cuticle and yellow cuticle.

serotinal, pertaining to or appearing in the autumn (Chapman); see vernal.

serotonin, toxic component in the venoms of insect stings (Gilmour, in CSIRO).

serous, of or pertaining to serum; of the nature of serum (T-B).

serpentine, winding like a serpent.

serpentine mine, a mine that is curved or coiled, becoming gradually larger to a headlike end (T-B); see mine.

serpentinous, serpentinus, a dirty, dark green (T-B).

Serphoidea, Proctotrupoidea, q.v. (Gordh, pers. comm., after Masner).

serra (pl., **serrae**), a saw or sawlike part (T-B; R. W. Brown).

serrata, in ♂ Blattopteroidea, right epiphallus, q.v. (Tuxen, after Crampton).

serrate, serratus (Latin), sawlike, i.e., with notched edges like the teeth of a saw, e.g., a serrate antenna with a toothlike extension arising from each flagellomere (T-B; McAlpine).

serrate-dentate, serratodentatus, toothed, the tooth edges themselves being saw-toothed (T-B).

serration, a tooth, as of a saw (T-B); a series of such teeth (T-B).

serratulate, with small teeth or serrations (T-B).

Serricornia, Coleoptera in which the antennae are serrate or saw-toothed (T-B).

serriferous, possessing a sawlike ovipositor in the ♀, as in sawflies (Hymenoptera: Symphyta) (T-B).

serriform, sawlike (T-B).

serrula (pl., **serrulae**), in ♀ Hymenoptera, subserrations on sawteeth (Symphyta) or sting barbs (Apocrita) along ventral ramus of gonapophysis VIII (Tuxen, after E. L. Smith).

serrulate, finely serrated; with minute teeth or notches (T-B).

serum, plasma, q.v., of hemolymph (T-B).

sesamex, a synergist for pyrethrum and allethrin; chemically 2-(2-ethoxyethoxy)ethyl-3,4-(methylenedioxy)phenyl acetal of acetaldehyde; slightly toxic to mammals, acute oral LD_{50} for rats 2000 to 2270 mg/kg (Pfadt).

Sesioidea, superfamily within the division Ditrysia (Lepidoptera), including the families Bracodidae, Sesiidae, and Choreutidae, formerly included within the Yponomeutoidea; a group of small to medium-sized, often brightly colored moths (Davis, pers. comm.).

sesqui-, Latin prefix; one and one half (T-B).

sesquialter, one and one half (T-B).

sesquialterous fascia, a continued fascia traversing both wings (T-B).

sesquialterous ocellus, an ocellate spot with a smaller one by it, termed sesquiocellus (T-B).

sesquiocellus, a large ocellate spot including a smaller one (T-B).

sesquitertial, occupying the fourth part of anything (T-B).

sessile, attached or fastened, incapable of moving from place to place (Borror et al.); attached directly without a stem or petiole, e.g., in Symphyta (Hymenoptera), having the abdomen broadly attached for nearly its full width to the thorax (T-B; Borror et al.).

Sessiliventres, Hymenoptera having no narrow constriction between the thorax and the abdomen, i.e., Symphyta, q.v. (T-B; Leftwich).

seta (pl., **setae**), a sclerotized hairlike projection of cuticula arising from a single trichogen cell and surrounded at the base by a small cuticular ring (Peterson); in Ephemeroptera, cerci, q.v. (Tuxen); see macrotrichia.

seta interna, in larval Chironomidae (Diptera), seta on inner dorsomedial seta of mandible with 3–40 usually pectinate branches (Saether).

seta premandibularis, in larval Chironomidae (Diptera), spinelike, usually small seta situated to each side on tormal bar between base of premandible and ungula (Saether).

seta sensualis, in Poduromorpha (Collembola), a seta thinner than adjacent setae and generally different in length, found in characteristic position on trunk segments (Christiansen and Bellinger).

seta subdentalis, in larval Chironomidae (Diptera), bristlelike, peglike, lanceolate or scalelike, filiform or pectinate seta ventrally on inner margin of mandible below mandibular teeth (Saether).

setaceous, setaceus (Latin), bristle-shaped; slender, gradually tapering to a tip (T-B); see setiform.

setae acetabuli, in ♂ Siphonaptera, usually one or 2 long setae at posterior margin of basimere behind acetabulum (Tuxen).

setae anteriores (S I), in larval Chironomidae (Diptera), pair of simple and bristlelike, bifurcate or highly dissected pectinate or plumose sensilla chaetica mesally on labrum above sclerotized labral margin (Saether).

setae caudales, in Ephemeroptera, cerci, q.v. (Tuxen, after Palmén).

setae genitales (sing., **seta genitalis**), in ♀ Siphonaptera, setae on inner surface of tergum VIII near its posterior margin (Tuxen).

setae maxillares, in larval Chironomidae (Diptera), strong setae of maxilla, 2 placed close together on palpiger (stipes) and 2 close together on cardo (Saether).

setae minuscula (S III), in larval Chironomidae (Diptera), pair of small to minute hairlike sensilla chaetica usually between and slightly above setae posteriores on labrum (Saether).

setae posteriores (S II), in larval Chironomidae (Diptera), pair of usually simple, occasionally pectinate, bristlelike sensilla chaetica above and slightly lateral to setae anteriores on labrum (Saether).

setae submenti, in larval Chironomidae (Diptera), simple, bifid, branched or plumose pair of setae immediately below mentum, anteriorly on submentum (Saether).

setal, of or pertaining to a seta (T-B); setalike (T-B).

setal alveolus, alveolus, q.v. (T-B).

setal area, in larval Trichoptera, one of 3 paired primary setal regions (sa_1, sa_2, and sa_3) on the mesonotum and metanotum (Wiggins).

setal map, in larval Lepidoptera, a diagrammatic drawing showing the chaetotaxy or arrangement of the setae on one-half of a bilaterally symmetrical thoracic or abdominal segment, the top edge being the dorsomeson and the lower edge being the ventromeson (Peterson).

setal membrane, the membranous floor of the socket, or alveolus, supporting the seta (T-B, after Snodgrass).

setal pattern, chaetotaxy, q.v. (Teskey, in McAlpine).

setal sense organ, trichoid sensillum, q.v. (T-B, after Snodgrass).

setal wart, in adult Trichopera, setiferous wart on the dorsum of the head or thorax (Mey, pers. comm.).

setarious, in adult Diptera, aristate, q.v. (T-B, after Say).

setate, setiferous, q.v. (Borror et al.).

setation, in larval Lepidoptera, chaetotaxy, q.v. (CSIRO).

setiferous, set with or bearing setae (T-B); see setose.

setiferous pad, in ♂ *Phoebis* (Lepidoptera: Pieridae), crista, q.v, (Tuxen, after Klots).

setiferous sense organ, trichoid sensillum, q.v., or hair plate, q.v. (T-B).

setiferous tubercle, a raised structure bearing a seta or setae (T-B); see styloconic sensillum and verruca.

setiform, setiformis (Latin), bristle or seta-shaped, e.g., setiform empodium of some adult Diptera (T-B; McAlpine); see setaceous.

setigenous, giving rise to or producing setae (T-B); see setiferous.

setigeris, tibial comb, q.v. (T-B, after MacGillivray).

setigerous, setiferous, q.v. (T-B).

setigerous tubercles, in Diptera, tubercles occurring on the scutellum or legs, each bearing a spine or bristle on its top (T-B, after Curran).

setimeres, in ♂ Ascalaphidae (Planipennia), long, strong appendages of the pulvilli (Tuxen, after Tjeder).

setiparous, setigerous, q.v. (T-B).

Setiplapia, Perloidea, q.v. (Borror et al.; Riek, in CSIRO).

setireme, the hairy, oarlike leg of aquatic insects (T-B).

setose, setous, setosus (Latin), furnished or covered with setae or stiff hairs (T-B); see setiferous and setulose.

setula (pl., **setulae**), a small stiff seta (T-B); in adult Diptera, the small, sharp process at the end of the subcosta (T-B); very small, usually nonpigmented bristles or cone-shaped structures on the ambulatory areas of maggots (Diptera), etc. (Peterson); see spicule.

setule, setula, q.v. (T-B).

setulose, bearing short, blunt bristles (Borror et al.).

Sevin (trade name), carbaryl, q.v. (Pfadt).

sex, as a number, 6; the physical difference between males and females, usually indicated by the sign of Mars (♂) for the male, and of Venus (♀) for the female (T-B); see neuter.

sex attractants, pheromones produced by ♀ insects that attract ♂ (Gilmour, in CSIRO).

sex brand, in ♂ Rhopalocera (Lepidoptera), a patch of dense androconia or specialized scent scales on the wing (Common and Waterhouse); see brand.

sex chromosome, a special chromosome, not occurring in identical number or structure in the 2 sexes and usually concerned with sex determination, e.g., the X chromosome or the Y chromosome (Mayr); see autosome.

sex comb, in certain ♂ Drosophilidae (Diptera), comb on first tarsomere of the foreleg (McAlpine).

sex determination, mechanism by which ♂ as opposed to ♀ offspring are produced (Chapman); see haplodiploidy.

sex hormone, hormone produced by the gonads (Chapman).

sex-limited character, a character occurring in one sex only (Mayr); see secondary sexual characters and sex-linked character.

sex-linked character, a character controlled by a gene located in the sex chromosome (Mayr); see sex-limited character.

sex mark, in ♂ Rhopalocera, sex brand, q.v. (Common and Waterhouse).

sex pheromones, pheromones serving as sex attractants (Borror et al.).

sexual, having sex or pertaining to sex (T-B).

sexual dimorphism, the phenotypic difference between the 2 sexes of a species (Mayr).

sexual reproduction, reproduction resulting in a diploid zygote with a maternal and a paternal chromosome set (Mayr); see parthenogenesis.

sexual selection, concept that competition for mates among members of one sex is responsible for the evolution of those traits peculiar to that sex, including all the various anatomical, physiological, and behavioral mechanisms involved in mate selection (Matthews and Matthews, after Darwin).

sexuales, in Aphidoidea and Coccoidea (Hemiptera: Sternorrhyncha), sexually reproductive (macropterous, brachypterous, or apterous) males or oviparous apterous females (T-B; Chapman, after Imms).

sexupara (pl., **sexuparae**), in Aphidoidea (Hemiptera: Sternorrhyncha), an alate, parthenogenetic ♀ that produces males and sexual females and oviparae (T-B; Chapman, after Imms)

shaft, in ♂ Plecoptera, penial shaft, q.v. (Tuxen).

shaft (of aedeagus), in ♂ Auchenorrhyncha (Hemiptera), tubular part of aedeagus (Tuxen, after Young).

shaft of antenna, flagellum, q.v. (T-B, after Klots).

shaft of sting, in ♀ Hymenoptera, stylet, q.v. (Tuxen, after Snodgrass).

shagreen, in pupal Chironomidae (Diptera), pattern of spinules or minute tubercles on abdominal segments (Saether).

shagreened, covered with a closely set roughness, like the rough-surfaced horse leather termed shagreen; like shark leather (T-B; Harris); see scabriculous.

shank(s), tibia, q.v. (T-B); in ♂ Auchenorrhyncha (Hemiptera), slender basal portions of stylets caudad of their attachment to genital capsule (Tuxen, after Oman).

shank fever, trench fever, q.v. (Adkins, pers. comm.).

shard, a chitinous sheath or elytron (T-B).

sharp, with a pointed tip or thin edge (T-B).

sheath, a structure enclosing others (T-B); in ♂ Lepidoptera, diaphragma, q.v. (Tuxen, after Evans); in ♀ Hymenoptera, second gonocoxa, q.v. (Tuxen).

sheath of aedeagus, in ♂ Caelifera, sheath of penis, q.v. (Tuxen, after Roberts).

sheath (of intromittent organ), in ♂ Lepidoptera, anellus, manica (Tuxen, after Evans).

sheath of ovipositor, in ♀ Hymenoptera, gonoplacs, q.v. (Tuxen, after Snodgrass).

sheath of penis, in ♂ Odonata, ligula, q.v. (Tuxen, after Calvert); in ♂ Caelifera (Orthoptera), sheath covering apical part of penis (Tuxen, after Dirsh).

sheath of sting, in ♀ Hymenoptera, gonapophyses, q.v. (Tuxen, after Snodgrass) or gonoplacs, q.v. (Tuxen, after Snodgrass).

sheet, in ♀ Incurvariidae (Lepidoptera), the tubular, sclerotized abdominal tergum VIII which forms part of a piercing ovipositor (Tuxen, after Wood).

sheet membrane, in ♀ Incurvariidae (Lepidoptera), the membranous abdominal sternum VIII which, together with its corresponding tergum, forms a piercing ovipositor (Tuxen, after Wood).

shell glands, the highly modified nephridia in Crustacea (T-B).

shellac, commercial product, consisting of cleaned lac (T-B; Woodward et al., in CSIRO); see lac.

shield, a sclerotized plate covering the greater part of the dorsal half of a segment, e.g., prothoracic shield of many larval Coleoptera and Lepidoptera (Peterson); in ♂ Hymenoptera, gonostylus + volsella (transl. "bouclier" Radoszkowski, in Tuxen).

shin, tibia, q.v. (T-B).

shivering, in some insects, preflight thoracic warm-up involving numerous patterns of flight muscle activation (Matthews and Matthews).

short-horned grasshoppers, members of the Acridoidea and Eumastacoidea (Orthoptera) (Key, pers. comm.); see locust.

short-tongued bees, group of bees within the Apoidea (Hymenoptera), including the Melittidae, Colletidae, and Halictidae, possessing adults with a glossa that is shorter than the prementum (Riek, in CSIRO); see long-tongued bees.

shoulder, loosely applied to any obtuse angulation; humeral angle, q.v., of wing (T-B); in adult Coleoptera, humerus, q.v., of elytron (T-B); in adult Lepidoptera, the anterior angles of the thorax (T-B); in Heteroptera (Hemiptera), humerus, q.v., of prothorax (T-B); in Orthoptera, humeral angle, q.v., of pronotum (T-B); in ♂ Lepidoptera, sclerotized costal margin of valva (Tuxen, after Chapman).

shoulder excrescence, in ♂ Lepidoptera, prominence of costa (Tuxen, after Warren).

shovel, in Ephemeroptera, the expanded flattened leg joints of burrowing nymphs (T-B, after Klots).

Sialida, hypothesized monophyletic group including the Megaloptera and Planipennia (Boudreaux).

sialisterium, salivary gland, q.v. (T-B).

Sialoidea, Megaloptera, q.v. (Borror et al.); Sialida, q.v. (Boudreaux, after Handlirsch).

sibling species, cryptic species, q.v. (Mayr).

sic (Latin), thus; used to indicate that spelling, references or other datum is exactly as given; generally used in parenthesis and frequently followed by an exclamation point (T-B).

sickle, in ♂ Lepidoptera, uncus, q.v. (Tuxen, after Chapman).

sicula, in ♂ Lepidoptera, uncus or teguman + uncus, q.v. (Tuxen, after Rambur).

side lobes, in ♂ Lepidoptera, paired, separate arms of gnathos (Tuxen, after Buchanan White); in ♀ Limnephilidae (Trichoptera), lateral parts of vulvar scale (Tuxen).

side lobes of pygofer, in ♂ Auchenorrhyncha (Hemiptera), caudally protracted lateral elongations of pygofer (Tuxen).

side piece, in ♂ Diptera (esp. Culicidae), basistylus, q.v. (Tuxen).

side pieces, in ♂ Trichoptera, lateral processes, q.v. (Tuxen).

side plates, in ♂ Eosentomoidea (Protura), lateral continuations distally on acroperiphallus (Tuxen).

side processes, in ♂ *Erebia* (Lepidoptera: Satyridae), part of gathos (Tuxen, after Chapman).

side prong, in ♀ Coleophoridae (Lepidoptera), lateromedial sclerotized structure with short, dark spines on caudal part of ductus bursae (Tuxen, after Toll).

Siebold's organ, a chordotonal organ on the foretibiae of locusts (Orthoptera: Caelifera), consisting of a series of scolopophores of the subintegumental type (T-B, after Comstock).

sienna, reddish-brown (T-B).

sieve plate, in some larval Diptera, Coleoptera, and Lepidoptera, a plate with large numbers of small pores serving to prevent the entry of dust or, especially in aquatic forms, water into the tracheal system (Chapman); in pupal Chironomidae (Diptera), plastron plate, q.v. (Saether).

sieve pore, in Heteroptera (Hemiptera), peg plates, q.v.; in adult Chironomidae (Diptera), apparent pore with several holes in middle of the tentorium in broad part just anterior to narrowing (Saether).

sievelike pores, in Coccoidea (Hemiptera: Sternorrhyncha), dermal disk pores with irregular divisions (Kosztarab and Korár).

sifter, device used to extract small arthropods from litter (Borror et al.).

sigma (pl., **sigmata**), in ♀ Culicidae (Diptera), parts of preatrial sclerite on each side of insula (Tuxen, after Gerry).

sigma seta, in larval Lepidoptera, ventral group, q.v., of setae (Peterson, after Fracker).

sigma virus, the agent of carbon dioxide sensitivity in various species of fruit flies (Diptera), the virion being cylindrical with one hemisperical end and averaging in size 70 by 180 millimicrons (Steinhaus and Martignoni).

sigmoid, shaped like the Greek letter sigma or the English S (T-B).

sigmoidal, sigmoid, q.v. (T-B).

sign, in invertebrate pathology, any objective aberration or manifestation of disease indicated by a change in structure (Steinhaus and Martignoni).

sign stimuli, releasers, q.v. (Matthews and Matthews).

signate, signatus, marked with signatures or lines resembling letters or characters (T-B).

signaturae, signatures, surface markings with a resemblance to letters or characters (T-B).

signum (Latin) (pl., **signa**), mark (R. W. Brown); in ♀ Lepidoptera, sclerotized, usually spined or scobinate structures in wall of corpus bursae (Tuxen, after Pierce); in ♀ *Glossina* (Diptera: Glossinidae), a sclerite in uterine wall (Tuxen); in adult Aculeata (Hymenoptera), anteroventral line on mesopleuron (Carpenter, pers. comm., after Richards, and after Bohart and Menke).

signum bursae, in ♀ Lepidoptera, signum, q.v. (T-B, after Klots).

signum dentatum, in ♀ Lepidoptera and *Sialis* (Megaloptera), a toothed plate inside of the bursa copulatrix to which muscles are attached (Chapman).

silica aerogel, a sorptive dust that is insecticidal, killing insects be dessication; prepared by treating sodium silicate with sulfuric acid, drying, and then grinding to small particle size (Pfadt).

silent host, a host that harbors a pathogen but shows no obvious signs of disease (Adkins, pers. comm.).

silk, a continuous, filamentous, hardened protein produced by the labial glands of larval Lepidoptera, Trichoptera, Siphonaptera, and some Hymenoptera, by the ♀ accessory glands in *Hydrophilus* (Coleoptera: Hydrophilidae), silk glands in basitarsus of foreleg in Embiidina, and by the Malpighian tubules in some larval Planipennia, used by Trichoptera in prey capture, as anchor lines, in retreat or case construction, and by all of the above insects to construct cocoons for pupa or eggs (T-B; Chapman).

silk-button gall, small, brown, hairy galls shaped like buttons with a central pit, produced on oak (*Quercus*) leaves by the gall wasp *Neuroterus numismalis* (Hymenoptera: Cynipidae) (Leftwich).

silk ejector, in Embiidina, one of the hollow setalike tubes on ventral surface of first and second tarsomeres of foreleg through which silk from the silk glands is secreted (Ross, in CSIRO).

silk galleries, in Embiidina, galleries, q.v. (Ross, in CSIRO); in Lepidoptera, tunnels spun by larvae within which they feed (Common, in CSIRO).

silk glands, glands which secrete liquids which harden into silk on exposure to the air (T-B); see silk.

silk press, in larval Lepidoptera, a structure, resembling a salivary pump, that moulds the silk into a thread (T-B, after Snodgrass; Chapman).

silk toxicity, a lethal hyperaminoacidemia in the silkworm, *Bombyx mori* (Lepidoptera: Bombycidae), caused by silk retention due to structural and functional lesions of the silk glands, as a result of endocrine disturbances, genetic factors, or infectious microorganisms (Steinhaus and Martignoni).

Silurian Period, geological period within the Paleozoic Era, between the Ordovician Period and the Devonian Period, extending between about 440 and 400 million years before the present (Riek, in CSIRO).

silverfish, a member of the order Zygentoma (Watson, in CSIRO).

silvicolous, inhabiting forests or woodlands (T-B).

simple, unmodified by any condition causing complexity (T-B; Borror et al.); not forked, toothed, branched, or divided (Borror et al.).

simple eye, in adult insects, ocellus, q.v. (T-B); in larval insects, stemma, q.v. (Peterson).

simple lateral eyes, in some adult insects, single or grouped eyes or true ocelli (not ommatidia) placed at the sides of the head (T-B, after Snodgrass).

simple ocellus, an ocellate spot with only the parts termed iris and pupil (T-B).

simple pore, in Coccoidea, e.g., Aclerdidae and Kermesidae (Hemiptera: Sternorrhyncha), flat, round pore, without divisions (Miller, in Stehr); see bilocular pore, trilocular pore, quadrilocular pore, quiquelocular pore, and multilocular pore.

sine tipo (Latin), without type (T-B).

Sinentomoidea, a suborder of Protura containing the family Sinentomidae, having spiracles present on thoracic segments II–III, and abdomen with pectinated structure (Nosek).

single band of crochets, in larval Lepdioptera, crochets arranged in a mesoseries (Peterson).

sinistrad, toward the left side (T-B).

sinistral, extending to or on the left side of the midline (T-B).

sinistrocaudad, extending obliquely from the left toward the tail (T-B).

sinistrocephalad, extending obliquely from the left toward the head (T-B).

sinistron, the left side of the insect body (T-B, after MacGillivray).

sinuate, sinuated, sinuatus (Latin), cut into sinuses; wavy, applying specifically to edges and margins (T-B); see sinuous.

sinuatoconvex, sinuate and convex (T-B).

sinuatolobate, sinuate and lobed (T-B).

sinuatotruncate, truncate with the margin sinuate (T-B).

sinuatoundulate, having linear markings or structures with obtuse sinuses (T-B).

sinuous, undulating, i.e., curved in and out (T-B).

sinus (Latin), pocket; recess (T-B; R. W. Brown).

sinus penis, in ♂ Lepidoptera, manica, q.v. (Tuxen, after Kusnezov).

sinus vaginalis (pl., **sinus vaginales**), in ♀ Lepidoptera, the whole receptive genital cavity caudad of abdominal segment VII (Tuxen, after Kusnezov).

Siphlonuroidea, superfamily proposed for the Siphlonuridae and Baetidae (Hennig, after Demoulin); see Baetoidea.

sipho, in ♂ Coccinellidae (Coleoptera), penis, q.v. (Tuxen, after Sharp and Muir).

siphon, any tubular external process or structure (T-B); proboscis, q.v. (T-B); in some larval Nematocera (Diptera), respiratory siphon, q.v. (T-B); respiratory tube or siphon, air tube, etc.

Siphonaptera, apterous, laterally compressed, endopterygote order of Neoptera (Insecta), including the fleas, being ectoparasites of birds and mammals with piercing and sucking mouthparts; larvae apodous and vermiform, usually living in the nests of the host; and pupae adecticous and exarate (T-B; Dunnet, in CSIRO).

siphonet, in Aphididae (Hemiptera: Sternorrhyncha), cornicle, q.v. (T-B).

siphoning mouthparts, in adult Lepidoptera, proboscis, q.v. through which liquids are siphoned usually without piercing (Borror et al.); see sucking mouthparts.

siphoning-sucking mouthparts, siphoning mouthparts, q.v. (Borror et al.).

Siphoniulida, order within the Helminthomorpha (Diplopoda), including 2 species of *Siphoniulus* (Siphoniulidae), known from Guatemala (Hoffman, in Parker).

Siphonophora, Coccinellidae; a term preoccupied in the Coelenterates (T-B).

Siphonophorida, order within the Helminthomorpha (Diplopoda), including the Siphonorhinidae, Siphonophoridae, and Nematozoniidae (Hoffman, in Parker).

siphonuli (sing., **siphonulus**), in Aphididae (Hemiptera: Sternorrhyncha), cornicles, q.v. (T-B).

siphuncle, in Aphididae (Hemiptera: Sternorrhyncha), cornicle, q.v. (T-B).

Siphunculata, Anoplura (Phthiraptera), q.v. (T-B; Leftwich); Anoplura + Ischnocera (Phthiraptera) (Boudreaux).

siphunculate, having or possessing a siphon or tube (T-B).

siphunculus (pl., **siphunculi**), proboscis, q.v. (T-B); in Aphididae (Hemiptera: Sternorrhyncha), cornicle, q.v. (T-B).

Siricoidea, superfamily within the Symphyta (Hymenoptera), including the families Siricidae, Orussidae, Xiphydriidae, and Anaxyelidae, possessing adults with mesoscutellum completely separated from scutum by a suture; axillae defined, and scrobal grooves present for reception of the basal segments of the antennae (Riek, in CSIRO; Borror et al.); see Orussoidea.

sistens type, in Aphididae (Hemiptera: Sternorrhyncha), nymphs of the third generation which remain undeveloped for a time (T-B, after Comstock); in Adelgidae (Hemiptera: Sternorrhyncha), first generation of the exsales (Stoetzel, pers. comm.).

sistentes (sing., **sistens**), in Aphididae (Hemiptera: Sternorrhyncha), aliencolae, q.v. (T-B).

sister group, the most closely related monophyletic group of another monophyletic group (Hennig).

sitophore sclerite, in Psocoptera and some Phthiraptera, cibarial sclerite, q.v. (T-B, after Snodgrass).

sixth longitudinal vein, in adult Diptera, first anal vein (1A) (T-B).

skeletal, of or pertaining to the exoskeleton (T-B).

skeleton, exoskeleton, q.v. (T-B).

skipper, member of the Hesperioidea (Lepidoptera) (T-B); jumping larva of some Piophilidae (Diptera), found in cheese and other provisions (T-B; Peterson; Borror et al.).

skimming, expansion skating, q.v.

skototaxis, a reflex response by which an insect will move towards a dark object or the darkest part of a room (Leftwich); see negative phototaxis.

slaty, colored with a very dark blackish gray with a reddish tinge (T-B).

slavery, dulosis, q.v. (Wilson).

sleeping sickness, African sleeping sickness, q.v. (Borror et al.).

slough, to shed or cast off, as a skin (T-B); see ecdysis.

slug caterpillar, limaciform larva, q.v., of Limacodidae (Lepidoptera) (T-B).

slurry, a thin mixture of water and any of several fine insoluble materials, as clay, derris or cubé powder, and so on (Pfadt).

s.m. interspace, submedian interspace, q.v. (T-B).

small crossvein, in adult Diptera, radial-medial crossvein q.v. (T-B, after Curran).

small intestine, ileum, q.v. (T-B).

smaltinus, dull grayish blue (T-B).

smaragdine, smaragdinus (Latin), emerald-colored, i.e., brilliant green (T-B; R. W. Brown).

smell, olfaction, q.v. (Borror et al.).

Smit's organ, in ♀ *Rhadinopsylla* (Siphonaptera: Ctenophthalmidae), a patch of minute spicules situated on the inner surface of the tergal pleurite of segment IX in the females of some species of (Rothschild and Traub).

snakefly, a member of the Raphidioptera (Borror et al.).

snout, in adult Curculionoidea (Coleoptera), rostrum, q.v. (T-B).

social, living in more or less organized communities or aggregations of individuals, as certain Hymenoptera (T-B); see social insect.

social bees, eusocial bees belonging to the family Apidae (Hymenoptera) (Borror et al.); see solitary bees.

social facilitation, a group effect in which there is an increase of an activity merely from the sight or sound (or other form of stimulation) coming from other individuals engaged in the same activity (Wilson).

social insect, in the strict sense, an insect that belongs to a eusocial species, e.g., an ant (Hymenoptera: Formicidae), a termite (Isoptera), or one of the eusocial wasps (Hymenoptera: Vespidae) or bees (Hymenoptera: Apoidea) (Wilson); in the broad sense, an insect that belongs to a presocial or eusocial species (Wilson).

social homeostasis, the maintenance of steady states at the level of the society either by control of the nest microclimate or by regulation of the population density, behavior, and physiology of the group members as a whole (Wilson).

social hormones, pheromones, q.v. (Tulloch).

social parasite, symphile, q.v. (T-B).

social parasitism, the coexistence in the same nest of 2 species of social insects, of which one is parasitically dependent upon the other (Wilson); the relationship between symphiles and their social insect hosts (Wilson); see inquilinism.

social symbiosis, social parasitism, q.v. (T-B).

social wasps, eusocial wasps belonging to the family Vespidae (Hymenoptera) (Borror et al.); see solitary wasps.

society, a group of individuals belonging to the same species and organized in a cooperative manner, implying some amount of reciprocal communication among the members (Wilson).

socii (sing., **socius**), lateral appendicular processes of the tenth segment in Trichoptera and Lepidoptera, possibly homologous with the cercuslike appendages on the tenth segment in lower Hymenoptera

(T-B, after Snodgrass); in ♂ Trichoptera, superior appendages, q.v. (Tuxen); in ♂ Lepidoptera, sclerotized, paired, hairy pads, sometimes petiolate, on caudal margin of tegumen ventrad of base of uncus (Tuxen, after Pierce).

sociobiology, the study of all aspects of communication and social organization (Wilson).

socioli (sing., **sociolus**), in ♂ Lepidoptera, projections of socii (Tuxen, after Diakonoff).

sociotomy, in termites (Isoptera), colony fission, q.v. (Wilson).

socket, in adult Lepidoptera, alveolus, q.v., of a scale (Downey and Allyn).

socle, in ♂ Auchenorrhyncha (Hemiptera), the enlarged basal part of aedeagus (Tuxen); in adult Lepidoptera, alveolus, q.v., of a scale or trichoid sensillum.

sodium cyanide, NaCN, a white, granular, highly poisonous powder, used in insect killing bottles (T-B).

sodium selenate, Na_2SeO_4, an inorganic systemic insecticide and acaricide that is applied to soil; highly toxic to warm-blooded animals (Pfadt).

soft palate, in adult Culicidae (Diptera), the part of the clypeopalatum between the dorsal and posterior hard plates (Harbach and Knight, after Nuttall and Shipley).

soldier(s), a member of a worker subcaste usually specialized for colony defense (Wilson); in termites (Isoptera), sexually undeveloped form, in which the head is much enlarged, and the mandibles are modified in various ways, and used in defense of the colony (T-B; Krishna, pers. comm.); in Aphidoidea (Hemiptera: Sternorrhyncha), aggressive immature forms that "bite" with their stylets (Pemphigidae), or used frontal horns (Hormaphididae) to defend the colony against predators (Myazaki); in certain ants (Hymenoptera: Formicidae), major worker, q.v. (T-B).

soldier nymph, in Isoptera, presoldier, q.v. (Krishna, pers. comm.).

soldier termite, in Isoptera, soldier, q.v. (Leftwich).

sole bladder(s), in ♂ Embiidina, ventral papillae on basitarsus of hind leg (Ross, in CSIRO); in Aphidoidea (Hemiptera: Sternorrhyncha), membranous swelling apicoventrally on tibia, making aphids capable of walking on smooth surfaces without slipping (Miyazaki, after Mordvilka).

solea (Latin) (pl., **soleae**), the underside of the tarsus and the pulvilli (T-B).

solenophage, a blood-feeding insect that obtains blood directly from venules or small veins (Adkins, pers. comm.); see telmophage.

Solifugae, order within the Arachnida, including the windscorpions, possessing a distinctly segmented opisthosoma without a taillike prolongation, pedipalps not chelate, chelicerae very large, usually about as long as prosoma, and extending foward, and body slightly narrowed at middle (Borror et al.).

solimeres, in some ♂ Chrysopidae (Planipennia), clawlike projecting apices of apodemes of abdominal sternum IX (Tuxen, after Tjeder).

solitaria phase, in locusts (Orthoptera: Acrididae), solitary phase, q.v. (Key, in CSIRO).

solitary, solitarius (Latin), occurring singly or in pairs, i.e., not in colonies (T-B).

solitary bees, bees (Hymenoptera: Apoidea), e.g., mining bees (Andrenidae and Halictidae), carpenter bees (Xylocopidae), and cuckoo bees (Nomadidae), in which each ♀ makes her own nest without the cooperation of others, and there are no separate queen and worker castes (Leftwich; Riek, in CSIRO); see social bees.

solitary phase, a form or phase occurring in certain Phasmida, Orthoptera (Acrididae), larval Lepidoptera, and a few other insects, characteristic of low-density populations (Norris, in CSIRO); see gregarious phase.

solitary wasps, wasps (Hymenoptera: Apocrita) that do not live in colonies, e.g., Eumeninae and Masarinae (Vespidae), Pompilidae, and Sphecidae (Leftwich; Riek, in CSIRO); see social wasps.

Solpugida, Solifugae, q.v. (Borror et al.).

solum (Latin) (pl., **sola**), floor (R. W. Brown); in ♂ Siphonaptera, short sclerite, between the 2 deflexi capsulae, to which the virga dorsalis is attached (Tuxen, after Smit).

solute, the substance dissolved in a solvent to form a solution (T-B).

solvent, any substance, solid or liquid, in which another dissolves (T-B).

soma (Latin) (pl., **somata**), body (R. W. Brown); the body of an animal excluding the germ cells (T-B).

somatic, relating to the soma (T-B).

somatic cells, the cells of the animal's body other than the germ cells (T-B).

somatic layer, the external layer of the mesoderm, applied to the walls of the alimentary canal (T-B, after Snodgrass); see splanchnic layer.

somatic nerves, a series of paired bundles of nerve fibers emerging from the ganglia of the central nervous system (T-B, after Wardle).

somatogenesis, environmentally-induced anatomical changes (T-B).

somatome, metamere, q.v. (Boudreaux).

somatoplasm, soma, q.v., excluding the germ cells (T-B).

somatopleure, somatic layer, q.v. (T-B).

somatotheca, gasterotheca, q.v. (T-B).

somite, a body segment of the adult insect (T-B); in the embryo, metamere, q.v. (T-B).

sonagram, a graphic representation of the vocalization of an animal (Mayr); a sound spectrogram recording the frequency spectrum of a sound as a function of time (Matthews and Matthews).

song, stereotyped sounds functioning in intraspecific communication (Borror et al.).

sonifaction, the production of sound (T-B); see sound-producing mechanisms.

sonoridic, sound producing; applied to stridulating organs (T-B).

sordid, sordidus (Latin), dirty; dull (T-B).

sorghum stunt mosaic, disease of sorghum caused by a rhabdovirus

transmitted propagatively by *Graminella* ((Hemiptera: Auchenorrhyncha: Cicadellidae) (Nault and Ammar).

sotto disease, bacillary paralysis, q.v. (Steinhaus and Martignoni).

sound-producing mechanisms, in insects: (1) stridulation, q.v.; (2) vi-
bration of special membranes called tymbals, e.g., Cicadoidea, Cicadelloidea, and Fulgoroidea (Hemiptera: Auchenorrhyncha), or
microtymbals (Lepidoptera: Arctiidae) (Fenton and Rhoeder); (3) by
striking some part of the body against the substrate, e.g., head of
some Anobiidae (Coleoptera), legs of some grasshoppers (Orthoptera), or tip of abdomen of some Plecoptera and Blattaria; (4) by
forcibly ejecting air or liquid from some body opening, e.g., popping
sound of pygidial glands expelling fluid in *Brachinus* (Coleoptera:
Carabidae), whistling sound produced by air forced through pharynx in *Acherontia atropos* (L.) (Lepidoptera: Sphingidae) (see whistle),
and hissing produced by expelling air through spiracles in
Gromphadorina (Blattaria); (5) humming or buzzing produced by vi-
bration of wings or other body parts; and (6) sounds produced by
general activities such as feeding and moving about (Borror et al.).

sowbug, a terrestrial member of the Isopoda commonly found under
stones, boards, or bark (Borror et al.).

sowda, onchocerciasis, q.v (Adkins, pers. comm.).

spadiceous, bright-brown (T-B).

spado (Latin), in bees (Apoidea) and ants (Formicidae) (Hymenoptera),
worker, q.v. (T-B).

spangle gall, small, flat, red gall about 1 mm across on the surface of
the leaves of oak (*Quercus* spp.) produced by gall wasp *Neuroterus
quercusbaccarum* and related species (Hymenoptera: Cynipidae)
(Leftwich).

spanogyny, the tendency of mosquito (Diptera: Culicidae) colonies
which normally require blood meals to die out when maintained on
vegetable food (Tulloch).

sparing agent, a chemical that can serve as a substitute for certain
functions (Chapman).

sparsate, sparse, q.v. (T-B; Harris).

sparse, sparsus (Latin), scattered; spread irregularly and some distance apart; thin, e.g., pile or hairs (T-B; Harris); see conflected and
dispersed.

spatha (Latin) (pl., **spathae**), a broad blade (T-B; R. W. Brown); in ♂
Tipulidae (Diptera), ejaculator apodeme, q.v. (Tuxen, after Westhoff); in ♂ Hymenoptera, parameres, q.v. (T-B, after Snodgrass;
Tuxen, after Boulangé); in ♂ Aculeata (Hymenoptera), partially de-
sclerotized, distally produced body of combined gonapophyses IX
and notum (less distal rhaches) extending independently on either
side of gonapophysis (T-B, after J. B. Smith; Tuxen, after E.L.
Smith).

spathal rod, in ♂ Hymenoptera, thickening of spatha extending to
ergot (Tuxen).

spathula (pl., **spathulae**), in ♂ *Polyura* (Lepidoptera: Apaturidae), a
broad, flat juxta (Tuxen, after Roepke).

spathulate, sword-shaped; narrow and flat at the base and enlarged at the apex (T-B); see spatulate.

spatial orientation, the self-controlled maintenance or change of an organism's body relative to environmental space (Matthews and Matthews).

spatula (Latin), small, broad, bladelike process (T-B, after Snodgrass; R. W. Brown); in larval Cecidomyiidae (Diptera), sternal spatula, q.v. (T-B).

spatula sternale, in larval Cecidomyiidae (Diptera), sternal spatula, q.v. (Teskey, in McAlpine).

spatulate, rounded and broad at the tip, attenuate at base (T-B); spoon-shaped (Borror et al.).

spatulate setae, lamellate setae with slender stem gradually broadened to apex, e.g., on median volsella of ♂ Chironomidae (Diptera) (Saether).

special secretory cells (of spermatheca), in ♀ Chironomidae (Diptera), secretory cells surrounding spermathecal ducts and appearing as small hairs or bubbles to each side of duct (Saether).

specialization, the restricted adaptation or function of an animal or of a structure (T-B).

specialized, remote from the primitive type; adapted to more special conditions of existence or to particular functions (T-B); see generalized.

specialized end of suranal plate, in ♂ Lepidoptera, scaphium, q.v. (Tuxen, after Packard).

speciation, the splitting of a phyletic line; the process of multiplication of species; the origin of discontinuities between populations caused by the development of reproductive isolating mechanisms (Mayr); see allopatric speciation and sympatric speciation.

species (Latin), (sing. and pl.; abbreviated **sp.**, one species, or **spp.**, 2 or more species), form; kind (T-B; R. W. Brown); an aggregation of individuals alike in appearance and structure, mating freely and producing young that themselves mate freely and bear fertile offspring resembling each other and their parents, including all varieties and races (T-B, after J. B. Smith); groups of actually (or potentially) interbreeding natural populations which are reproductively isolated from other such groups (Mayr); the rank next below the genus group, being the basic rank of zoological classification (ICZN); a taxon at the rank of species (ICZN); see biological species, population, and subspecies.

species group, in the hierarchy of classification, the lowest-ranking group of taxa the names of which are regulated by the Code, including all taxa at the ranks of species and subspecies (ICZN).

species-group name, a specific name or a subspecific name (ICZN).

species indeterminata (Latin), indeterminate species; abbrev., sp. indet., sp. ind. (T-B); see incerae sedis.

species inquirenda (pl., **species inquirendae**), a doubtfully identified species needing further identification (ICZN); see incertae sedis.

species name, a scientific name of a taxon at the rank of species (ICZN); a binomen, q.v. (ICZN).

species nova (Latin), new species; one heretofore undescribed; abbrev., sp. nov., sp. n. (T-B); see new species.

species odor, the odor found on the bodies of social insects which is peculiar to a given species (Wilson); see nest odor.

specific character, a feature or structure common to all individuals of a species, by means of which they may be distinguished from individuals of other species (T-B).

specific name, the second name in a binomen and in a trinomen (ICZN).

specillum (pl., **specilla**), in ♂ Plecoptera, accessory sclerotic structures arising from of near gonopore (Tuxen, after Brinck).

specimen, an individual (ICZN); a group of individuals derived by vegetative or asexual mulitiplication from a single individual and forming a single entity (e.g., a sponge or a coral colony) (ICZN),

speciogenesis, speciation, q.v. (T-B, after J. C. Chamberlain).

specular, mirrorlike (T-B).

specular membrane, in Cicadidae (Hemiptera: Auchenorrhyncha), tympanum, q.v., or tymbal, q.v. (T-B).

speculum (pl., **specula**), a transparent area or spot on wings of some Lepidoptera; in ♂ Orthoptera, the glassy areas at base of tegmina in ♂ Orthoptera that serve as sounding boards (T-B); a spot on the neck of some larval Lepidoptera; in adult Ichneumonoidea, upper area of mesepisternum (Gauld and Bolton); in many adult Chalcididae (Hymenoptera), a hairless area of wing membrane running obliquely from parastigma to hind margin of wing (Gauld and Bolton).

sperm (sing. and pl.), mature, haploid ♂ gamete, derived from spermatid, being generally filamentous in form with a head and a tail (T-B; Tulloch; Chapman).

sperm canal, in eggs of Pentatomomorpha (Hemiptera: Heteroptera), central canal surrounded by a spongy respiratory layer in micropylar region (Woodward et al., in CSIRO).

sperm capsule, in Odonata, spermatodesm, q.v. (T-B, after Imms).

sperm conveyor, in ♂ Plecoptera, supraanal lobe, q.v. (Tuxen, after Walker).

sperm duct, in ♂ Diptera, ejaculatory duct, q.v. (McAlpine).

sperm pump, in ♂ Psyllidae and Aleyrodidae (Hemiptera: Sternorrhyncha), a muscular part of ductus ejaculatorius (Tuxen); in ♂ Diptera, Siphonaptera, and Mecoptera, modified basal portion of ductus ejaculatorius (Tuxen; Boudreaux, after Kristensen).

sperm reservoir, in ♂ Heteroptera (Hemiptera), ejaculatory reservoir, q.v. (Tuxen, after Khanna); in ♀ *Cimex* (Heteroptera: Cimicidae), conceptaculum seminis (Tuxen, after Davis).

sperm sac, in *Blattella* (Blattaria: Blattellidae), sperm-containing sac within spermatophore (Chapman, after Khalifa); in ♂ Odonata, large dorsal dilation of the common sperm duct in which sperm are stored before being transferred to the accessory genitalia (O'Farrell, in CSIRO); in ♂ Diptera, sac at base of aedeagus functioning as part of sperm pump in species that do not produce a spermatophore (McAlpine).

sperm tube, testis follicle, q.v. (T-B, after Snodgrass).

spermalege (pl., **spermalegia**), in some Cimicoidea (Hemiptera: Heteroptera), an organ (organs) on ♀ pregenital abdominal segments receiving the sperm during traumatic insemination and lacking a direct communication with the genital apparatus itself; usually consisting of an external integumental pouch (ectospermalege) and an internal mesodermal part (mesospermalege) (Carayon, in Usinger).

spermaphore sclerite, in ♀ Psocoptera, gonopore plate, q.v. (Mockford).

spermapore, in ♀ Psocoptera, opening of ductus spermathecae on abdominal sternum IX (Tuxen, after Pearman).

spermatheca (pl., **spermathecae**), in ♀ insects, receptacle of the sperm during coition (T-B; Tuxen); in ♀ Heteroptera (Hemiptera), receptaculum seminis, q.v., vermiform gland, q.v., or spermathecal tube, q.v. (Tuxen, after Sharp; Andersen), in ♀ *Dysdercus* (Pyrrhocoridae), Gerridae (Hemiptera: Heteroptera), diverticulum ductus, q.v. (Tuxen, Singh, Pendergrast), in ♀ Cimicidae (Hemiptera: Heteroptera), conceptaculum seminis, q.v. (Tuxen, after Berlese), in ♀ Reduviidae (Hemiptera: Heteroptera), (paired tubular) pseudospermathecae, q.v. (Tuxen, after Pendergrast); in ♀ Lepidoptera, receptaculum seminis, q.v. (Tuxen) or bursa copulatrix, q.v. (Tuxen, after Kirby and Spence); in ♀ Chironomidae (Diptera), ectodermal invaginations around distal ends of gonoducts, consisting of entire caecum including spermathecal capsule, spermathecal gland (when present), and spermathecal duct (Saether).

spermathecal, of or pertaining to the spermatheca (T-B).

spermathecal apodemes, in ♀ Panorpidae (Mecoptera), gonoclavi, q.v. (Byers).

spermathecal bulb, in ♀ Gerromorpha (Hemiptera: Heteroptera), ductus receptaculi (in part), q.v. (Tuxen, after Pendergrast); in ♀ Heteroptera (excl. Gerromorpha), capsula seminalis, q.v. (Tuxen, after Scudder).

spermathecal capsule, in ♀ Diptera, any one of the one to 3 enlarged reservoirs differented at the inner end or ends of the spermathecal ducts (Harbach and Knight).

spermathecal capsule pore, in ♀ Culicidae (Diptera), one of the minute pores located near the orifice of the spermathecal capsule (Harbach and Knight).

spermathecal chamber, in ♀ Heteroptera (Hemiptera), pars intermedialis (in a vermiform gland), q.v. (Tuxen, after Davis).

spermathecal duct, in ♀ insects, ductus spermathecae, q.v. (Tuxen); in ♀ Heteroptera (Hemiptera), ductus receptaculi, q.v., of the spermatheca (receptaculum seminis) and vermiform gland, (Tuxen, after Davis).

spermathecal eminence, in ♀ Culicidae (Diptera), a median projection extending into the vagina from the roof and bearing the apertures of the spermathecal ducts and accessory gland duct (Harbach and Knight, after Christophers).

spermathecal eminence spicule, in some ♀ Culicidae (Diptera), one of the outgrowths of the spermathecal eminence, usually borne along the cephalic margin (Harbach and Knight).

spermathecal furrow, in ♀ Isoptera, spermatic groove, q.v. (Tuxen, after Weesner).

spermathecal gland, a special gland opening into the duct of the spermatheca (T-B, after Imms); in ♀ insects, a diverticulum of ductus spermathecae secreting a fluid in which the sperm are discharged (Tuxen); in ♀ Miridae, Piesmatidae (Hemiptera: Heteroptera), capsula seminalis + glandula apicalis (in a vermiform gland), q.v. (Tuxen, after Davis); in ♀ Heteroptera (Hemiptera), vermiform gland, q.v., (Tuxen, after Scudder); in ♀ *Agonoscelis* (Pentatomidae) and other Heteroptera, glandula apicalis, q.v. (Tuxen, after Whitfield); in ♀ Lepidoptera, glandula receptaculi, q.v. (Tuxen).

spermathecal openings, in ♀ Diptera, one or more openings of spermathecal duct; in Blephariceridae, Tanyderidae, and some Tipulidae consisting of 3 separate openings on abdominal sternite IX; in most Nematocera, a single opening on sternite IX, and in most other Diptera, a single internal opening in the dorsal wall of the genital chamber (McAlpine).

spermathecal pore, in ♀ Dermaptera, the opening of spermatheca into genital chamber (Tuxen, after Nel).

spermathecal pump, in ♀ Heteroptera (Hemiptera), pars intermedialis, q.v. (Tuxen, after Scudder).

spermathecal rod, in ♀ Mecoptera, medigynium, q.v. (Tuxen, after Potter).

spermathecal sclerite, in most ♀ Trichoptera, a sclerite in the dorsal wall of the genital chamber bearing the opening of the ductus spermathecae (Nielsen).

spermathecal spout, in ♀ Orthoptera, seminal papilla, q.v. (Tuxen, after Snodgrass).

spermathecal tube, in infraorder Gerromorpha and some other Heteroptera, an elongate, looped, spermatheca with glandular cells in its walls (Andersen); see spermatheca.

spermatic duct, in ♀ *Cimex* (Heteroptera: Cimicidae), duct arising from fusion of vasa deferentia (transl. "Samengang" Landois, in Tuxen).

spermatic groove, in ♀ Isoptera, median groove or furrow in roof of vestibulum, extending from external opening of spermathecal duct backward, sometimes up to opening of accessory glands (Tuxen, after Holmgren).

spermatic furrow, in ♂ *Cimex* (Heteroptera: Cimicidae), groove of left paramere in which runs the interlocked phallus (transl. "Samenrinne" Landois, in Tuxen).

spermatid, haploid product of second meiotic division of secondary spermatocyte which later transforms into a sperm (T-B; Chapman); see spermatocyte.

spermatocyte, diploid cell arising from a spermatogonia, the primary spermatocyte arising from spermatogonia by mitosis and the secondary spermatocyte arising from the first meiotic division of the primary spermatocyte (T-B; Chapman).

spermatodesm, in Odonata and some Orthoptera, sperm bundle in which the sperm are anchored together by their acrosomes and enclosed in a muff of mucopolysaccaride (Chapman).

spermatogenesis, the development of sperm from spermatogonia (T-B; Chapman); see spermiogenesis.

spermatogonia (sing., **spermatogonium**), descendents of the ♂ germ cells, located in the germarium of the testis follicle, which later give rise to spermatocytes (T-B; Chapman).

spermatogonial cyst, a cellular envelope or capsule enclosing a group of spermatogonia (T-B); see cyst.

spermatophore, capsule, sometimes with a stalk, formed by ♂ colleterial glands and containing sperm to be transferred to ♀, indirectly (Collembola, Diplura, Archaeognatha, Zygentoma) or directly (Orthoptera, Coleoptera, Megaloptera, Raphidioptera, Planipennia, Lepidoptera) (Tuxen; Sturm, pers. comm., after Schaller); see spermatophorum.

spermatophore cup, in ♂ Orthoptera, endophallic cavity, q.v. (Tuxen, after Packard).

spermatophore sac, in ♂ Caelifera (Orthoptera), the sac into which the gonopore opens (Tuxen); in ♂ Caelifera (Orthoptera), extension of ejaculatory sac near gonopore, distally extending to phallotreme (Tuxen, after Dirsh); in ♂ Grylloidea (Orthoptera), dorsal cavity, q.v. (Tuxen, after Walker); in ♂ Heteroptera (Hemiptera), ductus seminis distalis, q.v. (Tuxen, after Davey).

spermatophorum (pl., **spermatophora**), in Lepidoptera, encapsulated mass of spermatozoa, or the capsule of such a mass, formed by ♂ and transferred to ♀ bursa copulatrix during copulation, comprising collum spermatophori and corpus spermatophori (Tuxen, after Petersen); spermatophore, q.v. (T-B).

spermatophragma, in adult Lepidoptera, sphragis, q.v. (Tuxen, after Cholodkowsky).

spermatotheca, in ♀ insects, spermatheca, q.v. (Tuxen).

spermatozooid ducts, in Tachardiidae (Hemiptera: Sternorrhyncha: Coccoidea), elongate ducts that narrow from broad apex to slender dermal orifice (Miller, in Stehr).

spermatozoon (pl., **spermatozoa**), sperm, q.v. (T-B; Chapman).

spermiogenesis, the transformation of spermatids into sperm (Chapman); see spermatogenesis.

spermodes, in Cimicidae (Hemiptera: Heteroptera), intraepithelial network of canals in the walls of the pedicels and paired oviducts through which the spermatozoa pass from conceptacula seminis to the ovarioles (Carayon, in Usinger).

spermophagy, feeding on seeds and at least parts of the protective fruit that covers them (Wood).

spermora, the mouth of the duct of the spermatheca (T-B, after

MacGillivray); in ♀ Isoptera, external opening of spermathecal duct (Tuxen, after Geyer).

Sphaeriiformia, a group within the Myxophaga (Coleoptera) that includes the single superfamily Sphaerioidea (Crowson).

Sphaerioidea, single superfamily within the Myxophaga (Coleoptera), including the Sphaeriidae, Lepiceridae, Hydroscaphidae, and Torridinicolidae (Britton, in CSIRO); see Myxophaga.

Sphaeroceroidea, superfamily within the Acalyptratae (Diptera: Muscomorpha), including the familes Sphaeroceridae, Heleomyzidae, Trixoscelididae, Chyromyidae, Tethinidae and Rhinotoridae (McAlpine).

Sphecoidea, superfamily within the Apocrita (Hymenoptera), including solitary wasps of the family Sphecidae possessing adults with unbranched body hairs, posterior lateral lobes of pronotum not reaching to tegula, metapleural glands absent, and medial tibial spur of hind tibia modified into a calcar (Riek, in CSIRO); Sphecoidea + Apoidea (Gauld and Bolton, after Brothers).

sphecology, the study of wasps (Wilson).

sphecophile, a predator, parasite or guest in the nests of wasps (Tulloch, after Gaul); an organism that must spend at least part of its life cycle with wasp colonies (Wilson).

spherical, in the form of a sphere (T-B).

spherocyte, spherule cell, q.v. (Tulloch, after Bogojavlensky).

spheroidal, more or less spherical (T-B).

spheroidocyte, round, usually medium-sized hemocyte with several fatlike droplets and variable number of granular and other less distinct inclusions and sometimes crystals, and sending out threadlike pseudopodia in vitro (Tulloch, after Jones).

spheroidosis, a disease of larval Lepidoptera and Coleoptera, caused by an agent of the poxvirus group, in which large numbers of virus-containing crystals, called spheroids, appear in the cytoplasm of the fatbody cells (Steinhaus and Martignoni).

spherular cells, spherule cells, q.v. (Tulloch, after Chorine).

spherulate, provided with one or more rows of minute tubercles (T-B; Harris, after R. W. Brown); see perlate and tuberculate.

spherule, a minute sphere or globule (T-B); a nonrefringent granule in hemocyte cytoplasm (T-B).

spherule cell, in Coleoptera, Lepidoptera, and Diptera, round or oval hemocyte with large, nonrefringent, usually acidophilic inclusions frequently filling the whole cell, functioning in formation of fatbody and in intermediate metabolism (Tulloch; Chapman).

sphincter, a closing or constricting muscle about any opening (T-B).

sphingiform, similar in form to a sphingid caterpillar (Lepidoptera: Sphingidae), possessing a cylindrical body, with setae very short or wanting and no other armature except a mediodorsal horn or button on the eigth abdominal segment (Peterson).

Sphingoidea, superfamily within the division Ditrysia (Lepidoptera), including only hawk moths of the family Sphingidae (Common, in CSIRO).

sphingophily, insect-flower pollination syndrome involving hawk moths (Lepidoptera: Sphingidae) (Matthews and Matthews, after Baker and Hurd).

sphragidophor, in Lepidoptera, adjective, descriptive of a species which forms a sphragis (Tuxen, after Hering).

sphragis (pl., **sphragides**), in Lepidoptera, external structure, formed by ♂ and attached to ♀ abdomen during copulation, which more or less prevents subsequent copulations by ♀, consisting of a hardened glandular secretions (T-B, after Tillyard; Tulloch; Tuxen, after Eltringham); see mating plug.

sphragophor, in Lepidoptera, sphragidophor, q.v. (Tuxen, after Bryk).

Spicipalpia, infraorder within the Annulipalpia (Trichoptera), including the superfamilies Hydroptiloidea and Rhyacophiloidea, possessing small apical spicule on ultimate segment of adult maxillary palp (Weaver); see Curvipalpia.

spicranial notch, in larval Lepidoptera, V-shaped dorsomedial space delimited laterally by the caudal projections of the head capsule (Stehr), see cervical triangle, vertical triangle.

spicula (pl., **spiculae**), in ♀ Hymenoptera, sting, q.v. (T-B), or ovipositor, q.v. (T-B), or first gonapophyses, q.v. (Tuxen, after Westwood); in ♂ *Euthalia* (Lepidoptera: Nymphalidae), cornutus, q.v. (Tuxen, after Roepke); see spicule.

spicule(s), a small needlelike spine (T-B); in ♂ Coleoptera, one or 2 sclerotized bodies (rudiments of genital segment) attached by membranes to outside of genital tube (Tuxen); see spicula.

spiculiform, shaped like a slender, needlelike process (T-B).

spiculose, having the appearance of or possessing spicules (Peterson).

spiculose area of tergum VIII, in some ♂ Ceratophylloidea (Siphonaptera), a fairly well-defined area on the inner surface near the dorsal margin of abdominal tergum VIII beset with numerous spicules (Rothschild and Traub).

spiculum (pl., **spicula**), in ♂ Coleoptera, spicules, q.v. (Tuxen); in ♂ Hymenoptera, anterior median apodeme of abdominal sternum IX (Tuxen, after Kluge); see spicule.

spiculum gastrale, in ♂ Coleoptera, spicules, q.v. (Tuxen); in ♂ Lepidoptera, saccus, q.v. (Tuxen, after Peytoureau).

spiculum ventrale, in ♀ Coleoptera, endoskeletal rodlike sclerite present in forms with an ovipositor and serving as attachment for its muscles (Tuxen).

spider, a member of the order Araneae (Arachnida) (Borror et al.).

spider-lick, Paederus vesicular dermatitis, q.v. (Adkins, pers. comm.).

spider mite, plant-feeding mite belonging to the family Tetranychidae (Acari) (Borror et al.).

spike potential, action potential, q.v. (Chapman).

spiked pea gall, small green gall resembling peas with spikes, formed on the leaves of roses by larvae of the gall wasp *Diplolepis nervosa* (Hymenoptera: Cynipidae) (Leftwich); see pea gall.

spina (pl., **spinae**), the unpaired median apodemal process of a spinasternum (T-B, after Imms, Snodgrass); in ♂ Lepidoptera, superuncus, q.v. (Tuxen, after LeDoux).

spinasternum, one of the spina-bearing intersegmental sclerites of the thoracic venter, associated, or united, with the preceding sternum, and sometimes become part of the definitive prosternum or mesosternum, but not the metasternum (T-B, after Snodgrass); in ♂ *Inocellia* (Raphidioptera: Inocellidae), arcessus, q.v. (Tuxen, after Acker); in ♂ *Coniopteryx* (Planipennia: Coniopterygidae), entoprocessus, q.v. (Tuxen, after Acker); in ♂ *Mantispa* (Mantispidae) and *Lomamyia* (Berothidae) (Planipennia), penisfilum, q.v. (Tuxen, after Acker); in ♂ Osmylidae (Planipennia), subarcus, q.v. (Tuxen, after Acker); in ♂ *Chrysopa iberica* (Planipennia), gonapsis, q.v. (Tuxen, after Hölzel).

spinate, produced into an acuminate spine (T-B).

spindle cell, plasmatocyte, q.v. (Tulloch, after Lazarenko).

spindle-shaped, fusiform, q.v. (T-B).

spindle virosis, spheroidosis, q.v. (Steinhaus and Martignoni).

spindlelike, fusiform, q.v. (Peterson).

spine, a multicellular, more or less thornlike process or outgrowth of the cuticula not separated from it by a joint (T-B, after Comstock); in adult Siphonaptera, ctenidial spine, q.v. (Rothschild and Traub); see seta and spur.

spine of aedeagal lobe, in ♂ Chironomidae (Diptera), median volsella, q.v., or endomere, q.v. (Saether).

spine of penis cavity, in ♂ Chironomidae (Diptera), virga, q.v. (Saether).

spinelike wax rays, in Aleyrodidae (Hemiptera: Sternorrhyncha), ribbons of straight or curled cylindrical wax rods of dorsal submargin of pupa (Gill).

spined, spinose, q.v. (T-B, Harris).

spined body, in ♀ Coleophoridae (Lepidoptera), usually elongate, spinous, sclerotized structure in interior of bursa copulatrix (Tuxen, after Toll).

spinelet, small spines not much longer than wide (Rothschild and Traub); see spicule.

spinellae (sing., **spinella**), in ♂ Neuropteroidea, small, hard, toothlike structures, sometimes abundantly present on gonosaccus (Tuxen, after Tjeder).

spines of aedeagus, in ♂ Mecoptera, dorsal lobes, q.v. (Tuxen, after Tjeder).

spines of lamina, in ♂ Odonata, pair of spines on lamina anterior proximally in fenestra (Tuxen).

spinescent 8-shaped pores, in teneral ♀ Kermesidae (Hemiptera: Sternorrhyncha: Coccoidea), pores with an oval or circular sclerotized ring, cone-shaped teeth dorsally, and saclike ventrally, located in transverse bands on middorsum (Bullington and Kosztarab).

spinet, in Orthoptera, immovable (nonarticulated) sharp projection (usually on the hind tibiae) (Otte, pers. comm.); see spine.

spiniferous, bearing, or clothed with, spines (T-B).

spiniferous area, in ♀ Siphonaptera, area spiculosa, q.v. (Tuxen, after Jordan and Rothschild).

spiniform, in the form or shape of a spine (T-B).

spiniform bristle, in adult Siphonaptera, a bristle articulated with and arising from an alveolus (Lewis, pers. comm.); see seta.

spinneret, small tubular appendage from which silk threads are exuded by spiders and by many larval insects, being located posteriorly on the abdomen in the former but usually located on the labium of a larva, e.g., in larval Lepidopera (T-B; Peterson; Leftwich; Common, in CSIRO).

spinning bristle, in Embiidina, silk ejector, q.v. (T-B).

spinning glands, in Psocoptera, the glands which produce the viscid secretion which forms the silk (T-B).

spinose, spinosus (Latin), **spinous,** armed with thorny spines, more elongate than echinate (T-B; Harris, after R. W. Brown); see echinate and spinulate.

spinous-radiate, beset with spines in a circle, either concatenate, united at their bases, or setaceous, like bristles (T-B).

spinula (pl., **spinulae**), spinule, q.v. (T-B).

spinula pileoli (pl., **spinulae pileoli**), in ♂ *Zygaena* (Lepidoptera: Zygaenidae), fine spine of pileolus (Tuxen, after Loritz).

spinulae, slender cuticular outgrowths lacking innervation; in larval Chironomidae (Diptera), usually 2–6 sclerotized, mostly pointed scales in each lateral corner of membranous labral area, situated just mesad of triangular sclerite (Saether).

spinulae crassae (sing., **spinula crassa**), in ♂ *Zygaena* (Lepidoptera: Zygaenidae), median, coarse-spined region of lamina ventralis of aedoeagus (Tuxen, after Loritz).

spinulae membranulae intercoronariae, in ♂ *Zygaena* (Lepidoptera: Zygaenidae), spines in intercoronal membrane of lamina dorsalis of aedoeagus (Tuxen, after Loritz).

spinulae (of anal point), in adult Chironomidae (Diptera), basiconic pegs, q.v. (Saether).

spinulae tenues (sing., **spinula tenuis**), in ♂ *Zygaena* (Lepidoptera: Zygaenidae), coarse spines of distal region of lamina ventralis of aedoeagus (Tuxen, after Loritz).

spinulate, set with numerous small, thorny spines; minutely spinose (T-B; Harris, after R. W. Brown); see echinulate.

spinule, a small spine (T-B); see microtrichia.

spinulose, spinulosus (Latin), spinulate, q.v. (T-B; Harris).

spinulose processes, in ♂ *Aphelocheirus* (Heteroptera: Naucoridae), oblong and paired inarticulated processes of posterior ventral border of pygophore, probably parandria or pseudophallic organs (transl. "processus spinuleux" Poisson, in Tuxen).

spinus, in ♂ Diptera, epiphallus, q.v. (Tuxen, after Zumpt and Heinz; McAlpine).

spinus titillatorius, in ♂ Blattopteroidea, hypophallus, q.v. (Tuxen, after Wesché); in ♂ Diptera, (spinelike) epiphallus, q.v. (Tuxen; Colless and McAlpine, in CSIRO).

spiny bud gall, spiny gall on the flower buds of witch hazel caused by *Hamamelistes spinosus* (Hemiptera: Sternorrhyncha; Aphididae) (Borror et al.); see cone gall and spiny witch-hazel gall.

spiny gall, hedgehog oak gall, q.v., or pea galls, q.v. (Leftwich).

spiny witch-hazel gall, open-type gall formed from folded leaves of North America witch-hazel *Hamamelis virginea* by gall aphid *Hamamelistes spinosus* (Hemiptera: Sternorrhyncha: Aphididae) (Leftwich); see cone gall and spiny bud gall.

spira, in some ♀ Cynipidae (Hymenoptera), coiled ovipositor (Tuxen).

spiracle, spiracula (Latin) (pl., **spiraculae**), external opening of the tracheal system (T-B; Chapman).

spiracle cover lobe, in some Apocrita (Hymenoptera), pronotal lobe, q.v., covering mesothoracic spiracle (Riek, in CSIRO).

spiracular, of or pertaining to a spiracle (T-B).

spiracular area, in some adult Hymenoptera, the anterior of the 3 areas between the lateral and the pleural carinae on the propodeum (T-B).

spiracular atrium, the pitlike or tubular chamber forming the exterior part of the spiracle (T-B, after Snodgrass).

spiracular bristle, in adult Diptera, setae located on periphery of pro- or metathoracic spiracles (Borror et al.).

spiracular brush, in larval Psephenidae (Coleoptera), a conspicuous brush of setae on each side of abdominal tergite IX, close to, and facing, the large spiracle on each side of the posterior edge of abdominal segment VIII, serving to keep the spiracle free of silt (Britton, in CSIRO).

spiracular cleft, a deep, closed or open, cavity surrounding a spiracle; if closed one or more moveable liplike structures may be present (Peterson).

spiracular depression, in Coccoidea (Hemiptera: Sternorrhyncha), indentation on the thoracic margin with thick setae where the spiracular furrows end (T-B, after MacGillivray; Kosztarab and Kozár).

spiracular disc, in amphipneustic and metapneustic Diptera larvae, disclike area on caudal segment possessing respiratory openings (Peterson; Teskey, in McAlpine).

spiracular disk, in larval Diptera, spiracular disc, q.v. (Peterson).

spiracular field, in larval Diptera, spiracular disc, q.v. (Peterson).

spiracular filaments, in larval Diptera, remnants of spiracular tracheae when spiracles are absent (Teskey, in McAlpine).

spiracular frame, peritreme, q.v. (Peterson).

spiracular furrow, in Coccoidea, e.g., Coccidae (Hemiptera: Sternorrhyncha), depressed area leading from spiracular atrium to body margin, usually lined with wax pores (Miller, in Stehr); see spiracular depression and spiracular pore band.

spiracular gill, in some pupal and larval aquatic Diptera and Coleoptera, an extension of the cuticle surrounding a spiracle and bearing a plastron connected to the spiracle by aeropyles (Chapman).

spiracular glands, in larval Diptera, epidermal glands opening on the surface of the spiracular plate and secreting a hydrofuge substance (Teskey, in McAlpine).

spiracular hairs, in larval Schizophora (Diptera: Muscomorpha), hairs located at the outer end of each spiracular opening (Teskey, in McAlpine).

spiracular indentation, in Coccoidea (Hemiptera: Sternorrhyncha), spiracular depression, q.v. (Kosztarab and Kozár).

spiracular line, in larval Lepidoptera, the lateral line which includes the spiracles (T-B).

spiracular muscles, in insects, those muscles connected with each spiracle, usually an occlusor and a dilator (T-B, after Snodgrass).

spiracular opening, one of the openings of a spiracle (Teskey, in McAlpine).

spiracular papillae, in larval Schizophora (Diptera: Muscomorpha), papillae, bearing openings, projecting from spiracular stalk (Teskey, in McAlpine).

spiracular plate(s), peritreme, q.v. (Borror et al.); in larval Diptera, more or less well-defined plate on which are located the spiracular opening and the ecdysial scar (Teskey, in McAlpine); in ♀ Hymenoptera, eighth hemitergites, q.v. (Tuxen).

spiracular pore band, in most nymphs and ♀ Coccoidea (Hemiptera: Sternorrhyncha), rows or bands of multilocular pores, extending from each thoracic spiracle to body margin, being replaced by pore clusters in Ceroccocidae (Miller, in Stehr; Kosztarab and Kozár); see spiracular furrow.

spiracular sclerite, in adult Culicidae (Diptera), a small sclerite of the metapleuron located immediately below the metathoracic spiracle (Harbach and Knight, after Owen).

spiracular setae, in Coccoidea (Hemiptera: Sternorrhyncha), thick fleshy setae, normally in groups of 2 or 3 on body margin at end of spiracular furrow, in a depression (T-B, after MacGillivray; Kosztarab and Kozár).

spiracular slits, in larval Muscomorpha (Diptera), elongate to ovoid openings in the posterior spiracle (Ferrar).

spiracular sound organ, an organ formed from a series of leaflike folds inside the tracheae of a few Diptera and Coleoptera, producing a high pitched sound when air is rapidly expelled from the spiracles (Leftwich).

spiracular stalk, in larval Muscomorpha (Diptera), elevation bearing anterior spiracle (Teskey, in McAlpine).

spiracular trachea, the short, usually unbranched trachea rising directly from the spiracle (T-B, after Snodgrass).

spiral, rolled up like a watch spring, or twisted like a corkscrew (T-B).

spiral fiber, taenidium, q.v. (T-B).

spiral process of aedeagus, in ♂ Hydroptilidae (Trichoptera), paramere, q.v. (Tuxen, after Ross).

spiral process of the vesica, in Heteroptera (Hemiptera), cricoid sclerite, q.v. (Štys, pers. comm.).

spiral thread, taenidium, q.v. (T-B).

spiral tongue, in adult Lepidoptera, proboscis, q.v. (T-B).

spiralis (pl., **spirales**), axillary cord, q.v., of wing (T-B, after MacGillivray).

spirignath, in adult Lepidoptera, proboscis, q.v. (T-B).

spiritrompe, in adult Lepidoptera, proboscis, q.v. (T-B).

Spirobolida, order within the superorder Helminthomorpha (Diplopoda), the members of which possess one pair of legs on the fifth segment, ventrally closed third segment, stipites of gnathochilarium widely separated by mentum and laminae linguales, and terminal segment of body without setae-bearing papillae (Borror et al.).

spirochaete, bacterium, belonging to the order Spirochaetales, in which the cell is slender, spiral in shape, flexible and 0.003–0.500 mm long, being pathogens and also an essential part of the symbiosis between termites (Isoptera) and flagellate protozoans (Allaby).

spiroplasma, bacterium of the genus *Spiroplasma* (family Sprioplasmataceae), lacking a cell wall and often forming helical filaments, being parasitic on plants or arthropods (Allaby).

Spirostreptida, order within the superorder Helminthomorpha (Diplopoda), the members of which possess one pair of legs on segment 4 and 2 pairs of legs on segment 5, stipites of gnathochilarium widely separated by mentum and laminae linguales, and terminal segment of body without setae-bearing papillae (Borror et al.).

spittle, in Cercopidae (Hemiptera: Auchenorrhyncha), a frothy mass enveloping the nymph, passing from the anus and derived in part from a fluid produced by specialized cells of the proximal region of the Malpighian tubules (T-B; Woodward et al., in CSIRO; Chapman; O'Brien, pers. comm.).

spittle insect, spittlebug, q.v. (T-B, after Wardle).

spittlebug, a member of the Cercopoidea (Hemiptera: Auchenorrhyncha) (Woodward et al., in CSIRO).

splanchnic, of or pertaining to the viscera (T-B); visceral.

splanchnic layer, the inner layer of the mesoderm applied to the walls of the alimentary canal (T-B, after Snodgrass); see somatic layer.

splanchnic nerves, the nerves arising from the last abdominal ganglion and passing to the hind gut and to the reproductive system (T-B, after Imms).

splanchnocyte, prohemocyte, q.v. (T-B, after Wardle).

splanchnopleure, splanchnic layer, q.v. (T-B).

splendens, splendent, shining; glossy (T-B, after Kirby and Spence).

splenic organ, phagocytic organ, q.v. (T-B).

splitter, in taxonomy, one who divides taxa very finely, to express every shade of difference and relationship, through the formal recognition of separate taxa and their elaborate categorical ranking (T-B, after J. B. Smith; Mayr); see lumper.

spoile, exuviae, q.v. (T-B).

spongiform, resembling a sponge; soft and porous (T-B).

sponging mouthparts, in nonbiting higher Diptera, proboscis, q.v., lacking stylets and with large labella, with which liquid is sopped up (Borror et al.).

spongioplasm, spongioplasma, reticulum, q.v., of muscle (T-B, after Wardle).

spongiose, spongy, spungeous, spongelike; of a soft elastic tissue resembling a sponge (T-B).

spongy fossula, in Heteroptera (Hemiptera), fossula spongiosa, q.v.

spongy parenchyma, in galls produced by Cynipidae (Hymenoptera), the material occupying the central portion of a gall and constituting the major material of all the spongy and more hollow oak-apples of the genus *Cynips* (T-B, after Kinsey).

spontaneous discharge, production of an impulse in a nerve axon in the absense of a sensory imput (Chapman).

spoon, in honey bee (Hymenoptera: Apidae), labellum, q.v. (T-B); in ♂ Hesperiidae (Lepidoptera), spoon-shaped, usually ventrodistal, process of inner face of valva (transl. "cuiller" Reverdin, in Tuxen); in ♂ Lepidoptera, distal elongation, probably of sacculus (transl. "cuiller" Viette, in Tuxen).

spoonshaped mucro, in Collembola, dorsally concave mucro, with lamellae higher than rachis (Christiansen and Bellinger).

spore, among fungi, a microscopic, vegetative propagule functioning in reproduction and dispersal (Allaby); among bacteria, a differentiated cell functioning as a propagule or as a resistant structure allowing the organism to survive adverse environmental conditions (Allaby).

sporoblast, one of the nucleated bodies in the *Plasmodium* oocyst (T-B).

sporogony, within the oocyst of *Plasmodium,* the malarial protozoan, asexual reproduction by multiple fission of the zygote, producing the sporozoites (T-B; Tulloch; Allaby).

sporogony phase, the phase in the life cycle of *Plasmodium* within the insect host, during which there is sexual production of sporozoites (T-B).

Sporozoa, subphylum of the Protozoa, including, e.g., Plasodiidae, in which the life cycle includes a spore-forming or cyst-forming stage, being parasites of many different animals (Allaby).

sporozoan, a member of the Sporozoa.

sporozoite, the minute organism produced in the oocyst of the protozoan malarial parasite *Plasmodium,* being the stage of the malarial organism produced by the oocyst which is stored in the salivary gland of the mosquito (Diptera: Culicidae), and infects the vertebrate host during the blood feeding (T-B; Tulloch).

sport, an aberration or a mutation (T-B).

spotted fever, Rocky Mountain spotted fever, q.v. (Borror et al.).

spotted wilt disease, disease of tomatoes and other plants transmitted by at least 5 species of thrips, particularly the onion thrips, *Thrips tabaci* (Thysanoptera: Thripidae) (Mound).

spread, movement by some portion of a species that results in a major modification of its geographical range (Steinhaus and Martignoni, after R. F. Smith); see dispersal.

spreading board, specially constructed platform used in spreading the wings of insects so that they will be properly positioned when the specimen dries, esp. Lepidoptera (Borror et al.).

spring, in Collembola, furcula, q.v. (T-B).

Spring disease, a disease of the cutworm *Euxoa segetum* (Lepidoptera: Noctuidae), caused by the bacterium *Pseudomonas septica* (Steinhaus and Martignoni).

springs of penis, in ♂ Siphonaptera, virga penis, q.v. (Tuxen).

springtail, a member of the order Collembola (Wallace and Mackerras, in CSIRO).

spruce cone-gall, a compact conelike gall formed by the swelling of the spruce needles at the tips of young shoots attacked by the *Adelges abietis* (Hemiptera: Sternorrhyncha: Adelgidae) (Leftwich).

spur(s), thick cuticular appendage or spine connected to the body wall by a joint, generally on the tibia (T-B, after Comstock; Leftwich); in ♂ Ephemeroptera, penial spines, q.v. (Tuxen, after Needham, Traver, and Hsu); in ♂ Siphonaptera, processus basimeris ventralis, q.v. (Tuxen, after Jordan); in ♀ Incurvariidae (Lepidoptera), apophyses anteriores and posteriores (Tuxen, after Wood); see tibial spurs.

spur formula, a numerical expression of the arrangement of spurs, e.g., in Trichoptera 2-3-4, indicating 2 spurs on the foretibia, 3 on the midtibia, and 4 on the hind tibia (T-B, after J. B. Smith).

spurious, spurius (Latin), false (T-B; R. W. Brown).

spurious claw, in spiders (Arachnida: Araneae), a stout bristle that looks like a claw (Borror et al.).

spurious legs, aborted anterior legs in certain diurnal Lepidoptera, esp. Nymphalidae (T-B, after J. B. Smith).

spurious ocellus, an ocellate spot without any definite iris or pupil (T-B).

spurious vein(s), certain folds or thickenings in the wing surface which resemble veins so nearly as to be readily mistaken for them; sufficiently constant to be useful in classification (T-B); in adult Syrphidae (Diptera), a veinlike thickening of the wing membrane between radius (R) and media (M) (T-B, after Wardle).

spurs of tibia, tibial spurs, q.v. (Saether).

squama (pl., **squamae**), any scalelike structure (T-B; Leftwich); in adult Odonata, palpiger, q.v. (Borror et al.): in adult Dermaptera, sclerotized portion of remigium of wing (Giles, in CSIRO); in ♀ Miridae (Hemiptera: Heteroptera), ovivalvula, q.v. (Tuxen, after Wagner); in adult Lepidoptera, tegula, q.v. (T-B; Chapman); in adult Diptera, calypter (T-B; Chapman; McAlpine); in adult Chironomidae (Diptera), proximal lobe of wing (Saether); in ♂ Hymenoptera, digitus, q.v. (Tuxen, after Salt) or gonostylus, q.v. (Tuxen, after Thomson); see lamella.

squama bifurcata, in ♀ Psocoptera, valvae dorsales, q.v. (Tuxen, after Ribaga).

squama fimbriata, in larval Chironomidae (Diptera), labral lamella, q.v. (Saether).

squama genitale, in Protura, the whole genital armature (Tuxen, after Berlese).

squama palpifera, palpifer, q.v. (T-B).

squama platia, in larval Chironomidae (Diptera), labral lamella, q.v. (Saether).

squamate, scaly; covered with scales (T-B; Harris, after R. W. Brown); see cataphracted, imbricate, and scutate.

squame, squama, q.v. (T-B).

squame scale, a decumbent scale (Harbach and Knight).

squamiform, having a scalelike form (T-B).

squamose, squamosus (Latin), **squamous,** squamate, q.v. (T-B; Harris).

squamula (pl., **squamulae**), tegula, q.v. (T-B); in Diptera, calypter, q.v. (T-B; McAlpine); in ♀ Psocoptera, valvae externae, q.v. (Tuxen, after Kolbe).

squamula alaris, in adult Diptera, upper calypter, q.v. (T-B, after Comstock; McAlpine).

squamula penis, in ♂ Blattopteroidea, left epiphallus, q.v. (Tuxen, after Berlese).

squamula thoracalis, in adult Diptera, lower calypter, q.v. (T-B, after Comstock).

squamula thoracica, in adult Diptera, lower calypter, q.v. (McAlpine).

squamule, squamula, q.v. (T-B).

squamulose, squamulosus (Latin), **squamulous,** covered with small scales (T-B).

squamulum, in adult Siphonaptera, a small sclerite, shaped like the cervical link plate, situated at or near the anterior dorsal corner of the metasternum (Lewis, pers. comm.).

squarrose, squarrosus (Latin), **squarrous,** rough with elevations; scurfy; rough with loose scales differing in direction or not parallel in direction (T-B; Harris, after Marchant and Charles, Jaeger, and Stearn); pulverulent, rugose, salebrose, and scabrous.

ST$_{50}$, median survival time, q.v. (Steinhaus and Martignoni).

stabbers, in Anoplura (Phthiraptera), stylets, q.v., of sucking apparatus (T-B; Chapman).

stadium (pl., **stadia**), the time interval between 2 moults (T-B; Tulloch; Stehr); see instar.

stage, life stage, q.v. (T-B).

stalk, pedicel, q.v., of antenna (T-B).

stalk of leaf-shaped ventral sclerite, in ♂ Siphonaptera, vesicula, q.v. (Tuxen, after Sharif).

stalked, with a stalk or stem; with a narrow stemlike base; of veins, fused together to form a single vein (Borror et al.); see pedunculate and petiolate.

stalked bodies, corpora pedunculata, q.v. (T-B).

standard, an accepted, or agreed upon, object, thing or definition to which all others in its category are referred (T-B).

standard deviation (SD), the square root of the sum of the squared deviations (d) from the mean divided by the sample size minus one (n-1); (Mayr).

$$SD = \sqrt{\frac{\Sigma d^2}{(n-1)}}$$

standard error (**of the mean**) (**SE**), standard deviation divided by the square root of the sample size (n); (Mayr).

$$SE = \frac{SD}{\sqrt{n}}$$

stapes, in ♂ Heteroptera (Hemiptera), basal plates (the 2 as a whole), q.v. (Tuxen, after Bonhag and Wick).

staphyla, a group of gongylidia, the swollen hyphal tips produced by fungi that live in symbiosis with attine ants (Hymenoptera: Formicidae) (Wilson).

Staphyliniformia, group within the Polyphaga (Coleoptera), including the superfamilies Staphylinoidea, Hydrophiloidea, and Histeroidea (Britton, in CSIRO).

Staphylinoidea, superfamily within the Polyphaga (Coleoptera), including the Staphylinidae and other families, possessing adults with M-Cu loop absent in hind wing, at least one membranous basal abdominal segment, antenna not elbowed, and with at most, a loose club; larvae with galea and lacinia more or less fused (Britton, in CSIRO).

statary phase, the period in the activity cycle of an army ant (Hymenoptera: Formicidae) colony during which the colony is relatively quiescent and does not move from site to site, and the queen lays the eggs and the bulk of the brood is in the egg and pupal stages (Wilson); see nomadic phase.

static, passive; at rest or in equilibrium (T-B).

static organ, a structure which aids in preserving balance (T-B); in *Phylloxera* (Hemiptera: Sternorrhyncha: Phylloxeridae), Johnston's organ, q.v. (T-B, after Stauffacher); see halter.

static sense, the sense of balance or of maintaining position in the air or elsewhere (T-B).

statodynamic sense, the sense which regulates the position of an animal, through its awareness to its relation in space to the objects by which it is surrounded (T-B); see proprioreception.

statolith, static organ, q.v. (T-B).

statumen penis (pl., **statumina penis**), in ♂ Anoplura (Phthiraptera), unpaired sclerite in wall of genital sac continuous with base of penis (Tuxen).

stearic acid, $C_{18}H_{36}O_2$, a common fatty acid component of storage fats (Gilmour, in CSIRO).

steatocyte, a form of plasmatocyte which detaches itself from the imaginal adipose tissue to destroy the larval fat cells (T-B, after Henneguy).

stellate, stellated, stelliform, resembling a star; star-shaped; with a star-shaped structure (T-B).

stellate cell, plasmatocytelike cell often appliqued to epidermis and other tissues (Tulloch, after Wigglesworth).

stelocyttares, social wasps (Hymenoptera: Vespidae), in which the comb layers of the nest are supported by pillars and not connected with the envelope (T-B); see poecilocyttares and phragmocyttares.

stelocyttarous, pertaining to nests, and especially wasp nests (Hymenoptera: Vespidae), in which the combs are attached to the support by pillars (Wilson).

stem, in ♂ Odonata, first segment of prophallus, articulated to apex of vesicula spermalis (Tuxen, after Fraser); in ♂ Coleoptera, penis, q.v. (Tuxen, after Hopkins); in adult Diptera, stalk of halter (McAlpine).

stem group, a group of fossil taxa that are more closely related to one recent group than to any other recent group (Hennig).

stem mother, in Aphididae (Hemiptera: Sternorrhyncha), fundratrix, q.v. (T-B; Leftwich).

stem of aedeagus, in ♂ Auchenorrhyncha (Hemiptera), shaft (of aedeagus), q.v. (Tuxen).

stem species, a species which persists unchanged even after daughter species have separated off (Hennig).

stem vein, in adult Diptera, basal section of radius (McAlpine); in adult Chironomidae (Diptera), brachiolum, q.v. (Saether).

stemapoda (stemapoda), in larval Notodontidae (Lepidoptera), elongated anal prolegs (Peterson).

stemmata (sing., **stemma**), simple eyes of the often circular, lateral eye-groups in holometabolous larvae (T-B); small tubercles borne by antennae (T-B).

stemmatal group, in larval Lepidoptera, primary setae SD1 and SD2 located on thoracic and abdominal segments dorsocaudad of spiracle (Stehr, after Hinton).

stemmatic bulla, in some Nematocera (Diptera), dark bulla near the posterior margin of the compound eye, assumed to be a remnant of the larval eye (McAlpine).

Stemmiulida, order within the Helminthomorpha (Diplopoda), including the single family Stemmiulidae, containing species that inhabit the Old and New World tropics (Hoffman, in Parker).

Stempffer's process, in ♂ *Aricia anteros* (Lepidoptera: Lycaenidae: Plebeiinae), modification of uncus (Tuxen, after Nabokov).

stenazygos, in ♂ Coleoptera, the tubular, not enlarged part of azygos, i.e. ductus ejaculatorius (Tuxen).

stenazygotic portion, in ♂ Coleoptera, stenazygos, q.v. (Tuxen).

steno-, Greek prefix; narrow (T-B).

stenocephalous, stenocephalus, with a narrow, elongated head (T-B).

stenocostal area, in some Tingidae (Hemiptera: Heteroptera), a narrow marginal strip of the costal area on forewing (Štys, pers. comm.).

stenogamous, as applied to Culicidae (Diptera), those capable of mating in small cages, i.e., without a swarming flight of the males; (Tulloch, after Roubaud); see eurygamous.

stenogamy, the ability to mate in a confined space (Leftwich).

stenogastric, having a shortened abdomen or gaster (T-B).

stenopterous, having narrowed, but complete, wings, e.g., in Thysanoptera and Mymaridae (Hymenoptera) (T-B).

stenorhynchan, narrow-beaked or snouted (T-B).

stenothermal, restricted to living within a narrow range of temperatures (T-B).

stenotopic, restricted to a single type of habitat.

stenovalent, stenotopic, q.v. (Tulloch).

stenusin, in adult *Stenus* (Coleoptera: Staphylinidae), terpenoid produced by pygidial glands that lowers the surface tension of the water and makes the surface of the beetle hydrophobic (Chapman).

Stephanoidea, superfamily within the Apocrita (Hymenoptera) including the family Stephanidae, possessing adults with a subantennal groove for reception of basal articles of antenna, spurs of hind tibia not modified for preening, petiolate gaster, and antenna with more than 14 articles (Riek, in CSIRO; Gauld and Bolton).

stercoraceous, dung-inhabiting or frequenting (T-B); see coprophagous.

stercoral, relating or pertaining to excrement (T-B).

stereokinesis, a phenomenon by which the reflex movements and responses of an insect to light or other stimulus are inhibited by the action of tactile stimuli, e.g., when an insect remains motionless when in contact with a solid body, particularly with a rough surface, even if disturbed, sometimes resulting in crowding of insects (Tulloch; Leftwich).

stereotropism, negative thigmotropism, i.e., the avoidance of contact (T-B); see stereokinesis.

sterigma (pl., **sterigmata**), in ♀ Lepidoptera, the entire complex of sclerotized structures surrounding ostium bursae, consisting of lamella antevaginalis and lamella postvaginalis (Tuxen, after Bryk).

sterile, not capable of reproducing (T-B).

sterile caste, in Isoptera, the soldier and the worker caste, in which the sexual organs are atrophied and nonfunctional (Krishna, pers. comm.).

sterility, structural or functional inability to reproduce (T-B).

sterna, pl. of sternum, q.v. (T-B).

sternacosta, the transverse internal ridge of the sternal suture through the bases of the sternal apophyses (T-B, after Snodgrass).

sternacostal suture, the external suture of the sternacosta, separating the basisternum from the sternellum (T-B, after Snodgrass).

sternal, of or pertaining to the sternum (T-B).

sternal apodeme, in adult Hymenoptera, anterodorsal apodeme of a sternum (Tuxen).

sternal apophyseal pit, the external depression marking the point of origin of the sternal apophysis (Harbach and Knight).

sternal apophyses, the lateral apodemal arms of the eusternum, in higher insects united on a median base, the whole structure forming the furca (T-B, after Snodgrass).

sternal coxal process, the projection of the sternum serving for the ventral point of articulation within the coxa (Harbach and Knight).

sternal laterale, in certain of the lower insects, a plate found at each side of the sternum or of the presternum (T-B, after Snodgrass).

sternal orifice, in Perlidae (Plecoptera), a peculiar slit on each side of the sternum, extending inward and ending blindly (T-B).

sternal plate, sternum, q.v., consisting of a single plate (Leftwich).

sternal processes, in some ♂ Muscomorpha (Diptera), esp. Calytratae, lobes, tubercles, setae, and other modifications on abdominal sternum V (McAlpine).

sternal spatula, in larval Cecidomyiidae (Diptera), an elongate, sclerotized process on prosternum (T-B; Colless and McAlpine, in CSIRO; Teskey, in McAlpine).

sternal valves, in ♀ Diptera, hypogynial valves, q.v. (Colless and McAlpine, in CSIRO; McAlpine).

sternannum, basisternum, q.v. (T-B, after MacGillivray).

sternapodeme, in ♂ Chironomidae (Diptera), bridgelike apodeme connecting gonocoxites, connected with coxapodemes laterally and articulating with phallapodeme posteriorly (Saether); gonocoxal apodeme, q.v. (McAlpine).

sternaulus (pl., **sternauli**), in some adult Ichneumonoidea (Hymenoptera), a furrow on either side of the sternopleuron in the position of a sternopleural suture (T-B; Riek, in CSIRO).

sternellar, pertaining to the sternellum (T-B).

sternellum, the second sclerite of the ventral part of each thoracic segment, frequently divided into longitudinal parts which may be widely separated (T-B, after J. B. Smith); the area of the eusternum posterior to the bases of the sternal apophyses or the sternocoxal suture (T-B, after Snodgrass; Chapman); in ♂ Odonata, fenestra, q.v. (Tuxen, after Thompson); in ♂ Lepidoptera, transtilla (Tuxen, after Forbes).

sternepimeron, katepimeron, q.v. (T-B, after MacGillivray).

sternepisternum, katepisternum, q.v. (T-B, after MacGillivray).

sternite, a subdivision of a sternum, or any one of the sclerotic components of a definite sternum (T-B, after Snodgrass; Harbach and Knight); in ♀ Blattopteroidea, valvulae internae (Tuxen, after Lacaze-Duthiers).

sternite VIII, in ♀ *Agulla* (Raphidioptera: Raphidiidae), gonapophyses posteriores, q.v. (Tuxen, after Ferris and Pennebaker).

sternocoxal, of or pertaining to the sternum and coxa together.

sternomacula, in ♂ Plecoptera, sensory area along median line of certain abdominal sterna (Tuxen, after Crampton).

sternopleural, of or pertaining to the sternopleura, or sternopleurite (T-B).

sternopleural bristle, in adult Diptera, katepisternal seta, q.v. (T-B, after Comstock; Borror et al.).

sternopleural suture, in adult Diptera, anapleural suture, q.v. (T-B).

sternopleurite, the infracoxal sclerotization of a generalized thoracic pleuron, generally united with the primary sternum, forming part of the eusternum (T-B, after Snodgrass; Chapman); katepisternum, q.v. (McAlpine, after Crampton).

sternopleuron (pl., **sternopleura**), katepisternum, q.v., of mesothorax (T-B, after Comstock); in adult Diptera, katepisternum, q.v. (T-B, after J. B. Smith); in adult Chironomidae (Diptera), preepisternum, q.v. (Saether); combined plate resulting from the fusion of the sternum with the episternum (T-B, after Imms; Mackerras, in CSIRO); combined plate resulting from fusion of sternum with the katepisternum (Mackerras, in CSIRO); see sternopleurite.

sternorhabdite, in larval Hymenoptera, structure or tubercle giving rise to part of ovipositor (T-B); in ♀ Odonata, style, q.v. (Tuxen, after Tillyard); in ♀ Blattopteroidea, valvulae inferiores, q.v. (Tuxen, after Lacaze-Duthiers).

Sternorrhyncha, division within the Hemiptera, including the Psylloidea, Aleyrodoidea, Aphidoidea, and Coccoidea, possessing tarsi with fewer than 3 tarsomeres, and forewings, when present, without or with few closed cells (T-B; Woodward et al., in CSIRO). see Auchenorrhyncha, Coleorrhyncha, and Heteroptera.

Sternoxia, group proposed to include the Buprestoidea and the Elateroidea (Coleoptera) (Britton, in CSIRO).

sternum (pl., **sterna**), the entire ventral division of any segment (T-B); the definite sternum, which in the thorax usually includes the sternopleurites and may include the posteriorly adjacent intersegmental spinasternum (T-B, after Snodgrass); see eusternum.

sternum IX, in ♂ *Eupithecia* (Lepidoptera: Geometridae), weak, shield-shaped sclerite at midventral part of vinculum (Tuxen, after Schroeder).

sternum X, in ♂ Lepidoptera, subscaphium, q.v. (Tuxen, after Schroeder).

sterol, compound, e.g., cholesterol, obtained by insects from food, forming part of the lipoprotein structure of cells, and forming the starting point or the synthesis of certain hormones (Gilmour, in CSIRO; Chapman).

stethidium, thorax, q.v. (T-B).

Stewart's disease, Stewart's wilt, q.v. (Borror et al.).

Stewart's wilt, disease of corn plants caused by the bacterium *Erwinia stewarti* and transmitted circulatively by corn flea beetle, *Chaetocnema pulicaria,* and corn rootworms, *Diabrotica* spp. (Coleoptera: Chrysomelidae), and the seedcorn maggot, *Hylemya patura* (Diptera: Anthomyiidae) (Borror et al.).

stick-insect, a member of the order Phasmida (Key, in CSIRO).

stick-lac, branches and twigs with the dried lac insects (Hemiptera: Sternorrhyncha: Coccoidea) on them (T-B); see lac.

stigma (pl., **stigmata**), spiracle, q.v. (T-B; Leftwich); pterostigma, q.v., of wing (T-B; Leftwich); in Fulgoroidea (Hemiptera: Auchenorrhyncha), a thickened colored spot in the forewing just behind apex of the costal cell (O'Brien, pers. comm.); on forewing of Hesperiidae (Lepidoptera), brand, q.v. (T-B).

stigma metathoracis, in adult Diptera, posterior (meta-) thoracic spiracle, q.v. (T-B).

stigma plate, in ticks (Acari: Ixodida), the plate in which a spiracle is set (Matheson).

stigma vein, in adult Chalcidoidea (Hymenoptera), stigmal vein, q.v. (T-B).

stigmal border, in adult Psocoptera, a pigmented and somewhat sclerotized posterior border of the pterostigma in Psocidae and some other groups (transl. and shortened from "Metastigmalsaum" Enderlein, Roesler).

stigmal sensillum (of wing), in adult Chironomidae (Diptera), campaniform sensillum, q.v. (Saether).

stigmal vein, in adult Chalcidoidea and Scelionidae (Hymenoptera: Apocrita), a short vein extending posteriorly from the marginal vein of the wing, usually a little beyond the middle of the wing (Riek, in CSIRO; Borror et al.; Gauld and Bolton); see postmarginal vein.

stigmapophysis, in adult Psocoptera, small blunt process of radius and subcosta of forewing at base of pterostigma, under which the costa of the hind wing rests in repose (transl. of "stigmapophyse" Badonnel).

stigmasac, stigmapophysis, q.v. (Thornton, pers. comm.).

stigmasaum, in Psocoptera, stigmal border, q.v. (Mockford).

stigmatal bristle, in adult Diptera, proepimeral seta, q.v. (McAlpine).

stigmatal field, in larval Diptera, spiracular disc, q.v. (Peterson).

stigmatal line, in larval Lepidoptera, spiracular line, q.v. (T-B).

stigmatal spine, in some larval Diptera, an exsertile structure in the anal siphon consisting of the modified terminal spiracles (Philip).

stigmatic, of or pertaining to a stigma (T-B); see spiracular.

stigmatic cicatrix, or **scar,** the remains of an original spiracle after a moult (T-B, after Imms).

stigmatic cords, the spiracular branches when in the form of delicate cords (T-B, after Imms).

stigmatic furrow, in Coccoidea (Hemiptera: Sternorrhyncha), a trough which extends from the atrium of each spiracle to the cluster of stigmatic setae situated on the margin (Bimpel, Miller, and Davidson); see spiracular furrow.

stigmatiferous, bearing spiracles or stigmata (T-B).

stigmatonome, a blotch-shaped leaf mine caused by a larva feeding out in all directions (Hering); see blotch mine.

Stigmelloidea, Nepticuloidea, q.v. (Borror et al.).

stigmergy, in social insects, the guidance of work performed by individual colony members by the evidences of work previously accomplished rather than by direct signals from nestmates (Wilson, after Grassé).

stilt prolegs, unusually long prolegs which raise the larva when walking (T-B).

stilting, in *Schistocera* and other Acrididae (Orthoptera: Acrididae), extension of the legs at high temperatures, raising the body off the ground permitting circulation of air all around the body (Chapman).

stimuli, the small acute spines on some larvae, especially wood borers (T-B); in ♂ Ephemeroptera, penial spines, q.v. (Tuxen, after Eaton).

stimulus, any of the distrubing forces or conditions in an organism, external or internal, which tend to cause a response (T-B).

stimulus filtering, process by which stimuli pass through a hierarchically organized neural information system ultimately to the release of a particlular behavioral response (Matthews and Matthews).

stimulus generalization, a learning phenomenon in which a response is elicted from a stimulus similar to, but not identical with, the original conditioning stimulus (Matthews and Matthews).

sting, in ♀ Aculeata (Hymenoptera), modified ovipositor, used in defense, hunting, and aggression (Tuxen).

sting barb, in ♀ Apocrita (Hymenoptera), subdivisions on (usually) gonapophyses VIII (Tuxen, after E. L. Smith).

sting bulb, in ♀ Hymenoptera, bulb of sting, q.v. (Tuxen).

sting palp, in ♀ Hymenoptera, gonoplac, q.v. (Tuxen).

sting sheath, in ♀ Hymenoptera, gonoplac, q.v. (Tuxen).

stinging Hymenoptera, Aculeata, q.v. (Borror et al.).

stingless bee, a bee belonging to the subfamily Meliponinae (Hymenoptera: Apidae) (Wilson; Eickwort, pers. comm.).

stink gland, gland secreting substances with disagreeable odor that acts to deter would-be predators (T-B; Leftwich); see cervical glands, defensive glands, and metathoracic scent glands.

stipa, in ♂ Hymenoptera, parapenial lobe, q.v. (Tuxen, after Radoszkowski).

stipes (pl., **stipites**), the basic sclerite of the maxilla, immediately distad to the cardo and bearing the galea, lacinia, and maxillary palpus, articulating partly with the head, partly to the cardo (T-B; Peterson; Harbach and Knight; Chapman); in ♂ Protura, basal, unpaired part of phallus to which the paired styli are articulated (Tuxen, after Berlese); in ♀ Protura, supposed (nonexistent) basal part of acrogynium (Tuxen, after Berlese); in ♂ Hymenoptera, gonoforceps, q.v. (Tuxen, after Boulangé), parapenial lobe, q.v. (Tuxen, after Hagens), gonocoxites + gonostyli + volsellae (Tuxen, after Kluge), gonocoxites + gonostyli (Tuxen, after Morice), or gonocoxites, q.v. (Tuxen, after Thomson).

stipital, of or pertaining to the stipes or stipites (T-B).

stipital flexor, the muscle that bends or flexes the stipes (T-B).

stipital lobe, in some larval Notodontidae (Lepidoptera), a projection of the stipes, variously shaped, sometimes larger than the rest of the maxilla, surface frequently with numerous acanthae and microtrichia (Grimes and Neunzig).

stipital region, prementum, q.v. (T-B).

stipital sclerite, in larval Ichneumonoidea (Hymenoptera), sclerotic rod that supports the maxilla ventrally (Gauld and Bolton).

stipitate, supported on a stalk or pedicel (T-B).

stipites labii, labial stipes (Peterson); see prementum.

stipitocardinal, of or pertaining to both the stipes and the cardo (T-B).

stipitocardinal rod, in adult Culicidae (Diptera), the fused cardo and stipes (Harbach and Knight).

stipodema, in specialized Diptera, the apodeme of the labrum (T-B, after MacGillivray).

stipple, stippled, stippling, numerous points or dots; shading effects produced by dots, points or other small marks (Peterson).

stipula (pl., **stipulae**), prementum, q.v. (T-B, after MacGillivray).

stirofos, $C_{10}H_9Cl_4O_4P$, a synthetic insecticide; an organophosphate, 2-chloro-1-(2,4,5-trichlorophenyl)vinyl dimethyl phosphate; slightly toxic to mammals; acute oral LD_{50} for rats 4000 to 5000 mg/kg (Pfadt).

St. Louis encephalitis, a virus disease affecting the brain, producing languor, apathy, lethargy, and death; transmitted by certain Culicidae (Diptera) and mites (Acari) (Pfadt).

Stobbe's glands, in ♂ Noctuidae (Lepidoptera), special glands in the second abdominal segment producing an aphrodisiac pheromone dispersed by a brush of hairlike scales (Chapman).

stochastic theory of mass behavior, the theory that transition probabilities in the behavior of individual social insects are programmed to produce optimal mass responses of the colony as a whole, that the probabilities have been determined by the selection at the colony level, and that they represent a sensitive adaptation to the particular environmental conditions in which the species has existed during recent evolutionary time (Wilson).

stoma (pl., **stomata**), spiracle, q.v. (T-B).

stomach, midgut, q.v. (T-B).

stomach mouth, stomodaeal valve, q.v. (T-B, after Snodgrass).

stomachic, of or pertaining to the stomach (T-B).

stomachic ganglion, hypocerebral ganglion, q.v. (T-B).

stomatodaeum, stomodeum, q.v. (T-B).

stomatogastric nervous system, ganglia and associated nerves innervating the foregut and midgut, including the frontal ganglion, hypocerebral ganglion, and ingluvial ganglia (Chapman).

stomatotheca, the part of the pupa covering the mouth structures (T-B).

Stomatopoda, order within the Malacostraca (Crustacea), including marine forms, possessing a large abdomen that is broader than the cephalothorax (Borror et al.).

stomodaeum, stomodeum, q.v.

stomodeal food, the partly digested food which is transferred from mouth to mouth by social insects (Tulloch); see trophallaxis.

stomodeal nervous system, stomatogastric nervous system, q.v. (T-B, after Snodgrass).

stomodeal trophallaxis, trophallaxis in which the material originates from the mouth (Wilson).

stomodeal valve, the cylindrical or funnel-shaped invagination of the posterior end of the stomodaeum into the midgut (T-B, after Snodgrass; Chapman).

stomodeum, foregut, q.v. (T-B, after Snodgrass; Chapman); in the embryo, the anterior ectodermal invagination of the developing alimentary canal (T-B; Chapman).

stomogastric nerve, recurrent nerve, q.v. (T-B).

stomogastric nervous system, stomatogastric nervous system, q.v. (T-B).

stone brood, a disease of larval and adult honey bees (Hymenoptera:

Apidae), caused by the fungi *Aspergillus flavus* and, less frequently, *Aspergillus fumigatus,* in which diseased larvae usually die in the sealed stage, before pupation (Steinhaus and Martignoni).

stone centipede, a member of the order Lithobiomorpha (Chilopoda) (Borror et al.).

stonefly, a member of the order Plecoptera (Riek, in CSIRO).

storage excretion, storing the waste products of metabolism within the body in an insoluble form (Tulloch); see excretion.

storage pot, container of soft cerumen used for the storage of food in the nests of social bees (Hymenoptera: Apoidea), some of the pots constructed by the Meliponinae containing only honey (honey pot) and others only pollen (pollen pot) (Wilson).

straight run, the middle run made by a honey bee (Hymenoptera: Apidae) worker during the waggle dance and the element that contains most of the symbolic information concerning the location of the target outside the hive (Wilson).

strain, an infraspecific group of organisms having characteristic properties.

strainer, in nymphs of certain Ephemeroptera, a row of stiff hairs located on the foretibiae or on the mouthparts, used in straining out plankton (T-B, after Klots).

stramineous, stramineus (Latin), straw-colored, i.e., pale yellow (T-B, after Kirby and Spence).

strangulate, strongly constricted and contracted, as if by bands or cords, to form a waist (T-B).

strata, in ecology, groups of consocies (and animals not so grouped) occupying the recognizable vertical divisions of a uniform area (Folsom and Wardle).

stratal orientation, spatial orientation to resources or stresses that are extensive in a layer or vertical gradation (Matthews and Matthews, after Jander).

stratified, arranged or made up in layers.

Stratiomyoidea, superfamily within the infraorder Tabanomorpha (Diptera), including the Stratiomyidae, Xylomyidae, and Xylophagidae (McAlpine); see Tabanoidea.

Strepsiptera, endopterygote order of Neoptera (Insecta), with reduced mandibulate mouthparts, extreme development of the metathorax, reduced prothorax, without differentiated trochanters, adult males free-living, with hind wings and small elytriform forewings, females larviform, viviparous, with heteromorphosis during larval growth, the first instar free-living and active, later instars parasitic (T-B; Riek, in CSIRO).

stress, a syndrome of bodily changes, caused by some force, condition, or circumstance in or on an organism or on one of its physiological or anatomical systems (Steinhaus and Martignoni); see trauma.

stressor, any stimulus, or succession of stimuli, that tends to disrupt the normal homeostasis of an animal; factor that produces stress (Steinhaus and Martignoni).

stretch receptors, sensilla with multipolar nerve cells with free nerve endings, occurring in connective tissue or associated with the muscles, functioning as proprioreceptors, and stimulated by stretching (Chapman).

stria (pl., **striae**), in general, any fine longitudinal impressed line (T-B); in Coleoptera, a longitudinal depressed line or furrow, frequently punctured, extending from the base to the apex of the elytra (T-B); in adult Lepidoptera, a fine transverse line (T-B).

striarium, in adult Siphonaptera, a well defined area on the metepimeron or basal abdominal sternite with the striae arranged parallel to each other and placed particularly close together (Rothschild and Traub).

striate, striated, striatus (Latin), marked with parallel, fine, longitudinal, impressed lines or furrows (T-B; Harris, after Munz, Marchant and Charles, Jaeger, and R. W. Brown); see strigate and striolate.

striate band, in Protura, an anterior serrate line or lines on the dorsum and venter of abdominal segment VIII (Bellinger, pers. comm.).

striated band, in adult Arctiidae (Lepidoptera), tymbal, q.v.

striated border, regular layer of microvilli forming surface of cells adjacent to the lumen of midgut and Malpighian tubules (T-B, after Snodgrass; Leftwich; Chapman).

striated hem, striated border, q.v., of midgut (T-B).

striated muscle, muscle marked by minute transverse lines, including muscle in which the contraction is voluntary.

striate-punctate, having loose punctured striae (T-B).

striation, stria, q.v. (Saether).

Strickland Code, a code of nomenclature prepared by a committee of the British Association for the Advancement of Science under the secretaryship of H. E. Strickland and first published in 1842 (Mayr); see International Code of Zoological Nomenclature.

stridulate, to make a creaking, grating or hissing sound or noise, by rubbing 2 ridged or roughened surfaces against each other (T-B).

stridulating organ, structure(s) used in making sounds, in general, consisting of a file or filelike organ and an opposing scraper or rasp (T-B, after Imms); see sound-producing mechanisms.

stridulation, the sound produced by rubbing one surface or one structure upon or against another, both being suitably roughened (T-B); the act of stridulating or making creaking sounds (T-B), e.g, in certain Blaberidae (Blattaria) by rubbing the pronotum against the tegmina (Roth and Hartman).

stridulation mechanism, mechanism by which sounds are produced with stridulating organs (McAlpine); see file, plectrum, rasp, scraper, sound-producing mechanisms, stridulitrum, and stridulum.

stridulation organ, stridulating organ, q.v. (McAlpine).

stridulatory, connected with or of the nature of stridulation (T-B).

stridulatory file, file, q.v. (McAlpine).

stridulatory organs, stridulating organs, q.v. (CSIRO).

stridulitrum, in Heteroptera (Hemiptera), file, q.v., of stridulatory organ (Schuh, pers. comm.).

stridulum, in Orthoptera, file, q.v., in Acridoidea occurring on the hind femora, abdomen, or forewings, and in ♂ Ensifera occuring on the underside of Cu_2 of the wing (Otte, pers. comm.).

striga (pl., **strigae**), a narrow, transverse line or slender streak, either surface or impressed (T-B).

strigate, having narrow, transverse lines or streaks, either raised or impressed; composed of fine, short lines (T-B; Harris); see hatched, striate, and strigulate.

strigil, strigile, strigilis, scraper, q.v. (T-B); antennal cleaner, q.v. (T-B); in ♂ Corixidae (Hemiptera: Heteroptera), the peculiar structure on abdominal dorsum VI, sometimes shaped like a currycomb (T-B); in adult Lepidoptera, epiphysis, q.v. (Chapman); in adult Apocrita (Hymenoptera), a curved, comblike, moveable spur on the distal end of foretibia (T-B, after Comstock; Gauld and Bolton).

strigilation, the licking of secretions from the body of another animal (Wilson).

strigilator, any of various myrmecophiles or termitophiles that feed by licking the surface of the bodies of the ants (Hymenoptera: Formicidae), or termites (Isoptera), with which they live. e.g., the wingless cricket *Myrmecophila* (Orthoptera: Myrmecophilidae) (T-B, after W. M. Wheeler).

strigilla (pl., **strigillae**), in ♀ Siphonaptera, fine, usually circular ridges on inner wall of bulga and hilla (Tuxen, after Peus).

strigillate, stridulate, q.v. (T-B).

strigillation, stridulation, q.v. (T-B); see strigilation.

strigose, hispid, q.v. (T-B).

strigose lunate vitta, in *Ligyrocoris* (Hemiptera: Heteroptera: Lygaeidae), a crescent-shaped roughened area anteroventrally on the abdomen, functioning as a stridulitrum (T-B).

strigose ventral areas, in certain Pentatomidae (Hemiptera: Heteroptera), roughened ventral areas of abdominal sterna IV and V, producing sound when rubbed by the wartlike tubercles on the hind tibiae (T-B).

strigula, a fine short transverse mark or line (T-B).

strigulate, strigulated, finely or minutely strigate; with numerous short and fine transverse lines, either raised or impressed (T-B; Harris, after R. W. Brown); see striolate.

striolate, striolatus (Latin), minutely or finely striate; with numerous parallel and very fine longitudinal impressed lines or furrows (T-B; Harris, after R. W. Brown); see strigulate.

striole, a rudimentary stria (T-B).

striopunctate, punctatostriatus, q.v. (T-B).

stripe, a longitudinal streak of color different from the ground color (T-B).

strips, in ♂ Trichoptera, sclerotized productions of the phallic shield or abdominal segment IX continuing in the same plane as the genital chamber membranes (Morse); see periphaliic processes.

strongly, markedly or decidedly (T-B).

Strophandria, Tenthredinoidea, q.v. (Hennig, after Crampton, Ross).

strophandrous copulation, in ♂ Tenthredinoidea and some Xyelidae

(Hymenoptera), entire genitalia rotated 180° permitting copulation end-to-end (Tuxen, after Crampton); see orthandrous copulation.

strophe, spiral curling of the parts of the postabdomen of males of higher Diptera to bring the parts into a protected position at rest (Steyskal).

structural colors, colors produced by the scattering, interference, or diffraction of light (T-B; Chapman).

structure, an organ, appendage, or part (T-B).

struma (pl., **strumae**), among larval Coccinellidae (Coleoptera), a shortened parascolus usually appearing as a distinct moundlike projection of the body wall bearing a few chalazae (Peterson, after Gage).

strut(s), in ♂ Coleoptera, paired or unpaired processes (apophyses, apodemes) of penis or tegmen (Tuxen); in some ♂ Osmylidae (Planipennia), baculum, q.v. (Tuxen, after Killington); in ♂ Aradidae (Hemiptera: Heteroptera), inferior process, q.v. (Tuxen, after Leston); in ♂ Reduviidae (including Phymatinae) (Hemiptera: Heteroptera), sclerotizations of distal segment of phallus (true endosoma) into wall of distal part of ductus seminis, beginning proximally at level of distal end of ligamentary processes (pedicle) (Tuxen, after Singh-Pruthi); in adult Chironomidae (Diptera), apodeme, phallapodeme, superior volsella, sternapodeme, or coxapodeme, q.v. (Saether).

stump vein, in adult Diptera, incomplete basal connection of fourth radial vein with the third radial vein (McAlpine).

stupeous, stupose, q.v. (T-B).

stupose, covered with tufts of hair or matted filaments.

stupulose, stupulosus, finely stupose (T-B).

stylate, having or provided with a style or stylus (T-B); stylelike (Borror et al.).

style(s), in ♀ Odonata, a pair of tactile, fingerlike processes apically on lateral gonapophyses (Tuxen); in ♀ Caelifera (Orthoptera), the terminal part of the ventral ovipositor valves (Agarwala); in ♂ Auchenorrhyncha and ♂ Heteroptera (Hemiptera), parameres, q.v. (Tuxen, after Ribaut); in ♀ Coleoptera, styli, q.v. (Tuxen); in ♂ Hesperiidae (Lepidoptera), a projecting process of inner face of dorsal part of valva, being part of ampula or costa (Tuxen, after Rambur); in ♂ *Erebia* (Lepidoptera: Satyridae), styles (Tuxen, after Chapman); in adult Diptera, stylus, q.v., or antenna (Leftwich); in larval Chironomidae (Diptera), apical or slightly subapical peg- to bladelike style on second antennal segment (Saether); see stylus.

styled valves, in ♂ Diptera, gonopods, q.v. (Tuxen).

stylet(s), a small style or stiff process (T-B); a needlelike structure (Borror et al.); in ♂ Plecoptera, accessory, lateral, sclerotic processes of supraanal lobe (Tuxen); in Thysanoptera, Hemiptera, Anoplura (Phthiraptera), and some Diptera, one or more of the mouthparts modified for piercing and/or sucking and/or injection of saliva (T-B; Chapman); in ♀ Auchenorrhyncha (Hemiptera), first gonapophyses, q.v. (Tuxen); in ♀ Coleoptera, styli, q.v. (Tuxen); in ♂ Hesperiidae (Lepidoptera), uncus or tegumen + uncus (Tuxen, after Rambur); in ♀ Aculeata (Hymenoptera), the fused portions of second gonapophyses (Tuxen, after Snodgrass) (see sting).

stylet groove, in Heteroptera (Hemiptera), labial groove, q.v. (Štys, pers. comm.).

stylet sac, in Anoplura (Phthiraptera), a ventral diverticulum extending from the buccal funnel to the posterior region of the head (T-B, after Imms; Calaby, in CSIRO).

stylet sheath, in many plant-feeding Hemiptera, a more or less permanent duct, surrounding the mouthparts between the plant surface and the phloem, composed of tanned lipoprotein derived from the saliva (Gilmour, in CSIRO); in ♀ Aculeata (Hymenoptera), third valvulae, q.v. (T-B, after Imms).

styli genitales, in ♂ Auchenorrhyncha (Hemiptera), styles, q.v. (Tuxen).

styli linguales, in Diplopoda, the supporting rods of the hypopharynx (T-B, after Packard).

stylifer, in ♂ Hesperiidae (Lepidoptera), style (Tuxen, after Chapman).

styliform, in the shape of a stylus (T-B); terminating in a long slender point, like the aristate antennae of some Diptera (T-B).

styliform appendage, in Psocoptera, (chisellike) lacinia, q.v. (T-B, after Ribaga).

styliger, in ♂ Ephemeroptera, united coxites of forceps of abdominal sternum IX (Tuxen, after Snodgrass); in ♂ Isoptera, basal structure of abdominal sternum IX bearing styli (Tuxen, after Crampton).

styliger plate, in ♂ Ephemeroptera, styliger, q.v. (Tuxen).

stylocavernula (pl., **stylocavernulae**), in some ♂ Bittacidae (Mecoptera), small, probably sensory organ on stylus (Tuxen, after Tjeder).

styloconic sensillum, an olfactory cuticular sense organ consisting of one or more pegs of the basiconic type elevated on a style or cone (T-B, after Imms).

styloides, in ♂ Gerridae (Hemiptera: Heteroptera), parandria, q.v. (Tuxen, after Matsuda).

styloids, in ♀ Heteroptera (Hemiptera), posteroexternal processes of gonocoxites IX, more or less developed and frequently missing (Tuxen, after Ekblom).

Stylopidae, either one family within the Strepsiptera or sometimes synonymous with the Strepsiptera when the group is considered a family of Coleoptera (CSIRO; Leftwich); see Stylopoidea.

stylopization, parasitization by ♀ and ♂ puparia of Strepsiptera (T-B, after Wardle; Kinzelbach).

stylopized, parasitized by Strepsiptera (T-B; Leftwich).

Stylopoidea, superfamily for the Strepsiptera when treated as a group within the Coleoptera (Brittion, after Crowson, in CSIRO).

Stylops, Strepsiptera, q.v., or a genus within the Stylopidae (Strepsiptera) (T-B; Leftwich).

stylose, bearing a style (T-B, after Curran).

stylostome, the tube formed by the host as a result of the feeding of a chigger; in secreting salivary fluids, the chigger partially digests the skin tissues, which induces the host to form a proteinaceous tube walling off the injury (Pfadt).

stylotrachealis, a long tube bearing a stigma arising from the head case as in some pupal Diptera (T-B).

stylus (pl., **styli**), a small, pointed, nonarticulated process (T-B); distal part of gonopod, moveably attached to basal segment of gonopod (coxopodite) or to abdominal sternum (T-B, after Imms; Tuxen; Chapman); in ♂ Protura, the distal paired part of phallus consisting of basistylus and acrostylus Tuxen); in ♀ Protura, distal part of squama genitalis (Tuxen); in many Archaeognatha, coxal stylets, q.v. (Sturm, pers. comm., after Janetschek); in ♂ Ephemeroptera, genostyles, q.v. (Tuxen, after Crampton); in ♀ Odonata, styles, q.v. (Tuxen, after Walker); in ♀ Blattopteroidea, apophyses internae, q.v. (Tuxen, after Berlese); in ♂ Coccoidea (Hemiptera: Sternorhyncha), penis sheath, q.v. (Tuxen); in ♂ Heteroptera (Hemiptera), parameres, q.v. (Tuxen, after Seidenstücker); in ♂ *Neoneuromus* (Megaloptera), catoprocessus, q.v. (Tuxen, after Acker); in ♂ *Sisyra* (Sisyridae) and *Dilara* (Dilaridae) (Planipennia), entoprocessus, q.v. (Tuxen, after Acker); in ♂ Psychopsidae and Hemerobiidae (Planipennia), arcessus, q.v. (Tuxen, after Acker); in ♂ Diptera, dististylus, q.v., (in Muscomorpha) surstyli, q.v. (Tuxen), or paraphallus, q.v. (Tuxen, after Rohdendorf); in adult Diptera, e.g., Stratiomyidae, the last flagellomere of antenna (T-B; McAlpine) (see arista); in ♂ Chironomidae (Diptera), gonostylus, q.v. (Saether); in ♂ Siphonaptera, telomere, q.v. (Tuxen); in ♂ Hymenoptera, genostylus, q.v. (Tuxen, after Berlese); see style and stylet.

stylus analis, in Auchenorrhyncha (Hemiptera), anal style, q.v. (Tuxen).

sub-, Latin prefix; under, slightly less than, or not quite so (T-B: Harris).

subacute, moderately acute (T-B).

subadult, any individual beyond the earliest juvenile stages but not yet sexually mature (Christiansen and Bellinger).

subaduncate, somewhat hooked or curved (T-B).

subalar, below the wing (T-B).

subalar area, in adult Hymenoptera, subalar prominence, q.v. (Gauld and Bolton).

subalar knob, in adult Diptera, greater ampulla, q.v. (McAlpine).

subalar muscles, muscles arising from the coxa and epimeron of a wing-bearing segment and inserting on the subalare (T-B, after Snodgrass; Borror et al.).

subalar pit, in some adult Hymenoptera, an impression behind the slightly below subalar prominence (Gauld and Bolton).

subalar prominence, in some adult Hymenoptera, complexly raised portion of mesepisternum below the wing insertion (Gauld and Bolton).

subalar ridge, in adult Diptera, subalare, q.v. (McAlpine).

subalar sclerite, a sclerite of the pleural region below the wing (T-B, after Crampton); subalare, q.v. (Chapman).

subalare, the epimeral epipleurite, located behind the pleural wing process, giving insertion to the posterior pleural muscle of the wing (T-B, after Snodgrass; Chapman); see basalare.

subalifer, pleural wing process, q.v. (McAlpine).

subanal, ventrad of the anus (Peterson).

subanal appendages, structures of the caudal segment located below the anus (Peterson); in larval Megalodontoidea (Hymenoptera: Symphyta), paired segmented structures, located ventral to the lateral ends of the anal slit (Gauld and Bolton).

subanal hook, in ♂ Plecoptera, copulatory hook, q.v. (Tuxen, after Frison).

subanal lamina, paraproct, q.v. (T-B, after Heymons).

subanal lobe(s), in ♂ Plecoptera, subanal plates, q.v. (Tuxen, after Needham and Claassen); in larval Symphyta (Hymenoptera), membranous lobe of abdominal segment X below the anus (Gauld and Bolton); see suranal lobe.

subanal microtrichia, in adult Lepidoptera, a dense concentration of often curved, minute spines along the ventral anal margin of the forewing which intermesh into similar spines on the metascutum to hold the forewing at rest (Davis, after Common); see metascutal microtrichia.

subanal plate, in Orthoptera, subgenital plate, q.v. (T-B); in ♀ Diptera, ventral plate of proctiger (Tuxen, after Crampton).

subanal plates, in ♂ Plecoptera, a pair of sclerotized plates behind abdominal sternum X (if this is present) (Tuxen); in ♀ Plecoptera, a pair of large plates behind sternum X (if this is present) (Tuxen); in ♀ Isoptera, paraprocts, q.v. (Tuxen, after Fuller); in ♀ Hepialidae (Lepidoptera), central, ventral, paired sclerites of genital region (transl. "plaques sous-anales" Bourgogne, in Tuxen).

subanal retinaculum, in Lepidoptera, a row of stiff scales near the anal margin on the ventral surface of the forewing which catch the subcostal pseudofrenulum in some Gracillariidae (Davis); see retinaculum.

subanal styli, in ♂ Isoptera, styli, q.v. (Tuxen).

subanale (pl., **subanalia**), in adult Mecoptera, abdominal sternum XI covering anus from below (Tuxen); in ♀ Neuropteroidea, abdominal sternum XI covering anus from below (Tuxen).

subantennal groove, in adult Diptera, antennal groove, q.v. (T-B, after Curran).

subantennal process, in some Derbidae (Hemiptera: Auchenorrhyncha: Fulgoroidea), a foliaceous extrusion of the gena under the antennae (Fennah).

subantennal suture, in certain insects (e.g., Blattaria), a prominent suture extending downward from each antennal suture to the subgenal suture (T-B, after Snodgrass); see frontogenal suture.

subapical, located just proximad of the apex (Borror et al.).

subapical lines, in many Flatidae (Hemiptera: Auchenorrhyncha: Fulgoroidea), one or 2 continuous lines of crossveins near the apical border of the forewings (Metcalf).

subapical lobe, in ♂ *Culex* (Diptera: Culicidae), a lobe at apical end of basistylus (coxite), when this is divided into a dorsal and ventral flap (T-B; Tuxen; Harbach and Knight, after Edwards).

subapical sclerite, in ♂ Siphonaptera, sclerotization of ventroapical margin of palliolum (Tuxen, after Peus).

subapical style, in larval Chironomidae (Diptera), style, q.v. (Saether).

subappendiculae, in ♂ Ephemeroptera, penial spines, q.v. (Tuxen, after Crampton).

subapterous, almost wingless; with rudimentary wings only (T-B); see micropterous.

subarcus, in some ♂ Osmylidae (Planipennia), arch-formed transverse structure close above parameres (Tuxen, after Tjeder).

subarticle, in Archaeognatha, subdivision of an antennal segment (Wygodzinsky); see annulus and flagellomere.

subbasal, located just distad of the base (Borror et al.).

subbasal process, in ♂ *Culex* (Diptera: Culicidae), small peglike structure arising ventrally just above the basal lateral arm of paraproct, articulating with lateral basal process of the outer division of the lateral plate (Harbach and Knight, after Sirivanakarn).

subcallus (pl., **subcalli**), in some Tabanomorpha (Diptera), anterior shining area on frons immediately above the insertion of the antennae (Pechumen and Teskey, in McAlpine).

subcardo, proximal sclerite of cardo (T-B).

subcercal plates, in Ephemeroptera, paraprocts, q.v. (Tuxen, after Crampton).

subclass, a major subdivision of a class, containing a group of related orders (T-B; Borror et al.).

subclavate, somewhat thickened toward tip, but not quite club-shaped (T-B).

subclypeal pump, in certain adult Diptera, cibarial pump, q.v. (T-B).

subclypeal tube, in certain Diptera, cibarium, q.v. (T-B).

subcontiguous, not quite contiguous or touching (T-B).

subcordate, somewhat resembling the shape of a heart (T-B).

subcoriaceous, somewhat leathery (T-B).

subcorneal, lying under or beneath the cornea (T-B).

subcortical, beneath the bark of trees (T-B).

subcosta (Sc), the second, usually unbranched, longitudinal wing vein posterior to the costa, articulating basally with the first axillary sclerite (T-B, after Comstock; Chapman); in Hymenoptera, radius, q.v. (T-B, after Packard); see subcostal vein.

subcostal area, in Tingidae (Hemiptera: Heteroptera), anterior submarginal area of forewing (T-B; Drake and Ruhoff).

subcostal blood sinus, in wings of ♂ Embiidina a tapered sinus that becomes turgid with blood pressure during flight in position of subcostal vein (Ross).

subcostal break, in adult Diptera, costal break just proximal to where the subcosta joins the costa or to the point where it would join the costa if the subcosta was complete (McAlpine).

subcostal cell, any one of the cells margined anteriorly by the subcosta (T-B).

subcostal crossvein, in *Progomphus* (Odonata: Gomphidae), a single crossvein between subcosta and radius next the body or proximad of all other antenodal crossveins (T-B, after Garman).

subcostal fold or furrow, the depression between the costa and the radius (T-B).

subcostal plate, in Neoptera and Odonata, the basal wing sclerite from which costa and subcosta originate (Ross et al., after Hamilton).

subcostal-radial crossvein (sc-r), crossvein between subcosta and radius (McAlpine).

subcostal retinaculum, in adult frenate Lepidoptera, a cuticular flap or group of specialized scales on the ventral side of the subcostal or costal area of the forewing engaging the frenulum of the hind wing, usually being developed in the ♂ (Braun, after Tillyard).

subcostal sclerite, in adult Diptera, sclerite linking the subcosta with the first axillary sclerite (McAlpine).

subcostal seta, in adult Culicidae (Diptera), one of the setae occurring in a group on the base of the subcosta on the ventral surface of the wing (Harbach and Knight, after Knight and Laffoon).

subcostal vein, in adult Diptera, first radial vein (R_1) (T-B, after Schiner); in adult Lepidoptera, radius, q.v. (T-B); see subcosta.

subcoxa, the proximal part of the limb basis or the coxa, when differentiated or divided from the coxa (e.g., Collembola), usually incorporated into the pleural wall of the body segment (T-B, after Snodgrass); in Archaeognatha and Zygentoma, coxite, q.v. (Tuxen, after Silvestri).

subcoxal, lying under or below the coxa; of or pertaining to the subcoxa (T-B).

subcoxal pleurites, in the Chilopoda, small sclerites of various shapes more or less closely associated with the bases of the coxae (T-B, after Snodgrass).

subcranial cavity, in adult Diptera, ventral cavity of cranium from which protrude the mouthparts (McAlpine).

subcranial margin, in adult Diptera, margin of subcranial cavity (Colless and McAlpine, in CSIRO).

subcristate, with a moderately elevated ridge or keel on the pronotum, as in some Orthoptera (T-B).

subcutaneous, under or beneath the integument (T-B).

subcuticle, endocuticle, q.v. (Leftwich).

subcuticular, occurring or found under the cuticle (T-B); under the cuticle (T-B).

subdiscal vein, in adult Hymenoptera, vein forming the posterior margin the third discoidal cell, i.e., first branch of anterior cubitus (CuA) (Riek, in CSIRO; Borror et al.).

subdiscoidal vein, subdiscal vein, q.v. (Borror et al.).

subdorsal, below the dorsum and above the spiracles (T-B).

subdorsal incrassation, in adult Siphonaptera, an elliptical incrassation arising well below the dorsal margin of the frons and some distance above and in front of the base of the antennal fossa (Rothschild and Traub).

subdorsal line, in larval Lepidoptera, a longitudinal line to the side of the dorsal line and between it and the lateral line, or, if there is an addorsal line, between that and the lateral line (T-B).

subdorsal retinaculum, in adult frenate Lepidoptera, a tuft of hairs or row of stiff scales arising near the ventral base of the forewing which engages the frenulum from the hind wing; normally developed along cubital vein in ♀ (Braun, after Tillyard).

subdorsal ridge, in slug caterpillars (Lepidoptera: Limacodidae), a raised longitudinal line along the subdorsal row of abdominal tubercles (T-B).

subepaulet, in adult Diptera, humeral plate, q.v. (Colless and Mc Alpine, in CSIRO).

subepidermal, lying below or beneath the epidermis (T-B).

subepidermal nerve plexus, in soft-skinned larvae, a mass of nerve fibers from multipolar nerve cells beneath the epidermis (Chapman).

subequal, similar, but not equal in size, form or length (T-B; Borror et al.).

suberect, not quite upright (T-B).

suberoded, suberose, suberosus, having the appearance of being gnawed (T-B).

subesophageal ganglion, suboesophageal ganglion, q.v. (Borror et al.).

subfalcate, a little excavated below the apex, in the wing (T-B).

subfamily (pl., **subfamilies**), major subdivision of a family, containing a related group of tribes or genera, whose name ends in "-inae" (T-B; Borror et al.); a rank of the family group below family (ICZN); a taxon of the rank of subfamily (ICZN).

subfamily name, a scientific name of a taxon at the rank of subfamily (ICZN).

subfossorial, adapted for digging but not greatly modified (T-B).

subfrontal, close to the front; immediately behind the anterior margin (T-B).

subfrontal shoot, in Orthoptera, a dusky band on the hind wing of grasshoppers just back from the frontal margin of the wing and extending nearly to the base (T-B, after Walden).

subfulcrum, a sclerite between mentum and palpiger, being rarely present (T-B).

subfusiform, not quite fusiform (T-B).

subgalea, parastipes, q.v. (T-B).

subgena, the usually narrow lateral margin of the cranium, below the gena in hypognathous insects, set off by the subgenal sulcus above the gnathal appendages, consisting of the pleurostoma and hypostoma (Chapman).

subgenal, lying below the gena, of or pertaining to the subgena (T-B).

subgenal bridge, hypostomal bridge, q.v. (Teskey, in McAlpine).

subgenal margin, subgena, q.v. (Saether).

subgenal region, subgena, q.v. (T-B, after Snodgrass).

subgenal ridge, an internal ridge formed by the inward projection of the subgenal sulcus (T-B, after Snodgrass).

subgenal sulcus, the lateral submarginal groove of the cranium just above the bases of the gnathal appendages, extending between the anterior tentorial pit and the posterior tentorial pit (Chapman, after Snodgrass).

subgenal suture, subgenal sulcus, q.v. (T-B, after Snodgrass).

subgeneric name, a scientific name of a taxon of the rank of subgenus (T-B; ICZN)

subgeniculate, not quite geniculate (T-B).

subgenital lamina, in Orthoptera, subgenital plate, q.v. (T-B).

subgenital lobe, in ♀ Phthiraptera, membranous or sclerotized lobe extending from abdominal sternum VIII to cover genital opening (Tuxen, after Schmutz; Lyal); in ♂ Phasmida, poculum, q.v. (Key, pers. comm.); in ♀ Phasmida, operculum, q.v (Tuxen, after Snodgrass).

subgenital plate, in adult insects, a plate below the genitalia (T-B, after Tillyard; Tuxen, after Snodgrass); in ♀ Ephemeroptera, produced part of abdominal sternum VII (Tuxen, after Walker); in most ♂ Plecoptera, produced part of abdominal sternum IX covering gonopore (Tuxen); in most ♀ Plecoptera, sternum VIII (Zwick, pers. comm.); in ♀ Nemourinae (Plecoptera: Nemouridae), modified sternum VII (Zwick, pers. comm.); in ♀ Dermaptera, the enlarged abdominal sternum VII forming floor of genital chamber (Tuxen, after Nel); in ♂ Grylloblattodea, left coxopodite, q.v. (Tuxen); in ♂ Blattopteroidea, abdominal sternum VII of females and abdominal sternum IX of males (Alsop, pers. comm., after McKittrick; Boudreaux); in ♂ Orthoptera, ninth sternal lobe (Tuxen); in ♀ Orthoptera, abdominal sternum IX (Key, pers. comm.); in ♀ Caelifera, abdominal sternum VIII (Tuxen); in ♂ Embiidina, abdominal sternum VIII (Tuxen, after Imms); in ♀ Embiidina, abdominal sternum VIII (Tuxen, after Imms); in ♂ Zoraptera, abdominal sternum VIII (Tuxen, after Gurney); in ♀ Psocoptera, lamina subgenitalis, q.v. (Tuxen); in Phthiraptera, one or more well-sclerotized sternal plates lying ventral to genital chamber (Tuxen); in ♂ Auchenorrhyncha (Hemiptera), genital plates, q.v. (Tuxen); in ♂ Psyllidae (Hemiptera: Auchenorrhyncha), abdominal sternum IX (Tuxen, after Stough); in ♂ Aleyrodidae (Hemiptera: Sternorrhyncha), abdominal sternum IX (Tuxen); in ♀ Aphididae (Hemiptera: Sternorrhyncha), genital plate, q.v. (Tuxen); in Heteroptera (Hemiptera), any ♂ or ♀ abdominal sternum (usually VII, in ♀ Enicocephalidae VIII), or a specialized part of it, produced caudad to cover genital segments, genitalia, or genital opening (Štys, pers. comm.); in ♂ Miridae (Hemiptera: Heteroptera), inferior process, q.v. (Tuxen, after Carvalho and Southwood); in ♂ Neuropteroidea, abdominal sternum IX, q.v. (Tuxen, after Morton); in ♂ Coniopterygidae (Planipennia), hypandrium, q.v. (Tuxen, after Withycombe); in ♀ *Neuronema* and *Hemerobius* (Planipennia: Hemerobiidae), postgenitale, q.v. (Tuxen, after

Tjeder); in ♂ *Boreus* (Mecoptera: Boreidae), abdominal sternum IX (Tuxen); in ♀ Mecoptera, subgenitale, q.v. (Tuxen, after Carpenter), separate or fused sclerotized posterior extensions of abdominal sternum VIII (Byers); in ♀ Tipulidae (Diptera), hypogynium, q.v. (McAlpine); in ♂ Hydroptilidae (Trichptera), sclerotized oval or U-shaped structure ventrad of phallus, q.v. (Kelley); in ♀ Lepidoptera, lamella antevaginalis, q.v. (transl. "subgenitalplatte" Klapálek, in Tuxen); in ♂ Hymenoptera, abdominal sternum IX (Tuxen, after Dreisbach); in ♀ Hymenoptera, abdominal sternum VII (Tuxen).

subgenital process, in ♀ Phthiraptera, subgenital lobe, q.v. (Tuxen, after Clay; Lyal).

subgenital scale, in ♀ Coleophoridae (Lepidoptera), lodix (Tuxen, after Toll).

subgenital valve, in ♂ Mecoptera, hypovalvae, q.v. (Tuxen, after Crampton).

subgenitale, in ♀ Neuroptera, subgenital plate, covering abdominal segment VIII from below (Tuxen); in ♀ Mecoptera, plate covering abdominal segment IX (in Bittacidae also VIII) from below (Tuxen).

subgenual organ, a chordotonal organ in the proximal part of the tibia that is sensitive to vibrations (T-B; Chapman).

subgenus (pl., **subgenera**), a major subdivision of the genus, containing a group of related species, whose name is capitalized and placed in parentheses following the generic name (Borror et al.); the rank of the genus group below genus (ICZN); a taxon at the rank of subgenus (ICZN).

subgenus name, subgeneric name, q.v. (ICZN).

subglobose, not quite globose (T-B).

subglobular, not quite globular (T-B).

subhamuli (sing., **suhamulus**), in ♂ Siphonaptera, a pair of sclerites distad of the hamuli (Tuxen, after Peus).

subharpal plate, in ♂ *Hesperia* (Lepidoptera: Hesperiidae), sclerotized plate in median, proximal region of valva (Tuxen, after Warren).

subhumeral microtrichia, in adult Lepidoptera, a dense patch of minute spines on the ventral surface of the humeral sclerite of the forewing intermeshing with the mesepimeral microtrichia and holding the forewings at rest (Davis).

subhypodermal colors, subcutaneous colors contained in the fatbody and hemolymph (T-B, after Imms).

subhypostomal sclerite(s), in larval Muscomorpha (Diptera), anteroventral sclerite or pair of sclerites between the anterior arms of the intermediate sclerite (Ferrar).

subimaginal, of or pertaining to the subimago (T-B).

subimago (pl., **subimagoes**, **subimagines**), in Ephemeroptera, the winged developmental stage immediately preceding the reproductively mature adult (imago) (Peters, pers. comm.).

subintegumental scolophore, sense organ in which the nerve ending is free within the body cavity (T-B, after Comstock).

subjective synonym, each of 2 or more synonyms based on different name-bearing types (ICZN).

sublabrum, epipharynx, q.v. (T-B).

sublamina, in ♂ Blattopteroidea, hypophallus, q.v. (Tuxen, after Crampton).

sublateral, just inside the lateral margin.

sublateral bristles, in adult Diptera, bristles situated in a line with the intraalars but in front of the suture; the anterior 2 are sometimes included as posthumerals, but the term is deceptive (T-B, after Curran).

sublateral line, longitudinal line lying between the median line or meson and the lateral line (McAlpine).

subligula, in ♂ Lepidoptera, subscaphium, q.v. (Tuxen).

sublingual, lying beneath the tongue (T-B).

sublingual gland, in the honey bee (Hymenoptera: Apidae), ventral pharyngeal gland, q.v. (T-B, after Bordas).

submacropterous, of wings, slightly reduced and probably functional; in Heteroptera (Hemiptera), condition of the wings in which the corium and clavus of the forewings are fully developed with the membrane being slightly to greatly reduced, the hind wings generally being functional (Slater); see brachypterous.

submargin, the part of a surface just within the margin (T-B).

submarginal cell, in adult Hymenoptera, one or more cells of the wing lying immediately behind the marginal cells (Borror et al.).

submarginal dorsal tubercle, in Coccidae (Hemiptera: Sternorrhyncha: Coccoidea), circular slcerotized tubercle surrounding a central invaginated duct, located in dorsal submarginal row (Kosztarab and Kozár).

submarginal striae, proplegmatium, q.v. (Peterson).

submarginal tubercle, in Coccoidea (Hemiptera: Sternorrhyncha), submarginal dorsal tubercle, q.v. (T-B).

submarginal vein, in adult Chalcidoidea (Hymenoptera), a vein immediately behind and paralleling the costal margin of the wing (T-B, after Comstock; Riek, in CSIRO; Borror et al.); see marginal vein and postmarginal vein.

submedia, second axillary sclerite, q.v. (T-B, after MacGillivray).

submedian cell, in adult Hymenoptera, cell immediately posterior to fused media (M) and cubitus anterior (CuA), in the basal posterior portion of the wing (Borror et al.; Riek, in CSIRO).

submedian interspace, in the forewings of Lepidoptera, the area between the cubitus anterior (CuA) and the first anal vein (1A) (T-B).

submedian lobes (of fulcrum), in ♂ Siphonaptera, lobus fulcri medialis, q.v. (Tuxen, after Peus).

submedian mesal lobes (of apodemal strut), in ♂ Siphonaptera, lobus fulcri medialis, q.v. (Tuxen, after Peus).

submental, pertaining to the submentum (T-B).

submental peduncle, gulamentum, q.v. (T-B).

submental plate, in larval Chironomidae (Diptera), ventromental plate, q.v. (Saether).

submentum, the proximal division of the postmentum, by means of which the labium is attached to the head (T-B; Chapman, after Snodgrass); in larval Coleoptera, an unpaired median area lying approximately between the maxillary cardines on the underside of the head (Peterson, after Böving and Craighead); in larval Chironomidae (Diptera), gulamentum, q.v. (Saether); see mentum.

subnodal sector, in adult Odonata, radial sector (R$_s$), q.v. (T-B).

subnodus, in adult Odonata, an oblique crossvein, the continuation of the nodus below the first radial vein (T-B, after Tillyard).

subnymph, the resting or pupal stage of ♀ Coccoidea (Hemiptera: Sternorrhyncha) (T-B); see pseudopupa.

subocellate, spotted as if with ocellate spots without the pupil (T-B).

subocular, beneath or below the eye (T-B).

subocular sulcus, in certain Orthoptera, a groove extending from the circumocular sulcus to the subgenal sulcus beneath the compound eye (Chapman, after Snodgrass); in adult Hymenoptera, malar sulcus, q.v. (Gauld and Bolton); see frontogenal suture.

subocular suture, subocular sulcus, q.v. (T-B, after Snodgrass).

suboesophageal, lying under or beneath the oesophagus (T-B).

suboesophageal body, in the insect embryo, a group of large binucleate cells of mesodermal origin closely associated with the posterior end of the stomodeum (Chapman).

suboesophageal commissure, postoesophageal commissure, q.v. (T-B, after Snodgrass).

suboesophageal ganglion, ganglionic center of the head lying beneath the oesophagus, formed by the fusion of the ganglia of the mandibular, maxillary, and labial segments (T-B; Chapman).

suborbital, in larval Chironomidae (Diptera), cephalic seta S6 situated on gena anterior and slightly ventral to eye spots (Saether).

suborder, a major subdivision of an order, containing a group of related superfamilies or families (T-B; Borror et al.).

subordinate taxon, a taxon at a lower rank than the taxon of the same coordinate group with which it is compared (ICZN).

subovate, not quite ovate (T-B).

subovipositor, in ♀ Neotrephinae (Heteroptera: Helotrephidae), a somewhat regressed ovipositor (Tuxen, after China).

subpapilla, in some ♂ Mecoptera, subanale, q.v. (Tuxen, after Crampton).

subparallel, nearly parallel (T-B).

subpectinate, somewhat less than fully pectinate (T-B).

subpedunculate, not quite pedunculate (T-B).

subpharyngeal nerve, in some insects, one of a pair of small nerves arising from the suboesophageal tritocerebral commissure, or from the anterior end of the suboesophageal ganglion (T-B, after Snodgrass).

subphylum (pl., **subphyla**), a major subdivision of a phylum, containing a group of related classes (Borror et al.).

subprimary setae, in certain caterpillars (Lepidoptera), those primary setae found in later instars but not in the first (T-B, after Comstock); see primary setae and secondary setae.

subpunctate, subpunctatus, slightly punctured (T-B).

subpyriform, not quite pear-shaped (T-B).

subquadrangle, subquadrilateral, q.v. (T-B, after Comstock; Borror et al.).

subquadrate, not quite a square (T-B).

subquadrilateral, in adult Zygoptera (Odonata), cubital cell immediately behind the quadrilateral (O'Farrell, in CSIRO).

subrectal sclerite, in ♂ some Chrysopidae (Planipennia), tignum, q.v. (Tuxen, after Zimmermann).

subreniform, not quite kidney-shaped (T-B).

subreniform spot, a rounded spot or outline, below and sometimes attached to the reniform spot in *Catocala* and some allied Noctuidae (Lepidoptera) (T-B).

subscaphium (pl., **subscaphia**), in ♂ Geometridae and some other Lepidoptera, sclerotization of ventral part of tuba analis, sometimes being fused with the caudad, conjoined part of gnathos (Tuxen, after Pierce); in ♂ Lepidoptera, gnathos or gnathos + subscaphium (Tuxen, after Kusnezov) or uncus (Tuxen, after Rebel); in ♂ Coleophoridae (Lepidoptera), tegumen, q.v. (Tuxen, after Toll).

subscutellum, in adult Diptera, esp. Tachinidae, a convex, transverse ridge or lobe on mediotergite (Colless and McAlpine, in CSIRO; McAlpine).

subsegment, in the arthropod podite, a secondary division of a segment into 2 or more nonmusculated segments (T-B, Snodgrass); see antennomere, flagellomere, and tarsomere.

subsellate, nearly like or approaching the form of a saddle (T-B).

subsequent designation, the designation of the name-bearing type of a nominal taxon published after the nominal taxon was established (ICZN).

subsequent monotypy, the situation arising when a nominal genus or subgenus was established before 1931 without any included nominal species, and when only a single taxonomic species denoted by an available name was first subsequently referred to it (ICZN).

subsequent spelling, any spelling of an available name other than the original spelling (ICZN).

subserrate, denticulate, q.v. (T-B).

subsidiary spine, in larval Chironomidae (Diptera), accessory blade, q.v. (Saether).

subsinuate, slightly sinuate (T-B).

subsocial, applied to the condition or to the group showing it in which the adults care for their nymphs or larvae for some period of time (Wilson); see presocial.

subspecies, (sing. and pl.; abbrev. **ssp.** for one, **sspp.** for 2 or more), a geographically defined aggregate of local populations which differs from other such subdivisions of the species (Mayr); the rank of the species group below species; the lowest rank at which names are regulated by the Code (ICZN); a taxon at the rank of subspecies (ICZN).

subspecies name, a scientific name of a taxon at the rank of subspecies (ICZN); trinomen, q.v. (ICZN).

subspecific name, the third name in a trinomen (ICZN).

subspiniform, not quite spinelike or spine-shaped (T-B).

subspiracular area, in adult Culicidae (Diptera), the rather indefinite area of the anterior mesanepisternum lying below the hypostigmal area between the proepimeron and the postspiracular area (Harbach and Knight, after Edwards).

subspiracular line, in larval Lepidoptera, a stripe or line below the spiracles (T-B).

subspiracular seta, in adult Culicidae (Diptera), one of the setae rarely occurring on the subspiracular area of the anterior mesanepisternum (Harbach and Knight).

substemmatal group, in larval Lepidoptera, primary setae SS1–SS3 located on the head ventral of the stemmata (Stehr).

substitute king, in Isoptera, ♂ supplementary reproductive, q.v. (T-B, after Comstock).

substitute queen, in Isoptera, ♀ supplementary reproductive, q.v. (T-B, after Comstock).

substomodaeal commissure, postoesophageal commissure, q.v. (T-B).

substrate, a substance which is acted on by an enzyme (T-B); the material such as fecal matter or leaf parts upon which certain ants (Hymenoptera: Formicidae) raise fungi (T-B).

substriate, substriatus, slightly striate (T-B).

subter (Latin), below; beneath (R. W. Brown).

subteres, subterete, nearly but not quite cylindrical (T-B).

subterminal, below the end or not quite attaining the end (T-B).

subterminal transverse space, in adult moths (Lepidoptera), the area between the transverse posterior line and the subterminal line (T-B, after J. B. Smith).

subterranean, living underground; beneath the surface of the soil or ground (T-B).

subtile, subtilis (Latin), thin; fine; slender; acute (T-B; R. W. Brown).

subtriangle, in adult Odonata, the cell in the wing behind the triangle (T-B, after Garman).

subtriangular space, in adult Odonata, triangle, q.v. (T-B).

subtribe, a rank of the family below tribe (ICZN); a taxon at the rank of subtribe (ICZN).

subtropical, bordering the tropics (T-B).

subulate, subuliform, subulatus (Latin), awl-shaped, i.e., linear at base, attenuate at tip (T-B).

subulate setae, in ♂ Chironomidae (Diptera), lamellate setae on median volsella, being basally slender and gradually narrowing into a hairlike apical point (Saether).

subulicorn antenna, an awl-shaped antenna; linear at base, attenuate at tip (T-B).

Subulicornia, the Odonata and Ephemeroptera considered as one group (T-B, after Lameere); see Paleoptera.

Subulipalpia, Setipalpia, q.v. (Borror et al.).

subunci (sing., **subuncus**), in ♂ Lepidoptera, paired structures arising from lateroventral margins of tegumen below base of uncus, distinguishable from gnathos and socii (Tuxen, after Niculescu); in ♂ Lycaenidae (Lepidoptera), falces, q.v. (Tuxen, after Chapman).

subvaginal plate, in ♀ Auchenorrhyncha (Hemiptera), sclerite between pregenital sternite and external orifice of vagina (Tuxen, after Fennah).

subvalvae (sing., **subvalva**), in ♀ Plecoptera, posterior parts of lateral lobes of subgenital plate (produced parts of abdominal sternum VIII) (Tuxen, after Crampton).

subventral flange, in ♂ Embiidina, usually flattened subventral part of bifid apex of left or right tergal process (Ross, in Tuxen).

subventral group of setae, in larval Lepidoptera, primary setae SV1 to SV3 located subventrally on apodal segments and at bases of thoracic legs and abdominal prolegs (Stehr, after Hinton).

subventral line, in larval Lepidoptera, a lateral stripe or line just dorsad of legs and prolegs and between the lateral and ventral lines (T-B, after J. B. Smith).

subventral lobe, central lobe, q.v. (Tuxen, after Walker).

subventral ridge, in slug caterpillars (Lepidoptera: Limacodidae), a longitudinal raised line along the subventral series of abdominal tubercles (T-B).

subventral space, in slug caterpillars (Lepidoptera: Limacodidae), the area on each side, between the lateral ridge and the lower edge of the body, in which spiracles are situated (T-B).

subvibrissal setae, in adult Diptera, setae along the anteroventral margin of the gena (McAlpine).

subvibrissal setulae, subvibrissal setae, q.v. (McAlpine).

succincti, chrysalides of butterflies (Lepidoptera) which are held in place by a silken cord around the body (T-B); see girdle and suspensi.

succineous, succineus, resembling amber or amber-colored (brownish-yellow) (T-B).

succinic acid, $(CH_2CO_2H)_2$, an organic acid, being an intermediate in glucose oxidation, commonly found in high concentrations in the hemolymph (Gilmour, in CSIRO).

succursal nest, in social insects, the permanent resting or hiding place built by workers, but not a true nest as no brood is reared in it (Tulloch, after Gaul).

sucker(s), a disc variously placed by which certain aquatic insects adhere to surfaces, e.g., paired abdominal suckers on the venter of abdominal segments II–VII in larval Blephariceridae (Diptera) and discs on ventral surface of tarsomeres 1–3 of the foreleg in certain ♂ Dytiscidae (Coleoptera) (T-B; Chapman); see suction disc.

sucking disc, in larval Blephariceridae (Diptera), sucker, q.v. (Colless and McAlpine, in CSIRO).

sucking insects, insects that suck blood, nectar, plant sap or other liquid food with mouthparts modified for sucking, i.e., a proboscis or similarly formed structure (Leftwich).

sucking louse, a member of the suborder Anoplura (Phthiraptera) (Calaby, in CSIRO).

sucking mouthparts, mouthparts adapted for sucking fluid (Borror, et); see piercing-sucking mouthparts and siphoning mouthparts.

sucking pump, in insects with sucking mouthparts, cibarial pump, q.v., pharyngeal pump, q.v., or the 2 combined (T-B).

sucking spears, in larval Hemerobiidae (Planipennia), the specialized mandibles and maxillae used for puncturing prey and sucking its juices (T-B).

sucking stomach, in adult Lepidoptera, crop, q.v. (T-B).

sucrase, enzyme that splits sucrose into glucose and fructose (T-B).

sucrose, $C_{12}H_{12}O_{11}$, dissacharide consisting of glucose and fructose joined together by a beta linkage (T-B; Chapman).

suction disc, in some larval Neuropteroidea, one or 2 suckerlike structures at the end of the abdomen (Riek, in CSIRO); in larval Mecoptera (excl. Nannochoristidae), weakly modified apex of abdomen (Riek, in CSIRO); in larval Blephariceridae and some Psychodinae (Psychodidae) (Diptera), sucker, q.v. (Teskey, in McAlpine); see sucker.

Suctoria, Siphonaptera, q.v. (T-B; Boudreaux, after DeGeer).

suctorial, adapted for sucking (T-B); see haustellate.

suctorial mandibles, in some adult and larval Coleoptera, mandibles with tubelike channels through which fluid food is imbibed, e.g., larval Dytiscidae (Britton, in CSIRO).

suffulted pupil, the pupil of an ocellate spot which grades into another color (T-B).

suffused, clouded or obscured by a darker color (T-B).

suffusion, a clouding, or spreading of one shade over another (T-B).

sugar beet curly top, disease of sugar beets caused by an isometric virus and transmitted circulatively by leafhoppers, *Ciculifer tenellus* and *C. opacipennis* (Hemiptera: Auchenorrhyncha: Cicadellidae) (Borror et al.).

sugar beet yellows, viral disease of sugar beets, lettuce, or spinach transmitted semipersistently by aphid *Myzus persicae* (Hemiptera: Sternorrhyncha: Aphididae) (Borror et al.).

sugarcane mosaic, viral disease of sugarcane, sorghum, and corn transmitted nopersistently by aphids (Hemiptera: Sternorrhyncha: Aphididae) (Borror et al.).

sugaring, attracting insects by spreading a sugary mixture on tree trunks, stumps, etc. (Borror et al.).

sulcate, sulcated, sulcatus (Latin), deeply furrowed or grooved (T-B; Harris); see canaliculate and porcate.

sulci, pl. of sulcus, q.v. (T-B).

sulciform, groove-shaped or groovelike (T-B).

sulcus (pl., **sulci**), groove with a purely functional origin (T-B; Chapman, after Snodgrass); see suture.

sulfaquinoxaline, an organic sulfur-containing compound used in veterinary medicine; N'-(2-quinoxalinyl) sulfanilamide (Pfadt).

sulfotepp, a synthetic insecticide and acaricide; an organophosphate, tetraethyl dithiopyrophosphate; highly toxic to mammals, acute oral LD_{50} for rats 7 to 10 mg/kg (Pfadt).

sulfoxide, a synergist for pyrethrum; 1,2-methylenedioxy-4-[2-(octyl-sulfinyl)propyl]benzene; slightly toxic to warmblooded animals, acute oral LD_{50} for rats 2000 to 2500 mg/kg (Pfadt).

sulfureous, sulfureus (Latin), sulphur yellow, q.v. (T-B).

sulphur yellow, light yellow (T-B); see flavous (T-B).

sumac gall, an irregular, smooth, fruitlike gall on the sumac tree *Rhus cotinoides* produced by aphid *Melaphis rhuis* (Hemiptera: Sternor-rhyncha: Aphididae) (Leftwich).

sun-compass reaction, flight oriented to the position of the sun (Chapman); light-compass reaction, q.v. (Leftwich).

sunken organ, in adult Chironomidae (Diptera), sensillum capitatum, q.v. (Saether).

sunscorpion, windscorpion, q.v. (Borror et al.).

sunspider, windscorpion, q.v. (Borror et al.).

super-, Latin prefix; over; above; beyond (T-B).

superans, exceeding in size and length (T-B).

superciliary, set or placed above the eyes (T-B).

supercilium (pl., **supercilia**), an arched line like an eyebrow sometimes found above an eye spot or ocellus (T-B); a hair (or hairs) above the upper margin of the compound eye (T-B).

superclass, in classification, an aggregate of 2 or more classes (T-B).

supercontraction, in some visceral muscles, the capaciity of the sar-comeres to shorten by more than half their length (Chapman).

supercooling point, temperature at which ice crystals start to form within the insect (Chapman).

superdevelopment, hypermetamorphosis, q.v. (Leftwich).

superfamily (pl., **superfamilies**), a group of closely related families, whose name ends in "-oidea" (T-B; Borror et al.); a rank of the family group above family, being the highest rank at which names are regulated by the Code (ICZN); a taxon of the rank of superfam-ily (ICZN).

superfamily name, a scientific name of a taxon at the rank of super-family (ICZN).

superficial germ band, one that remains ventral in position and in which blastokinesis does not take place (T-B, after Folsom and War-dle).

superficies, the surface (T-B).

superficies externa, the outer surface of any organ or part (T-B).

superficies inferia, the under or lower surface of any organ or part (T-B).

superficies interna, the inner surface of any organ or part (T-B).

Supericornia, Heteroptera with the antennae inserted on the upper parts of the sides of the head, e.g., Coreidae (T-B); see Infericornia.

superinfection, in invertebrate pathology, a fresh infection added to the one of the same nature already present (Steinhaus and Marti-gnoni); see reinfection and secondary infection.

superior (Latin), higher (R. W. Brown).

superior anal appendages, in Odonata, anal appendages, q.v. (Tuxen, after Garman).

superior antenna, one set on the upper part of the head (T-B).

superior apophyses, in ♀ Orthoptera, short processes from upper basal parts of posterior valvulae, connected with inferior intervalvula in Caelifera, but ending free in Ensifera (Ander, in Tuxen).

superior appendage(s), in ♂ Zygoptera (Odonata), cerci, q.v. (Borror et al.); in ♂ Plecoptera, subanal plates, q.v. (Tuxen, after Tillyard); in adult Neuroptera, ectoproct, q.v. (Tuxen, after Tjeder); in ♂ Trichoptera, passively movable, setose, paired dorsolateral appendages on abdominal segment X, often lacking or fused with abdominal segment X in which case the term may be applied to other structures of abdominal segment X (Tuxen), occurring only in Limnephilidae according to Schmid (for whom otherwise superficially similar structures are appendices preanales in other families), also in ♀ Limnephilidae but on abdominal segment IX, thus not homologous (Tuxen, after Nielsen); in ♂ Chironomidae (Diptera), superior volsella, q.v. (Saether).

superior intervalvula, in ♀ Orthoptera, transverse sclerite connecting bases of posterior valvulae, being inconspicuous in Caelifera (Ander, in Tuxen).

superior lobe, an upper lobe (T-B).

superior oil, a dormant spray of high paraffinic and low aromatic content, characteristics which provide increased plant safety and satisfactory insecticidal action (Pfadt).

superior orbit, vertical orbit, q.v. (T-B, after MacGillivray).

superior orbital setae, orbital setae, q.v. (McAlpine).

superior orbital setulae, orbital setulae, q.v. (McAlpine).

superior process(es), in ♀ Aleyrodiidae (Hemiptera: Sternorrhyncha), dorsal gonapophysis, q.v. (Tuxen); in ♂ Heteroptera (Hemiptera), paired bare sclerotizations, processes, etc., of the diaphragm, lateral to the anal tube and dorsal to the bases of parameres (trans. "processus supérieurs" Dupuis, in Tuxen); in ♂ Lepidoptera, uncus, q.v. (Tuxen, after McLachlan).

superior taxon, a taxon at a higher rank than the taxon of the same coordinate group with which it is compared (ICZN).

superior valvulae, in ♀ Phasmida, outgrowths of coxopodite of abdominal segment IX (Günther, in Tuxen).

superior volsella, in adult Chironomidae (Diptera), apparent mesodorsal appendage, lobe or area of ♂ gonocoxite IX (Saether); see endomere and volsella.

superior wings, forewings, q.v. (T-B).

superiors, in adult Odonata, anal appendages, q.v. (T-B, after Garman).

superlinguae (sing., **superlingua**), in apterygote insects, larval Ephemeroptera, and Dermaptera, a pair of lateral lobes of the hypopharynx (T-B; Chapman); in larval Chironomidae (Diptera), paraligula, q.v. (Saether).

superlingual segment, the fifth segment of the head, between the mandibular and maxillary segments (T-B); see head.

superne, above; relating to the upper surface (T-B).

supernormal sign stimulus, a signal which is even more effective in eliciting a given behavior than the natural signal (Matthews and Matthews).

supernumerary, additional or added, of cells, veins or other structures (T-B).

supernumerary cells, additional cells in the wings of Diptera, produced by extra crossveins (e.g., in Nemestrinidae, Bombyliidae, etc.) (T-B, after Curran).

supernumerary crossveins, crossveins, other than those normally present (T-B, after Curran).

supernumerary radial crossvein, in adult Tanyderidae and Tipulidae (Diptera: Tipulomorpha), crossvein between fourth and fifth branches of radius (McAlpine).

supernumerary segment, in Cecidomyiidae (Diptera), a segment between the head and the first thoracic segment (T-B).

superorder, a group of allied orders, such as the Acercaria (T-B).

superorganism, any society, such as a colony of a eusocial insect species, possessing features of organization analogous to the physiological properties of a single organism, e.g., with reproductive castes (analogous to gonads) and worker castes (analogous to somatic tissue), and sometimes with exchange of nutrients by trophallaxis (analogous to the circulatory system), and so forth (Wilson).

superparasitism, multiparasitism where more individuals of a single species are attempting to develop on a host than that host can nourish to optimal size (Gauld and Bolton).

superposed, placed one above the other, as the frontal tufts in some moths (Lepidoptera) (T-B).

superposition eye, clear-zone eye, q.v. (T-B, after Snodgrass; Borror et al.).

superposition image, a phenomenon in noctural insects in which the pigmented sheaths surrounding the ommatidia can be retracted so that the points of light which normally form a mosaic image will merge together and overlap giving a less distinct but brighter image (T-B, after Imms; Leftwich); see apposition image.

superprocessus, in ♂ Neuropteroidea, dorsal, backward directed process of each paramere (Tuxen, after Tjeder).

supersedure, in honey bees (Hymenoptera: Apidae), the replacement of the resident queen, usually an old and sickly individual, with a new queen reared by the workers, a process distinct from colony multiplication by swarming (Wilson).

superspecies, a monophyletic group of entirely or largely allopatric species (Mayr); see semispecies.

supertriangle, in adult Odonata, the wing cell just in front of the triangle (T-B, after Garman); the area from the arculus to the distal angle of the triangle in Anisoptera (T-B).

superuncus (pl., **superunci**), in ♂ Lepidoptera, esp. Papilionidae, mediodorsal, uncuslike process of caudal margin of abdominal tergum VIII (Tuxen, after Kusnezov).

supination, twisting of the wing so that the ventral face of the wing faces obliquely foward, caused by the pulling down of the trailing edge of the wing by the subalar muscle (Chapman).

supine surface, the upper surface (T-B).

supplement, in adult Odonata, an adventitious vein formed by a number of crossveins being lined up to form a continuous vein, located behind and more or less parallel to one of the main longitudinal veins (T-B, after Comstock; Borror et al.); see accessory vein and intercalary vein.

supplemental anal loop, in some genera of Aeschninae (Odonata: Aeschnidae), a second anal loop (T-B, after Comstock).

supplemental process, accessory process of antenna, q.v. (Peterson).

supplementary joint, accessory process of antenna, q.v. (Peterson).

supplementary knife-blade, in ♀ Incurvariidae (Lepidoptera), sclerotized part separated longitudinally from body of "knife-blade" (Tuxen, after Wood).

supplementary lobes, in ♂ Coleoptera, paired processes (apophyses, apodemes) of tegmen or penis (transl. "lobes supplémentaires" Lindroth and Palmén, in Tuxen).

supplementary media, radius, in adult Odonata, extra longitudinal veins in the wings between M_3 and M_4 and M_4 and Cu_1 (T-B, after Garman).

supplementary reproductive, in Isoptera, an individual, nymphoid or ergatoid, q.v., apterous neotenic or brachypterous neotenic, which becomes a functional reproductive in the colony of its origin without reaching the imago or alate form and without leaving the parent colony, sometimes replacing, sometimes supplementing a primary reproductive (king or queen); also includes adultoids (Krishna, pers. comm.).

supplementary scales, intercalary plates, q.v. (T-B, after MacGillivray).

supplementary sectors, interposed sectors, q.v. (T-B).

supplementary setae, setae in addition to those usually present (Christiansen and Bellinger).

support filament, on the maxilla of Protura, a tube running backwards from the base of the lobi externi at the level of the cardo, extending into a heart-shaped expansion (trans. Italian "filamento di sostegno" Berlese, in Tuxen).

supporting plate, in ♀ Hymenoptera, gonangulum, q.v. (Tuxen, after Imms).

suppression, the use of the Commission of its plenary power to rule (1) that a work is unpublished or unavailable for nomenclatural purposes; or (2) that an available name is either (a) never to be used as a valid name (totally supresed, or partially supressed), or (b) only to be used as a valid name under stated conditions (conditionally suppressed); or (3) that a nomenclatural act is invalid (ICZN).

suppressed name, a scientific name that the Commission has ruled to be unpublished or unavailable (ICZN).

suppressed work, a work that the Commission has ruled to be unpublished or unavailable (ICZN).

supra-, Latin prefix; above; over; beyond (T-B).

supra citato (Latin), cited above; abbrev., supr. cit. (T-B).

supraalar, in pupal Chironomidae (Diptera), seta on thorax above wing sheath (Saether).

supraalar area, in adult Diptera, the lateral margin of the scutum immediately above the attachment of the wing (Harbach and Knight; McAlpine).

supraalar bristles, in adult Diptera, supraalar setae, q.v. (T-B, after Comstock; Borror et al.).

supraalar callus, in adult Chironomidae (Diptera), eminence in front of and to either side of scutellum (Saether).

supraalar cavity, in adult Diptera, supraalar depression, q.v. (T-B).

supraalar depression, in adult Diptera, e.g. Blephariceridae, Deuterophlebiidae, Simuliidae, and Thaumaleidae, a distinct concavity in supraalar area (T-B; McAlpine).

supraalar groove, in adult Diptera, supraalar depression, q.v. (T-B, after Comstock; Harbach and Knight); in adult Hymenoptera, a groove or depression just above the bases of the wing (T-B, after J. B. Smith).

supraalar ridge, in adult Diptera, upper margin of supraalar depression (McAlpine).

supraalar scale, in adult Culicidae (Diptera), one of the scales occurring on the supraalar area of the scutum (Harbach and Knight).

supraalar setae, in adult Diptera, longitudinal row of setae on the scutum above the root of the wing, lateral to the intraalar setae (McAlpine).

supraalars, in adult Chironomidae (Diptera), setae of supraalar callus (Saether); see supraalar setae.

supraanal, above the anus (T-B).

supraanal appendages, in Odonata, anal appendages, q.v. (T-B, after Imms; Tuxen).

supraanal hook, in ♂ Lepidoptera, uncus, q.v. (T-B); in ♂ Plecoptera, epiproct, q.v. (Tuxen, after Hynes).

supraanal lobe, in adult Plecoptera, epiproct, q.v. (Tuxen; Zwick, pers. comm.).

supraanal membrane, supraanal pad, q.v. (T-B; Tuxen).

supraanal pad, the reduced epiproct in certain orders of insects, beneath the end of abdominal tergum X (T-B, after Snodgrass; Tuxen).

supraanal plate, in Ephemeroptera, epiproct, q.v. (Tuxen); in Blattopteroidea, abdominal tergum X (Tuxen); in Isoptera, epiproct, q.v. (Tuxen); in Grylloblattodea, epiproct, q.v. (Tuxen); in Orthoptera, epiproct or tergiproct, q.v., or part thereof (Tuxen, after Walker); in Dermaptera, penultimate sternite, q.v. (Tuxen); in ♂ Plecoptera, epiproct, q.v. (Tuxen; Zwick, pers. comm.); in ♂ Psyllidae (Hemiptera: Sternorrhyncha), proctiger, q.v. (Tuxen); in Tachardiidae (Hemiptera: Sternorrhyncha: Coccoidea), sclerotized area laterad of anal opening but not forming an operculum (Miller, in Stehr); in ♂ *Nymphes* (Planipennia: Nymphidae), mediuncus, q.v. (Tuxen, after

Crampton); in ♂ Diptera, dorsal plate of proctiger (Tuxen, after Crampton).

supraanal process, in ♂ Plecoptera, supraanal lobe, q.v. (Tuxen, after Needham and Claassen).

supraanal seta, in larval Chironomidae (Diptera), seta to each side dorsally on anal segment just above anal tubules (Saether).

supraanale (pl., **supraanalia**), in some adult Neuropteroidea, plate covering anus from above (Tjeder, in Tuxen); in adult Mecoptera, abdominal tergum XI covering anus from above (Tjeder, in Tuxen).

supracerebral glands, the pair of salivary glands situated above the brain in bees (Hymenoptera: Apoidea) (T-B).

supracervical setulae, in adult Diptera, group of small setae on occiput above occipital foramen (McAlpine).

suprachorionic layer(s), in the eggs of insects, the layer or layers deposited over the chorion (Cobben); see cement layer and extrachorion.

Supracide (trade name), methidathion, q.v. (Pfadt).

supraclypeal area, in adult Hymenoptera, the region of the head between the antennal sockets, the clypeus and the frontal crest (T-B).

supraclypeal mark, in adult bees (Hymenoptera: Apoidea), a patch of light color above the clypeus (T-B).

supraclypeus, postclypeus, q.v. (T-B).

supracoxal, lying above or over the coxa (T-B).

supradistal plate, in some ♂ Enicocephalidae (Hemiptera: Heteroptera), dorsal cover of ♂ genitalia (Štys).

supraepimeron, anepimeron, q.v. (T-B, after MacGillivray).

supraepisternum, anepisternum, q.v. (T-B, after Imms).

suprageneric, of a taxon: one at a rank higher than genus (ICZN).

supragenital plate, in ♀ Integripalpia (Trichoptera), mostly unpaired sclerite of abdominal segment X above the genital opening in (Nielsen; Schmid).

supraneural bridge, in the honey bee (Hymenoptera: Apidae), the fused endosternites (T-B).

supraoesophageal, situated above the oesophagus (T-B).

supraoesophageal center, brain, q.v. (T-B).

supraoesophageal ganglion, brain, q.v. (T-B).

supraorbital, situated above the eye (T-B); in larval Chironomidae (Diptera), cephalic seta S7 situated on gena above eye spots (Saether).

supraorganism, superorganism, q.v.

suprapapilla, in some ♂ Mecoptera, supranale, q.v. (Tuxen, after Crampton).

suprarami of cingulum, in ♂ Cyrtacanthacridinae (Orthoptera: Acrididae), dorsal projections of cingulum (Tuxen, after Eades).

suprascutella, in adult Hymenoptera, postscutellum, q.v. (T-B, after MacGillivray).

supraspecific, term applied to a category or phenomenon above the species level (Mayr).

supraspinal cord, ventral diaphragm, q.v. (T-B, after Packard).

supraspinal vessel, pericardial sinus, q.v. (T-B).

supraspiracular line, in larval Lepidoptera, a line or stripe above the spiracles (T-B).

suprasquamal ridge, in adult Diptera, a ridge running from the base of the lower calypter to the anterolateral angle of the scutellum (McAlpine).

suprastigmatal line, supraspiracular line, q.v. (T-B).

suprastomodeal, over or above the stomodeum (T-B).

supratentoria (sing., **supratentorium**), slender threadlike, or large, arms arising from the lateral margin of a pretentorium or of the corpotentorium (T-B, after MacGillivray).

supratriangular crossveins, in Odonata, veins crossing the supratriangular space (T-B).

supratriangular space, in adult Anisoptera (Odonata), an area just above the triangle, occupying nearly the same position as the quadrilateral of Zygoptera (Odonata) (T-B).

supratympanal organ, subgenual organ, q.v. (T-B, after Comstock).

supravalva (pl., **supravalvae**), in ♂ Lithosiinae (Lepidoptera: Arctiidae), dorsocaudad directed extension of basis valvae, often running along dorsal margin of valvae (Tuxen, after Birket-Smith).

supravibrissal setae, in adult Diptera, esp. Tachinidae, setae on facial ridge (McAlpine).

suranal, supraanal, q.v. (T-B).

suranal fork, in locusts (Orthoptera: Acrididae), a structure at the base of the suranal plate (T-B, after Packard), possibly being a toothed cercus.

suranal furcula, in ♂ Orthoptera, suranal fork, q.v. (T-B).

suranal lobe, in insect larvae, lobe dorsad of the anus (Peterson); see subanal lobe.

suranal plate, in adult Ephemeroptera and Isoptera, epiproct, q.v. (Tuxen); in ♀ Plecoptera, epiproct, q.v. (Tuxen, after Crampton); in ♂ Orthoptera, supraanal plate, q.v. (T-B); in ♂ Heteroptera (Hemiptera), anal tube, q.v. (Tuxen, after Matsuda); in larval Lepidoptera, anal plate, q.v. (T-B); in ♂ Ceratocampini (Lepidoptera: Saturniidae), tegumen + uncus (Tuxen, after Packard).

suranal process, a sclerotized process on the meson of the suranal lobe (Peterson); in larval Symphyta (Hymenoptera), postcornu, q.v. (Gauld and Bolton).

surculus (pl., **surculi**), in ♂ Plebeiinae (Lepidoptera: Lycaenidae), paired, sclerotized structure of manica (Tuxen, after Nabokov).

surface pheromone, a pheromone with an active space restricted so close to the body of the sending organism that direct contact, or something approaching it, must be made with the body in order to perceive the pheromone, e.g., the colony odors of many species (Wilson).

surgonopods, in ♂ Auchenorrhyncha (Hemiptera), anal hooks, q.v. (Tuxen, after Crampton); in adult Neuropteroidea, ectoproct, q.v. (Tuxen, after Crampton); in ♂ Mecoptera, lobes of epandrium, q.v. (Tuxen, after Crampton); in ♂ Trichoptera, superior appendages, q.v. (Tuxen).

surpapilla, in some ♂ Mecoptera, supranale, q.v. (Tuxen, after Crampton).

surpedal area, postepipleurite, q.v. (Peterson).

surra, disease of domestic animals in parts of Africa, Asia, and South America, caused by the protozoan *Trypanosoma evansi* (Trypanosomatidae) and transmitted by horse flies (Diptera: Tabanidae) (Allaby).

surstylar lobes, in adult Diptera, surstyluslike lobes of epiandrium (McAlpine).

surstyli (sing., **surstylus**), in ♂ Mecoptera, processes of epiandrium, q.v. (Tuxen, after Crampton); in ♂ Diptera, secondary lobate differentiations of epiandrium (Tuxen, after Crampton); see inner surstyli and outer surstyli.

sursum, upward (T-B).

susceptible, in invertebrate pathology, the state of being readily affected or acted upon by an injurious agent (Steinhaus and Martignoni).

suspensi, chrysalides of butterflies (Lepidoptera) which are suspended by the tail only (T-B); see succincti.

suspension, a system of solid particles dispersed in a liquid (Pfadt).

suspensor, the column or partition of carton or wax attaching strata of comb in the nests of bees and wasps (Hymenoptera: Aculeata) (Tulloch, after Gaul).

suspensorial apodemes, in ♂ Heteroptera (Hemiptera), apodemes of diaphragm (dorsoproximal extensions of edges of median groove) to which are appended basal plates of articulatory apparatus (Tuxen, after Štys).

suspensorium (pl., **suspensoria**), a dorsal strand of cells by which the gonad is attached to the coelomic wall (T-B); structures or muscles from which others suspend or hang (T-B); in ♂ Hepialidae (Lepidoptera), support for penis formed by 2 processes of tegumen meeting ventral to it (Tuxen, after Eyer); in ♂ Mnesarchaeidae (Lepidoptera), concave, unpaired sclerite supporting aedoeagus from below (ventrad) (Tuxen, after Philpott); in larval Chironomidae (Diptera), pecten hypopharyngis, q.v. (Saether).

suspensorium of the hypopharynx, suspensory sclerites, q.v. (T-B, after Snodgrass).

suspensory arms, in ♂ Heteroptera (Hemiptera), suspensorial apodemes, q.v. (Tuxen, after Davis).

suspensory ligament, combined filaments of ovarioles inserted into the body wall or the dorsal diaphragm, suspending the developing ovaries in the hemocoel (T-B, after Snodgrass; Chapman).

suspensory ligaments, in ♂ Tingidae (Hemiptera: Heteroptera), suspensorial apodemes, q.v. (Tuxen, after Livingstone).

suspensory muscles, dilator muscles, q.v. (T-B).

suspensory plates, in ♂ Tingidae (Hemiptera: Heteroptera), edges of median groove (Tuxen, after Livingstone).

suspensory processes, in ♂ Heteroptera (Hemiptera), suspensorial apodemes, q.v. (Tuxen, after Dupuis and Carvalho).

suspensory sclerite(s), paired sclerites in the lateral wall of the adoral face of the hypopharynx, extending upward to end in the lateral wall of the stomodaeum, receiving muscles from the frons, and hinged distally with lingual sclerites (Chapman, after Snodgrass).

sustentacular apodeme, in ♂ Syrphidae (Diptera), phallosome, q.v. (Tuxen, after Metcalf).

sustentors, the 2 posterior projections of a butterfly (Lepidoptera: Rhopalocera) chrysalis (T-B).

sutural, of or pertaining to a suture (T-B).

sutural area, in the family Tingidae (Hemiptera: Heteroptera), the inner-apical portion of the forewing, narrow in short-winged forms, expanding in long-winged forms; corresponding to the membrane of the forewing in the other Heteroptera (T-B).

suture, groove marking the line of fusion of 2 formerly distinct plates (T-B; Chapman, after Snodgrass); the line of juncture of elytra, tegmina, or hemelytra (T-B); see sulcus.

suturiform, fused together so that only a slight impressed line is visible (T-B).

swell body s.l., in ♂ Heteroptera (Hemiptera), endosoma, q.v. (Tuxen, after Ekblom).

swell body s.str., in ♂ Heteroptera (Hemiptera), conjunctiva, q.v. (Tuxen, after Ekblom).

swarming, in honey bees (Hymenoptera: Apoidea), the normal method of colony reproduction in which the queen and a large number of workers depart suddenly from the parental nest and fly to some exposed site, where they cluster while scout workers fly in search of a suitable new nest cavity (T-B; Wilson); in ants (Hymenoptera: Formicidae), the mass exodus of winged reproductive forms from the nests during the nuptial flight (Wilson); in many Nematocera (Diptera) and Enicocephalidae (Hemiptera: Heteroptera), aggregating in a mating swarm, q.v.

sweeping, collecting technique involving swinging a reenforced net through vegetation (Borror et al.).

sweepstake route, route over which dispersal is possible but extremely difficult for most organisms (Mackerras, in CSIRO).

swim hair, in pupal Chironomidae (Diptera), fringe, q.v. (Saether).

swimmerets, in some larval aquatic Neuroptera, gill- or platelike structures serving as oars or organs of locomotion (T-B); in Crustacea, an abdominal appendage that functions as a swimming organ (Borror et al.).

swimming fan, in some Veliidae, e.g., *Rhagovelia* (Hemiptera: Heteroptera: Veliidae), the fanlike structure usually formed from a modified ventral arolium, and which aids in swimming on flowing water (Andersen).

swimming fringe, in pupal Chironomidae (Diptera), fringe, q.v. (Saether).

swimming paddles, in pupal Culicidae (Diptera), anal paddles, q.v. (T-B).

swine pox, a virus disease of swine characterized by small, red skin lesions, weakness, loss of appetite, chills, and fever; trnsmitted by the hog louse, *Haematopinus suis* (Phthiraptera: Anoplura: Haematopinidae) (Pfadt).

sword-shaped seta, in larval Chironomidae (Diptera), seta subdentalis, q.v. (Saether).

sylvan, silvicolous, q.v. (T-B).

sylvatic plague, plague in wild rodents (Borror et al.); see bubonic plague.

symbiogenesis, the method of origin of social symbiotic relation among ants (Hymenoptera: Formicidae) and other insects (T-B).

symbiont, an organism that lives in symbiosis with another species (T-B; Wilson).

symbiosis, the intimate, relatively protracted, and dependent relationship of members of one species with those of another, consisting of 3 principle kinds: commensalism, mutualism, and parasitism (T-B; Wilson).

symbiote, symbiont, q.v. (T-B).

symbiotic, living together in a state of symbiosis (T-B).

symmetrical, evenly developed on both sides (T-B); see asymmetrical.

symmetry, a definite pattern of body organization, which is capable of division into similar halves or radii (T-B; Borror et al.); see bilateral symmetry.

sympathetic nervous system, stomatogastric nervous system, q.v. (T-B).

sympatric hybridization, the occasional production of hybrid individuals between 2 otherwise well-defined sympatric species (Mayr).

sympatric speciation, speciation without geographic isolation; the acquisition of isolating mechanisms within a deme (Mayr); see host race.

sympatry, the occurrence of 2 or more populations in the same area; more precisely, the existence of a population in breeding condition within the cruising range of individuals of another population (Mayr).

symphile, a symbiont, in particular a social insect or other kind of arthopod, which is accepted to some extent by an insect colony and communicates with it amicably, generally being licked, fed, and transported to the host brood chambers, or treated to a combination of these actions (T-B; Wilson).

symphily, the relation borne to ants (Hymenoptera: Formicidae) by the true guests which inhabit their nests and are fed and tended; rendering in return some substance or service desired by the ants (T-B); see metochy and synecthry.

Symphiogastra, Heterogastra, q.v. (Britton, after Kolbe, in CSIRO).

Symphyla, class of slender, unpigmented myriapods (Arthropoda), characterized by small size (1–8 mm in length), unbranched antennae, 10–12 pairs of legs, and genital openings located near the anterior end of the body (T-B; Mackerras, in CSIRO; Borror et al.).

Symphypleona, suborder within the Collembola, including only the family Sminthuridae, possessing a globose body with the thorax and the first 4 abdominal sternites fused (Wallace and Mackerras, in CSIRO).

symphysis, a joining together of 2 sclerites by a soft membrane, permitting a slight motion (T-B).

Symphyta, suborder within the Hymenoptera, including sawflies and horntails of the superfamilies Xyeloidea, Mealodontoidea, Tenthredinoidea, Siricoidea, Orussoidea and Ceproidea, possessing adults with abdomen broadly sessile at its base and without a marked constriction, even when hinged, between segments I and II, and thorax with 2 pairs of spiracles, neither visible dorsally; larvae more or less eruciform (Riek, in CSIRO; Gauld and Bolton).

symplesiomorphic, sharing a relatively primitive state of a homologous character among 2 or more species; see plesiomorphic.

symplesiomorphy, the sharing of one or more primitive character states by several species; a shared primitive character (Hennig); see synapomorphy.

symptom, in invertebrate pathology, an objective aberration in function (including behavior), indicating disease (Steinhaus and Martignoni); see sign.

symptomatology, the science that treats the symptoms and signs of disease; study of the aggregate of symptoms and signs of a disease (Steinhaus and Martignoni).

syn-, Greek prefix; with; together (T-B).

synanthropic, associated with and living with man, in his dwellings, other building, or produce (Gauld and Bolton).

synapomorphic, the sharing of relatively derived or specialized state of 2 or more homologous characters; see apomorphic.

synapomorphy, the sharing of one or more derived character states (apomorphies) by several species; a shared derived character (Hennig); see symplesiomorphy.

synaporium, an animal association formed owing to unfavorable conditions or disease (Steinhaus and Martignoni).

synapse, site at which nerve cells are closely opposed so that activity of one is influenced by another, located primarily within the central nervous system (T-B, after Snodgrass; Chapman).

Synaptera, Apterygota, q.v. (T-B).

synapterous, primitively wingless (T-B).

synaptic, of or pertaining to a synapse (T-B).

synaptic gap, narrow space between membranes of nerve cells within a synapse (Chapman).

synaptic plexus, mass of nerve axons of retinula cells located immediately beneath a dorsal ocellus (Chapman).

synarthrosis, articulation without motion (T-B).

syncephalon, in Arthropoda, a secondary composite head composed of the prostomium and one or more somites following it (T-B, after Snodgrass).

syncerebrum, in insects, brain, q.v. (T-B).

synchronic species, species which occur at the same time level (Mayr); see allochronic species.

synchronous, happening at the same time (T-B).

synchronous flashing, a phenomenon observed occasionally in the tropics, e.g., in Thailand, when large numbers of fireflies (Coleoptera: Lampyridae) or other luminescent insects flash rhythmically in unison, this usually taking place at dusk (Leftwich).

synchrony, synchronism; identity of time (T-B).

synciput, the part of the vertex lying between the eyes (T-B).

syncytial, of or pertaining to the syncytium (T-B).

syncytium, the masses of protoplasm with scattered nuclei, from which the egg, nutritive and epithelial cells arise in the insect ovary (T-B, after Packard); a protoplasmic mass formed by the fusion of several protoplasts without the fusion of the individual nuclei (T-B, after Daubenmire).

syndesis, a method of articulation where 2 parts are connected by a membrane which permits considerable motion between them.

syndiacony, the relationship between ants (Hymenoptera: Formicidae) and plants (such as fungi) wherein both obtain some benefit from the other (Tulloch, after Forel).

syndrome, in invertebrate pathology, a group of signs characteristic of a particular disease; a running together or concurrence of symptoms associated with any morbid process (Steinhaus and Martignoni).

synechthran, a symbiont, usually a scavenger, a parasite, or a predator, which is treated with hostilty by the host colony (Wilson).

synecology, the study of whole plant and animal communities (Allaby); see antecology.

synecthry, the relation borne to ants (Hymenoptera: Formicidae) by insects inhabiting their nests in spite of the efforts of the ants to destroy them (T-B); see symphily and metochy.

synergist, a chemical substance that when used with an insecticide, drug, etc., will result in greater total effect than the sum of their total individual effects (Pfadt).

syngonapophysis, in ♀ Emesinae (Heteroptera: Reduviidae), the fused gonoplacs (Tuxen, after Wygodzinsky).

synista, synistata, in Neuropteroidea, mouth structures which are undeveloped, forming an imperfect tubular structure (T-B); see elinguata.

synoecy, inquilinism, q.v. (T-B).

synoekete, inquiline, q.v. (T-B; Wilson).

synoenocytes, the localization of oenocytes as distinctive organs rather than scattered throughout the body (Tulloch).

synonym, each of 2 or more scientific names of the same rank used to denote the same taxon (ICZN); see junior synonym, objective synonym, senior synonym, and subjective synonym.

synonymous, having the character of a synonym or an identity of terminological application (T-B).

synonymy, the relationship between synonyms (ICZN); a list of synonyms (ICZN).

synoptic collection, a collection of specimens representing important or major taxa; a sample (Borror et al.).

synovigeric, developing successive numbers of eggs to maturity throughout adult life, e.g., ♀ idiobionts (Gauld and Bolton); see proovigeric.

synscleritous, union of tergite and sternite to form a complete ring (Tuxen); see discleritous.

synsternite, in many adult Apocrita (Hymenoptera), fused gastral sternites (Gauld and Bolton).

syntergite, in many adult Apocrita (Hymenoptera), fused gastral tergites (Gauld and Bolton).

syntergite 1 + 2, in adult Diptera, sclerite resulting from the fusion of tergites of abdominal segments I and II (McAlpine).

syntergosternite, in many ♂ Muscomorpha (Diptera), composite sclerite formed from fusion of tergal and sternal elements of the pregenital abdominal segments VI–VIII (McAlpine).

synthetic pyrethroid, pyrethroid, q.v.

synthlipsis, in Heteroptera (Hemiptera), minimum interocular distance (T-B, after Kirkaldy; Nieser; Štys).

synthorax, pterothorax, q.v. (T-B, after Imms; Mackerras, in CSIRO).

Syntonopterodea, extinct group of insects from the Upper Carboniferous, now placed within the Ephemeroptera (Boudreaux, after Laurentiaux).

syntrophy, in social insects, the feeding of symphiles or synoeketes by accident while caring for the brood (Tulloch).

syntype, each specimen of a type series from which neither a holotype nor a lectotype has been designated (ICZN).

synxenic cultivation, the rearing of one or more individuals of a single species in association with one or more known species of organisms (Steinhaus and Martignoni).

syringe, in Hemiptera, salivary pump, q.v. (T-B).

Syrphoidea, superfamily within the series Aschiza of the Muscomorpha (Diptera: Brachycera), including the Syrphidae and Pipunculidae, possessing adults with cell CuP markedly longer than cell M, R_{4+5} unbranched, and antenna usually with an arista (Colless and McAlpine, in CSIRO; McAlpine).

Systellognatha, Setipalpia, q.v. (Borror et al.).

system, an order of arrangement after a distinct plan or method (T-B).

systematic, in definite order or arranged according to a system (T-B).

systematics, the study of biological classification; organismal biology, q.v. (Mayr; ICZN); see taxonomy.

systematist, a student of classification in biology, who discriminates among taxa and recognizes groups according to affinity (T-B).

systemic insecticide, an insecticide capable of absorption into plant sap or animal blood and lethal to insects feeding on or within the treated host (Pfadt).

systole, contraction of the dorsal vessel that sends blood out of its anterior end (T-B; Chapman); see diastole.

systolic, of or pertaining to the systole (T-B).

Systox (trade name), demeton, q.v. (Pfadt).

T

t.a. line, transverse anterior line, q.v. (T-B).

t.p. line, transverse posterior line, q.v. (T-B).

Tabaniformia, Tabanomorpha, q.v. (Hennig).

Tabanoidea, superfamily within the Orthorrhapha (Diptera: Brachycera), including the Tabanidae and other families, possessing adults with enlarged, padlike epodium, which resembles the pulvilli (Colless and McAlpine, in CSIRO); superfamily within the infraorder Tabanomorpha (Diptera), including the Tabanidae, Rhagionidae, Athericidae and Pelecorhynchidae (McAlpine).

Tabanomorpha, infraorder within the suborder Brachycera (Diptera), including the Tabanoidea and Stratiomyoidea (McAlpine).

tabardillo, epidemic typhus, q.v. (Adkins, pers. comm.).

tachygenesis, the telescoping of development in immature insects (T-B); a shortened development involving the omission of several larval instars (Leftwich).

tactile, of or pertaining to the sense of touch (T-B); used for touching (T-B).

tactile papilla, accessory process of antenna, q.v. (Peterson).

tactile receptor, mechanoreceptor, q.v. (Leftwich).

tactile sense, mechanoreception, q.v. (T-B).

tactile sensillum, trichoid sensillum, q.v. (T-B); mechanoreceptor, q.v. (T-B).

tactile spine, trichoid sensillum, q.v. (Leftwich).

tactochemical, of or pertaining to perception by touch and chemical stimuli (T-B).

tadpole shrimps, members of the order Notostraca (Borror et al.).

taenia, a broad longitudinal stripe (T-B).

taeniate, taeniatus (Latin), with broad, longitudinal bands or ribbon-like markings; shaped like a tapeworm (T-B; Harris, after R. W. Brown, and Marchant and Charles).

taenidium (pl., **taenidia**), a spiral thickening of the intima, arranged along the tracheae, preventing the collapse of the latter (T-B; Chapman).

tagma (Greek) (pl., **tagmata**), something ordered or arranged (R. W. Brown); a group of segments forming a unit in the body of an arthropod, e.g., the head, thorax, and abdomen of an insect (T-B, after Snodgrass; Leftwich).

tagmosis, the organization of the body into groups of segments, more or less united, and forming distinct trunk sections or tagmata (T-B, after Snodgrass).

tail, an elongated terminal segment of the abdomen (T-B); in Aphididae (Hemiptera: Sternorrhyncha), cauda, q.v. (T-B; Stoetzel, in Stehr); in some adult Lepidoptera (esp. Papilionidae) and Neuropteroidea, an elongated process on the hind wing (T-B).

tail of spermatheca, in ♀ Siphonaptera, hilla, q.v. (Tuxen).

tailless whipscorpion, a member of the Amblypygi (Borror et al.).

talus, the ankle; the apex of the tibia, where the tarsus is attached.

tandem, one behind the other, the 2 connected or attached together (Borror et al.).

tandem running, in certain ant (Hymenoptera: Formicidae) species, a form of communication, used by the workers during exploration or recruitment, in which one individual follows closely behind another, frequently contacting the abdomen of the leader with its antennae (Wilson).

tangent, tangential, touching, set in or meeting at a tangent; applied to ornamentation and processes (T-B).

tangium, in ♀ Hymenoptera, ventral ramus, q.v. (Tuxen, after Ross).

tangoreceptor, trichoid sensillum, q.v. (T-B).

tannin, complex nonnitrogenous compound containing phenols, glycosides, or hydroxy acids, occurring widely in plants, being toxic substances with astringent properties rendering plant tissues unpalatable to many herbivores (Allaby).

tanning, sclerotization, q.v. (Chapman).

Tanyderoidea, superfamily within the infraorder Tipulomorpha (Diptera: Nematocera), including the family Tanyderidae (McAlpine); see Tipuloidea.

Tanypezoidea, Diopsoidea, q.v. (Colless and McAlpine, in CSIRO).

tapetum, in adult Noctuidae and some other moths (Lepidoptera) with clear-zone eyes, layer of tracheae running through the eye parallel with and forming a sheath around each ommatidium, reflecting light back into the ommatidium (T-B; Chapman); in the dorsal ocelli of cockroaches (Blattaria), a reflective layer at the back of the receptor cells (Chapman).

tapeworm, a parasitic worm belonging to the class Cestoda, e.g., *Dipylidium caninum* transmitted to man by dog flea, *Ctenocephalides canis,* and *Hymenolepis diminuta* transmitted to man by the rat flea, *Xenopsylla cheopis* (Siphonaptera: Pulicidae) (Borror et al.; Allaby).

tapinoma-odor, the peculiar rancid butter smell of some Dolichoderinae (Hymenoptera: Formicidae), produced by a secretion from anal glands (T-B, after W. M. Wheeler).

taraxanthin, pigment in the hemolymph of pupal *Hylophora* (Lepidoptera: Saturniidae) (Chapman).

Tardigrada, class within the Arthropoda, including the water bears, found in water, moss, and other damp places, being of minute size (1 mm or less in length) and possessing 4 pairs of fleshy unsegmented legs, each of which bears several claws (Borror et al.).

tarsal, of or pertaining to the tarsus (T-B).

tarsal bladder, pretarsal bladder, q.v. (Reed, in CSIRO).

tarsal claw, pretarsal claw, q.v. (T-B; Borro et al.).

tarsal formula, the number of tarsomeres on the fore, mid, and hind tarsi, respectively (Borror et al.).

tarsal lobes, in some Coleoptera, euphantulae, q.v. (T-B).

tarsal organs, tarsal taste organ, q.v. (Tulloch).

tarsal paronychium, in Aleyrodidae (Hemiptera: Sternorrhyncha), the tarsal surface thickened and clothed with microsetae on the plantar surface (Gill); see euphantulae.

tarsal pulvilli, euphantulae, q.v. (T-B).

tarsal segment, tarsomere, q.v. (McAlpine).

tarsal spine, in adult Diptera, pseudospur, q.v. (Saether).

tarsal spur, in adult Diptera, pseudospur, q.v. (Saether).

tarsal taste organ, one of many chemoreceptors, q.v., on the tarsi of some Lepidoptera and possibly other insects (Leftwich).

tarsation, touching with the tarsi, especially the touching of another insect as a tactile signal (Wilson).

tarsite, tarsomere, q.v. (T-B).

tarsomere, subdivision or article of the tarsus, usually numbering from 2–5 (T-B, after Snodgrass; Borror et al.; Chapman).

tarsule, tarsulus (Latin), pretarsus, q.v. (T-B, after Crampton).

tarsungulus, in larval Polyphaga (Coleoptera), the terminal clawlike segment of the leg formed by fusion of the tarsus and the claw (Peterson; Britton, in CSIRO).

tarsus (pl., **tarsi**), the leg segment attached to the apex of the tibia, bearing the pretarsus and consisting of from one to 5 tarsomeres (T-B; Chapman).

Tartarides, Schizomida, q.v. (Borror et al.).

taste, chemoreception in which chemicals are perceived in the liquid state at relatively high concentrations with contact chemoreceptors (Chapman); see olfaction.

taste cup, coeloconic sensillum, q.v. (T-B).

taste organ, chemoreceptor, q.v. (Leftwich).

taster, palpus, q.v., or antenna, q.v. (T-B).

tau group, in larval Lepidoptera, an indefinite group of setae between pi and sigma groups, consisting of pi, tau, omega, or other setae (Peterson).

tautonomy, tautonymy, q.v. (T-B).

tautonymous name, a scientific name exhibiting tautonymy (ICZN).

tautonymy, the use of the same word for the name of a genus and of one of its included species and/or subspecies (ICZN); see absolute tautonymy, Linnaean tautonymy, and virtual tautonymy.

tawny, brownish-yellow (T-B).

taxis (pl., **taxes**), any oriented heading of an animal, whether moving or stationary (Matthews and Matthews); movement toward or away from a stimulus (Borror et al.); see tropism.

taxon (pl., **taxa**), any taxonomic unit (e.g., a family, a subgenus, a species), whether named or not, including its subordinate taxa and individuals, whether their names are regulated by the Code (e.g., species) or not (e.g., class) (ICZN); see ichnotaxon, infrasubspecific taxon, nominal taxon, nominotypical taxon, subordinate taxon, superior taxon, taxonomic taxon, and zoological taxon.

taxonomic, taxonomical, relating to classification (T-B).

taxonomic category, designates rank or level in a hierarchic classification, being a class, the members of which are all taxa assigned to a given rank (Mayr).

taxonomic character, any attribute of a member of a taxon by which it differs or may differ from a member of a different group (Mayr).

taxonomic group, a taxon with all its subordinate taxa and their individuals, e.g., the taxonomic group Insecta consists of all insects and their taxa (ICZN).

taxonomic hierarchy, a system of classification based on taxa of decreasing inclusiveness from the kingdom Animalia to the smallest distinguishable groups of individuals (ICZN).

taxonomic taxon, a taxon (e.g., family, genus, species) including whatever nominal taxon and individuals a zoologist at any time considers it to contain in his or her endeavor to define the boundaries of a zoological taxon, denoted by the valid name determined from available names of its included nominal taxa (ICZN).

taxonomic unit, taxon, q.v. (Key, in CSIRO).

taxonomy, the theory and practice of classifying organisms (Mayr; ICZN); the arranging of species and groups thereof into a system which exhibits their relationship to each other and their places in a natural classification (T-B, after Ferris).

tectate, tectiform, q.v. (T-B).

tectiform, rooflike, sloping from a median ridge, like the forewings of Cicadidae (Homoptera: Auchenorrhyncha) (T-B).

tectorium (pl., **tectoria**), in ♂ Lycaenidae (Lepidoptera), structure arising from a point cephalad of the valvae, forming on each side a broad, sclerotized curtain which more or less surrounds and overhangs the aedoeagus (Tuxen, after Bethune-Baker).

tectum (Latin) (pl., **tecta**), roof (R. W. Brown); in ♂ Siphonaptera, the roof of the genital capsule, including the crescent sclerites, satellite sclerites and the central sclerites (Tuxen, after Jordan; Rothschild and Traub); in ♂ Mecoptera, median backward-projecting portion of tergum IV, or epiandrium, q.v. (Tuxen, after Crampton).

teges (pl., **tegites**), in larval Scarabaeoidea (Coleoptera), a continuous, patch of setae on the raster, occupying either the hind part or almost the whole of abdominal sternum X when the palidium is absent; or single and transverse, or paired, longitudinal and short; occasionally divided anteriorly into 2 parts with the campus in between (T-B, after Böving).

tegillum (pl., **tegilla**), in larval Scarabaeoidea (Coleoptera), a patch of setae on each side as abdominal sternum X on the raster, outside of a pair of palidia (T-B, after Böving); in ♂ Siphonaptera, small dorsal sclerite in the roof of the capsula, between the tectum and tubus interior (Tuxen, after Smit).

tegmen (pl., **tegmina**), a covering (T-B); in Blattaria, Mantodea, Orthoptera and certain Auchenorrhyncha (Hemiptera), the hardened leathery or horny forewing usually with reduced venation (T-B; Leftwich); in Heteroptera (Hemiptera), only slightly sclerotized forewing not differentiated into proximal coriaceous and distal membraneous part, or hemelytron, q.v. (T-B); in ♂ Coleoptera, the single or divided sclerite situated basally (proximad) of the penis and often surrounding it when in repose, usually divided into basal piece and parameres (Tuxen) or applied to basal piece, q.v., alone (Tuxen, after Muir); in ♂ Lepidoptera, tegumen, q.v. (Tuxen, after Huebner); in ♂ Tabanoidea (Diptera), aedeagal sheath, q.v. (McAlpine); see elytron.

tegmenite, in ♂ Coleoptera, isolated basal sclerite of the tegmen, situated on the second connecting membrane (Tuxen, after Arnett).

tegula (pl., **tegulae**), a sclerite carried at the extreme base of the costa of the forewing, being very large and overlapping the wing base in Lepidoptera and also well-developed in Hymenoptera and Diptera (T-B, after Imms; McAlpine); in adult Diptera, alula, q.v. (T-B, after Comstock); in ♂ Orthoptera, cingulum, q.v. (Tuxen); see humeral plate and patagium.

tegular arms, in Lepidoptera, the internal structures which support the tegular plates (T-B, after Comstock).

tegular plate, in adult Lepidoptera, the structure of the notum which bears the tegula of the forewing (T-B, after Comstock).

tegumen (pl., **tegumina**), in ♂ *Nymphes* (Planipennia: Nymphidae), mediuncus, q.v. (Tuxen, after Crampton); in ♂ Lepidoptera, abdominal tergum IX + cephalic elements of tergum X, more or less expanded caudad and lateroventrad to form a roof- or hoodlike structure (Tuxen, after Petersen); in ♂ Rhopalocera (Lepidoptera), tegumen (Petersen) + uncus + vinculum (Tuxen, after Buchanan White); in ♂ Papilionidae (Lepidoptera), broadly expanded tergum VIII minus superuncus (Tuxen, after Gosse).

tegument, integument, q.v. (T-B).

tegumentary, integumentary, q.v. (T-B).

tegumentary nerve, one of a pair of slender nerves arising from the dorsal lobe of the deutocerebrum and passing to the vertex (T-B, after Imms); see antennal nerve.

teleaform larva, in Hymenoptera with a hypermetamorphosis (e.g., Proctotrupoidea), a larva which resembles the first-instar larva of *Teleas* (Scelionidae), with prominently hooked or curved, ventrally-directed, cephalic protuberances, and having one or more girdles of setae about the abdomen (T-B, after Imms; Gauld and Bolton).

teleodont, a form of ♂ Lucanidae (Coleoptera) bearing the largest mandibles (T-B); see mesodont and priodont.

teleological, purposive or purposeful (T-B).

teleology, a form of anthropomorphism in which processes in nature are directed toward some discernible goal (T-B; Matthews and Matthews).

teleomorphic phase, in Muscomorpha (Diptera), the pupal phase with adult external structures (legs, wings, and proboscis) becoming visible though the pupal integument during replacement of pupal body wall by the adult body wall, the pupal integument still enclosing the unpigmented insect (Peterson, after Dean).

telescope, to run segments into each other (T-B); or to run together or eliminate stages in the development of an animal (T-B).

telescopic, arranged so that one portion of an organ or process may be drawn into another, like the joints of a telescope (T-B).

Telmatobia, Ochteroidea, q.v. (Hennig, after Rieger).

telmophage, a blood-feeding insect that obtains blood directly from a pool of blood formed in tissue after the mouthparts have lacerated blood vessels (Adkins, pers. comm.).

telofilum, in Thysanura and Ephemeroptera, filum terminale, q.v. (Tuxen, after Crampton).

telomere(s), in ♂ insects, distal segment of paramere (Tuxen, after Snodgrass); in ♂ Chironomidae (Diptera), gonostylus, q.v. (Saether); in ♂ Siphonaptera, moveable process, q.v. (Tuxen, after Smit); in ♂ Trichoptera, apical segment of a divided paramere (T-B, after Snodgrass); see harpago.

telomeres dorsalis, in ♂ Siphonaptera, dorsal (or anterior) telomere when 2 are present (Tuxen, after Smit).

telomeres ventralis, in ♂ Siphonaptera, ventral (or posterior) telomere when 2 are present (Tuxen, after J. B. Smith).

Telomerida, hypothesized monophyletic group including the Hymenoptera, Neuropteroidea, and Panorpoidea (Boudreaux).

telophragma, Krause's membrane, q.v. (T-B, after Folsom and Wardle).

telopodite, the primary six-segmented shaft of the insect limb distal to the coxopodite, the basal segment of which is the first trochanter (basipodite) (T-B, after Snodgrass); in ♂ Thysanura, parameres, q.v. (Tuxen, after Escherich); in ♂ Siphonaptera, telomere, q.v. (Tuxen, after Enderlein); in ♀ Thysanura, gonapophyses, q.v. (Tuxen, after Escherich).

telotarsus, the distal of the 2 principal subsegments of the tarsus in Arachnida and Chilopoda (T-B, after Snodgrass).

telotaxis, orientation as if with a purposive end in view (T-B; Leftwich); a reaction in which an insect or other organism orients itself and moves in a direct direction towards the source of a stimulus (Leftwich); see phototelotaxis.

telotrophic egg tube, telotrophic ovariole, q.v. (T-B).

telotrophic ovariole, in Heteroptera (Hemiptera) and many Polyphaga (Coleoptera), an ovariole with trophic tissue in the germarium, connected to each developing oocyte by a cytoplasmic nutritive cord (Chapman).

telson (Greek), end; boundary (R. W. Brown); the primitive terminal body segment in arthropods, which bears the anus and corresponds to the periproct of annelids and probably not a true body somite (T-B, after Snodgrass); the terminal region of the abdomen, found in the embryos of many insects, but rarely (Protura) in the adult (T-B, after Imms; Chapman); the terminal part of the insect abdomen that bears the anus (T-B, after Wardle); in Coccoidea (Hemiptera: Sternorrhyncha), the single plate representing the continuous lateral pilacerores of the meson of the eighth segment, i.e., postanal plate (T-B, after MacGillivray); in Dermaptera, plate of opisthomeres, q.v., that may be lost or fused with the metapygidium (Tuxen).

telum (Latin), a spear-shaped process (T-B); telson, q.v. (T-B).

temones, in ♂ Coleoptera, paired processes (apophyses, apodemes) of the penis or tegmen (Lindroth and Palmén, in Tuxen).

temple, the part of the head above and behind the compound eyes; in some adult Odonata, postocular lobe (O'Farrell, in CSIRO); in adult Hymenoptera, upper part of gena (Gauld and Bolton).

temporal, of or relating to the temple of the head.

temporal foveolae, in Orthoptera, foveate depressions on the margins of the vertex near the front border of the eye (Key, pers. comm.).

temporal orbit, in adult Hymenoptera, genal orbit, q.v. (Gauld and Bolton).

temporal summation, cummulative effect of successive impulses arriving at a synapse, initiating a postsynaptic impulse (Chapman).

temporals, in adult Chironomidae (Diptera), setae located behind, dorsal, mesal and between eyes, including postorbitals, orbitals, inner and outer verticals, and frontals (Saether).

temporary parasitism, temporary social parasitism, q.v. (Matthews and Matthews).

temporary polyethism, age polyethism, q.v. (Wilson).

temporary social parasitism, parasitism in which the queen of one species enters an alien nest, usually belonging to another species, kills or renders infertile the resident queen, and takes her place, the colony then becoming increasingly dominated by the offspring of the parasite queen as the host workers die off from natural causes (Wilson).

tenacula, in ♂ Diptera, retinacula, q.v. (Tuxen).

tenacular ridges, in Collembola, the sclerotizations on the inner bases of the dentes with which the tenacular teeth engage (Christiansen and Bellinger).

tenaculum, in Collembola, a minute organ with 2 divergent prongs, situated medially on the ventral surface of the third abdominal segment, serving to hold the furcula in place (T-B; Borror et al.); in ♂ Hymenoptera, gonostylus, q.v. (Tuxen, after Radoszkowski).

tendinous, of or pertaining to a tendon (T-B); of the character of a tendon (T-B).

tendo, the anal area of the hind wings when it forms a groove for the abdomen (T-B); in adult Trichoptera, a small elliptical space at the base of the hind wings near the base of the anal veins and behind the trochlea (T-B).

tendon, a slender, chitinous plate, band, or cup-shaped piece, to which muscles are attached for moving appendages (T-B); in ♂ *Zorotypus zimmermani* (Zoraptera), part of the complicated genital structure (Tuxen); in ♂ Trichoptera, thin band-shaped structure, joining phallobase with clasper and/or abdominal segment X (Ross); in Lepidoptera, frenulum, q.v. (T-B, after Kirby and Spence); in ♂ *Hadena* (Lepidoptera: Noctuidae), costal hook of harpe, transtilla auct. (Tuxen, after Forbes); see apodeme.

tendon of sternum IX, in ♂ Siphonaptera, apophysis, q.v. (Tuxen).

tendril, in some ♂ Collembola, an elongate, usually coiled seta of the dorsal abdominal organ (Christiansen and Bellinger).

Tenebrionoidea, superfamily within the Polyphaga (Coleoptera), including the families Tenebrionidae, Mycetophagidae, Ciidae, Melandryidae, Mordellidae, Rhipophoridae, Meloidae, and many others, possessing adults without a transverse suture on metasternum, hind tarsus with 4 or fewer articles, trochanter obliquely attached, so that femur is in contact with coxa, and ♂ aedeagus with tegmen lying dorsal to median lobe (Lawrence, in Parker).

tenent, adapted for holding on, clinging or clasping (T-B).

tenent hair(s), adhesive setae located on the underside of the tarsi, aiding insects in walking on smooth surfaces (T-B; Leftwich); in Collembola, apically expanded setae situated near apices of tibiotarsus, overhanging pretarsus and claws, may be clavate, capitate or setiform (Richards); see euplantulae.

teneral, condition of the adult shortly after eclosion when its cuticle is not fully sclerotized or fully mature in color (T-B); an insect in the teneral condition.

teneral period, period during which an insect is teneral (Chapman).

tension receptor, stretch receptor, q.v. (Leftwich).

tensor, a muscle which stretches a membrane (T-B).

tentacle, tentacule, tentaculum (Latin), (pl., **tentaculi**), feeler (T-B; R. W. Brown); see maxillary tentacle.

tentacular, of or pertaining to organs of touch or tentacles (T-B).

tentaculate, tentaculatus, having tenticles (T-B).

tentaculiferous, bearing tentacles (T-B).

Tenthredinoidea, superfamily within the Symphyta (Hymenoptera), including the Tenthredinidae, Parsidae, Argidae, Blasticotomidae, Cimbicidae, and Diprionidae, possessing adults with narrow, emarginate pronotum, foretibia with 2 apical spurs, forewing lacking intercostal vein, second radial crossvein of forewing distal to second radiomedial crossvein, and base of ♂ parameres absent (Gauld and Bolton, after Königsmann; Schauff, pers. comm.).

tentiform, shaped like a tent (T-B).

tentiform mine, blotch mine in which the leaf is thrown into a fold on one side (T-B).

tentorial arms, anterior tentorial arms, q.v., and posterior tentorial arms, q.v. (T-B).

tentorial bar, in larval, pupal, and adult Culicidae (Diptera), the right or left half of the tentorium comprised mainly of the united anterior and posterior tentorial bars (Harbach and Knight).

tentorial bridge, posterior tentorial arms, q.v., which are continuous in a transverse bar (T-B, after Snodgrass); in larval Coleoptera, bridge within the head between the posterior ends of the hypostomata (Peterson, after Böving and Craighead).

tentorial foveae, in adult Hymenoptera, anterior tentorial pits, q.v. (T-B).

tentorial macula, one of the dark spots where the dorsal arms of the tentorium unite with the epicranial wall in the neighborhood of the antennae, e.g., in Dermaptera (T-B, after Snodgrass; Popham).

tentorial pits, the external depressions in the cranial wall at the roots of the tentorial arms (T-B, after Snodgrass); see anterior tentorial pits and posterior tentorial pits.

tentorium, endoskeleton of the head, serving as a brace and site for attachment of muscles (T-B; Chapman).

tentoropharyngeal sclerite, in larval Muscomorpha (Diptera), major part of cephalopharyngeal skeleton consisting of a pair of reclining, somewhat U-shaped sclerites on either side of the pharynx (Teskey, in McAlpine); paraclypeal phragma, q.v. (Ferrar).

tenuis (Latin), stretched; expanded (T-B; R. W. Brown).

tenuivirus, an RNA plant virus of Gramineae, transmitted propagatively by Delphacidae (Hemiptera: Sternorrhyncha) (Nault and Ammar).

Tephritoidea, superfamily within the series Schizophora of the Muscomorpha (Diptera: Brachycera), including the Tephritidae and other families, possessing males with abdominal segment VI vestigial or absent, aedeagus very long and coiled, and females with abdominal segment VII more or less enlarged and forming an ovipositor sheath, the subsequent segments forming an elongate ovipositor (Colless and McAlpine, in CSIRO).

teratocyte, a cell that has originated from an uneclosed parasitoid and which is liberated into the body cavity of the host when the parasitoid hatches, often being a remnant of the trophamnion (Tulloch, after Paillot, Jones; Gauld and Bolton); see pseudogermes.

teratogyne, in ants (Hymenoptera: Formicidae), an aberrant form of ♀ present in a colony either as the only form or coexisting with other females, i.e., with normal or with alpha-females; originally designated as beta-females by Wheeler (Tulloch).

teratological specimen, an abnormal specimen or a monstrosity (ICZN).

teratology, the study of structural abnormalities, especially monstrosities and malformations (Mayr; Steinhaus and Martignoni).

terebella, a sawlike ovipositor (T-B); see saw and terebra.

terebra (pl., **terebrae**), a borer or piercer (T-B); a mandibular sclerite articulated to the basalis, forming the point of the structure and equivalent to the galea of the maxilla (T-B); in ♀ Odonata, the combined anterior and median gonapophyses (Tuxen, after Tillyard); in ♀ Cordulegasteridae (Odonata), the enormously hypertrophied anterior gonapophyses (Tuxen, after authors); in ♀ Psocoptera, lamina subgenitalis, q.v. (Tuxen, after Kolbe); in ♀ Terebrantia (Thysanoptera), ovipositor, q.v. (Tuxen); in ♀ Tenthredinidae (Hymenoptera), sawlike ovipositor, q.v. (Tuxen).

terebrant, adapted for boring (Leftwich); having a piercing or boring organ which may be either a modified ovipositor or more rarely a modified proboscis (T-B; Leftwich).

terebrant Hymenoptera, members of the Apocrita (Hymenoptera), having an ovipositor for piercing or boring, rather than a sting (Riek, in CSIRO); see aculeate.

Terebrantes, terebrant Hymenoptera, q.v. (Leftwich); see aculeate Hymenoptera.

Terebrantia, suborder of Thysanoptera, including the Thripidae, Aeolothripidae, Merothripidae, Heterothripidae, Adiheterothripidae, Fauriellidae and Uzelothripidae possessing females with saw-like ovipositor and apex of abdomen conical, males with apex of abdomen rounded, and wings carried side by side along the dorsum when at rest (Mound et al.); terebrant Hymenoptera, q.v. (T-B).

terebrate, terebrant, q.v. (Leftwich).

teres, terete, cylindrical or nearly so (T-B).

tergal, belonging to the tergum (T-B); see dorsal.

tergal apodeme (of tergum IX), in ♂ Siphonaptera, apodeme of tergum IX, q.v. (Tuxen, after Snodgrass).

tergal apophyse, in ♀ Orthoptera, acrotergite, q.v. (Tuxen, after Snodgrass).

tergal arms, in ♂ Tipulidae (Diptera), surstyli, q.v. (McAlpine, after Byers).

tergal fissure, in adult Diptera, lateral transverse groove on the scutum between median and posterior notal wing processes (McAlpine).

tergal glands, in ♂ Blattaria, specialized glandular area (indicated by groups of setae, or fossae or depressions with or without setae) on one or more abdominal terga, used in sexual behavior and in maneuvering the ♀ and arresting her movement in the proper position for mating (Roth).

tergal plate, in anopheline larvae (Diptera: Culicidae), a small sclerite occurring anteriorly on the dorsal midline of abdominal segments I–VIII (Harbach and Knight, after Imms).

tergal processes, in ♂ Grylloblattodea, ventrolateral arms, q.v. (Tuxen, after Snodgrass); in ♂ Embiidina, caudal processes of left and right hemitergite of abdominal segment X (Ross, in Tuxen).

tergal valves, in ♀ Diptera, cerci, q.v. (Tuxen).

tergiferous, bearing on the back (T-B), e.g., ♂ *Belostoma* (Hemiptera: Heteroptera: Belostomatidae), which carries eggs on its back.

tergiproct, in Caelifera (Orthoptera), the combined, caudal part of abdominal tergum X and epiproct (Tuxen, after Ander).

tergite, a dorsal sclerite or part of a segment, especially when such consists of a single sclerite (T-B); see notum and tergum.

tergopleural, of or pertaining to the upper and lateral portion of a segment (T-B).

tergopleural apodeme, in adult Lepidoptera, a strongly sclerotized apodeme of the mesothorax on which the tergopleural muscle of the forewing is inserted (Common, in CSIRO).

tergorhabdites, in ♀ Blattopteroidea, valvulae superiores, q.v. (Tuxen, after Lacaze-Duthiers); plates on the inner surface of the abdominal wall (T-B).

tergosternal, of or pertaining to the tergum and sternum together (T-B).

tergosternal muscle, flight muscle lying to side of the median dorsal muscle in the anterior part of the segment, attached dorsally on the anterior lateral areas of the tergum and ventrally on the basisternum before the coxae (T-B, after Snodgrass).

tergosternum, in ♂ Diptera, hypandrium, q.v. (Tuxen, after Zumpt and Heinz).

tergum (pl., **terga**), the upper or dorsal surface of any body segment of an insect, whether consisting of one or more than one sclerite (T-B); the large sclerite on the dorsal surface of a segment (Chapman); see notum and tergite.

termen, apical margin, q.v., of wing (T-B).

terminal, situated at the tip or extremity (T-B); see basal.

terminal anastomosis, lamina ganglionaris, q.v., of optic lobe (T-B).

terminal apparatus, in ♀ Grylloidea (Orthoptera), the specialized structures in the apex of the ovipositor (Tuxen).

terminal appendage of tail of spermatheca, in ♀ Siphonaptera, papilla, q.v. (Tuxen).

terminal arborizations, the fine branching fibrils ending the axon and the collateral ends (T-B).

terminal bulb, in ♀ Gerridae (Hemiptera: Heteroptera), capsula seminalis (in part), q.v. (Tuxen, after Brinkhurst).

terminal chamber, in ♂ Heteroptera (Hemiptera), genital chamber, q.v. (Tuxen, after Sharp).

terminal disease, in invertebrate pathology, a disease which ends the life of an organism (Steinhaus and Martignoni).

terminal filament(s), the cellular end thread of an ovariole (T-B) (see suspensory ligament); in Ephemeroptera, cerci and filum terminale, q.v. (Tuxen); in nymphs of Plecoptera, e.g., Gripopterygidae and Australoperlidae, filamentous appendages at the dorsal apex of the abdomen believed to be remnants of abdominal segment XI (Zwick, pers. comm., after Illies).

terminal fold, in ♂ Zygoptera (Odonata), preputial fold, q.v. (Tuxen, after Kennedy).

terminal line, in adult Lepidoptera, a line along the outer margin or termen of the wings (T-B).

terminal plate, in ♂ *Sialis* (Megaloptera: Sialidae), fused ectoprocts (Tuxen, after Ross); in Lycaenidae (Lepidoptera), sterigma, q.v. (Tuxen, after Chapman).

terminal proleg, in larval Diptera, proleg on terminal abdominal segment (Teskey, in McAlpine); see anal proleg.

terminal segment, in ♂ Heteroptera (Hemiptera), pygophore, q.v. (Tuxen, after Sharp).

terminal segment of penis, in ♂ Odonata, glans, q.v. (Tuxen, after Borror).

terminal space, in certain adult Lepidoptera, the area between the subterminal tranverse line (s.t. line) and the terminal line of the wing (T-B, after J. B. Smith).

terminal taxon, a taxon whose name is indicated at the end of a branch of a cladogram.

terminal ventral process, in ♂ *Glossosoma* (Trichoptera: Glossosomatidae), probably unpaired paramere (Tuxen, after McLachlan).

terminalia, the terminal abdominal segments (and their parts) modified to form the genital segments (T-B, after Crampton).

termitarium (pl., **termitaria**), a nest, natural or artificial, or a colony, of termites (Isoptera) (T-B).

termite, a member of the order Isoptera (T-B; Gay, in CSIRO).

termitiform, resembling a termite (Isoptera) (Peterson).

termitology, the study of termites (Isoptera) (Wilson).

termitophile, a termite (Isoptera) insect guest, of another order (T-B, after Comstock); inquiline in the nest of termites (Isoptera) (Leftwich); an organism that must spend at least part of its life cycle with termite (Isoptera) colonies (Wilson).

termitophilous, termite (Isoptera) loving; applied to the insect and other guests habitually living in a termite colony with and among the termites (T-B).

terpene, any hydrocarbon composed of 2 or more isoprene units (Allaby).

terpenoids, complex volatile compounds frequently employed as pheromones, e.g., geraniol and pinene (Gilmour, in CSIRO).

terrestrial, living on the land, as opposed to being aquatic (T-B).

territorialism, territoriality, q.v. (Norris, in CSIRO).

territoriality, broadly, any space-associated intolerance of others and, more narrowly, an intolerance based on real estate holdings (Matthews and Matthews).

tertian malaria, malignant tertian malaria, q.v. (Borror et al.).

tertiary fringe scale, in adult Culicidae (Diptera), one of the small linear scales set in 2 rows on the wing margin, on the dorsal surface just inside the row of fringe scales and the other on the ventral surface just inside the row of secondary fringe scales, being poorly developed in males (Harbach and Knight, after Knight and Laffoon).

Tertiary Period, period within the Cenozoic Era, extending between about 70 and 1 million years before the present (Riek, in CSIRO).

tertiary reproductive, in termites (Isoptera), ergatoid reproductive, q.v. (Wilson).

tessellate, tessellated, tessellatus (Latin), made up of squares like a chess board, either in sculpture or in color (T-B; Harris, after Marchant and Charles, and Munz); see cancellate and clathrate.

tessellated membrane, any membrane with a surface resembling a mosaic (Harbach and Knight).

tesselated membranous area, in mosquito larvae (Diptera: Culicidae), the area composed of the palatal tessellated area, the lateral palatal penicular area and the anteromedian palatal penicular area (Harbach and Knight, after Pao and Knight).

test, in most Coccoidea (Hemiptera: Sternorrhyncha), scale, q.v. (T-B); in Diaspididae (Hemiptera: Sternorrhyncha: Coccoidea), covering consisting of exuviae, secreted waxy material, and excrement (Kosztarab and Kozár); in Psylloidea (Hemiptera: Sternorrhyncha), lerp, q.v. (Woodward et al., in CSIRO).

testaceous, testaceus, bearing a hard covering (T-B); brownish-yellow (T-B).

testicular, of or pertaining to the testis (T-B).

testicular follicle, testis follicle, q.v. (T-B).

testicular tube, testis follicle, q.v. (T-B).

testiculate, shaped like a testicle (T-B).

testis (pl., **testes**), usually paired ♂ gonad, consisting of a number of testis follicles, bound by a peritoneal sheath, connecting with the seminal vesicle via the vas deferens (T-B; Chapman).

testis follicle, tubular structure within a testis within which spermatogenesis takes place (Chapman).

testudinate, testudinatus, resembling the shell of a tortoise, i.e., roofed, arched, or vaulted (T-B).

testudinarious, testudinarius, with brown, black, and yellow markings, like tortoise-shell (T-B).

Tethys Sea, ancient sea separating Laurasia from Gondwanaland (Mackerras, in CSIRO).

tetra-, Greek prefix; four (T-B).

tetradactyle, with 4 fingers or fingerlike processes (T-B).

tetragonal, tetragonum (Latin), having 4 sides or angles; quadrangular (T-B).

Tetramera, the Coleoptera with 4 tarsomeres in each tarsus (T-B).

tetramerous, having tarsi each with 4 tarsomeres (T-B).

Tetraptera, old name proposed for all insects with 4 naked, membranous reticulated wings (T-B).

tetrapterous, having 4 wings (Leftwich).

tetrapyroles, class of chemicals consisting of 4 pyroles joined together, including pigments such as porphyrins and bilins (Chapman).

Tetrigoidea, superfamily within the Caelifera (Orthoptera), including only the family Tetrigidae, possessing fore- and midtarsi each with 2 tarsomeres, hind tarsus with 3 tarsomeres, and pronotum produced posteriorly so as to overlie dorsally the rest of the thorax and at least the first few abdominal segments (Key, in CSIRO).

Tettigonioidea, superfamily within the Ensifera (Orthoptera), including long-horned grasshoppers, or katydids, of the families Tettigoniidae and Prophalangopsidae, possessing tarsi with 4 tarsomeres, tegminized forewings, and fore- and midtibiae very rarely with ventral articulated spines (Key, in CSIRO).

Texas cattle fever, disease of cattle caused by *Babesia bigemina* (Protozoa: Piroplasmea) and transmitted by the cattle tick, *Boophilus annulatus* (Say) (Acari) (Borror et al.); see babesioses.

thamnophilous, living in thickets or dense shrubbery (T-B).

thanatosis, feigning death, i.e., remaining motionless for a period of time if disturbed (Norris, in CSIRO).

Thaumastocoridea, superfamily recognized by some authors, within the infraorder Cimicomorpha (Hemiptera: Heteroptera), including the single family Thaumastocoridae (Schuh).

theca (pl., **thecae**), any protective case or covering, e.g., the chitinous covering of a pupa (T-B; Leftwich); in ♂ Odonata, vesicula spermalis, q.v. (Tuxen, after Rathke); in ♂ Blattopteroidea, right epiphallus (Tuxen, after Wesché); in ♂ Auchenorrhyncha (Hemiptera), a fold or sheath from the phallobase partly or totally enclosing the aedeagus (Tuxen); in ♂ Heteroptera (Hemiptera), phallotheca, q.v. (Tuxen, after Sharp); in ♂ Lepidoptera, anellus, (Tuxen, after Snodgrass); in ♂ Diptera, basiphallus, q.v. (Tuxen; McAlpine); in many adult Muscomorpha (Diptera), conspicuous ventral sclerite of the proboscis corresponding to the prementum (Colless and McAlpine, in CSIRO).

thecal, of or pertaining to a theca (T-B).

Thelyphonida, Uropygi, q.v. (Borror et al.).

thelyotoky, thelytoky, q.v. (T-B).

thelytoky, parthenogenesis in which only females are produced (T-B; Chapman); the production of females from unfertilized eggs (Wilson); see amphitoky and arrhenotoky.

thermal sense, perception of temperature (T-B).

thermocline, in a body of water, a narrow dividing stratum between the epilimnion and hypolimnion, q.v. (Tulloch).

thermometabolism, the dependence of metabolic activity on temperature (T-B).

thermotropism, the reaction of an organism to temperature changes (T-B).

thiamin, essential vitamin in the diets of insects (Gilmour, in CSIRO).

thigh, femur, q.v. (T-B).

thigmotactic, contact-loving; applied to species that tend to live close together or in touch, one with the other (T-B).

thigmotaxis, a locomotory response, sometimes an inhibition of movement, caused by the stimulus of touch, causing many insects and other small animals to cling to surfaces or crevices with which they come into contact (T-B; Leftwich); see stereokinesis.

thigmotropism, reaction to contact or touch (T-B).

third axillary, third axillary sclerite, q.v. (T-B, after Snodgrass).

third axillary plate, in adult Diptera, third axillary sclerite, q.v. (McAlpine).

third axillary sclerite, Y-shaped axillary sclerite articulating anteriorly with second axillary sclerite, distally with base of anal veins, and proximally with posterior notal process, upon which the flexor muscle inserts (Chapman; Harbach and Knight).

third clasper, in ♂ Chironomidae, superior volsella, q.v. (Saether).

third-form reproductive, in Isoptera, ergatoid reproductive, q.v. (E. M. Miller).

third gonapophyses, in ♀ Heteroptera (Hemiptera), gonoplacs, q.v. (Tuxen, after Davis); in ♀ Phymatidae (Hemiptera: Heteroptera), ? gonocoxites IX (Tuxen, after Davis); in ♂ Hymenoptera, gonobase + gonocoxites + gonostyli (Tuxen, after Rohwer).

third longitudinal vein, in adult Diptera, posterior branch of radius, R_{4+5} (T-B, after Williston).

third ramus, in ♀ Heteroptera (Hemiptera), (unorthodox usage) anterior connecting leaf of gonapophysis IX, q.v. (Tuxen, after Southwood).

third segment of penis, in ♂ Odonata, body of penis, q.v. (Tuxen, after Borror) or glans, q.v. (Tuxen, after Selys-Longchamps).

third submarginal cross-nervure, in adult Hymenoptera, third radio-medial crossvein (T-B, after Norton).

third valves, in ♀ Isoptera, dorsal valves, q.v. (Tuxen).

third valvulae, in ♀ insects, gonoplacs, q.v. (Tuxen, after Snodgrass); in ♀ Odonata, lateral gonapophyses, q.v. (Tuxen, after Snodgrass); in ♀ Blattopteroidea, valvulae superiores, q.v. (Tuxen, after Snodgrass); in ♀ Isoptera, dorsal valves, q.v. (Tuxen); in ♀ Orthoptera, posterior valvulae, q.v. (Tuxen, after Snodgrass); in ♀ Psocoptera, valvae externae, q.v. (Tuxen, after Broadhead); in ♀ Auchenorrhyncha (Hemiptera), saw-case, q.v. (Tuxen, after Fennah); in ♀ Heteroptera (Hemiptera), gonoplacs, q.v. (Tuxen, after Snodgrass); in ♀ Hymenoptera, gonoplacs, q.v. (Tuxen, after Michener).

thoracic, belonging or attached to the thorax (T-B).

thoracic brush, in adult Chironomidae (Diptera), scopula thoracalis, q.v. (Saether).

thoracic dorsal bristles, in Diptera, the specialized bristles on the dorsum of the thorax, e.g., the dorsocentrals, scutellars, acrosticuals (T-B).

thoracic ganglia, the first 3 ganglia of the ventral nerve cord, posterior to the suboesophageal ganglion, primitively situated one in each of the thoracic segments, controlling the locomotory organs (T-B, after Imms).

thoracic horn, in pupal Chironomidae (Diptera), variously-shaped and ornamented organ anteriorly on each side of cephalothorax (Saether); respiratory horn or trumpet, q.v.

thoracic leg, the jointed appendage of a thoracic segment of insect larvae, as distinguished from abdominal or prolegs (T-B).

thoracic region, the second of the 3 regions into which the embryonic trunk segments become segregated, the future locomotor center of the insect by the development of its appendages (legs and wings) as locomotory organs (T-B, after Snodgrass).

thoracic salivary gland, in the honey bee (Hymenoptera: Apidae), labial gland, q.v. (T-B, after Imms).

thoracic squama, in adult Diptera, lower calypter, q.v. (Chapman).

thoracic sternal gills, in nymphs of Ephemeroptera, single membranous outgrowths that occur on the midsternal line of each thoracic segment of some taxa (T-B, after Needham and Murphy).

thoracic tracheal folds, in Aleyrodidae (Hemiptera: Sternorrhyncha), folds on venter of pupa leading from the spiracles to the body margin, providing air passage (Gill).

thoracico-abdominal segment, propodeum, q.v. (T-B).

thorax, middle portion of the body between the head and abdomen, consisting of 3 segments (prothorax, mesothorax, and metathorax), each of which usually bear a pair of articulated legs (T-B; Chapman); see mesosoma, pterothorax, and thoracic region.

thorn, in some Collembola, enlarged conical granule located dorsally on the dens (Christiansen and Bellinger).

thread plate, an epithelial plate of the embryo from which the terminal threads of the ovarian tubes originate (T-B).

thread press, in larval Lepidoptera, silk press, q.v. (T-B).

threonine, an essential amino acid in the diets of insects (Gilmour, in CSIRO).

threshold of development, the temperature at which, on the descending scale, development definitely ceases and at which, on the ascending scale, development is initiated (Tulloch, after Uvarov).

threshold of response, the measurable level of stimulus required to release a response (Matthews and Matthews).

thrips (sing. and pl.), member of the order Thysanoptera (Reed, in CSIRO).

thumb, in any digitate organ or structure, the thick outer finger; any thick blunt branch arising from a structure (T-B).

thylactium, an external galllike cyst in the abdomen of the host, containing the parasitic larva of Dryinidae (Hymenoptera) (T-B; Riek, in CSIRO).

thyridial cell, in adult Trichoptera, the cell formed by the first fork of the media, i.e., cell M, located behind the thyridium (T-B; Riek, in CSIRO).

thyridiate, thyridiatus, broken so as to permit folding or bending, as a wing vein (T-B).

thyridium (pl., **thyridia**), in some adult Neuropteroidea, small, whitish, or almost transparent spots near the anastomosis of the disc of the wings (T-B); in adult Trichoptera, a hyaline spot on the first fork of the median vein (T-B); in adult Ichneumonidae and some Aculeata (Hymenoptera), a differently sculptured, elliptical or more or less oval, area located anteriorly on abdominal tergite III, and sometimes on abdominal tergite IV (T-B; Gauld and Bolton).

Thyridoidea, superfamily of the infraorder Ditrysia (Lepidoptera) containing one family Thyrididae, adults being small to medium-sized moths with broad wings and often stout bodies, naked proboscis, one- or two-segmented maxillary palpi, without tympanal organs; larvae with 2 prespiracular (L) setae on prothorax, without secondary setae, crochets in uni- or biordinal circle; pupae without dorsal spines, not protruded at ecdysis (Common).

thyroid, in adult Diptera, a prominent plate on the posterior wall of the haustellum (T-B, after Snodgrass).

thyrsus, a cluster (T-B).

Thysanoptera, order of exopterygote Neoptera (Insecta), including small, usually slender insects with asymmetrical rasping mouthparts, tarsi with eversible apical bladders, wings, when present, short, narrow, with reduced venation and wide marginal fringe, cerci absent, and metamorphosis gradual, but with 2 or 3 preimaginal resting stages (T-B; Reed, in CSIRO).

Thysanopterida, Thysanoptera, q.v. (Boudreaux).

Thysanopteroidea, Thysanoptera, q.v. (Boudreaux, after Weber).

Thysanura, Zygentoma, q.v. (Sturm, pers. comm., after Birket-Smith, Wygodzinsky; Borror et al.); Entognatha + Archaeognatha + Zygentoma, q.v. (Sturm, pers. comm., after Latreille); Diplura + Archaeognatha + Zygentoma (Sturm, pers. comm., after Grassi); Archaeognatha + Zygentoma (T-B; Sturm, pers. comm., after Börner).

Thysanura Entotrophica, Diplura, q.v. (T-B).

thysanuriform larva, oligopod larva resembling a member of the Zygentoma, being common among beetles (Coleoptera), mayflies (Ephemeroptera), dragonflies (Odonata), etc. (T-B); see campodeiform larva and elateriform larva.

tibia (pl., **tibiae**), the fourth segment of the leg, between the femur and the tibia (T-B; Chapman).

tibiaflexis, femorotibial joint, q.v. (T-B, after MacGillvray).

tibial, of or pertaining to the tibia (T-B).

tibial comb, in adult Chironomidae (Diptera), either row of spiniform setae at apex of hind tibia, or structures formed by a series of basally fused spinules on mid- and hind tibiae or nonarticulated comblike structure (Saether); a strigil or scraper, q.v.

tibial epiphysis, in adult Lepidoptera, epiphysis, q.v. (T-B).

tibial gland, in adult *Dolichopus* (Diptera: Dolichopodidae), gland on hind tibia (McAlpine, after Kazjakina).

tibial keels, in ♂ Corduliidae and Synthemidae (Odonata: Anisoptera), fused rows of comblike spines on tibia (O'Farrell, in CSIRO).

tibial organ, in adult Chloropidae (Diptera), specialized sensory area on the hind tibia (McAlpine, after Anderson).

tibial scale, in adult Chironomidae (Saether), oval extension of tibia at apex which may be spiniform at its tip (Saether).

tibial spur formula, in Isoptera, a formula expressing the number of tibial spurs present in the fore- mid- and hind tibia, respectively, expressed as 3:3:3; 3:2:2, and so forth (Krishna, pers. comm.).

tibial spurs, the spur or spurs frequently borne near to or at the end of the tibia (T-B); see comb.

tibial thumb, in *Pediculus* (Phthiraptera: Pediculidae), an extension of the inner distal end of the tibia, apposed to the claw for grasping hairs, etc. (T-B).

tibiarolium, fossula spongiosa, q.v. (T-B, after MacGillivray).

tibiofemoral, femorotibial, q.v. (T-B).

tibiotarsal organ, in Sminthuridae (Collembola), complex structure found on tibiotarsus (T-B; Christiansen and Bellinger).

tibiotarsal segment, tibiotarsus, q.v. (T-B).

tibiotarsus, in Collembola, fourth leg segment from the base, arising from the femur and bearing the pretarsus apically (Christiansen and Bellinger).

tick, a member of the suborder Ixodida (Acari), including the families Ixodidae (hard ticks) and the Argasidae (soft ticks) (Borror et al.).

tick fever, African tick fever, q.v., or Colorado tick fever, q.v. (Borror et al.).

tick paralysis, paralysis in vertebrates caused by venom from ♀ ticks (Acari) feeding on the neck or near the base of the skull (Borror et al.).

tigellus (pl., **tigelli**), in ♂ Plecoptera, long, slender spine arising from part of subanal plates (Tuxen, after Brinck).

tignum (pl., **tigna**), in some ♂ Chrysopidae (Planipennia), transverse arched structure between subanale and gonarcus (Tuxen, after Tjeder).

tiller, in cereal grains, a sucker or shoot from the root or near the main stalk (T-B).

timbal, in Cicadidae (Hemiptera: Auchenorrhyncha), at the base of the abdomen, the membranous area in the lateral cavity on the lateral wall of the partition separating the 2 cavities of the chordotonal organ (T-B, after Comstock); the shelllike drum in cicadas, at the base of the abdomen, used in producing sound, also termed the tympanum (T-B, after Imms).

Timematidea, in Phasmida, infraorder of Timematodea, including the single superfamily Timematoidea (Kevan).

Timematodea, suborder within the Phasmida, containing the infraorder Timematidea (Kevan).

Timematoidea, in Phasmida, superfamily in infraorder Timematidea containing the single family Timematidae, containing the single genus *Timema* (Kevan).

tineoid apodemes, in adult Tineoidea, Yponomeutoidea and Gelechioidea (Lepidoptera), paired, relatively slender apodemes protruding from the anterior margin of the abdominal sternite II, usually at the anterior end of rodlike thickenings (venulae) of sternum II, providing articulation with the metathorax (Brock).

Tinaeoidea, Tineoidea, q.v. (Borror et al.).

tinctorial pattern, color pattern (T-B).

Tineoidea, the most primitive superfamily within the division Ditrysia (Lepidoptera), including the families Arrhenophanidae, Eriocottidae, Psychidae, and Tineidae, being very small to medium sized moths without chaetosema, with maxillary palpi often five-segmented and folded, ♀ usually with elongate, telescoping ovipositor bearing 3 or more pairs of apophyses; pupa with dorsal abdominal spines, and larvae frequently living in tubes or portable cases (Davis).

Tingoidea, superfamily within the infraorder Cimicomorpha of the Heteroptera (Hemiptera), including only the phytophagous Tingidae (lace bugs); see also Miroidea.

tip, the extremity; the part furthest removed from the base (T-B); see apex.

Tiphioidea, superfamily within the Aculeata (Hymenoptera), including the Tiphiidae, Sapygidae, Mutillidae, Sierolomorphidae, and Bradynobaenidae (Gauld and Bolton, after Brown); included within the Vespoidea (*sensu* Gauld and Bolton, after Brothers).

Tipuloidea, superfamily within the Nematocera (Diptera), including the Tipulidae and Trichoceridae (Borror et al.); superfamily within the infraorder Tipulomorpha, including the Tipulidae (McAlpine); see Trichoceroidea.

Tipulomorpha, Polyneura, q.v. (Hennig); division within the Nematocera (Diptera), including the Tipulidae, Ptychopteridae, and Trichoceridae, possessing long-legged, long-winged adults with V-shaped suture and bilobed postphragma on mesonotum (Colless and

McAlpine, in CSIRO); infraorder within the Nematocera (Diptera), including the Tanyderoidea (Tanyderidae) and Tipuloidea (Tipulidae) (McAlpine).

Tischerioidea, superfamily of infraorder Heteroneura (Lepidoptera) containing one family Tischeriidae, adults being small moths with short proboscis scaled at base, minute maxillary palpi, wings simple veins, ♀ genitalia monotrysian; larvae leaf-mining, thoracic legs two-segmented, prolegs on abdominal segments III–VI with transverse bands of crochets; pupae in larval mine, with dorsal spines, protruded from mine at ecdysis (Munroe).

tissue culture, study of cells, tissues and organs explanted from animals and maintained or grown in vitro for more than 24 hours (Steinhaus and Martignoni); see cell culture, organ culture, and primary culture.

tissue water, water produced in the cells as a by-product of metabolism.

titillator(s), in ♂ insects, spines, small plates, or slender processes at distal extremity of aedeagus (Tuxen); in ♂ Ephemeroptera, penial spines, q.v. (Tuxen); in ♂ Blattopteroidea, part of left epiphallus (Tuxen, after Crampton); in ♂ Plecoptera, intermediate appendage, q.v. (Tuxen, after Kempny), principal part of sclerotized armature of penis (Tuxen, after Klapálek), specillum, q.v. (Tuxen, after Klapálek), filament, q.v. (Tuxen, after Klapálek), stylets, q.v. (Tuxen, after Klapálek), or (in *Leuctra*) subanal plates, q.v. (Tuxen, after Needham and Claassen); in ♂ Ensifera (Orthoptera), paired sclerotizations above dorsal phallic lobes (Tuxen); in ♂ Caelifera (Orthoptera), epiphallus, q.v. (Tuxen); in ♂ Heteroptera (Hemiptera), processus phallothecae, q.v. (Tuxen, after Baker) or processus phallothecae and conjunctivae (Tuxen, after Larsén); in ♂ Mecoptera, (ventral) parameres, q.v. (Tuxen, after Klapálek); in Bittacidae (Mecoptera), penisfilum, q.v. (Esben-Petersen); in ♂ Trichoptera, parameres, q.v. (Tuxen, after authors).

titillator cavity, in ♂ Tettigonioidea (Orthoptera), a cavity dorsad of dorsal phallic lobes in which the titillator is concealed when not everted (Tuxen, after Ander).

toe, in ♂ Auchenorrhyncha (Hemiptera), lateral apical point of style, e.g., in *Macrosteles* (Tuxen, after Dorst).

token stimulus, a releaser without any inherent relevance to survival (Matthews and Matthews).

tomentose, tomentosus, covered with tomentum (T-B).

tomentum (Latin), a form of pubescence composed of short, matted, woolly hair (T-B).

tongue, hypopharynx, q.v., or proboscis, q.v. (T-B; Leftwich); in adult Hymenoptera, glossa, q.v. (T-B); in ♂ Heteroptera (Hemiptera), inferior process, q.v. (Tuxen, after Schaefer).

tongue-shaped lobe, in ♀ Trichoptera, central sclerite, q.v. (Tuxen, after Nielsen; Flint, pers. comm.).

tongueworm, a member of the class Pentastomida (Borror et al.).

tonic, pertaining to the tone or strength of the system or of a structure or organ (T-B).

tonofibrillae, cuticular fibrils connecting the muscle fibers with the inner surface of the cuticle (T-B, after Snodgrass; Chapman); see attachment fibers and microtubules.

tonotropism, reaction to sound (T-B).

tonus, the condition of a muscle which remains in a continuous state of partial contraction enabling an animal to maintain its posture (Leftwich).

tooth, an acute angulation (T-B); a short pointed process from an appendage or margin (T-B); a very stout heavy spicule with a blunt apex (Harbach and Knight).

toothed-plate, in ♂ Dermaptera, plate in wall of preputial sac bearing numerous fine cuticular processes, which grip the wall of ♀ vagina during copulation (Tuxen, after Popham).

topazine, topazinus, topaz-colored, i.e., a crystalline pale-yellow (T-B).

topochemical sense, the perception of scents along a path or on either side of it, enabling ants (Hymenoptera: Formicidae), or other insects to follow a track previously used by themselves or by other insects and to return to it (Leftwich).

topographic orientation, object orientation with an elaboration of the approach phase of orientation (Matthews and Matthews, after Jander).

topotype, a term, not regulated by the Code, for a specimen originating from the type locality of the species or subspecies to which it is thought to belong, whether or not the specimen is part of the type series (ICZN).

torma (pl., **tormae**), a small sclerite on the posterior lateral margin of the epipharynx on each side, onto which insert muscles that close the labrum against the mandibles (T-B, after Snodgrass; Chapman) (see suspensory sclerites); in larval Scarabaeoidea (Coleoptera), a dark scleroma at each end of the clypeolabral suture, extending transversely toward the midline of the epipharynx, varying in size and shape according to the species (T-B, after Böving) (see dexiotorma and laeotorma); in larval Culicidae (Diptera), an elongate, detached, usually very dark sclerite transmitting movement to the lateral palatal brush (Harbach and Knight).

tormal apodemal bar, in some culicine larvae (Diptera: Culicidae), the darkly pigmented, well-sclerotized, curved, barlike unit of the tormal apodeme, connected to the lateral tormal process by a pale flexible part of the tormal apodeme (Harbach and Knight, after Laffoon and Knight).

tormal apodeme, any apodeme of a torma (Harbach and Knight).

tormal bar, in larval Chironomidae (Diptera), sclerotized medial part of labral margin consisting of mesal arms of tormae fused with secondary sclerotizations of labral margin (labralia) to transverse bar (Saether).

tormal sclerite, in larval Culicidae (Diptera), torma, intertorma, or anterior palatal bar, q.v. (T-B, after Menees).

tormal seta, in larval Chironomidae (Diptera), seta premandibularis, q.v. (Saether).

tormogen cell, the epidermal cell associated with a seta, forming the setal membrane or socket (T-B, after Snodgrass; Chapman); see alveolus and trichogen cell.

tornal, relating to the tornus (T-B).

tornus, in adult Lepidoptera, anal angle, q.v., of wing (T-B; Mackerras, in CSIRO).

torose, torosus (Latin), **torous,** superficially swelling in knots, knobs, or protuberances; knobby; swollen or with a knobby or knotted shape (T-B; Harris, after R. W. Brown, and Marchant and Charles); see nodulate, torulose, tuberculate and verrucose.

torpid, quiescent, q.v. (T-B).

torqueate, with a ring or collar (T-B).

torquillus, rotula, q.v. (T-B).

torsion, a twisting (T-B).

tortilis (Latin), tortuosus, q.v. (T-B; R. W. Brown).

tortricoid apodemes, in adult Tortricoidea and most higher Lepidoptera, paired, short apodemes protruding from the anterior margin of abdominal sternite II, usually lacking venulae on sternum II, providing articulation with the metathorax (Brock).

Tortricoidea, superfamily within the Ditrysia (Lepidoptera), including small moths of the family Tortricidae (Common, in CSIRO).

tortulose, tortulosus (Latin), **tortulous,** torulose, q.v. (T-B, after J. B. Smith).

tortuose, tortuosus (Latin), **tortuous,** twisted; winding (T-B; R. W. Brown).

torulose, torulosus (Latin), **torulous,** minutely torose; with numerous small knobs or knots (T-B; Harris, after R. W. Brown); see torose.

torulose antenna, antenna in which the articles have swellings (T-B).

torulus (pl., **toruli**), basal socket of antenna (T-B; Mackerras, in CSIRO).

torus, a thickened part or pedicel on which an organ is borne, e.g., the base of an antenna (Leftwich); pedicel, q.v., of antenna (Mackerras, in CSIRO).

totaglossa, ligula, q.v., consisting of the fused glossae and paraglossae without a line of division (T-B, after MacGillivray); in larval Symphyta (Hymenoptera), median terminal lobe, q.v. (Gauld and Bolton).

total cleavage, holoblastic cleavage, q.v. (Boudreaux).

total hemocyte count, the number of hemocytes per cubic millimeter of hemolymph, i.e., a measure of the number of circulating cells (Tulloch, after Jones).

totidem, in all parts; entirely (T-B).

touch, mechanoreception, q.v. (Gilmour, in CSIRO).

touffe, touffe flacherie, q.v. (Steinhaus and Martignoni).

touffe flacherie, a noninfectious flacherie of the silkworm, *Bombyx mori* (Lepidoptera: Bombycidae), known to appear in rearing establishments after sudden abnormal increases in environmental temperature and humidity, and particularly affecting fifth-instar larvae (Steinhaus and Martignoni).

toxemia, a condition produced by the dissemination of toxins in the blood (Steinhaus and Martignoni).

toxic, poisonous (T-B).

toxicognath, in centipedes (Chilopoda), poison jaw, being modified legs located on the first body segment behind the head (Borror et al.).

toxinosis, any disease caused by the action of a toxin (Steinhaus and Martignoni).

trabecula centralis, in adult Siphonaptera, area communis, q.v. (Lewis, pers. comm.).

trabeculae (sing., **trabecula**), in Coleoptera, cuticular columns separating blood spaces between dorsal and ventral surfaces of elytron (Chapman); in scales of Lepidoptera, internal struts between superior and inferior lamellae (Chapman); in Diptera larvae, cross struts or serrations strengthening rima on each side of the spiracular opening (Teskey, in McAlpine).

trabeculum (pl., **trabecula**), rounded, lobular masses of the protocerebrum, from which arise the stalks bearing the mushroom bodies (T-B, after J. B. Smith); in certain Phthiraptera, a paired movable appendage in front of the antennae (T-B).

trabes, in ♂ Coccinellidae (Coleoptera), a process on tegumen (Tuxen, after Verhoeff).

trachea (pl., **tracheae**), a spirally-ringed, internal, elastic air tube in insects; an element of the respiratory system (T-B).

tracheal air sacs, air sacs, q.v. (Gilmour, in CSIRO).

tracheal capillary, trachiole, q.v. (T-B).

tracheal commissures, transverse tracheal trunks continuous from one side of the body to the other (T-B, after Snodgrass).

tracheal end cell, in light producing organ of *Photuris* (Coleoptera: Lampyridae), large cell enclosing tracheole where it joins a trachea (Chapman).

tracheal gills, in aquatic insects, the flattened or filamentous processes with thin cuticle and a network of tracheoles immediately beneath the surface, through which oxygen is absorbed from the water, including caudal gills, q.v., and rectal gills, q.v. (T-B; Chapman).

tracheal gill theory or **hypothesis,** a theory of the origin of the insect wings, in which they are derived from the thoracic tracheal gills of aquatic insects, which have lost their original function and have become adapted for the purposes of flight on the migration of the insects to land (T-B, after Gegenbaur).

tracheal orifice, the primary opening at the point of formation of a trachea, whether exposed externally or concealed in a secondary atrial depression of the body wall (T-B, after Snodgrass).

tracheal sac, in adult *Bittacomorpha* (Diptera: Ptychopteridae), tracheal sac within enlarged first tarsomere (McAlpine).

tracheal system, the part of the respiratory system composed of the tracheae and tracheoles (T-B, after Snodgrass).

tracheal vesicles, in some larval Chaoboridae and some Culicidae (Diptera), dilations of dorsal tracheal trunks which help the larvae maintain their position in the water (Teskey, in McAlpine).

tracheary, relating to or composed of tracheae (T-B).

Tracheata, Atelocerata, q.v. (Hennig); name for a group of arthropods with tracheae, including Arachnida, Onychophora, Hexapoda, and Myriapoda (Boudreaux, after Haeckel).

tracheate, supplied with tracheae (T-B); an arthropod with tracheae (T-B).

tracheation, the arrangement or system of distribution of tracheae (T-B).

trachein, a colloidal or jellylike material forming the walls of the tracheal air sacs in aquatic larvae such as *Chaoborus* (Diptera: Culicidae: Chaoborinae) (Leftwich).

tracheoblast, cell derived from epidermal cells of the lining of the trachea that produces a tracheole intracellulary (Tulloch; Chapman).

tracheoid area, in pupal Culicidae (Diptera), the proximal part of the trumpet meatus when showing more or less distinct transverse striations on the external surface (Harbach and Knight, after Knight).

tracheole, fine tube arising from a trachea retaining its cuticular lining a moulting (T-B; Chapman).

tractium, in ♀ Hymenoptera, ventral ramus, q.v. (Tuxen, after Ross).

Tragplatte, in ♂ Diptera, aedeagal apodeme, q.v. (McAlpine).

tragus, in pupal Culicidae (Diptera), a more or less elaborate lobe sometimes occurring on the rim of the pinna of a laticorn trumpet (Harbach and Knight, after Reid and Knight).

trail parasitism, see trophic parasitism (Wilson).

trail pheromone, a substance laid down in the form of a trail by one animal and followed by another member of the same species, e.g. termites (Isoptera) and ants (Hymenoptera: Formicidae) (Wilson; Chapman).

trail substance, trail pheromone, q.v. (Wilson).

trajectory, the path in the air of a moving object (T-B).

tramosericeous, tramosericeus, satiny (T-B).

trans-, Latin prefix; over; beyond; a complete change (T-B).

transaminases, enzymes, particularly active in the fat body, involved in amino acid synthesis (Gilmour, in CSIRO).

transcutal suture, in adult Diptera, transverse suture, q.v., or scutal suture, q.v. (McAlpine).

transecting behavior, traveling in a straight line at a right angle to the longest axis of exposed space (Matthews and Matthews).

transection, a cut across, at right angles to the body; a transverse section (T-B).

transepimeral suture, in adult Diptera, suture dividing epimeron into an anepimeron and a katepimeron (McAlpine).

transfaunation, transfer of symbiotic fauna (usually mutualistic protozoa) from one host to another (Steinhaus and Martignoni).

transformational mimicry, mimicry in which different instars imitate different models (Matthews and Matthews).

transfrontal bristles, in Diptera, the lower frontal bristles that are often directed across the frontal vitta (T-B, after Comstock).

transiens phase, in locusts (Orthoptera: Acrididae), intermediate phase between solitary phase and gregarious phase (Key, in CSIRO).

transitional cell, chromophile, q.v. (Tulloch, after Jones).

translucent, allowing light to pass through, but not necessarily transparent (T-B; Borror et al.); see opaque.

translucent pores, in Coccoidea (Hemiptera: Sternorrhyncha), small clear areas on surface of trochanter or hind coxa, femur, or tibia (Kosztarab and Kozár).

translucid, translucent, q.v. (T-B).

transmission, in medical entomology, the passage of a parasite from the intermediate host to the definitive host, and visa versa (T-B, after Matheson); see transport host and vector.

transmontane, beyond or on the other side of the mountains; see cismontane.

transnotal suture, in Nematocera, a transverse suture on the pronotum separating the antepronotum from the postpronotum (Harbach and Knight, after Owen).

transovarial transmission, transovarian transmission, q.v. (Tulloch, after Philip).

transovarian transmission, the transmission of microorganisms from one generation to the next by way of the egg (Steinhaus and Martignoni).

transpiration, the act or process of exhaling or passing off liquids as vapor (T-B).

transport host, one partner in a phoretic relationships; the animal that transports a pathogenic microoorganism to which it is nonsusceptable; mechanial vector (Steinhaus and Martignoni).

transscutal articulation, in some adult Symphyta and Chalcididae (Hymenoptera), transverse line of flexibility between the forewing bases that subdivides the mesoscutum (Gibson; Gauld and Bolton); see axilla.

transscutal suture, the transverse suture dividing the scutum into an anterior and a posterior region (T-B, after Crampton); in certain Hymenoptera, transcutal articulation, q.v. (T-B, after Snodgrass).

transscutellar suture, in the higher Diptera, the suture which cuts through the anterior part of the scutellum between the lateral extremities of the scutoscutellar suture (T-B, after Snodgrass).

transstadial transmission, the transmission of microorganisms from one stage of the host to the next, thoughout part or all of the host's life cycle (Tulloch, after Philip; Steinhaus and Martignoni).

transtilla (pl., **transtillae**), in ♂ Geometridae and other Lepidoptera, a sclerotized structure in dorsal part of diaphragma, typically a transverse bar connecting dorsoproximal edges of valvae, sometimes interrupted mesally, sometimes dentate or with variously shaped processes, and part of fultura superior (Tuxen, after Pierce); in ♂ Lepidoptera, also applied by various authors to appendices angulares (part of costa), gnathos, or peniculi (Tuxen).

transtilla knob, in ♂ Lepidoptera, projection arising from each ectal end of transtilla when mesal part of transtilla is absent (Tuxen, after Diakonoff).

transverse, transversus (Latin), broader than long (T-B); running accross (T-B); at right angles to the longitudinal axis (T-B; Borror et al.).

transverse anterior line, in adult moths (Lepidoptera), the line which crosses the forewing one-third or less of the distance from the base (T-B).

transverse arch, in some ♂ Chrysopidae (Planipennia), tignum, q.v. (Tuxen, after Adams).

transverse connective, in larval Diptera, transverse tracheal tube connecting dorsal and lateral trunks on each side (Teskey, in McAlpine).

transverse cord, in certain Plecoptera, a nearly continuous series of crossveins extending across each wing just beyond the middle (T-B, after Comstock).

transverse genital slit, in ♀ Strepsiptera, opening of brood canal ventrally between head and thorax (Tuxen, after Pierce).

transverse grid bar, in larval Culicidae (Diptera), one of the transverse sclerotizations supporting the bases of individual cratal setae (Harbach and Knight).

transverse group of crochets, said of crochets arranged transversely or accross the longitudinal axis of the body in a single uniserial or multiserial band, or in 2 such bands (Peterson).

transverse impression, in adult Diptera, genal groove, q.v. (T-B, after Comstock; McAlpine).

transverse marginal vein, in adult Hymenoptera, radial crossvein (r), q.v., posterior to distal end of pterostigma (Borror et al.).

transverse median vein, in adult Hymenoptera, a crossvein between the discoidal vein and the anal vein (Borror et al.).

transverse moulting suture, in Aleyrodidae (Hemiptera: Sternorrhyncha), the transverse suture at posterior end of longitudinal moulting suture (Gill).

transverse muscles, in insects, those muscles which lie internal to the longitudinals, including dorsal transverse and ventral transverse muscles (T-B, after Snodgrass).

transverse orientation, orientation in which the body is positioned at a fixed angle relative to the stimulus (Matthews and Matthews).

transverse plane, anatomical plane of body at right angles to the longitudinal axis and to the sagittal and horizontal planes (McAlpine).

transverse plate, in Coccoidea (Hemiptera: Sternorrhyncha), the transverse cephalic part of the ovisac (T-B, after MacGillivray).

transverse posterior line, a line crossing the forewings of certain Lepidoptera, two-thirds or more of the way from the base (T-B, after J. B. Smith).

transverse process of epiphallus, in ♂ Orthoptera, lophus, q.v. (Tuxen, after Snodgrass).

transverse radial vein, in adult Hymenoptera, transverse marginal vein, q.v. (Borror et al.).

transverse septum, in ♂ Coreidae (Hemiptera: Heteroptera), inferior process, q.v. (Tuxen, after Brown).

transverse sternapodeme, in ♂ Chironomidae (Diptera), that part of the sternapodeme which is between dorsolateral projections (Saether); part of gonocoxal apodeme.

transverse strut, in ♂ Fulgoroidea (Hemiptera: Auchenorrhyncha), a sclerotized rod with which the claspers are connected to each other and then to the base of the aedeagus (O'Brien, pers. comm.).

transverse sulcus, in many Orthoptera, the transverse groove of the pronotum (T-B).

transverse suture, in adult Diptera, transverse suture dividing the scutum into an anterior presutural area and a posterior postsutural area (T-B, after Comstock; Borror et al.; McAlpine).

transverse tubular (T-) system, in muscle fibers a system of transverse invaginations of the plasma membrane (Chapman).

transverse vein, crossvein, q.v. (Leftwich).

trap-nesting, providing artificial nesting sites in the field, especially for bees and wasps (Hymenoptera: Aculeata) (Gauld and Bolton).

trapeziform, in the form or shape of a trapezium (T-B).

trapezium, a four-sided figure in which no 2 sides are parallel (T-B).

trapezoid, trapezoidal, in the form of a four-sided figure of which 2 sides are parallel and 2 are not (T-B).

trauma, in invertebrate pathology, wounds or injuries caused directly by violent contact of external objects with the body of an animal (Steinhaus and Martignoni); see stress.

traumatic insemination, in many Cimicoidea and some Nabidae (Hemiptera: Heteroptera), puncturing the body wall or the wall of inner ♀ genitalia by ♂ phallus during mating, and deposition of sperm outside the usual reproductive tract (Carayon, in Usinger); see hemocoelic insemination.

treehopper, a member of the family Membracidae (Hemiptera: Auchenorrhyncha).

trehalase, enzyme catalysing the hydrolysis of the carbohydrate trehalose (Chapman).

trehalose, dissacharide, consisting of 2 glucose molecules, occurring in all insects and commonly the most abundant sugar in the hemolymph (Chapman).

trehalose-6-phosphate, intermediate metabolite in the production of trehalose from glucose-1-phosphate (Gilmour, in CSIRO).

Trematoda, a sometimes recognized group of parasitic flatworms, including the Digenea (Allaby).

trematode, a member of the Trematoda.

trench fever, disease of humans caused by *Rochalimaea quintana* (Rickettsiaceae) and transmitted by *Pediculus humanus humanus* (Phthiraptera: Anoplura), causing pain, malaise, and fever (Allaby).

tri-, both Latin and Greek prefix; three (T-B).

triad, an arrangement in threes of the veins of the insect wing (T-B).

trial-and-error learning, learning in which a particular stimulus becomes associated with a motor reaction as a result of reinforcement in some subsequent behavior (Chapman).

triangle, in adult Anisoptera (Odonata), a triangular cell near the base of the wing bordered on proximal side by posterior cubitus (CuP) (T-B, after Garman; O'Farrell, in CSIRO).

triangular, triangulus (Latin), having 3 angles.

triangular piece, in *Pieris brassicae* (Lepidoptera: Pieridae), tegumen + uncus (transl. "Triangelstück" Harold, in Tuxen).

triangular plate, in ♀ Apoidea (Hymenoptera), gonangulum, q.v. (Tuxen, after Snodgrass).

triangular sclerite, in larval Chironomidae (Diptera), anterior triangular sclerite of labral margin (Saether).

triangular valve, in ♀ Lepidoptera, signum, q.v. (Tuxen, Griffith).

triangulate, triangular, q.v. (T-B).

triangulum (pl., **triangula**), in ♀ Pentatomidae (Hemiptera: Heteroptera), median piece issuing from the fusion of median line of gonapophyses of abdominal segment VIII (Tuxen, after Verhoeff).

triangulum occipitale, in larval Chironomidae (Diptera), area enclosed by primary and secondary postoccipital margin (Saether).

triarticular, triarticulate, triarticulatus (Latin), composed of 3 segments or articles (T-B).

Triassic Period, earliest period within the Mesosoic Era, extending between about 225 and 180 million years before the present (Riek, in CSIRO).

tribe, a subdivision of a subfamily, containing a group of genera, the name of which ends in "-ini" (T-B; Borror et al.); a rank of the family group below subfamily (ICZN); a taxon at the rank of tribe (ICZN).

tricarinate, with 3 carinae or keels (T-B).

tricerores, in *Pseudococcus* (Hemiptera: Coccoidea: Pseudococcidae), trilocular pores, q.v. (T-B, after MacGillivray).

trichiation, chaetotaxy, q.v. (Mackerras, in CSIRO).

trichobothrium (pl., **trichobothria**), in many terrestrial arthropods, fine sensory hairs arising from a cupuliform base (von Kéler); in spiders (Arachnida: Araneae), minute sensory hairs on the tarsi (Borror et al.); in Collembola, ♂ Archaeognatha, and Diplura, long sensory setae each supported on a tubercle or boss (Wallace and Mackerras, in CSIRO); in many Heteroptera (Hemiptera), specialized slender sensory setae arising from spots, tubercles, or pits (bothria) on the abdominal venter (Pentatomorpha), the head (many families), antennal segment 2 (Reduvioidea), the scutellum (Nabidae: Prostemmatinae), and the meso- and metafemora (Miridae) (Schuh); see bothriotricha.

Trichoceroidea, superfamily within the Psychodomorpha (Diptera: Nematocera), including the family Trichoceridae (McAlpine).

trichodes, trichomes, q.v. (T-B).

trichogen, trichogen cell, q.v. (T-B, after Snodgrass; Leftwich).

trichogen cell, the epidermal cell that generates a seta (T-B, after Snodgrass).

trichogenous cell, trichogen cell, q.v. (T-B).

trichoid, formed like a trichia or hair; trichialike (T-B).

trichoid sensillum, a hairlike projection of the cuticle articulated with the body wall by a membranous socket (alveolus), functioning as mechanoreceptors or less often as chemoreceptors (T-B; Chapman).

trichomes, modified hairs present on certain myrmecophilous insects which give off secretions that ants (Hymenoptera: Formicidae) imbibe, e.g., base of abdomen in Holoptilinae (Heteroptera: Reduviidae); adult Paussini (Coleoptera: Carabidae); on elytra of *Chlamydopsis* (Coleoptera: Histeridae); and base of abdomen of adult Clavigerinae (Pselaphidae) (Tulloch; Woodward et al., Britton, in CSIRO).

Trichopora, those members of the Heteroptera (Hemiptera) with trichobothria on the pregenital abdominal sterna, i.e., Pentatomomorpha less Aradidae (Štys, pers. comm.).

trichophore, a cylindrical internal cavity of the cuticula beneath the base of a seta; contains the distal parts of the cells associated with the seta (T-B, after Snodgrass).

trichopore, the opening in the cuticula beneath a seta, giving passage to the hair-forming process of the trichogen cell (T-B, after Snodgrass).

Trichoptera, endopterygote order of Neoptera (Insecta) with adults possessing reduced mouthparts, forewing with anal veins looped, anterior cubitus (CuA) forked in both wings, and body and wings covered with hairs and at times with some scales; larvae aquatic, with a pair of terminal abdominal prolegs; pupae decticous (T-B; Riek, in CSIRO).

Trichopterida, Amphiesmenoptera, q.v. (Boudreaux).

trichosors, in adult Neuropteroidea, short, setose thickenings of wing margin interposed between tips of longitudinal veins (Riek, in CSIRO).

trichostichal bristles, in adult Diptera, metapleural bristles, q.v. (T-B, after Comstock).

Trichotelocera, Dipsocoromorpha, q.v. (Schuh, pers. comm.).

trichotomous, divided into 3 parts (T-B).

trichroism, the condition of any given part exhibiting 3 different colors in different individuals of the same species, e.g., the hind wings of certain heliconiine Nymphalidae (Lepidoptera) (T-B).

tricuspid, tricuspidate, tricuspidatus (Latin), divided into 3 cusps or points (T-B).

tridactyle, tridactylous, tridactylus (Latin), three-toed or three-clawed (T-B).

Tridactyloidea, superfamily within the suborder Caelifera (Orthoptera), including the families Tridactylidae and Cylindrachetidae, having the prosternum directly connected to the pronotum by a precoxal bridge, foretarsus with 1 or 2 tarsomeres, midtarsus with 2 tarsomeres, hind tarsus with a single article, arolium absent, abdomen with 9 fully sclerotized sterna in both sexes, sternum IX constituting the subgenital plate lacking both styles and sternal lobe, and paraporct bearing a sclerotized hook in ♂ (Key, in CSIRO).

trident, in certain nymphal Ephemeroptera, a tooth on the mandible with 3 long points (T-B, after Needham).

trident organ, in ♀ Micropterigidae (Lepidoptera), fork organ, q.v. (Tuxen, after Philpott).

tridentlike structure, in ♀ Hydroptilidae (Trichoptera), vaginal sclerite, q.v. (Tuxen, after Mosely; Flint, pers. comm.).

tridentate, tridentatus (Latin), with 3 teeth.

trifasciate, trifasciatus (Latin), with 3 fascia or bands of color (T-B).

trifid, cleft in 3 (T-B).

trifine subfamilies, in Noctuidae (Lepidoptera), those subfamilies in which adults are characterized by the second medial vein (M_2) of hind wing being reduced and well removed from third medial vein (M_3), so that CuA appears to be three-branched (Kitching), e.g., Heliothidinae, Noctuinae, Hadeninae, Culliinae, Amphipyrinae, and Acronictinae (Common, in CSIRO); see quadrifine subfamilies.

Trifidae, trifine subfamilies, q.v. (Forbes).

trifurcate, trifurcatus (Latin), 3 times forked (T-B).

trigamma, in the lepidopterous wing, a three-pronged fork, the prongs of which are veins M_3, Cu_{1a}, and Cu_{1b} (T-B, after Imms).

triglycerides, fats, especially storage fats in insects, consisting of glycerol and 3 fatty acids (Gilmour, in CSIRO).

Trignatha, a group recognized to include the Chilopoda, Symphyla, and Hexapoda (Hennig, after Tiegs, Manton).

trigonal, triangular; an area bounded by a triangle (T-B).

Trigonaloidea, superfamily within the Apocrita (Hymenoptera), including the family Trigonalidae, adults having antennae with more than 16 articles, closed basal cells in hind wing, forewing with a distinct costal cell, pronotum without a dorsal surface in median area and not reaching back above tegulae, pronotum with pronotal lobe reaching back to tegula, margined with close fine hairs, no antennal groove, and spurs of hind tibia not modified for preening (Riek, in CSIRO; Schauff, pers. comm.).

trigonapophyses, in ♂ Culicidae (Diptera), parameres, q.v. (Tuxen, after Brölemann).

trigonate, trigonatus, trigonous, three-angled (T-B).

trigonulum, in adult Odonata, triangle, q.v. (T-B).

trilateral, having 3 sides (T-B).

trilineate, trilineatus (Latin), three-lined (T-B).

trilobate, trilobatus (Latin), **trilobe, trilobed,** having 3 lobes (T-B).

trilobate type, in some ♂ Coleoptera, a symmetrical type of aedeagus with well-developed, sclerotized basal piece and sclerotized to which articulate the parameres and to which the penus is firmly fixed by the first connecting membrane; judged to be the most primitive type among those exhibited by the Coleoptera (Lindroth and Palmén, in Tuxen).

Trilobita, an extinct subphylum of Arthropoda from the Paleozoic Era, including the trilobites, a marine group possessing 3 londitudinal divisions of the elongate and flattened body, the 2 lateral divisions consisting of the paraterga (Borror et al.).

trilobites, members of the Trilobita (Borror et al.).

Trilobitodea, Trilobitoidea, q.v. (Boudreaux).

Trilobitoidea, an extinct group of arthropods from the mid-Cambrian Burgess Shales, similar to the Trilobita, but lacking laterally delimited paraterga (Boudreaux, after Stormer).

Trilobitomorpha, hypothesized monophyletic group including the Trilobita and Trilobitoidea (Boudreaux, after Størmer).

trilocular pores, in nymphs and females of Coccoidea (Hemiptera: Sternorrhyncha), pores with 3 openings (Woodward et al., in CSIRO; Kosztarab and Kozár); see simple pore, bilocular pore, and multilocular pore.

Trimera, a grouping of the Psocoptera having three-segmented tarsi (T-B); the series of Coleoptera in which there are only 3 tarsal joints present.

trimerous, in 3 parts or pieces, e.g., tarsi with 3 articles (T-B).

trimorphism, the phenomenon of having 3 forms in color or structure in one and the same species; or, in ants (Hymenoptera: Formicidae), and termites (Isoptera), in one and the same worker caste (T-B).

trinomen (pl., **trinomina**), the combination of a generic name, a specific name, and a subspecific name, that together constitute a scientific name of a subspecies (ICZN).

trinomial, trinomen, q.v. (T-B).

trinominal name, trinomen, q.v. (ICZN).

trinominal nomenclature, an extension of the binominal system of nomenclature to permit the designation of subspecies by a three-word name (Mayr).

triommatidoidea, in some apterous and immature Aphidoidea, reduced compound eyes each consisting of 3 separate lenses (Woodward et al., in CSIRO).

triordinal crochets, in larval Lepidoptera, crochets with their proximal ends in a single row but their distal ends of 3 alternating lengths (Peterson); see uniordinal crochets and biordinal crochets.

tripartite, in 3 parts (T-B).

tripectinate, having 3 rows of comblike branches, e.g., tripectinate antenna (T-B; Borror et al.),; see bipectinate and pectinate.

triphasic allometry, polymorphism in which the allometric regression line, when plotted on a double logrithmic scale, "breaks" at 2 points and consists of 3 segments; in ants (Hymenoptera: Formicidae), the 2 terminal segments usually have slight to moderately high slopes and the middle segment has a very high slope (Wilson).

triploblastic, consisting of 3 germ layers, ectoderm, mesoderm and endoderm, from which complex organ systems are developed—the primitive embryonic cellular pattern (T-B, after Klots).

triploid, a cell or individual with 3 haploid chromosome sets, one of the forms of polyploidy (Mayr).

Triplosoboidea, extinct superfamily of Ephemeroptera from the Upper Carboniferous in Europe, including the Triplosobidae (Landa and Soldán).

tripod, in ♂ *Pyrgus* (Lepidoptera: Hesperiidae), forked process of tegumen (transl. "trépied" Reverdin, in Tuxen).

tripupillate, having 3 pupils within an ocellar spot (T-B).

triquetral, triquetrous, triquetrus (Latin), triangular, q.v. (T-B; R. W. Brown).

triradiate, with 3 arms or branches (T-B; Christiansen and Bellinger).

triregional, divided into 3 distinct parts or regions (T-B).

tritocerebral, of or pertaining to the tritocerebrum (T-B).

tritocerebral commissure, postoesophageal commissure, q.v. (Gilmour, in CSIRO).

tritocerebral segment, intercalary segment, q.v. (T-B).

tritocerebrum, small part of the brain consisting of a pair of lobes beneath the deutocerebrum formed from the ganglia of the intercalary segment of the head (T-B, after J. B. Smith; Chapman).

tritonymph, a third stage nymph (Tulloch).

Tritopolyphaga, name for a group including the Bostrychiformia and Cucujiformia (Coleoptera) (Hennig, after Schilder).

triturating, adapted for grinding or crushing (T-B).

triturating basket, in adult Zeugloptera (Lepidoptera), hypopharynx modified for grinding pollen grains (Common, in CSIRO).

triundulate, with 3 waves or undulations (T-B).

triungulid, triungulin, q.v. (T-B, after Folsom and Wardle).

triungulin, the active, tiny, first instar campodeiform larva of some insects that undergo hypermetamorphosis, some predaceous Coleoptera (esp. Meloidae), and Planipennia (Mantispidae) (Peterson); in Strepsiptera, triunguliniform larva, q.v. (Peterson); see planidium.

triungulin larva, triungulin, q.v. (Borror et al.).

triunguliniform larva, in Strepsiptera, active, legless, first-instar larva (Kinzelbach, pers. comm.).

triunguloid, triungulin, q.v. (Peterson).

trivial name, vernacular name, q.v. (T-B; Mayr).

trivittate, trivittatus (Latin), with 3 stripes or vittae (T-B).

trivoltine, having 3 generations in a year or season (T-B).

Trochalopoda, that grouping of Heteroptera in which the posterior coxae are nearly globose and the articulation is a ball and socket joint (T-B); see Pagiopoda.

trochantellus, in some adult Apocrita (Hymenoptera), proximal end of femur, appearing as an apparent second segment of the trochanter (Riek, in CSIRO; Gauld and Bolton).

trochanter, a segment of the insect leg between the coxa and the femur, sometimes divided (Odonata), and sometimes fused with the femur (T-B); see trochantellus.

trochanteral, of or pertaining to the trochanter (T-B).

trochanteral brush, in larval Trichoptera, tuft of hairs on the distal part of trochanter (Wiggins).

trochanteral organ, in Katiannidae, a shortened, slightly expanded distal seta located in a conspicuous pit, and in Entomobryidae (Collembola), a series of short differentiated setae, on the inner surface of the trochanter (Christiansen and Bellinger).

trochanteral spine, in Sminthuridae (Collembola), a blunt, or distinctly capitate, or pointed, translucent spine on the inner side of at least the metathoracic trochanter (Richards).

trochanterellus, in adult Hymenoptera, trochanter, q.v. (T-B).

trochanterofemoral, of or pertaining to the trochanter and the femur jointly (T-B).

trochantin, in some Pterygota (Insecta), free sclerotized remnant of coxopleurite located at the base of the leg, providing a second point of pleural articulation with the coxa (T-B; Chapman); any small sclerite interposed between 2 others, e.g., on the mouthparts (Leftwich).

trochantin of the mandible, pleurostoma, q.v. (T-B, after Imms).

trochantinal, of or pertaining to the trochantin (T-B).

trochantinopleura, coxopleurite, q.v. (T-B).

trochiformis, cylindroconic (T-B).

trochlea (pl., **trochleae**), in Cicadidae (Hemiptera: Auchenorrhyncha), the thickened base of the hind wing (T-B); in adult Trichoptera, a small elliptical space at base of hind wing behind origin of media (T-B).

trochlearis, pulley-shaped; like a cylinder contracted medially (T-B).

trochus (Latin), any small segment intercalated between the normal segments in an articulated structure or part (T-B).

Troctomorpha, suborder of Psocoptera, including the Nanopsocetae and Amphientometae, possessing adults with tarsi with 3 (exceptionally 2) tarsomeres, pterostigma not thickened, and antennae with 11 to 17 articles and with some flagellomeres secondarily annulated (Smithers, after Badonnel, in CSIRO).

Trogiomorpha, suborder of Psocoptera, including the Atropetae and Psocatropetae, possessing adults with tarsi with 3 tarsomeres, paraprocts with strong posterior spine, pterostigma not thickened or absent, antennae with 20 or more articles and never secondarily annulated (Pearman; Badonnel).

troglobite, obligate inhabitant of caves (Norris, in CSIRO).

troglophile, facultative inhabitant of caves (Norris, in CSIRO).

trogolodytic, living underground exclusively (Tulloch).

trophallactic glands, certain glands which produce the exudate or secretion given by larvae to the adults after being fed (T-B).

trophallaxis, in eusocial insects, the exchange of alimentary liquid among colony members and quest organisms, either mutually or unilaterally (T-B, after W. M. Wheeler; Wilson); see stomodeal trophallaxis and proctodeal trophallaxis.

trophamnion, in parasitic insects with polyembryony, e.g., parasitic Hymenoptera, cytoplasm of the egg associated with the paranuclear mass that surrounds the embryonic region and serves in passing nutriment from the host to the embryo (T-B, after Imms; Chapman).

trophi, mouthparts, q.v. (T-B).

trophic, of or pertaining to food or eating (T-B).

trophic core, in telotrophic ovarioles, mass of cytoplasm at distal end that provides nutrients to the developing oocytes through nutritive cords (Chapman).

trophic egg, in social insects, an egg, degenerate in form and inviable, which is fed to other members of the colony (Wilson).

trophic membrane, in Strepsiptera and paedogenetic Cecidomyiidae, e.g. *Miastor,* (Diptera), membrane derived from the mother in hemocoelic viviparity which nourishes the eggs (Hinton and Mackerras, in CSIRO).

trophic parasitism, the intrusion of one species into the social system of another, as, for example, by utilization of the trail system, in order to steal food (Wilson).

trophic plasticity, in insects, the ability to become adapted to new foods (T-B).

trophic sac, in Phthiraptera, stylet sac, q.v. (Calaby, in CSIRO).

trophic symbiosis, trophobiosis, q.v. (T-B).

trophidium, first larval stage of *Pseudomyrmex* (Hymenoptera: Formicidae) (Tulloch).

trophobiont, an organism living either within or without the nest of a social species, which is cared for and protected by that species, and which produces secretions attractive to the social insects (Tulloch, after Gaul).

trophobiosis, the relationship in which ants (Hymenoptera: Formicidae) receive honeydew from members of the Auchenorrhyncha and Sternorrhyncha (Hemiptera) or certain caterpillars (Lepidoptera) and provide these insects with protection in return (Wilson).

trophocyte, cell that elaborates nutritive materials, comprising the majority of the fat body, functioning as nurse cells in meroistic ovarioles, or serving as nutritive cells within testis follicles (T-B, after Snodgrass; Chapman).

trophogenesis, the origin of different caste traits from differetnial feeding of the immature stages (opposed to genetic control of castes and blastogenesis) (Wilson).

trophogeny, the determination of caste differences by nutritional mechanisms (Tulloch, after Gaul).

trophoporic field, in social insects, the habitat or area supplying the colony with food (Tulloch).

trophothylax, in Pseudomyrmecinae (Hymenoptera: Formicidae), a food pocket in abdominal segment I of the larva (T-B; Leftwich).

trophozoite, first stage in the asexual development of the malaria parasite, *Plasmodium* spp. (Plasmodiidae), infecting red blood cells, derived from a merozoite produced either in the liver paranchymal cells or from another red blood cell (T-B; Borror et al.); see schizont.

tropic, pertaining to or of the nature of a tropism (T-B).

tropic behavior, that form of behavior which is made up of predominantly simple reflex actions (T-B, after Wardle).

tropical, belonging to the tropical region of the earth (T-B).

tropical splenomegaly, kala-azar, q.v. (Adkins, pers. comm.).

tropicopolitan, pantropical, q.v. (T-B).

tropism, a reflex response whereby an insect turns in a particular direction in relation to a stimulus, being either positive (turning toward the stimulus) or negative (turning away from the stimulus) (T-B; Leftwich; Borror et al.); stationary orientation toward a stimulus, refering primarily to plants (Matthews and Matthews); see taxis.

tropomyosin, protein present in small quantities in the contractile elements of muscle fibers (Chapman).

troponin, protein present in small quantities in the contractile elements of muscle fibers (Chapman).

tropotaxis, a response involving the turning of an insect followed by movement in a definite direction in relation to the stimulus, combining a tropism and a taxis (T-B; Leftwich); phototropotaxis.

trough-shaped mucro, in Collembola, elongate and dorsally-grooved mucro (Christiansen and Bellinger).

true bug, bug, q.v.

true clasps, in ♂ Lepidoptera, valvae, q.v. (Tuxen, after Burgess).

trulleum (Latin) (pl., **trullea**), basin (R. W. Brown); in ♂ Hepialidae (Lepidoptera), median sclerotization hinged to dorsal margin of juxta (Tuxen, after Philpott).

trumpet, in pupal Culicidae (Diptera), the paired, usually movable, dorsolateral appendage of the cephalothorax containing the mesothoracic spiracle (T-B; Harbach and Knight, after Meinert).

trumpet mine, a leaf mine in which a trumpet-shaped cavity is formed with one end wider than the other, e.g., that made by the larva of *Tischeria malifoliella* (Lepidoptera: Tischeriidae) in apple leaves (T-B; Leftwich).

truncate, truncatus (Latin), cut off squarely at the tip (T-B).

truncate wing, in insects, one shortened straight across, as in *Drosophila* (Diptera: Drosophilidae) laboratory mutants (T-B).

truncation, truncature, a square cutting off (T-B).

truncus, trunk, q.v. (T-B).

trunk, thorax, q.v. (T-B); the combined thorax and abdomen, e.g., Collembola (T-B; Christiansen and Bellinger); in Aculeata (Hymenoptera), alitrunk, q.v. (Brown, pers. comm.).

truss cell, in adult Myrmeleontoidea (Planipennia), hypostigmatic cell, q.v. (T-B, after Wardle; Borror et al.).

Trypanosomatidae, family of parasitic protozoans in which the cells are extremely variable in form, depending on the host and the conditions, the species being parasitic in vertebrates, invertebrates, and plants (Allaby); see trypanosomiasis.

trypanosome, a member of the Trypanosomatidae (T-B).

trypanosomiasis, a disease caused by infection with *Trypanosoma* (Trypanosomatidae), transmitted by Triatominae (Heteroptera: Reduviidae) and Tabanidae (Diptera) (Woodward et al., Colless and Mc Alpine, in CSIRO).

trypsin, a mammalian protease (T-B; Gilmour, in CSIRO).

tryptophan, $C_{11}H_{12}O_2N_2$, an essential amino acid in the diet of insects (Gilmour, in CSIRO).

tsetse fly, one of the Glossinidae (Diptera), which carry African sleeping-sickness (trypanosomiasis) (T-B).

tsutsugamushi disease, scrub typhus, q.v. (Borror et al.).

tuba analis (pl., **tubae anales**), in Auchenorrhyncha (Hemiptera), anal tube, q.v. (Tuxen); in Lepidoptera, posterior part of digestive tract, enclosed by genital structures, ending at anus (Tuxen, after Diakonoff).

tube, a slender, hollow, cylindrical body; in ♂ *Zorotypus zimmermanni* Gurn. (Zoraptera), part of the complicated genital structure (Tuxen); in larval Culicidae (Diptera), respiratory siphon, q.v. (T-B).

tubercle, a small knoblike or rounded protuberance (T-B; Borror et al.); in adult Sphecoidea (Hymenoptera), pronotal lobe, q.v. (T-B, after Rohwer); in caterpillars (Lepidoptera), body structures, sometimes bearing setae, e.g., pinaculum, verruca, q.v. (T-B; Peterson).

tubercula sensitiva (sing., **tuberculum sensitivum**), in ♀ Japygidae (Diplura), 2 small lobes on sides of papilla genitalis (Tuxen, after Silvestri).

tuberculate, covered or furnished with rounded, projecting lobes; more strongly projecting than granulate, papillate, or pustulate (T-B; Harris, after Stearn, Jaeger, and R. W. Brown); see nodulate, torose, and verrucose.

tuberculate pits, in adult Tipulidae (Diptera), prescutal pits, q.v. (T-B, after Curran; McAlpine).

tubercule, tubercle, q.v. (T-B).

tuberculiform, shaped like a pimple or tubercle (T-B).

tuberculose, tuberculosus (Latin), **tuberculous,** tuberculate, q.v. (T-B; Harris).

tuberculus (pl., **tuberculi**), tubercle, q.v. (T-B); in ♀ Culicidae (Diptera), one or more small, rounded, pale, buttonlike structures situated on the insula (Harbach and Knight, after Reinert).

tuberiferous, bearing tubercles (T-B).

tubular colleterial glands, in ♀ *Sycanus* (Hemiptera: Heteroptera: Reduviidae), a bipartite vermiform gland or 2 long pseudospermathecae (Tuxen, after Kershaw).

tubular ducts, in ♀ Coccoidea (Hemiptera: Sternorrhyncha), dermal ducts of various sizes and shapes producing wax (Woodward et al., after Ezzat and McConnell, in CSIRO).

tubular glands, in Asterolecaniidae (Hemiptera: Sternorrhyncha: Coccoidea), small tubes extending through the cuticle into the body cavity (T-B, after Green).

tubular muscle, synchronous skeletal muscle in which the myofibrils are arranged radially round a central cytoplasmic core containing the nuclei (Chapman); see close-packed muscle.

tubular piece, in ♀ Integripalpia (Trichoptera), part of abdominal segment X forming a sclerotized tube carrying the anus (Nielsen).

tubular portion (of phallus), in ♂ Tingidae (Hemiptera: Heteroptera), endosoma, q.v. (Tuxen, after Drake and Davis).

tubular pseudospermathecae, in ♀ Pachynomidae (Hemiptera: Heteroptera), (paired tubular) pseudospermathecae, q.v. (Tuxen, after Drake and Davis).

tubular spinnerets, in Coccoidea (Hemiptera: Sternorrhyncha), dorsal pores, q.v. (T-B, after MacGillivray).

tubular type, in ♀ Coleoptera, genitalia with separate bursa copulatrix (Lindroth and Palmén, in Tuxen).

tubules, in larval Chironomidae (Diptera), anal tubules, q.v., or blood gills, q.v. (Saether).

tubuli, in Coccoidea (Hemiptera: Sternorrhyncha), dorsal pores, q.v. (T-B, after MacGillivray).

tubuli anales, in larval Chironomidae (Diptera), anal tubules, q.v. (Saether).

tubuli laterales, in larval Chironomidae (Diptera), lateral tubules, which are near the anal tubules, q.v. (Saether).

tubuli ventrales, in larval Chironomidae (Diptera), ventral tubules, which are near the anal and lateral tubules, q.v. (Saether).

Tubulifera, suborder of Thysanoptera, including only the Phlaeothripidae, possessing females with reduced, chutelike ovipositor, abdominal segment X tubular in both sexes, and with wings devoid of microtrichia, with unsocketed fringe cilia, and overlapping along the dorsum when at rest (T-B; Reed, in CSIRO; Mound et al.).

tubulose, tubulosus, tubulous, formed like a tube; fistulous (T-B).

tubulus (pl., **tubuli**), in ♀ Lepidoptera, tubular, telescoping ovipositor (Tuxen, after Kirby and Spence); in ♀ Diptera, the slender, flexible abdominal segments forming the ovipositor (T-B); see oviscapt and ovipositor.

tubus (Latin), pipe (R. W. Brown).

tubus interior (pl., **tubi interiores**), in ♂ Siphonaptera, terminal, sclerotized continuation of endophallus lying in longitudinal axis of aedeagus (Tuxen, after Peus).

tuft, a group of more or less parallel setae arising from a given area or verruca (Peterson).

tularemia, disease of man and rodents caused by the bacterium *Francisella tularensis* and transmitted by deer flies, *Chrysops* spp. (Diptera: Tabanida), and ticks (Acari: Ixodidae) (Borror et al.).

tullilus (pl., **tullili**), pulvillus, q.v. (T-B, after MacGillivray).

tumefaction, abnormal tissue formation in insects having characteristics in common with vertebrate neoplasms but whose nature is unknown (Steinhaus and Martignoni, after Harshbarger and Taylor); tumor, q.v. (Steinhaus and Martignoni).

tumescence, a swelling (T-B).

tumescent, somewhat swollen (T-B).

tumid, tumidus (Latin), swollen (T-B; R. W. Brown).

tumor, any swelling, whether edema or a mass resulting from malformation, inflammation of repair (Steinhaus and Martignoni); neoplasm, q.v. (Steinhaus and Martignoni).

tumulus (Latin), mound (R. W. Brown); the pile of loose earth around the entrance of a new insect burrow (Michener).

tunica, in Sminthuridae (Collembola), a connection between the basal lateral teeth, extending across the outer edge of the unguis in Entomobryomorpha, and an inflated outer sheath along the dorsal edge of the unguis (Christiansen and Bellinger); in ♂ *Bombyx mori* (Lepidoptera: Bombycidae), diaphragma, q.v. (Tuxen, after Malpighi).

tunica externa, tunica interna, in Diptera, the outer and inner envelopes, respectively, surrounding the single saclike testis (T-B, after Snodgrass).

tunica intima, an inner lining or membrane (T-B); the inner layer of the silk glands (T-B).

tunica propria, in ovarioles, an elastic membrane inside the outer ovariole sheath (Chapman).

tunicate, tunicatus (Latin), covered by one another like a set of funnels, as the articles of some antennae (T-B).

turbinate, turbinatus (Latin), top-shaped; conical (T-B; R. W. Brown); see pyriform.

turbinate eye, in ♂ Ephemeroptera, upper portion of divided compound eye raised on a broad stalk (T-B; Riek, in CSIRO; Borror et al.).

turgid, turgidus (Latin), inflated; swollen; distended (T-B; R. W. Brown); see tumid.

Turner's circling, the circling of the homecoming insect as it approaches the nest entrance (Tulloch, after Gaul).

turreted, of a head, one produced anteriorly and in a triangular point above (T-B).

turritus, towering; rising conelike, as a surface (T-B).

twin ocellus, two ocellate spots joined together (T-B).

twisted-winged parasite, a member of the order Strepsiptera (Borror et al.).

two-winged fly, a member of the order Diptera (Colless and McAlpine, in CSIRO).

tyloid(s), in ♂ Trigonalidae and many ♂ Ichneumonidae and Braconidae (Hymenoptera), a large longitudinal keel or sensory patch on the ventral side of several flagellar segments (T-B; Riek, in CSIRO; Gauld and Bolton).

tylus (pl., **tyli**), in ♀ Ischnocera (Phthiraptera), second gonapophysis or gonoplac, q.v. (Tuxen, after von Kéler; Lyal); in Heteroptera (Hemiptera), the distal part of the clypeus or anteclypeal region (T-B); in larval Scarabaeoidea (Coleoptera), a sclerome covering, completely or partly, the fused epizygal, coryphal and haplomeral elements, produced toward the pedium as a single obtuse point or a few rounded lobes (T-B, after Böving).

tymbal, in ♀ and some ♂ Auchenorrhyncha and some Pentatomidae (Heteroptera) (Hemiptera), a sound producing membrane on abdominal segment I (Matthews and Matthews; Chapman).

tymbal organ, in adult Arctiidae (Lepidoptera), sound-producing organs located on each metepisternum, composed of a series of transverse, parallel ridges (= microtymbals) and grooves (Ferguson); see tymbal.

tympanal, of the nature of or pertaining to a tympanum or stretched membrane (T-B).

tympanal air chamber, a space inside of the tympanum into which air is admitted by a spiracle near its margin (T-B, after Comstock).

tympanal fossa, in adult Diptera, a largely membranous area between the suprasquamal ridge and the lower margin of the postalar wall (McAlpine).

tympanal frame, in Lepidoptera, a supporting framework on dorsal, posterior and ventral sides of the tympanal membrane of the thoracic tympana; morphologically part postnotal, part epimeral (Richards).

tympanal hood, in adult Noctuoidea (Lepidoptera), counter tympanic hood, q.v. (Borror et al.).

tympanal organ, organ sensitive to vibrations, on the foretibiae in Grylloidea and Tettigonioidea (Orthoptera), on the mesothorax of some Nepomorpha (Hemiptera: Heteroptera), on the metathorax of Noctuoidea (Lepidoptera), and on the first abdominal tergite in Acrididoidea (Orthoptera), Cicadidae and other Auchenorrhyncha (Hemiptera), and Dudgeoneidae, Pyraloidea, Drepanoidea, Uranioidea, and Geometroidea (Lepidoptera), consisting of a thin area of cuticle, the tympanic membrane, an inner air sac, and a chordotonal organ attached to the inside of the tympanic membrane or adjacent to it (T-B; Chapman).

tympanal pockets, in Lepidoptera, pockets in the tympanal frame; typically 4 in number (never more) and designated by numbers I–IV from anterodorsal to posteroventral (Richards).

tympanal ridge, in adult Diptera, a riblike sclerite strengthening the tympanal fossa (McAlpine).

tympanic membrane, a thin, membranous cuticular portion of tympanal organ, sensitive to vibrations (Chapman).

tympanic pit, in many adult Muscomorpha (Diptera), membranous pit, enclosed by lowermost arms of forked tympanal ridge, opening toward the base of the wing (McAlpine).

tympanule, tympanal organ, q.v. (T-B).

tympanum, tympanal organ, q.v. (T-B, after Imms); tympanic membrane, q.v. (Chapman).

Tyndall scattering, reflection of blue wavelengths in all directions due to granules with dimensions similar to the wavelengths of blue light, e.g., in adult Odonata (Chapman).

type, a particular kind of specimen (ICZN); see allotype, cotype, holotype, lectotype, name-bearing type, neotype, paralectotype, paratype, syntype, topotype (T-B).

type by absolute tautonomy, absolute tautonymy, q.v. (T-B).

type by elimination, fixation by elimination, q.v. (T-B).

type by original designation, original designation, q.v. (T-B).

type by virtual tautonomy, virtual tautonymy, q.v. (T-B).

type designation, fixation, q.v. (Mayr).

type fixation, fixation, q.v. (ICZN).

type genus, the nominal genus that is the name-bearing type of a nominal family-group taxon (ICZN).

type horizon, the geological stratum from which the name-bearing type of a nominal species or subspecies was collected (ICZN).

type host, the host species with which the name-bearing type of a nominal species or subspecies is associated (ICZN).

type locality, the geographical (and, where relavent, stratigraphical) place of capture or collection of the name-bearing type of a nominal species or subspecies, or the place from which it, or its wild progenitor, began its unnatural journey if the name-bearing type was captured or collected after being transported by boat vehicle, aircraft, or other human or mechanical means (ICZN).

type method, the method by which the name for a taxon is unambiguously associated with a definite zoological object belonging to the taxon (Mayr).

type series, the series of specimens, defined in the Code, which either constitutes the name-bearing type (syntypes) of a nominal species, subspecies, or form which the name-bearing type has been or may be designated (ICZN).

type selection, fixation, q.v. (Mayr).

type species, the nominal species that is the name-bearing type of a nominal genus or subgenus (ICZN).

type specimen, holotype, lectotype, or neotype (ICZN); any specimen (syntype) of the type series (ICZN).

typhoid fever, bacterial disease of man caused by *Salmonella typhi* transmitted by the house fly, *Musca domestica* (Diptera: Muscidae), various blow flies (Diptera: Calliphoridae), and various flesh flies (Diptera: Sarcophagidae), and through contaminated drinking water (Borror et al.; Allaby).

typhus fever, a disease caused by *Rickettsia* (Rickettsiaceae); see boutonneuse fever, endemic typhus, epidemic typhus, scrub typhus, and Rocky Mountain spotted fever.

typical, of the normal or usual form of a species (T-B); agreeing with the type (T-B).

typical host, a host in which the pathogenic microorganism (or parasite) is commonly found (Steinhaus and Martignoni, after Hopps and Price).

typological thinking, a concept in which variation is disregarded and members of the population are considered as replicas of the "type," the Platonic *eidos* (Mayr).

tyrosinase, copper salt of tyrosine, important in the hardening and darkening of the larval cuticle to form the puparium of Muscomorpha (Diptera) (T-B; Chapman).

tyrosine, an amino acid with a hydroxyphenol group, involved in the production of dopaquinone and melanin (T-B; Chapman)

U

U-shaped band, in some anopheline larvae (Diptera: Culicidae), a sclerotized strip of cuticle located posteriorly at the base of the spiracular apparatus and connecting the pecten plates of opposite sides of abdominal segment VIII, being partly homologous with the siphon of other mosquito larvae (Harbach and Knight, after Marshall).

U-shaped rod, in larval Culicidae (Diptera), the U-shaped thickened basal rim of the mandible (Harbach and Knight, after Rao and Knight).

UDP-glucose, uridine diphosphate glucose, q.v. (Gilmour, in CSIRO).

UDPAG, uridine diphosphate acetylglucosamine, q.v. (Chapman).

ugly nest, a nest made by the larvae of certain tortricid moths (Lepidoptera: Tortricidae), particularly those of *Cacoecia,* in which leaves, that later turn brown, are tied together with silk threads (Leftwich).

uliginous, uliginosus, muddy, or pertaining to mud (T-B).

ulnar area, in Orthoptera, median area, q.v. (T-B)

ulnar vein, in Auchenorrhyncha (Hemiptera) and Orthoptera, cubitus anterior, q.v. (T-B).

ulnoid, in adult Culicidae (Diptera), a line of thickening formed at the posterior end of the alula when the wing is extended (Harbach and Knight, after Prashad).

ulona, the thick, fleshy mouthparts of Orthoptera (T-B, after Fabricius).

Ulonata, Orthoptera, q.v. (T-B, after Fabricius).

ultramarine, dark blue (T-B).

ultranodal sector, in Odonata, postnodal sector, q.v. (T-B, after J. B. Smith).

ultraviolet, the rays of the solar spectrum, of short wave length (2920–4000 Å), beyond the visible spectrum (T-B).

ultraviolet perception, ultraviolet vision, q.v. (Gilmour, in CSIRO).

ultraviolet vision, the ability of most insects to perceive light frequencies in the ultraviolet range (Leftwich).

umber, yellowish-brown (T-B).

umbilicate, umbilicated, umbilicatus (Latin), navel-shaped, or resembling a navel (T-B).

umbilicus (Latin), a navel (T-B; R. W. Brown); a navellike depression (T-B).

umbo (Latin) (pl., **umbones**), boss; knob; shield (T-B; R. W. Brown); in the plural, 2 movable spines on the sides of the prothorax in some Coleoptera (T-B, after J. B. Smith).

umbonate, umbonated, umbonatus (Latin), bossed; with an elevated knob (T-B).

umbra (Latin), shadow; shade (T-B; R. W. Brown).

umbraculate, umbraculatus, bearing an umbrella-shaped projection, e.g., on the head of some Orthoptera (T-B, after Kirby and Spence).

umbrella organ, campaniform sensillum, q.v. (T-B).

umbrose, umbrosus (Latin), shaded or clouded (T-B).

un-, a Saxon prefix; not (T-B).

unarmed, without spurs, spines or armature of any kind (T-B).

unavailable name, a scientific name that does not conform to the Code, or that is an excluded name under the Code (ICZN).

unavailable nomenclatural act, one published in an unavailable work or that does not conform to the provisions of the Code (ICZN).

unavailable work, a published work (1) that was issued before 1758; or (2) that does not conform to the Principle of Binominal Nomenclature; or (3) that the Commission has ruled to be unavailable (ICZN).

unci (sing., **uncus**), in ♂ Odonata, hamuli, q.v. (T-B); see uncus.

unciform, hook-shaped (T-B).

unciform sclerotization, in ♀ Siphonaptera, single or double sclerotization on the anterior part of abdominal tergum VIII, usually covered by the flange of abdominal sternum VII (Tuxen, after Smit; Rothschild and Traub).

uncinate, uncinatus (Latin), hooked; barbed (T-B; R. W. Brown), e.g., an uncinate spine (T-B).

uncinus (pl., **uncini**), hook; barb (R. W. Brown); in some ♂ *Semidalis* (Planipennia: Coniopterygidae), external hook membranously connected to apex of each paramere (Tuxen, after Tjeder); in *Chrysopa* (Planipennia: Chrysopidae), entoprocessus, q.v. (Tuxen, after Principi).

uncus (pl., **unci**), hook; barb (R. W. Brown); a hooklike process on the distal inner margin of the maxillary mala, perhaps a remnant of the lacinia, e.g., in larval *Carpophilus* (Coleoptera: Nitidulidae) (Peterson); in ♂ Blattopteroidea, right epiphallus (Tuxen, after Berlese); in ♂ Zoraptera, dorsocephalad directed lobe on abdominal terga X–XI (Tuxen, after Bolivar); in ♂ some Phthiraptera, lower endomere, q.v. (Tuxen); in ♂ Auchenorrhyncha (Hemiptera), anal hooks, q.v. (Tuxen); in ♂ *Nymphes* (Planipennia: Nymphidae), mediuncus, q.v. (Tuxen, after Crampton); in ♂ Lepidoptera, abdominal tergum X, middorsal structure, usually strongly sclerotized, extending caudad from the caudal margin of the tegumen (Tuxen, after Peytoureau), superuncus, q.v. (Tuxen, after Gosse), subscaphium, q.v. (Tuxen, after Rebel), tegumen + uncus (Tuxen, after Roepke), gnathos, q.v. (Tuxen, after Stitz), or (in Hesperiidae) stylet, q.v. (Tuxen, after Rambur); in ♂ Culicidae (Diptera), parts of parameres (Tuxen, after Howard, Dyar and Knab); in ♂ Hymenoptera, paramere, q.v. (Tuxen), penis, q.v. (Tuxen, after Franklin), or aedoeagus, q.v. (Tuxen, after Williams) or in most adult Chalcididae, hooked apex of stigmal vein (Gauld and Bolton); see unguis.

uncus anticus (pl., **unci antici**), in ♂ *Enispe*, middorsal caudad extending process of the tegumen (abdominal tergum IX) (Tuxen, after Stichel), or in ♂ *Discophora necho* Felder (Lepidoptera: Nymphalidae), single, middorsal, process of the uncus (abdominal tergum X) (Tuxen, after Roepke).

uncus head, in ♂ Lepidoptera, fused and thickened end of the otherwise paired uncus (transl. "uncuskopf" Tuxen).

uncus-socii, in ♂ *Zygaena* (Lepidoptera: Zygaenidae), paired uncus lobes (Tuxen, after Loritz).

undate, undatus (Latin), undulate, q.v. (T-B).

undatergum, telson, q.v. (T-B, after MacGillivray).

undose, undosus (Latin), with undulating, broad, nearly parallel depressions running more or less into each other; wavy, resembling ripple-marks on a sandy beach (T-B; Harris); see vermiculate.

undulated, undulatus, wavy (T-B; R. W. Brown).

undulating tube, in ♀ Gerridae (Hemiptera: Heteroptera), ductus receptaculi, q.v. (Tuxen, after Brinkhurst).

undulatory, undulated, q.v. (Christiansen and Bellinger).

unequal, unlike in size, form, development or other characters (T-B).

ungual, of or pertaining to an unguis or claw (T-B).

ungual digitule, in Coccoidea (Hemiptera: Sternorrhyncha), digitule, q.v. (T-B, after MacGillivray).

unguiculate, unguiculatus, furnished with claws (T-B).

unguiculus (pl., **unguiculi**), a small claw or clawlike process (T-B; R. W. Brown); in most Collembola, the ventral, smaller appendage borne by the pretarsus (T-B; Christiansen and Bellinger).

unguifer, median dorsal process or sclerite of the last tarsomere with which the claws are articulated (T-B, after Snodgrass; Chapman).

unguiflexor, pretarsal depressor muscle, q.v. (T-B).

unguiform, shaped like a claw (T-B).

unguis (Latin) (pl., **ungues**), claw, q.v. (T-B; R. W. Brown); clawlike structure of the maxilla (T-B, after Kirby and Spence); in Collembola, the dorsal, larger appendage borne by the preparsus (Christiansen and Bellinger); in Aphididae (Hemiptera: Sternorrhyncha), portion of ultimate antennal segment distal of the primary sensorium (T-B; Stoetzel, in Stehr); in ♂ Lepidoptera, uncus, q.v. (Tuxen, after Malpighi); see uncus.

unguitractor, pretarsal depressor muscle, q.v. (T-B); see unguitractor plate.

unguitractor plate, the ventral sclerite of the pretarsus, articulating with auxiliae or claws distally and giving rise to the unguitractor tendon proximally (T-B, after Snodgrass; Chapman).

unguitractor tendon, the tendon that runs from the unguitractor to the pretarsal depressor muscle (T-B; Chapman).

ungula (Latin), hoof (R. W. Brown); the terminal tarsomere (T-B); unguis, q.v. (T-B); in larval Chironomidae (Diptera), U-shaped sclerite surrounding the epipharyngeal area laterally, carrying the basal sclerite posteriorly, anterior opening being closed by tormal bar, usually bearing chaetulae basales on lower, inner, posterolateral margins (Saether).

ungulate, shaped like a horse's hoof (T-B, after Say); having claws (T-B).

uni-, Latin prefix; one (T-B).

unicapsular, with only one capsule (T-B).

unicellular, consisting of one cell only (T-B).

unicolonial, pertaining to a population of social insects in which there are no behavioral colony boundaries (opposed to multicolonial) (Wilson).

unicolorate, unicolorous, unicoloratus, of one color throughout (T-B).

unicornous, with only one horn (T-B).

unidentate, with one tooth only (T-B).

unifollicular, consisting of one follicle only (T-B).

uniforous spiracle, spiracle having one entrance (Peterson).

unilabiate, having one lip only (T-B).

unilateral, on one side only (T-B).

unilocular, having one cell or cavity only (T-B).

uninominal name, a scientific name consisting of one word and used for a taxon of higher rank than the species group (ICZN).

uninominal nomenclature, the designation of a taxon by a scientific name consisting of a single word, being required for taxa above species rank (Mayr).

uniordinal crochets, in larval Lepidoptera, crochets that are arranged in a single row and are of a single length throughout or somewhat shorter towards the end of the row (Peterson, after Fracker); see biordinal crochets and triordinal crochets.

uniplicate, with a single fold or line of folding (T-B).

unipolar, having only one pole (T-B).

unipolar cell, a nerve cell with only one nerve proceeding from it (T-B).

unique, one only; unlike any other; in general, applied to an only known specimen of a species or group (T-B).

Uniramia, hypothesized monophyletic group, including the Onychophora, Myriapoda, and Hexapoda, the members of which are characterized by a single pair of antennae, uniramous appendages, and whole-limb jaws (Borror et al., after Manton).

uniserial crochets, in larval Lepidoptera, crochets arranged in a single row or series with their bases in a continuous line (T-B, after Imms; Peterson, after Fracker).

unisetaceous, unisetose, q.v. (Christiansen and Bellinger).

unisetose, having only one bristle or seta (T-B).

unisexual, of one sex only, e.g., some species of Aphididae (Hemiptera: Sternorrhyncha), Curculionidae (Coleoptera), and Cynipidae (Hymenoptera), in which only parthenogenetic females are known (T-B; Borror et al.); see bisexual.

univariate analysis, a biometric analysis of a single character (Mayr); see multivariate analysis.

univoltine, having one generation in a year (T-B); see bivoltine and multivoltine.

unjustified emendation, any emendation other than a justified emendation (ICZN).

unjustified original spelling, the spelling of a family-group name based upon unjustified emendation of a generic name (ICZN).

unpaired accessory gland, in ♀ Heteroptera (Hemiptera), vermiform gland, q.v. (Tuxen, after Carayon, Usinger and Wygodzinsky).

unpublished work, a work that is not published within the meanings of the Code (ICZN).

unsclerotized, not sclerotized (T-B).

unspecialized, generalized, not restricted or adapted to particular functions or conditions (T-B).

upper anal appendage, in ♂ Bittacidae (Mecoptera), epiandrium, q.v. (Tuxen, after Esben-Petersen).

upper appendage, in ♂ Bittacidae (Mecoptera), epiandrium, q.v. (Tuxen, after Esben-Petersen).

upper arm of clasper, in ♂ Pentatomoidea (Hemiptera: Heteroptera), superior process, q.v. (Tuxen, after McDonald).

Upper Austral Zone, cool temperate North America (T-B).

upper calypter, in adult Diptera, posterior wing lobe, distal to the lower calypter and proximal to the alula, believed to be homologous with the jugal region of other higher insects (Harbach and Knight; McAlpine).

upper field, in Orthoptera, anal field, q.v., of tegmen (T-B).

upper flap of the side-piece, in ♂ Culicidae (Diptera), the ventral (prerotation sense) surface of the goncoxite (Harbach and Knight, after Edwards).

upper frontal setae, in adult Diptera, frontal setae on the upper portion of the frontal plate (McAlpine).

upper genital styles, in ♂ *Empoasca* (Hemiptera: Auchenorrhyncha: Cicadellidae), appendages of the pygofer (Tuxen).

upper manubrium, in ♂ Siphonaptera, apodeme of tergum IX, q.v. (Tuxen).

upper margin, in Orthoptera, anal margin, q.v., of closed tegmen (T-B, after Thomas).

upper median area, in adult Hymenoptera, areola, q.v. (T-B).

upper mesepimeral scale, in adult Culicidae (Diptera), one of the scales occurring in a group on the dorsoposterior quarter of the mesanepimeron (Harbach and Knight).

upper mesepimeral seta, in adult Culicidae (Diptera), one of the setae occurring in a group on the upper posterior area of the mesanepimeron before the mesothoracic spiracle (Harbach and Knight, after Edwards).

upper meskatepisternal scale, in adult Culicidae (Diptera), one of the scales occurring in a group located immediately below the upper meskatepisternal setae (Harbach and Knight).

upper meskatepisternal seta, in adult Culicidae (Diptera), one of the setae occurring in more or less a horizontal line on the upper part of the meskatepisternum (Harbach and Knight).

upper ocular seta, in adult Culicidae (Diptera), one of the ocular setae occurring along the dorsal margin of the compound eye (Harbach and Knight).

upper orbital setae, in adult Diptera, orbital setae on the upper portion of the orbital plate (McAlpine).

upper organ, in ♂ Lepidoptera, tegumen + uncus (Scudder and Burgess).

upper penis cover, in ♂ Trichoptera, dorsal plate, q.v. (Tuxen).

upper penis lobe, in ♂ Odonata, median lobe of the flagella or the projection from the apical border of the glans (Tuxen, after Kimmins).

upper plate, in ♀ Psyllidae (Hemiptera: Sternorrhyncha), dorsal plate, q.v. (Tuxen).

upper pleurotergite, in adult Culicidae (Diptera), the upper division of the pleurotergite (Harbach and Knight).

upper pleurotergite apodeme, in adult Culicidae (Diptera), an apodeme borne along the upper margin of the upper pleurotergite, giving support to the walls of the mesopostnotum (Harbach and Knight).

upper postpronotal scale, in adult Culicidae (Diptera), one of the scales usually occurring in a large group on the dorsal part of the postpronotum (Harbach and Knight).

upper prealar scale, in adult Culicidae (Diptera), one of the scales occurring principally on the prealar knob among and above the prealar setae (Harbach and Knight).

upper proepisternal scale, in adult Culicidae (Diptera), one of the scales occurring in a group on the proepisternum above the base of the forecoxa (Harbach and Knight).

upper proepisternal seta, in adult Culicidae (Diptera), one of the proepisternal setae occurring in a group above the forecoxa (Harbach and Knight).

upper radial, in adult Lepidoptera, first median vein (M_1) (T-B, after J. B. Smith).

upper rhabdopoda, in $\male$ Ephemeroptera, penis, q.v. (Tuxen, after Packard).

upper sector of triangle, in adult Odonata, first branch of cubitus (Cu_1) (T-B).

Upper Sonoran Faunal Area, dry, cold temperate, western North America (T-B).

upper vaginal lip, in $\female$ Culicidae (Diptera), the sclerotized and pigmented rim of the roof of the vagina, articulating anteriorly with the lower vaginal lip at the hinge (Harbach and Knight, after Curtin and Jones).

upper vaginal sclerite, in $\female$ Culicidae (Diptera), a pigmented sclerite of the vaginal roof other than the upper vaginal lip (Harbach and Knight, after Reinert).

upper valve, in $\female$ Psyllidae (Hemiptera: Sternorrhyncha), dorsal plate, q.v. (Tuxen).

upper valves, in $\female$ Aleyrodidae (Hemiptera: Sternorrhyncha), dorsal valves, q.v. (Tuxen).

upright egg, in Lepidoptera, an egg, when deposited, that is symmetrical in horizontal section, with the micropylar axis vertical and the micropyle at the top (Common, after Chapman).

uranidin, a yellow coloring matter in some Coleoptera and Lepidoptera (T-B).

Uranioidea, superfamily of the infraorder Ditrysia (Lepidoptera) containing one family Uraniidae, possessing adults with large chaetosemata, naked proboscis, broad wings, hind wing often with tails or projections, abdomen with tympanal organs at base in $\female$ and at junction of segments II and III in $\male$; larvae with secondary setae few or absent, crochets in biordinal mesoseries; pupae stout, without dorsal spines (Common).

urate, ammonium, potassium, sodium, or calcium salt of uric acid (T-B; Chapman).

urate cells, in the fat body of Collembola, Blattaria, and larval Apocrita (Hymenoptera), cells scattered among the trophocytes functioning in storage excretion of uric acid as urate crystals or granules (T-B, after Snodgrass; Chapman).

urceolate, pitcher-shaped; swelling in the middle like a pitcher (T-B).

urea, $CO(NH_2)_2$, urine product of nitrogen metabolism produced from allantoic acid through the action of the enzyme allantoicase, commonly represented in small amounts in the excreta of insects (Chapman).

ureter, the stalk connecting Malpighian tubules, when they form large tufts, with the alimentary canal (T-B).

uric acid, $C_5H_4N_4O_3$, main product of nitrogen excretion, synthesized in the fat body by a pathway that incorporates nitrogen and carbon into the molecule from a variety of sources (formate, glycine, aspartate etc.) (Gilmour, in CSIRO).

uricase, enzyme catalyzing the transformation of uric acid to allantoin (Chapman).

uricose glands, utriculi majores tubules of the accessory sex glands of ♂ cockroaches (Blattaria) (mostly in the Blattellidae) which store large amounts of uric acid, and pour it over the spermatophore during copulation, being glands serving as storage-excretory organs of uric acid between matings and active excretory organs during copulation (Roth and Dateo); in some species the uric acid is eaten by the ♀ after the spermatophore is expelled and she incorporates it into the ootheca (Schal and Bell).

uridine diphosphate acetylglucosamine (UDPAG), condensed uridine triphosphate and acetylglucosamine-1-phospate, involved in the production of chitin (Chapman).

uridine diphosphate glucose (UDP-glucose), condensed uridine triphosphate and glucose-1-phosphate, involved in the production of glycogen (Gilmour, in CSIRO).

uridine triphosphate (UTP), nucleotide involved in the production of glycogen from glucose molecules and chitin from acetyl glucosamine units (Gilmour, in CSIRO; Chapman).

urinary vessels, Malpighian tubules, q.v. (T-B); anal glands, q.v. (T-B).

urine, colorless liquid within the lumen of the Malpighian tubules containing soluble nitrogenous waste products (Gilmour, in CSIRO).

urite, sternite, q.v. (T-B).

urogomphi (sing., **urogmphus**), in larval Coleoptera, usually paired processes from the posterior end of the tergum of the ninth abdominal segment, being jointed and movable by muscles, or unjointed and immoveable (T-B, after Böving and Craighead; Peterson).

urolora (sing., **urolorum**), in ♀ Trichoptera and Lepidoptera, apodemes, q.v. (Tuxen, after Crampton).

uromere, abdominal segment (T-B).

uropatagia, paraprocts, q.v. (T-B).

uropod (pl., **uropoda**), any of the abdominal appendages of arthropods (T-B); proleg, q.v. (Peterson); in Malacostraca (Crustacea), one of the terminal (usually lobelike) pair of abdominal appendages (Borror et al.; Boudreaux).

Uropygi, order within the Arachnida, including the whipscorpions, possessing a distinctly segmented opisthosoma with a long, whiplike prolongation that does not end in a sting and lacking comblike organs on the second ventral segment, pedipalps much stouter than legs, and eyes (Borror et al.).

Uropygida, Uropygi, q.v. (Boudreaux).

uropygium, oviscapt, q.v. (T-B).

urosome, abdomen, q.v. (T-B).

urosternite, the sternal or under piece of the uromeres (T-B).

urotergite, an abdominal tergite (T-B).

urticating, nettling; causing a stinging or burning sensation of the skin (T-B).

urticating hairs, in certain caterpillars (Lepidoptera) and adult insects, hairs or setae connected with cutaneous poison glands, through which venom issues, or barbed hairs which cause mechanical irritation (T-B).

urtication, the rash produced by certain insects by means of poisonous hairs or secretions (T-B).

U-shaped notal ridge, the scuto-scutellar suture.

ustulate, ustulatus, marked with brown, giving or having a scorched appearance (T-B).

uta, espundia, q.v. (Adkins, pers. comm.).

uterine, of or pertaining to the uterus (T-B).

uterine glands, in ♀ Diptera, opening of uterus in viviparous forms (Tuxen, after Snodgrass).

uterus (pl., **uteri**), in ♀ Reduviidae (Hemiptera: Heteroptera), oviductus communis (broadened distal part), q.v. (Tuxen, after Galliard); in ♀ Coleoptera, basal part of the vagina (Tuxen, after Bissell) or median oviduct, q.v. (Tuxen); in ♀ Lepidoptera, vagina, q.v. (Tuxen, after authors); in ♀ *Bombyx mori* (Lepidoptera: Bombycidae), bursa copulatrix or corpus bursae, q.v. (Tuxen, after Malpighi); in ♀ Pieridae and Tineidae (*Monopis*) (Lepidoptera), greatly expanded portion of the vestibulum where, in certain viviparous forms, one or more larvae develop (Tuxen, after Kusnezov, Diakonoff); in viviparous ♀ Diptera, a pouch of the anterior part of the genital chamber, into the anterior end of which open the oviduct, ductus spermathecae and accessory glands, the last being uterine glands probably not homologous with accessory glands of abdominal segment IX (Tuxen, after Snodgrass).

uterus masculinus, in Symphyla, a pouch or sac into which the ductus ejaculatorius opens (T-B).

utilitarian, for useful ends or purposes (T-B).

UTP, uridine triphospate, q.v. (Gilmour, in CSIRO).

utricle, utriculus, q.v. (T-B).

utricular, utriculate, utriculatus, furnished with utricli (T-B).

utriculi breviores, small vesicular sacs connected with the seminal vesicles in crickets (Orthoptera: Grylloidea) and some other insects (T-B).

utriculi majores, large vesicular sacs or tubular structures connected with the seminal vesicles in crickets (Orthoptera: Grylloidea) and some other insects (T-B).

utriculus (pl., **utriculi**), a small sac (T-B; R. W. Brown); a cell (T-B); in some ♂ Sialidae (Megaloptera), one of a pair of weak tubelike organs on each side of the mediuncus (Tjeder, in Tuxen); in ♀ Lepidoptera, larger, saclike reservoir of spermatheca (Weidner).

utrimque, similarly placed on both sides (T-B).

V

V setae, in larval and pupal Chironomidae (Diptera), ventral setae including O-setae, normally occurring in 4–5 pairs on abdominal sternites II–VII (Saether).

V-shaped notal ridge, the endoskeletal ridge of the mesonotum or metanotum, its arms divergent posteriorly, marked externally by the scutoscutellar suture, q.v. (T-B, after Snodgrass).

V-shaped ridge, in many larval Culicidae (Diptera), a ridge extending anteriorly outward from the U-shaped rod near the postartis of the mandible (Harbach and Knight).

vacuolate, vacuolated, with vacuoles or small cavities, empty or filled with a watery fluid (T-B).

vacuole, membrane-based sac found in many cells, normally acting as a storage organ (Allaby).

vagabond gall, leaf gall of poplar trees caused by *Pemphigus vagabundus* (Hemiptera: Sternorrhyncha: Aphididae) (Borror et al.); see leaf petiole gall.

vagility, capacity to disperse (Mackerras, in CSIRO).

vagina (pl., **vaginae**), in ♀ insects, tubular part of the genital chamber nearest the oviductus communis (median oviduct), into the anterior of which opens the spermatheca (Tuxen); in ♀ Protura, oviductus communis, q.v. (Tuxen); in ♀ Isoptera, vestibulum, q.v. (Tuxen); in ♀ Phasmida, posterior opening of the bursa copulatrix (Tuxen); in ♀ Orthoptera, oviductus communis, q.v. (Tuxen); in ♀ Auchenorrhyncha (Hemiptera), saw-case, q.v. (Tuxen); in ♀ Coccoidea and Aphididae (Hemiptera: Sternorrhyncha), vulva, q.v. (Tuxen); in ♀ Heteroptera (Hemiptera), pars communis of the ectodermal genital ducts, distally to the oviductus communis (Tuxen, after Heberdey); in ♀ Medocostidae (Hemiptera: Heteroptera), vestibulum, q.v. (Tuxen, after Štys); in ♀ Coleoptera, distal (terminal) part of the oviductus communis receiving the penis during copulation (Tuxen); in ♀ Lepidoptera with monotrysian type of genitalia, the portion of the oviductus communis between the vestibulum and the ostium oviductus (Tuxen, Cholodkowsky); in ♀ Lepidoptera, entire oviductus communis posterior to the entrance of the ductus seminalis or ductus receptaculi (Tuxen, after authors), ductus bursae, q.v. (Tuxen, after Burgess), bursa copulatrix or corpus bursae, q.v. (Tuxen, after Jordan), genital cavity, q.v. (Tuxen, after Malpighi), or ostium bursae, q.v. (Tuxen, after Scudder); in ♀ Siphonaptera, deep and narrow pocket proximal to the genital chamber (Tuxen, after Snodgrass) or camera genitalis, q.v. (Tuxen, after Lass); in ♀ Diptera, posterior portion of the genital chamber (McAlpine); .

vagina inferior, in ♀ Blattopteroidea, valvulae inferiores, q.v. (Tuxen, after Brunner v. Wattenwyl).

vagina superior, in ♀ Blattopteroidea, valvulae superiores, q.v. (Tuxen, after Brunner v. Wattenwyl).

vagina superior interna, in ♀ Blattopteroidea, valvulae internae, q.v. (Tuxen, after Brunner v. Wattenwyl).

vagina tubiformis, in ♀ Lepidoptera, a tubular ovipositor, q.v. (Tuxen, after Burmeister).

vaginae, in ♀ Blattopteroidea, valvulae, q.v. (Tuxen, after Brunner v. Wattenwyl).

vaginal, resembling a sheath (T-B); of or pertaining to the vagina (T-B).

vaginal aperture, in ♀ Lepidoptera, ostium bursae, q.v. (Tuxen, after Rothschild and Jordan).

vaginal apodeme, in many ♀ Nematocera and orthorrhaphous Brachycera (Diptera), genital fork, q.v. (Tuxen; McAlpine); in ♀ Chironomidae (Diptera), gonapophysis IX, notum, rmaus, q.v. (Saether).

vaginal armature, in ♀ Lepidoptera, sterigma, q.v. (Tuxen, after Rothschild and Jordan).

vaginal atrium, in ♀ Diptera, distal part of the vagina (van Emden and Hennig, in Tuxen).

vaginal clamp, in ♀ Siphonaptera, a muscular, barlike structure, sometimes forming a ball and socket type of clamp arising from the floor of the vagina and inserting into a corresponding cavity in its dorsal wall, thus effectively closing the entrance to the oviduct (Rothschild and Traub).

vaginal knobs, in ♀ Plecoptera, lateral sclerotizations at the opening of genital duct (Zwick, pers. comm., after Aubert).

vaginal papilla, in ♀ Dytiscidae (Coleoptera), terminal end of vagina protruding through the vulva (transl. "vaginalpapille" Lindroth and Palmén, in Tuxen).

vaginal pouch, in ♀ Heteroptera (Hemiptera), variably formed pouch that may bear ringed glands (Tuxen, after Pendergrast).

vaginal valves, in ♀ Plecoptera, vaginal knobs, q.v. (Tuxen, after Wu).

Vaginata, Coleoptera, q.v. (T-B).

vaginate, vaginated, vaginatus, ensheathed (T-B).

vaginate type, in ♂ Coleoptera, a type of aedeagus in which the basal piece together with the parameres is elongated, forming a pipe or a (dorsal or ventral) channel though which the penis moves, e.g., certain Tenebrionoidea (Tuxen, after Jeannel and Paulian).

vaginula (pl., **vaginulae**), in ♀ Hymenoptera, gonoplac, q.v. (Tuxen, after Kirby and Spence).

vagus nerve, the system of nerves and ganglia cephalad of the supraoesophageal ganglion (T-B, after Comstock and Kellogg); see frontal ganglion.

vagus nervous system, stomatogastric nervous system, q.v. (T-B, after Comstock).

valgate, valgatus, enlarged at the bottom; club-footed (T-B).

valid name, the correct scientific name for a taxon under the provisions of the Code (ICZN).

valid nomenclatural act, one that is correct under the provisions of the Code (ICZN).

valine, essential amino acid in the diet of insects (Gilmour, in CSIRO).

vallar bristle, in some adult Sciomyzidae (Diptera), bristle arising from the subalare (McAlpine).

vallar ridge, in adult Diptera, subalare, q.v. (McAlpine).

vallum penis, in ♂ Lepidoptera, anellus, q.v. (Tuxen, after Kusnezov).

valvae (sing., **valva**), in ♂ Trichoptera, inferior appendages, q.v. (Tuxen, after Zander); in ♂ Lepidoptera, paired, presumably clasping organs, believed to be derived in part or wholly from intersegmental membrane of abdominal segments IX–X and/or gonopods of abdominal segment IX (styli, coxites or parameres), typically a flattened sac, open proximally (Tuxen, after Huebner); in ♀ Thysanoptera, blades of ovipositor (Tuxen); in ♀ Lepidoptera, navicula, q.v. (Tuxen, after Fruhstorfer) or papillae anales, q.v. (Tuxen); in ♀ Trichoptera, lateral or vertical plates issued from abdominal segment VIII (Nielsen) or segment IV in Leptocoridae (Schmid).

valvae anales, in Orthoptera, paraprocts, q.v. (Tuxen).

valvae dorsales (sing., **valva dorsalis**), in ♀ Psocoptera, median processes of the gonapophyses of abdominal segment IX (Tuxen).

valvae externae (sing., **valva externa**), in ♂ Hymenoptera, gonocoxites + gonostyli (Tuxen, after Zander); in ♀ Psocoptera, lateral processes of gonapophyses of abdominal segment IX (Tuxen).

valvae inferae (sing., **valva infera**), in ♀ Japygidae (Diplura), 2 lower blades carried by the papilla genitalis (Tuxen, after Silvestri).

valvae inferiores, in ♀ Diptera, hypogynial valves, q.v. (Tuxen).

valvae internae, in ♂ *Chloroclystis* (Lepidoptera: Geometridae), fulterior interior, q.v. (Tuxen, after Meixner); in ♂ Hymenoptera, digitus or volsella, q.v. (Tuxen, after Zander).

valvae superae (sing., **valva supera**), in ♀ Japygidae (Diplura), 2 upper blades carried by the papilla genitalis (Silvestri).

valvae ventrales (sing., **valva ventralis**), in ♀ Psocoptera, first valvulae, q.v. (Tuxen; Mockford, pers. comm.).

valvar strut, in ♂ Hymenoptera, dorsal ramus (of gonapophysis IX), q.v. (Tuxen, after Ross).

valvate, having or resembling a valve (T-B).

valve(s), a lid or cover to an aperture or opening, which opens in one direction but closes in the other (T-B); internal valvelike lobe of the heart wall between the chambers, said to be present in certain larval Diptera (T-B, after Snodgrass); in adult Hymenoptera, valvula, q.v., of maxilla (T-B, after J. B. Smith); in Coccoidea (Hemiptera: Sternorrhyncha), anal plate, q.v. (T-B, after Green); in ♂ Caelifera (Orthoptera), one of a pair of valvelike lobes projecting from the posterior end of the cingulum (Tuxen, after Dirsh); in ♂ Zoraptera, clasping organs, q.v. (Tuxen, after Paulian); in ♂ Aleyrodidae (Hemiptera: Sternorrhyncha), claspers, q.v. (Tuxen); in ♂ Auchenorrhyncha (Hemiptera), genital valve, q.v. (T-B, after J. B. Smith); in ♂ Coleoptera, parameres, q.v. (Tuxen); in ♂ Panorpidae (Mecoptera), paired, appressed lobes of aedeagus, distinct from parameres (Byers); in ♂ Lepidoptera, valvae, q.v. (T-B); in ♀ Diplura, valvae superae and inferae, q.v. (Tuxen, after Pagés); in ♀ Odonata, lateral gonapophyses, q.v. (Tuxen, after Tillyard); in ♀ Orthoptera, valvulae, q.v. (Tuxen, after Chopard); in ♀ Phasmida, gonapophyses, q.v. (Tuxen); in ♀ Boreidae (Mecoptera), gonapophyses laterales, q.v. (Tuxen, after Esben-Petersen); in ♀ Lepidoptera, papillae anales, q.v. (Tuxen); in ♀ Chironomidae (Diptera), gonapophysis VIII, q.v. (Saether); in ♀ Chironomidae (Diptera), gonocoxite IX, q.v. (Saether); in ♀ Aculeata (Hymenoptera), a flap on the first valvulae extending into the bulb of the sting (Tuxen, after Snodgrass).

valvellae (sing., **valvella**), in ♂ Lithosiinae (Lepidoptera: Arctiidae), a pair of periphallic structures mesad of the valvae and laterad or dorsolaterad of the juxta, often distended dorsad, supposed derivatives of the gonapophyses (Tuxen, after Birket-Smith).

valvibulla, in ♀ Orthoptera, dorsal-basal part of the inner valvulae (Tuxen, after Crampton).

valvifers, in ♀ insects, first and second gonocoxae, q.v. (Tuxen, after Snodgrass); in ♀ Odonata, median gonapophyses, q.v. (Tuxen, after Crampton); in ♀ Grylloblattodea, a pair of sclerites at the base of the ovipositor articulating with the base of the first and third valvulae as well as with abdominal tergum IX, being vestiges of abdominal sternum IX (Tuxen); in ♀ Orthoptera, sclerite at the base of the posterior valvulae, being rarely visible in Caelifera (Tuxen); in ♀ Thysanoptera, triangular basal sclerites attached to the ovipositor (Tuxen, after Doeksen); in ♀ Auchenorrhyncha (Hemiptera), ventrolateral sclerites of abdominal segments VIII and IX to which the valves are attached (Tuxen); in ♀ Coleoptera, paraprocts, q.v. (Tuxen, after Tanner); in ♀ Chironomidae (Diptera), gonocoxite IX, q.v. (Saether).

valvifers (**1st** and **2nd**), in ♀ Heteroptera (Hemiptera), gonocoxites (VIII and IX), q.v. (Tuxen, after Snodgrass).

valvijugum, in ♀ Orthoptera, inferior intervalvula, q.v. (Tuxen, after Crampton).

valvilli, in ♀ Ichneumonoidea and Apocrita (Hymenoptera), one or more small articulating flaps on first gonapophyses (Gauld and Bolton).

valvipons, in ♀ Orthoptera, inferior intervalvula, q.v. (Tuxen, after Crampton).

valvula(e), a small valve or valvelike process (T-B); paraproct, q.v. (T-B, after Burmeister); in adult Eumeninae (Vespidae), translucent processes bordering propodeal foramen (Carpenter, pers. comm., after Carpenter and Cumming); in ♂ Tortricidae (Lepidoptera), process at the base of the valvula (Tuxen, after Diakonoff); in ♂ Lepidoptera, sacculus (Tuxen, after Hering); in ♂ Lepidoptera, central and ventrocaudal region of the valva, ventrad of the cucullus, in Noctuidae (Lepidoptera) homologous with valvula (Pierce) and in Rhopalocera absent, being positionally replaced by the harpe (Tuxen, after Sibatani et al.); in ♂ Coleophoridae (Lepidoptera), dorsal, lightly sclerotized lobe of the valva (Tuxen, after Toll); in ♀ Phasmida, gonapophyses, q.v. (Tuxen); in ♀ Orthoptera, the 3 pairs of blades forming the ovipositor (in all groups with an orthopteroid ovipositor) (Tuxen); in ♀ Psocoptera, valvae dorsales, q.v. (Tuxen, after Kolbe); in ♀ Heteroptera (Hemiptera), gonapophyses (VIII and IX) and styloids, q.v. (Tuxen, after Snodgrass); in ♀ Raphidiidae (Raphidioptera), styli, q.v. (Tuxen, after Friedrich); in ♀ Mecoptera, lamnae, q.v. (Tuxen, after Grell); in ♂ Geometridae (Lepidoptera), central region of the valva, typically lightly sclerotized, lying between the costa and sacculus (Tuxen, after Pierce); in ♀ Lepidoptera, papillae anales, q.v. (Tuxen); in adult Hymenoptera, the expanded platelike galea of the maxilla (T-B); in ♀ Hymenoptera, gonapophyses, q.v. (Tuxen).

valvula analis dorsalis, in adult Zygentoma, valvula supraanalis, q.v. (Tuxen, after Börner).

valvula analis superior, in Plecoptera, supraanal lobe, q.v. (Tuxen, after Klapálek).

valvula genitalis, in ♂ *Tinea* (Lepidoptera: Tineidae) and *Tortrix* (Lepidoptera: Tortricidae), manica (Tuxen, after Stitz); in ♂ Auchenorrhyncha (Hemiptera), genital valve, q.v. (Tuxen).

valvula supraanalis (pl., **valvulae supraanales**), in adult Zygentoma, small plate below the filum terminale, regarded as a remnant of the telson (Tuxen, after Denis); in Plecoptera, supraanal lobe, q.v. (Tuxen, after Klapálek).

valvula vulvae, in most ♀ Anisoptera (Odonata), first gonapophyses, q.v., reduced to 2 small flaps guarding the entrance to the vagina (Tuxen, after Tillyard).

valvulae anales, in ♀ Lepidoptera, papillae anales, q.v. (Tuxen).

valvulae anales inferiores, in Plecoptera, subanal plates, q.v. (Tuxen, after Klapálek).

valvulae anales laterales, in adult Archaeognatha and Zygentoma, paraprocts, q.v. (Tuxen, after Börner).

valvula inferior (pl., **valvulae inferiores**), in ♀ insects, first gonapophyses, q.v. (Tuxen); in ♀ Diptera, hypogynial valves, q.v. (Tuxen).

valvula interna (pl., **valvulae internae**), in ♂ *Calliphora* (Diptera: Calliphoridae), cerci, q.v. (Tuxen, after Lowne); in ♀ Blattopteroidea, second gonapophyses, q.v. (Tuxen).

valvula lateralis (pl., **valvulae laterales**), in ♂ Calliphoridae (Diptera), surstyli, q.v. (Tuxen); in ♀ Auchenorrhyncha (Hemiptera), the lateral parts of the pygofer (Tuxen, after Sahlberg).

valvulae mediae, in ♂ Muscomorpha (Diptera), cerci, q.v. (Tuxen).

valvulae mediales, in ♂ Muscomorpha (Diptera), cerci, q.v. (Tuxen).

valvulae ovipositores, in ♀ Orthoptera, valvulae, q.v. (Tuxen, after Brunner v. Wattenwyl).

valvulae subanales, in Plecoptera, subanal plates, q.v. (Tuxen, after Klapálek).

valvula superioris (pl., **valvulae superiores**), in ♀ Blattopteroidea, upper pair of valves forming the ovipositor (Tuxen); in ♀ Heteroptera (Hemiptera), gonoplacs, q.v. (Tuxen, after Christophers and Crass).

valvulae vaginales, in ♀ Siphonaptera, abdominal sternum IX (Tuxen, after Lass).

valvular, valvelike, having the functions of a valve, or of or pertaining to a valve (T-B).

valvular process, in ♀ Odonata, style, q.v. (Tuxen).

valvular stria, rhachal remnant (proximal rhachis) on the base of the ramus of gonapophysis IX (Tuxen, after Wong).

valvular tube, in ♀ Idiostolidae (Hemiptera: Heteroptera), vestibulum, q.v. (Tuxen, after Schaefer).

valvule(s), valvula, q.v. (T-B); in ♂ Odonata, gonapophyses, q.v. (Tuxen, after Tillyard); in ♀ Orthoptera, valvulae, q.v. (Tuxen).

valvura, in ♂ Hymenoptera, ventral ramus (of gonapophysis IX), q.v. (Tuxen, after Ross).

vannal area, anal area, q.v., of wing (Mackerras, in CSIRO).

vannal lobe, in adult Hymenoptera, claval lobe, q.v. (Borror et al.).

vannal fold, claval furrow, q.v. (T-B).

vannal notch, preaxillary excision, q.v. (Gauld and Bolton).

vannal region, clavus, q.v., of wing (T-B, after Snodgrass).

vannal veins, the veins associated at their bases with the third axillary sclerite, and occupying the vannal region of the wing; the "anal" veins except the first, or postcubitus (T-B, after Snodgrass).

vannus, fanlike expansion of the clavus of the hind wing separated from the remigium by the claval furrow (T-B; Leftwich; Chapman).

van't Hoff's Rule, an observational rule which states that, within appropriate limits, the metabolic rate of a living system doubles with each 10° elevation in temperature (Tulloch).

variance (Var), the square of the standard deviation (Mayr); the sum of squared deviations from mean (d) divided by the sample size minus one (n-1);

$$\text{Var} = \frac{\Sigma d^2}{n-1}$$

variant spellings, different spellings of specific or subspecific names that are deemed to be identical for the purposes of the Principle of Homonymy (ICZN).

variation, differences displayed by individuals within a species (T-B; Allaby); see continuous variation, discontinuous variation, and polymorphism.

varicose, varicosus (Latin), irregularly swollen (T-B).

variegate, variegated, variegatus (Latin), of several colors in indefinite pattern (T-B).

varietas (Latin), variety; abbrev., v., var. (T-B).

variety, an ambiguous term of classical (Linnaean) taxonomy for a heterogeneous group of phenomena including nongenetic variations of the phenotype, morphs, domestic breeds, and geographic races (Mayr).

variola (Latin), **variole,** a pocklike mark (T-B).

variolate, pitted as if by small pox; full of irregular indentations (varioles) (T-B; Harris, after R. W. Brown); see cicatrose, impressed, and lacunose.

variolose, variolosus (Latin), **variolous,** variolate, q.v. (T-B).

vas ejaculatorium, in ♂ Lepidoptera, ductus ejaculatorius, q.v. (Tuxen).

vas deferens (pl., **vasa deferentia**), in ♂ insects, the paired mesodermal ducts which carry spermatozoa from testes, opening separately or united into the ectodermal ductus ejaculatorius (T-B; Tuxen).

vas efferens (pl., **vasa efferentia**), in ♂ insects, ducts leading from the testis follicles of the testis to the vas deferens (T-B; Tuxen; Chapman).

vasa mucosa, Malpighian tubules, q.v. (T-B).

vascular, of or relating to vessels or ducts (T-B).

vasiform, vessel-shaped (T-B).

vasiform orifice, in Aleyrodidae (Hemiptera: Sternorrhyncha), the anal structure that contains the operculum and lingula (Stoetzel, in Stehr).

vector, intermediate host, q.v. (T-B); an arthropod or other animal carrying a microorganism pathogenic for members of another species (Steinhaus and Martignoni); see transport host.

vegetative functions, in the living organism, all those functions which together work to maintain life, e.g., respiration and digestion (T-B, after Snodgrass).

vegetative phase, in invertebrate pathology, the period in the virus infection in which there is actual multiplication of viral material, preceding the final infective stage (Steinhaus and Martignoni).

vein, sclerotized, tubular structure supporting the membrane of the wings (T-B; Chapman); see venation.

veinlet, any small veins in the insect wing (T-B); in Orthoptera, a minute transverse rib or ridge between longitudinal veins (T-B); see accessory vein, crossvein, intercalary vein, and intercostula.

velum (pl., **vela**), a membrane (T-B); a membranous appendage of the spurs at the apex of the anterior tibia (T-B); a translucent flattened lateral expansion of the basal part of a seta or spicule (Harbach and Knight); in ♀ Chrysopidae (Planipennia), a pair of sail-formed processes from the dorsal side of the boxlike spermatheca (Tuxen, after Tjeder); in ♂ Coleoptera, thin membrane forming part of apical and marginal portions of a paramere (Tuxen, after Brundin); in ♂ Lepidoptera, specialized sclerotized structure of abdominal sternum VIII (Tuxen, after Eltringham); in ♂ Siphonaptera, arch-shaped enlargement of the dorsal wall of the aedeagus cephalad above the aedeagal apodeme (Tuxen, after Peus); in adult bees (Hymenoptera: Apoidea), a broad process at the inner end of the foretibia (T-B).

velum penis, the thin membranous covering of the ♂ intromittent organ (T-B); see anellus.

velutinous, velutinus (Latin), velvety; clothed with dense, soft, short hair, like velvet (T-B; R. W. Brown).

vena, vein, q.v. (T-B).

vena arcuata, jugal bar, q.v. (T-B, after Snodgrass).

vena cardinalis, the second jugal vein, usually appearing as a basal branch of the vena arcuata (T-B, after Snodgrass).

vena dividens, in Orthoptera and Blattaria, cubitus posterior,, q.v. (T-B, after Comstock, Tillyard, J. B. Smith, Snodgrass).

vena media, media (M), q.v., of wing (T-B).

vena plicata, on the wings of Dermaptera, the vein around which the folding occurs (T-B).

vena spuria, spurious vein, q.v. (T-B, after Wardle; Leftwich).

venation, the complete system of veins of a wing (T-B).

venational fields, primary groups of wing veins, including costal, subcostal, radial, median, cubital, and anal (Mackerras, in CSIRO).

venom, toxic fluid injected into prey or enemies causing death, paralysis, or pain (Chapman); in ♀ aculeate Hymenoptera, the secretion of the accessory or poison gland (Tulloch).

venom glands, poison glands, q.v. (Gilmour, in CSIRO).

venomous, capable of injecting a venom via a bite or sting (Borror et al.).

venose, venosus (Latin), **venous,** furnished with veins or veinlike markings; of or pertaining to veins (T-B; Harris).

vent, anus, q.v. (Tuxen).

venter, the under surface of the abdomen as a whole (T-B); the entire ventral side of an animal (Peterson; Borror et al.).

ventilation tracheae, tracheae with collapsible walls, responding to varying surrounding pressure (T-B, after Snodgrass).

ventose, ventosus (Latin), inflated; puffed out (T-B).

ventrad, toward the venter; in the direction of the venter (T-B).

ventral, pertaining to the under surface of the abdomen (T-B); pertaining to the under surface of the body (Peterson).

ventral aedeagal bridge, in ♂ Culicidae (Diptera), the transverse sclerotization connecting the aedeagal sclerites furthest from the anus (Harbach and Knight, after Knight and Laffoon).

ventral aedeagal sclerites, in ♂ Cyrtacanthacridinae (Orthoptera: Acrididae), ventral, solidly sclerotized structures in the phallotreme membrane (Tuxen, after Eades).

ventral aedeagal valve, in ♂ Caelifera (Orthoptera), ventral pair of sclerotizations in the endophallic membrane limiting the phallotreme duct (Tuxen).

ventral aedeagal valves, in ♂ Cyrtacanthacridinae (Orthoptera: Acrididae), posterior (ventral) apical processes or lobes of the aedeagus (Tuxen, after Eades).

ventral apical lobe of penis, in ♂ Siphonaptera, hamuli, q.v. (Tuxen, after Jordan and Rothschild).

ventral apotome, in larval Trichoptera, gular sclerite of the head capsule, sometimes separated into anterior and posterior ventral apotomes, q.v. (Wiggins).

ventral appendage, in ♂ Plecoptera, vesicle, q.v. (Tuxen, after Hanson); in Chironomidae (Diptera), inferior volsella, q.v. (Saether).

ventral appendages, in ♂ Mecoptera, hypovalvae, q.v. (Tuxen, after Banks).

ventral appendices of penis, in ♂ Caelifera (Orthoptera), a pair of valves attached below the apical valves of the penis (Tuxen, after Dirsh).

ventral appendix, in adult Hymenoptera, proximal part of the ventral ramus of gonapophyses (transl. "ventralforsatz" Oeser, in Tuxen).

ventral arch, in larval Sciomyzidae (Diptera), strong, dentate structure of the cephalopharyngeal skeleton below the base of the mandibles (Teskey, in McAlpine).

ventral arm, in ♂ *Culex* (Diptera: Culicidae), the lateral pointed process of the inner division of the lateral plate of the phallosome, being homologous with the leaflets of the aedeagus in *Anopheles* (Harbach and Knight, after Sundararaman).

ventral basivalvular sclerite, in ♀ Caelifera (Orthoptera), ventral sclerite of ventral ovipositor valve (Tuxen).

ventral bridge, in ♂ Hymenoptera, ventral sclerotic bridge between bases of penis valves (Tuxen, after Michener).

ventral brush, in larval Culicidae (Diptera), series of long setae located medially on abdominal sterum IX (Peterson), or a more or less linear series of irregularly paired setae borne on the midline of abdominal segment X (Harbach and Knight, after Dyar).

ventral chain, ventral nerve cord, q.v. (T-B).

ventral chitin rod, in ♂ Nepidae (Hemiptera: Heteroptera), ligamentary processes, q.v. (Tuxen, after Hamilton).

ventral circulus, in Pseudococcidae (Hemiptera: Sternorrhyncha: Coccoidea), circulus, q.v. (Kosztarab, pers.comm.).

ventral comb, in Trichoptera, a transverse row of fine teeth on abdominal sternum VI (T-B; Wey, pers. comm.).

ventral condyle, in Dicondylia (Insecta), a secondary condyle located anteroventrally on the mandible (T-B, after MacGillivray); see dorsal condyle.

ventral connectives, in ♂ Heteroptera (Hemiptera), suspensorial apodemes, q.v. (Tuxen, after Baker).

ventral cornua, in larval Muscomorpha (Diptera), paired arms arising from tentoropharyngeal sclerite and fused with the pharynx (Teskey, in McAlpine).

ventral diaphragm, a horizontal septum just above the nerve cord cutting off the perineural sinus from the perivisceral sinus (T-B, after Imms; Chapman).

ventral ecdysial line, any ventral preformed line of weakness along which the cuticle splits (usually) or bends during ecdysis (Harbach and Knight).

ventral epandrial plate, in adult Diptera, abdominal sternite X, q.v. (McAlpine).

ventral epandrial sclerite, in ♂ Brachycera (Diptera), abdominal sternite X, q.v. (McAlpine, after Hennig).

ventral face of the leg, in Diptera, the lower aspect of the leg when it is laterally extended.

ventral flap, in ♂ Culicidae (Diptera), part of the basistylus (coxite) when divided by a median strip of thin membrane (van Emden and Hennig, in Tuxen); in ♀ Ephemeroptera, subgenital plate, q.v. (Tuxen, after Phillips).

ventral fringe, in many larval Culicidae (Diptera), one of the pharyngeal fringes borne ventral to the lateral pharyngeal sclerite in the lateral margin of the pharynx (Harbach and Knight); see primary ventral fringe and secondary ventral fringes.

ventral genital valve, in ♂ Psyllidae (Hemiptera: Sternorrhyncha), hypandrium, q.v. (Tuxen, after Crawford).

ventral glands, glands in the ventral part of the head of some insects (Thysanura, Ephemeroptera, Odonata, Dermaptera, Acrididae [Orthoptera], and Phasmida), corresponding to the thoracic and prothoracic glands of other insects and a source of the moulting hormone (Leftwich); in Diaspididae (Hemiptera: Coccoidea), circumgenital pores, q.v. (T-B, after MacGillivray); in larval Lepidoptera and Tenthredinidae (Hymenoptera), eversible glands located on the venter (Peterson).

ventral gonapophyses, in ♀ Psocoptera, valvae ventrales, q.v. (Tuxen); in ♀ Aleyrodidae (Hemiptera: Sternorrhyncha), lateral valves, q.v. (Tuxen).

ventral gonocoxal bridge, in ♂ Hymenoptera, basal sclerotic bridge between gonocoxites on venter (Tuxen, after Michener).

ventral grouped glands, in Diaspididae (Hemiptera: Coccoidea), circumgenital pores, q.v. (T-B).

ventral groove, in Collembola, a channel in the cuticle running from the apex of labium to the anterior surface of the ventral tube (T-B; Christiansen and Bellinger); in Pentatomidae (Hemiptera: Heteroptera), a median lengthwise groove on the abdomen (T-B).

ventral group of setae (V), in larval Lepidoptera, primary seta V1 located on thoracic and abdominal segments, on the inner base of thoracic legs and abdominal prolegs, and in a similar positin on other segments (Stehr, after Hinton); see adventral tubercle.

ventral heart, ventral diaphragm, q.v. (T-B).

ventral incrassation, in ♂ Siphonaptera, the sclerotization of the ventral margin of the clasper (Rothschild and Traub).

ventral lamella, in some ♂ Siphonaptera, a ventral lobe arising from the lateral wall of the aedeagus, folded or pendant, smooth, striated or spiculose (Rothschild and Traub).

ventral lamella of proctiger, in ♂ Asilidae (Diptera), abdominal sternite X, q.v. (McAlpine, after Karl).

ventral lamina, in ♀ Plecoptera, subgenital plate, q.v. (Tuxen, after Morton).

ventral laterotergites, in Heteroptera (Hemiptera), ventrally situated laterotergites, distinct from dorsal laterotergites but generally fused with the sternum and usually bearing spiracles (Štys, pers. comm.).

ventral light reaction, transverse orientation in which the ventral surface of the body is kept perpendicular to a directed source of light at all times (Matthews and Matthews).

ventral lobe, in ♂ Plecoptera, vesicle, q.v. (Tuxen, after Needham and Claassen); in ♂ Caelifera (Orthoptera), an extension of the ectophallic membrane (sometimes sclerotized) surrounding the aedeagus ventrally and more or less laterally (Tuxen); in ♂ Auchenorrhyncha (Hemiptera), ventral lobular part of the first valvulae (Tuxen, after Fennah); in Gerromorpha (Hemiptera: Heteroptera), buccula, q.v. (Andersen).

ventral lobe of penis, in ♂ Caelifera (Orthoptera), ventral aedeagal valve, q.v. (Tuxen, after Walker); in ♂ Ensifera (Orthoptera), ventral phallic lobe, q.v. (Tuxen, after Walker).

ventral locomotory welts, in larval Diptera, especially Muscomorpha, a ventral patch of spines on each abdominal segment that aids in locomotion (Ferrar).

ventral maxillary suture, in some culicine larvae (Diptera: Culicidae), a groove or furrow on the ventral surface of the maxillary body between the galeastipes and laciniastipes, extending from a point mesal to the maxillary brush to the basal notch (Harbach and Knight).

ventral muscle, in insects, muscle in which the fibers are typically longitudinal and attached on the intersegmental folds or on the antecostae of successive sterna (T-B, after Snodgrass).

ventral nerve cord, the chain of ventral ganglia, beginning anteriorly with the tritocerebral ganglia (T-B); the ventral chain of thoracic and abdominal ganglia (T-B, after Snodgrass).

ventral nodule, in some ♂ *Embia* (Embiidina: Embiidae), rounded, wartlike nodule on the midventral surface of the left paraproct (Ross, in Tuxen).

ventral oral brush, in many culicine larvae (Diptera: Culicidae), a covering of filaments located on the posterior margin of the ventral oral sclerite, apparently functioning to clean the mandibular sweepers and to retain food particles in the pharynx (Harbach and Knight).

ventral oral fringe, in many larval Culicidae (Diptera), usually one or 2 rows of small flattened filaments located on the ventral margin of the mouth between the ventral oral sclerite and the labiohypopharynx (Harbach and Knight).

ventral oral sclerite, in many larval Culicidae (Diptera), a small rounded plate located just inside the mouth on the midline of the ventral wall of the pharynx at about the level of the dorsal oral sclerite (Harbach and Knight).

ventral parameres, in Aeolothripidae (Thysanoptera), ventral appendages of the periandrium phallobase (Priesner, in Tuxen); in ♂

Neopanorpa (Mecoptera: Panorpidae), paired ventral processes from base of the aedeagus (Tuxen, after Byers).

ventral paratergites, in Heteroptera (Hemiptera), ventral laterotergites, q.v. (Štys, pers. comm.).

ventral phallic lobes, in ♂ Ensifera (Orthoptera), paired ventral lobes of phallus, q.v. (Ander, in Tuxen).

ventral phallic valves, in ♂ Mecoptera, (ventral) parameres, q.v. (Tuxen, after Crampton).

ventral phallomere, in ♂ Blattopteroidea, hypophallus, q.v. (Tuxen, after Snodgrass).

ventral pharyngeal gland, in the honey bee (Hymenoptera: Apoidea), a transverse row of cells opening into the floor of the pharynx between the ducts of the lateral pharyngeal glands (T-B, after Snodgrass).

ventral pharyngeal ridges, in larval Muscomorpha (Diptera), a series of longitudinal ridges between the ventral cornua of the tentoropharyngeal sclerite used as a filter to concentrate food (Ferrar).

ventral pharyngeal sclerite, in many larval Culicidae (Diptera), a narrow band of sometimes lightly sclerotized cuticle extending along the lateroventral margin of the pharynx from the anterior part of the ventral oral sclerite (Harbach and Knight).

ventral plate(s), a layer of columnar cells of the blastoderm on the ventral side of the egg, which later becomes the germ band (T-B, after Imms); in ♂ Plecoptera, subgenital plate, q.v. (Tuxen, after Morton); in some ♂ Enicocephalidae (Hemiptera: Heteroptera), fused genital plates (Štys); in ♂ Lepidoptera, median, band-shaped or shield-shaped plate formed by fusion of the distal ends of the arms of the gnathos, ventrad of the tuba analis (Tuxen, after Busck and Heinrich), sternum VIII (Tuxen, after Pierce), or (in *Hesperia*: Hesperiidae) part of the sacculus (Tuxen, after Warren); in ♂ Simuliidae (Diptera), sclerotized ventral portion of the aedeagus (McAlpine); in ♀ Ephemeroptera, postgenital plate, q.v. (Tuxen, after Kimmins); in ♀ Plecoptera, subgenital plate, q.v. (Tuxen, after Banks); in Phthiraptera, subgenital plate, q.v. (Tuxen); in ♀ Psyllidae (Hemiptera: Sternorrhyncha), the ventral one of the genital plates enclosing the ovipositor (Tuxen); in ♀ Staphylinidae (Coleoptera), sclerotized plate in intersegmental membrane of the vulva (transl. "ventralplatte" Brundin) (Tuxen); in ♀ Hydroptilidae (Trichoptera), the outlet of an unpaired structure, situated on the ventral side of abdominal segment VIII (Tuxen); in ♀ Polycentropodidae and Hydropsychidae (Trichoptera), paired platelike processes of venter VIII (Tuxen); in ♀ *Eupithecia* (Lepidoptera: Geometridae), lodix (Tuxen, after McDunnough).

ventral premental spicules, in larval Culicidae and Dixidae (Diptera: Nematocera), a variable collection of blades, filaments, spinules and other spicules borne on the ventral margin of the labiohypopharynx (Harbach and Knight).

ventral process, in ♂ Plecoptera, vesicle, q.v. (Tuxen, after Mosely); in ♂ Urostylidae (Hemiptera: Heteroptera), hypandrium, q.v. (Tuxen, after Yang); in ♂ Trichoptera, unpaired, but sometimes bilobed, ventral projection from abdominal segment IX (Tuxen); in ♂ Chironomidae (Diptera), inferior volsella, q.v. (Saether).

ventral process (of corpus of clasper), in ♂ Siphonaptera, processus basimeris ventralis, q.v. (Tuxen, after Peus).

ventral process of left phallomere, in ♂ Blattopteroidea, phallus, q.v. (Tuxen, after Beier).

ventral process of sternum IX, in ♂ Embiidina, left paraproct, q.v. (Tuxen, after Imms).

ventral process of sternum X, in ♂ *Coniopteryx* (Planipennia: Coniopterygidae), entoprocessus, q.v. (Tuxen, after Killington).

ventral proctigeral sclerite, in ♂ Empididae (Diptera), abdominal sternite X, q.v. (McAlpine, after Ulrich).

ventral prolegs, in larval Holometabola, all prolegs on the ventral aspect of any abdominal segments, except the last, which are called anal prolegs (Peterson).

ventral ptyche, in ♀ Hymenoptera, longitudinal mesal fold in the corium of each gonapophsis VIII, marking the ventral limit of the egg canal (Tuxen, after E.L. Smith).

ventral ramus, in ♂ Hymenoptera, ventral ramus of gonapophysis IX (Tuxen, after E. L. Smith); in ♀ Hymenoptera, ventral apodeme running the length of a gonopod and connecting it basally to a gonocoxite (Tuxen, after E. L. Smith); in larval Culicidae (Diptera), a branch of each cibarial bar extending along the lateral margin of the labiohypopharynx (Harbach and Knight).

ventral receptacle, in certain ♀ acalyptrate Diptera, diverticulum, functioning as a sperm reservoir, arising from the anteroventral portion of the genital chamber (McAlpine).

ventral ridge of sacculus, in ♂ Coleophoridae (Lepidoptera), sacculus, q.v. (Tuxen, after Toll).

ventral scale, in Diaspididae (Hemiptera: Sternorrhyncha: Coccoidea), the thin wax layer produced by the insect, between its venter and the host plant (T-B: Kosztarab and Kozár).

ventral sclerite(s), in ♀ Trichoptera, central sclerite, q.v. (Flint, pers. comm.); in ♂ Siphonaptera, hamuli, q.v. (Tuxen, after Jordan).

ventral sclerite of ventral ovipositor valve, in ♀ Caelifera (Orthoptera), ventral basivalvular sclerite, q.v. (Agarwala).

ventral sensory organs, in larval Muscomorpha (Diptera), sensory lobes on the head segment; sometimes called maxillary palpi, but possibly not homologous with them (Ferrar).

ventral scopa, in some ♀ Apoidea (Hymenoptera), hirsute area on venter of abdomen used in collecting pollen (Gauld and Bolton); see scopa.

ventral seta, in adult Culicidae (Diptera), one of 4 small peglike cibarial setae borne ventrally at the posterior margin of the cibarium (Harbach and Knight).

ventral sinus, perineural sinus, q.v. (T-B, after Snodgrass).

ventral sole plate, in larval Trichoptera, the ventral sclerite bridging the flexible membranous connection between the lateral sclerite and the anal claw of an anal proleg (Wiggins).

ventral spine, in Pentatomoidea (Hemiptera: Heteroptera), a spinelike projection anteriorly from the second or third true abdominal sternum, directed toward the head and lying at times between the coxae (T-B); in ♀ *Enallagma, Aciagrion,* and some *Ischnura* (Odonata: Zygoptera), a small spine on ventroapical border of abdominal segment VIII (Tuxen).

ventral stylet, in mouthparts of Phthiraptera, the lower paired stylet, basally attached to the stylet sac (T-B, after Imms).

ventral teeth, in larval Culicidae (Diptera), a row of closely associated teeth located ventrally on the mesodistal margin of the mandible (Harbach and Knight, after Foote).

ventral tentorial arm, in adult Culicidae (Diptera), a small ventral process on the anterior tentorial arms (Harbach and Knight).

ventral terminal sclerites, in ♂ Siphonaptera, hamuli, q.v. (Tuxen, after Jordan).

ventral titillators, in ♂ Mecoptera, (ventral) parameres, q.v. (Tuxen, after Issiki).

ventral trachea, the ventral segmental trachea orginating at a spiracle (T-B, after Snodgrass).

ventral tracheal commissure, tracheal commissure that crosses below the ventral nerve cord (T-B, after Snodgrass).

ventral tracheal trunk, a longitudinal ventral tracheal trunk uniting the series of ventral tracheae (T-B, after Snodgrass).

ventral tube, in Collembola, median lobe projecting ventrally from first abdominal segment, bearing a pair of eversible vesicles at the apex (T-B; Wallace and Mackerras, in CSIRO; Chapman).

ventral tubules, in larval Chironomidae (Diptera), one or 2 pairs of tubules ventrally on the abdominal segment XI (Saether).

ventral valve(s), in ♀ insects, first gonapophyses, q.v. (Tuxen); in ♂ *Sialis* (Megaloptera: Sialidae), abdominal sternum IX, q.v. (Tuxen, after McLachlan); in ♂ *Neopanorpa* (Mecoptera: Panorpidae), ventral paired, appressed lobes of aedeagus, distinct from parameres (Tuxen, after Byers); in ♂ Mecoptera, parameres, q.v. (Tuxen, after Carpenter); in ♀ Ephemeroptera, subgenital plate, q.v. (Tuxen, after Tillyard); in ♀ Aleyrodidae (Hemiptera: Sternorrhyncha), lateral valves, q.v. (Tuxen, after Deshpande); in ♀ Psyllidae (Hemiptera: Sternorrhyncha), ventral plate, q.v. (Tuxen).

ventral valve of aedeagus, in ♂ Orthoptera, ventral aedeagal valve, q.v. (Tuxen, after Roberts).

ventral valves of ovipositor, in ♀ Plecoptera, a pair of sclerotized processes arising from or near the hind margin of abdominal sternum VIII (above subgenital plate) (Tuxen, after Walker).

ventral valvulae, in ♀ insects, first gonapophyses, q.v. (Tuxen).

ventricle, a chamber of the insect heart (T-B).

ventricose, ventricosus, distended; inflated (T-B).

ventricular, of or pertaining to a ventricle (T-B).

ventricular ganglion, hypocerebral ganglion, q.v. (T-B).

ventricular valve, in certain insects, a small internal circular fold or ring of long cells projecting from the posterior margin of the mesenteric epithelium and acting as an occlusor mechanism (T-B, after Snodgrass); a mechanism of the insect heart which prevents the backward flow of hemolymph (T-B, after Imms).

ventriculus (Latin), midgut, q.v. (T-B; Leftwich).

ventrimeson, the midline of the ventral surface of the body (T-B).

ventrite, sternite, q.v. (T-B, after Ferris; Mackerras, in CSIRO).

ventrocaudal angle of sacculus, in ♂ Coleophoridae (Lepidoptera), ventrocaudal angle of the more or less projecting, mesal part of the valva (Tuxen, after Toll).

ventrocephalad, toward the lower side and anteriorly (T-B).

ventrocephalic median extension, in ♀ Caelifera (Orthoptera), a pouch running forward from the cephalic extremity of the bursa copulatrix (Key).

ventrodorsal, extending from belly to back, ventral to dorsal surface (T-B; Peterson).

ventroflexion, in ♂ Diptera, bending or folding of the apical portion of the abdomen anteroventrally (McAlpine).

ventrolateral, on the lower surface and to one side of the midline (T-B; Christiansen and Bellinger).

ventrolateral arms, in ♂ Grylloblattodea, a pair of processes from ventrolateral margin of abdominal tergum X (Tuxen, after Walker).

ventrolateral lobe, in ♀ Chironomidae (Diptera), ventrolateral lobe of gonapophysis VIII when this is divided (Saether).

ventrolateral plate, in larval Culicidae (Diptera), the area of the prementum lateral to the lateral premental teeth and ventral to the salivary meatus (Harbach and Knight, after Pao and Knight).

ventrolateral suture, in larval Coleoptera, a continuous longitudinal groove, in the thorax running immediately above the 2 scleromes, episternum and epimeron, or when these are indistinct or absent, above the hypopleural area to which they belong; in the abdomen running above hypopleural area and between the pitlike impressions where the ventral and dorsal wedges of the intersegmental membrane meet when they are present (Peterson, after Böving and Craighead).

ventromedian cervical sclerite, in some larva Culicidae (Diptera), primarily *Aedes,* a small pigmented plate occurring on the ventral median area of the cervix (Harbach and Knight, after Reinert).

ventromedian process, in ♂ Urostylidae (Hemiptera: Heteroptera), hypandrium, q.v. (Tuxen, after Yang).

ventromental beard, in some larval Chironomidae (Diptera), e.g., Prodiamesinae, setae on dorsal, inner surface of ventromental plate (Saether); see cardinal beard.

ventromental plate, in larval Chironomidae (Diptera), free lateral parts of ventromentum (Saether).

ventromentum, in larval Chironomidae (Diptera), ventral wall of double-walled mentum including ventromental plates (Saether); in some larval Culicidae and Chironomidae (Diptera: Nematocera), the lower and more proximal of the 2 transverse, usually projecting, specialized subdivisions produced when the mentum is completely (in mosquito larvae) or incompletely (in chironomid larvae) divided by a transverse inflection of membrane (Harbach and Knight); see hypostoma.

ventromeson, the intersection of the meson with the ventral surface of the body (Peterson).

ventroposterior, on the lower surface and behind the midline (Christiansen and Bellinger).

ventroposterior apodemes, in ♂ Heteroptera (Hemiptera), ductifer, q.v. (Tuxen, after Schaefer).

ventrovalvae, in ♂ Mecoptera, (ventral) parameres, q.v. (Tuxen, after Crampton).

ventrovalvulae, in ♀ insects, first gonapophyses, q.v. (Tuxen, after Crampton); in ♀ Plecoptera, lateral lobes of the subgenital plate (produced parts of abdominal sternum VIII) (Tuxen, after Crampton).

venula (pl., **venulae**), a small vena (R. W. Brown); in adult Lepidoptera, rodlike sclerotized thickenings of abdominal sternum II, usually found in Tineoidea, Yponomeutoidea and Gelechioidea (Minet).

venule, branch of a main longitudinal vein of the insect wing (T-B); crossvein, q.v. (Leftwich).

verbenol, volatile cyclic alcohol, serving as an antiaggregative pheromone, produced by ♂ and ♀ bark beetles (Coleoptera: Scolytidae) (Chapman).

verbenone, volatile cyclic ketone, serving as an antiaggregative pheronone, produced by ♂ and ♀ bark beetles (Coleoptera: Scolytidae) (Chapman).

verdohaem, a pigment produced as a product of the break down of hemoglobin by the midgut cells of *Rhodnius* (Hemiptera: Heteroptera: Reduviidae) (Chapman).

Vericloacia, Annulipalpia, q.v. (Weaver).

vermian, wormlike (T-B); see vermicular and vermiculate.

vermicular, worm-shaped or wormlike in general body form (T-B; Harris, after Munz, and Stearn); see cariose, undose, and vermiculate.

vermiculate, vermiculatus (Latin), with superficial, tortuous markings resembling the tracks of a worm (T-B; Harris, after Stearn); see cariose, undose, and vermicular.

vermicule, a little worm or grub (T-B); see maggot.

vermiculus (pl., **vermiculi**), in ♂ Lepidoptera, part of the harpe (Tuxen, after Hering).

vermiform, worm-shaped (T-B); see vermicular.

vermiform cell, extremely elongated (75 to over 300 μ) plasmatocyte-like cells found in larvae and pupae of certain Lepidoptera (Tulloch, after Yeager) and Diptera (Tulloch, after Jones), and rarely present in some Coleoptera at pupation (Tulloch, after Jones).

vermiform gland, in ♀ Cimicomorpha (Hemiptera: Heteroptera), an organ homologous with the spermatheca but without sperm-storing function (Tuxen, after Drake and Davis).

vermiform larva, in Orthoptera, pronymph, q.v. (Key, in CSIRO); in Diptera, maggot, q.v., or acephalous larva, q.v. (Borror et al.).

vernacular name, a name of an animal or animals in a language used for general purposes as opposed to a name proposed only for zoological nomenclature (ICZN); see scientific name.

vernal, of or pertaining to the spring (T-B).

vernantia, ecdysis, q.v. (T-B).

verriculate, verriculatus, with tufts of erect parallel hairs or bristles (T-B).

verricule, verriculus, a dense tuft of upright hairs (T-B); in some larval Lepidoptera, pencils of secondary setae borne on flat plates (Common, in CSIRO).

verruca (pl., **verrucae**), a wart or wartlike prominence (T-B; R. W. Brown); in larval Lepidoptera, somewhat elevated portions of the cuticle bearing tufts of secondary setae (T-B, after Imms; Common, in CSIRO); see verrucule.

verrucate, verrucose, q.v. (Harris).

verrucose, verrucosus (Latin), **verrucous,** covered with irregularly shaped lobes or wartlike protuberances (T-B; Harris, after Stearn); see nodulate, torose, and tuberculate.

verruculose, verruculosus (Latin), **verruculous,** verrucose, q.v. (T-B; Harris).

verruga peruana, mild, cutaneous form of Carrion's disease (Adkins, pers. comm.); see oroya fever.

versatile, moving freely in every direction.

versicolor, versicolorate, versicoloratus, versicolorous, with several colors, indeterminately restricted; changeable in color (T-B).

Versonian cell, apical cell, q.v., of testis follicle (T-B; Leftwich).

Verson's cell, apical cell, q.v., of testis follicle (T-B; Leftwich).

Verson's glands, in larval Lepidoptera, moulting glands, q.v. (T-B, after Snodgrass; Leftwich).

vertex, the top of the head between the eyes, frons and occiput, anterior to the occipital suture (T-B; Borror et al.).

vertexal, occurring on or near the vertex, or directed toward it.

vertical, in pupal Chironomidae (Diptera), lateral and anterior-most seta on the ocular field (Saether).

vertical arm, in ♂ Siphonaptera, proximal arm, q.v. (Tuxen).

vertical bristles, in adult Diptera, 2 pairs of bristles, the inner vertical bristles and the outer vertical bristles, more or less behind the upper and inner corner of the eyes (T-B, after Comstock; McAlpine).

vertical cephalic bristles, in adult Diptera, vertical bristles, q.v. (T-B).

vertical classification, classification which stresses common ancestral and descendant groups of a phyletic line in a single higher taxon, separating them from contemporaneous taxa having reached a similar grade of evolutionary change (Mayr); see horizontal classification and natural classification.

vertical furrows, in adult Hymenoptera, the portions of the antennal furrows situated on the dorsal aspect of the head, extending from the lateral ocelli to the caudal aspect of the head, being rarely wanting and usually more distinctly marked than the other portions of the antennal furrows (T-B).

vertical margin, in adult Diptera, the limit between the front and the occiput (T-B).

vertical orbit, the margin of vertex adjacent to the dorsal aspect of a compound eye (T-B, after MacGillivray).

vertical plates, in Diptera larvae, tentorial phragmata, q.v. (Teskey, in McAlpine); in adult Diptera, orbital plates, q.v. (McAlpine).

vertical process, in ♂ Pyrrhocoridae (Hemiptera: Heteroptera), inferior process, q.v. (Tuxen, after Freeman).

vertical setae, in larval Lepidoptera, microscopic setae V1–V3 located near the posterior margin on each side of the vertex of the head, and thought to be proprioceptors (Hinton); setae MD1–MD3 (Stehr).

vertical triangle, in adult Diptera, ocellar triangle, q.v. (T-B, after Comstock; McAlpine); in larval Lepidoptera, epicranial notch, q.v. (Peterson, after Fracker).

verticals, in adult Diptera, vertical bristles, q.v. (T-B).

verticil, in certain Diptera, one of the whorls of long fine sensitive setae on a flagellomere of the antenna (T-B).

verticillate, verticillatus (Latin), whorled; set with whorls, especially setae (T-B).

verticillate antenna, antenna in which each flagellomere has a whorl of long extensions, e.g., adult Cecidomyiidae and Tipulidae (Diptera) (T-B; McAlpine); see plumose and pencil.

vesica (pl., **vesicae**), in ♂ insects, a specially developed endophallus (Tuxen); in ♂ Cicadidae (Hemiptera: Auchenorrhyncha), membranous retractile apical part of aedeagus (Tuxen, after Orian); in ♂ Heteroptera (Hemiptera), distal part of an endosoma differentiated to form 2 segments (Tuxen, after Singh-Pruthi); in ♂ Lygaeidae (Hemiptera: Heteroptera), disticonjunctiva, q.v. (Tuxen, after Ashlock); in ♂ Coleoptera, internal sac, q.v. (Tuxen, after Snodgrass); in ♂ Lepidoptera, flexible, eversible tube, sometimes very long, lying in the aedoeagus (Tuxen, after Pierce), or vesicula seminis, q.v. (Tuxen, after Hering); in ♂ Diptera, ejaculator, q.v. (Tuxen), hypophallus, q.v. (Tuxen, after Zumpt and Heinz), or sperm sac (McAlpine).

vesica appendages, in ♂ Heteroptera (Hemiptera), processus vesicae, q.v. (Tuxen, after Singh-Pruthi).

vesica penis, in ♂ Anoplura (Phthiraptera), endophallus, q.v. (Clay, in Tuxen; Lyal).

vesica processes, in ♂ Heteroptera (Hemiptera), processus vesicae, q.v. (Tuxen, after Dupuis and Carvalho).

vesica seminalis, in ♂ Lepidoptera, enlargement of the ductus ejaculatorius or vas deferens at the juncture with the duct of the glandulae accessoriae (Tuxen, after Burmeister).

vesicant, vesicating, vesicatory, blister-raising, e.g., the spanishfly *Lytta vesicatoria* (Coleoptera: Meloidae), and its congeners (T-B).

vesicle, a little sac, bladder or cyst, being sometimes extensible (T-B; Borror et al.); in some beetles (Coleoptera) and caterpillars (Lepidoptera), an extensible organ producing odors or secretions (T-B); in ♂ Odonata, vesicula spermalis, q.v. (Tuxen, after Calvert); in ♂ Nemouridae (Plecoptera), spatulate structure arising from anterior part of abdominal sternum IX (subgenital plate) (Tuxen, after Kimmins); in ♂ Thysanoptera, epiphallus, q.v. (Tuxen), endotheca, q.v. (Heming), or endophallus, q.v. (Lyal); in ♂ Siphonaptera, vesicula, q.v. (Tuxen, after Jordan et al.); in larval Culicidae (Diptera), a tiny conical, rounded or ridgelike elevation, occurring in rows or polygonal patterns on the cranium (Harbach and Knight, after Dahl); in ♀ Lepidoptera, sclerotized enlargement of distal end of efferent canal (Dugdale); see eversible vesicle.

vesicula (pl., **vesiculae**), small bladder (R. W. Brown); in ♂ Diptera, ejaculator, q.v. (Tuxen); in ♂ Siphonaptera, prominent, semicircular cup-shaped expansion at the base of the tubus interior (Tuxen, after Jordan); see vesicle.

vesicula seminalis (pl., **vesiculae seminales**), in ♂ insects, paired, vesicular dilatation of vasa deferentia for storage of spermatozoa (Tuxen).

vesicula spermalis, in ♂ Odonata, flasklike vesicle at the base of the prophallus for reception of spermatophores (Fraser and Asahina, in Tuxen).

vesicular, vesiculous, pertaining to or consisting of vesicles or small sacs or bladders (T-B).

vesicular glands, in Machilidae (Archaeognatha), pairs of glands in the coxites of the pregenital abdominal segments, possibly associated with moulting (Bitsch and Palevody).

vesiculate, bladderlike; having a swollen appearance (T-B).

vesiculate larva, in endoparasitic Braconidae (Hymenoptera), eucephalous larva with proctodeum evaginated to form a more or less external spherical vesicle (Gauld and Bolton).

vesparium, a natural or artificial nest of a colony of Vespinae (Hymenoptera: Vespidae) (Tulloch, after Gaul).

Vespoidea, superfamily within the Apocrita (Hymenoptera), including the Vespidae possessing angulate posterior lateral lobes of the pronotum, reaching back to and ending above the tegula, metapleural glands lacking, and lateral pronotum and mesopleuron meeting with carinate margins and with very little free movement between them (Riek, in CSIRO); Vespoidea + Scolioidea + Formicoidea + Pompiloidea + Tiphioidea (Gauld and Bolton, after Brothers).

vespophiles, inquilines in wasp (Hymenoptera: Vespidae), nests, e.g., rove beetle *Velleius* (Coleoptera: Staphylinidae) (Leftwich).

vestibule, atrium, q.v. (T-B); in ♀ Ephemeroptera, vestibulum, q.v. (Tuxen, after Morgan); in ♀ Lepidoptera, sinus vaginalis, q.v. (Tuxen, after authors); .

vestibulum (pl., **vestibula**), in ♀ Ephemeroptera, invagination from behind abdominal sternum VII, forming a more or less shallow and modified pouch into which the oviducts open (Tuxen, after Snodgrass); in ♀ Isoptera, invagination cavity formed by inflection of the body wall behind (above) abdominal sternum VII when the latter is prolonged beyond abdominal sternum VIII (Tuxen, after Snodgrass); in ♀ Reduviidae (Hemiptera: Heteroptera), oviductus communis (broadened distal part), q.v. (Tuxen, after Davey); in ♀ Miridae (Hemiptera: Heteroptera), the more or less individualized tubular space between the gonapophyses distal to the genuine vulva in the ovipositor-shaped type of genitalia (Davis); in ♀ Lepidoptera, the more or less dilated, cephalad part of the oviductus communis into which open the ductus seminalis and ductus receptaculi (Tuxen, after Petersen).

vestibulum vaginae, in ♀ Siphonaptera, dorsal vaginal ingrowth, caudad of the ostium bursae (Tuxen, after Dampf).

vestige, the remains of a previously functional part or organ (T-B).

vestigial, small, poorly developed, degenerate, or nonfunctional (T-B; Borror et al.).

vestiture, the general surface covering comprised of cuticular projections, e.g., setae, scales, or spicules (T-B; Harbach and Knight).

vesture, vestiture, q.v. (T-B).

vexillum (pl., **vexilla**), in adult Hymenoptera, an expansion on the tip of the tarsus of certain fossorial groups (T-B); in ♂ Siphonaptera, membranous appendage, q.v. (Tuxen, after Smit).

vibrant, having a rapid motion to and fro (T-B).

vibratile, formed for or having vibratory motion (T-B).

vibrissa (pl., **vibrissae**), whisker; stiff tectile hair (R. W. Brown); in adult Diptera, one or more stout setae on the vibrissal angle (T-B; Colless and McAlpine, in CSIRO); see mystax.

vibrissal angle, in adult Diptera, angular prominence at the ventral termination of the facial ridge, frequently bearing one or more vibrissae (T-B, after Curran; McAlpine).

vibrissal ridge, in adult Diptera, facial ridge, q.v. (T-B, after Comstock; McAlpine).

vibrissarium, in adult Schizophora (Diptera: Muscomorpha), genal groove, q.v. (McAlpine).

vice (Latin), in place of (T-B).

vide (Latin), see (T-B).

vide etiam (Latin), see also; abbrev., v. et. (T-B).

villiform, of the form or character of a villus or soft fine hair (T-B).

villose, villosate, villosus (Latin), **villous,** soft-haired; covered with long hairs which give a woolly appearance; covered with soft flexible hairs thickly set (T-B, after Kirby and Spence).

villus (pl., **villi**), a small fine hair (T-B); a minute, slender, flexible, filamentlike spicule (Harbach and Knight); a short, hairlike or papillate process on the surface of certain absorbent and sensory organs (T-B).

vinaceous, claret-colored, i.e., purplish-red.

vinculum (pl., **vincula**), in ♂ Lepidoptera, abdominal sternum IX, typically a flat, U-shaped ring, its dorsal extremities articulating with pedunculi (Tuxen, after Pierce); in ♂ Lepidoptera genitalia, the entire coxosternal plate of the ninth abdominal segment (T-B, after Snodgrass); in ♂ Calliphoridae (Diptera), hypandrium, q.v. (Tuxen, after Hall).

vinculum strut, in ♂ Lycaenidae (Lepidoptera), thickened ridge on the vinculum (Tuxen, after Clench).

vinegaroon, whipscorpion, q.v. (Borror et al.).

vinous, vinaceous, q.v. (T-B).

violaceous, violaceus (Latin), violet-color (T-B).

violet, a bluish-purple (T-B).

viral transmission, transmission of viruses to plants and animals, often by insect vectors; see circulative transmission, foregut-borne transmission, and propagatively transmission.

viremia, the presence of virus in the hemolymph or blood (Steinhaus and Martignoni).

virescent, turning or becoming green (T-B); see viridescent.

virga (pl., **virgae**), in ♂ insects, terminal phallic spine, usually arising from the endophallus (Tuxen, after Snodgrass); in ♂ Plecoptera, filament, q.v. (Tuxen, after Crampton); in ♂ Dermaptera, sclerotized distal portion of the ejaculatory duct (Tuxen, after Zacher); in ♂ Blattopteroidea, phallus, q.v. (Tuxen, after Berlese); in ♂ Heteroptera (Hemiptera), vesica, q.v. (Tuxen, after Crampton); in ♂ Coleoptera, flagellum, q.v. (Tuxen, after Snodgrass); in ♂ Lepidoptera, cornuti (Tuxen, after Snodgrass); in ♂ Siphonaptera, elongate strengthenings in the dorsal and ventral wall of the endophallus, virga dorsalis and ventralis (Tuxen, after Peus); in ♂ Chironomidae (Diptera), terminal group of spines sometimes attached to the distal end of the endophallus (Saether).

virga dorsalis (pl., **virgae dorsales**), in ♂ Siphonaptera, elongate strengthening in the dorsal wall of the endophallus (Tuxen, after Peus).

virga excitata (pl., **virgae excitatae**), in ♂ Lycaenidae (Lepidoptera), dorsobasal process of the valva, extending caudad, more or less capable of independent motion, perhaps for stimulation of ♀ (Tuxen, after Bethune-Baker).

virga penis (pl., **virgae penes**), in ♂ Siphonaptera, a rod, in most species paired, below the penis, caudad ending in tubus interior, cephalad often coiled up near the penis base (Tuxen, after Smit).

virga ventralis (pl., **virgae ventrales**), in ♂ Siphonaptera, elongate strengthening in the ventral wall of the endophallus (Tuxen, after Peus).

viridescent, greenish (T-B); see virescent.

viridis (Latin), green (T-B; R. W. Brown).

virion, the mature virus, being either a naked or enveloped nucleocapsid (Steinhaus and Martignoni).

virtual tautonymy, the nearly identical spelling, or the same origin or meaning, of a generic or subgeneric name and the specific or subspecific name in a binomen or trinomen (ICZN).

virulence, in invertebrate pathology, the quality or property of being virulent; the quality of being poisonous; the ability of a microorganism to invade and injure the tissues of its host; the relative capacity of a microorganism to overcome the body defenses of the host (Steinhaus and Martignoni); see pathogenicity.

virus, an ultramicroscopic infectious agent capable of passing through porcelain bacterial filters, which can be cultivated only in the presence of living cells, being common pathogens of plants and animals (T-B; Tulloch); see geminivirus, marafivirus, reovirus, rhabdovirus, and tenuivirus.

viscera, the internal organs of the body (T-B).

visceral, pertaining to or attached to the viscera (T-B).

visceral muscle, muscle that moves the viscera, having one or, more commonly, no attachment to the body wall (Chapman)

visceral nervous system, stomatogastric nervous system, q.v. (T-B).

visceral segment, pregenital segment, q.v. (T-B).

visceral sinus, perivisceral sinus, q.v. (T-B).

visceral trachea, the median segmental trachea originating at a spiracle, branching to the alimentary canal, the fat tissue, and the reproductive organs (T-B, after Snodgrass).

visceral tracheal trunk, a longitudinal tracheal trunk closely associated with the walls of the alimentary canal (T-B, after Snodgrass).

visceronome, a serpentine larval mine tightly coiled or folded like an intestine (Hering).

viscid, viscidus (Latin), sticky (T-B; R. W. Brown).

viscous, thick, sticky or semifluid (T-B).

vision, light sense (Borror et al.).

visual, of or pertaining to vision or light (T-B).

visual cell, retinula cell, q.v. (T-B, after Imms).

visual organ, crystalline body, q.v. (T-B, after J.E.V. Boas).

visual sense, vision, q.v. (T-B).

vitamin, an organic substance that is required in small amounts in the diet since they cannot be synthesized, commonly a structural component of a coenzyme (T-B; Tulloch, after Rockstein; Chapman).

vitellarium, proximal portion of an ovariole in which the oocytes grow as yolk is deposited in them (T-B; Chapman).

vitelline, vitellinus (Latin), yellow, with a slight tinge of red, like the yolk of an egg (T-B).

vitelline membrane, outer layer of the oocyte, surrounding the yolk (T-B; Chapman).

vitellogenesis, the deposition of yolk in the oocyte (Chapman).

vitellogenin, principal type of yolk protein synthesized and released from the fat body and absorbed by the developing oocytes (Chapman).

vitellogenous, producing the vitellus or yolk (T-B).

vitellophage, endodermal yolk cell, derived from energids, involved in the breakdown of the yolk at all stages of development and later forming part of the midgut epithelium (T-B; Chapman).

vitellus, yolk, q.v. (T-B).

vitrella (pl., **vitrellae**), Semper cell, q.v., or corneagen cell, q.v. (T-B; Leftwich).

vitreous, vitreus (Latin), glassy or transparent (T-B).

vitreous body, crystalline cone, q.v. (T-B, after Comstock; Leftwich); corneagen cells, q.v. (T-B, after Imms).

vitreous layer, corneagen layer, q.v. (T-B).

vitta (pl., **vittae**), a broad longitudinal stripe (T-B, after Kirby and Spence); in ♂ Carposinidae (Lepidoptera), a long ribbonlike, distal process of sinistral apical process of the asymmetrical aedoeagus (Tuxen, after Philpott).

vitta frontalis, in adult Diptera, frontal vitta, q.v. (T-B).

vittate, vittatus (Latin), striped; longitudinally striped or plaited (T-B; Harris).

viviparity, the bearing of living young instead of eggs by the ♀ (T-B); in the broad sense, retention of the embryo within the ♀ at least until it has almost reached blastokinesis (Chapman); in the narrow sense, retention of the embryo within the ♀, where it receives nourishment directly from the parent in addition or instead of from the yolk (Chapman); see adenotrophic viviparity, hemocoelous viviparity, ovoviviparity, and pseudoplacental viviparity (Chapman).

viviparous, displaying viviparity (T-B; Chapman); see ovoviviparous.

vocal cords, on thorax of adult Diptera, spiracular sound organs, q.v. (T-B).

void, to excrete waste products; emptiness; an empty space (T-B).

volant, flying or capable of flight (T-B).

volatile, readily vaporized (T-B).

volsella (pl., **volsellae**), pincers (R. W. Brown); in ♂ *Agulla* (Raphidioptera: Raphidiidae), parameres, q.v. (Tuxen, after Michener); in ♂ Chironomidae (Diptera), accessory clasping apparatus derived from fragments of either or both of gonocoxite IX and gonapophysis IX, appearing as appendages, lobes or field of gonocoxites or at bases of gonocoxites (Saether); in ♂ Hymenoptera, inner ventral fragmentum of paramere (Tuxen, after Snodgrass; Gauld and Bolton).

volsellar bridge, in ♂ Hymenoptera, sclerotic bridge between bases of volsellae (Tuxen, after Michener).

volsellar strut, in ♂ Hymenoptera, the internal longitudinal ridge strengthening volsella (Tuxen, after Michener).

vom Rath's organ, in adult Lepidoptera, a group of sensilla on the labial palpi of most moths, usually located in a shallow or deep depression near the tip (Common); see sensory pit.

vomer, in ♂ Phasmida, vomer subanalis, q.v. (Tuxen, after Snodgrass).

vomer subanalis, in ♂ Phasmida, moveable sclerotization from abdominal sternum X, functioning during copulation (Tuxen, after Pantel).

vomit drop, the drop of regurgitated substance that appears at the end of the proboscis of flies (T-B, after Matheson).

vulgar, vulgaris (Latin), common; commonplace; ordinary (T-B, after J. B. Smith; R. W. Brown); see vernacular.

vultus, face, q.v. (T-B).

vulva (pl., **vulvae**), in ♀ insects, external opening of the genital chamber or vagina (Tuxen); in ♀ Heteroptera (Hemiptera), the broad (plate-shaped type of genitalia) or strengthened (ovipositor-shaped type) external opening of the vagina (Tuxen, after Larsén); in ♀ Miridae (Hemiptera: Heteroptera), vestibulum, q.v. (Tuxen, after Kullenberg); in ♀ Lepidoptera, ostium bursae, ostium oviductus or vagina, q.v. (Tuxen, after authors).

vulvar annulus, in ♀ *Panorpa* (Mecoptera: Panorpidae), genital plates, q.v., or medigynium, q.v. (Ferris and Rees).

vulvar hook, in some ♀ *Goniodes* (Phthiraptera: Ischnocera), sclerotized process on each side of the vulva, i.e., first gonapophysis (transl. "Pforthaken" von Kéler, in Tuxen; Lyal).

vulvar lamina, in ♀ Anisoptera (Odonata), the posterior margin of abdominal sternum VIII (T-B; Borror et al.); in ♀ Plecoptera, subgenital plate, q.v. (Tuxen, after J. B. Smith).

vulvar retractor apodemes, in ♀ *Panorpa* (Mecoptera: Panorpidae), gonoclavi, q.v. (Ferris and Rees).

vulvar scale(s), in ♀ Odonata, lateral gonapophyses, q.v. (Tuxen, after Tillyard and Fraser); in ♀ Odonata, vulvar lamina, q.v. (T-B); in many ♀ Integripalpia (Trichoptera), a subgenital plate formed from the median lobe of abdominal sternite VIII and side lobes of abdominal segment IX (Nielsen).

vulvar sclerites, in ♀ Dytiscidae (Coleoptera), a pair of sclerites ventrad of vulva (Lindroth and Palmén, in Tuxen).

vulvar spine, in ♀ Odonata, ventral spine, q.v. (Tuxen, after Garman).

W

waggle dance, the dance whereby workers of various species of honey bees (*Apis,* Hymenoptera: Apidae) communicate the location of food finds and new nest sites, consisting basically of a run through a figure-eight pattern, with the middle, transverse line of the eight containing the information about the direction and distance of the target (Wilson).

Wagner's organ, in ♂ Ceratophyllidae (Siphonaptera), paired cuticular invaginations near the base of abdominal sternum VIII (Lewis, pers. comm.).

waist, in ants (Hymenoptera: Formicidae), pedicel, q.v., of abdomen (Brown, pers. comm.).

Waldtracht disease, poisoning of adult honey bees (Hymenoptera: Apidae), foraging on honeydew from conifers, usually spruce (Steinhaus and Martignoni).

walking leaf, a member of the Phylloidea (Phasmida) (Carlberg, pers. comm.); see walking stick.

walking stick, a member of the order Phasmida (Borror et al.); see walking leaf.

wall, the retaining sides of an organ or structure; the boundary of a cell or cavity (T-B).

Wallacea, biogeographic transition zone between Wallace's line and Weber's line, including Sulawesi (Mackerras, in CSIRO).

wandering phase, in Diptera, post feeding larva that migrates from the food supply to a safe place for pupation (Ferrar).

wanting, absent.

war fever, epidemic typhus, q.v. (Adkins, pers. comm.).

warning coloration, bright colors or markings on animals which are poisonous or otherwise dangerous, giving them the advantage of being recognized and avoided by predators, e.g., black and yellow stripes of a wasp (Hymenoptera) (T-B, after Folsom and Wardle; Leftwich); see aposematic.

wart, a spongy excrescence, more or less cylindric, with a truncated tip (T-B); in adult Trichoptera, setal wart, q.v. (T-B); see tubercle and verruca .

washed, with continuous pigment pattern but with faint areas (Christiansen and Bellinger).

Wasmannian mimicry, mimetic resemblance which facilitates cohabitation with a mimic's host, its model, e.g., beetles (Coleoptera) and other guests of ants (Hymenoptera: Formicidae) (Matthews and Matthews, after Rettenmeyer).

wasp, a general term referring to members of the Aculeata (Hymenoptera) other than the Formicidae (ants) and Apoidea (bees), but also as a combining form for other members of the Apocrita.

Wassersucht, watery disintegration, q.v. (Steinhaus and Martignoni).

water bear, a member of the class Tardigrada (Borror et al.).

water bug, member of the infraorder Nepomorpha (Hemiptera: Heteroptera) (Hennig).

watery disintegration, a lethal disease of cockchafer grubs, *Melolontha* (Coleoptera: Scarabaeidae), caused by a virus, in which the diseased larvae appear transparent, especially in the abdomen, following atrophy and disintegration of the fat body (Steinhaus and Martignoni).

wavey setae, in pupal Podonominae (Diptera: Chironomidae), long and stout setae, bent sharply twice somewhat proximal of middle and ending in a hook, inserted at caudolateral angles of abdominal segment VIII and on anal lobe (Saether).

wax, a complex mixture of lipids, providing a waterproofing layer on the surface of the cuticle or, in Coccoidea and related insects (Hemiptera: Sternorrhyncha), a protective covering (scale), or, in bees (Hymenoptera: Apoidea), used to construct larval cells (beeswax) (T-B; Chapman).

wax-bearing plates, in nymphal Fulgoroidea (Hemiptera: Auchenorrhyncha), areas containing wax producing glands on abdominal terga VI–VIII (O'Brien, in Stehr); see wax plate.

wax cutters, in adult honey bees (Hymenoptera: Apidae), pincerlike structures on the hind leg (T-B).

wax glands, any glands which secrete a waxy product (T-B); in Sternorrhyncha (Hemiptera), any of several dermal glands that secrete copious amounts of wax (T-B; Stoetzel, in Stehr); in adult Coniopterygidae (Planipennia), glands situated on the head, thorax, and abdomen secreting a whitish or greyish meal (Riek, in CSIRO); in bees (Hymenoptera: Apoidea), abdominal glands that produce beeswax (Chapman).

wax layer, a layer of the epicuticle known to be responsible for waterproofing the cuticle (Tulloch, after Richards); see wax.

wax pick, a spur or spine on the midleg of the honey bee (Hymenoptera: Apidae), used for removing wax and pollen from the ventral part of the body (Leftwich).

wax pincers, in honey bees (Hymenoptera: Apidae), wax cutters, q.v. (T-B, after Folsom and Wardle).

wax plate, in Aleyrodidae and Coccoidea (Hemiptera: Sternorrhyncha), the plate onto which the secretions of wax glands are poured (T-B).

wax pore, in Coccoidea (Hemiptera: Sternorrhyncha), a cuticular pore through which wax is secreted (T-B).

wax scale, in worker bees (Hymenoptera: Apoidea), one of the scales secreted in the wax pocket or gland (T-B).

wax shears, in honey bees (Hymenoptera: Apidae), wax cutters, q.v. (T-B).

waxen, waxlike; waxy; of the color or appearance of wax (T-B).

weakly, feebly, not markedly (T-B).

web spinner, a member of the order Embiidina (Ross, in CSIRO).

wedge-shaped plates, in Coccoidea (Hemiptera: Sternorrhyncha), mesal plates, q.v (T-B, after MacGillivray).

weighting, character weighting, q.v. (Mayr).

Weismann's ring, ring gland, q.v. (Tulloch; Leftwich).

wet wax, in ♀ *Ceroplastes* (Hemiptera: Sternorrhyncha: Coccoidea: Coccidae), wax produced by instars 3 and 4 with a pastelike texture and when squeezed produces a drop of liquid, flowing around dry wax filaments of previous instars, leaving only the tips exposed, forming a scale (Miller, in Stehr).

whalebone plate, in ♀ Incurvariidae (Lepidoptera), lateral, ribbed dilation of "knife-blade" (Tuxen, after Wood).

wheat streak mosaic, viral disease of wheat and corn transmitted semipersistently by the mite *Eriophyes tipulae* (Acari: Eriophyidae) (Borror et al.).

whip-lash dermatitis, a smear lesion caused by the brushing activity to remove the beetles, *Pachypaederus puncticollis* and *Paederus sabacus* (Coleoptera: Staphylinidae) from the skin (Britton, in CSIRO; Adkins, pers. comm.); see Paederus vesicular dermatitis.

whipscorpion, a member of the order Uropygi (Borror et al.); see micro whipscorpion, short-tailed whipscorpion, and tailless whipscorpion.

whipspider, tailless whipscorpion, q.v. (Borror et al.).

whistle, in *Acherontia* (Lepidoptera: Sphingidae), sound producing apparatus at the base of the proboscis, including the epipharynx, making a high-pitched sound when an air stream is passed through it (Chapman); see sound-producing mechanisms.

white cuticle, chitinous endocuticle of the serosal cuticle of the egg, responsible for the toughness of the egg (Tulloch; Chapman); see yellow cuticle.

white head, an abnormality occurring during the development of honey bees (Hymenoptera: Apidae), characterized by the lack of brown pigment in the cuticle of the head and of the first pair of legs, resulting from a lack of oxygen to the prothorax and head (Steinhaus and Martignoni).

white muscardine, a mycosis of various larval, pupal, and adult insects, caused by the hypomecetous fungus *Beauveria bassiana,* with infection occurring by mycelial penetration through the insect integument and with hyphae filling the body cavity after death followed by the emergence of typically white mycelial growth and conidia, covering the insect body (Steinhaus and Martignoni).

white soldier, in Isoptera, presoldier, q.v. (Krishna, pers. comm.).

whitefly, a member of the family Aleyrodidae (Hemiptera: Sternorrhyncha) (Woodward et al., in CSIRO).

whitlow, paronychium, q.v. (T-B).

whorl, a ring of hairs set about a joint or center like the spokes of a wheel (T-B).

wilt disease, nucleopolyhedrosis of gypsy moth caterpillars, *Lymantria dispar* (Lepidoptera: Lymantriidae) (Steinhaus and Martignoni); nucleopolyhedrosis of larval Lepidoptera (Steinhaus and Martignoni); spotted wilt disease, q.v., of plants (Borror et al.).

windscorpion, member of the order Solifugae (Borror et al.).

wing(s), in adult insects or subimago of Ephemeroptera, paired membranous appendages, supported by veins, located on the mesothorax or metathorax, functioning in flight (T-B; Chapman) (see elytron, hind wings, hemelytron, forewings, and tegmen); in larval Muscomorpha (Diptera), cornua, q.v. (Ferrar).

wing base, the proximal part of the wing between the bases of the veins and the body, containing the humeral and axillary sclerites (T-B, after Snodgrass).

wing bone, vein, q.v. (T-B).

wing brush, in adult Chironomidae (Diptera), scopula alaris, q.v. (Saether).

wing bud, larval histoblast from which a wing of the adult arise (T-B); in pupal Siphonaptera, wing rudiments (Dunnet, in CSIRO); see wing pad.

wing case, in hemimetabolous insects, wing pad, q.v. (T-B, after Tillyard); in adult Coleoptera, elytron, q.v. (T-B; Leftwich); in Blattaria, Mantodea, and Orthoptera, tegmen, q.v. (Leftwich); see wing cover.

wing cell, any area of an insect wing between or bounded by veins, being either a closed cell, q.v., or an open cell (T-B; McAlpine).

wing-coupling mechanism, in some Pterygota, the manner in which the forewing and hind wing are engaged in flight; see wing-locking mechanism.

wing cover, portion of cuticle of a nymph or pupa that covers a rudiment of the adult wing (T-B); forewing of adult when it is thicker than the hind wing and covers it at rest, e.g., elytron (Coleoptera), tegmen (Blattaria and Orthoptera), and hemelytron (Hemiptera: Heteroptera) (T-B; Leftwich).

wing fringe, in many winged insects, one or more rows of setae or scalesprojecting beyond the wing margin (Harbach and Knight).

wing-holding setae, in macropterous Tubulifera (Thysanoptera), sigmoidal or sickle-shaped setae on the abdominal tergites that package wings in repose (Stannard).

wing-locking mechanism, in adult Neoptera, means by which the wings are held in place in repose (Nichols, pers. comm.); in Euheteroptera (Hemiptera: Heteroptera), the modification of the costal margin of the forewing and the mesothorax to retain the wing firmly in postion in repose (trans. "Druckknofsystem" after Cobben) (see frenum); see wing-coupling mechanism.

wing-locking microtrichia, in adult Lepidoptera, an area of microtrichia beneath and near the base of the forewing which enmeshes with an area of similar microtrichia on the metascutum, locking the folded wings in place (Common); in Micropterigidae similar microtrichia beneath the hind wing also enmesh with microtrichia on the axillary cord (Kristensen).

wing membrane, membrane, q.v., of wing (Harbach and Knight).

wing muscles of the heart, aliform muscles, q.v. (T-B).

wing pads, the encased undeveloped wings of the nymphs of Hemimetabola, which show behind the thorax as 2 lateral flattish structures (T-B).

wing regions, the principal areas of the wings differentiated in the wing-flexing insects (Neoptera), and often separated by distinct lines of folding, including the wing base, remigium, clavus, and jugum (T-B, after Snodgrass).

wing scale, in adult Isoptera, basal part of wing remaining on the imago after the main portion of the wing is shed along the basal suture (Emerson); in adult Hymenoptera, tegula, q.v., or humeral plate, q.v. (T-B); in adult Lepidoptera, scale, q.v., on wing (Leftwich).

wing sheaths, wing pads, q.v. (T-B).

wing spot, in adult Culicidae (Diptera), spots on the wings formed by light- and dark-colored scales (Harbach and Knight, after Christophers).

wing stump, in Isoptera, wing scale, q.v. (Thorne, pers. comm.).

wing teeth, in Collembola, the large tarsal teeth in some species (T-B).

wing veins, veins, q.v. (T-B; Leftwich).

wing venation, venation, q.v. (T-B).

winged spiracle, a spiracle located in the center of an inverted V-shaped pigment area e.g., in Cimicidae (Hemiptera: Heteroptera) (Peterson).

winglet, vestigial wing (T-B).

wings of the heart, aliform muscles, q.v. (T-B).

Winkler bag, a cloth mesh bag, containing litter sample, which is suspended over a funnel that catches escaping insects directing them into a collecting bottle (Gauld and Bolton).

winter cocoon, hibernaculum, q.v. (Peterson).

Wipfelkrankheit (German), a nucleopolyhedrosis of the larva of the nun moth, *Lymantria monacha* (Lepidoptera: Lymantriidae), causing diseased caterpillars to proceed to the tops ("Wipfeln") of trees (Steinhaus and Martignoni).

Wipfelsucht, Wipfelkrankheit, q.v. (Steinhaus and Martignoni).

wireworm, soil-inhabiting larva of Elateridae (Coleoptera) that feeds upon plant roots (Leftwich); see elateriform larva.

witch hazel cone-gall, cone-shaped gall on leaves of American witchhazel *Hamamelis virginea* caused by the aphid *Hormaphis hamamelidis* (Hemiptera: Sternorrhyncha: Aphididae) (Leftwich; Borror et al.).

witch's broom, alfalfa witch's-broom, q.v. (Borror et al.).

wood louse, sowbug, q.v.

woolly oak gall, leaf gall on oak (*Quercus* spp.) caused by *Callirhytis lanata* (Hymenoptera: Cynipidae) (Borror et al.).

work of an animal, the result of the activity of an animal (e.g., burrows, borings, galls, nests, worm tubes, cocoons, tracks), but not part of the animal and applying to trace fossils but not to such fossil evidence as internal molds, external impressions, and replacements (ICZN); see ichnotaxon.

worker, a member of the nonreproductive, laboring caste in semisocial and eusocial species, presupposing the existence also of royal (reproductive) castes (Wilson); in Termitidae (Isoptera), individuals which lack wing buds and have reduced pterothorax, eyes, and genital apparatus (Wilson); in the social Hymenoptera, females, either unable to reproduce or able to lay fewer eggs than the queen, their function including nest-building, foraging, tending the brood, and defending the colony (T-B, after Imms; Brown, pers. comm.); see gamergate.

worker jelly, in honey bees (Hymenoptera: Apoidea), a secreted material supplied by workers to larvae in regular brood cells that causes the latter to develop into workers (see royal jelly) (Wilson).

wound tumor, disease of clover caused by an isometric virus and transmitted propagatively by leafhoppers, *Agallia constricta* and *Agalliopsis novella* (Hemiptera: Auchenorrhyncha: Cicadellidae) (Borror et al.).

wrack, organic debris cast up on the shore, especially at the high tide line.

wrinkled, rugose, q.v. (Harris).

writhled, rugose, q.v. (T-B; Harris).

X

X-chromosome, the chromosome which in part, at least, determines the sex of an individual, i.e., paired in the ♀, single in the ♂ of most dioecious organisms (Tulloch).

X-disease, peach X-disease, q.v. (Borror et al.).

x organ, in Heteroptera (Hemiptera), epipharyngeal sense organ, q.v. (Cobben; Andersen)

x seta, in ♂ Chironomidae (Diptera), e.g., Podonominae, ventral seta on the apical lobe of the gonostylus (Saether).

XA mixture, killing fluid for larvae consisting of 50 ml of xylene and 50 ml of 95% ethyl alcohol (Borror et al.).

xanthic, yellowish, q.v. (T-B).

xanthine, $C_5H_4N_4O_2$, purine precursor of uric acid (Gilmour, in CSIRO),

xanthine dehydrogenase, enzyme catalyzing conversion of xanthine into uric acid (Gilmour, in CSIRO).

xanthochroism, in adult Hymenoptera, e.g., *Bembicinus* (Sphecidae), condition in which males are entirely sandy yellow instead of the normal black and yellow markings (Riek, in CSIRO).

xanthommatin, ommochrome producing brown color on the bodies and wings of insects (Gilmour, in CSIRO).

xanthophyll, carotenoid pigment found in plant cells, being an oxidized derivative of a carotene, commonly found in hemolymph of phytophagous insects (T-B; Tulloch; Chapman).

xanthopsin, a yellow-colored substance impregnating the retinular elements in night eyes of insects (T-B, after Imms).

xanthopterin, pterine pigment, producing yellow color, commonly found in the wings of Pieridae (Lepidoptera) (Chapman).

xanthopterine, pterine pigment producing yellow coloration in insects (Tulloch); see xanthopterin.

xanthos (Greek), **xanthous,** yellow (T-B; R. W. Brown).

xenic cultivation, the rearing of one or more individuals of one species in association with an unknown number of species of other organisms (Steinhaus and Martignoni).

xenobiosis, the relation in which colonies of one ant species (Hymenoptera: Formicidae), live in the nests of another species and move freely among the hosts, obtaining food from them by regurgitation or other means but keeping their brood separate (T-B, after J. B. Smith; Wilson).

xenodiagnosis, the use of noninfected insects, which are fed on an individual suspected of having a disease transmitted by these insects, followed by incubation in the body of the insect and diagnosis, being used mainly in the diagnosis of Chagas' disease (Adkins, pers. comm.).

xenoma, a symbiotic complex formed by hypertrophing host cells and multiplying intracellular parasites, such as certain microsporidians (Steinhaus and Martignoni, after Weissenberg).

xerophilous, living in dry places (T-B).

xerothermic fauna, that fauna which is found in warm, dry conditons (Tulloch, after Forel).

xiphos (Greek), sword; saber (R. W. Brown); see xiphus.

Xiphosura, subclass within the class Merostomata, including horseshoe crabs (Borror et al.).

xiphosuran, a member of the Xiphosura (T-B; Borror et al.).

Xiphosurida, Xyphosura, q.v. (Boudreaux).

xiphus, see xyphus.

Xyeloidea, superfamily within the Symphyta (Hymenoptera), including the family Xyelidae, possessing adults with antennae with a very long third article, formed by the fusion of several antennomeres (Gauld and Bolton, after Königsmann).

xylan, a yellow, gummy polysaccharide found in woody tissues, yielding xylose upon hydrolysis.

xylanase, an enzyme which catalyzes the hydrolysis of xylan, found in wood-feeding Coleoptera (T-B).

xylem, plant tissue consisting of various types of cells, which transports water and dissolved substances to the leaves, possessing vertical systems of dead cells with thick, lignified walls (Allaby); the wood of trees and shrubs; see cambium and phloem.

xylene, xylol, $C_6H_4(CH_3)_2$, a colorless, transparent, volatile, nonpolar liquid, used in clearing tissues for microscopic mounts and as a solvent for Canada balsam (T-B).

xyloid, woodlike in aspect (T-B).

xylomycetophagy, the cultivation and utilization of a symbiotic fungus as a food source (Wood).

xylophagous, feeding on xylem or wood (Gauld and Bolton).

xylophagy, living on and feeding directly on xylem or wood tissues (Wood).

Xyphosurida, Xyphosura, q.v. (Boudreaux).

xyphus, xiphus, a spinous triangular process of the prosternum and/or mesosternum in many Heteroptera (Hemiptera) and some other insects (T-B).

Y

y organ, in Heteroptera (Hemiptera), epipharyngeal sense organ, q.v. (Cobben; Andersen)

y seta, in ♂ Chironomidae (Diptera), e.g., Podonominae, dorsal seta on the apical lobe of the gonostylus (Saether).

Y-shaped dorsal sclerite of phallotheca, in ♂ Siphonaptera, solum, q.v. (Tuxen, after Sharif).

Y-vein, 2 adjacent veins fusing distally, forming a Y-shaped figure (Borror et al.).

yaw, in flying or swimming insects, rotation about the vertical axis (Chapman).

yaws, tropical disease of man caused by the spirochaete, *Treponema pertenue,* producing ulcerative lesions on skin and mucous membranes, and later bone lesions, transmitted by certain Muscidae and Chloropidae (Diptera) (Borror et al.; Allaby).

yeast, a fungus that can exist in the form of single cells, reproducing by fission or budding (Allaby).

yellow body, an amorphous mass formed by the shed epithelium of the larval midgut at pupation (Tulloch).

yellow cuticle, epicuticle of the serosal cuticle of the egg, responsible for the impermeability of the egg to salt ions (Tulloch; Chapman).

yellow dwarf, potato yellow dwarf, q.v. (Borror et al.).

yellow fever, viral disease of man and monkeys in the American and African tropics and subtropics transmitted by various mosquitoes, esp. *Aedes aegypti* (Diptera: Culicidae) (Borror et al.).

yellow jacket (yellow-jacket or **yellowjacket),** in the United States, any one of a number of ground-nesting wasps of the genus *Vespula* (Wilson).

yellow pan trap, shallow tray with bright yellow interior and dark exterior filled with a killing solution and placed into the ground, being used to attract and collect small insects, esp. small Hymenoptera (Gauld and Bolton).

yolk, nutritive matter of the egg, consisting of proteins or lipids, as distinguished from the cellular portion (T-B; Tulloch; Chapman).

yolk cells, vitellophages, q.v. (T-B, after Snodgrass).

yolk cleavage, the division of the yolk into masses containing from one to several cleavage nuclei (T-B, after Snodgrass).

Yponomeutoidea, a superfamily of the division Ditrysia (Lepidoptera) including such families as Acrolepiidae, Argyresthiidae, Lyonetiidae, Ochsenheimeriidae, Plutellidae, and Yponomeutidae, possessing naked haustellum, maxillary palpi 1–4 segmented and unfolded, R_5 to termen of forewing, ♂ with pleural lobes from abdominal segment VIII, and pupa without dorsal spines (Kyrki).

Z

zanthopsin, xanothopsin, q.v. (T-B, after Imms).

Zeitgeber (German), a cyclical environmental cue synchronizing or entraining a circadian rhythm (Matthews and Matthews).

zero (0-) setae, in larval and pupal Chironomidae (Diptera), O-setae, q.v. (Saether).

Zeugloptera, the most primitive suborder of Lepidoptera, consisting of the single superfamily Micropterigoidea, possessing mandibulate adults (no haustellum) with ascoid antennal sensilla, ♀ with cloaca, dectious pupa, larva with an unpaired medial seta on frontoclypeus and up to 8 pairs of unmusculated prolegs (Kristensen).

zona (Latin), a belt or zone (T-B).

zona periferica sinus penis, in ♂ Lepidoptera, funicular, caudal part of the manica (Tuxen, after Kusnezov).

zonal orientation, spatial orientation to resources or stresses that are extensive in a horizontal gradation (Matthews and Matthews, after Jander).

zone, in ♂ Lepidoptera, line around aedoeagus where manica attaches to it (Tuxen, after Chapman).

zone of growth, in the testis follicle, the region between the germarium and the zone of maturation in which the primary spermatogonia, enclosed in cysts, divide and increase in size to form spermatocytes (T-B, after Snodgrass; Chapman, after Wigglesworth).

zone of maturation, in the testis follicle, the region between the zone of growth and the zone of maturation in which each spermatocyte undergoes 2 meiotic divisions (reduction) to produce spermatids (Chapman, after Wigglesworth).

zone of transformation, in the testis follicle, region following the zone of maturation in which the spermatids develop into spermatozoa, a process known as spermiogenesis (Chapman, after Wigglesworth);

zone of maturation + zone of transformation (T-B, after Snodgrass).

zonite, arthromere or somite, q.v. (T-B).

zoogeography, the study of the distribution of animals, particularly historical aspects (T-B); see biogeography and phytogeography.

zoological formulae, excluded from provisions of the Code; modifications of available names throughout a taxonomic group by the addition of a standard prefix or suffix in order to indicate that the taxa named are members of that group (ICZN).

zoological nomenclature, the system of scientific names for zoological taxa and the provisions for the formation, treatment, and use of those names (ICZN); see nomenclature.

zoological taxon, a natural taxon of animals, named or unnamed (ICZN).

zoologist, one who studies animals (ICZN).

zoonite or **zoonule,** somite, q.v. (T-B).

zoonosis (pl., **zoonoses**), disease of lower (or extra-human) vertebrates transmissible to man in which arthropods may play an intermediary role (Tulloch, after Philip); any disease in man acquired from one of the lower animals, including invertebrates (Steinhaus and Martignoni); human pathogens maintained in other vertebrate host (Adkins, pers. comm.).

zoonotic, referring to zoonoses (Tulloch).

zoophagous, feeding on animals (T-B; Borror et al.); see necrophagous, predaceous, and sarcophagous.

zoophilous, of plants, adapted to pollination by animals.

zooplankton, plankton consisting of microscopic animals, including protozoa, small Crustacea, and larvae of many different kinds of other animals (Allaby); see phytoplankton.

zoosuccivorous, animal-fluid suckers; referring to insects that suck blood or other body-fluids (T-B); see hematophagous.

Zoraptera, order of endopterygote Neoptera (Insecta), including small insects with moniliform antennae, a Y-shaped epicranial suture, mandibulate mouthparts, tarsi with 2 tarsomeres, wings when present membranous and with reduced venation, cerci short, and females with ovipositor greatly reduced or absent (Smithers, in CSIRO).

Zorapterida, Zoraptera, q.v. (Boudreaux).

Zygaenoidea, a superfamily of the division Ditrysia (Lepidoptera), including the families Limacodidae, Megalopygidae, Dalceridae, Cyclotornidae, Epipyropidae, and Zygaenidae, possessing adults with reduced or absent maxillary palpi, M present or vestigial within discal cell, CuP present, tympanal organs absent, pupa with appendages largely free, and often stout, sluggish larvae (Common, in CSIRO).

Zygentoma, order of more or less flattened, cursorial, primitively wingless insects, including the families Lepidotrichidae, Maindroniidae, Nicoletiidae, Lepismatidae, possessing dicondylar mandible, five-segmented maxillary palpus, compound eyes absent or with few ommatidia, thorax not strongly arched, pleura exposed, and coxae lacking styles (Sturm, after Börner; Hennig); see Archaeognatha.

zygoma (Greek) (pl., **zygomata**), bar (R. W. Brown); in ♂ Caelifera (Orthoptera), the caudal transverse part of the cingulum (Ander, in Tuxen).

zygomatic adductors, the 2 sets of muscles together, between the 2 jaws of insects (T-B, after Snodgrass).

Zygoptera, suborder of Odonata, including the damselflies, adults having the fore- and hind wings similar in shape and venation, and nymphs which are usually slender, with 3 (rarely 2) caudal gills (T-B; O'Farrell, in CSIRO); see Anisoptera and Anisozygoptera.

zygopteroid, equally-winged; with fore- and hind wing similar in form and size, like in the Zygoptera (Odonata) (T-B).

zygopterous, of or pertaining to the Zygoptera (damselflies) (Odonata) (T-B).

zygopterous penis, in ♂ Zygoptera (Odonata), organ of transfer of the spermatophore originating from abdominal segment II (Fraser and Asahina, in Tuxen).

zygos (Greek), pair (R. W. Brown); in ♂ Coleoptera, paired portion of the internal genitalia (i.e., testes, seminal ducts and accessory glands) (Tuxen).

zygote, the fertilized egg or egg nucleus (T-B, after Snodgrass).

zygotic portion, in ♂ Coleoptera, zygos, q.v. (Tuxen).

zygous, paired (Tuxen).

zygum (pl., **zyga**), in larval Scarabaeoidea (Coleoptera), a sclerome pertaining to the region haptomerum and forming its anterior margin, typically appearing as a convex cross bar in front of the sensilla and heli, but often enlarged and carrying these structures (T-B, after Böving).

zymase, a complex of enzymes, found in yeast, decomposing sugar to alcohol and carbon dioxide (T-B; Tulloch).

zymogen, an inert substance in the living cell from which an enzyme is produced (T-B, after Wardle).

zymospecies, a species recognized soley on the basis of characters obtained through enzymes electrophoresis or comparable enzyme studies (Carlberg, pers. comm.).

PRINCIPAL SOURCES FOR THE CURRENT EDITION

BORROR, D. J., D. M. DELONG, AND C. A. TRIPLEHORN. 1981. An Introduction to the Study of Insects. Fifth Edition. Saunders College Publishing, Philadelphia. xi, 827 pp.

BOUDREAUX, H. B. 1979. Arthoropod Phylogeny with Special Reference to Insects. John Wiley and Sons, New York. viii + 320 pp.

CHAPMAN, R. F. 1982. The Insects, Structure and Function. Third Edition. Harvard University Press, Cambridge, Massachusetts. xvi, 919 pp.

CSIRO. 1970. The Insects of Australia. Melbourne University Press, Carlton, Victoria. xiii, 1029 pp.

GENERAL ASSEMBLY OF THE INTERNATIONAL UNION OF BIOLOGICAL SCIENCES. 1985. International Code of Zoological Nomenclature. Third Edition. International Trust for Zoological Nomenclature in association with British Museum (Natural History), London, and University of California Press, Berkeley and Los Angeles. xx, 338 pp.

HARBACH, R. E. AND K. L. KNIGHT. 1980. Taxonomist's Glossary of Mosquito Anatomy. Plexus Publishing, Inc., Marlton, New Jersey. xi, 415 pp

HARRIS, R. A. 1979. A glossary of surface microsculpturing. Occasional Papers in Entomology, California Department of Food and Agriculture 28:1–31.

HENNIG. W. 1969. Die Stammesgeschichte der Insekten. Waldemar Kramer, Frankfurt am Mein. 436 pp. [Translation: Hennig, W. 1981. Insect Phylogeny. John Wiley and Sons, Chichester, United Kingdom. xxii + 514 pp.]

LEFTWICH, A. W. 1976. A Dictionary of Entomology. Crane Russak, New York; Constable, London. 360 pp.

MATTHEWS, R. W. AND J. R. MATTHEWS. 1978. Insect Behavior. Wiley, New York. xiii, 507 pp.

MAYR, E. 1969. Principles of Systematic Zoology. McGraw-Hill Book Company, New York. xi, 428 pp.

MCALPINE, J. F. ET AL. (eds.). 1981. Manual of Nearctic Diptera. Volume 1. Research Branch, Agriculture Canada, Ottawa. vi, 674 pp.

PARKER, S. P. (ed.). 1982. Synopsis and Classification of Living Organisms. Vol. 2. McGraw-Hill Book Company, New York.

PETERSON, A. 1948. Larvae of Insects. Part I. Lepidoptera and Hymenoptera. Edwards Bros., Ann Arbor, Michigan. 315 pp.

PETERSON, A. 1951. Larvae of Insects. Part II. Coleoptera, Diptera, Neuroptera, Siphonaptera, Mecoptera, Trichoptera. Edwards Bros., Ann Arbor, Michigan. v, 416 pp.

PFADT, R. E. (ed.). 1978. Fundamentals of Applied Entomology. Third Edition. MacMillan Publishing Co., New York. 798 pp.

SAETHER, O. A. 1980. Glossary of chironomid morphology terminology (Diptera: Chironomidae). Entomologica Scandinavica, Supplementum 14:1–51.

STEINHAUS, E. A. AND M. E. MARTIGNONI. 1970. An Abridged Glossary of Terms Used in Invertebrate Pathology. Second Edition. Pacific Northwest Forest and Range Experiment Station, United States Department of Agriculture, Forest Service. vi, 38 pp.

TORRE-BUENO, J. R. DE LA. 1937. A Glossary of Entomology. Brooklyn Entomological Society, Brooklyn, New York. ix, 336 pp., 9 pls.

TULLOCH, G. S. 1962. Torre-Bueno's Glossary of Entomology, Supplement A. Brooklyn Entomological Society, Brooklyn, New York. 36 pp.

TUXEN, S. L. (ed.). 1970. Taxonomist's Glossary of Genitalia in Insects. 2nd rev. and enl. ed. Munksgaard, Copenhagen. 359 pp.

WILSON, E. O. 1971. The Insect Societies. The Belknap Press of Harvard University Press, Cambridge, Massachusetts. x, 548 pp.

ADDITIONAL SOURCES FOR THE CURRENT ADDITION

ACHTERBERG, C. VAN. 1979. A revision of the subfamily Zelinae auct. (Hymenoptera: Braconidae). Tijdschr. Entomol. 122:241–479.

AGARWALA, S. B. D. 1952. A comparative study of the ovipositor in the Acrididae—II. Indian J. Entomol. 14:61–75.

ALBRECHT, F. O. AND R. E. BLACKITH. 1957. Phase and moulting polymorphism in locusts. Evolution 11:166–177.

ALLABY, M. (ed.). 1985. The Oxford Dictionary of Natural History. Oxford University Press, UK. xiv + 688 pp.

AMEDEGNATO, C. 1976. Structure et évolution des genitalia chez les Acrididae et familles apparentées. Acrida 5(1):1–15.

ANDERSEN, N. M. 1982. The Semiaquatic Bugs (Hemiptera, Gerromorpha). Phylogeny, Adaptations, Biogeography, and Classification. Entomonograph, Volume 3. Scandinavian Science Press, Ltd., Klampenborg, Denmark. 455 pp.

ASPÖCK, H., U. ASPÖCK, AND H. HÖLZEL. 1980. Die Neuropteren Europas. 2 Volumes. Goecke and Evers, Krefeld, West Germany. 495 pp and 355 pp.

BADONNEL, A. 1943. Psocoptères. Faune de France. 42:1–164.

BADONNEL, A. 1951. Ordre des Psocoptères. Pp. 1301–1340. In: Grassé, P. P. (ed.), Traité de Zoologie. Volume 10. Masson, Paris.

BARTH, R. 1955. Maennliche Duftorgane brasilianischer Lepidopteren. 10. Mitteilung: Hemiceras proximata Dogn. (Notodontidae). An. Acad. Bras. Cienc. 27:539–544.

BERLESE, A. 1909. Monografia dei Myrientomata. Redia 6:1–182.

BETTEN, C. 1934. The caddis flies or Trichoptera of New York State. N. Y. State Mus. Bull. 292:1–576, pls. 1–67.

BICCHIERAI, M. C. AND G. P. MORETTI. 1984. Presumed scent-organ on the anterior wing of male Beraeodes minutus L. (Abstract). p. 35. In: Morse, J. C. (ed.), Proceedings of the 4th International Symposium on Trichoptera, Clemson, South Carolina, 11–16 July 1983. Series Entomologica, Volume 30. Dr. W. Junk Publishers, The Hague.

BICCHIERAI, M. C. AND G. P. MORETTI. 1987. Prosternal horn and

Gilson's gland in certain limnephilid larvae. Pp. 3–9. *In*: Bournaud, M. and H. Tachet (eds.), Proceedings of the 5th International Symposium on Trichoptera, Lyon, France, 21–26 July 1986. Series Entomologica, Volume 39. Dr. W. Junk Publishers, Dordrecht.

BIRKET-SMITH, S. J. R. 1971. On the abdominal morphology of Thysanura (Archaeognatha and Thysanura *s.str.*). Entomol. Scand. Suppl. 6:1–67.

BITSCH, J. AND C. PALEVODY. 1973. L'épithelium absorbant des vésicules coxales des Machilides (Insecta Thysanura). Z. Zellforsch. Mikrosk. Anat. 143:169–182.

BITSCH, J. AND C. PALEVODY. 1976. Ultrastructure des glandes vésiculaires des Machilidae (Insecta, Thysanura) pendant l'intermue. Arch. Zool. Exp. Gen. 117:141–168.

BLACKMAN, R. L. AND V. F. EASTOP. 1984. Aphids on the World's Crops: An Identification and Information Guide. John Wiley and Sons, Chicester. 466 pp.

BOHART, R. M. AND A. S. MENKE. 1976. Sphecid Wasps of the World. University of California Press, Berkeley. ix + 695 pp.

BÖRNER, C. 1904. Zur Systematik der Hexapoden. Zool. Anz. 27:511–533.

BÖRNER, C. 1939. Die Grundlagen meines Lepidopterensystems. Verh. VII. Int. Kongr. Entomol., Berlin 2:1372–1424.

BRAUN, A. S. 1924. The frenulum and its retinaculum in the Lepidoptera. Ann. Entomol. Soc. Am. 18(3): 234–256.

BRINDLE, A. 1973. The Dermaptera of Africa, Part I. Mus. Roy. Afr. Centr., Ann. Ser. Octavo, Sci. Zool. 205:1–335.

BRINDLE, A. 1978. The Dermaptera of Africa, Part II. Mus. R. Afr. Centr., Ann. Ser. Octavo, Sci. Zool. 225:1–204.

BROADHEAD, E. 1950. A revision of the genus *Liposcelis* Motschulsky with notes on the position of this genus in the order Corrodentia and on the variability of ten *Liposcelis* species. Trans. R. Entomol. Soc. Lond. 101:335–388.

BROCK, J. P. 1971. A contribution towards an understanding of the morphology and phylogeny of the ditrysian Lepidoptera. J. Nat. Hist. 5:29–102.

BROTHERS, D. J. 1975. Phylogeny and classification of the aculeate Hymenoptera, with special reference to Mutillidae. Univ. Kans. Sci. Bull. 50:483–648.

BRUES, C. T., A. L. MELANDER, AND F. M. CARPENTER. 1954. Classification of Insects. Bull. Mus. Comp. Zool. Harv. Univ. 108:1–917.

BRUIJNING, C. F. A. 1948. Studies on Malayan Blattidae. Zool. Meded. 29:1–174.

BULLINGTON, S. W. AND M. KOSZTARAB. 1985. I. Revision of the family Kermesidae (Homoptera) in the Nearctic Region based on adult and third instar females. Va. Agric. Exp. Sta. Bull. No. 85-11:1–118.

BURMEISTER, H. 1838. Handbuch der Entomologie. Theod. Chr. Friedr. Enzlin, Berlin.

BYERS, G. W. 1954. Notes on North American Mecoptera. Ann. Entomol. Soc. Amer. 47:484–510.

CARAYON, J. 1971. Notes et documents sur l'appareil odorant métathoracique des Hémiptères. Ann. Soc. Entomol. France. (N.S.) 7:737–770.

CARAYON, J. 1974. Ètude dur les Hémiptères Plokiophilidae. Ann. Soc. Entomol. Fr. 10:499–525.

CARAYON, J. 1984. Les androconies de certains Hémiptères Scutelleridae. Ann. Soc. Entomol. Fr. 20:113–134.

CARLBERG, U. 1981. Defensive secretion if stick insects. J. Chem. Ecol. 7:905–906.

CARLBERG, U. 1987. Chemical defence in Phasmida vs. Mantodea (Insecta). Zool. Anz. 218:369–373.

CARPENTER, J. M. AND J. M. CUMMING. 1985. A character analysis of the North American potter wasps (Hymenoptera, Vespidae: Eumeninae). J. Nat. Hist. 79:877–916.

CARTER, C. I. 1971. Conifer woolly aphids (Adelgidae) in Britain. Forestry Comm. Bull. No. 42:1–49.

CHENG, F. Y. 1957. Revision of the Chinese Mecoptera. Bull. Mus. Comp. Zool. Harv. Univ. 116:1–118.

CHISHOLM, I. E., AND T. LEWIS. 1984. A new look at thrips (Thysanoptera) mouthparts, their action and effects of feeding on plant tissue. Bull. Entomol. Res. 74:663–675.

CHOE, J. C. 1989. A new species Zorotypus gurneyi from Panama and redescription of Z. barberi Gurney (Zoraptera: Zorotypidae). Ann. Entomol. Soc. Amer. 82: in press.

CHOPARD, L. 1949. Anatomie, Systematique, Biologie. In: Grasse, P. P. (ed.), Traité de Zoolgie. Volume 9. Insectes. Masson, Paris.

CHRISTIANSEN, K. A. AND P. F. BELLINGER. 1980–81. The Collembola of North America North of the Rio Grande. Grinnell College, Grinnell, Iowa. 1322 pp.

CLARK, J. T. 1976. The eggs of stick insects (Phasmida): a review with descriptions of the eggs of eleven species. Syst. Entomol. 1:95–105.

COBBEN, R. H. 1957. Beitrag zur Kenntnis der Uferwanzen (Hem. Het. Fam. Salidae). Entomol. Ber., Amsterdam. 17:245–257.

COBBEN, R. H. 1961. A new genus and four new species of Saldidae (Heteroptera). Entomol. Ber., Amsterdam. 21:96–106.

COBBEN, R. H. 1968. Evolutionary Trends in Heteroptera. Part 1. Eggs, Architecture of the Shell, Gross Embryology and Eclosion. Centre for Agricultural Publishing, Wageningen, Netherlands. 475 pp.

COBBEN, R. H. 1978. Evolutionary Trends in Heteroptera. Part 2. Mouthpart-structures and Feeding Strategies. Medelingen Landbouwhogeschool 78-5. H. Veeman, Wageningen, Netherlands. 407 pp.

COMMON, I. F. B. 1969. A wing-locking or stridulatory device in Lepidoptera. J. Austr. Entomol. Soc. 8:121–125.

COMMON, I. F. B. 1988. Moths of Australia. Melbourne University Press.

COMMON I. F. B. AND D. F. WATERHOUSE. 1982. Butterflies of Australia. Revised Edition. Angus and Robertson, Sydney. 682 pp.

COMSTOCK, J. H. 1918. The Wings of Insects. Comstock Publishing Co., Ithaca, New York. 430 pp.

CONDE, B. 1947. Description de quatre Protoures nouveaux du sud-ouest de la France. Coll. Mus. Zool. Nancy 2:5–12.

CRAMPTON, G. C. 1931. The genitalia and terminal structures of the male of the archaic Mecopteron, *Notiothauma reedi* compared with related Holometabola from the standpoint of phylogeny. Psyche 38: 1–21.

CRICHTON, M. I. 1957. The structure and function of the mouthparts of the adult caddis flies (Trichoptera). Phil. Trans. R. Soc. Lond. Ser. B Biol. Sci. 241:45–91.

CROSBY, T. K. 1973. Dyar's rule predated by Brook's rule. N. Z. Entomol. 5:175–176.

CROSSKEY, R. W. 1981. Simuliid taxonomy—the contemporary scene. *In*: Laird, M. (ed.), Blackflies: The Future for Biological Methods in Integrated Control. Academic Press, New York.

CROWSON, R. A. 1981. The Biology of the Coleoptera. Academic Press, New York. xiii + 802 pp.

DANIELS, G. 1979. The genus *Ptecticus* Loew from Australia, New Guinea and the Bismark and Solomon Archipelagos (Diptera: Stratiomyidae). Rec. Austr. Mus. 32(18):563–588.

DAVIS, D. R. 1975. Systematics and zoogeography of the family Neopseustidae with the proposal of a new superfamily (Lepidoptera: Neopseustoidea). Smithson. Contr. Zool. 210:1–45.

DAVIS, D. R. 1978. A revision of the North American moths of the superfamily Eriocranioidea with the proposal of a new family Acanthopteroctetidae (Lepidoptera). Smithson. Contr. Zool. 251:1–131.

DAVIS, D. R. 1986. A new family of monotrysian moths from Austral South America (Lepidoptera: Palaephatidae), with a phylogenetic review of the Monotrysia. Smithson. Contr. Zool. 434:1–202.

DAVIS, D. R. AND E. S. NIELSEN. 1980. Description of a new genus and two new species of Neopseustidae from South America, with discussion of phylogeny and biological observations (Lepidoptera: Neopseustoidea). Steenstrupia 6:253–289.

DENIS, J. R. 1965. Super-Ordre des Ectotrophes. Pp. 209–275. *In*: Grassé, P.P. (ed.). Traité de Zoologie. Volume 9. Insectes. Masson, Paris.

DIAKONOFF, A. 1952. Microlepidoptera of New Gunea, Part 1. Verh. Akad. Wet. Amst. 49:1–167.

DIXON, A. F. G. 1985. Aphid Ecology. Blackie, Glasgow and London. 157 pp.

DOWNEY, J. C., AND A. C. ALLYN. 1975. Wing-scale morphology and nomenclature. Bull. Allyn Mus. 31: 1–32.

DRAKE, C. J. AND N. T. DAVIS. 1960. The morphology, phylogeny, and higher classification of the family Tingidae, including a description of a new genus and species of the subfamily Vianaidinae (Hemiptera: Heteroptera). Entomol. Am. 39:1–100.

DRAKE, C. J. AND F. A. RUHOFF. 1965. Lacebugs of the World: A Catalog (Hemiptera: Tingidae). Smithson. Inst. U. S. Nat. Mus. Bull. 243:1–634.

DUGDALE, J. S. 1974. Female genital configuration in the classification of Lepidoptera. N. Z. J. Zool. 1:127–246.

EMERSON, A. E. 1965. A review of the Mastotermitidae (Isoptera), including a new fossil genus from Brazil. Am. Mus. Novit. 2236:1–46.

EMERSON, K. C. 1982. Mallophaga. Pp. 409–415. *In*: Parker, S. P. (ed.). Synopsis and Classification of Living Organisms. McGraw-Hill Book Company, New York.

ENDERLEIN, G. 1925. Ordnung: Flechtlinge, Copeognatha. *In*: Brohmer, P., P. Ehrmann, and G. Ulmer (eds.). Die Tierwelt Mitteleuropas. Leipzig, IV Band, 2. Lief, 10:1–16.

ERWIN, T. L. 1974. Studies of the subtrive Tachyina (Coleoptera: Carabidae: Bembidiini), Part 2: A revision of the New World-Australian genus *Pericompsus* LeConte. Smithson. Contr. Zool. 162:1–96.

FALCO, R. C. AND D. FISH. 1988. Ticks parasitizing humans in a lyme disease endemic area in southern New York State. Amer. J. Epidemiol. 128(5):1146–1152.

FENNAH, R. G. 1952. On the generic classification of Derbidae (Fulgoroidea), with descriptions of new Neotropical species. Trans. R. Entomol. Soc. Lond. 103:109–170.

FENTON, M. B. AND K. D. ROEDER. 1974. The microtymbals of some Arctiidae. J. Lepid. Soc. 28:205–211.

FERGUSON, D. C. 1985. Contributions toward reclassification of the world genera of the tribe Arctiini, Part 1—Introduction and a revision of the *Neoarctia-Grammia* group (Lepidoptera: Arctiidae; Arctiinae). Entomography 3:181–275.

FERRAR, P. 1987. A guide to the breeding habits and immature stages of Diptera Cyclorrhapha. Entomonograph 8(1):1–478 (text). E. J. Brill/Scandinavian Science Press, Leiden, Copenhagen.

FERRIS, G. F. AND B. E. REES. 1939. The morphology of *Panorpa nuptialis* (Gerstaecker) (Mecoptera: Panorpidae). Microentomology 4:79–108.

FEUERBORN, H. J. 1922. Das Problem der geschechtlichen Zuchtwahl im Lichte neuer Beobachtungen. Naturwiss. Wochenschrift 21: 1–12.

FLYNN, J. E. AND J. P. KRAMER. 1983. Taxonomic study of the planthopper *Cedusa* in the Americas (Homoptera: Fulgoroidea: Derbidae). Entomography 2:121–260.

FORBES, W. T. M. 1954. Lepidoptera of New York and neighboring states. Part 3. Noctuidae. Mem. Cornell Univ. Agric. Exp. Sta. 329:1–433.

FRANK, J. H. AND K. KANAMITSU. 1987. *Paederus,* sensu lato (Coleoptera: Staphylinidae): Natural history and medical importance. J. Med. Entomol. 24:155–191.

GAULD, I. AND B. BOLTON (EDS.). 1988. The Hymenoptera. British Museum (Natural History) and Oxford University Press, UK. xi + 332 pp.

GIBBS, G. W. 1979. Some notes on the biology and status of the Mnesarchaeidae (Lepidoptera). N. Z. Entomol. 7:2–9.

GIBSON, G. A. P. 1985. Some pro- and mesothoracic structures important for phylogenetic analysis of Hymenoptera, with a review of terms used for the structures. Can. Entomol. 117:1395–1443.

GILES, E. T. 1963. The comparative external morphology and affinities of the Dermaptera. Trans. R. Entomol. Soc. Lond. 115(4):95–164.

GILES, E. T. 1974. The relationship between the Hemimerina and the other Dermaptera: a case for reinstating the Hemimerina within the Dermaptera, based upon a numerical procedure. Trans. R. Entomol. Soc. Lond. 126(2):189–206.

GILL, R. J. In Press. The morphology of whiteflies. In: Gurling, D. (ed.). Whiteflies: Bionomics, Pest Status, and Management. Intercept Scientific, Medical, and Technical Publications, Dorset, UK.

GOEL, S. C. AND C. W. SCHAEFER. 1970. The structure of the pulvillus and its taxonomic value in the land Heteroptera (Hemiptera). Ann. Entomol. Soc. Am. 63:307–313.

GRASSÉ, P. P. 1959. La reconstruction du nid et les coordinations interindividuelles, chez *Bellicositermes natalensis* et *Cubitermes* sp. La théorie de la stigmergie: Essai d'interpretation du comportment des Termites constructeurs. Insectes Soc. 6:41–84.

GRASSÉ, P. P. AND C. NOIROT. 1954. *Apicotermes arquieri* (Isoptère): Ses constructions, sa biologie. Considérations générales sur la sous-famille des Apicotermitinae nov. Ann. Sci. Nat. Zool. Biol. Anim. (11)16:345–388.

GRIFFITHS, G. C. D. 1972. The Phylogenetic Classification of Diptera Cyclorrhapha with Special Reference to the Structure of the Male Postabdomen. Series Entomologica, Volume 8. Dr. W. Junk N. V., The Hague. 340 pp.

GRIMES, L. R., AND H. H. NEUNZIG. 1986. Morphological survey of the maxillae in last stage larvae of the suborder Ditrysia (Lepidoptera): Mesal lobes (laciniogaleae). Ann. Entomol. Soc. Am. 79:510–526.

HAPP, G. M., J. D. STRANDBERG, AND C. M. HAPP. 1966. The terpene-producing glands of a phasmid insect–cell morphology and histochemistry. J. Morphol. 119:143–160.

HEMING, B. S. 1970a. Postembryonic development of the female reproductive system in *Frankliniella fusca* (Thripidae) and *Haplothrips verbasci* (Phlaeothripidae) (Thysanoptera). Misc. Pub. Entomol. Soc. Am. 7:199–234.

HEMING, B. S. 1970b. Postembryonic development of the male reproductive system in *Frankliniella fusca* (Thripidae) and *Haplothrips verbasci* (Phlaeothripidae) (Thysanoptera). Misc. Pub. Entomol. Soc. Am. 7:237–272.

HEMING, B. S. 1971. Functional morphology of the thysanopteran pretarsus. Can. J. Zool. 49:91–108.

HEMING, B. S. 1978. Structure and function of the mouthparts in larvae of *Haplothrips verbasci* (Osborn) (Thysanoptera, Tubulifera, Phlaeothripidae). J. Morphol. 156:1–38.

HEMING, B. S. 1980. Development of the mouthparts in embryos of *Haplothrips verbasci* (Osborn) (Insecta, Thysanoptera, Phlaeothripidae). J. Morphol. 164:234–263.

HEMING, B. S. 1989. Chapter 28. Thysanoptera. In: Stehr, F.W. (ed.)

Immature Insects. Volume 2. Kendall/Hunt Publishing Company, Dubuque, Iowa, (in press).

HENRY, C. S. 1982. Neuroptera. Pp. 470–482. *In*: S. P. Parker (ed.), Synopsis and Classification of Living Organisms. Volume 2. Mc-Graw-Hill Book Company, New York.

HERING, E. M. 1951. Biology of the Leafminers. W. Junk, Gravenhage. 420 pp.

HINCKS, W. D. A. 1959. A systematic monograph of the Dermaptera of the World based on material in the British Museum (Natural History). Part two. Pygidicranidae excluding Diplatyinae. London, British Museum (Natural History), London. ix + 218 pp.

HINCKS, W. D. AND E. J. POPHAM. 1970. Dermaptera. Pp. 75–80. *In*: Tuxen, S. L. (ed.). Taxonomist's Glossary of Genitalia in Insects. Second Edition. Munksgaard, Copenhagen.

HINTON, H. E. 1946. On the homology and the nomenclature of the setae of lepidopterous larvae, with some notes on the phylogeny of the Lepidoptera. Trans. R. Entomol. Soc. Lond. 97:1–37.

HINTON, H. E. 1948. The dorsal cranial areas of caterpillars. Ann. Mag. Nat. Hist. (11)14:843–852.

HODKINSON, I. D. AND I. M. WHITE. 1979. Homoptera Psylloidea. Handbooks for the Indentification of British Insects. Vol. 2, Part 5(a). Royal Entomological Society of London, UK.

HOPKINS, G. H. E. AND M. ROTHSCHILD. 1953–1966. An Illustrated Catalogue of the Rothschild Collection of Fleas (Siphonaptera) in the British Museum (Natural History). Volumes 1–4. British Museum of Natural History, London.

HUNGERFORD, H. B. 1948. The Corixidae of the Western Hemipshere (Hemiptera). Univ. Kans. Sci. Bull. 32:1–827.

IMMS. A. D. 1959. Outlines of Entomology. Fifth Edition. Revised by O. W. Richards and R. B. Davies. Methuen & Co. Ltd., London. 224 pp.

JACOBS, W. AND F. SEIDEL. 1975. Systematische Zoologie: Insekten. Stuttgart. 377 pp.

JANETSCHEK, H. 1954. Über Felsenspringer der Mittelmeerländer (Thysanura, Machilidae). Eos Rev. Esp. Entomol. 30:163–314.

JANETSCHEK, H. 1970. Protura (Beintastler). Handbuch Zoologie Berl. 4:1–72.

JANETSCHEK, H. 1972. On phylogenetic interrelationships of the Thysanura and its allies. Acta Salamant. Ser. Cienc. 36:305–315.

JORDAN, K. 1923. On the comb-bearing flap present on the fourth abdominal segment in the males of certain Notodontidae. Novit. Zool. 30:153–154.

KAESTNER, A. 1972–1973. Lehrbuch der Speziellen Zoologie. Volume I/3. Insecta. Stuttgart.

KELLEY, R. W. 1984. Phylogeny, morphology and classification of the micro-caddisfly genus *Oxyethira* Eaton (Trichoptera: Hydroptilidae). Trans. Am. Entomol. Soc. 110:435–463.

KEVAN, D. K. McE. 1982. Phasmatoptera. Pp. 379–383. *In*: Parker, S. P. (ed.), Synopsis and Classification of Living Organisms. McGraw-Hill Book Company, New York.

KEY, K. H. L. 1957. Kentromorphic phases in three species of Phasmatodea. Austr. J. Zool. 5:247–284.

KEY, K. H. L. 1983. On the identity of a structure of the bursa copulatrix in morabine grasshoppers (Orthoptera: Eumastacidae). J. Austr. Entomol. Soc. 22:245–296.

KEY, K. L. H. 1985. Monograph of the Monistriini and Peasidini (Orthoptera: Pyrgomorphidae). Austr. J. Zool. Suppl. 107:1–213.

KITCHING, I. J. 1984. An historical review of the higher classification of the Noctuidae (Lepidoptera). Bull. Br. Mus. Nat. Hist. Entomol. 49: 153–254.

KLUGE, A. G. AND J. S. FARRIS. 1969. Quantitative phyletics and the evolution of anurans. Syst. Zool. 18:1–36.

KOMNICK, H. 1977. Chloride cells and chloride epithelia of aquatic insects. Int. Rev. Cytol. 49:285–329.

KOSZTARAB, M. 1982. Homoptera. Pp. 447–470. In: Parker, S. P. (ed.). Synopsis and Classification of Living Organisms. Volume 2. McGraw-Hill Book Company, New York.

KOSZTARAB, M. AND F. KOZÁR. 1988. Scale Insects of Central Europe. Dr. W. Junk Publishers, Dordrecht. 456 pp.

KRAMER, J. P. 1973. Revision of the American planthoppers of the genus Stobaera (Homoptera: Delphacidae) with new distributional data and host plant records. Proc. Entomol. Soc. Wash. 75:379–402.

KRISHNA, K. AND FRANCES M. WEESNER (EDS.). 1969–1970. Biology of termites. Academic Press, New York and London. 1:1–598, 2:1–643.

KRISTENSEN, N. P. 1976. Remarks on the family-level phylogeny of butterflies (Insecta, Lepidoptera, Rhopalocera). Z. Zool. Syst. Evolutionsforsch. 14:25–33.

KRISTENSEN, N. P. 1984. Studies on the morphology and systematics of primitive Lepidoptera (Insecta). Steenstrupia 10:141–191.

KRITENSEN, N. P. AND E. S. NIELSEN. 1981. Intrinsic proboscis musculature in non-ditrysian Lepidoptera-Glossata: Structure and phylogenetic significance. Entomol. Scand. Suppl. 15:299–304.

KYRKI, J. 1984. The Yponomeutoidea: A reassessment of the superfamily and its suprageneric groups (Lepidoptera). Entomol. Scand. 15: 71–84.

LANDA, V. AND T. SOLDÁN. 1985. Phylogeny and higher classification of the order Ephemeroptera: A discussion from the comparative anatomical point of view. Studie CSAV 4(1985):1–121.

LARINK, O. 1983. Embryonic and postembryonic development of Machilidae and Lepismatidae (Insecta: Archaeognatha et Zygentoma). Entomol. Gen. 8:119–133.

LENT, H. AND P. WYGODZINSKY. 1979. Revision of the Triatominae (Hemiptera, Reduviidae), and their significance as vectors of Chagas's disease. Bull. Am. Mus. Nat. Hist. 163:123–520.

LONDT, J. B. H. 1974. Corneus spots in insects. J. Entomol. Soc. South. Afr. 37:5–14.

LYAL, H. C. 1985. Phylogeny and classification of the Psocodea, with particular reference to the lice (Psocodea: Phthiraptera). Syst. Entomol. 10:145–165.

LYAL, C. H. C. 1986. External genitalia of Psocodea, with particular reference to lice (Phthiraptera). Zool. Jb. Anat. 114:277–292.

MCLACHLAN, R. 1874–1880. A monographic revision and synopsis of the Trichoptera of the European fauna. Napier Printers, London.

MAES, K. 1985. A comparative study of the abdominal tympanal organs in Pyralidae (Lepidoptera). Nota Lepid. 8:341–350.

MARKL, W. 1954. Vergleichend-morphologische Studien zur Systematik und Klassifikation der Myrmeleoniden (Insecta, Neuroptera). Verh. Naturforsch. Ges. Basel 65:178–263.

MARTYNOV, V. 1922. The interpretation of the wing venation and tracheation of the Odonata and Agnatha. Rev. Russe Entomol. 18:145–174 (translation in Psyche 37:245–281).

MAYNARD, E. A. 1951. A Monograph of the Collembola or Springtail Insects of New York State. Comstock Publishing Company, Inc., Ithaca, NY. 339 pp.

MCCAFFERTY, W. P. AND G. F. EDMUNDS, JR. 1979. The higher classification of the Ephemeroptera and its evolutionary basis. Ann. Entomol. Soc. Am. 72:5–12.

MCKITTRICK, F. A. 1964. Evolutionary studies of cockroaches. Cornell Agric. Exp. Sta., Mem. 389:1–197.

MEAD, F. W. AND J. P. KRAMER. 1982. Taxonomic study of the planthopper genus Oliarius in the United States (Homoptera: Fulgoroidea: Cixiidae). Trans. Am. Entomol. Soc. 107:381–569.

MENKE, A. S. (ED.). 1979. The semiaquatic and aquatic Hemiptera of California (Heteroptera: Hemiptera). Bull. Calif. Insect Surv. 21: i–xi, 1–166.

MICHENER, C. D. 1974. The Social Behavior of Bees. A Comparative Study. The Belknap Press of Harvard University Press, Cambridge, Massachusetts. xii + 404 pp.

MILLER, E. M. 1969. Caste differentiation in the lower termites. Pp. 283–310. In: Krishna, K. and F.M. Weesner (eds.) Biology of Termites. Volume I. Academic Press, New York.

MILLER, N. C. E. 1956. The Biology of the Heteroptera. Leonard Hill Books, London. 162 pp.

MINET, J. 1983. Étude morphologique et phylogénétique des organes tympaniques des Pyraloidea. 1-Généralités et homologies (Lep. Glossata). Ann. Soc. Entomol. Fr. 19:175–207.

MINKS, A. K. AND P. HARREWIJN (EDS.). 1987. Aphids: Their Biology, Natural Enemies and Control. Volume A. Elsevier, Amsterdam. 450 pp.

MITTER, C. 1988. Taxonomic potential of some internal reproductive structures in Catocala (Lepidoptera: Noctuidae) and related genera. Ann. Entomol. Soc. Am. 81:10–18.

MIYAMOTO, S. 1961. Comparative morphology of alimentary organs of Heteroptera, with the phylogenetic consideration. Sieboldia Acta Biol. 2:197–259, 49 pls.

MOCKFORD, E. L. 1965. A new genus of hump-backed psocids from Mexico and southwestern United States (Psocoptera: Psocidae). Folia Entomol. Mex. 11:3–13.

MOCKFORD, E. L. 1974. Records and descriptions of Cuban Psocoptera. Entomol. Am. 48:103–215.

MOCKFORD, E. L. 1975. Genus *Eremopsocus* McLachlan: Distinction from *Cerastipsocus* Kolbe and review of species (Psocoptera: Psocidae). Psyche 82:244–258.

MOCKFORD, E. L. AND A. N. GARCIA ALDRETE. 1976. A new species and notes on the taxonomic positions of *Asiopsocus* Günther (Psocoptera). Southwest. Nat. 21:335–346.

MORSE, J. C. 1975. A phylogeny and revision of the caddisfly genus *Ceraclea* (Trichoptera, Leptoceridae). Contr. Am. Entomol. Inst. 11: 1–97.

MORTON, K. J. 1902. Notes on the females of Artic and northern species of *Apatania*. Entomol. Mon. Mag. 38:150–157, pl. III.

MOUND, L. A. 1973. Thrips and whitefly. Pp. 229–242. *In*: Gibbs, A. J. (ed.). Viruses and Invertebrates. North Holland Publishing Company, Amsterdam.

MOUND, L. A. AND A. K. WALKER. 1982. Terebrantia (Insecta: Thysanoptera). Fauna of N. Z. 1:5–113.

MOUND, L. A., B. S. HEMING, AND J. M. PALMER. 1980. Phylogenetic relationships between the families of recent Thysanoptera (Insecta). Zool. J. Linn. Soc. 69:111–149.

MOUND, L. A., G. D. MORISON, B. R. PITKIN, AND J. M. PALMER. 1976. Thysanoptera. Handbooks for the Identification of British Insects. Volume 1, Part 11. Royal Entomological Society of London, UK. 79 pp.

MUNROE, E. 1982. Lepidoptera. Pp. 612–652. *In*: S. P. Parker (ed.), Synopsis and Classification of Living Organisms. Volume 2. McGraw Hill Book Company, New York.

NAULT, L. R. AND E. D. AMMAR. 1989. Leafhopper and planthopper transmission of plant viruses. Ann. Rev. Entomol. 34:503–529.

NAULT, L. R. AND J. G. RODRIGUEZ. 1985. The Leafhoppers and Planthoppers. John Wiley and Sons, New York.

NEBOISS, A. 1986. Atlas of Trichoptera of the SW Pacific-Australian Region. Dr. W. Junk Publishers, Dordrecht, viii + 286 pp.

NEEDHAM, J. G. AND H. E. MURPHY. 1924. Neotropical mayflies. Bull. Lloyd Lib. 24, Entomol. Ser. 4:1–79.

NEL, R. J. 1929. Studies on the development of the genitalia and the genital ducts in insects. I. Female of Orthoptera and Dermaptera. Q. J. Microsc. Sci. 73:25–85.

NEW, T. R. 1984. Intergeneric relationships in recent Nymphidae. Pp. 125–131. *In*: Gepp, J., H. Aspöck, and H. Hölzel (eds.). Proceedings of the 1st International Symposium on Neuropterology, Graz, Austria. 265 pp.

NIELSEN, A. 1943. *Apatidea auricula* Forsslund from a Norwegian mountain lake: Description of the imago and notes on the biology. Entomol. Medd. 23:18–30.

NIELSEN, A. 1957. A comparative study of the genital segments and their appendages in male Trichoptera. Biol. Skr. 8:1–159.

NIELSEN, A. 1980. A comparative study of the genital segments and the genital chamber in female Trichoptera. Biol. Skr. 23:1–200.

NIESER, N. 1975. The water bugs (Heteroptera: Nepomorpha) of the Guyana region. Studies Fauna Suriname Other Guyanas 59:1–310, 24 pls.

NOIROT, C. 1969. Formation of castes in the higher termites. Pp. 311–350. In: Krishna, K. and F.M. Weesner (eds.). Biology of Termites. Volume I. Academic Press, New York.

NOIROT, C. AND C. NOIROT-TIMOTHÉE. 1969. The digestive system. Pp. 49–88. In: Krishna, K. and F. M. Weesner (eds.). Biology of Termites. Volume I. Academic Press, New York.

NOSEK, J. 1973. The European Protura. Their Taxonomy, Ecology and Distribution with Keys for Determination. Museum d'Histoire Naturelle, Geneve. 354 pp.

PACLT, J. 1956. Biologie der primär flügellosen Insekten. Gustav Fischer, Jena. vi + 258 pp.

PAPÁČEK, J., P. ŠTYS, AND M. TONNER. 1988. A new subfamily of Helotrephidae (Heteroptera, Nepomorpha) from southeast Asia. Acta Entomol. Bohemoslov. 85:120–152, pls. i–iii.

PARKER, K. D. AND K. M. RUDALL. 1955. Calcium citrate in an insect. Biochem. Biophys. Acta 17:287.

PAULIAN, R. 1949. Découverte de l'ordre des Zoraptères à Madagascar et description d'une nouvelle esp ce. Mem. Inst. Sci. Madagascar, A 3:77–80.

PEARMAN, J. V. 1936. The taxonomy of the Psocoptera: Preliminary sketch. Proc. R. Ent. Soc. Lond. 5:58–62.

PEARMAN, J. V. 1942. Third note on Psocoptera from warehouses. Entomol. Mon. Mag. 78:289–292.

PEARMAN, J. V. 1946. A specific characterization of *Liposcelis divinatorius* (Mueller) and *mendax* sp. n. (Psocoptera). Entomologist, London 79: 235–244.

PEARMAN, J. V. 1951. Additional species of Brtish Psocoptera. Entomol. Mon. Mag. 87:84–89.

PENNY, N. D. 1975. Evolution of the extant Mecoptera. J. Kans. Entomol. Soc. 48:331–350.

POLHEMUS, J. T. 1985. Shore Bugs (Heteroptera, Hemiptera; Saldidae). A World Overview and Taxonomy of Middle America Forms. The Different Drummer, Englewood, Colorado. 252 pp.

POPHAM, E. J. 1959. The anatomy in relation to feeding habits of *Forficula auricularia* L. and other Dermaptera. Proc. Zool. Soc. Lond. 133: 251–300.

POPHAM, E. J. 1964 (1965). The functional morphology of the reproductive organs of the common earwig, *Forficula auricularia* and other Dermaptera with reference to the natural classification of the order. J. Zool., London 146:1–43.

POPHAM, E. J. 1984. The genus *Hemimerus*, insect parasites of the giant rat. Nyala 10:39–42.

POPHAM, E. J. 1985. The mutual affinities of the major earwig taxa (Insecta, Dermaptera). Z. Zool. Syst. Evolutionsforsch. 23:194–214.

POWELL, J. A. 1973. A systematic monograph of the New World ethmiid moths (Lepidoptera: Gelechioidea). Smithson. Contr. Zool. 120:1–302.

RATH, O. VOM. 1887. Über die Hautsinnesorgane der Insecten. Zool. Anz. 10:627–631, 645–649.

REMINGTON, C. L. 1954. The suprageneric classification of the order Thysanura (Insecta). Ann. Entomol. Soc. Amer. 47:277–286.

RICHARDS, O. W. 1962. A Revisional Study of the Masarid Wasps. London, British Museum (Natural History), London. vii + 294 pp.

RICHARDS, O. W. 1977. Hymenoptera. Introduction and Key to Families. Handbooks for the Identification of British Insects. Vol. 6, Number 1. Second Edition. Royal Entomological Society of London. 200 pp.

RICHARDS, O. W. 1978. The social wasps of the Americas excluding the Vespinae. Publ. Br. Mus. Nat. Hist. 785:1–580.

RICHARDS, O. W. AND M. J. RICHARDS. 1951. Observations on the social wasps of South America. Trans. R. Entomol. Soc. Lond. 102:1–170.

RICHARDS, W. R. 1968. Generic classification, evolution and biogeography of the Sminthuridae of the World (Collembola). Mem. Ent. Soc. Can. 53:1–54.

RICKLEFS, R. E. 1979. Ecology. 2nd Edition. Chiron Press, New York.

ROSS, E. S. 1987. Studies in the insect order Embiidina: A revision of the family Clothodidae. Proc. Cal. Acad. Sci. 45:9–34.

ROSS, H.H. 1944. The caddis flies, or Trichoptera, of Illinois. Ill. Nat. Hist. Surv. Bull. 23:1–326.

ROSS, H.H. 1956. Evolution and Classification of the Mountain Caddisflies. University of Illinois Press, Urbana. 213 pp.

ROSS, H. H., C. A. ROSS, AND J. R. P. ROSS. 1982. A Textbook of Entomology. Fourth Edition. John Wiley & Sons, New York.

ROTH, L. M. 1969. The evolution of male tergal glands in the Blattaria. Ann. Entomol. Soc. Am. 62:176–208.

ROTH, L. M. AND G. P. DATEO. 1965. Uric acid storage and excretion by accessory sex glands of male cockroaches. J. Insect Physiol. 11:1023–1029.

ROTH, L. M. AND H. B. HARTMAN. 1967. Sound production and its evolution in the Blattaria. Ann. Entomol. Soc. Am. 60:740–752.

ROTHSCHILD, M. AND R. TRAUB. 1971. Illustrated Catalogue of the Rothschild Collection of Fleas. Volume V (Glossary). British Museum (Natural History), London, UK.

RUDOLPH, D. 1982. Site, process and mechanism of active uptake of water vapour from the atmosphere in the Psocoptera. J. Insect Physiol. 28(3):205–212.

RUSSELL, L. M. 1948. The North American species of white-flies of the genus *Trialeurodes*. U. S. Dept. Agric. Misc. Publ. 635:1—85.

RUSSELL, L. M. 1986. The whitefly genus *Aleurocerus* Bondar (Hemiptera, Homoptera, Aleyrodidae). Entomography 4:137–183.

SAKAI, S. 1982. A new proposed classification of the Dermaptera with special reference to the check list of the Dermaptera of the World. Bull. Daito Bunka Univ. 20:1–108.

SCHAL, C. AND W. J. BELL. 1982. Ecological correlates of paternal investment of urates in the tropical cockroach. Science 281:171–173.

SCHALLER, F. 1971. Indirect sperm transfer by soil Arthropods. Ann. Rev. Entomol. 16:407–440.

SCHMID, F. 1980. Genera des Trichoptères du Canada et des états adjacents. Les insectes et Arachnides du Canada. Partie 7. Direction de la Recherche, Agriculture Canada. Publ. 1692, 296 pp.

SCHNEIDER, D. 1964. Insect antennae. Ann. Rev. Entomol. 9:103–122.

SCHUH, R. T. 1976. Pretarsal structure in the Miridae (Hemitera) with a cladistic analysis of relationships within the family. Am. Mus. Novit. 2601:1–39.

SCHUH, R. T. 1986. The influence of cladistics on heteropteran classification. Ann. Rev. Entomol. 31:67–93.

SELLICK, J. T. S. 1987. The micropylar plate of the eggs of Phasmatodea, and its taxonomic significance. Pp. 133–139. In: Mazzini, M. and V. Scali, (eds.). First. International Symposium on Stick-Insects. Siena,

SELLICK, J. T. C. 1988. The capitula of phasmid eggs: An update with review of the current state of phasmid ootaxonomy. Zool. J. Linn. Soc. 93:273–282.

SETTY, L. R. 1931. The biology of Bittacus stigmaterus Say (Mecoptera: Bittacusidae). Ann. Entomol. Soc. Am. 24:467–484.

SHAROV, A. G. 1957. Peculiar Paleozoic wingless insects belonging to a new order Monura (Insecta: Apterygota). Dokl. Akad. Nauk SSSR 115:795–798. [In Russian].

SHARPLIN, J. 1964. Wing base structure in Lepidoptera III. Taxonomic characters. Can. Entomol. 96:943–949.

SLATER, J. A. 1977. The incidence and evolutionary significance of wing polymorphism in lygaeid bugs with particular reference to those of South Africa. Biotropica 9:217–229.

SLATER, J. A. 1979. The systematics, phylogeny, and zoogeography of the Blissinae of the World (Hemiptera: Lygaeidae). Bull. Am. Mus. Nat. Hist. 165:1–180.

SMIT, F. G. A. M. 1973. Siphonaptera (fleas). Pp. 325–371. In: Smith, K. G. V. (ed.), Insects and other Arthoropods of Medical Importance. British Musem (Hatural History), London.

SMIT, F. G. A. M. 1987. An Illustrated Catalogue of the Rothschild Collection of Fleas. Volume VII. Malacopsylloidea. British Museum (Natural History), London.

SNIDER, R. J. AND S. J. LORING. 1984. Occurrence and external morphology of proprioceptors (oval organs) among North American Sminthurinae (Collembola: Sminthuridae). Ann. Soc. R. Zool. Belg. 114:35–42.

SNODGRASS, R. E. 1935. Principles of Insect Morphology. McGraw-Hill Publishing Company, New York. ix + 667 pp.

SNODGRASS, R. E. 1944. The feeding apparatus of biting and sucking insects affecting man and animals. Smithson. Misc. Collect. 104:1–113.

SNODGRASS, R. E. 1952. A Textbook of Arthropod Anatomy. Comstock Publishing Associates, Ithaca, New York. viii + 363 pp.

SNODGRASS, R. E. 1957. A revised interpretation of the external reproductive organs of male insects. Smithson. Misc. Collect. 135:1–60.

SPEIGHT, M. C. D. 1969. The prothoracic morphology of acalypterates (Diptera) and its use in systematics. Trans. R. Entomol. Soc. Lond. 121:325–421.

STANGE, L. A. 1970. Revision of the ant-lion tribe Brachynemurini of North America (Neuroptera: Myrmeleontidae). Univ. Calif. Publ. Entomol. 55:i–vi, 1–192.

STANNARD, L. J. 1957. The phylogeny and classification of the North American genera of the suborder Tubulifera (Thysanoptera). Ill. Biol. Monogr. 25:215–552.

STEHR, F. W. (ED.). 1987. Immature Insects. Volume 1. Kendall/Hunt Publishing Company, Dubuque, Iowa. xiv + 754 pp.

STEHR, F. W. (ED.). 1989. Immature Insects. Volume 2. Kendall/Hunt Publishing Company, Dubuque, Iowa. In press.

STEINMANN, H. 1986. Dermaptera, Catadermaptera I. Das Tierreich, Volume 102. W. de Gruyter, Berlin & New York. xiv + 343 pp.

STRONG, L. 1975. Defence glands in the giant spiny phasmid *Extatosoma tiaratum*. J. Entomol. Ser. A Physiol. & Behavior. 50:65–72.

STUCKENBERG, B. R. 1973. The Athericidae, a new family in the lower Brachycera (Diptera). Ann. Natal Mus. 21:649–673.

STURM, H. 1986. Aspekte des Paarungsverhaltens bei den Machiloidea (Archaeognatha, Insecta). Braunschw. Schr. 2:507–518.

ŠTYS, P. 1980. *Australostolus monteithi* gen. n., sp. n.—first record of an Australian aenictopecheine bug (Heteroptera, Enicocephalidae). Acta Entomol. Bohemoslov. 77:303–321.

ŠTYS, P. 1981. A new relict subfamily, genus and species of Enicocephalidae from New Caledonia (Heteroptera). Acta Entomol. Bohemoslov. 78:412–429.

ŠTYS, P. AND I. KERZHNER. 1975. The rank and nomenclature of higher taxa in recent Heteroptera. Acta Entomol. Bohemoslov. 72:65–79.

TAKAHASHI, R. 1921. The metamorphosis of Thysanoptera with notes on that of Coccidae. Zool. Mag. Tokyo 33:80–85.

TILLYARD, R. J. 1918. The panorpoid complex. A study of the phylogeny of the holometabolous insects, with special reference to the subclasses Panorpoidea and Neuropteroidea. Introduction. Proc. Linn. Soc. N. S. Wales 43:265–284.

TJEDER, B. 1957. Neuroptera-Planipennia. The Lace-wings of Southern Africa. 1. Introduction and families Coniopterygidae, Sisyridae, and Osmylidae. Pp. 95–188. *In*: Hanström, B. P. Brinck, and G. Rudebec (eds.), South African Animal Life, Volume 4. Swedish Natural Science Research Council, Stockholm.

TUXEN, S. L. 1964. The Protura. A Revision of the Species of the World with Keys for Determination. Hermann, Paris. 360 pp.

TUXEN, S. L. (ED.). 1970. Taxonomist's Glossary of Genitalia in Insects, Second edition. Munksgaard, Copenhagen.

USINGER, R. L. 1966. Monograph of Cimicidae (Hemiptera-

Heteroptera). Entomological Society of America, Thomas Say Foundation, College Park, Maryland. Volume 7, ix + 585 pp.

UVAROV, B. 1966. Grasshoppers and Locusts: A Handbook of General Acridology. Volume 1. Cambridge Universty Press, UK. 481 pp.

VANCE, T. C. 1974. Larvae of the Sericothripini (Thysanoptera: Thripidae), with reference to other larvae of the Terebrantia of Illinois. Ill. Nat. Hist. Surv. Bull. 31(5):144–208.

VICKERY, V. R. 1983. Catalogue of Australian stick insects (Phasmida, Phasmatodea, Phasmatoptera, or Cheleutoptera). C.S.I.R.O. Austr. Div. Entomol. Tech. Pap. 20:1–19.

VICKERY, V. R. AND D. K. KEVAN. 1983. A monograph of the orthopteroid insects of Canada and adjacent regions. Lyman Entomol. Museum Res. Lab. Mem. 13:1–680.

WEAVER, J. S. III. 1984. The evolution and classification of Trichoptera, Part 1: The groundplan of the Trichoptera. Pp. 413–419. *In*: Morse, J. C. (ed.). Proceedings of the Fourth International Symposium on Trichoptera. Series Entomologica Volume 30. W. Junk, The Hague.

WEBER, H. 1954. Grundriss der Insektenkunde. Third Edition. Gustav Fischer, Stuttgart. 428 pp.

WEIDNER, H. 1934. Beiträge zur Morphologie und Physiologie des Genitalapparates der weiblichen Lepidopteren. Z. Angew. Entomol. 21:239–289.

WESTWOOD, J. O. 1839. An Introduction to the Modern Classification of Insects. Volume 1. London.

WHITE, I. M. AND I. D. HODKINSON. 1982. Psylloidea (Nymphal Stages). Hemiptera, Homoptera. Handbooks for the Indentification of British Insects. Volume 2, Part 5(b). Royal Entomological Society of London, UK. 50 pp.

WIGGINS, G. B. 1977. Larvae of the North American caddisfly genera (Trichoptera). University of Toronto Press, Toronto and Buffalo. xi + 401 pp.

WILEY, E. O. 1981. Phylogenetics: The Theory and Practice of Phylogenetic Systematics. John Wiley and Sons, Inc., New York. xv + 439 pp.

WILLE, A. 1960. The phylogeny and relationship between insect orders. Rev. Biol. Trop. 8:93–122.

WOOD, S. L. 1982. The bark and ambrosia beetles of North and Central America (Coleoptera: Scolytidae), a taxonomic monograph. Mem. Great Basin Nat. 6:1–1359.

WYGODZINSKY, P. W. 1957. Thysanura from the Pelagic Islands. Boll. Soc. Entomol. Ital. 87:109–113.

WYGODZINSKY, P. W. AND K. SMITH. 1980. Survey of the Microcoryphia (Insecta) of the Northeastern United States and Adjacent Provinces of Canada. Amer. Mus. Nov. 2701:1–17.

WYGODZINSKY, P. AND P. ŠTYS. 1982. Two new primitive genera and species of Enicocephalidae from Singapore (Heteroptera). Acta Entomol. Bohemoslov. 79:127–142.

NON-ENGLISH LANGUAGE GLOSSARIES AND SOURCES

BENOIT, P. (ED). 1975. Noms français d'insectes au Canada avec noms latins et anglais correspondants. Quatri me édition. Ministère de l'Agriculture du Quebec. 214 pp. FRENCH.

CARVALHO, M. B. AND G. P. DE ARRUNDA. 1967. Glossário de termos técnicos de entomologia. Boletim Técnico Instituto de Pesquisas Agronomicas de Pernambuco 24:1–87. PORTUGUESE.

ERICSON, R. O. 1961. A glossary of foreign-language terms in entomology. U.S.D.A., A.R.S., Agric. Handbook No. 218: ix, 1–59. CZECH, DANISH, DUTCH, GERMAN, POLISH, RUSSIAN, SWEDISH.

FRIESE, G. 1964. Insekten; Taschenlexikon der Entomologie unter besonderer Berücksichtigung der Fauna Mitteleuropas. Bibliographisches Institut, Leipzig. 295 pp. GERMAN.

GHIDINI, G. M. [no date]. Glossario di entomologia. La Scuola, Brescia. 1206 pp. ITALIAN.

GREIFF, M. 1985. Spanish-English-Spanish Lexicon of Entomological and Related Terms, with Indexes of Spanish Common Names of Arthropods and Their Latin and English Equivalents. Commonwealth Institute of Entomology, London. SPANISH.

ISHIDA, M. 1933. The Dictionary of Terms Used in Entomology. Masota Ishida, Sapporo, Japan. ix, 294 pp. JAPANESE.

JACOBS, W. 1974. Taschenlexikon zur Biologie der Insekten mit besonderer Berücksichtigung mitteleuropäischer Arten. Gustav Fischer Verlag, Stuttgart. 635 pp. GERMAN.

JACOBS, W. AND F. SEIDEL. 1975. Systematische Zoologie: Insekten. G. Fischer, Stuttgart. 377 pp. GERMAN.

KÉLER, S. VON. 1963. Entomologisches Wörterbuch, mit besonderer Berücksichtigung der morphologischen Terminologie. Akademie-Verlag, Berlin. 774 pp. GERMAN.

LALIBERTE, J. L. 1982. Aide-mémoire à l'usage de l'amateur. Glossaire entomologique. Fabreries (Suppl.) 11:1–84. FRENCH.

LAUX, W. AND G. SCHMIDT. 1979. Russische Namen von Arthropoden pflanzenschutzlicher Bedeutung. Mitteilungen aus der Biologischen Bundesanstalt für Land- und Forstwirtschaft, Berlin-Dahlem 188: 1–86. RUSSIAN.

LIU CHUNG-LUOH. (ED). 1965. Ying han k'ung ch'ung hsüeh tz'u tien. Science Press, Peking. vi, 385 pp. (transl. Torre-Bueno, J. R. de la. 1962. A Glossary of Entomology. Third Printing with appendix by Tulloch). CHINESE.

SÉGUY, E. 1967. Dicionnaire des termes techniques d'entomologie élémentaire. P. Lechevalier, Paris. 465 pp. FRENCH.

SHCHEGHOLEVA, V. N. 1958. Slovar'- spravochnik entomologa. 2. perer. i dep. izd. Gos. izdvo sel' khoz. litry, Moskva. 631 pp. RUSSIAN.

SHIRAKI, T. 1971. A Glossary of Entomology. Hokuryu-Kan, Tokyo. 1098 pp. JAPANESE.

STEINMANN, H. & L. ZOMBORI. 1981. Terminologia insectorum morphologica. Fauna Hungariae 146:1)210. HUNGARIAN.

VANEKOVA, Z. (ED.). 1968. Skodlive cinitele v pol'nohospodarskej a lesnej vyrobe (Harmful agents in agricuture and forestry). Chemicke Zavody Juraja Dimitrova, Bratislava. 140 pp. CZECH, GERMAN, RUSSIAN, SLOVAK.

SOURCES TO ENGLISH COMMON NAMES OF INSECTS

CARNE, P. B. ET AL. 1980. Scientific and Common Names of Insects and Allied Forms Occurring in Australia. Commonwealth Scientific and Industrial Research Organization, Canberra, Australia. 95 pp.

FERRO, D. N. 1977. Standard Names for Common Insects of New Zealand. No. 2:1–42.

MERINO-RODRIGUEZ, M. 1964. Elsevier's Lexicon of Parasites and Diseases in Livestock. Elsevier, Amsterdam. 125 pp.

MERINO-RODRIGUEZ, M. 1966. Elsevier's Lexicon of Plant Pests and Diseases. Elsevier, Amsterdam. 351 pp.

SEYMOUR, P. 1980. Invertebrates of Economic Importance in Britain: Common and Scientific Names. HMSO, London. viii + 132 pp.

WERNER, F. G. (ED.). 1982. Common Names of Insects and Related Organisms. Entomological Society of America, College Park, Maryland. 133 pp.

OTHER USEFUL REFERENCES

ALLABY, M. (ED.). 1985. The Oxford Dictionary of Natural History. Oxford University Press, Oxford. xiv + 688 pp.

BROWN, R. W. 1956. Composition of Scientific Words. Revised Edition. Published by the author. 882 pp.

BRUES, C. T., A. L. MELANDER, AND F. M. CARPENTER. 1954. Classification of Insects. Bull. Mus. Comp. Zool. 108:1–917. (An excellent set of keys to the families of insects, including references to many higher taxonomic categories not included in the *Glossary*).

GILBERT, P. 1977. A Compendium of the Biographical Literature on Deceased Entomologists. British Museum (Natural History), London. xiv + 455 pp.

GILBERT, P. AND C. J. HAMILTON. 1983. Entomology. A Guide to Information Sources. Mansell Publishing Co., London. 237 pp.

KING, R. C. AND W. D. STANSFIELD. 1985. A Dictionary of Genetics. Third Edition. Oxford University Press, New York.

LINCOLN, R. J., G. A. BOXSHALL, AND P. F. CLARK. 1982. A Dictionary of Ecology, Evolution and Systematics. Cambridge University Press, Cambridge. viii + 298 pp.

PARKER, S. P. (ED.). 1982. Synopsis and Classification of Living Organisms. Vol. 2. McGraw-Hill Book Company, New York. (An excellent source for family level information and higher taxonomic categories).

WOODS, ROBERT S. 1966. An English-Classical Dictionary for the use of Taxonomists. Pamona College. xiii + 331 pp.

NOTES